p. 28
38 - 39
40 - 41

McGraw-Hill Civil Engineering Series
Harmer E. Davis, *Consulting Editor*

APPLIED HYDROLOGY

McGraw-Hill Civil Engineering Series

HARMER E. DAVIS, *Consulting Editor*

BABBITT · Engineering in Public Health

BABBITT AND DOLAND · Water Supply Engineering

DAVIS, TROXELL, AND WISKOCIL · The Testing and Inspection of Engineering Materials

DUNHAM · Foundations of Structures

DUNHAM · The Theory and Practice of Reinforced Concrete

DUNHAM AND YOUNG · Contracts, Specifications, and Law for Engineers

GAYLORD AND GAYLORD · Structural Design

GOLZÉ · Reclamation in the United States

HENNES AND EKSE · Fundamentals of Transportation Engineering

HENRY · Design and Construction of Engineering Foundations

KRYNINE AND JUDD · Principles of Engineering Geology and Geotechnics

LINSLEY AND FRANZINI · Elements of Hydraulic Engineering

LINSLEY, KOHLER, AND PAULHUS · Applied Hydrology

MATSON, SMITH, AND HURD · Traffic Engineering

MEAD, MEAD, AND AKERMAN · Contracts, Specifications, and Engineering Relations

PEURIFOY · Construction Planning, Equipment, and Methods

TROXELL AND DAVIS · Composition and Properties of Concrete

TSCHEBOTARIOFF · Soil Mechanics, Foundations, and Earth Structures

URQUHART, O'ROURKE, AND WINTER · Design of Concrete Structures

WANG AND ECKEL · Elementary Theory of Structures

APPLIED HYDROLOGY

RAY K. LINSLEY, JR., *B.S.C.E., Assoc. M. ASCE, Member Am. Geophys. Union, Assistant Chief for Hydrology, Division of Climatological and Hydrologic Services, U.S. Weather Bureau, Associate Professor of Hydraulic Engineering, Stanford University*

MAX A. KOHLER, *B.S., Assoc. M. ASCE, Member Am. Geophys. Union, Chief, Procedure Development Section, Division of Climatological and Hydrologic Services, U. S. Weather Bureau*

JOSEPH L. H. PAULHUS, *B.S.C.E., M.S. in Meteorology, Assoc. M. ASCE, Member Am. Geophys. Union, Prof. Member Amer. Meteorological Soc., Chief, Cooperative Studies (Reclamation) Section, Division of Climatological and Hydrologic Services, U. S. Weather Bureau*

McGRAW-HILL BOOK COMPANY, INC.

New York Toronto London 1949

APPLIED HYDROLOGY

VI

PREFACE

There is abundant evidence that some principles of hydrology were known and applied at the dawn of history. Modern hydrology, however, is a product of the current century. In fact, the bulk of current theory and practice stems from the great expansion in flood-control and reclamation programs since 1935. During this period the useful application of hydrology has been demonstrated in many fields, such as highway and airport drainage, small water-supply projects, storm-sewer design, and others.

As a result of the rapid growth in activities within the field of hydrology during recent years, many technical papers have been written for scientific periodicals, and numerous special bulletins have been issued by several agencies. These numerous papers on a subject which is still young, as applied sciences go, display considerable lack of standardization of terminology, nomenclature, and techniques. Persons not engaged in the full-time practice of hydrology often find it difficult to orient themselves in the field.

This book is designed to meet the demand for a convenient text reference for general data, basic theory, and methods of application. The emphasis throughout has been on the presentation of methods for practical application of hydrology and on data which present the means and ranges of variation of the key elements in hydrology. Basic data are limited to the continental United States except in so far as foreign data have been judged pertinent to the practice of hydrology in this country. Techniques and problems discussed are those which are characteristic of hydrology in the United States. It is the hope of the authors that this book will prove useful as a text to the student in the field and a valuable reference and guide to those engineers who devote all or part of their professional efforts to hydrologic problems. No claim is made that it presents a complete coverage of the field. Much basic theory readily available from other sources has not been included, in the interest of conserving space. Many highly specialized and unusual applications of hydrology have been omitted in favor of detailed presentation of the more generally applicable techniques. It is believed, however, that ample references have been supplied for those who wish to carry their study beyond the scope of this book.

Every effort has been made to adopt a standardized terminology and nomenclature and to present well-established procedures. To this end the authors are indebted to their many friends and fellow workers who have generously assisted in the preparation of the material. A. L. Shands, W. C. Ackermann, T. J. Nordenson, W. C. Spreen, A. H. Williams, and C. F. Izzard contributed materially by reviewing portions of the manuscript.

THE AUTHORS

WASHINGTON, D.C.
July, 1949

CONTENTS

SYMBOLS AND ABBREVIATIONS

The following list of symbols has been adopted by the authors for this text. With few exceptions, no symbol is assigned a dual meaning. Well-recognized letter symbols used in the various sciences basic to hydrology have generally been followed, but, in order to avoid confusion, some variations on the less firmly established symbols have been adopted. Specific definitions of symbols and units have been given, where necessary, with each equation in the text.

LETTER SYMBOLS

A area
A_d drainage area
A_w water-surface area
a a coefficient
a_c cross-sectional area
a_h absolute humidity
a_s saturation absolute humidity
B width
B_t top width
b a coefficient
C capacitance in electrical circuit
$\mathbf{C}$ Chezy coefficient
C_d coefficient of discharge
C_P projection ratio
C_p coefficient of unit-hydrograph peak
C_s coefficient of skew
C_t coefficient of basin lag
c a coefficient or exponent
c_s sediment concentration
c_v vapor concentration
D depth
D_D drainage density
D_d drawdown
D_m mean depth in a cross section (a_c/B_t)
d diameter (or derivative)
E energy
E_a evaporation
e vapor pressure
$\mathbf{e}$ 2.71828 . . . (base of Napierian logarithms)
e_a vapor pressure of air
e_s saturation vapor pressure
e_w vapor pressure at a water surface
F force
F_a actual water-surface fall
F_c cyclostrophic force
F_d deflecting (Coriolis) force
F_g pressure-gradient force
F_i total volume of infiltration
F_m mean water-surface fall for steady flow
F_n normal water-surface fall for steady flow
F_s surface tension
F_t critical tractive force
f relative humidity
f_{av} average infiltration rate
f_c minimum infiltration capacity
f_i infiltration rate
f_0 initial infiltration capacity
f_p infiltration capacity
G_i bed-load transport per unit width
g stage or gage height
$\mathbf{g}$ acceleration of gravity
H quantity of heat
H_f latent heat of fusion
H_v latent heat of vaporization
h head
h_c height of capillary rise
h_v velocity head
I inflow rate

i rainfall intensity
i_e rate of excess rainfall (supply rate)
J frequency
j a coefficient
K channel-storage constant
K_c thermal conductivity
K_d thermal diffusivity
K_p coefficient of permeability
K_r coefficient of recession
K_w moisture conductivity of soil
k a coefficient or exponent
$\mathbf{k}$ von Kármán's constant (0.4)
L length of stream
L_o length of overland flow
l a distance
l_f fetch of wind
M quantity of snowmelt
M_c moisture content
M_i total suspended load per unit width
M_t silt discharge
m a coefficient or exponent
m rank in an array
$\mathbf{m}$ mass
N number of items
n a coefficient or exponent
$\mathbf{n}$ Manning or Kutter coefficient
O outflow rate
P precipitation
$\mathbf{P}$ probability
P_a antecedent-precipitation index
P_e precipitation excess
p pressure
p_a total air pressure
p_d partial pressure of dry air
pF logarithm of capillary potential ($\log_{10} \psi$)
Q volume of flow or runoff
Q_s volume of surface runoff
Q_t thermal quality of snow
q rate of discharge
q_c critical discharge for bed-load movement
q_h specific humidity
q_m steady-flow discharge
q_p unit-hydrograph peak flow
R hydraulic radius or resistance in an electrical circuit
$\mathbf{R}$ Reynolds number
R_B Bowen's ratio
R_b back radiation
R_g dry-air gas constant
R_i incident radiation
R_w water-vapor gas constant
r radius
r_d radius of drawdown around a well
r_e radius of the earth
r_o radius of orbit
S volume of channel storage
S_d depression-storage capacity
S_e surface retention (interception plus depression storage)
S_H heat storage
S_i interception-storage capacity
s slope
s_c critical slope
s_e slope of the energy gradient
s_m water-surface slope for steady flow
T temperature
T_a air temperature
T_d dewpoint temperature
T_e exceedance interval
T_p return period
T_r recurrence interval
T_s water- or snow-surface temperature
T_v virtual temperature
T_w wet-bulb temperature
t time
t_c time of runoff concentration
t_f duration of rainfall excess
t_o period of oscillation
t_P time from beginning of rain to peak
t_p basin lag
t_R duration of rainfall
t_r unit duration of rainfall ($t_p/5.5$)
t_t routing period
t_u lag in a reach
U unit-hydrograph ordinate
U_c consumptive use
u wave celerity
V volume
V_d volume of water in surface detention
V_i volume of water in interception storage
V_p porosity
V_s volume of water in depression storage
v velocity
v_a anticyclonic gradient-wind velocity
v_c critical velocity
v_d surface velocity
v_e cyclostrophic- (Eulerian) wind velocity
v_G geostrophic-wind velocity

- v_g grain velocity (sediment transport)
- v_l cyclonic gradient-wind velocity
- v_m mean velocity in a cross section
- v_s settling velocity (of sediment)
- v_w wind speed
- W weight
- $\mathbf{W}$ an infiltration index
- W_p precipitable water
- w unit weight of water (62.4 lb/ft^3)
- w_g unit weight of grains
- w_r mixing ratio
- X a variable
- X_f the mode of a distribution
- x horizontal coordinate or distance
- x a coefficient or exponent
- Y a variable
- Y' a computed value of Y
- Y_s specific yield of an aquifer
- y a vertical coordinate
- Z elevation
- Z_w set-up of water surface due to wind
- z_a wave amplitude
- beta β an angle
- epsilon ϵ eddy conductivity or diffusion coefficient
- eta η specific heat
- η_v specific heat by volume
- Theta Θ diffusion constant
- theta θ an angle
- kappa κ a coefficient
- Lambda Λ total potential
- lambda λ wave length
- mu μ coefficient of absolute viscosity
- nu ν coefficient of kinematic viscosity
- xi ξ a coefficient or exponent
- pi π 3.1416 . . .
- rho ρ density
- ρ_a density of moist air
- ρ_d density of dry air
- ρ_g density of suspended grains
- ρ_i density of ice
- ρ_v density of water vapor
- ρ_w density of water
- sigma σ standard deviation
- tau τ unit shear
- τ_c critical shear for bed-load movement
- τ_0 unit shear at channel bed
- Upsilon Υ du Boys coefficient
- Phi Φ an infiltration index
- phi ϕ latitude
- chi χ $v_s/\sqrt{\mathbf{g}Ds}$
- Psi Ψ specific gravity (also snow density)
- psi ψ capillary potential
- omega ω angular velocity

MATHEMATICAL SYMBOLS

- $\overline{Y}$ the bar over a symbol indicates an average
- $>$ greater than
- $<$ less than
- $f(\ )$ function of
- Σ summation
- $\hat{\sigma}$ the caret indicates an adjusted value
- Δ an increment of
- ∞ infinity
- ∂ partial derivative
- d derivative

ABBREVIATIONS

- A° absolute (Kelvin) temperature
- acre-ft acre-foot
- atm atmosphere
- Btu British thermal unit
- C° centigrade temperature
- cal calories
- cc cubic centimeter
- cfs cubic feet per second (second-foot)
- cgs centimeter-gram-second
- cm centimeter
- cm^3 cubic centimeter
- csm cubic feet per second per square mile
- F° Fahrenheit temperature
- fps feet per second

ft foot
ft-lb foot-pound
ft-lb-sec foot-pound-second
gal gallon
g gram
gpm gallons per minute
gps gallons per second
hr hour
in. inch
kg kilogram
km kilometer
kw kilowatt
lat latitude
lb pound
lin ft linear foot
log logarithm
m meter
mb millibar
min minute
mm millimeter
mph miles per hour
msl mean sea level
oz ounce
pt pint
sec secant or second
sech hyperbolic secant
sfd second-foot-day [(cubic foot per second)-day]
tan tangent

1
INTRODUCTION

Hydrology is that branch of physical geography dealing with the waters of the earth with special reference to properties, phenomena, and distribution. It treats specifically of the occurrence of water on the earth, the description of the earth with respect to water, the physical effects of water on the earth, and the relation of water to life on the earth.

The hydrologic cycle. The hydrologic cycle is the descriptive term applied to the general circulation of water from the seas to the atmosphere, to the ground, and back to the seas again. It is summarized graphically in Fig. 1-1.

The cycle may be considered to begin with the water of the oceans. Water from the ocean surface is evaporated into the atmosphere. This vapor is condensed by various processes and falls to the earth as precipitation. Some of this precipitation falls directly on the seas, and some falls on land surfaces. A portion of that falling on the land is retained temporarily in the soil, in surface depressions, and on vegetation and other objects until it is returned to the atmosphere by evaporation and transpiration. The remainder, moving by devious surface and underground channels to rivers, lakes, and eventually to the sea, is likewise subject to evaporation and transpiration throughout its travels.

Figure 1-1 and the foregoing description of the hydrologic cycle are necessarily oversimplified. Actually, all phases of the cycle are occurring simultaneously. On a world-wide basis the volumes of moisture involved in each phase of the cycle are relatively constant; but viewed in terms of a limited area, such as a small river basin, the quantities in any part of the cycle vary through wide limits. These variations are the primary subjects of study in hydrology. For example, a temporary unbalance of the cycle in which great volumes of water are concentrated in the streams results in a flood. Conversely, small or negligible amounts of water in the precipitation phase of the cycle lead to drought.

History of hydrology. Ancient Arabian wells and elaborate Chinese and Egyptian irrigation systems testify to the ability of early hydrologists,

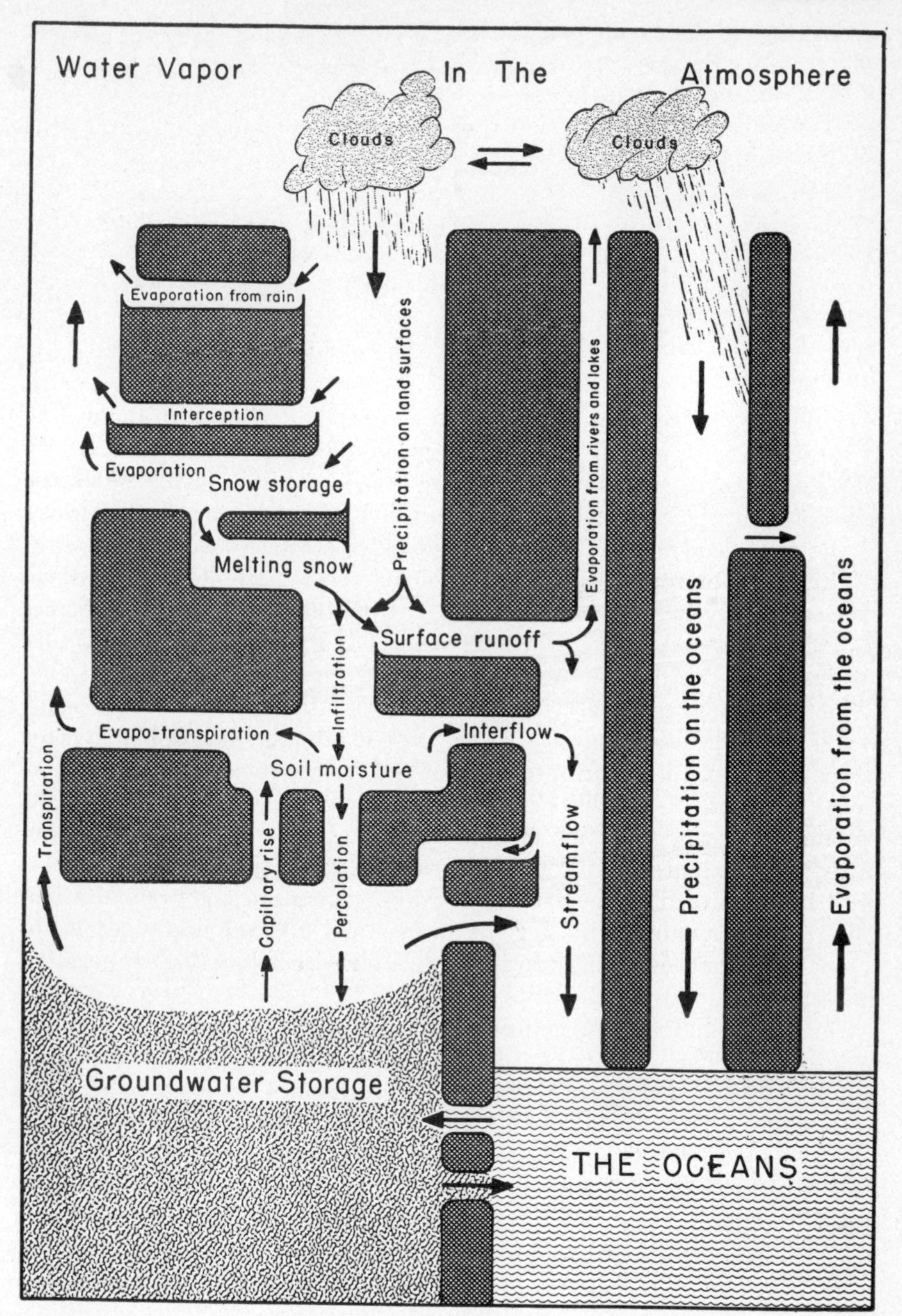

FIG. 1–1. The hydrologic cycle.

but hydrology as we know it today is a young science. Some qualitative phases of hydrology were developed during the late nineteenth century as a result of work in related sciences; but active, quantitative research in the field dates from studies in the early years of the present century by Horton, Sherman, Meyer, Mead, and others. The last two decades have witnessed a great advance stimulated by increased governmental interest in flood control, soil conservation, river navigation, and hydroelectric-power development.

Egyptian inscriptions dating from 3000 B.C. mention Nile River floods, and definite floodmarks for as early as 1800 B.C. have been found. There is evidence that rainfall measurements were made in India as early as the fourth century B.C. The problems of hydrology were principally a matter of philosophic speculation until recent years. Curiously enough, the greatest problem for the philosophers was that of describing the hydrologic cycle. Such men as Homer, Plato, and Aristotle felt that rainfall was quite inadequate to supply streamflow and formulated elaborate hypotheses to explain how the water welled up from great subterranean caverns connected with the sea. Attempts were made to explain occurrence of streams near mountaintops by assumptions involving vacuums, wind pressure, and a curvature of the ocean surface which made it somewhere higher than the mountains. Equally elaborate assumptions were necessary to explain how the salt-water source produced fresh-water streams.

Until the fifteenth century A.D. it was considered heresy to question the theories of the early philosophers. Finally, practical men, such as da Vinci and Palissy, expounded an outline of the hydrologic cycle quite similar to present-day conceptions. It was not until the seventeenth century that Pierre Perreault supplied the necessary quantitative proof by comparing measurements of rainfall and runoff for the Seine River in France and showing that the runoff volume was only about one-sixth the rainfall. Perreault's findings were soon supported by data collected by Mariotte, and a few years later the English astronomer Halley demonstrated by experiments that the moisture evaporated from the oceans was adequate to supply streamflow.

Under the leadership of Torricelli, Pitot, Bernoulli, de Chézy, Herschel, Venturi, and others, investigations moved forward rapidly in the study of fluid flow (hydraulics). Dams, bridges, levees, and canals were soon being designed by hydraulic engineers with a fair knowledge of fluid mechanics but with only the crudest sort of rules of thumb to estimate the probable quantities of water to which these structures might be subjected. As the number and size of structures increased and the potential economic loss from structural or operational failure multiplied, the demand for a more adequate basis for design increased, and modern hydrology found its start.

Scope and application of hydrology. There are three broad problems in hydrology: (1) the measurement, recording, and publication of basic data; (2) the analysis of these data to develop and expand the fundamental theories; (3) the application of these theories and data to a multitude of practical problems. The ensuing text discusses these problems in considerable detail. It will be seen that hydrology is a broad science drawing on many related fields and basic sciences for many of its data and much of its theory. Hydrologic techniques, however, are rather distinct from those generally encountered in other fields.

In terms of the hydrologic cycle, the scope of hydrology may be defined as that portion of the cycle from precipitation to reevaporation or return of the water to the seas. The remaining phases of the cycle are treated by the sciences of *oceanography* and *meteorology*. Hydrology also includes within its scope those waters of internal origin which become a part of the available water resources of the earth.

The International Association of Scientific Hydrology recognizes four subdivisions of the science. These are *potamology*, the study of surface streams; *limnology*, the study of lakes; *geohydrology*, relating to subsurface waters; and *cryology*, dealing with snow and ice. To these may well be added a fifth and very new branch, *hydrometeorology*, the study of the borderline problems between the fields of hydrology and meteorology. Actually, the phenomena of hydrology are so interrelated that few hydrologic problems do not encompass more than one of these branches. Thus, in the study of surface streams, one must consider all the other branches. No attempt has been made to segregate the material in this book in accordance with the subdivisions mentioned above.

2
CLIMATE

The hydrologic characteristics of an area are determined largely by (1) the climate of the region and (2) the geological structure of the area. In the general sense, climatic factors are most important because they determine, to a considerable extent, the surface features of a terrane. The magnitude and distribution of precipitation, the occurrence of snow and ice, and the effect of wind, temperature, and humidity on evaporation are among the climatic factors which establish the hydrologic features of a particular area. Hence, the hydrologist must have an understanding of the meteorological processes that determine a regional climate. The climate of an area depends on its location within the world-wide circulation pattern of the atmosphere, but the influence of this circulation is modified by the physiographic features of the area. These large-scale influences, which are not completely understood theoretically, are discussed in this chapter.

THE GENERAL CIRCULATION

In many fields it is possible to set up controlled experiments, vary one factor at a time, and study the consequences. Meteorologists, however, have to accept such variations as nature may offer—variations seldom so clean-cut as to permit the establishment of well-defined relationships. The atmosphere may be considered as a turbulent fluid subjected to strong thermal influences and moving over a rough, rotating spheroid. No fully satisfactory theoretical or experimental technique exists for the study of such fluid motions and, hence, the meteorologist does not yet have a universally accepted outline of the general circulation of the atmosphere. The following discussion is based on Rossby's concept[1] of the general circulation.

Thermal circulation. Most attempts to explain the mean-circulation pattern start with the hypothetical circulation that would exist on a non-rotating sphere. In this simplified case, a purely thermal circulation

[1] Rossby, C. G., The Scientific Basis of Modern Meteorology, from "Climate and Man," *U.S. Dept. Agr. Yearbook*, pp. 599-655, 1941.

would result, with the sun as the source of energy. About 40 per cent of the radiant energy reaching the earth's atmosphere is reflected back to space from the upper surface of clouds and through diffuse scattering by air molecules and dust. The remainder, except for a small loss through reflection, is absorbed by the earth and its atmosphere. In the earth's crust the solar radiation is transformed into heat and subsequently reradiated to space. Since the earth's mean temperature is essentially constant, it follows that this outflow of heat energy must balance the incoming radiation. Most of the outgoing radiation from the earth is absorbed by water vapor in the lower layers of the atmosphere and to some extent by ozone in the upper layers. Since the atmosphere emits radiation upward and

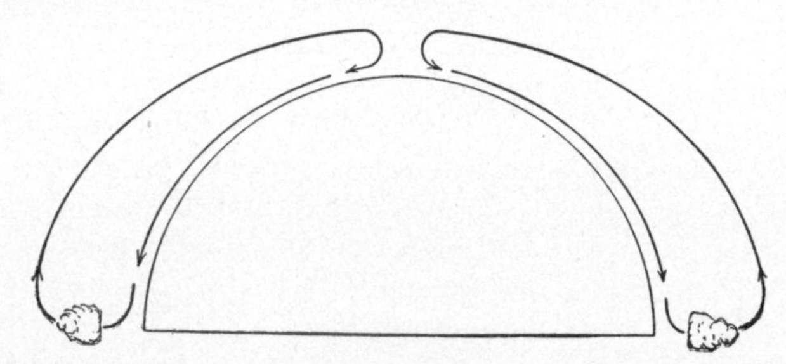

FIG. 2–1. Simple thermal circulation on a nonrotating earth.

downward but absorbs little except from the ground, its temperature must be lower than that of the ground. Similarly, the ground temperature is higher than it would be in the absence of an atmosphere, since some of the radiation emitted by the ground is returned to it by the atmosphere. This blanketing effect is known as the *greenhouse effect.*

Because more solar radiation is received at the equator than at higher latitudes, the air rises at the equator and flows toward the poles. To balance this poleward flow aloft, air in the lower layers must move toward the equator. Figure 2-1 shows the circulation as it would appear in the Northern Hemisphere on a nonrotating earth. The result is a net transport of heat northward, reducing the temperature contrast between equator and pole.

The circulation described above works like a simple heat engine. The difference between the heat energy received and that given off is converted into winds. Friction between the atmosphere and the earth's surface prevents the wind speeds from increasing indefinitely. Thus, friction converts the kinetic energy of the winds to heat energy, which is radiated back to space.

The circulation of Fig. 2-1 differs from that actually observed in the atmosphere because of two factors: (1) the earth's rotation; (2) the distribution of oceans and continents.

The effect of the earth's rotation. A parcel of air at rest relative to the earth's surface moves with a constant velocity in an orbit about the polar axis. If this parcel is forced northward in the Northern Hemisphere at a constant elevation, the radius of its orbit is necessarily reduced. It follows from the principle of conservation of angular momentum that its eastward velocity increases. Moreover, the eastward velocity of points on the surface of the earth decreases poleward. Because of these two effects, a poleward-moving parcel acquires a rapidly increasing speed from west to east relative to the earth's surface. Conversely, a parcel moving equatorward acquires a westward velocity. The earth's speed at the equator is about 1500 fps and at 60° lat is half this amount. A parcel at rest at the

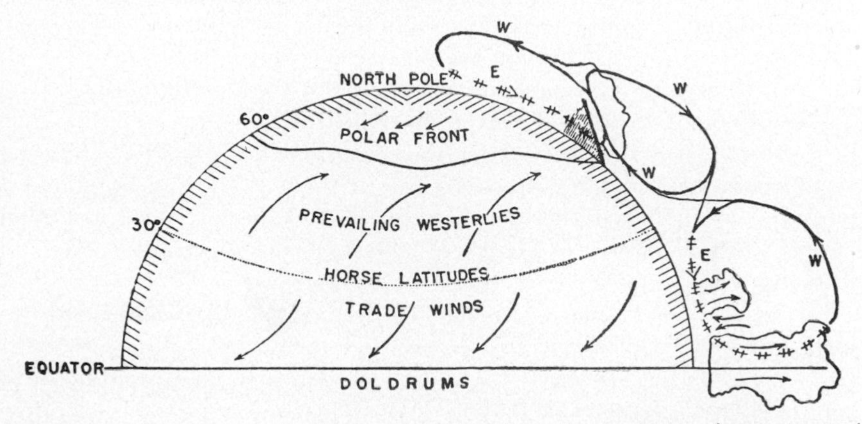

FIG. 2–2. The general circulation of the Northern Hemisphere. (*After Rossby.*)

equator would attain a theoretical velocity of 2250 fps if moved to 60° lat. Wind speeds of this magnitude are never observed because of friction and because such direct, large-scale displacements do not occur.

Prevailing westerly winds above 3 miles are evidence that this effect operates on the poleward flow aloft of air from the equator. However, the general easterly winds, which would be expected at the surface at all latitudes because of the southward return flow, are not observed. Obviously, if such easterly winds did exist the earth's rotation would be retarded through friction. Belts of easterly winds are observed below 30° and above 60° lat and general westerly winds between 30° and 60° lat.

This leads to the general circulation pattern shown in Fig. 2-2. Air rising at the equator and moving north acquires an eastward component because of the earth's rotation. By the time this air reaches about 30° lat (the *horse latitudes*), it has lost sufficient heat so that it tends to subside. The subsiding air divides into two branches—one branch, moving south, develops into the northeast trade winds, while the second continues northward and eastward in the middle latitudes.

The polar cell is also thermally produced. Loss of heat in the lower layers at the poles results in subsidence. The subsiding air spreads southward and because of the earth's rotation acquires a westward component. While moving southward this air is warmed, and at about 60° lat it rises and returns to the pole as southwesterly winds aloft.

The details of the circulation in the middle latitudes are not well established. The northeastward-moving branch of the air subsiding in the horse latitudes meets the westward-moving air at the southern extreme of the polar cell (*polar front*), where it is forced upward over the colder air and continues northward to the pole. If there were no escape for the air in the polar cell, this inflow from the middle cell would result in an accumulation at the pole. The release of air from the northern cell is accomplished, however, by outbreaks through the polar front which carry the excess air southward through the temperate zone and into the equatorial cell.

The effect of land and water distribution. If the surface of the earth were of uniform composition, the circulation described for a rotating earth would result in a high-pressure belt at the horse latitudes and a low-pressure belt at the periphery of the polar cell. However, the distribution of land and sea masses causes these belts to break down into centers of high and low pressure.

Chiefly because of continuous mixing, heat gains and losses are distributed through comparatively great depths in large bodies of water, while the land is affected only near its surface. Consequently, ocean-surface temperatures are far more equable than those of land surfaces. This condition is further emphasized by the lower specific heat of the soil and, during the winter, by the snow cover on the continents, which reflects much of the incident radiation back to space. Hence, in winter when the land surfaces are cold relative to the water surfaces, there is a tendency for high pressure to be intensified over the continents and for low pressure to become more pronounced over the oceans. These features are reflected in the semipermanent Icelandic and Aleutian lows and the high-pressure area over the North American Continent (Fig. 2-3). Under these conditions, the polar front is displaced far to the south over the continent. At the same time, the high-pressure belt at the horse latitudes retreats southward and is weakened over the ocean surfaces. In the summer season, the situation is somewhat reversed (Fig. 2-4). The pressure belts advance northward; the pressure centers in the subtropical high-pressure belt are located over oceans, and the lows in the polar trough are more prominent over the continents.

Cyclones and anticyclones. The main features of the mean, or general, circulation have a statistical rather than an actual permanence. At any time, the actual circulation of the atmosphere may depart widely from the mean picture. The permanent and semipermanent features are distorted or displaced by transitory systems, which disappear in the mean. Both permanent and transitory features can be typed as cyclones and anticyclones. A *cyclone* is a circular or nearly circular area of low atmospheric pressure in which the winds blow counterclockwise in the Northern Hemisphere. There are two main types of cyclones, the tropical and extratropical.

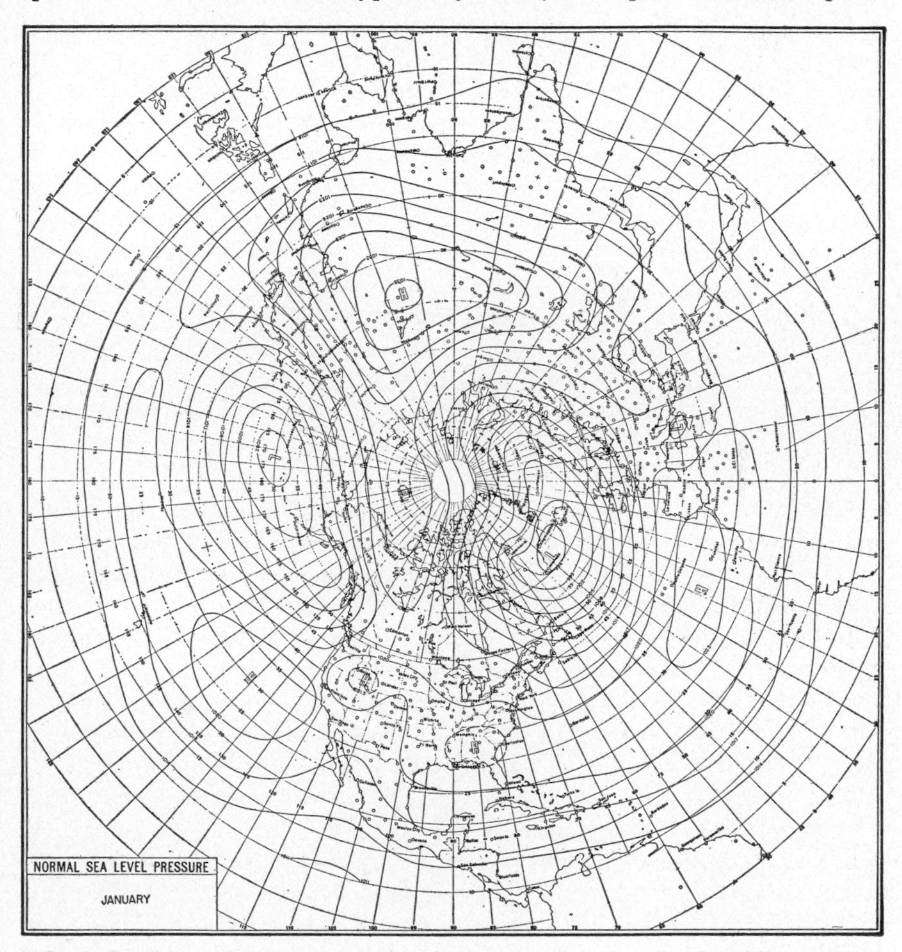

FIG. 2–3. Normal January sea-level pressure for the Northern Hemisphere. (*U.S. Weather Bureau.*)

Tropical cyclones are relatively small, very violent storms of tropical latitudes, also known as *hurricanes* and *typhoons*. Their diameter is usually between 50 and 300 miles, and winds near their center often exceed velocities of 100 mph. The center of such storms, known as the *eye*, is an area of very light winds and clearing skies. Tropical cyclones always develop over water and move westward with the trade winds of the equatorial belt.

Many curve poleward into the westerly winds of the Temperate Zone. The energy of tropical storms is rapidly dissipated as they move over large land masses because of increased friction and the lack of a moisture supply.

Extratropical cyclones, or *lows*, are low-pressure systems, usually larger and less violent than tropical cyclones. Their diameter may be as great

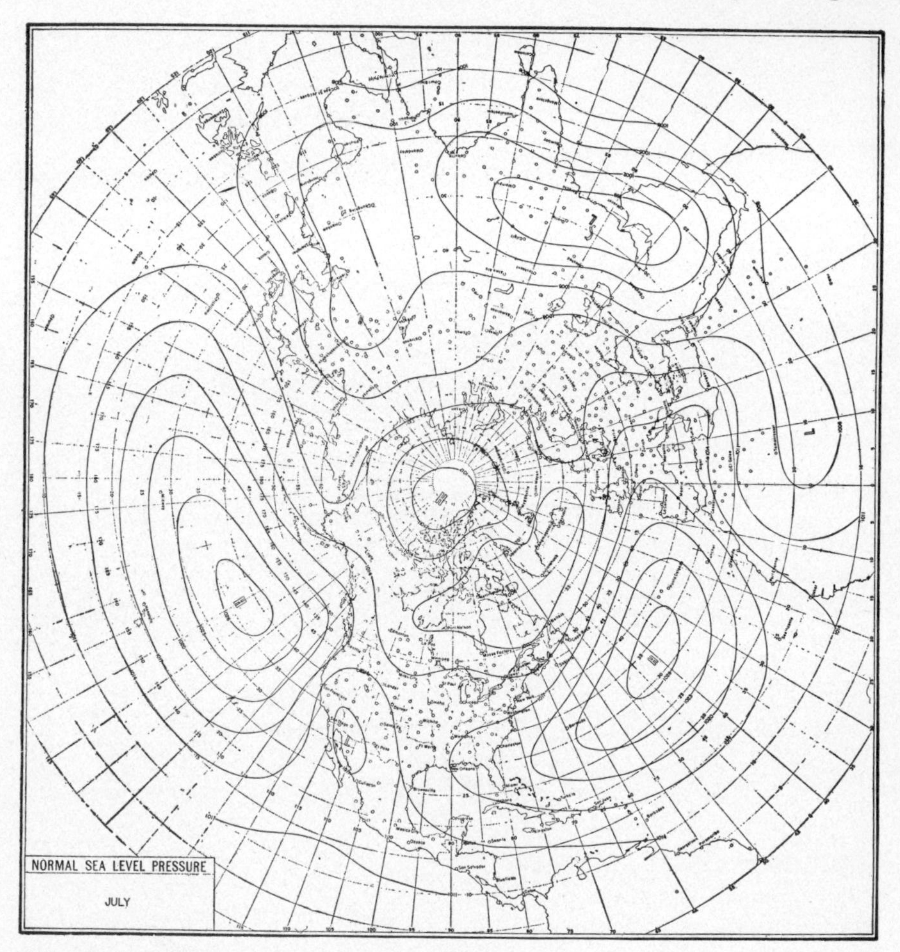

FIG. 2–4. Normal July sea-level pressure for the Northern Hemisphere. (*U.S. Weather Bureau.*)

as 1500 miles, and their winds range from strong or gale force near the center to light at the outer edge. These lows are usually formed where air masses of contrasting temperatures are brought into juxtaposition. Unlike the tropical cyclone, which affects only a small area, they may cause precipitation and cloudiness over many thousands of square miles. Finally, they have a frontal structure with which their origin, development, and dissolution are integrally associated. Figure 2-5 shows average tracks and daily movement of storms in the United States.

Some regions of the United States are subject to *thermal lows* formed by excessive heating at the surface. Such lows have no associated frontal system and usually cause no precipitation or cloudiness. Typical thermal

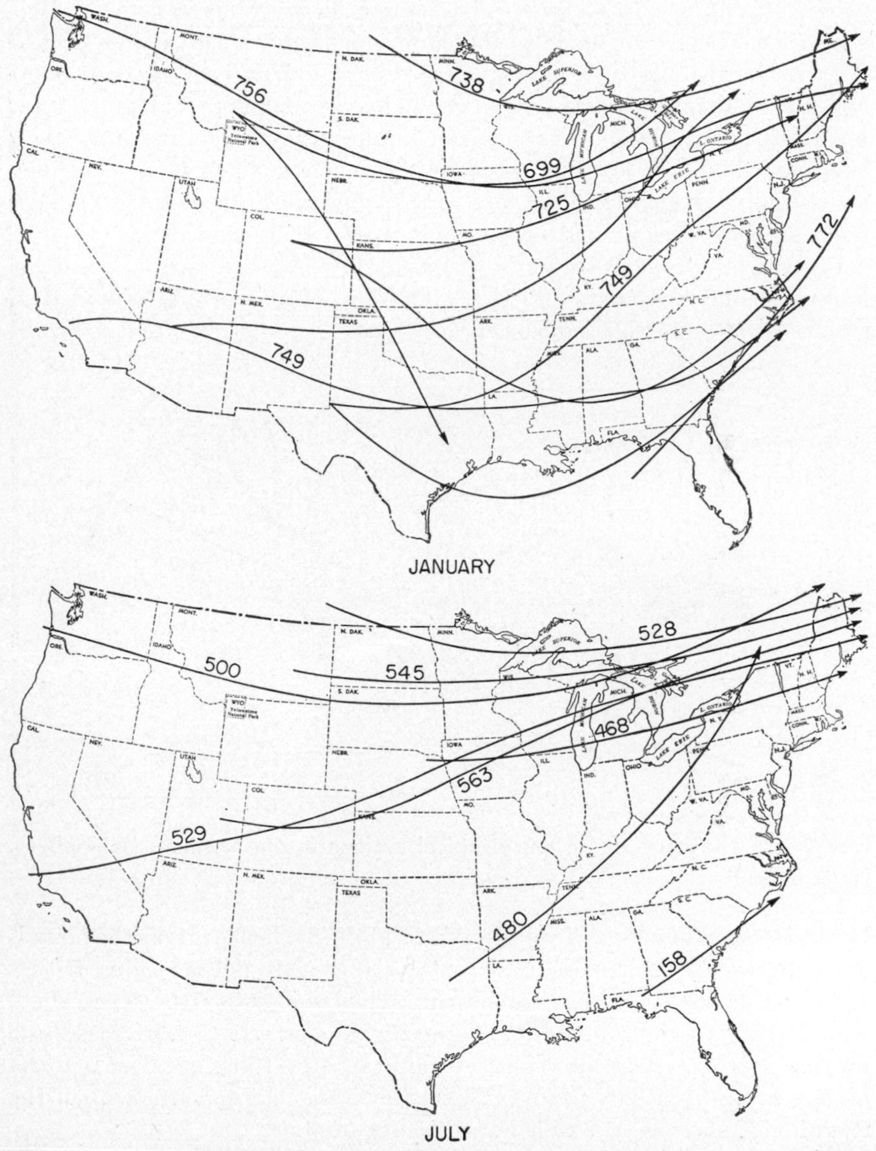

FIG. 2–5. Average tracks and daily movement (miles) of lows. (*After Bowie and Weightman.*)

lows form during the summer months over the Southwestern states and the Central Valley of California.

An *anticyclone* is an area of relatively high pressure with closed isobars, in which the winds flow spirally outward in a clockwise direction in the Northern Hemisphere. There are two kinds of anticyclones, cold and warm. *Cold anticyclones* are formed when air over a restricted area is cooled from below. They are, therefore, relatively shallow domes of cold air, rarely reaching elevations above 10,000 ft. *Warm*, or *dynamic, anticyclones*, on the other hand, are deep systems, and high pressure prevails far up into the atmosphere. As the name implies, they are warmer than their environment in the lower atmosphere; however, in the stratosphere they are actually colder. The winter North American anticyclone is cold, or thermal, while oceanic highs are usually warm, or dynamic.

Fronts. A *frontal surface* is the boundary between two adjacent air masses of different characteristics. The line of intersection of a frontal surface with the earth is called a *surface front*. An *upper-air front* is formed

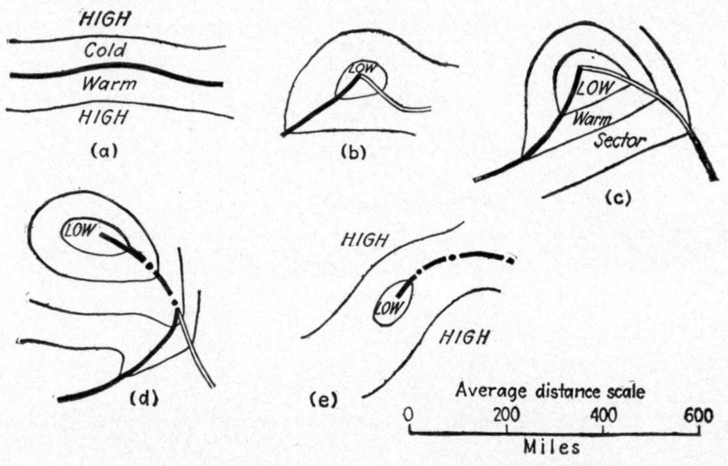

FIG. 2–6. Life cycle of an extratropical cyclone in the Northern Hemisphere. (*After Byers.*)

by the intersection of two frontal surfaces aloft and hence marks the boundary between three air masses. Frontal surfaces are not actually surfaces but rather layers or zones of transition. Their thickness is, however, small with respect to the dimensions of the air masses. If the air masses are moving so that warm air replaces colder air, the front is called a *warm front;* conversely, it is a *cold front* if cold air is displacing warm air. If the front is not moving, it is called a *stationary front.*

The life history of a typical extratropical cyclone is shown in Fig. 2-6. For reasons not yet completely understood, a wave is generated on the boundary between two air masses (Fig. 2-6*a*). Under conditions of dynamic stability, this wave moves along the front with little change in form. If the wave is unstable, it progresses through the successive stages

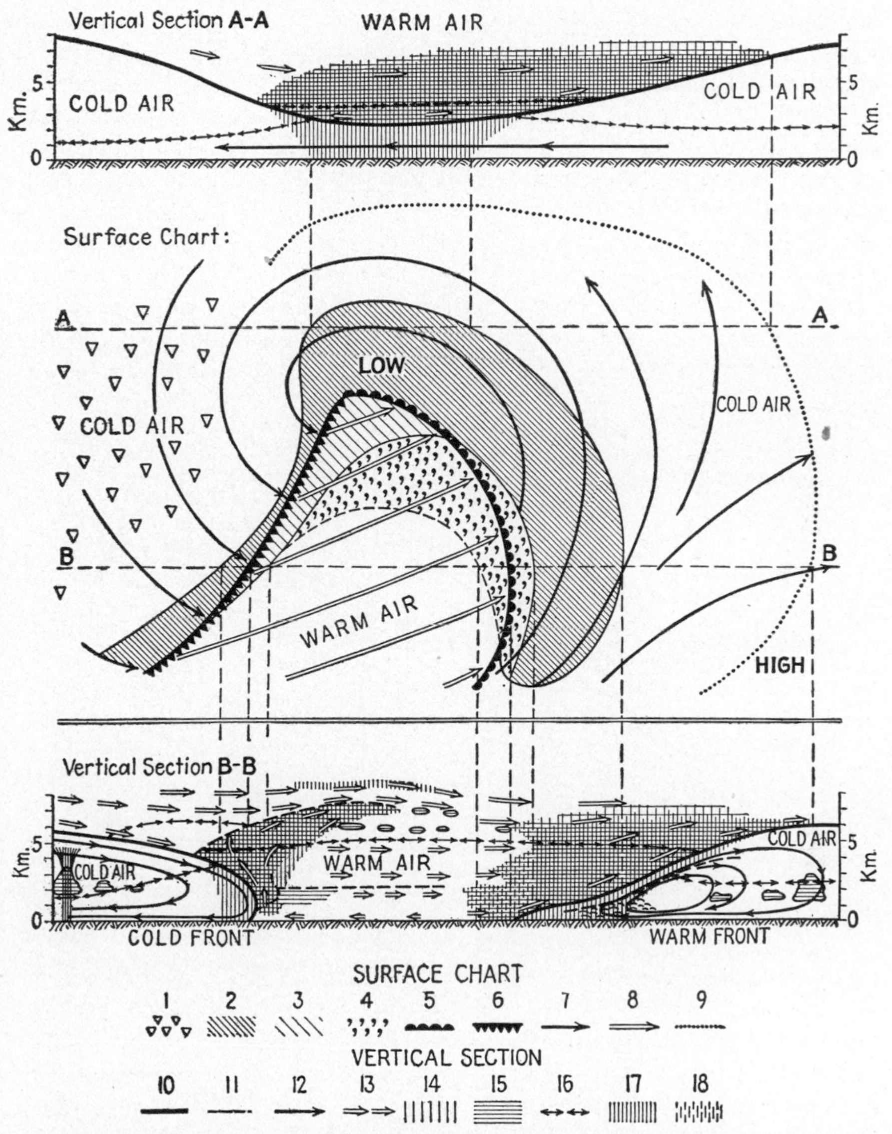

1, shower; 2, rain area in cold air; 3, rain area in warm air; 4, drizzle; 5, warm front; 6, cold front; 7, streamlines of the cold air; 8, streamlines of the warm air; 9, outer cirrostratus boundary; 10, frontal surface; 11, other discontinuity surface; 12, motion of the cold air relative to the center; 13, motion of the warm air relative to the center; 14, falling ice crystals; 15, suspended cloud particles; 16, lower ice-crystal boundary; 17, rain or snow; 18, drizzle.

FIG. 2–7. Model of a young extratropical cyclone. (*After Bergeron.*)

of Fig. 2-6. In stage *c* the cyclone is already deepening and has a well-formed, warm sector. This stage is shown in detail in Fig. 2-7. Warm air moving from the warm sector is forced upward along the warm-front surface, causing widespread precipitation ahead of the surface front. At the same time, the advancing wedge of cold air behind the cold front is lifting the warm air and causing convective showers behind the cold front. Rain also frequently occurs in the warm sector.

Cold fronts move faster than warm fronts and usually overtake them (Fig. 2-6*d*). This process is called *occlusion*, and the resulting surface front is called an *occluded front*. Two types of occlusions are possible,

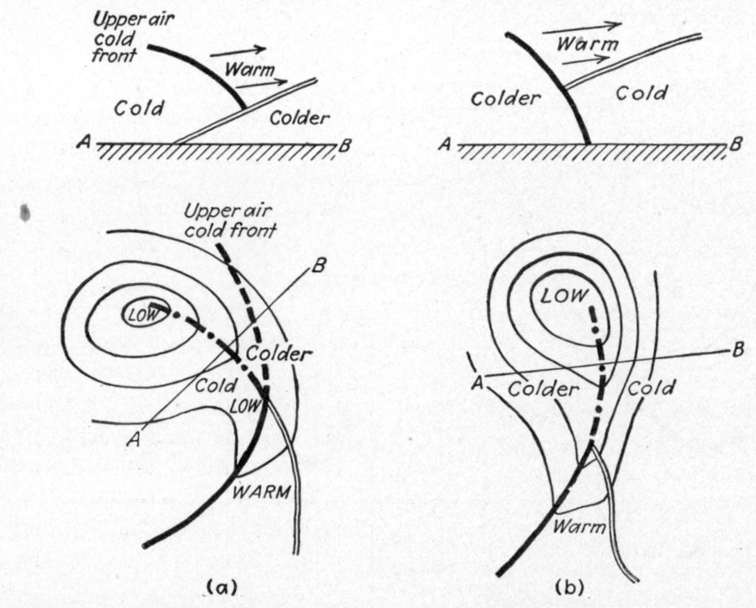

FIG. 2–8. Warm-type (a) and cold-type (b) occlusions. (*After Byers.*)

depending on the relative temperatures of the air masses on either side of the front. The *cold-type occlusion* develops when the air in advance of the front is warmer than that behind, while with the opposite temperature distribution the *warm-type occlusion* forms (Fig. 2-8). In both cases, an upper front is formed.

PHYSIOGRAPHIC INFLUENCES ON CLIMATE

Although the general circulation is the major factor in determining the climates of the world, physiographic features modify the circulational effects considerably to produce a wide variety of climates. The following discussion treats the general effects of these features on climate. Subsequent chapters describe in more detail the effects of physiography on specific meteorological elements.

Continental and oceanic influences. Excluding the influence of the general circulation, the distribution of continents and oceans provides the most important control on world climate. The winds created by the general circulation set up ocean currents which transport large amounts of warm water poleward and cold water equatorward. The Gulf Stream in the Atlantic and the Kuroshio in the Pacific are typical warm currents. The Kuroshio, or Japan Current, is responsible for the unusually mild climate along the coastline of the Gulf of Alaska. On the other hand, the cold, foggy summers along the coasts of Labrador and Newfoundland are caused by the cold Labrador Current.

In addition to the influence of the major ocean currents, coastal climates are sometimes affected by the phenomenon known as "upwelling." When prevailing winds result in the transport of surface water away from the coast, cold water from great depths is brought to the surface near the coast. When warm maritime air moves across this cold water, condensation takes place and fog and low clouds are formed. Cooling of the air from below results in stable conditions and light precipitation. Such conditions are in evidence along the California coast in summer.

Because of the difference in heat-storage characteristics of land and water masses, variations in atmospheric temperature are reduced and lag more over oceans than over land surfaces. The peaks and troughs of the annual march of temperature occur about one month later over oceans than over land. The influence of continents and oceans is not restricted to temperature. Wüst estimated that some 80,000 cubic miles of water is evaporated annually from the oceans, while only about 15,000 cubic miles is evaporated from lakes and land surfaces of continents. Thus, it is evident that air masses over the ocean carry relatively greater moisture charges than those over land. It is not possible to ignore entirely the effects of fronts, subsidence, and topography on the distribution of precipitation, but it can be stated in general that cloudiness, humidity, and precipitation decrease and sunshine increases inland with distance from the coastline. As a matter of interest, the total annual precipitation over continents is estimated to be about 24,000 cubic miles, of which about 9000 is returned to the sea by streamflow.

Thermal contrasts between land and ocean are responsible for diurnal wind reversals if not counteracted by large-scale circulation. During the day, the lower layers of air over the land are warmer than those over the ocean, and a pressure gradient is set up which causes a *sea breeze*, *i.e.*, a wind from the ocean to the land. At night the situation is reversed to produce a *land breeze.* According to Landsberg, sea breezes may often be felt as much as 30 to 40 miles inland, but the land breeze is much weaker and reaches only a few miles out to sea. Both land and sea breezes rarely extend above 1500 ft.

Seasonal temperature contrasts between land and water produce large-scale land and sea breezes called *monsoons*. In winter, high pressures over relatively cold land surfaces produce offshore winds, while in summer the reverse takes place. In a typical monsoon climate, the winters are clear and dry, and the summers are cloudy and wet. The outstanding example of a monsoon climate is that of India, but noticeable monsoon effects are also observed on the Spanish Peninsula and in Australia, China, portions of Africa, and Texas.

Influence of topography. Land forms and variations in elevation cause wide differences in climate within short distances. It is well known that temperature in the free atmosphere decreases with elevation at an average rate of about 3½ F° per 1000 ft up to the tropopause. Similar variation of surface temperature with altitude has been observed in mountain regions.

Air is cooled as it rises up the windward slope of a mountain range and is warmed as it descends on the leeward slope. If precipitation occurs during the ascent, the latent heat of condensation is realized and temperatures, level for level, are higher on the leeward slope. Temperature contrasts between the two slopes are further accentuated because of the more favorable radiation conditions on the leeward side, where cloudiness is less than on the windward.

A diurnal wind system, comparable to the land and sea breezes of the coast, is common in mountainous regions. During the day, surface temperatures along a mountain slope are higher than those at corresponding levels in the free air. Consequently, a convection current is generated such that heated air rises up the mountain slope (*valley breeze*) and is replaced by subsiding air over the valley. Similarly, the cooling of air at night by outgoing radiation leads to a gravitational flow downslope, known as the *mountain breeze*.

Large mountain ranges serve as climatic divides by acting as barriers which deflect the circulation in the lower atmosphere. Thus, maritime air masses approaching from the Pacific are either deflected or considerably modified by the western mountain ranges. It is observed that precipitation generally increases with elevation on both slopes but is considerably higher on the windward slope.

Effect of lakes. Heat storage in lakes acts to stabilize air temperatures, minimizing and lagging variations in the adjacent regions. Near large lakes with winds prevailing generally in one direction, both the annual and diurnal temperature ranges are lowest on the lee shore. In regions where the lakes freeze in winter, the exchange of the latent heat of fusion between the lakes and the air further modifies the temperature variations.

During the winter, air masses moving over the relatively warm surface of large lakes pick up an additional moisture charge and at the same time are made more unstable by heating from below. As a result, the amount and frequency of precipitation, fog, and cloudiness are greater on the leeward shore. In the summer, the stabilizing effect of the relatively cold lake surface on passing air masses reduces the amount of precipitation on the leeward shore.

3

TEMPERATURE IN THE ATMOSPHERE

In the preceding chapter the manner in which the atmosphere receives heat from the sun was discussed. Weather changes are associated with variations of atmospheric temperature. Since solar energy radiated by the sun is the principal source of heat for the surface of the earth, the rate at which heat is received is an important factor in meteorological processes.

HEAT TRANSFER

Insolation. The rate at which heat is delivered at any given place on the earth's surface in the form of solar rays depends on (1) the rate at which energy is radiated from the sun, (2) the distance of the earth from the sun, (3) the inclination of the rays to the surface, and (4) the portion of the incoming solar energy absorbed by the atmosphere. Solar radiant energy is received at the top of the atmosphere at the average rate of 1.94 $cal/cm^2/min$ on a surface normal to the solar rays. This rate is called the *solar constant*, but the incoming radiation actually fluctuates slightly. In January the earth is about 91 million miles from the sun and in July about 94 million miles. Since the intensity of radiation varies inversely with the square of the distance, the solar energy received in January is about 7 per cent greater than in July.

Because of the inclination of the earth's axis, the portions of the earth's surface receiving the most direct rays of the sun vary as the earth moves along its orbit. Thus, in July the Northern Hemisphere is tilted toward the sun and, although the earth is at its greatest distance from the sun, experiences its warmest weather because the angle of the solar rays to the earth's surface is greatest. Similarly, the earth's rotation results in a diurnal variation in the amount of radiation received at any point.

About 43 per cent of the solar radiation entering the top of the atmosphere is reflected or scattered back to space. Of the remainder, 12 per cent is absorbed by the water vapor in the atmosphere; 5 per cent by dust, clouds, and permanent gases, such as nitrogen, oxygen, and argon; and 40 per cent by the surface of the earth.

Instruments for measuring the intensity of incoming radiation are called *pyrheliometers.* Radiation-intensity observations are made at about 50 stations in the United States, but duration of sunshine is recorded at most Weather Bureau first-order stations. The instrument used for this purpose is the *Marvin sunshine recorder,* which is essentially a differential air thermometer. When exposed to solar rays, a black bulb absorbs more heat than a clear one, causing the air and alcohol vapor within it to expand and force a column of mercury to rise. When the mercury reaches two wires midway up the tube, it closes an electrical circuit. Unfortunately, the instrument is sensitive to diffuse radiation and temperature, as well as to direct sunshine. Since there is no objective standard for its adjustment, records for different stations are not comparable.

The *Smithsonian silver-disk pyrheliometer* is used by the U.S. Weather Bureau as a standard for measuring normal incident radiation. It has a sensitive, blackened silver disk at the lower end of a diaphragmed tube. The diaphragms of the tube exclude radiation to the silver disk except from the sun's disk and a small ring of the sky in immediate proximity to it. The silver disk is usually alternately exposed and shielded for 2-min periods. A bent mercurial thermometer is immersed in mercury in a sealed chamber in the side of the silver disk to measure its rate of heating and cooling.

The *Eppley thermoelectric pyrheliometer* is used for measuring total solar and sky radiation. This instrument consists of two concentric rings of equal area, one blackened and the other white, mounted inside a hermetically sealed glass bulb, which has been thoroughly dried and partially evacuated. The hot junctions of a multi-couple thermopile of gold-palladium and platinum-rhodium alloys are attached to the lower side of the black ring and the cold junctions to the lower side of the white ring. The differential in temperature between the two rings creates an electromotive force nearly proportional to the amount of radiation received.

In addition to the instruments described above, there are many other types of pyrheliometers. In order to obtain comparable measurements with the various instruments, they must be standardized to measure the radiation from the same portion of the sky. In this country, all pyrheliometers designed for measuring normal incident radiation have openings subtending an angle of 5°43′; *i.e.*, the ratio of tube length to diameter of receiving surface is 10 : 1.

Conduction and convection. Air in contact with the earth's surface is heated by *conduction,* the flow of heat energy through matter by means of internal molecular activity without any obvious motion of matter. In addition, most of the heat radiated by the earth's surface is absorbed by water vapor and carbon dioxide in the lower atmosphere. Other gases in contact with the water vapor and carbon dioxide are warmed by conduction.

Because air which is being heated decreases in density, the air which is in contact with the earth's surface and is warmed by conduction tends to become lighter. However, since the earth's surface consists of various substances, the air in contact with it is unevenly heated, with resulting differences in air density. Buoyancy forces lighter, warmer air to rise through the surrounding denser, cooler air. The ascending warm air expands because of lower atmospheric pressure and therefore cools. It is further cooled by conduction and mixing with surrounding air. When the ascending air has expanded and lost enough heat so that its density is the same as that of its environment, it stops rising. The rising warm air is, of course, replaced by the cooler surrounding air. The entire process is known as *convection*, which is the transport of heat by moving matter.

THE VERTICAL DISTRIBUTION OF TEMPERATURE

The net effect of all the processes which influence the temperature of the atmosphere results in a general decrease of temperature with height averaging about 3½ F° per 1000 ft in the troposphere and a nearly isothermal condition in the stratosphere. The rate of change of temperature with height is called the *vertical temperature gradient*, or *lapse rate*. Temperature lapse rates in the lower layers above a land surface show a great deal of variation. At night, when outgoing radiation lowers the temperature of the surface, the layer of air just above the ground is also cooled. It may lose sufficient heat so that its temperature is lower than that of the air immediately above. There is then an increase of temperature with elevation, or *temperature inversion*. Strong, surface winds tend to destroy such inversions by mixing. Temperature inversions are also found at the boundary of a layer of cold air with warm air flowing over it. Thus, upper-air soundings made ahead of an advancing warm front will show an inversion at the boundary between the colder air in the lower layers and the overrunning warm air.

After sunrise the ground is heated by solar radiation, the temperature of the air in contact with the surface begins to rise, and the night inversion begins to weaken. Further warming eventually destroys the inversion completely, and if the heating is continued, the lapse rate of the lower layers may reach the dry-adiabatic (0.54 F° per 100 ft). At this point, further heating results in a thorough mixing of the air. However, under optimum surface heating conditions, it is possible for the lapse rate of an extremely thin layer of air to exceed the dry-adiabatic. A rate of decrease of temperature with height greater than 0.54 F° per 100 ft is known as a *superadiabatic lapse rate*.

Cloudiness has an important influence on the net amount of radiation received or given off by the ground. By limiting the amount of heat lost by the ground, night cloudiness may prevent surface inversions from forming. In the daytime, cloudiness decreases the lapse rate in the lower layers by lessening the amount of heat received by the surface.

Dry-adiabatic lapse rate. A thermodynamic process in which no heat exchange occurs between the working system and its environment is called an *adiabatic process.* When a parcel of air at one level is forced to a lower level, the higher pressure at the lower level acts to decrease its volume. The work of compression is converted to heat energy and is manifested by rising temperatures. This warming of air adiabatically by compression is called *dynamic heating.* In nature, the process is not strictly adiabatic as some heat is lost or gained from the surrounding air. However, air is such a poor conductor and radiator of heat that, for meteorological purposes, the process is considered adiabatic. Conversely, a parcel of air which is lifted to a higher level is subjected to lower external pressure and expands. The rising parcel does work on the surrounding air by exerting pressure outward. The source of energy for this work is the heat in the ascending air, which must necessarily cool as it rises. The cooling of air adiabatically by expansion is called *dynamic cooling.*

The temperature of a particle of unsaturated air lifted adiabatically decreases at the rate of 0.54 F° per 100 ft (approx 1 C° per 100 m). This rate of decrease of temperature with height is known as the *dry-adiabatic lapse rate.* If a particle of unsaturated air were forced to descend adiabatically, its temperature would, of course, increase at the rate of 0.54 F° per 100 ft.

Saturated-adiabatic lapse rate. When a parcel of air saturated with water vapor is lifted adiabatically, it expands and cools dynamically. The cooling of the water vapor in the air causes condensation and results in the release of the latent heat of vaporization. This heat serves to reduce the rate of cooling of the rising parcel. For this reason, the *saturated-adiabatic lapse rate* is less than the dry-adiabatic. For the process to be truly adiabatic, the products of condensation must be carried along in suspension in the ascending air.

In the lower layers of the atmosphere, the average saturated-adiabatic lapse rate is 0.3 F° per 100 ft. Since the amount of water vapor which air can contain decreases with temperature, the rate at which heat is liberated by condensation must diminish as the saturated air is cooled. Therefore, at low temperatures, the saturated-adiabatic lapse rate approaches the dry-adiabatic.

At and below freezing, water vapor may condense into supercooled liquid water, ice crystals, or snow. When it condenses into the last two forms, the latent heat of fusion combines with the latent heat of vaporization to further reduce the rate of decrease of temperature of the rising air. The saturated-adiabatic lapse rate for condensation in the form of ice, therefore, is less than that for supercooled water, but there is a counteracting influence at temperatures below freezing because more condensation is possible when the space is saturated with respect to water than with respect to ice.

The saturated-adiabatic process is reversible, *i.e.*, a parcel of air which follows the saturated adiabat in rising will follow the same lapse rate in descending, provided that it retains all the original products of condensation. In nature, this process is rare, since the products of condensation are usually precipitated.

Pseudoadiabatic lapse rate. If the moisture which is being condensed in a rising parcel of saturated air is precipitated, the temperature of the air will decrease at the *pseudoadiabatic lapse rate.* The process is not strictly adiabatic, because some heat is carried away by the precipitation. As in the saturated-adiabatic process, the lapse rate at below freezing temperatures depends on whether the products of condensation are in the form of ice or supercooled water.

For ascending parcels of saturated air, the saturated-adiabatic and pseudoadiabatic processes yield lapse rates which do not differ significantly and, for most meteorological problems, are considered equal. However, the pseudoadiabatic process is irreversible, since the products of condensation are not retained. The descending air cannot remain saturated and warms at the dry-adiabatic lapse rate.

ATMOSPHERIC STABILITY

When the vertical distribution of temperature in a layer of the atmosphere is such that an element of air will resist vertical displacement, the lapse rate and the layer are said to be *stable.* If, on the other hand, the vertical distribution of temperature should be such that an air particle which is given either an upward or downward impulse continues to move away from its original level with increasing speed, the lapse rate and the layer are said to be *unstable.* A layer of air is in a state of *indifferent* or *neutral equilibrium* if its lapse rate is such that air particles do not resist or assist vertical displacement.

Unsaturated air. Unsaturated air is stable when its lapse rate is less than the dry-adiabatic. Thus, in Fig. 3-1, the temperature curves *C* and *D* indicate stable lapse rates for unsaturated air. A parcel of air being lifted adiabatically in an unsaturated layer having a lapse rate less than the dry-adiabatic becomes cooler than its environment. It is thus denser than its environment and tends to fall back to its initial level. Conversely, if the parcel is being forced downward, it becomes warmer than its environment and tends to return to the starting level.

If, on the other hand, the lapse rate of a layer of air is such that when a parcel of air within it is lifted or forced downward it will find itself warmer or colder, respectively, than its environment, the lapse rate and the air are said to be unstable. Thus, in Fig. 3-1, any curve to the left of B would represent superadiabatic, or unstable, lapse rates.

Curve A in Fig. 3-1 represents a lapse rate of 1.9 F° per 100 ft. This is known as the *autoconvective lapse rate.* In a layer of air having this lapse rate, the decrease of temperature with height compensates for the decrease of pressure so that the density of the air is the same at all levels. If the rate of decrease of temperature with height is greater than 1.9 F° per 100 ft, the density of the air increases with height. Since denser air aloft

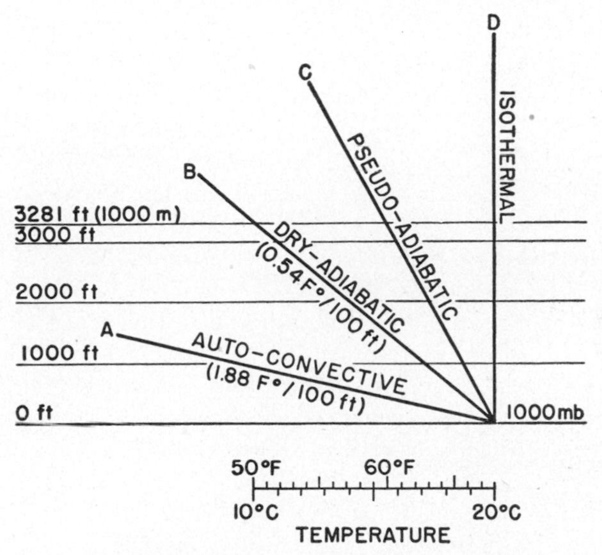

FIG. 3–1. Temperature lapse rates.

will sink into lighter air below without the application of any external force, such a lapse rate represents an exceedingly unstable condition, known as *mechanical instability.*

A layer of unsaturated air having a dry-adiabatic lapse rate is in neutral equilibrium, since vertically displaced parcels of air will always have the same temperature as their environment and, hence, remain in their new positions.

Saturated air. In saturated air, rates less than the pseudoadiabatic are stable (Fig. 3-1, curve C). Any layer of air, whether saturated or unsaturated, is stable if its lapse rate is less than the pseudoadiabatic. Saturated air having a lapse rate greater than the pseudoadiabatic is unstable. Moist, unsaturated air with a lapse rate between the dry-adiabatic and the pseudoadiabatic (between B and C, Fig. 3-1) is said to be in *conditional equilibrium, i.e.,* it may become unstable when lifted to the saturation level. Saturated air having a lapse rate equal to the pseudoadiabatic is in neutral equilibrium.

Effects of vertical displacement of layers of unsaturated air. If a layer of air is being displaced vertically without horizontal shrinking or stretching, the difference in pressure between the bottom and top remains constant, because the total weight of air in the layer remains unchanged. It can easily be shown that the lifting of an unsaturated layer changes its lapse rate so that it approaches but never reaches the dry-adiabatic. Thus, a layer of unsaturated air with a stable lapse rate, *i.e.*, less than the dry-adiabatic, has its stability decreased by lifting.

The downward displacement of a layer of unsaturated air has the opposite effect in that the lapse rate tends to depart from the dry-adiabatic. A layer having a lapse rate less than the dry-adiabatic has its stability increased, and one with a lapse rate greater than the dry-adiabatic becomes more unstable. Obviously, the stability of a layer of unsaturated air having a dry-adiabatic lapse rate will not be influenced by vertical displacement.

Convergence and divergence. A net horizontal inflow of air into the layer between two specified levels is called *convergence*. Since the air is not confined, convergence leads to vertical motion. Hence, if there is convergent flow at the surface, there must also be upward flow; if there is horizontal convergence at any level aloft, there must be either upward or downward motion. Convergence is usually associated with low-pressure centers. Thermal or forced vertical convection from a layer usually leads to horizontal convergence within the layer.

Divergence, the opposite of convergence, is a net outflow of air from a layer. The resulting deficit is compensated by a downward movement of air from aloft when divergence is at the surface or by either upward or downward movement when the divergent layer is at a higher level. Divergence is usually associated with anticyclones and occurs above the warm-front surface of extratropical cyclones.

The slow settling or sinking of a mass of air over a large area is known as *subsidence*. Subsidence is accompanied by divergence in the lower layers, because the sinking air cannot accumulate, or "pile up," in the region indefinitely. By depleting the air from the lower layers in a region, divergence leads to subsidence because the air aloft tends to sink and to replace the air which is flowing out from below.

These phenomena influence the stability of a layer of unsaturated air having a stable lapse rate (less than dry-adiabatic) as follows: (1) lifting and convergence of the layer act together to increase the lapse rate and, hence, to decrease the stability; (2) subsidence and divergence act together to decrease the lapse rate and thus increase the stability. However, these factors do not always act in the above combinations. When the opposite combinations occur, the effects usually tend to cancel out. The combination of subsidence and horizontal divergence in the lower layers of the atmosphere may act so effectively in decreasing the lapse rate that a temperature inversion, known as a *subsidence inversion*, may result.

Maximum cloudiness and precipitation are generally found over regions of maximum horizontal convergence near the surface, a phenomenon generally associated with cyclones. On the other hand, little cloudiness or precipitation is found over regions of maximum horizontal divergence near the surface, a condition usually related to anticyclones.

Effects of lifting air beyond the condensation level. If a layer of air which has more moisture and is nearer saturation at the bottom than at the top is lifted dry-adiabatically, condensation will occur in the lower portion first. Continued lifting will cause the saturated air to cool at the pseudoadiabatic rate, while the unsaturated air in the upper part of the layer will continue to cool at the dry-adiabatic rate.

Since the dry-adiabatic rate is greater than the pseudoadiabatic, the unsaturated air at the top of the layer will cool faster than the saturated air at the bottom. Consequently, the lapse rate within the layer increases, and further lifting may lead to a lapse rate greater than the pseudoadiabatic—an unstable condition for saturated air. A layer of air which, if lifted sufficiently, would acquire a lapse rate greater than the pseudoadiabatic after reaching saturation is said to be *convectively unstable*. Once the lapse rate of the saturated air exceeds the pseudoadiabatic, large-scale overturning will take place—a condition favorable for widespread thunderstorm activity. The importance of convective instability lies in the fact that stable air may become unstable through vertical motion of the air mass as a whole, such as is found on the windward side of mountain ranges and along frontal surfaces.

MEASUREMENT OF TEMPERATURE

Surface-air temperatures. In order to obtain the true temperature of the free air, it is very important that the temperature-measuring instruments be exposed properly. They must be placed in an open space where the circulation of air is quite unobstructed, but they cannot be exposed freely to the sky and the direct rays of the sun. This is usually accomplished in this country by mounting the instruments in an *instrument shelter*, which is nothing more than a white, wooden box with louvered sides which allow free movement of air. In addition to protecting the instruments from direct and reflected radiation, the shelter also serves to keep them dry.

In order that the observed temperatures may be representative of conditions in the free air, it is important that the location of the shelter be typical of the nearby area. The shelters are so installed that the thermometers are about 4½ ft above the ground. In cities, the shelters are sometimes necessarily installed on roofs of buildings, but temperatures obtained in such locations are of doubtful validity as an indication of the thermal climate of a city.

Most thermometers for measuring free-air temperature near the surface are of the liquid-in-glass type. The *maximum thermometer* automatically registers the highest temperature occurring since its last setting. The standard Weather Bureau instrument is similar to ordinary mercury thermometers, except that the bore of the tube is constricted near the bulb so that, as the temperature rises, the mercury in the tube is forced past the constriction in small drops but cannot retreat into the bulb when the temperature falls. This thermometer is usually exposed with its bulb slightly above the horizontal, is righted for a reading, and is set by whirling to force the mercury past the constriction into the bulb.

The *minimum thermometer* automatically registers the lowest temperature which occurs after it has been set. The U.S. Weather Bureau uses an alcohol thermometer with a glass index immersed in the liquid. This index resembles a pin with a head at both ends and is about ½ in. long. To set this thermometer, the bulb end is raised to allow the index to slide to the end of the alcohol column, where it rests because of surface tension. The thermometer is then placed in a horizontal position, and if the temperature falls lower than that prevailing at the time of setting, the index is pulled toward the bulb end. If the temperature should rise, the alcohol will expand past the index without displacing it.

The *thermograph* is an instrument designed to make an autographic record of temperature. The thermometric element is commonly either a bimetallic strip or a metal tube filled with liquid. In the first case, the bimetallic element has the form of a helical coil, one end being rigidly fastened to the instrument and the other linked to the pen. In the second case, the metal tube is made with a tendency to curl. This latter type is in general use in the U.S. Weather Bureau. The deformation of the tube, which is generally filled with alcohol, actuates a pen. The pen traces the record of temperature on a ruled sheet which is wrapped around a cylinder revolved by clockwork.

Electrical-resistance thermometers are convenient for indicating or recording temperatures at some distance from the point of measurement. They are essentially resistance bridges, with the thermic element (thermohm) forming one arm. The resistance of the thermic element varies with temperature and is indicated on a scale graduated in degrees of temperature. Thermocouples, gas bulb thermometers, and other special types of temperature-measuring equipment are frequently used in meeting special problems.

INTERPRETATION OF TEMPERATURE DATA

In order to avoid misusing published Weather Bureau temperature data, a knowledge of the terminology and methods of computation is necessary. The terms *average*, *mean*, and *normal* are all arithmetic means. In meteorology and climatology, the first two are often used interchangeably, but the normal, used as a standard of comparison, has a specialized significance—it is the average value over a specified period of years of any meteorological element for a particular date, month, or season of the year or for the year as a whole.

Definitions. The *mean daily temperature* is computed by averaging the daily extremes [(max + min)/2]. This gives a value which is usually too high but which is ordinarily within a degree from the true daily average. Most cooperative observers take temperature readings about sunset, and the temperatures are published as of the date the readings were made, even though the reported maximum or minimum may have occurred on the previous calendar day. Mean temperatures computed from evening readings will be slightly higher than those computed from midnight readings. For observations taken in the morning, the bias will usually be negative, but smaller than for evening observations.[1]

The *normal daily temperature* is the average daily mean temperature for a given date computed from a record of many years. The *daily range* in temperature is the difference between the highest and lowest temperatures recorded on a particular day. The *mean daily range* is the difference between the normal maximum and minimum temperatures for the same day.

The *mean monthly temperature* is the average of the mean monthly maximum and minimum temperatures. The *normal monthly temperature* is the average of the monthly means for a given month over a period of years. The *absolute monthly range* is the difference between the highest and lowest temperatures experienced during a particular month.

The *mean annual temperature* is the average of the monthly means for the year. The *normal annual temperature* is the average of the annual means over a period of many years. The *annual range* is the difference between the mean temperatures of the warmest and coldest months of the year. The *absolute range* is the difference between the highest and lowest temperatures recorded during the period of record.

The *degree day* is a departure of one degree per day in the daily mean temperature from an adopted reference temperature. The number of degree days for an individual day is the actual departure of the mean temperature from the standard, and the number of degree days in a month or other interval is the sum of all the daily values. Most published degree-day data

[1] Rumbaugh, W. F., The Effect of Time of Observations on the Mean Temperature, *Monthly Weather Rev.*, Vol. 62, pp. 375-376, 1934.

are based on a reference temperature of 65°F because, according to heating engineers, the minimum temperature for bodily comfort in the home is reached when the mean daily temperature falls below that value. Thus, in this instance, a day with a mean temperature of 60°F would have 5 degree days.

In hydrology, degree days are often used in connection with snowmelt computations. For this purpose, degree days above 32°F are usually

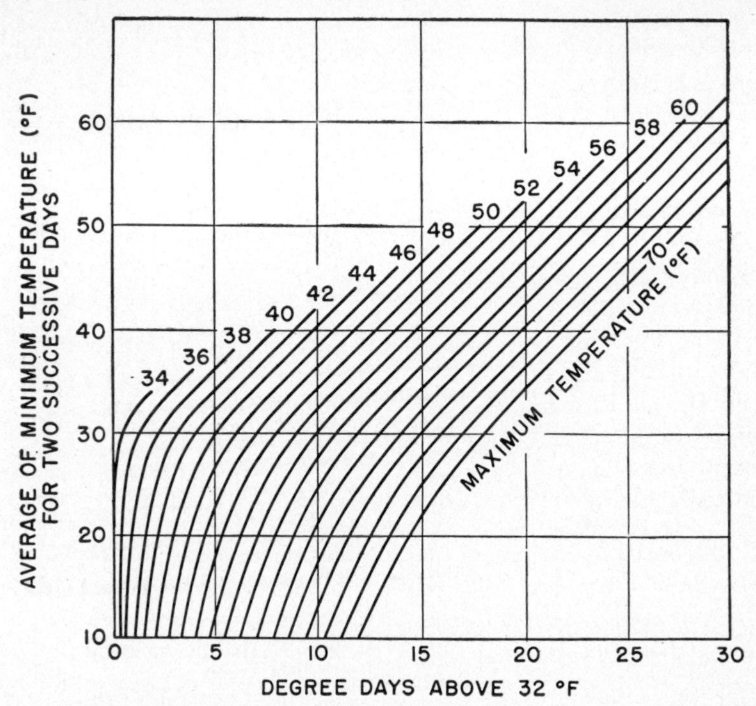

FIG. 3–2. Chart for computing degree days above 32°F from observed maximum and minimum temperatures. (*After Snyder.*)

summarized. By assuming a linear variation of temperature, Snyder[1] constructed curves (Fig. 3-2) giving degree days above 32°F based on the daily maximum temperature and the average of the preceding and following daily minimum temperatures.

The *accumulated temperature* is an index to both the amount and duration of an excess or deficiency of air temperature above or below an adopted standard and is usually expressed in degree days. The *accumulated excess* (or *deficiency*) of temperature is the algebraic sum of the daily departures from normal for the period from Jan. 1 to any date. It is the difference

[1] "Report of Cooperative Hydrologic Investigations," p. 94, Commonwealth of Pennsylvania, August, 1939 (mimeo.).

between the sum of the daily means and the sum of the daily normals. The *average daily excess* (or *deficiency*) is obtained by dividing the accumulated excess by the number of days in the period considered.

Adjustment of data. The "double-mass plotting" method of adjustment discussed in Chap. 6 is not directly applicable to temperature data. An analysis of this method will reveal the basic assumption that values at one station are, on the average, proportional to corresponding values at other stations, that is, $Y = bX$. While this is a valid assumption in dealing with precipitation data, the relation between temperatures for two adjacent stations is better represented by an equation of the form $Y = a + X$.

The homogeneity of a set of temperature data can be tested by plotting observed values at the station of interest against the average for several nearby stations and labeling the points with the year of the observation. A significant change in exposure will be evidenced by a shift in the regression line. Ordinarily, the regression lines will be nearly parallel, so that the early records may be adjusted to the present exposure by simply adding a constant.

Changing the exposure of the thermometers may have an effect upon maximum temperatures different from the effect on minimum temperatures. Further, the adjustment constants may change with season of the year. Therefore, adjustment constants should be determined by months (for maximum and minimum data separately). When the monthly constants are plotted against date, they should conform to a smooth curve.

GEOGRAPHICAL DISTRIBUTION OF TEMPERATURE

Latitudinal variation. Since atmospheric temperature is controlled chiefly by incoming solar radiation, its distribution depends largely on latitude. Despite considerable departures due to other influences, the general orientation of the sea-level isotherms is east and west. The annual range of temperature is also related to latitude. In the tropics, where the daily amount of solar radiation changes only slightly throughout the year, the annual range of temperature is slight; at the poles the yearly variation of incoming solar radiation and the annual range of temperature are larger. Figures 3-3 and 3-4 are maps of mean temperatures for January and July, respectively, in the United States.

Influence of land and water masses. Since land surfaces warm more rapidly than water surfaces under the influence of incoming radiation and cool more rapidly through outgoing radiation, the distribution of land and water over the earth is an important factor in modifying the latitudinal variation of temperature. In summer, when the incoming radiation exceeds the outgoing, land surfaces become warmer than water surfaces; in winter, the outgoing radiation exceeds the incoming, and land surfaces cool more rapidly than water. Hence, the temperature of the air in the lower levels near the earth's surface shows a greater annual range over land than over oceans. A similar but less marked effect is experienced between day and night. At many coastal stations, the moderating influence of the water is particularly effective because of the sea breeze, which reduces

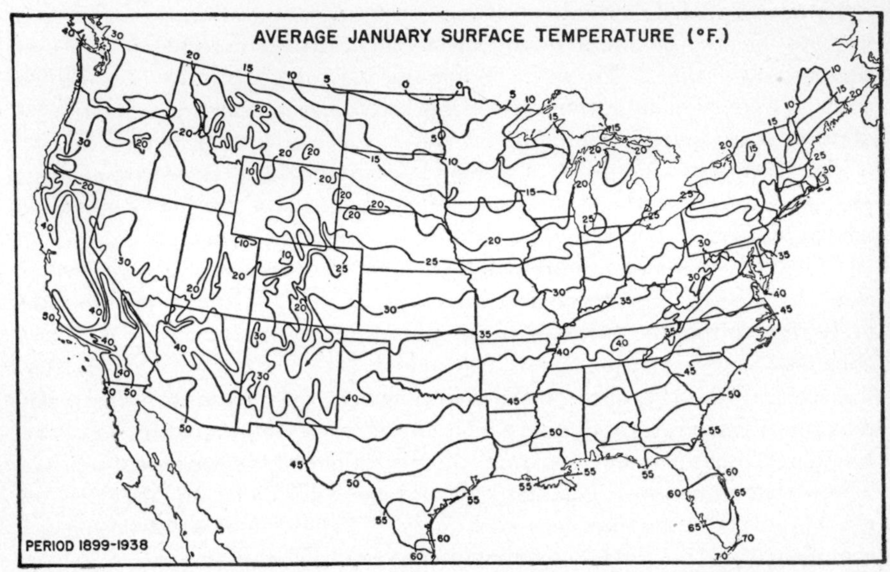

FIG. 3–3. Average January surface temperature. (*U.S. Weather Bureau.*)

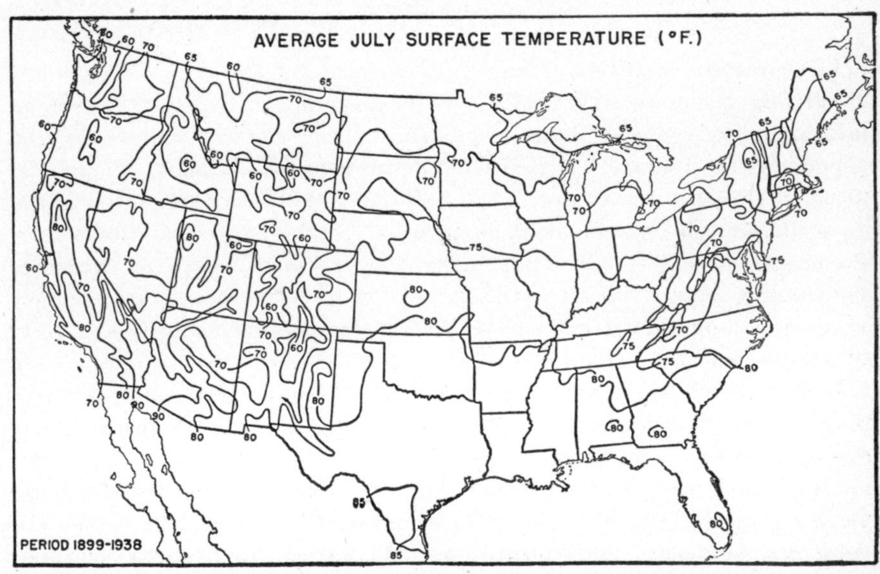

FIG. 3–4. Average July surface temperature. (*U.S. Weather Bureau.*)

temperatures in the hottest part of the day. The effects of land and water distribution on temperature often completely mask the latitudinal variation. This influence is most marked along the Pacific Coast because of the prevailing westerly winds. In Figs. 3-3 and 3-4, the isotherms near the Pacific Coast have a general north-south orientation rather than east-west.

Orographic influences. Surface air temperatures usually decrease with elevation. A high mountain station ordinarily experiences lower temperatures than a station farther down the slope. Studies of temperatures in mountainous regions have shown that the average rate of decrease of surface air temperature along mountain slopes is usually between 3 and 5 F° per 1000 ft. However, at night, temperatures at the bottom of a slope are often lower than at higher elevations, because of gravity drainage of cold air into the valleys.

In the daytime, the orientation of a slope influences the temperature to a considerable extent. In general, western slopes on symmetrical hills have higher temperatures, level for level, than do eastern slopes. A southern slope receives more insolation than would a horizontal surface in the same location, because the solar rays are more nearly perpendicular to the slope. A northern slope receives less insolation than either the southern slope or the horizontal surface because the rays strike it more obliquely and do not reach it at all for much of the day. Hence, temperatures are lower on northern slopes, as evidenced by the later disappearance of snow.

Because of the greater effectiveness of radiation at high levels, there is a tendency for large daily and annual ranges of temperature at high elevations. On mountain slopes, however, the tendency is offset by air drainage and mixing. Large diurnal temperature ranges are particularly characteristic of plateaus.

Effects of vegetation. While trees are very effective in absorbing incident radiation, little of this radiation is transmitted to the soil. During the day the temperature of the air near the surface is lower than that just above the treetops. At night, the treetops act as radiating surfaces, and the soil beneath is protected from excessive heat losses. Minimum temperatures under a forest canopy are therefore higher than in the open. On the other hand, the shading effect of the trees tends to keep the daily maximum temperature somewhat lower. The annual mean temperature in a forested area may be 2 to 4 F° lower than the mean in comparable open country. The difference is greatest during the summer season and becomes rather small in winter; hence, the annual range of temperature is less in forested regions.

Other types of vegetative cover, while less effective than forests, result in more equable temperatures than are experienced over bare soil. It is true, however, that frost is often observed on grass when nearby solid rock at the same level is devoid of any condensate. This phenomenon can be attributed to the poor conductivity of grass. The heat which is radiated from the grass is not readily replaced by heat from the lower soil, as is the case for rock. On clear nights, the temperature of grass has been found to be more than 18 F° lower than that of the underlying soil.

Effects of cities. In a large city, the amount of heat which is produced annually is roughly equal to one-third of the solar radiation reaching an equivalent area. The mean annual temperature of cities averages about 2 F° higher than in their immediate vicinities. The greatest difference occurs in winter, because the amount of heat then produced is at a maximum. The daily minimum temperatures in cities are much higher than in the suburbs. The contrast is especially marked on clear nights, when city haze restricts radiation. The difference in daily maximum temperatures is relatively small.

Any comparison of city and country temperatures must recognize the difference resulting from roof exposures in cities. On clear, still nights, when radiative cooling is particularly effective, roof-top minima may be as much as 15 F° higher than at the ground in an elevation difference of 100 ft. However, on cloudy or windy nights, a slight gradient in the opposite direction will be observed. Maximum temperatures are ordinarily lower at roof level than at the ground. On the average, roof exposures indicate slightly lower temperatures than adjacent ground stations.

TEMPERATURE VARIATIONS WITH TIME

Cycles. A study of temperature records may reveal many apparent periodic changes. These so-called "cycles" are quite numerous and of widely varying lengths. Some investigators[1] have tried to associate temperature cycles with variations in solar radiation. However, with the exception of diurnal and annual variations, no persistent, regular cycles of appreciable magnitude have been found in the data now available. Kincer[2] made a study of temperature records, which indicates that the available period of record is not adequate to define cycles. His data show a small upward trend in temperature over the past 50 to 75 years.

Annual variation. The annual march of air temperature follows the soil-surface temperature and, hence, the radiation intensities. The maximum and minimum points in the annual cycle, for continental areas, occur about 1 month after the solstices. At oceanic stations, this lag is about 2 months. In the United States, January is usually the coldest month and

[1] Clayton, H. H., "Solar Relations to Weather and Life," 2 vols., Clayton Weather Service, Canton, Mass., 1943.

Abbot, C. G., "Solar Radiation and Weather Studies," *Smithsonian Inst. Misc. Collections*, Vol. 94, No. 10, 1935.

[2] Kincer, J. B., Our Changing Climate, *Trans. Am. Geophys. Union*, Vol. 27, pp. 342-347, 1946.

July the warmest. The amplitude of the annual range, *i.e.*, the difference between the average temperatures of the coldest and warmest months of the year, varies with latitude, elevation, and distance from the ocean.

Diurnal variation. The diurnal temperature change is produced by the daily fluctuation in incoming solar radiation. The temperature begins to rise at sunrise but does not reach its maximum at continental stations until 1 to 3 hr after the sun has reached its highest altitude. Over oceanic stations, this lag is only about ½ hr. Minimum temperatures are usually reached about sunrise. During the night, when solar radiation is absent, temperature is affected only by radiative cooling. Consequently, the typical diurnal temperature curve is not symmetrical, the period from maximum to minimum being longer.

The diurnal temperature range, *i.e.*, the difference between the daily maximum and minimum, is affected by the state of the sky. On overcast days, the maximum temperature is lower because of reduced insolation. On the other hand, the minimum is higher because the clouds reduce the amount of outgoing radiation. The diurnal temperature range is much smaller over oceans than over continents, the daily maximum being lower and the minimum higher.

4

ATMOSPHERIC HUMIDITY

Water vapor is one of the regular constituents of the atmosphere, although at times only very small amounts may be present. The profound influence of atmospheric moisture on temperature has been discussed in preceding chapters. By absorbing and reradiating terrestrial radiation, atmospheric vapor serves to stabilize the earth's temperature. The release of latent heat of condensation or sublimation within a rising parcel of air maintains temperature lapse rates that are less than in dry air. More important to the hydrologist, however, is the fact that this moisture is the source of precipitation and also materially controls the rates of evaporation from land and water surfaces. It is thus an extremely important factor in the hydrologic cycle.

PROPERTIES OF VAPOR

Vaporization. Most atmospheric vapor is formed by evaporation from water surfaces at ordinary temperatures (Chap. 8). The change from the liquid to the gaseous state is called *vaporization*, or *evaporation*. Vaporization of liquid water occurs because some of its molecules possess sufficient kinetic energy to carry them out through the surface of the water in opposition to the attractive forces which tend to hold them within the body of the liquid. Since an increase in the temperature of a liquid is accompanied by an increase in the speed of its molecules and by a decrease in surface tension, the rate of vaporization increases with temperature. Molecules may leave an ice surface in the same manner as they leave a liquid. This process, whereby a solid passes directly to the vapor state without passing through the intermediate liquid state, is called *sublimation*.

Vapor pressure. Any gas exerts a pressure because of the kinetic energy of its molecules. In a mixture, each gas exerts a *partial pressure* independent of the other gases. The partial pressure exerted by water vapor is called *vapor pressure*. If the total pressure of humid air in a closed container were p and the water vapor were removed, the final pressure p' due to the dry air alone would be less than p. The difference $p - p'$ resulting from the removal of the water vapor is the vapor pressure e.

For practical purposes, the maximum amount of water vapor that can exist in any given space is a function of temperature and is independent of the coexistence of other gases. When a given space contains the maximum amount of water vapor for a given temperature, the space is said to be *saturated*. The expression, "the air is saturated," is often used for "the space is saturated" but is not strictly correct. The *saturation vapor pressure* is the pressure exerted by the vapor in a saturated space. For all practical purposes, it is the maximum vapor pressure possible at a given temperature. There is a slight variation of saturation vapor pressure with atmospheric pressure, but this variation is so small that it may be neglected. Supersaturation exists if a space contains more vapor molecules than the amount necessary to saturate it. This condition does not occur to any appreciable extent in the atmosphere.

If samples of ice and water at a temperature below freezing are placed in confined spaces and the vapor pressure is measured over each, the vapor pressure over water is found to be slightly higher. The difference is at a maximum at about 10°F, but the ratio of the vapor pressures increases with decreasing temperature (Fig. 4-1). Most psychrometric tables are based on conditions over ice for temperatures below 32°F.

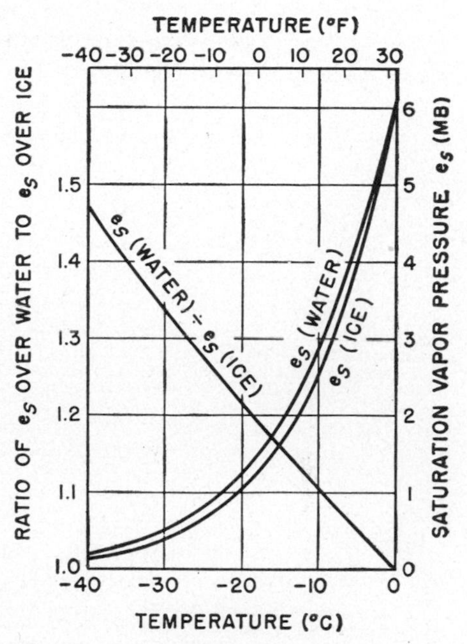

FIG. 4-1. Variation of vapor pressure with temperature below the normal freezing point.

Condensation. Condensation is the process by which vapor changes to the liquid or solid state. In a space in contact with a water surface, condensation and vaporization always go on simultaneously. The rate of vaporization exceeds the rate of condensation if the space is not yet saturated. In a state of saturation, the rates of condensation and vaporization balance. When supersaturation exists in the atmosphere, condensation normally occurs if suitable nuclei are present.

Water-vapor molecules can sublime without going through the liquid stage. Since the saturation vapor pressure over ice is less than that over water at the same temperature, the introduction of ice in a space saturated with respect to supercooled liquid water (liquid water below the freezing point) at the same or higher temperature will result in the direct condensation of vapor on the ice. This is an important factor in the production of heavy rain (Chap. 6).

Latent heat of vaporization or condensation. Vaporization results in the removal of heat energy from the liquid being vaporized, while condensation adds heat energy to the liquid on which condensation occurs. The *latent heat of vaporization* is the amount of heat absorbed by a unit mass of a substance, without change in temperature, while passing from the liquid to the vapor state. The reverse change of state releases an equivalent amount of heat known as the *latent heat of condensation.*

The heat of vaporization of water varies with temperature but may be determined accurately up to 40°C by the formula

$$H_v = 594.9 - 0.51T \tag{4-1}$$

where H_v is the latent heat in calories per gram of water and T is the temperature (°C).

Latent heat of fusion. The latent heat of fusion is the amount of heat absorbed by a unit mass of substance, without change in temperature, while passing from a solid to a liquid. It may be defined as the amount of heat required to convert one gram of ice into liquid water without change in temperature. When 1 g of liquid water freezes into ice, the latent heat of fusion (79.7 cal/g) is liberated.

Latent heat of sublimation. The latent heat of sublimation is the heat absorbed by a unit mass of substance, without change in temperature, while passing directly from a solid to a vapor state. It is the amount of heat required to convert one gram of ice into vapor at the same temperature without passing through the intermediate liquid state. It is equal to the sum of the latent heat of vaporization and the latent heat of fusion. Hence, at 0°C it is about 675 cal/g. Direct condensation of vapor into ice at the same temperature, without passing through the liquid state, liberates an equal amount of heat.

Density of moist air. The specific gravity of water vapor as compared with that of dry air at the same temperature and pressure is 0.622. The density of water vapor ρ_v in grams per cubic centimeter is

$$\rho_v = 0.622 \frac{e}{R_g T} \tag{4-2}$$

where T is the absolute temperature (°C) and R_g, the dry-air gas constant, equals 2.87×10^3 when the vapor pressure e is in millibars.

The density of dry air ρ_d in grams per cubic centimeter is

$$\rho_d = \frac{p_d}{R_g T_a} \tag{4-3}$$

where p_d is the pressure in millibars.

The density of moist air is equal to the mass of water vapor plus the mass of dry air in a unit volume of the mixture. If p_a is the total pressure of the moist air, $(p_a - e)$ will be the partial pressure of the dry air alone. Adding Eqs. (4-2) and (4-3) and substituting $(p_a - e)$ for p_d,

$$\rho_a = \frac{p_a}{R_g T_a}\left(1 - 0.378\,\frac{e}{p_a}\right) \tag{4-4}$$

This equation shows that moist air is lighter than dry air.

The *virtual temperature*, T_v, of moist air is the temperature at which dry air under the same pressure would have the equivalent density. Hence,

$$T_v = \frac{T_a}{1 - 0.378(e/p_a)} \tag{4-5}$$

Combining Eqs. (4-4) and (4-5),

$$\rho_a = \frac{p_a}{R_g T_v} \tag{4-6}$$

HUMIDITY EXPRESSIONS

Vapor pressure. As defined earlier in this chapter, the vapor pressure e is the partial pressure of the water vapor in the atmosphere. It is usually expressed in millibars and can be computed by the empirical psychrometric equation

$$e = e_s - 0.000367 p_a (T_a - T_w)\left(1 + \frac{T_w - 32}{1571}\right) \tag{4-7}$$

where p_a is the atmospheric pressure (mb), T_a is the dry-bulb temperature (°F), T_w is the wet-bulb temperature (°F), and e_s is the saturation vapor pressure corresponding to T_w.

Absolute humidity. The absolute humidity a_h is the mass of water vapor per unit volume of space. It is usually expressed in grams per cubic meter and can be computed by

$$a_h = 217\,\frac{e}{T_a} \tag{4-8}$$

where T_a is the absolute temperature (°C). It should be noted that absolute humidity is equivalent to vapor density and that Eq. (4-8) is the same as Eq. (4-2), except for units.

Relative humidity. The relative humidity f is the percentage ratio of the amount of moisture in a given space to the amount which that volume could contain if it were saturated. Hence, it is also the ratio of the actual vapor pressure to the saturation vapor pressure:

$$f = 100\,\frac{a_h}{a_s} = 100\,\frac{e}{e_s} \tag{4-9}$$

Dewpoint. The dewpoint T_d is the temperature at which air becomes saturated when cooled under constant pressure and with constant water-vapor content. It may also be defined as that temperature which has a saturation vapor pressure equal to the existing vapor pressure.

Specific humidity. The specific humidity q_h is the mass of water vapor per unit mass of moist air. It is usually expressed in grams per kilogram of moist air and can be computed by

$$q_h = 622 \frac{e}{p_a - 0.378e} \tag{4-10}$$

Since p_a is of the order of one hundred times e, the negative term in the denominator is ordinarily omitted and Eq. (4-10) becomes

$$q_h = 622 \frac{e}{p_a} \tag{4-11}$$

Mixing ratio. The mixing ratio w_r is the mass of water vapor per unit mass of perfectly dry air in a humid mixture. Usually expressed in grams per kilogram of dry air, it is given by

$$w_r = 622 \frac{e}{p_a - e} \tag{4-12}$$

It should be noted that there is little numerical difference between the specific humidity and the mixing ratio, and for many purposes they are considered equal.

Precipitable water. The total amount of water vapor in the atmosphere is frequently expressed as the depth of precipitable water W_p in inches. This term is a misnomer, since no natural precipitation process removes all the moisture from the air. The equation for computing the depth of precipitable water from upper-air soundings[1] is

$$W_p = 0.0004 \int_{p_1}^{p_0} q_h \, dp \tag{4-13}$$

where q_h is the specific humidity in grams per kilogram and p is pressure in millibars. In practice, the amount of precipitable water in a column of air of any considerable height is computed by increments of pressure using the formula

$$\Delta W_p = 0.0004 \bar{q}_h \, \Delta p \tag{4-14}$$

and summing ΔW_p throughout the column. The value of $\bar{q}_h$ is generally taken as the average of the specific humidity at the top and bottom of each layer.

In saturated air with a pseudoadiabatic lapse rate, the precipitable water in a column of air is a function of surface temperature and the weight of

[1] Solot, S., Computation of Depth of Precipitable Water in a Column of Air, *Monthly Weather Rev.*, Vol. 67, pp. 100-103, 1939.

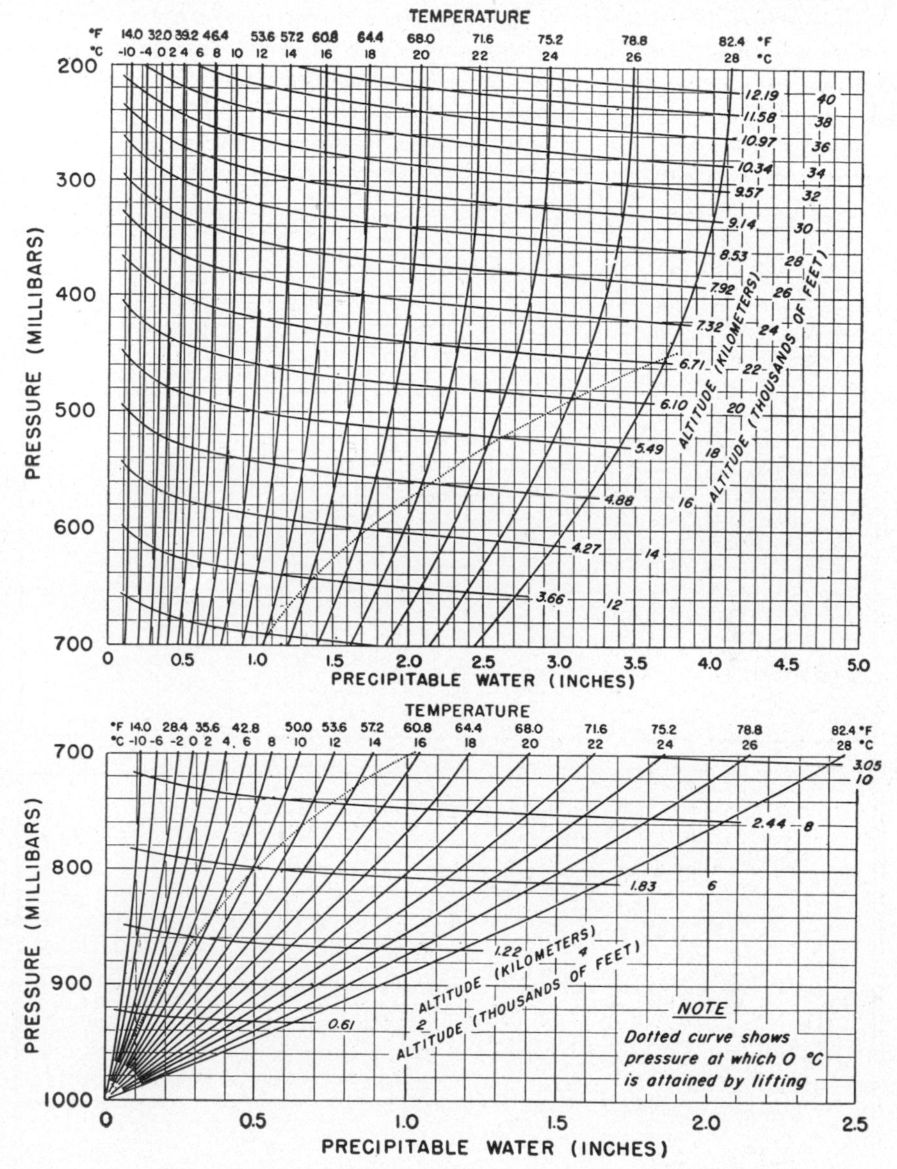

FIG. 4–2. Depths of precipitable water in a column of air of given height above 1000 mb as a function of dewpoint, assuming saturation and pseudoadiabatic lapse rate. (*U.S. Weather Bureau.*)

the air (Δp) only. Figure 4-2 shows the relation for a column with its base at sea level and a pressure of 1000 mb. The dewpoint is substituted for the surface temperature when the air is not saturated. The depth of precipitable water for any layer can be obtained by entering the chart with the pressure for the top and bottom of the layer and subtracting. In any

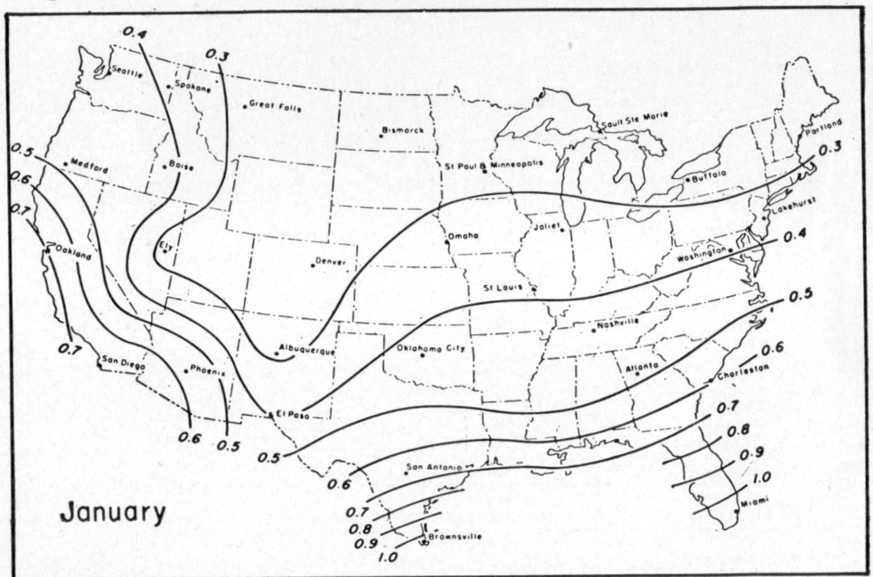

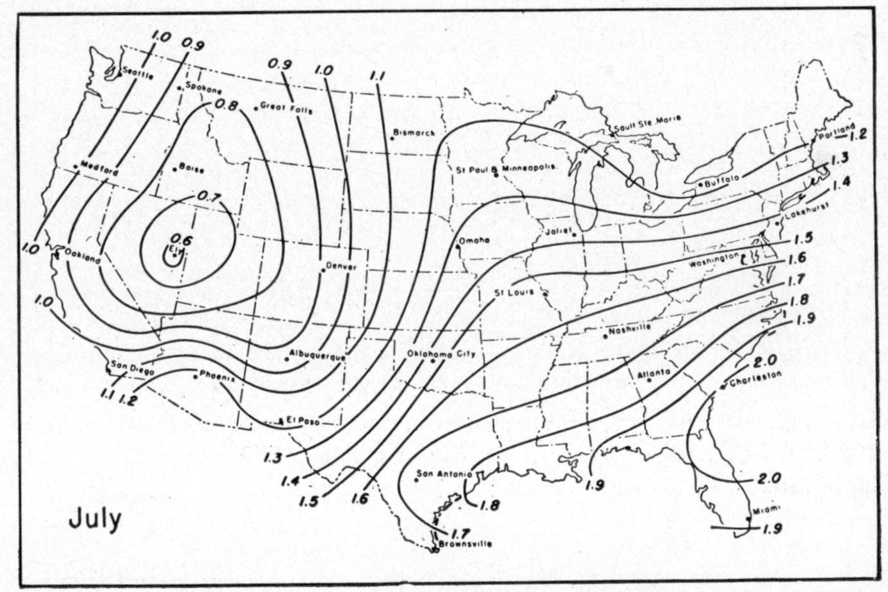

FIG. 4–3. Mean precipitable water from the

case, the temperature, or dewpoint, must be reduced pseudoadiabatically to 1000 mb before entering the chart.

The true average daily precipitable water for a given period is to be obtained only by averaging the depths computed separately for each day. Since such a procedure entails a large amount of work, the maps of Fig. 4-3

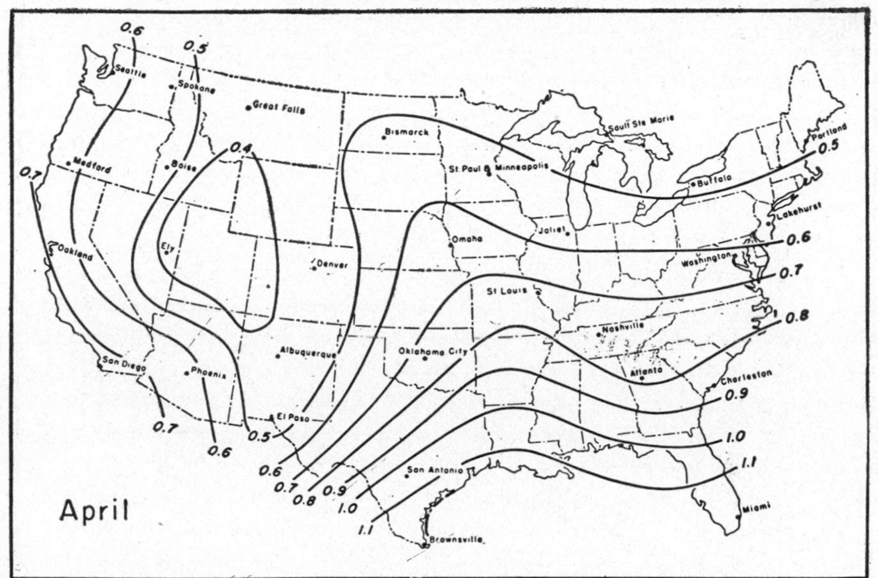

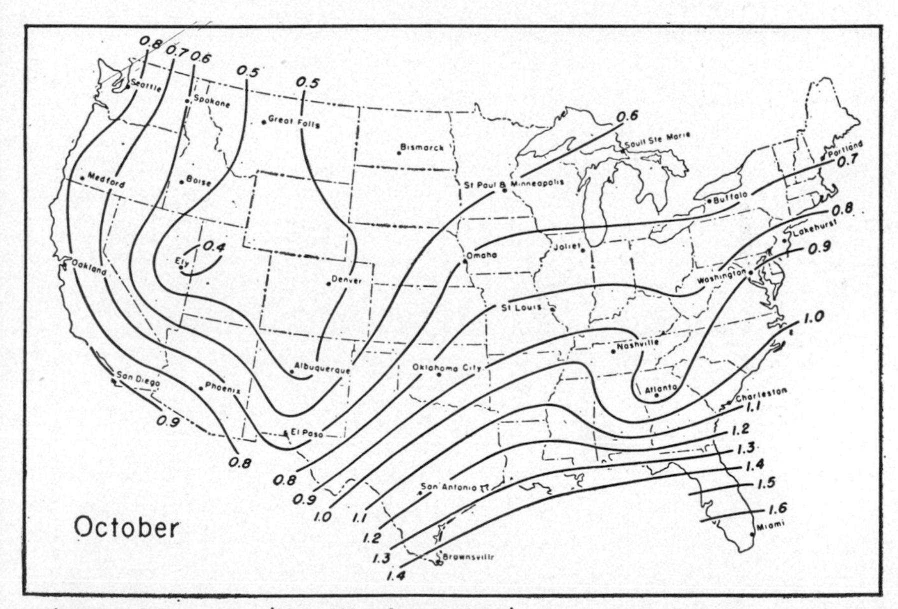

surface to 8 km, msl. (*U.S. Weather Bureau.*)

are based on mean monthly values of upper-air data from radio soundings. The maps show depths of precipitable water in the atmosphere below 8 km, msl (26,250 ft). Precipitable water above 8 km is negligible.

Conservatism of humidity expressions. Each of the above quantities has a particular advantage over the others for a specific purpose. In order to appreciate fully the difference between these terms, their conservatism must be considered. *Conservatism* is the relative constancy of an air-mass property despite the activity of atmospheric processes which tend to change its magnitude. Since the magnitude of all atmospheric properties is constantly changing, conservatism is relative. No measure of humidity is conservative for processes involving changes of water content, *i.e.*, evaporation and condensation, but vapor pressure, dewpoint, specific humidity, and mixing ratio are usually considered conservative properties.

Absolute and relative humidity vary as the result of changes in temperature or pressure, even though there is no actual removal or addition of water vapor. Since most atmospheric processes produce large variations in either pressure or temperature, absolute and relative humidity are highly variable, or nonconservative. The absolute humidity has limited use in meteorology, but the relative humidity is a popular quantity, because many meteorological and physiological phenomena involving atmospheric moisture depend on the degree of saturation and not on the quantity of water vapor.

Vapor pressure and dewpoint depend on the amount of moisture in a unit volume of air and therefore are not conservative for processes involving changes in pressures, such as adiabatic expansion or compression. Under dry-adiabatic conditions, the variation of dewpoint in ascending or descending air is about 1 F° per 1000 ft. The two quantities remain constant for temperature changes in unsaturated air at constant pressure and hence are conservative for radiational heating or cooling. The dewpoint is widely used as an expression of the amount of moisture in the air and is the quantity usually shown on weather maps. The specific humidity and mixing ratio are conservative for any process not involving the actual removal or addition of water vapor.

MEASUREMENT OF ATMOSPHERIC HUMIDITY

Although numerous instruments[1] have been devised for measuring the amount of water vapor in the atmosphere, the measurement of humidity is one of the least accurate instrumental procedures in meteorology.

Instruments. The instrument generally used for making official measurements of humidity in the surface layers of the atmosphere is the *psychrometer*. It consists of two thermometers, one of which has its bulb

[1] Middleton, W. E. K., "Meteorological Instruments," pp. 85-101, University of Toronto Press, Toronto, 1942.

covered with a closely fitting jacket of clean muslin saturated with water. The thermometers are ventilated by whirling or by use of a fan or bellows. Because of evaporation, the reading of the moistened (wet-bulb) thermometer is lower than that of the dry bulb, and this difference in degrees is called the *wet-bulb depression.* By reference to appropriate tables,[1] the dewpoint, relative humidity, and vapor pressure may be obtained.

The *hair hygrometer* consists of a frame in which a strand of hair is kept at approximately constant tension. Changes in length of the hair corresponding to changes in relative humidity are transmitted to a pointer. This instrument is seldom used for meteorological purposes, but it is an inexpensive humidity indicator and is often found in homes and offices. The *hair hygrograph* is essentially a hair hygrometer, but the hair activates a pen, which records on a rotating drum. The *hygrothermograph* combines the registration of both relative humidity and temperature on one record sheet.

The *dewpoint hygrometer* is a device used to determine the dewpoint directly. It usually consists of a highly polished metal vessel containing a suitable liquid, which is cooled by any of several methods. The temperature of the liquid at the moment condensation begins to occur on the metal surface is the dewpoint. The instrument can be made self-recording by observing the metal surface photoelectrically. The use of this instrument has been restricted mostly to laboratory research.

The *spectroscopic hygrometer* measures the selective absorption of light by water vapor in certain bands of the spectrum. This instrument can be used to determine the average moisture content between it and a light source. It has been used to measure the total atmospheric moisture with the sun as a light source.[2]

Errors in measurement. All humidity-measuring instruments are subject to errors from improper observational technique, but the ordinary psychrometer invites more errors of this type than any other device. First, two thermometers must be read. This doubles the chances of misreading. An error of a few tenths of a degree is not serious at summer temperatures but, in the case of extremely low temperatures, may render the measurement absurd. Second, sling and whirling psychrometers must be stopped to permit reading. In dry weather, the readings have to be made at very short intervals to avoid missing the lowest wet-bulb temperature, as the mercury will begin to rise as soon as the muslin becomes dry. Third, the latent heat of fusion causes the mercury in the wet-bulb thermometer to lag at the freezing point, which is sometimes mistaken for the

[1] "Psychrometric Tables," W. B. No. 235, U.S. Weather Bureau, Washington, D. C., 1941.

[2] Foster, N. B., and L. W. Foskett, A Spectrophotometer for the Determination of the Water Vapor in a Vertical Column of the Atmosphere, *J. Optical Soc. Am.*, Vol. 35, pp. 601-610, 1945.

wet-bulb temperature. In addition to these errors are those resulting from the conduction of heat down the thermometer stem, insufficient ventilation, dirty or thick muslin, and impure water — all of which tend to make the measurements too high.

The hair hygrometer and hygrograph are also relatively inaccurate instruments. Besides altering its length with changes in relative humidity, the hair expands with increasing temperature. The magnitude of this effect seems to be about 4 per cent as much per Fahrenheit degree as the mean change of length for 1 per cent relative humidity. The response of the hair to changes in relative humidity is relatively slow and depends a great deal on temperature. The lag increases with decreasing temperature, becoming almost infinite at −40°F. These errors reach significant proportions in upper-air soundings, where large ranges in temperature and sharp variations of humidity with height are observed.

GEOGRAPHICAL DISTRIBUTION OF ATMOSPHERIC HUMIDITY

Latitudinal variation. There is a general tendency for atmospheric moisture to decrease with increasing latitude, although other influences distort this distribution considerably (Fig. 4-3). Relative humidity, being an inverse function of temperature, tends to increase with latitude. However, the general subsidence in the vicinity of the horse latitudes causes a slight decrease in average relative humidity from the equator to 30° lat.

Influence of land and water masses. Since the source of atmospheric moisture is the earth's surface, it follows that the water-vapor content of the atmosphere over a region depends to a considerable extent on the type of surface. It can be reasonably expected that, other factors being the same, atmospheric moisture is greater over water than over land. Although Fig. 4-3 shows the mean depth of precipitable water over the United States only, the influence of water masses is marked, especially where the prevailing winds (Fig. 5-7) are off the sea.

Orographic influence. Since the earth's surface is the source of atmospheric moisture, the maximum water-vapor content is almost always at the ground. Furthermore, the amount of water vapor which can exist in a given volume varies with temperature, which generally decreases with elevation. These two effects result in a decrease of moisture content with elevation, the rate of decrease usually being greatest near the surface. Practically all atmospheric moisture is contained in the lowest 8 km. High-altitude stations have less atmospheric moisture above them than have sea-level stations when other effects are similar. Although there is little supporting evidence, it appears reasonable to expect that the moisture content measured at a mountain station would be somewhat greater than that measured in the free air at the same level.

Effects of vegetation. During the growing season, plants add water vapor to the air by transpiration. Bare soil, on the other hand, can become extremely dry. Furthermore, when wet from recent rain or dew, a vegetative cover offers a larger evaporative surface than does bare soil. Consequently, air over vegetation usually has a higher moisture content than air over bare soil.

HUMIDITY VARIATIONS WITH TIME

Annual variation. The annual variation of the atmospheric-moisture content is, in most regions, practically parallel to that of temperature, *i.e.*, a summer maximum and a winter minimum. This is not true of relative humidity, however, except between the equator and about 30° lat. At higher latitudes, the relative humidity is greater in winter despite low absolute humidity, because of low temperatures and correspondingly low saturation vapor pressures. Hence, although the actual vapor pressure usually has a summer maximum, the relative humidity may be at a minimum during that season.

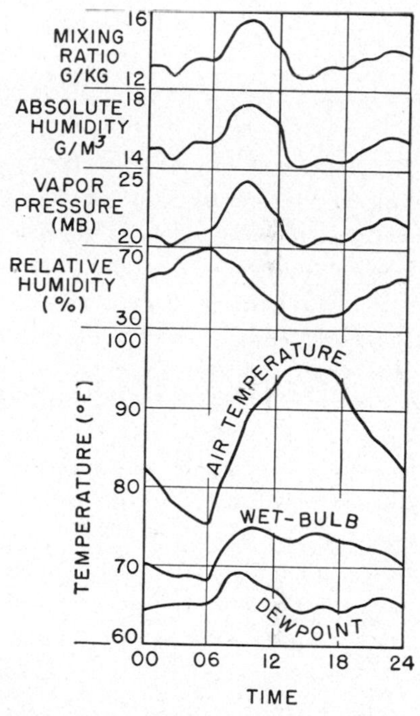

FIG. 4–4. Diurnal variation of atmospheric moisture at the surface, Ft. Worth, Texas, Aug. 23, 1947.

Diurnal variation. Other things being equal, evaporation increases with temperature. Hence, the diurnal variation of atmospheric moisture should be somewhat similar to that of temperature. This is true over the ocean, where atmospheric humidity is at a minimum in the early morning hours and at a maximum in the early afternoon. Over land, however, starting from a minimum in the early morning hours, the atmospheric-water content in the lower layers increases rapidly to a maximum sometime in the forenoon, decreases to a secondary minimum in the afternoon, and increases again toward evening (Fig. 4-4). The afternoon minimum is due to two effects, (1) in the forenoon the surface soil is being depleted of moisture by evaporation at a greater rate than it can be replaced by the transport of water from lower soil layers so that it is gradually drying out, and (2) the turbulent transport of vapor from the surface to higher levels increases during midday.

The diurnal variation of the relative humidity is in general opposite to that of temperature. The maximum usually occurs in the early morning and the minimum in the early afternoon. In regions influenced by sea breezes, the relative humidity may increase during the day. The decrease of relative humidity with height is generally greater at night than in daytime. At night the relative humidity at 2 in. above the ground may be as much as 40 per cent greater than that at the 6-ft level. When insolation is very strong (as at midday), the surface layers may become so warm that the relative humidity increases upward in the lower layers.

5

WINDS

Wind is an important agent in the hydrologic cycle, since there could be no significant moisture transport without air movement. Chapter 2 discusses the large-scale wind phenomena which effect this transport. Precipitation rates, reservoir evaporation, and many other hydrologic phenomena are directly affected by wind. In addition, the determination of design storms by modern hydrometeorological analysis requires a careful study of the wind structure of major storms. In the absence of observed wind data, the necessary information must frequently be deduced from a consideration of the factors controlling winds.

Air flowing nearly horizontally is ordinarily known as *wind*. A stream of air moving in any other direction, especially in the vertical, is called an *air current*. Winds are mainly the result of horizontal differences in pressure. In the absence of other factors tending to influence wind, it should be expected that its direction would be from high to low pressure and that its speed would vary with the pressure gradient. Observation shows that the latter is true but that wind direction is mainly along the isobars, with a slight drift toward lower pressure. The relationship between wind direction and pressure center is expressed by Buys Ballot's law: *If an observer stands with his back to the wind, the lower pressure is on his left in the Northern Hemisphere and on his right in the Southern Hemisphere.* Obviously, the horizontal motion of the air is also affected by forces other than pressure.

FORCES AFFECTING WINDS

Pressure-gradient force. The horizontal pressure gradient at a point is the greatest decrease of pressure per unit horizontal distance. It is usually determined by dividing the difference in pressure Δp between two adjacent isobars, one on each side of the point, by the shortest distance l between them. Thus, in Fig. 5-1 the horizontal pressure gradient at O is $(p_2 - p_1)/l$ or, more precisely, $\partial p/\partial l$.

The horizontal pressure gradient represents the force acting on a unit cube of air as a result of the pressure difference between opposite sides and is always understood to be directed from high to low pressure. The *pressure-gradient force*, F_g, acting on a unit mass of air, is the horizontal pressure gradient divided by the air density ρ_a, that is, $(\partial p/\partial l)/\rho_a$. This force increases as the distance between isobars decreases and, for a given horizontal pressure gradient, it increases when the air density diminishes.

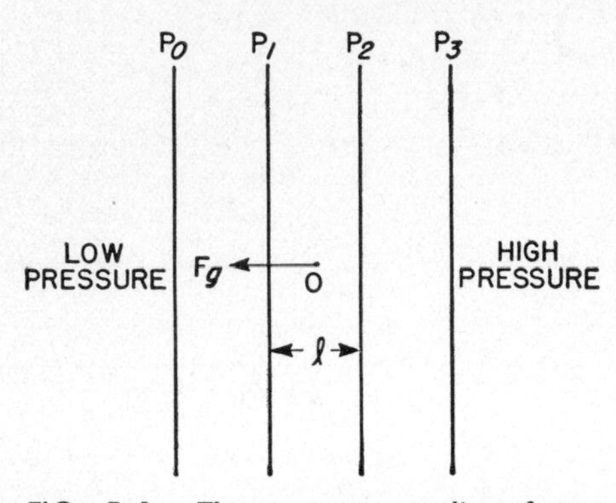

FIG. 5–1. The pressure-gradient force.

Deflecting force. Let us assume the earth's surface in the vicinity of the North Pole to be a horizontal plane which rotates about the polar axis with the angular velocity of the earth (Fig. 5-2). To an observer in space, a particle projected from O toward A travels the straight path OA. However, during the time t required to cover the distance OA, point A moves to A'. An observer standing at O and originally facing A is facing A' at the end of time t, so that from his standpoint the path of the particle appears to be along the curve OA. Therefore, to an observer in the Northern Hemisphere, the particle appears to be deflected to its right. In the Southern Hemisphere, the deflection is to the left of the instantaneous direction of motion. This apparent deflection is known as the *Coriolis effect*.

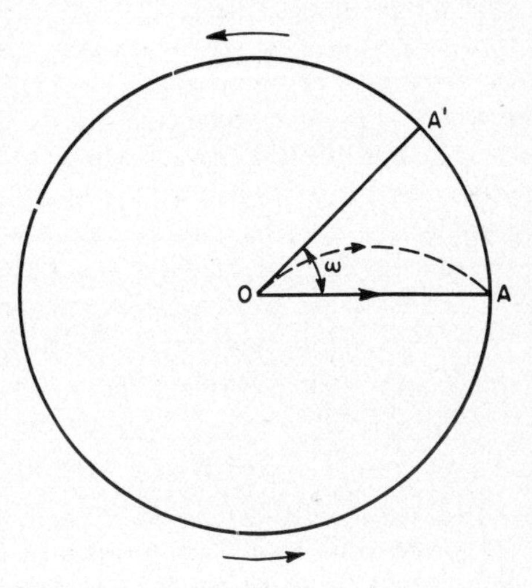

FIG. 5–2. Deflection due to the earth's rotation.

The apparent *deflecting force*, F_d, per unit mass can be expressed by the term $2\omega v \sin \phi$, where ω is the angular velocity of the earth's rotation about its axis, v is the velocity of the air particle, and ϕ is the latitude. The term $2\omega \sin \phi$ is commonly known as the *Coriolis parameter*. This force always acts at right angles to the instantaneous direction of motion and hence affects direction but not speed. Its magnitude is independent of the horizontal direction of air movement.

Cyclostrophic force. When isobars are curved, centrifugal force tends to drive the air outward across the isobars. Consider a particle of unit mass moving with velocity v along a circle of radius r on the earth's surface (Fig. 5-3). The centrifugal force v^2/r tending to drive the particle outward can be resolved into two components, F_n normal and F_c tangent to the earth's surface. The angle θ between the centrifugal force and its horizontal component is equal to the angle subtended at the earth's center by radius r. By trigonometry it can easily be shown that $F_c = v^2/(r_e \tan \theta)$, where r_e is the earth's radius. The horizontal force F_c, known as the *cyclostrophic force,* increases as the radius of curvature of the isobars decreases. In the case of straight isobars, the trajectory is a great circle, and the cyclostrophic force is zero.

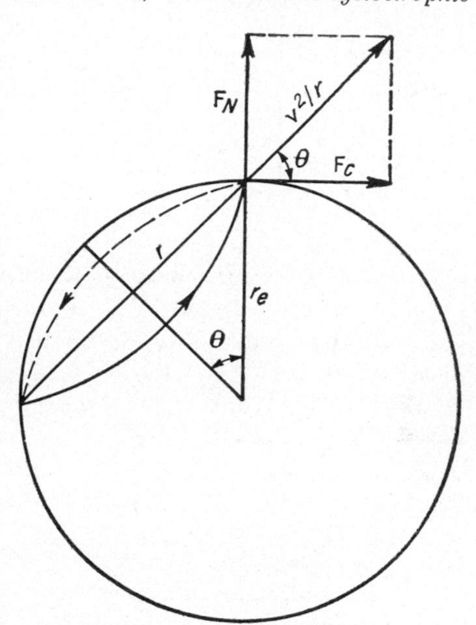

FIG. 5-3. Cyclostrophic force.

Friction. Friction always acts to reduce velocity and, hence, the Coriolis and cyclostrophic forces, which are functions of velocity. The Coriolis force always acts against the pressure-gradient force, but the cyclostrophic force may act either with or against the pressure gradient. With a cyclonic pressure system, a reduction in F_d and F_c causes the wind to drift inward toward the low pressure. In an anticyclonic system F_d and F_c act against each other, but in middle and higher latitudes F_d is much greater than F_c, and the net effect of friction is to cause an outward drift of wind in the direction of the pressure gradient. The angle at which the wind blows across the isobars averages about 30° over land under normal conditions. The frictional force diminishes with height and usually becomes negligible about 2000 ft above the ground.

DYNAMIC CLASSIFICATION OF WINDS

Geostrophic wind. The *geostrophic wind* is the steady horizontal flow of air which results when the only two active forces, namely, the pressure-gradient force F_g and the deflecting force F_d, balance each other. This condition can exist only when the isobars are straight and parallel (Fig. 5-4). The geostrophic-wind velocity v_G can then be expressed by

$$v_G = \frac{1}{2\omega\rho_a \sin \phi} \frac{\partial p}{\partial l} \tag{5-1}$$

Although Eq. (5-1) is valid only for straight isobars, it is often used to compute winds along isobars of slight curvature. Under normal conditions, it is a convenient method for estimating wind velocity just above the friction layer (about 2000 ft) when only the pressure field at the surface is known. In practice, the geostrophic-wind velocity is usually measured graphically with a special scale, which takes into account the latitude, map projection, isobaric interval, air density, and units of velocity.

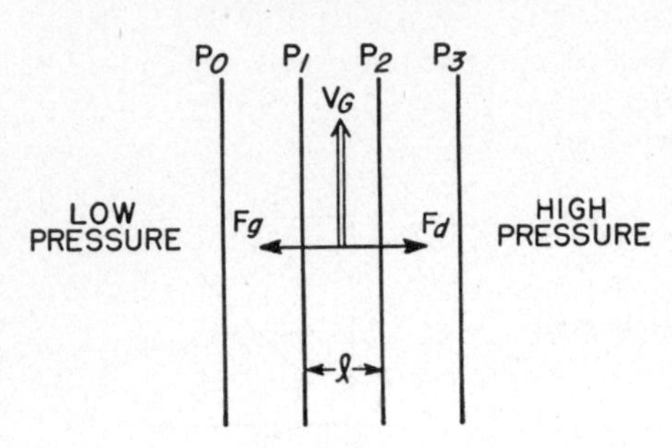

FIG. 5-4. Geostrophic wind in the Northern Hemisphere.

Gradient wind. The gradient wind is steady, horizontal, frictionless atmospheric motion along curved isobars in an unchanging pressure field when the pressure-gradient, deflecting, and cyclostrophic forces are in equilibrium. Thus, the geostrophic wind is merely a special case of gradient wind in which the radius of curvature of the isobars is infinite. The gradient wind is usually a reasonable approximation to the true wind above the friction layer.

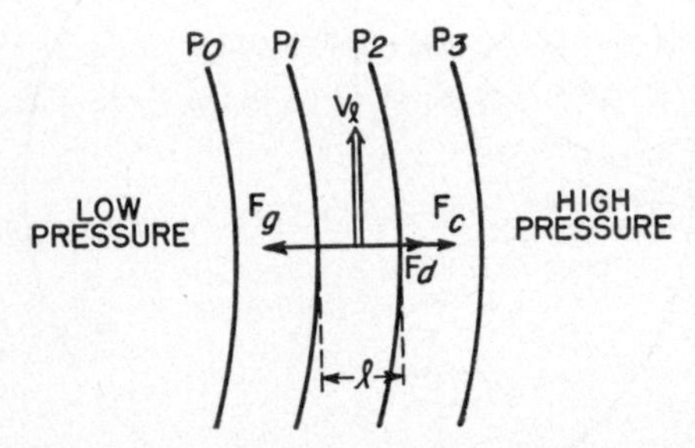

FIG. 5-5. Cyclonic gradient wind in the Northern Hemisphere.

Figure 5-5 illustrates the case of gradient wind v_l associated with a cyclone. The pressure-gradient force F_g balances the sum of the deflecting force F_d and the cyclostrophic force F_c, and

$$\frac{1}{\rho_a}\frac{\partial p}{\partial l} = 2\omega v_l \sin\phi + \frac{v_l^2}{r_e \tan\theta} \tag{5-2}$$

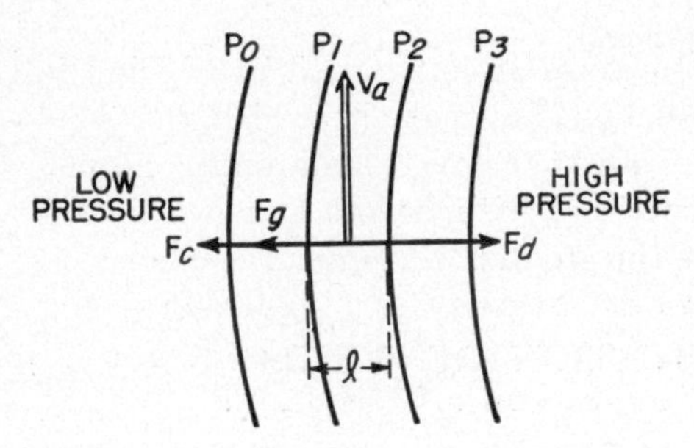

FIG. 5-6. Anticyclonic gradient wind in the Northern Hemisphere.

The anticyclonic gradient wind v_a is illustrated in Fig. 5-6. As for the cyclonic case, F_g and F_d act in opposite directions, but the isobars are now convex toward lower pressure; hence F_c acts in the same direction as F_g, and

$$\frac{1}{\rho_a}\frac{\partial p}{\partial l} = 2\omega v_a \sin\phi - \frac{v_a^2}{r_e \tan\theta} \tag{5-3}$$

From Eqs. (5-1) and (5-2), we obtain

$$v_l - v_G = -\frac{v_l^2}{(2\omega \sin \phi)(r_e \tan \theta)} \tag{5-4}$$

and, from Eqs. (5-1) and (5-3),

$$v_a - v_G = \frac{v_a^2}{(2\omega \sin \phi)(r_e \tan \theta)} \tag{5-5}$$

Obviously, the difference between the gradient wind and the geostrophic wind decreases as the radius of curvature of the isobars increases. The geostrophic wind may therefore be used as a good approximation to the true wind above the friction layer when the radius of curvature of the isobars is not too small. However, the geostrophic wind is always an overestimate of the gradient wind in a cyclone and an underestimate in an anticyclone.

Cyclostrophic wind. The *cyclostrophic*, or *Eulerian, wind*, v_e, is a high-velocity, curving wind, as in a tropical cyclone, in which the chief controlling influence to balance the pressure-gradient force is the cyclostrophic force. In middle and high latitudes, the deflecting force in the gradient-wind equations outweighs the cyclostrophic force. In low latitudes, sin ϕ, and therefore F_d, is very small, and F_c becomes more important. Neglecting F_d, we may write

$$\frac{1}{\rho_a}\frac{\partial p}{\partial l} = \frac{v_e^2}{r_e \tan \theta} \tag{5-6}$$

or

$$v_e = \sqrt{\frac{r_e \tan \theta}{\rho_a}\frac{\partial p}{\partial l}} \tag{5-7}$$

Equation (5-7) cannot be satisfied when $\partial p/\partial l$ is negative, *i.e.*, when the pressure distribution is anticyclonic. Hence, it may be concluded that anticyclones cannot exist as stable systems at very low latitudes.

LOCALIZED WIND PHENOMENA

Foehns. When air is forced to flow up and across a mountain barrier, it cools dry adiabatically (5.4 F° per 1000 ft) until its temperature has dropped to the dewpoint. Condensation then occurs, leading to the formation of cloud over the mountain, and possible precipitation. Above the condensation level, the air cools at the saturated-adiabatic lapse rate (about 3 F° per 1000 ft). As it descends the lee side of the mountain, the air is warmed dry adiabatically so that, level for level, it is warmer than it was on the windward side. Having lost some moisture during its ascent, the air thus arrives on the plains beyond the mountain barrier as a warm, dry *foehn wind*, or *chinook*. The outstanding chinook of the United States is the warm, dry westerly wind along the eastern slopes of the

Rocky Mountains. It may occur at any season of the year, but its effects are most marked in winter, when it may cause a temperature rise of 20 to 30 F° in 15 min. The chinook causes ice and snow to disappear rapidly; hence it is sometimes called the "snow eater." The chinook may begin at any hour of the day or night and may last 3 to 4 days. Its velocity varies from a gentle breeze to a gale, and it may blow continuously or come in short spells interrupted by colder and calmer intervals. On the West Coast, the name chinook is sometimes given to a moist southwesterly wind from the Pacific Ocean. This wind is warm in winter and cool in summer, is commonly attended by clouds and rain, and is definitely not a true chinook, or foehn.

Tornadoes. The tornado, known popularly as a "twister" or "cyclone" in the central United States, where it most frequently occurs, is a violent rotary storm, ranging from about 40 ft to 1 mile in diameter. It usually occurs in the spring or summer and is observed as a heavy cumulonimbus from which hangs a funnel-shaped cloud marking the vortex, which may or may not reach the earth. It is attended by heavy precipitation, thunder, and usually hail. Winds blow spirally upward around the axis of the tornado cloud and have on occasions been estimated to exceed 300 mph. Vertical velocities within the funnel cloud may exceed 100 mph. The storm itself travels about 25 to 40 mph, and its path is usually 20 to 40 miles long but may be as long as 300 miles. It is believed that under favorable moisture and temperature conditions the tornado is induced aloft by the interaction of adjacent winds of opposite directions.

MEASUREMENT OF WIND

Since wind is air in motion, it has both direction and speed. The *wind direction* is the direction *from* which it is blowing; it is usually stated in terms of 16 compass points (N, NNE, NE, etc.) for surface winds and in terms of tens of degrees from north, measured clockwise, for winds aloft. Wind speed is usually indicated in miles per hour, but meters per second and knots are often used. For purposes of conversion from one unit to another, it is useful to remember that 1 m/sec = 2.2 mph and 1 knot = $1\frac{1}{7}$ mph, approximately.

Anemometers. Instruments for measuring the speed or force of the wind are called *anemometers*. The *propeller*, or *windmill*, *anemometer*, which has a horizontal axis of rotation, has not been widely used in meteorology but is gaining in popularity. The *air meter*, used by air-conditioning engineers for investigating air currents in mines, buildings, etc., is a windmill anemometer.

The *cup anemometer*, which is most commonly used for official meteorological observations, has a vertical axis of rotation. Both three- and four-cup types are in common use.

Pressure-tube anemometers make use of the fact that wind blowing into the mouth of a tube increases the pressure in the tube and that a current blowing across the mouth decreases the pressure inside the tube. These effects can be used singly or, preferably, in combination to measure wind speed. The Dines anemometer is probably the best known of this type. The pressure or difference in pressure in the tubes is measured with a manometer or pressure gage.

Exposure of wind instruments. Special investigations of winds may require unusual mounting and exposure of instruments. However, for ordinary meteorological purposes, when representative values of surface-air movement are sought, it is important that the instruments be exposed in a standard manner. Perhaps the greatest discrepancy between wind records of adjacent stations is due to the differences in the height of anemometers above the surface. Although it is known that wind speed varies greatly with altitude, little effort has been made to standardize the height of anemometer installations. The height may range from about 30 ft for a rural installation to hundreds of feet in the city, where anemometer supports, usually masts or towers, are often mounted on skyscrapers.

In the country the anemometer should be located as far away from trees as possible. If there are no large clearings, it should be mounted above treetop height. A roof installation on a large building practically ensures indicated speeds which are too high because, in addition to the effect due to elevation alone, the streamlines converge as the wind passes the building. Gustiness is usually higher for this type of installation.

Errors of measurement. In the measurement of surface winds, there is little doubt that differences resulting from nonuniform exposure of instruments usually exceed the errors due to instrumental deficiencies. However, there are some rather serious instrumental limitations. The cup anemometer registers too high a mean speed in a variable wind because the cup wheel accelerates more quickly than it loses speed. Pressure-plate anemometers of the pendulum type are seldom used because, unless designed with great care, resonance between the swinging plate and the gusts and lulls may cause false indications. All pressure-tube anemometers are subject to error because of changes in air density. Furthermore, in gusty winds those of the float-manometer type indicate fluctuations which are smaller than and out of phase with actual wind speeds.

GEOGRAPHICAL VARIATION OF WIND

Position in the general circulation. Because of the location of the United States in the general circulation pattern, the prevailing wind at the surface and aloft over most of the country is from a general westerly direction. There is a tendency for storms to follow certain established paths (Fig. 2-5), and winds in regions traversed by storm tracks are more variable. In the United States as a whole, winds are relatively variable because most of the country is frequented by migratory pressure systems. While there is a general tendency for wind speed to increase with latitude, this effect is more noticeable aloft than at the surface, where other influences are more pronounced.

Influence of land and water masses. A general discussion of these effects is given in Chap. 2. It should be noted that these influences are also associated with diurnal and seasonal effects. The monsoonal effect over Texas, the land and sea breezes of the coasts, and the lake breeze on the shores of large inland water bodies are winds influenced by the distribution of land and water masses.

Orographic influences. Winds in mountainous regions are very localized because of the orographic influences. On mountain summits and ridges the wind speed is usually higher than in the free air at the same elevation, because the orographic barriers tend to converge the flow of air, causing acceleration. The highest surface-wind speed ever recorded, 231 mph at Mt. Washington, New Hampshire (elev. 6262 ft), on Apr. 12, 1934, was undoubtedly the result of such convergence. On the lee of mountain barriers and in sheltered valleys, the winds are usually light. The wind direction is especially influenced by the orientation of barriers and valleys. The effects on air forced to flow across an orographic barrier are described earlier in this chapter (foehn).

There is a very noticeable diurnal effect on wind in mountainous regions. The mountain and valley breezes (Chap. 2) reflect these influences. Daytime heating and nocturnal cooling also cause plateaus to be windy by day and calm by night.

Effects of trees, buildings, etc. Trees, buildings, and other obstacles in the path of wind create eddies in the lower layer of the atmosphere. The friction resulting from these obstructions tends to reduce the wind speed and deflect the direction as described earlier in this chapter. Actual wind records show a gradual reduction of speed to be associated with the growth of cities. For instance, at Detroit the average wind speed decreased from 15 to 9 mph during the period 1909 to 1930, while wind records in the nearby open country showed no such variation.[1] The effects of surface friction become negligible above the gradient level (about 2000 ft).

Over land, the surface-wind speed averages about 40 per cent of that at the gradient level, and at sea about 70 per cent. The relationship between the wind speed at anemometer height and that at some higher level in the friction layer may be expressed by the empirical formula

$$\frac{v_w}{v_{w0}} = \left(\frac{Z}{Z_0}\right)^k \tag{5-8}$$

[1] Landsberg, H., "Physical Climatology," p. 123, Pennsylvania State College, State College, Pa., 1941.

where v_w is the wind speed at height Z above the surface, v_{w0} is the wind speed at anemometer level Z_0 (usually not less than 30 ft), and k is a constant, which is about $1/5$ for average conditions, about $1/7$ for winds over 35 mph or when convection is pronounced, and about $1/2$ for winds under 8 mph.

WIND VARIATION WITH TIME

Annual variation. The month-to-month variation of winds in the United States, both at the surface and aloft, is aptly illustrated in various summaries.[1] The seasonal variation at the surface and at 10,000 and 20,000 ft, msl, is shown in Fig. 5-7. Wind speeds are highest in winter because the temperature contrast between higher and lower latitudes (and hence the pressure gradient) is greatest. With the approach of spring, a monsoonal effect is observed along the Gulf Coast, with southeasterly winds prevailing up to about 1 mile. Over the Great Plains west of the Mississippi the winds up to about 1 mile become southerly, increasing the flow of humid air into that region. On the Pacific Coast the surface wind shows a marked tendency to blow onshore in Washington and Oregon, being mostly northwesterly. In general, middle and late summer is the calmest period of the year, and large-scale wind variations are less frequent. During the fall, the winds up to about 1 mile over the southeastern portion of the country tend to be northeasterly. Otherwise, the general tendency is somewhat similar to spring conditions.

Diurnal variation. Frictional forces are dependent, not only on the nature of the underlying surface, but also on the stability of the air. Since surface heating decreases atmospheric stability, frictional forces are usually minimized shortly after midday. Conversely, the effect of friction is at a maximum near sunrise, when the air reaches its greatest stability because of nighttime cooling. Hence, over land areas the surface-wind speed normally reaches a maximum in the early afternoon and decreases to a minimum about sunrise. This diurnal variation is significant only near the ground, and at levels above about 200 ft the maximum occurs at night and the minimum in the daytime.[2] This phenomenon is due to the fact that temperature inversions resulting from nighttime cooling minimize turbulence within a thin layer near the surface, while during the daytime the effect of friction is distributed through a much thicker layer. Wind direction, also being associated with friction, must experience a diurnal

[1] "Airway Meteorological Atlas for the United States," U.S. Weather Bureau, Washington, D.C., 1941.

"Normal Surface Wind Data for the United States," U.S. Weather Bureau, Washington, D.C., 1942.

[2] Hellman, G., Über die Bewegung der Luft in den untersten Schichten der Atmosphäre, *Meteorolog. Z.*, Vol. 34, pp. 273-285, 1917.

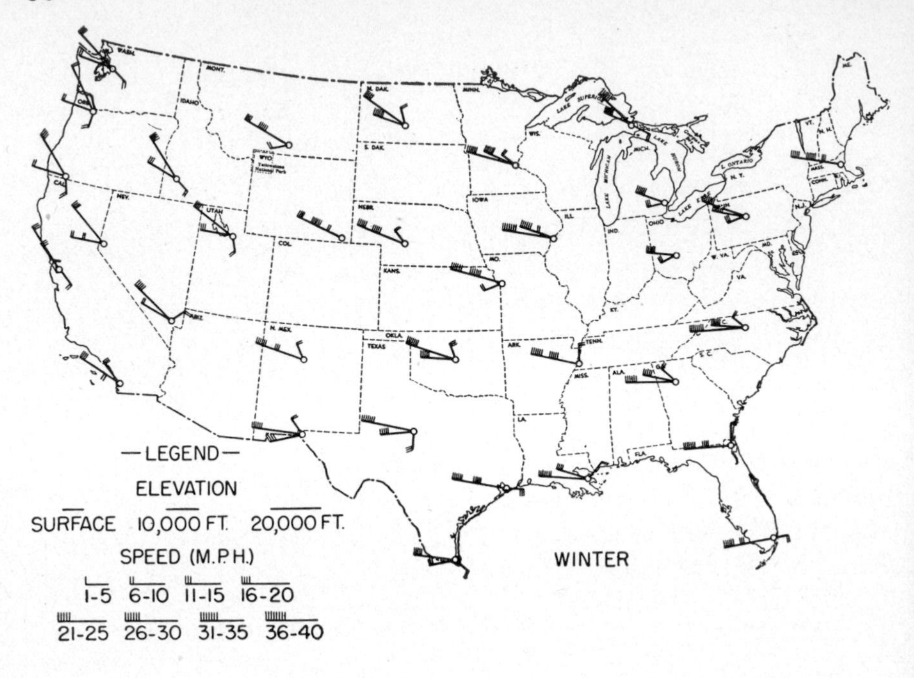

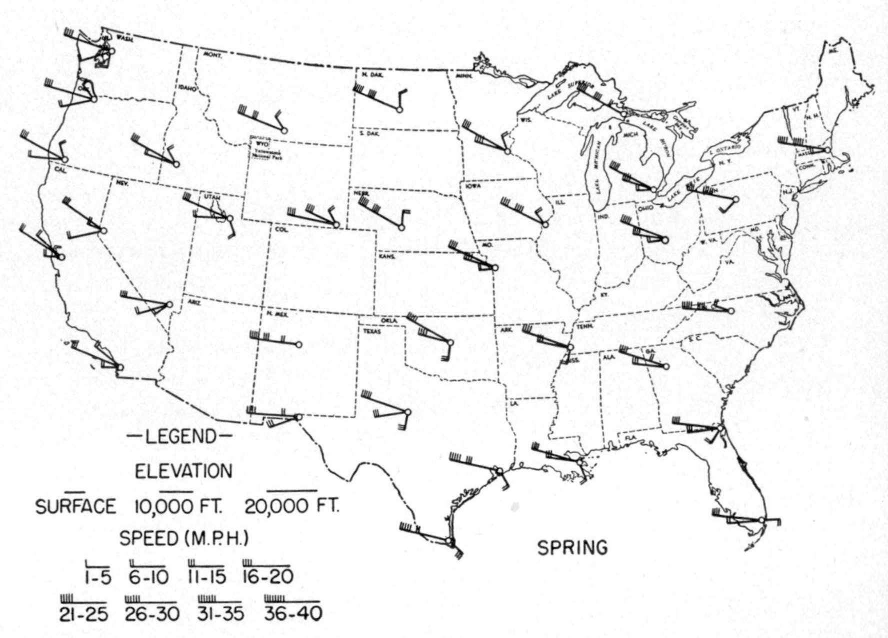

FIG. 5–7. Wind resultants at

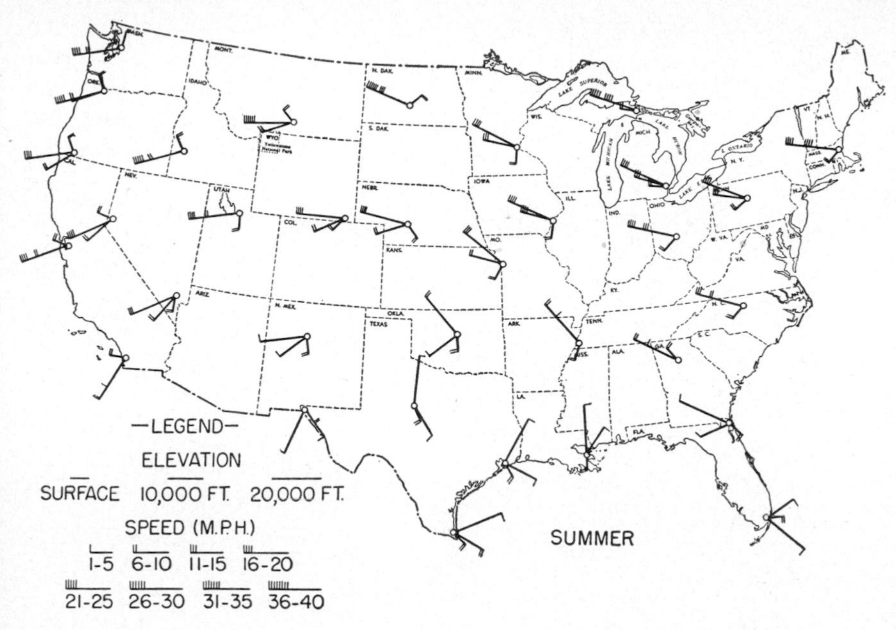

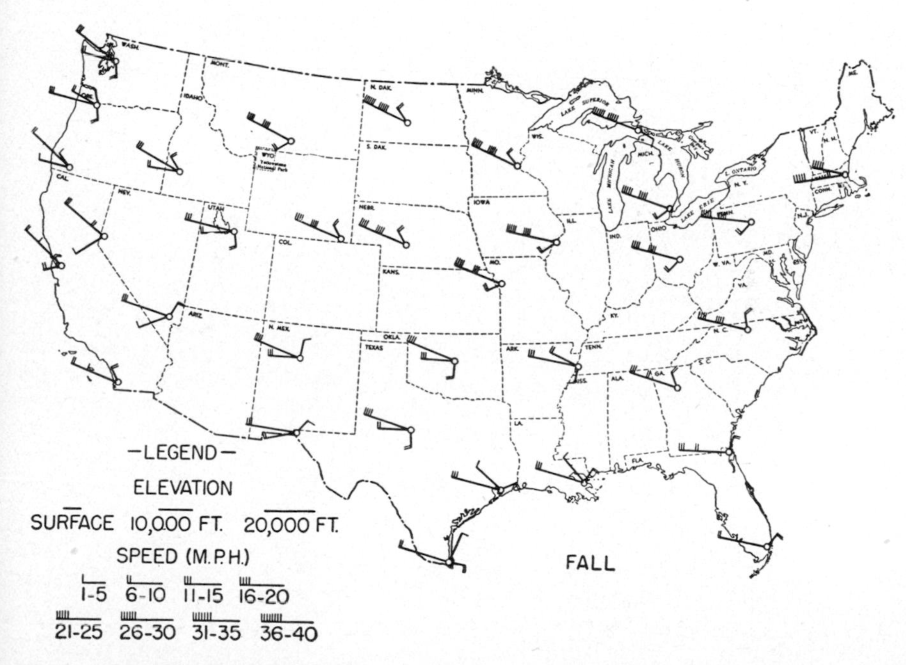

various levels for selected stations.

variation. Theoretically, the wind should veer (clockwise) with decreasing friction and back (counterclockwise) when friction increases. Observations indicate that this is true. Thus, in summary, it can be said that in a thin layer of air near the surface the winds back and decrease at night and veer and increase during the day. At higher levels in the friction layer, the winds veer and increase at night and back and decrease during the day. This diurnal variation of winds is most pronounced in summer.

Other important diurnal effects leading to phenomena such as the mountain, valley, land, and sea breezes have been described in Chap. 2. The diurnal variation of winds over large bodies of water has not been investigated thoroughly. It appears reasonable to expect that it would not be significant, because of the small diurnal variation in sea-surface temperatures.

6
PRECIPITATION

Hydrologists have long known that only about one-fourth of the total amount of precipitation which falls on continental areas is returned to the seas by direct runoff and underground flow. Hence, it was generally believed that continental evaporation constituted the principal source of moisture for continental precipitation. Many ideas for increasing local precipitation were based on the premise, now known to be erroneous, that more rainfall would result from increased atmospheric moisture through continental evaporation. Impounding of streamflow in lakes and ponds and selection of farm crops with high transpiration rates were among the methods suggested.

Moisture in the atmosphere, although essential to precipitation, is only one of several factors affecting precipitation amounts. Other things being equal, precipitation varies directly with available moisture. However, variations in other factors sometimes obscure the effect of moisture. For instance, the average moisture content of the air over San Diego, California, is greater than that over Seattle, Washington, throughout the year; yet the average annual precipitation at San Diego is about 10 in., while that at Seattle is near 35 in. Similarly, the abundance of moisture in the atmosphere over Lower California, where annual rainfall rarely exceeds 5 in., does little to alleviate desert conditions.

Within the United States, deficiencies in precipitation are usually attributable, not to inadequate atmospheric moisture, but rather to the ineffectiveness of other meteorological factors in the precipitation processes. The location of a region with respect to the general circulation system is primarily responsible for its climate. Orographic barriers often exert more influence on the climate of a region than does nearness to a moisture source.

Locally evaporated moisture can contribute to local precipitation only if the air remains stagnant. Since the complete absence of wind in the free air is rare, the moisture evaporated from a water surface, such as a lake, is distributed throughout a very large volume of air. The moisture content of air passing over the lake region of Wisconsin, where the ratio of water surface to land surface is 1 : 40, is increased by approximately 1 per cent.[1]

Moisture evaporated from land areas is generally absorbed by dry air masses which cross the continent without any appreciable reprecipitation and eventually pass out to sea. Hence, the chief source of precipitation over continents is moisture evaporated from ocean surfaces and carried inland by maritime air masses. Holzman has thoroughly discussed this topic, including the identification of those air masses which contribute the major portion of the precipitation over the United States and those which evaporate the moisture from land surfaces and carry it back to sea.

FORMATION OF PRECIPITATION

Precipitation elements. Atmospheric vapor may condense on condensation nuclei to form water droplets or, if supercooled, on sublimation nuclei to form ice crystals. Products of combustion, oxides of nitrogen, and salt crystals are the principal types of condensation nuclei. Crystalline materials, such as silica or quartz, and carbon dioxide are effective sublimation nuclei. Under ordinary fair-weather conditions, water droplets and ice crystals which constitute cloud or fog appear to float in the air. Actually, all cloud elements tend to settle toward the earth. The average cloud element, however, weighs so little that only a very slight upward motion of the air is needed to support it. The droplets in an ordinary cloud average about 0.01 mm (0.0004 in.) in diameter, and an upward air movement of 0.5 ft/min is sufficient to keep them from falling. Ice crystals of equivalent weight, because of their shape and larger size, can be supported by even lower velocities.

Under favorable conditions, water droplets and ice crystals increase in size until too heavy to be kept aloft, even with upward velocities much in excess of 0.5 ft/min, and begin to fall earthward. Frequently, the air below the cloud layer is unsaturated, and the falling drops are evaporated while passing through it. According to Findeisen,[2] the distance which a drop can fall through unsaturated air increases as the fourth power of its radius. Drops having a radius of 0.1 mm falling through air of 90 per cent relative humidity are evaporated in about 10 ft, while 0.5-mm drops can fall about 6500 ft. Obviously, a large number of falling cloud elements never reach the ground. For the purpose of hydrology, *precipitation* is defined as that water, in liquid or solid form, which reaches the earth.

[1] Holzman, B., Sources of Moisture for Precipitation in the United States, *U.S. Dept. Agr. Tech. Bull.* 589, 1937.

[2] Findeisen, W., Die Kolloidmeteorologischen Vorgänge bei der Niederschlagsbildung, *Meteorolog. Z.*, Vol. 55, pp. 127-128, 1938.

Although no definite drop size can be said to mark the boundary between cloud and precipitation elements, a radius of 0.1 mm has been generally accepted.[1] There are wide variations in individual cases, and the radius of most raindrops is usually much greater than 0.1 mm.

Colloidal stability of clouds. Clouds can be regarded as colloidal suspensions[2] of finely divided liquid and solid particles in the air. This concept has been the basis of most modern theories of condensation and precipitation. If cloud elements do not tend to coalesce, the cloud is *colloidally stable;* if they do, it is *colloidally unstable.* Colloidal instability is required for significant precipitation since condensation processes alone cannot produce droplets over 0.2 mm in diameter. The colloidal stability of a cloud is determined by the electrical charge, size, temperature, and relative motion of the cloud elements, as well as the coexistence of ice crystals and liquid droplets.

Electrical charge. The presence of cloud elements of opposite charges results in coalescence through electrostatic attraction. Because of the small charges and relatively large distances between elements, this attraction is not considered particularly effective. Moreover, that coalescence which does take place neutralizes the charges on the particles involved. It has been shown[3] that when the elements of a fog carry a relatively high unipolar charge, the fog will remain stable, or "dry," whereas fogs without charge are typical "wet," or misting, fogs. Thus, electrostatic forces can prevent coalescence, although they are not effective in promoting it. Colloidal instability due to nonuniform charge on cloud elements cannot result in precipitation of greater intensity than drizzle or mist.

Size of droplets. The vapor pressure of water varies slightly with curvature of the surface, *i.e.*, the larger the drop, the lower the vapor pressure. Thus, in a cloud consisting of large and small droplets, the mean vapor pressure of the air is higher than the vapor pressure over the large droplets and lower than that over the smaller. As a result, the small droplets tend to evaporate and condense on the larger drops. However, computations[4] show that this effect is negligible.

Temperature of cloud elements. In a mixture of cloud elements of different temperatures, there is a net transport of water from warm to cold elements because of differences in vapor pressure. The rate of change of saturation vapor pressure with temperature is greatest at high temperatures

[1] Suring, R., "Leitfaden der Meteorologie," p. 125, Tauchnitz, Leipzig, 1927.

[2] Schmauss, A., and A. Wigand, "Die Atmosphäre als Kolloid," Friedrich Vieweg & Sohn, Brunswick, 1939.

[3] Frankenberger, E., Über die Koagulation von Wolken und Nebel, *Physik. Z.*, Vol. 31, pp. 835-840, 1930.

[4] Humphreys, W. J., "Physics of the Air," 3d ed., p. 276, McGraw-Hill, New York, 1940.

(Appendix C), and therefore this effect may be an important cause of coalescence in relatively warm clouds (50°F or more).[1]

Motion of cloud elements. Since many turbulent clouds produce no precipitation, it may be presumed that the collision of cloud elements resulting from relative motion is ineffective in causing coalescence. However, relative motion does promote colloidal instability by bringing together elements of different electrical charge, size, and temperature.

Coexistence of ice crystals and water droplets. Saturation vapor pressure over ice is less than over water at the same temperature. Hence, the coexistence of ice and water elements in a cloud results in a net transport of moisture from the water to the ice particles. According to Bergeron[2] this effect is responsible for most precipitation and all heavy precipitation. None of the previous factors can result in appreciable precipitation at temperatures near or below freezing.

PRECIPITATION FORMS

Any product of condensation of atmospheric water vapor, whether formed in the free air or at the earth's surface, is a *hydrometeor*. Since the hydrologist is primarily interested in precipitation, only those hydrometeors referring to falling moisture are here defined. Among those hydrometeors not included are damp haze, fog, ice fog, drifting snow, blowing snow, frost, and rime.

Drizzle. Uniform precipitation consisting of water droplets less than 0.02 in. in diameter is called drizzle. It usually falls from stratiform clouds, and its intensity is generally less than 0.04 in./hr.

Rain. Rain consists of waterdrops generally larger than 0.02 in. in diameter. It is usually reported in three intensities, *light* for rates of fall from a trace to 0.10, *moderate* from 0.11 to 0.30, and *heavy* over 0.30 in./hr.

A drop falling through still air rapidly reaches a maximum downward velocity, the *terminal velocity*, where the resistance of the air balances the weight of the drop. Terminal velocities increase with drop size up to about 0.22 in. and then decrease because of increasing air resistance due to flattening of the drops (Table 6-1). For large diameters, the deformation is sufficient to break up the drops before they can attain the terminal velocity which would be expected for their dimensions.

Upward velocities exceeding the terminal velocities of the largest drops are not unusual in vigorous convective systems, so that drops of any size up to the maximum may be found in some clouds. The intensity of the

[1] Petterssen, S., "Weather Analysis and Forecasting," p. 46, McGraw-Hill, New York, 1940.

[2] Bergeron, T., On the Physics of Clouds, *Mem. Meteorolog. Assoc. Intern. Union Geod. Geophys.*, Lisbon, 1933, pp. 156-175.

upward movement of air thus determines the average size of drops in clouds and, consequently, in the falling precipitation. Since the velocity of the ascending current is generally not uniform everywhere under a cloud layer, there is no definite lower limit to the size of the falling drops.

TABLE 6-1. Terminal Velocity of Waterdrops

Drop diameter		Terminal velocities, fps	
Mm	In.	After Lenard*	After Laws†
0.5	0.02	11.5	
1.0	0.04	14.4	
1.5	0.06	18.7	18.1
2.0	0.08	19.4	21.6
3.0	0.12	22.6	26.4
4.0	0.16	25.3	29.1
5.0	0.20	26.2	30.3
5.5	0.22	26.2	30.5
6.0	0.24	25.9	30.5
6.5	0.26	25.6	

* Lenard, P., Über Regen, *Meteorolog. Z.*, Vol. 21, p. 254, 1904.

† Laws, J. O., Measurements of the Fall-velocity of Water-drops and Raindrops, *Trans. Am. Geophys. Union*, Vol. 22, pp. 709-721, 1941.

Glaze. The ice coating formed when rain or drizzle freezes as it comes in contact with cold objects at the ground is called *glaze*. It can occur only when the air temperature is near 32°F.

Sleet. When raindrops are frozen while falling through air below 32°F, transparent globular grains of ice known as *sleet*, or *ice pellets*, are formed. The pellets are ordinarily between 0.04 and 0.16 in. in diameter.

Snow. Precipitation in the form of ice crystals is snow. Single ice crystals can reach the ground, but usually a number of them coalesce and fall as *snowflakes*. Flakes as large as 8 by 15 in. have been reported[1] at Ft. Keogh, Montana. The density of freshly fallen snow varies greatly; 5 to 20 in. of snow is generally required to equal 1 in. of water. The average density is assumed to be about 0.1.

Snow pellets. Snow pellets, or *graupel*, are white, opaque, round, or occasionally conical grains of snowlike structure 0.02 to 0.20 in. in diameter. They are crisp and easily compressible and rebound when falling on hard ground. Because of its appearance, this form of precipitation is often called *tapioca snow*. Its intensities are reported as for snow.

Small hail. Translucent, round, or sometimes conical grains of frozen water, about 0.08 to 0.20 in. in diameter, are called small hail. Each grain

[1] Abbe, C., Gigantic Snowflakes, *Monthly Weather Rev.*, Vol. 43, p. 73, 1915.

consists of a snow-pellet nucleus covered by a thin layer of ice, which gives it a glazed appearance. Small hail is not crisp or easily compressible and when falling on hard ground does not ordinarily rebound or burst. It often occurs with rain and almost always when the temperature is above freezing. It should not be confused with true hail, which has a different size and structure and usually occurs with thunderstorms.

Hail. Precipitation in the form of balls or irregular lumps of ice over 0.2 in. in diameter is called hail. Hailstones are generally composed of alternating clear ice and opaque, snowlike layers as a result of repeated ascents and descents within the cloud during their formation. Thus, by the time the hailstones reach the ground they have acquired an onionlike structure. Some hailstones, however, do not undergo such vertical motion and reach the surface as lumps of clear ice. The formation of large hailstones requires ascending currents strong enough to support the hailstone while it grows. Vertical velocities as great as 50 fps are not rare in well-developed thunderstorms, and 120 fps has been reported under extremely unstable conditions. The thermodynamics of hailstone formation has been discussed by Schumann.[1]

Hail occurs almost exclusively in violent or prolonged thunderstorms and never with below-freezing temperatures at the ground. It is a late spring or summer rather than a winter phenomenon.

TYPES OF PRECIPITATION

In general, cloud or fog is formed by cooling air to below the saturation point. This cooling may be the result of one or more processes, but adiabatic cooling by reduction of pressure through lifting is the only process by which large masses of air can be cooled rapidly to below their dewpoint. The rate and amount of precipitation depend largely on the rate and amount of cooling and the moisture content of the air. Thus, the sole cause of any considerable quantity of precipitation is the ascent of moist air, and precipitation can therefore be classified according to the cause of the upward motion. In nature, however, several effects usually occur simultaneously, and many occurrences of precipitation cannot be classified as belonging to any single type.

Cyclonic precipitation. Precipitation associated with the passage of cyclones, or lows, is called cyclonic precipitation. This type can be classified into *nonfrontal* and *frontal*. Nonfrontal precipitation can occur in any kind of barometric depression. The lifting of the air is caused by horizontal convergence resulting from inflow into the low-pressure area.

Frontal precipitation is the result of lifting of warm air over cold. *Warm-front precipitation* is formed in the warm air which moves upward

[1] Schumann, T. E. W., The Theory of Hailstone Formation, *Quart. J. Roy. Meteorolog. Soc.*, Vol. 64, pp. 3-20, 1938.

over a wedge of cold air. The area of precipitation may extend two or three hundred miles ahead of the surface front, and the precipitation is generally light to moderate and nearly continuous until after the passage of the warm front. *Cold-front precipitation,* on the other hand, is of a showery nature and is formed in the warm air forced upward by an advancing wedge of cold air. Precipitation usually occurs near the surface front but may extend 100 miles or more ahead of it.

Convective precipitation. This type of precipitation results from the upward movement of air that is warmer than its surroundings. Being of lesser density, the ascending air has a tendency to continue rising until it reaches a level where it has the temperature of its environment. The temperature contrast causing convection may result from heating of surface air, cooling aloft, or mechanical lifting over a frontal surface or mountain barrier. Convective precipitation is of showery nature, and its intensity may vary from light showers to cloudbursts, depending on the temperature and moisture conditions.

Orographic precipitation. The precipitation caused by lifting of air over mountain barriers is called orographic precipitation. Orographic barriers often supply the lift to set off cyclonic or convective precipitation. For this reason, precipitation is heavier on windward slopes, with *rain shadows*, regions of lighter precipitation, on leeward slopes. Orographic precipitation not associated with cyclonic or convective action is ordinarily of low intensity.

MEASUREMENT OF PRECIPITATION

Rainfall is probably the meteorological element first measured by man.[1] There is evidence that rainfall records were kept in India in the fourth century B.C. It is known that rain gages of some sort were used in Korea in A.D. 1442. The modern type of gage came into use in Europe late in the fifteenth century. There are many types[2] of gages, but only those which are commonly used in the United States are discussed here.

All forms of precipitation are measured on the basis of the vertical depth of water or water equivalent which would accumulate on a level surface if all the precipitation remained where it fell. In the United States, all precipitation is measured in inches and hundredths. An amount less than 0.005 in. is recorded as a *trace*. Snow on the ground is measured on the basis of actual depth.

Nonrecording gages. Any open receptacle with vertical sides may serve as a rain gage, but in order to permit more accurate observations

[1] Horton, R. E., The Measurement of Rain and Snow, *J. New Engl. Water Works Assoc.*, Vol. 33, pp. 14-71, 1919.

[2] Middleton, W. E. K., "Meteorological Instruments," pp. 102-110, University of Toronto Press, Toronto, 1942.

certain refinements are necessary. The standard gage[1] (Fig. 6-1) of the U.S. Weather Bureau has a circular receiver 8 in. in diameter. The rainfall passes from the receiver to a cylindrical measuring tube 2.53 in. in diameter (area equal to one-tenth that of the receiver). When 1 in. of rain falls in the receiver, the measuring tube is filled to a depth of 10 in. With a stick graduated in inches and tenths, the rainfall can easily be measured to the nearest hundredth of an inch. When snow is expected,

FIG. 6–1. Overflow can, receiver, measuring tube, and stick for standard 8-in. precipitation gage. (*U.S. Weather Bureau.*)

the receiver and measuring tube are removed and the snow is caught in the overflow can. The snow is melted and poured into the measuring tube for measurement.

Recording gages. It is often important to know, not only the total amount of precipitation, but also its intensity, or rate of fall. Recording gages give a continuous record of precipitation in the form of a pen trace on a clock-driven chart. These gages may operate over extended periods without attention.

The U.S. Weather Bureau has adopted the *tipping-bucket gage* (Fig. 6-2) for its first-order stations. A 12-in. funnel collects the rainfall and conducts

[1] Instructions for Cooperative Observers, *U.S. Weather Bur. Circ. B* and *C*, 1941. Measurement of Precipitation, *U.S. Weather Bur. Circ. E*, 1936.

it to a pair of small buckets. The buckets are so designed that, when 0.01 in. of rainfall collects in one bucket, it tips and empties the water into a storage can, at the same time bringing the other bucket under the funnel. The tipping of the bucket actuates an electrical circuit, which causes a pen to make a notch on a recorder chart. The water in the storage reservoir is drawn off and measured in a tube, as with a standard gage. This type

FIG. 6–2. Tipping-bucket rain gage. (*U.S. Weather Bureau.*)

of gage is adapted to remote recording. It cannot, however, be used for measuring snow without heating.

Weighing-type recording gages (Fig. 6-3) are commonly used for field installations, because they record snow as well as rain. The precipitation passes through a collector into a bucket, which is supported on the platform of a spring or lever balance. By means of linkages, the increasing weight of the bucket and its contents is recorded on a chart. The chart thus shows a trace of accumulated amounts of precipitation.

Storage gages. The greatest depths of snowfall generally occur in mountainous regions difficult of access during winter. To obtain records from such regions, storage gages are used. These gages are the same in principle as the nonrecording and weighing-type gages described above, but they are designed to hold much greater amounts of precipitation. Recording gages designed to operate for 30 to 60 days without servicing

FIG. 6–3. Weighing-type precipitation gage. (*Leupold and Stevens Instrument Co.*)

and nonrecording gages with sufficient capacity for an entire season are now in use.

A wet snow, falling without wind, can build up around the lip of a gage into a doughnut-shaped deposit which almost completely closes the gage orifice. The usual cylindrical gage favors this sort of deposit, since the snow can freeze to the vertical walls and obtain support inside and out. To permit free fall of snow inside the gage, the upper portion should be in the shape of a frustrum of a cone. The side slope should not be less than 6 : 1

to minimize deposits on the exterior of the gage. Capping of the gage is a relatively infrequent phenomenon, and since the cap eventually melts and falls into the container, very little catch is lost. Properly heated collars would prevent capping entirely.

The orifice of a snow gage should be above the maximum anticipated snow depth. The design now in use by the U.S. Weather Bureau is made from 12-in. thin-walled pipe (Fig. 6-4), which serves both as container and tower. The gage is made in 5-ft sections so that any height in multiples of 5 ft is possible. Interim measurements are made with a stick or electric tape, while the initial charge and final measurement of a season's catch are accomplished by weighing the contents.

FIG. 6–4. Standpipe-type storage precipitation gage equipped with Alter shield. (*U.S. Weather Bureau.*)

Melting agents. To provide gages with capacity for large amounts of snowfall without making the container excessively large, it is necessary to melt the snow in the gage. This is usually accomplished by placing an initial charge of 29.6 per cent anhydrous calcium chloride brine (37.5 per cent commercial calcium chloride of 78 per cent purity) in the gage. Such a charge has a freezing point of −60°F and, when diluted by an equivalent amount of precipitation, will protect against a temperature of 16°F. Ethylene glycol and related commercial antifreeze agents are effective but are far more expensive than calcium chloride. Unlike calcium chloride, they are not corrosive and do not require special interior treatment of gages. Figure 6-5 shows the freezing point of various antifreeze agents.

Electrical heating of the collector ring and the use of bottled gas as a heat source have been explored, but as yet no reliable and economical solution has been found in this direction. The exterior of snow gages should be painted flat black to make maximum use of available solar radiation.

Since snow gages are often left for extended periods without attention, the contents must be protected against evaporation. This is accomplished by adding sufficient thin oil to the contents to cover the liquid surface completely. SAE 10 motor oil is very satisfactory.

Errors of precipitation measurements. There are several sources of error in the measurement of precipitation.[1] Most of the errors are individually negligible, and most result in too low a measurement. Except for mistakes in reading the scale of the gage, the usual observational errors

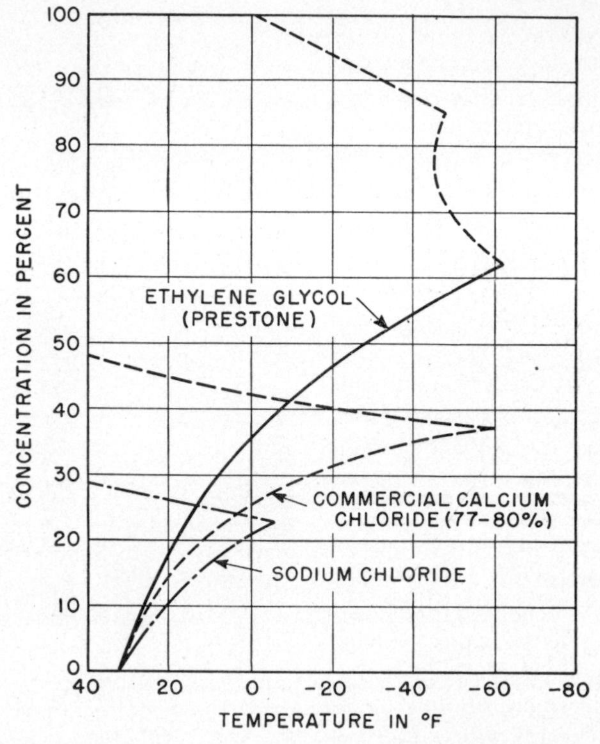

FIG. 6-5. Freezing-point variations for common antifreeze agents.

are generally small but consistent. Some observers fail to measure light amounts. Others allow the measuring stick to remain in the water too long, thus permitting the moisture to "creep" up the stick so that the reading obtained may be several hundredths of an inch too high. Though small, such errors are cumulative. Errors in scale readings, on the other hand, can be large but are usually compensating since there is as much chance of reading high as there is of reading low.

Instrumental errors may be quite large and are cumulative. The

[1] Horton, R. E., Measurement of Rainfall and Snow, *Monthly Weather Rev.*, Vol. 47, pp. 294-295, 1919.

Kleinschmidt, E., "Handbuch der meteorologischen Instrumente," pp. 283-286, Springer, Berlin, 1939.

measuring stick displaces water when introduced into the measuring tube, thus increasing the reading about 1 per cent. Bends or dents in the rim of the collector can so alter its receiving area that the amount of water measured no longer represents the true rainfall. During intense rains (5 to 6 in./hr), the bucket in a tipping-bucket gage will tip every 6 or 7 sec, while about 0.3 sec is required to complete a tip. During this time a small amount of water will flow into the already filled bucket. Under such conditions, this type of gage will record about 5 per cent too low.[1] The water which is caught in the reservoir is measured independently of the recorder count, and the difference is prorated throughout the period of excessive rainfall.

Some precipitation is required to moisten the funnel and inside surfaces of a gage. The amount of this moistening error depends on the roughness of the wetted surfaces. The loss, which is repeated for each rain occurring when the gage is dry, has been estimated to be about 0.01 in. Over a period of 1 year, losses may easily amount to 1 in., or 5 per cent of a 20-in. annual rainfall. Raindrop splash from the collector funnel may be expected to reduce the catch of gages with shallow collector rings. No data are available as to the magnitude of this error, but it is thought to be significant for large raindrops, especially when accompanied by strong winds.

When rain is falling vertically, a gage inclined at 10° from the vertical will catch 1.5 per cent less than it should. If the inclination of the gage is toward the wind and is less than twice the inclination of the rain, the gage will catch more than the true amount. While some investigators[2] believe that gages should be normal to land slopes, all Weather Bureau records are taken from vertical gages. Since the area of a basin is its projection on a horizontal plane, the measurement of precipitation normal to a slope would make it impractical to compute the true average depth. Moreover, it would be difficult to select a site for an inclined gage to be representative of a large area.

Effect of wind on snow. It has long been recognized that the vertical acceleration of air as it passes a precipitation gage imparts an upward acceleration to precipitation about to enter and results in an actual catch somewhat smaller than the true fall. As a result, shields[3] designed to

[1] Parsons, D. A., Calibration of a Weather Bureau Tipping-bucket Rain Gage, *Monthly Weather Rev.*, Vol. 69, p. 205, 1941.

[2] Storey, H. C., and E. L. Hamilton, A Comparative Study of Rain Gages, *Trans. Am. Geophys. Union*, Vol. 24, pp. 133-142, 1943.

Hayes, G. L., A Method of Measuring Rainfall on Windy Slopes, *Monthly Weather Rev.*, Vol. 72, pp. 111-114, 1944.

[3] Riesbol, H. S., Report on Exploratory Study of Rain Gage Shields and Enclosures at Coshocton, Ohio, *Trans. Am. Geophys. Union*, Vol. 21, pp. 474-482, 1940.

Brooks, C. F., Further Experiences with Shielded Precipitation Gages on Blue Hill and Mt. Washington, *Trans. Am. Geophys. Union*, Vol. 21, pp. 482-485, 1940.

deflect air currents away from the gage orifice have been used for a number of years. The Alter shield[1] (Fig. 6-4) has been adopted as standard by the U.S. Weather Bureau. German experiments[2] have shown that an unshielded gage may catch as little as 50 per cent of the true snowfall with winds of 30 mph. Observations in this country under natural conditions (average wind velocity probably less than 10 mph) indicate that shielding increases the catch by about 20 per cent when the gage is exposed in relatively open areas and by about 10 per cent in forest glades. The open construction of the Alter shield does not provide the opportunity for snow to build up as do solid shields, and the flexible design allows wind movement to aid in keeping the shield free of accumulated snow. Unfortunately, conditions favoring wet snow which accumulates rapidly are observed with little or no wind, and as a result even Alter shields may be expected to retain snow occasionally. The Nipher shield (Fig. 6-6) is more effective in reducing wind errors, but its solid construction prevents its use in areas of significant snowfall.

At the present time, relatively few gages are equipped with shields of any kind. It is generally considered that wind errors will be small if proper care is exercised in the selection of the gage location. The gages should be placed on level surfaces away from all possible updrafts. Roof exposures are rarely favorable. Low bushes, fences, or walls will serve as windbreaks, but in order that these protecting objects may not themselves intercept precipitation that would otherwise fall into the gage, they should be no nearer the gage than their own height.

The efficiency of a gage decreases as the gage is filled. Gerdel[3] showed that a gage having a large residual capacity will catch substantially greater amounts of snow than one which has only a small remaining volume. This effect is apparently the result of air currents set up over the liquid surface in a nearly full gage as compared with the relatively stagnant air in the depths of an empty gage. Hence, snow gages should have a large capacity and should be emptied while a considerable residual volume remains.

The precipitation-gage network. There are today about 3000 recording and 8000 nonrecording gages of various types in the United States, or one for approximately every 275 square miles on the average. The area of a standard 8-in. gage is 1/80,000,000 square mile. The extent of extrapolation from the gage record to the computed average depth over a large area is obvious. The network density necessary to obtain adequate

[1] Alter, J. C., Shielded Storage Precipitation Gages, *Monthly Weather Rev.*, Vol. 65, pp. 262-265, 1937.

[2] Röstad, A., Über die Wirkung des Nipherschen Schutztrichters, *Meteorolog. Z.*, Vol. 42, p. 266, 1925.

[3] Gerdel, R. W., "Snow Studies at Soda Springs, Calif.," *Ann. Rept. Coop. Snow Invest.*, U.S. Weather Bureau and University of Nevada, 1943-1944, p. 3.

records varies with the use to which the records are to be put and the characteristics of the region being studied. Studies of large storms or of long-term averages over large areas of fairly level terrane require only a relatively thin network of stations. Studies of intense local storms or of rainfall in mountainous areas may require a much denser network. In the storm of January, 1937, over the Clinch River in Tennessee, 9 Weather

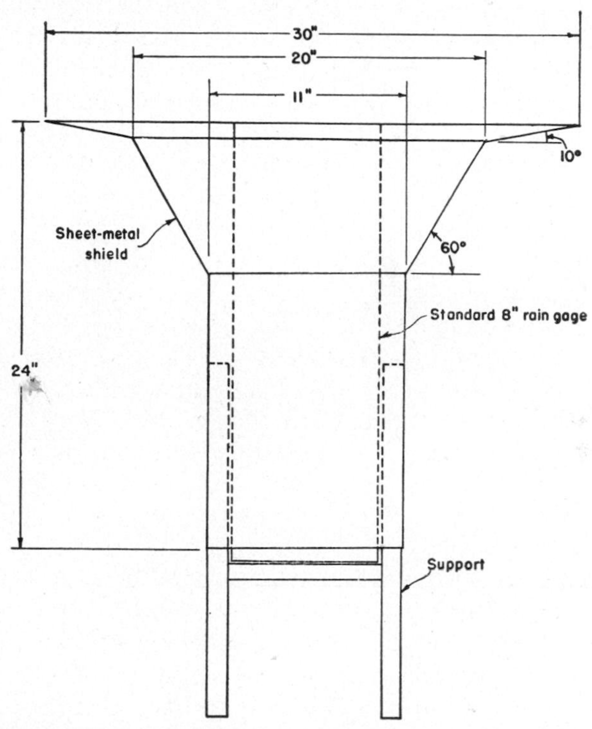

FIG. 6-6. Details of one form of modified Nipher shield.

Bureau gages with an average density of 1 gage per 328 square miles gave an average rainfall of 9.47 in. When 32 TVA gages were included in the average (1 gage per 72 square miles), it was increased to 10.65 in.[1] A similar comparison[2] for the Muskingum Basin is shown in Fig. 6-7.

When a storm occurs over a typical gage network, the probability that the center of the storm will be recorded by a gage varies with the network density. Little is known of the morphology of intense storms because of the general lack of data. The density of gage networks today is more

[1] Gay, R. W., Rainfall Records and Studies in the TVA, *Am. Meteorolog. Soc. Bull.*, Vol. 20, pp. 378-383, 1939.

[2] "Thunderstorm Rainfall," *Hydrometeorolog. Rept.* 5, U.S. Weather Bureau and Corps of Engrs., Vicksburg, Miss., 1947.

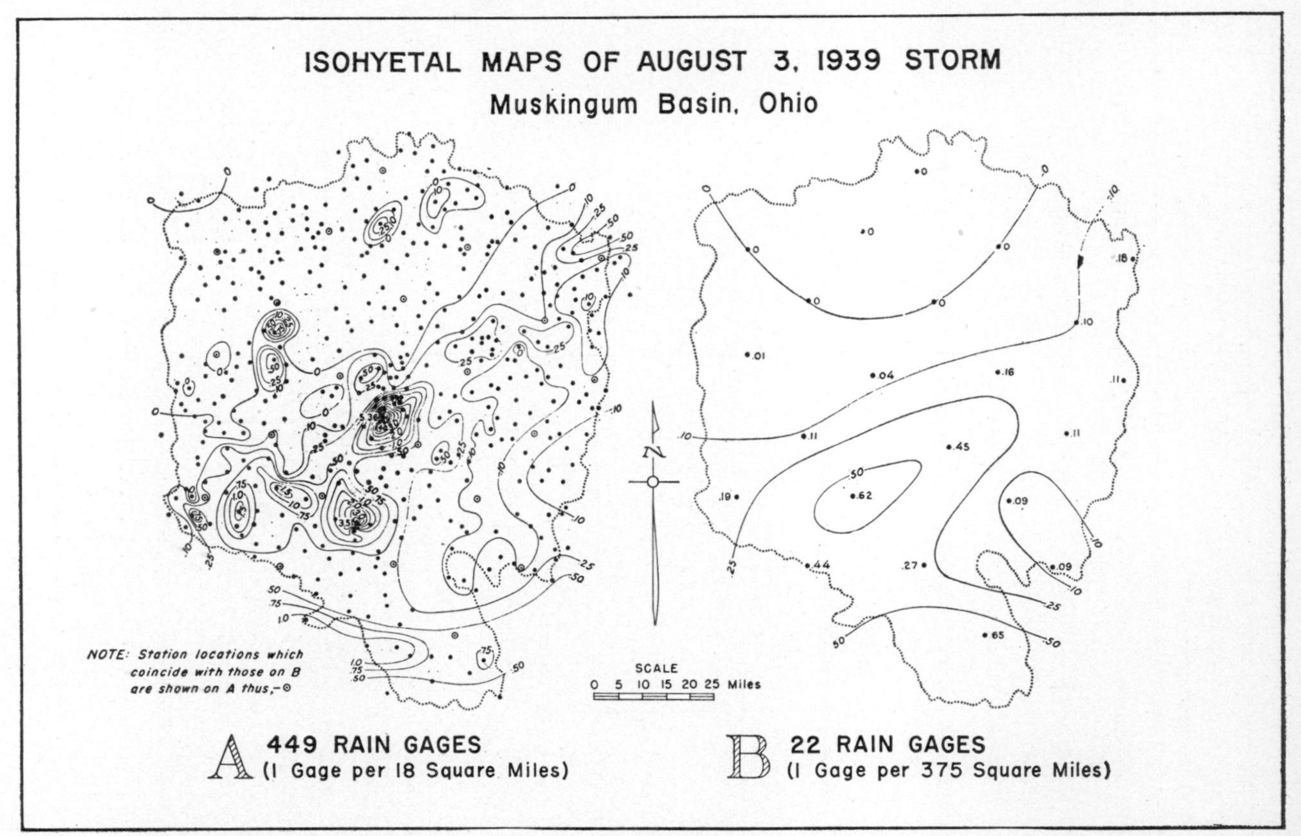

FIG. 6–7. Isohyetal maps showing the effect of network density on apparent storm pattern. (*U.S. Weather Bureau.*)

often based on economic reasons than on scientific standards. A network of precipitation stations should be planned so as to give an accurate picture of the areal distribution of precipitation. Stations should not be concentrated at points of expected heavy precipitation at the expense of low-precipitation areas, or vice versa. The accessibility of the gage site and its proximity to an observer often determine the specific location. Figure 6-8 was developed from an analysis of rainfall in the Muskingum Basin and shows the standard error of rainfall averages as a function of network density and area.

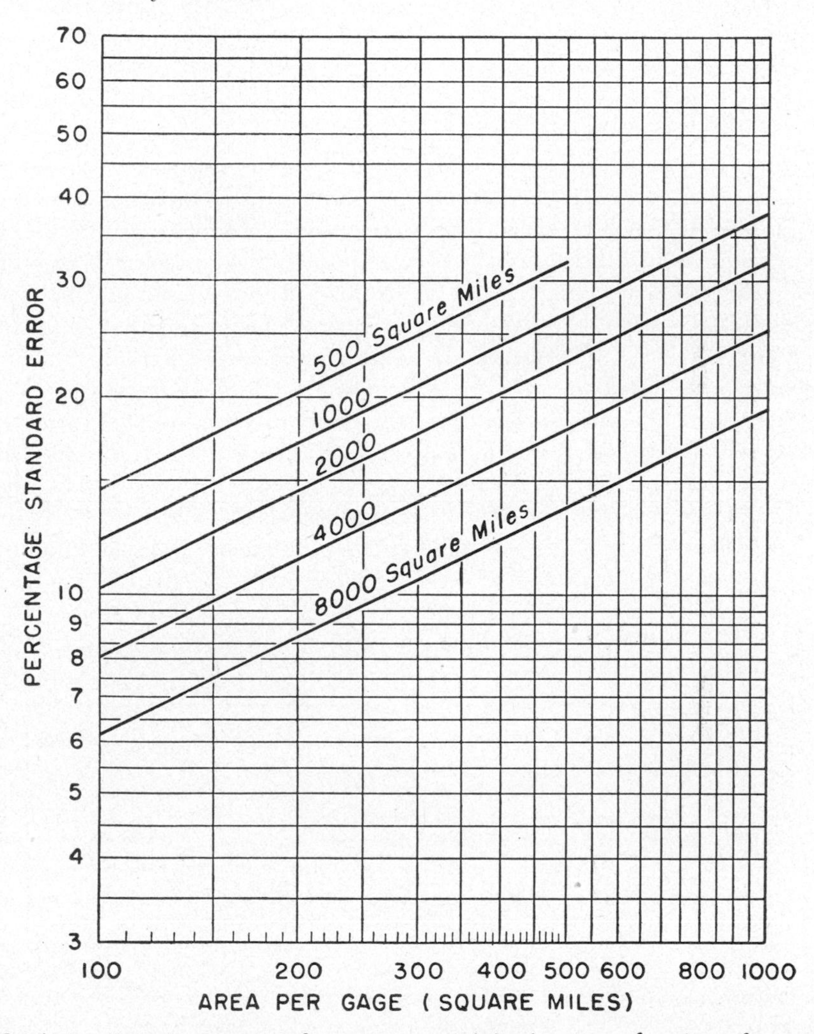

FIG. 6-8. Standard error of average precipitation as a function of network density and drainage area for the Muskingum Basin. (*U.S. Weather Bureau.*)

ADJUSTMENT OF PRECIPITATION DATA

In using precipitation in the solution of hydrologic problems, it is necessary to ascertain that time trends in the data are due to meteorological causes.[1] Quite frequently, these trends are the result of changes in the gage location, changes in the immediate surroundings (such as construction of buildings or growth of trees), and changes in observing technique. Slight changes in location are particularly significant in mountainous regions. Frequently, changes in gage location or exposure are not disclosed by the published record, since it has been Weather Bureau practice to continue a station under the same name as long as it remained in the general vicinity of its original site. The consistency of a record may be determined and the necessary adjustment accomplished by use of the *double-mass-curve* technique. This method of adjustment[2] is based upon a procedure that compares the accumulated annual or seasonal precipitation at the station to be tested with the concurrent accumulated values of mean precipitation for a group of base stations (Fig. 6-9). At least 10 base stations should be selected from within the immediate zone of environment of the station being tested. A decided change in the precipitation regime of the station is indicated by an abrupt change in the slope of the double-mass curve. The change in slope in Fig. 6-9 is accounted for by the fact that the station was moved from Hermit to near Hermit in 1923. On the basis of the difference in slope of the two sections of the curve, the records for Hermit should be adjusted by the factor $^{237}/_{278}$ to make the earlier years comparable with those for the present location. The consistency of the record for each of the base stations should be tested, and those stations showing inconsistent records should be dropped from the base before any other stations are tested or adjusted. In areas where there is a marked seasonal variation in precipitation types, better results may be obtained by using seasonal values instead of annual totals.

The double-mass adjustment technique is a useful tool when properly applied. A conservative approach is necessary, and underadjustment is to be preferred to overadjustment. The temptation is always present to use a series of short segments conforming as closely as possible to the plotted data. In every case, the data will show a tendency to fluctuate about a mean line, but a change in slope should not be shown unless it is supported by at least 5 years of data or by definite evidence of a change in exposure. Occasionally, a particular year will show an abnormal accumu-

[1] Kincer, J. B., Determination of Dependability of Rainfall Records by Comparison with Nearby Records, *Trans. Am. Geophys. Union*, Vol. 19, pp. 533-538, 1938.

[2] Merriam, C. F., Progress Report on the Analysis of Rainfall Data, *Trans. Am. Geophys. Union*, Vol. 19, pp. 529-532, 1938.

Kohler, M. A., Double-mass Analysis for Testing the Consistency of Records and for Making Required Adjustments, *Am. Meteorolog. Soc. Bull.*, Vol. 30, pp. 188-189, 1949.

lation, with the preceding and following years showing a consistent slope. In such cases, two parallel line segments should be used. There is a regional consistency in precipitation patterns for long periods of time, but this consistency becomes less pronounced for shorter periods. Therefore, the double-mass technique is not generally recommended for the adjustment of daily or storm amounts.

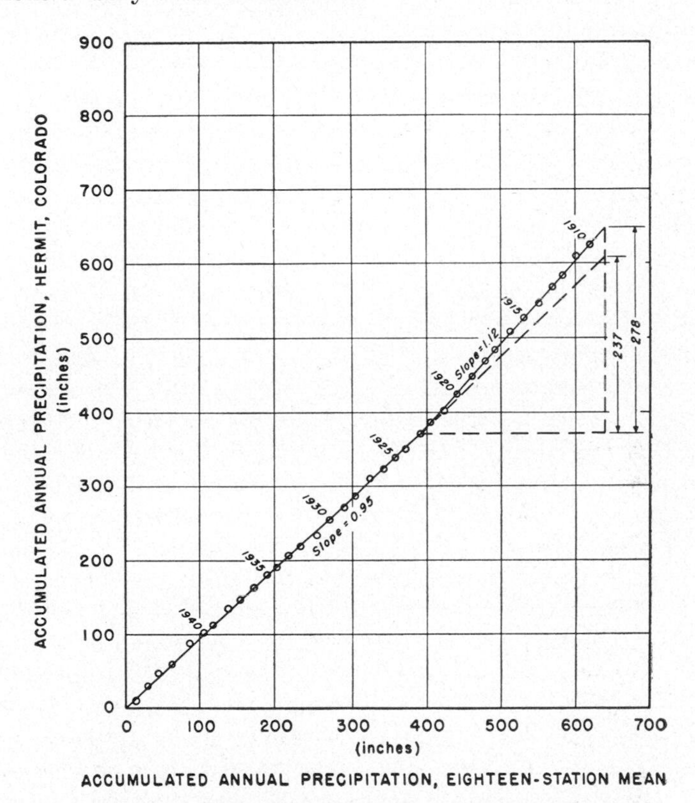

FIG. 6–9. Adjustment of precipitation data for Hermit, Colorado, by double-mass curve.

AVERAGE DEPTH OF PRECIPITATION OVER AREA

Since most hydrologic problems require a knowledge of the average depth of rainfall over a significant area such as a river basin, some procedure[1] must be used to convert the gage measurements to areal averages. The simplest procedure is to average arithmetically the amounts measured by the gages within the area. If the gages are distributed uniformly and

[1] Horton, R. E., Determining the Mean Precipitation of a Drainage Basin, *J. New Engl. Water Works Assoc.*, Vol. 38, pp. 1-47, 1924.

if the variation of individual gage catches from the mean is not large, this procedure is probably as accurate as any other method. Even in mountainous country, arithmetic averages will yield fairly accurate results if the orographic influences on precipitation are considered in the selection of gage sites.[1] In actual storm situations, however, the simple averaging of gage measurements sometimes gives unsatisfactory results because of nonuniform distribution of gages.

Thiessen method. A more formal method of computing average depths of precipitation over an area is that known as the *Thiessen method*, which gives weight to the areal distribution of stations. A Thiessen network[2] is constructed (Fig. 6-10) by locating the stations on a map and drawing the perpendicular bisectors to the lines connecting the stations. The polygons thus formed around each station are the boundaries of the effective area assumed to be controlled by the station, *i.e.*, the area which is closer to the station than to any other station. The area governed by each station is planimetered and expressed as a percentage of the whole area. Weighted average rainfall for the basin is computed by multiplying each station precipitation amount by its assigned percentage of area and totaling. The results are usually more accurate than the arithmetic average.[3] The inflexibility of this method is its greatest limitation. The weights for the adjacent stations must be changed each time a station is added to or taken from the network.

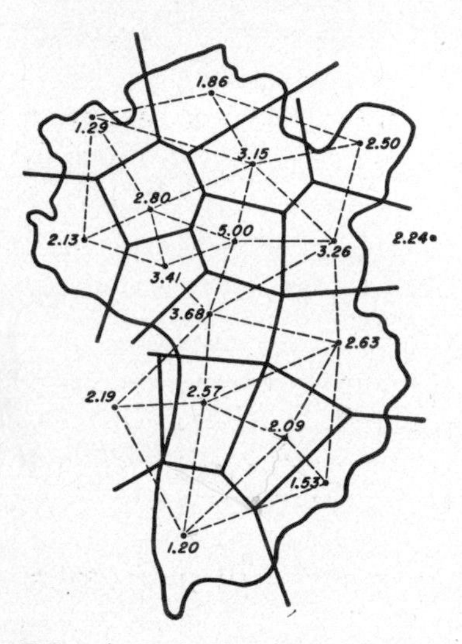

FIG. 6–10. Thiessen network (average precipitation = 2.54 in.).

The isohyetal method. Perhaps the most accurate method for computing average precipitation is the use of the *isohyetal map*. Such a map is constructed by plotting on a suitable base the precipitation for each station and then drawing, in proper relative position, contours of equal precipitation (*isohyets*) as shown in Fig. 6-11. The average precipitation for an area can be readily computed by weighting the average precipitation between

[1] Wilm, H. G., A. Z. Nelson, and H. C. Storey, An Analysis of Precipitation Measurements on Mountain Watersheds, *Monthly Weather Rev.*, Vol. 67, pp. 163-172, 1939.

[2] Thiessen, A. H., Precipitation Averages for Large Areas, *Monthly Weather Rev.*, Vol. 39, pp. 1082-1084, 1911.

[3] Horton, R. E., Accuracy of Areal Rainfall Estimates, *Monthly Weather Rev.*, Vol. 51, pp. 348-353, 1923.

contours (usually taken as one-half the sum of the two contour values) by the area between contours, totaling these values, and dividing by the total area. In some cases, it may be possible to estimate the average precipitation with a fair degree of accuracy by a simple inspection.

The isohyetal map permits the use and interpretation of all available data. It is particularly adapted to display and discussion work. If the shape of the isohyetal pattern is not definitely known, the isohyets may be interpolated[1] between stations. If there is indication of orographic precipitation, the contours may roughly follow the actual ground contours or the isohyets of seasonal precipitation. Orographic precipitation generally increases with altitude to the crest of a barrier. For very high barriers, however, the maximum precipitation on the windward slope quite often occurs below the crest. The lee sides of barriers usually show a sharp decline in precipitation downslope from the crest. If local centers of heavy precipitation are apparent, the isohyets can be spaced more closely around them.

DEPTH-AREA-DURATION ANALYSIS OF STORM PRECIPITATION

It is often necessary to analyze, not only the areal distribution of storm precipitation, but its time distribution as well.[2] While the time distribution can be approximated by inspection of the records, particularly if recording-gage data are available, mass curves are generally used for more detailed estimates.

Computation of depth-area data from isohyetal maps. Depth-area data (Fig. 6-12) are obtained by planimetering the total storm isohyetal map (Fig. 6-11). If the two isohyets bounding a given area are roughly parallel, the average depth over the area is assumed to be the average of the two isohyetal values. If the isohyetal pattern is irregular, the average depth may be higher or lower than the average of the encompassing isohyets.

Mass curves. A *mass curve* is a plot of accumulated precipitation against time (Fig. 6-13). By making use of observers' notes as to time of beginning and ending of precipitation, mass curves can be plotted from daily readings. Records from stations equipped with recording gages can be used to guide the construction of mass curves for adjacent nonrecording stations. The fact that the observation time is not the same at all stations is a decided advantage in the construction of mass curves. A

[1] Reed, W. G., and J. B. Kincer, The Preparation of Precipitation Charts, *Monthly Weather Rev.*, Vol. 45, pp. 233-235, 1917.

[2] Manual for Depth-Area-Duration Analysis of Storm Precipitation, *U.S. Weather Bur. Coop. Studies Tech. Paper* 1, 1946.

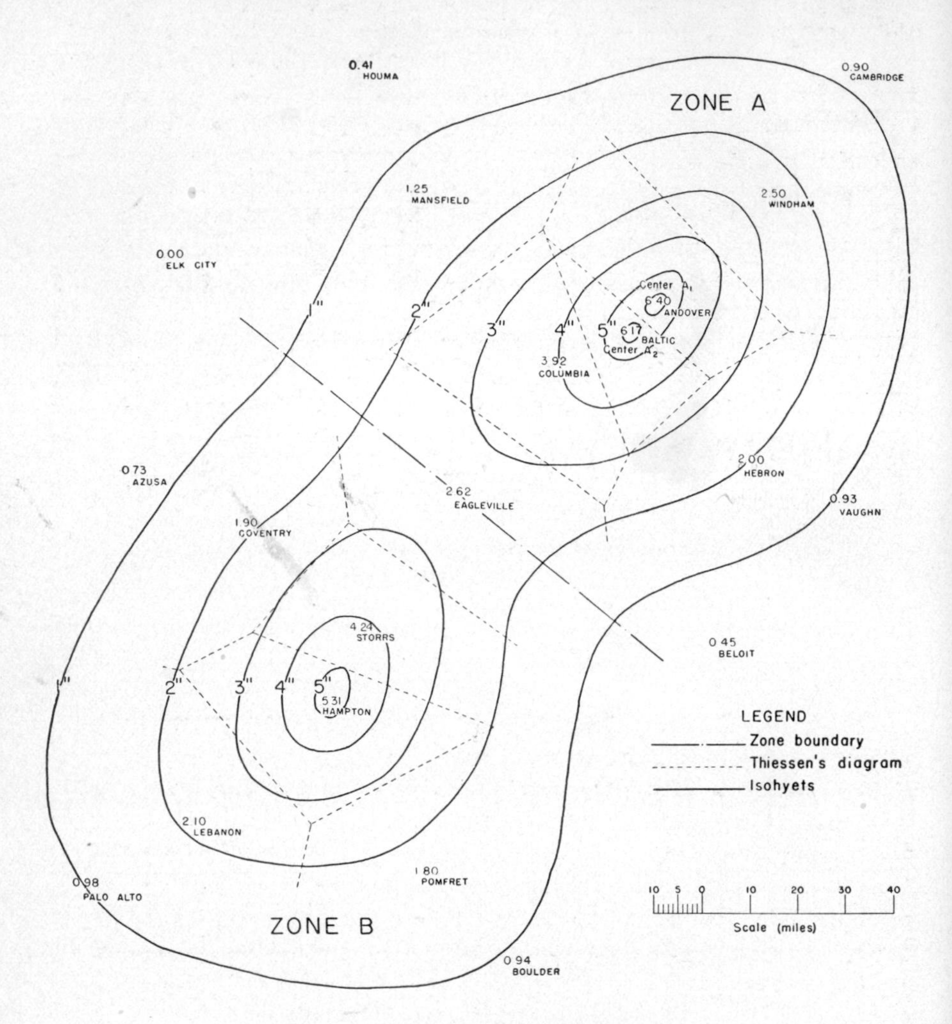

TOTAL-STORM ISOHYETAL MAP

(HYPOTHETICAL STORM)

FOR 24 HOURS

FROM 3 AM, SEPT. 1, 1947

TO 3 AM, SEPT. 2, 1947

FIG. 6–11. Total-storm isohyetal map.

LINE NO	RAINFALL CENTER OR ZONE	ISOHYET INCHES	AREA ENCLOSED		NET AREA IN SQ MI	AVERAGE DEPTH OF RAINFALL IN INCHES	VOLUME OF RAINFALL IN INCH – SQ. MI.		AVERAGE DEPTH OF RAINFALL IN INCHES (COL 9 ÷ COL 5)
			PLANIMETER READING	AREA IN SQ MI			INCREMENT (COL 6 X COL 7)	ACCUMULATIVE	
1	2	3	4	5	6	7	8	9	10
1	A	6.4	—	STATION	—	—	—	—	6.4
2	CENTER A_1	6	9	14	14	6.2	87	87	6.2
3									
4	CENTER A_2	6	7	11	11	6.1	67	67	6.1
5									
6	CENTER A_1+A_2	6	—	25	—	—	—	154	—
7		5	123	189	164	5.5	902	1056	5.6
8		4	531	815	626	4.5	2817	3873	4.8
9		3	1580	2424	1609	3.5	5632	9505	3.9
10		2*	3652	5602	3178	2.5	7945	17450	3.1
11		1*	6704	10284	4682	1.5	7023	24473	2.4
12									
13	B	5	36	55	55	5.3	292	292	5.3
14		4	31.9	489	434	4.5	1953	2245	4.6
15		3	1171	1796	1307	3.5	4574	6819	3.8
16		2*	3122	4789	2993	2.5	7482	14301	3.0
17		1*	6749	10353	5564	1.5	8346	22647	2.2
18									
19	COMBINATION OF ZONES								
20	A + B	2	—	10391	—	—	—	31751	3.1
21		1	—	20637	—	—	—	47120	2.3

* ISOHYET DOES NOT CLOSE WITHIN THIS ZONE

FIG. 6–12. Computation of depth-area data from isohyetal map.

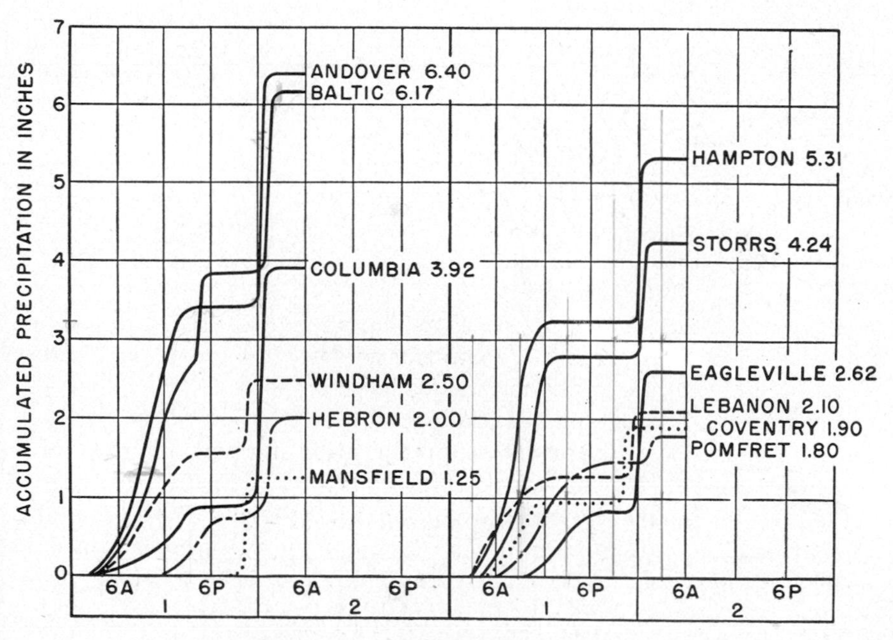

FIG. 6–13. Mass rainfall curves.

meteorological analysis of frontal passages and air-mass types is also helpful.[1]

Figure 6-14 shows tabulations of data scaled directly from the mass curves of Fig. 6-13. The 6-hr period used in the example is the most practical time unit for most storm analyses. Longer periods mask out variations in precipitation intensity, while the limitations of the basic data rarely justify the use of shorter periods. Stations in each zone are listed

LINE NO.	ZONE OR CENTER	STATION	ABSOLUTE MAX. PRECIP. DURATION IN HOURS				CONTEMPORANEOUS ACCUMULATED PRECIPITATION IN INCHES TIME IN HOURS AT END OF PERIOD									
			6	12	18	24	6 9A1	12 3P1	18 9P1	24 3A2	30	36	42	48	54	60
1	A	ANDOVER	3.0	3.4	5.6	6.4	1.3	3.4	3.4	6.4						
2		BALTIC	2.4	3.7	5.4	6.2	0.9	2.6	3.8	6.2						
3		COLUMBIA	3.0	3.3	3.8	3.9	0.2	0.8	0.9	3.9						
4		WINDHAM					0.8	1.5	1.6	2.5						
5		HEBRON					0.0	0.2	0.7	2.0						
6		MANSFIELD					0.0	0.0	0.0	1.2						
7																
8	B	HAMPTON	2.8	3.2	4.4	5.3	2.0	3.2	3.2	5.3						
9		STORRS	2.3	2.8	3.7	4.2	0.9	2.8	2.8	4.2						
10		EAGLEVILLE					0.0	0.5	0.8	2.6						
11		LEBANON					0.9	1.3	1.3	2.1						
12		COVENTRY					0.5	1.0	1.0	1.9						
13		POMFRET					0.2	1.1	1.5	1.8						
14																
15																
16																
17																
18																
19																
20																

FIG. 6-14. Tabulation of data from mass rainfall curves.

in order of precipitation depths for convenience in subsequent computations. "Absolute maximum precipitation" values shown in Fig. 6-14 need be tabulated only for stations in areas of relatively intense precipitation. These values are the highest that can be found by trial anywhere on the mass curves.

Accuracy in the determination of maximum short-period precipitation intensities over small areas (25 square miles or less) is of greater importance than for larger areas, where natural valley storage tends to smooth out the effects on a hydrograph of variations in precipitation. It is apparent, upon consideration of the scarcity of precipitation stations, that the probability of recording the highest point precipitation is very remote. It is considered reasonable, in the study of most large-area storms, to assume that the highest station precipitation represents the average depth over an appreciable area (usually taken as 10 square miles) rather than the maxi-

[1] Shands, A. L., and G. N. Brancato, Applied Meteorology: Mass Curves of Rainfall, *U.S. Weather Bur. Hydrometeorolog. Tech. Paper* 4, 1947.

mum point precipitation. Accordingly, absolute maximum depth-duration values assumed to apply to 10 square miles are obtained directly from the mass curve for the station that recorded the most intense precipitation for any duration. In some cases, it may be necessary to derive these data for two or more stations in order to determine the maxima for all durations.

The distribution over an area large enough to include several stations should be determined by prorating the average total-storm precipitation in proportion to the average of the mass curves for the stations in or near the area. Average mass curves are determined for the total area enclosed by each isohyet (Figs. 6-15 to 6-17). If six or more stations are available in the area within a given isohyet, the arithmetic average of the mass curves is satisfactory. The number of mass curves included in the average is of greater significance than the actual size of the area, provided that the areal distribution of stations is reasonably uniform. When fewer than six stations are available within an isohyet, it is customary to use a weighted mass curve, with the weights assigned on the basis of a Thiessen network. On this basis, a mass curve for a station controlling twice as much effective area as another station is given twice as much weight in computing the weighted mass curve. Data listed under the heading Encompassing Isohyet are obtained from Fig. 6-12. The Effective Area controlled by each station, in so far as the area within any isohyet is concerned, is that portion of the Thiessen polygon encompassed by the isohyet under consideration (Fig. 6-11). The size of each effective area is indicated in terms of planimeter readings, and the ratio of each to the total area within the isohyet is given in per cent under Station Weight. The mass-curve values (Fig. 6-14) are multiplied by the station weight and added to obtain the weighted mass curves. Both the average and weighted mass curves must be adjusted to the correct total as obtained by planimetering.

Combination of data from separate storm centers. The method discussed above applies to the computation of depth-area-duration data for individual storm centers. The total-storm isohyetal pattern was divided into zones chosen as closely as practicable to the principal rainfall centers. For areas larger than a single zone, the average mass curves for separate zones may be weighted in proportion to the areas within each isohyet in the respective zones or may be averaged directly. Both methods are shown in Fig. 6-17.

The combinations of data for contiguous zones that are necessary to determine the maximum average depth of precipitation for various areas and durations can be determined by trial. Only the combinations necessary to define maximum depth-area curves for the various durations are required. Consequently, combinations which yield low values may be eliminated by inspection. Maximum depth-duration curves should be computed for the separate zones and combinations of contiguous zones

SUBJECT: *Average Rainfall Depths and Maximum Depth-Duration Data (Zone A)*

STORM PERIOD: 19*47* *Sept. 1-2*
24 HOURS FROM *3* A.M. *Sept. 1*
TO *3* A.M. *Sept. 2*

Note
"Effective" area controlled by station is area bounded by Thiessen's diagram and designated isohyet. K=sq. mi /unit

Line No.	Center or Zone	Station or Item Description	Encompassing Isohyet			Effective Area Controlled by Sta.		Product of Accumulative Station Rainfall × Station Weight Except as Otherwise Noted — Time in Hours at End of Period (or Duration of Maximum Precipitation)																				Total
			Inches	Average P in inches	Area inclosed sq mi.	Planim Reading K=1534	Station weight in %	6	12	18	24	30	36	42	48	54	60	66	72	78	84	90	96	102	108	114	120	
								9a1	3p1	9p1	3a2																	
1	A	Andover (Absolute max. station precip.)						3.0	3.4	5.6	6.4																	
2		(e) End of period of max. precip.						2a2	3p1	1a2	3a2																	
3																												
4	A	Baltic (Absolute max. station. precip.)						2.4	3.7	5.4	6.2																	
5		(e) End of period of max. precip.						3a2	2a2	2a2	3a2																	
6																												
7																												
8	A	Andover	6	6.2	14	–	100	1.3	3.4	3.4	6.4																	
9	(Center A_1)	(b) Adjusted mass curve						1.3	3.3	3.3	6.2																	
10		(c) Adjusted increment						1.3	2.0	0.0	2.9																	
11		(d) Max. depth-duration						2.9	3.3	4.9	6.2																	
12		(e) End of period for (d)						3a2	3p1	3a2	3a2																	
13																												
14																												
15	A	Baltic	6	6.1	11	–	100	0.9	2.6	3.8	6.2																	
16	(Center A_2)	(b) Adjusted mass curve						0.9	2.6	3.7	6.1																	
17		(c) Adjusted increment						0.9	1.7	1.1	2.4																	
18		(d) Max. depth-duration						2.4	3.5	5.2	6.1																	
19		(e) End of period for (d)						3a2	3a2	3a2	3a2																	
20																												
21																												
22	A	Andover	5	5.6	189	67	54	0.70	1.84	1.84	3.46																	
23	(Center A_1+A_2)	Baltic				58	46	0.41	1.20	1.75	2.85																	
24																												
25		(a) Weighted mass curve				125	100	1.11	3.04	3.59	6.31																	
26		(b) Adjusted mass curve						1.0	2.7	3.2	5.6																	
27		(c) Adjusted increment						1.0	1.7	0.5	2.4																	
28		(d) Max. depth-duration						2.4	2.9	4.6	5.6																	
29		(e) End of period for (d)						3a2	3a2	3a2	3a2																	
30																												
31																												
32	A	Andover	4	4.8	815	253	47	0.61	1.60	1.60	3.01																	
33		Baltic				200	38	0.34	0.99	1.44	2.36																	
34		Columbia				78	15	0.03	0.12	0.14	0.58																	
35																												
36		(a) Weighted mass curve				531	100	0.98	2.71	3.18	5.95																	
37		(b) Adjusted mass curve						0.8	2.2	2.6	4.8																	
38		(c) Adjusted increment						0.8	1.4	0.4	2.2																	
39		(d) Max. depth-duration						2.2	2.6	4.0	4.8																	
40		(e) End of period for (d)						3a2	3a2	3a2	3a2																	

REMARKS:

SUBJECT: Average Rainfall Depths and Maximum Depth-Duration Data (Zone A)

Note: "Effective" area controlled by station is area bounded by Thiessen's diagram and designated isohyet. K=sq. mi./unit

STORM PERIOD: 1947 Sept. 1-2
24 HOURS FROM 3 AM. Sept. 1
TO 3 AM. Sept. 2

Line No.	Center or Zone	Station or Item Description	Encompassing Isohyet: Inches	Encompassing Isohyet: Average P in inches	Encompassing Isohyet: Area inclosed sq. mi.	Effective Area Controlled by Sta.: Planim. Reading K=1.534	Effective Area Controlled by Sta.: Station weight in %	Product of Accumulative Station Rainfall × Station Weight Except as Otherwise Noted — Time in Hours at End of Period (or Duration of Maximum Precipitation): 6	12	18	24	30	36	42	48	54	60	66	72	78	84	90	96	102	108	114	120	Total
								9a1	3p1	9p1	3a2																	
1	A	Andover	3	3.9	2424	505	32	0.42	1.09	1.09	2.05																	
2		Baltic				328	21	0.19	0.55	0.60	1.30																	
3		Columbia				524	33	0.07	0.26	0.30	1.29																	
4		Eagleville				34	2	0.00	0.01	0.02	0.05																	
5		Windham				140	9	0.07	0.14	0.14	0.22																	
6		Hebron				42	3	0.00	0.01	0.02	0.06																	
7																												
8		(a) Weighted mass curve				1573	100	0.75	2.06	2.37	4.97																	
9		(b) Adjusted mass curve						0.6	1.6	1.9	3.9																	
10		(c) Adjusted increment						0.6	1.0	0.3	2.0																	
11		(d) Max. depth-duration						2.0	2.3	3.3	3.9																	
12		(e) End of period for (d)						3a2	3a2	3a2	3a2																	
13																												
14																												
15	A	Andover	2	3.1	5602	700	19	0.25	0.65	0.65	1.22																	
16		Baltic				334	9	0.08	0.23	0.34	0.56																	
17		Columbia				820	23	0.05	0.18	0.21	0.90																	
18		Eagleville				518	14	0.00	0.07	0.11	0.36																	
19		Windham				628	17	0.14	0.26	0.27	0.42																	
20		Hebron				494	14	0.00	0.03	0.10	0.28																	
21		Mansfield				159	4	0.00	0.00	0.00	0.05																	
22																												
23		(a) Weighted mass curve				3653	100	0.52	1.42	1.68	3.79																	
24		(b) Adjusted mass curve						0.4	1.2	1.4	3.1																	
25		(c) Adjusted increment						0.4	0.8	0.2	1.7																	
26		(d) Max. depth-duration						1.7	1.9	2.7	3.1																	
27		(e) End of period for (d)						3a2	3a2	3a2	3a2																	
28																												
29																												
30		Computations Based on Unweighted Average of Mass Curves for Stations Inclosed by Various Isohyets																										
31																												
32																												
33	A	Sum of precip. at 6 stations	1	2.4	10,284	–	100	3.2	8.5	10.4	22.2																	
34																												
35		(a) Unweighted mass curve	(Average of 6 stations)					0.53	1.42	1.73	3.70																	
36		(b) Adjusted mass curve						0.3	0.9	1.1	2.4																	
37		(c) Adjusted increment						0.3	0.6	0.2	1.3																	
38		(d) Max. depth-duration						1.3	1.5	2.1	2.4																	
39		(e) End of period for (d)						3a2	3a2	3a2	3a2																	
40																												

REMARKS:

FIG. 6–15. Average rainfall depths and maximum depth-duration data (Zone A).

SUBJECT: Average Rainfall Depths and Maximum Depth-Duration Data (Zone B)

Note
"Effective" area controlled by station is area bounded by Thiessen's diagram and designated isohyet K=sq mi/unit

STORM PERIOD: 1947 Sept. 1-2
24 HOURS FROM 3 AM. Sept. 1
TO 3 AM. Sept. 2 :

Line No.	Center or Zone	Station or Item Description	Encompassing Isohyet			Effective Area Controlled by Sta.		Product of Accumulative Station Rainfall × Station Weight Except as Otherwise Noted — Time in Hours at End of Period (or Duration of Maximum Precipitation)																				Total
			Inches	Average P in inches	Area inclosed sq mi.	Planim. Reading K=1.534	Station weight in %	6	12	18	24	30	36	42	48	54	60	66	72	78	84	90	96	102	108	114	120	
								9a1	3p1	9p1	3a2																	
1	B	Hampton (Absolute max. station precip.)						2.8	3.2	4.4	5.3																	
2		(e) End of period of max. precip.						11a1	3p1	1a2	3a2																	
3																												
4																												
5	B	Hampton	5	5.3	55	–	100	2.0	3.2	3.2	5.3																	
6		(b) Adjusted mass curve						2.0	3.2	3.2	5.3																	
7		(c) Adjusted increment						2.0	1.2	0.0	2.1																	
8		(d) Max. depth-duration						2.1	3.2	3.3	5.3																	
9		(e) End of period for (d)						3a2	3p1	3a2	3a2																	
10																												
11																												
12	B	Hampton	4	4.6	489	211	66	1.32	2.11	2.11	3.50																	
13		Storrs				108	34	0.31	0.95	0.95	1.43																	
14																												
15		(a) Weighted mass curve				319	100	1.63	3.06	3.06	4.93																	
16		(b) Adjusted mass curve						1.5	2.9	2.9	4.6																	
17		(c) Adjusted increment						1.5	1.4	0.0	1.7																	
18		(d) Max depth-duration						1.7	2.9	3.1	4.6																	
19		(e) End of period for (d)						3a2	3p1	3a2	3a2																	
20																												
21																												
22	B	Hampton	3	3.8	.1796	576	49	0.98	1.57	1.57	2.60																	
23		Storrs				519	45	0.40	1.26	1.26	1.89																	
24		Eagleville				47	4	0.00	0.02	003	0.10																	
25		Lebanon				22	2	0.02	0.03	003	0.04																	
26		Coventry				3	0	0.00	0.00	0.00	0.00																	
27																												
28		(a) Weighted mass curve				1167	100	1.40	288	289	4.63																	
29		(b) Adjusted mass curve						1.1	2.4	2.4	3.8																	
30		(c) Adjusted increment						1.1	1.3	0.0	1.4																	
31		(d) Max. depth-duration						1.4	2.4	2.7	3.8																	
32		(e) End of period for (d)						3a2	3p1	3a2	3a2																	
33																												
34																												
35																												
36																												
37																												
38																												
39																												
40																												

REMARKS:

SUBJECT: Average Rainfall Depths and Maximum Depth-Duration Data (Zone B)

Note
"Effective" area controlled by station is area bounded by Thiessen's diagram and designated isohyet. K=sq mi /unit

STORM PERIOD: 1947, Sept. 1-2
24 HOURS FROM 3 A.M. Sept. 1
TO 3 A.M. Sept. 2

Line No.	Center or Zone	Station or Item Description	Encompassing Isohyet			Effective Area Controlled by Sta.		Product of Accumulative Station Rainfall × Station Weight Except as Otherwise Noted; Time in Hours at End of Period (or Duration of Maximum Precipitation)																				Total
			Inches	Average P in inches	Area inclosed sq mi	Planim. Reading K=1534	Station weight in %	6	12	18	24	30	36	42	48	54	60	66	72	78	84	90	96	102	108	114	120	
								9a1	3p1	9p1	3a2																	
1	B	Hampton	2	3.0	4789	798	26	0.52	0.83	0.83	1.38																	
2		Storrs				707	23	0.21	0.64	0.64	0.97																	
3		Eagleville				523	17	0.00	0.08	0.14	0.44																	
4		Lebanon				455	14	0.13	0.18	0.18	0.29																	
5		Coventry				357	11	0.06	0.11	0.11	0.21																	
6		Pomfret				273	9	0.02	0.10	0.14	0.16																	
7																												
8		(a) Weighted mass curve				3113	100	0.94	1.94	2.04	3.45																	
9		(b) Adjusted mass curve						0.8	1.7	1.8	3.0																	
10		(c) Adjusted increment						0.8	0.9	0.1	1.2																	
11		(d) Max. depth-duration						1.2	1.7	2.2	3.0																	
12		(e) End of period for (d)						3a2	3p1	3a2	3a2																	
13																												
14																												
15		Computations Based on Unweighted Average of Mass Curves for Stations Inclosed by Various Isohyets																										
16																												
17																												
18	B	Sum of precip. at 6 stations	1	2.2	10,353	–	100	4.5	9.9	10.6	17.9																	
19																												
20		(a) Unweighted mass curve	(Average of 6 stations)					0.75	1.65	1.77	2.98																	
21		(b) Adjusted mass curve						0.5	1.2	1.3	2.2																	
22		(c) Adjusted increment						0.5	0.7	0.1	0.9																	
23		(d) Max. depth-duration						0.9	1.2	1.7	2.2																	
24		(e) End of period for (d)						3a2	3p1	3a2	3a2																	
25																												
26																												
27																												
28																												
29																												
30																												
31																												
32																												
33																												
34																												
35																												
36																												
37																												
38																												
39																												
40																												

REMARKS:

FIG. 6–16. Average rainfall depths and maximum depth-duration data (Zone B).

SUBJECT: Average Rainfall Depths and Maximum Depth-Duration Data (Zones A and B in Combination)

Note
"Effective" area controlled by station is area bounded by Thiessen's diagram and designated isohyet. K = sq. mi./unit

STORM PERIOD: 1947, Sept. 1-2
24 HOURS FROM 3 A.M. Sept. 1
TO 3 A.M. Sept. 2

Line No.	Center or Zone	Station or Item Description	Encompassing Isohyet: Inches	Encompassing Isohyet: Average P in inches	Encompassing Isohyet: Area inclosed sq. mi.	Effective Area Controlled by Sta.: Planim. Reading K=/.534	Effective Area Controlled by Sta.: Station weight in %	Product of Accumulative Station Rainfall X Station Weight Except as Otherwise Noted — Time in Hours at End of Period (or Duration of Maximum Precipitation): 6	12	18	24	30	36	42	48	54	60	66	72	78	84	90	96	102	108	114	120	Total
								9a1	3p1	9p1	3a2																	
1	A	Item (a) × Zone Weight	2	3.1	5602	—	54	0.28	0.77	0.91	2.05																	
2	B	do.	2	3.0	4789	—	46	0.43	0.89	0.94	1.59																	
3	A+B	(a) Weighted mass curve	2	3.1	10,391	—	100	0.71	1.66	1.85	3.64																	
4		(b) Adjusted mass curve						0.6	1.4	1.6	3.1																	
5		(c) Adjusted increment						0.6	0.8	0.2	1.5																	
6		(d) Max. depth-duration						1.5	1.7	2.5	3.1																	
7		(e) End of period for (d)						3a2	3a2	3a2	3a2																	
8																												
9																												
10		Computations Based on Unweighted Average of Mass Curves for Stations Inclosed by Various Isohyets																										
11																												
12	A	Sum of precip. at 6 stations	1	2.4	10,284			3.2	8.5	10.4	22.2																	
13	B	" " " " 6 "	1	2.2	10,353			4.5	9.9	10.6	17.9																	
14	A+B	" " " " 12 "	1	2.3	20,637			7.7	18.4	21.0	40.1																	
15		(a) Unweighted mass curve	(Average of 12 stations)					0.64	1.53	1.75	3.34																	
16		(b) Adjusted mass curve						0.4	1.1	1.2	2.3																	
17		(c) Adjusted increment						0.4	0.7	0.1	1.1																	
18		(d) Max. depth-duration						1.1	1.2	1.9	2.3																	
19		(e) End of period for (d)						3a2	3a2	3a2	3a2																	
20																												
21																												
22																												
23																												
24																												
25																												
26																												
27																												
28																												
29																												
30																												
31																												
32																												
33																												
34																												
35																												
36																												
37																												
38																												
39																												
40																												

REMARKS:

FIG. 6–17. Average rainfall depths and maximum depth-duration data (Zones A and B in combination).

over which the total-storm rainfall was greatest. The maximum depth of precipitation during the longer durations will certainly be found in such regions, and it is very likely that maxima for shorter durations will be found here also. However, the greatest depth of precipitation over intermediate areas for the shorter durations can occur in regions where the total-storm precipitation is less than the maximum. Hence, combinations

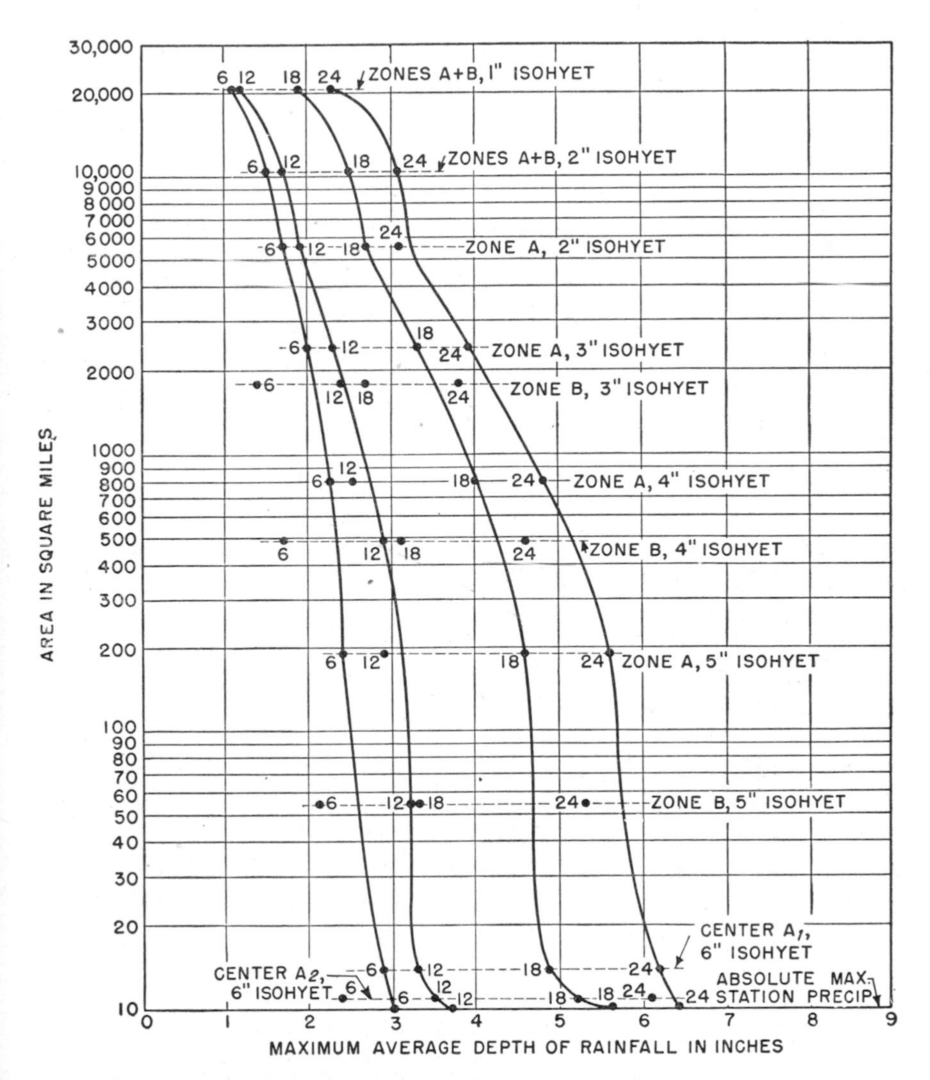

FIG. 6–18. Maximum depth-area-duration curves. The plotted points represent the maximum average depth over the area designated, within the number of hours indicated by the figures beside the points.

from zones having maximum storm totals should be compared with other plausible combinations to ensure that no maxima are overlooked.

Depending on the use to which the storm analysis is to be put, care should be exercised in combining data from zones where the topographical and meteorological influences are not comparable. For example, an average of precipitation over a mountain range and adjacent plains may be very misleading. Similarly, precipitation in two widely separated centers may be the result of unassociated meteorological causes.

Maximum depth-area-duration curves. For many design purposes it is necessary to determine the maximum depths of precipitation within a given storm for various areas and durations, *i.e.*, *maximum depth-area-duration curves.* Maximum depth-duration data for the area within any

AREA IN SQ. MI.	DURATION OF RAINFALL IN HOURS										
	6	12	18	24	30	36	48	60	72	96	120
10	3.0	3.7	5.6	6.4							
100	2.5	3.2	4.7	5.7							
200	2.4	3.1	4.6	5.6							
500	2.3	2.9	4.3	5.2							
1000	2.2	2.7	3.9	4.6							
2000	2.1	2.4	3.4	4.1							
5000	1.8	2.0	2.8	3.3							
10000	1.5	1.7	2.5	3.1							
20000	1.1	1.2	1.9	2.4							

FIG. 6–19. Maximum average depth of rainfall in inches.

isohyet are obtained by selection of maximum increments of precipitation from the adjusted mass-curve data of Figs. 6-15 to 6-17. The maximum 6-, 12-, 18-, and 24-hr values are computed by combining the highest adjacent 6-hr values (items *c* and *d*).

Maximum depth-duration values computed for various areas are plotted on semilog paper and an enveloping curve drawn for each duration (Fig. 6-18). Curves most satisfactorily defined are drawn first, and the remainder are interpolated to conform with plotted points and the shape of the more clearly defined curves. Depth-area curves derived from isohyetal maps for actual storms usually approach straight lines or flat curves when plotted on semilog paper with area on the logarithmic scale. Final results of the analysis are generally presented as in Fig. 6-19.

Depth-area formula. Horton [1] found that depth-area curves could be represented by

$$\bar{P} = P_0 e^{-kA^n} \tag{6-1}$$

[1] Horton, R. E., Discussion on Distribution of Intense Rainfall, *Trans. ASCE*, Vol. 87, pp. 578-585, 1924.

in which $\overline{P}$ is the average depth of rainfall for a given duration over an area A, P_0 is the highest amount at the center of the storm, and k and n are constants for a given storm.

The formula is useful for extrapolating storm data previously analyzed. Selecting two pairs of known values $\overline{P}_1, A_1$ and $\overline{P}_2, A_2$, and writing Eq. (6-1) in the form

$$\frac{\overline{P}}{P_0} = \mathbf{e}^{-kA^n} \tag{6-2}$$

values of $kA_1{}^n$ and $kA_2{}^n$ can be obtained from a table of exponentials. Calling these values X_1 and X_2, respectively, n can be determined from

$$\left(\frac{A_1}{A_2}\right)^n = \frac{X_1}{X_2} \tag{6-3}$$

and

$$k = \frac{X_1}{A_1{}^n} = \frac{X_2}{A_2{}^n} \tag{6-4}$$

Using storm data processed by the Miami Conservancy District,[1] Horton found that the envelope curve of 24-hr amounts for five great northern storms could be represented by

$$\overline{P} = 16\mathbf{e}^{-0.0883A^{0.24}} \tag{6-5}$$

and for five great southern storms by

$$\overline{P} = 22\mathbf{e}^{-0.112A^{0.23}} \tag{6-6}$$

Intensity-duration formulas. Many formulas have been derived to express the relationship between intensity and duration of point rainfall. For durations of 5 to 120 min, most formulas are of the general type

$$i = \frac{a}{t + b} \tag{6-7}$$

in which i is the average intensity for duration t, and a and b are coefficients which vary with locality. Meyer[2] has determined values of a and b for numerous localities east of the Rocky Mountains and has compared the results of formulas developed by other investigators.

For durations of over 2 hr, the relation between the average rainfall intensity and duration is more accurately expressed[3] by a formula of the type

$$i = \frac{c}{t^n} \tag{6-8}$$

in which c and n are constants having values dependent on locality.

[1] "Storm Rainfall of Eastern United States," *Tech. Rept.*, Part V, pp. 258-259, Miami Conservancy District, Dayton, rev. 1936.

[2] Meyer, A. F., "Elements of Hydrology," 2d ed., pp. 196-202, Wiley, New York, 1928.

[3] Bernard, M., Formulas for Rainfall Intensities of Long Duration, *Trans. ASCE*, Vol. 96, pp. 592-596, 1932.

In a study of 141 cases of rainfall with mean hourly intensity of 0.50 in. or greater, Breihan[1] found that, on the average, about 80 per cent of the rain fell at rates in excess of the mean hourly rate and about 45 per cent occurred at rates twice the mean hourly rate.

Obviously, intensity equations such as Eqs. (6-7) and (6-8) can be combined with Eq. (6-1) to obtain a general depth-area-duration function.

GEOGRAPHICAL DISTRIBUTION OF PRECIPITATION

The discussion of the general circulation in Chap. 2 indicates that the precipitation regime for any region is dependent to a large extent on the location of the region in the general circulation pattern. The latitude, distance from moisture source, and orography of a region also influence its precipitation. In most analyses of precipitation distribution, it is practically impossible to estimate the relative effectiveness of these influences.

Latitudinal variation. In general, precipitation is heaviest near the equator and decreases toward higher latitudes. However, the irregularity of the isohyets on the mean annual precipitation chart of the United States (Fig. 6-20) indicates that other factors are much more effective in influencing the geographical distribution of precipitation.

Distance from a moisture source. Since precipitation requires a source of moisture, it tends to be heavier near coastlines. The decrease of precipitation northward from the Gulf Coast is the most marked example of this effect in the United States (Fig. 6-20). Although obscured by the effects of orography, a similar variation is discernible in the western United States. Large inland bodies of water in regions of pronounced prevailing winds, such as the Great Lakes, also have a noticeable effect on the distribution of precipitation. In general, the occurrence of precipitation is more frequent on the lee shore. Precipitation amounts, on the other hand, show a seasonal trend, with winter precipitation heavier on the lee shore and summer precipitation heavier on the windward.

Orographic influences. Since precipitation is chiefly the result of lifting of air masses, amounts and frequency are usually greater on the windward side of orographic barriers. Conversely, since the downslope motion of air results in a decrease of relative humidity, regions on the lee of mountain ranges usually have relatively light precipitation. However, the air in passing over the ridge does not begin to descend immediately but continues to rise for some distance past the crest. Thus, for some distance (depending on the wind velocity) beyond the crest, relatively heavy amounts are observed. This is called the *spill-over effect*. The effect

[1] Breihan, E. R., Relation of Hourly Mean Rainfall to Actual Intensities, *Civil Eng.*, Vol. 10, pp. 303-305, 1940.

of a mountain barrier is sometimes felt some distance to the windward because the air begins to rise before reaching the barrier. This is known as the *upwind effect.*

Many investigators[1] have correlated precipitation with elevation. It is generally agreed that the level of maximum precipitation in the Sierra

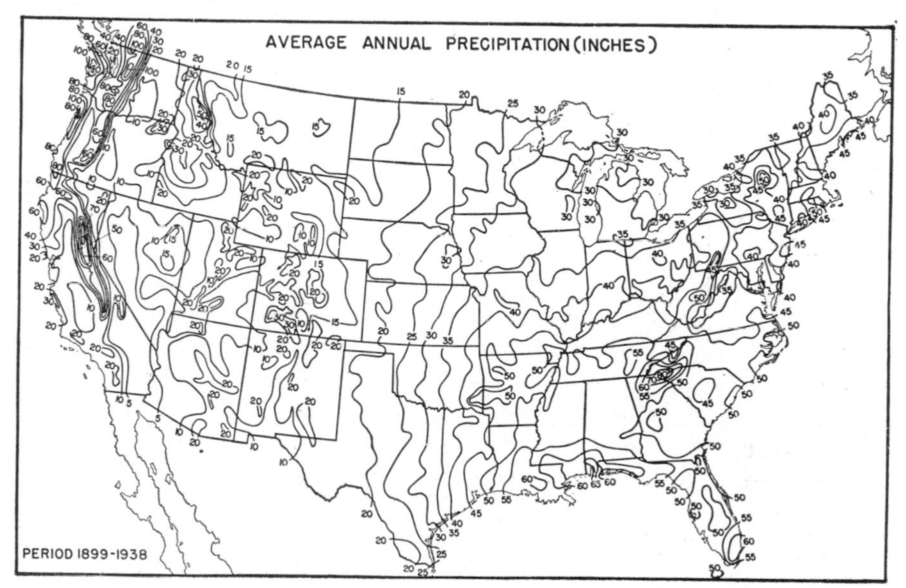

FIG. 6–20. Average annual precipitation. (*U.S. Weather Bureau.*)

Nevada is about 5000 ft and that it is higher in summer than in winter. Lee[2] stated that annual precipitation on the windward slope increases at the rate of 0.85 in. per 100 ft to 5000 ft and then decreases at 0.40 in. per 100 ft to the crest. Henry[3] recognized that orientation and inclination of the slope were important factors.

The best and most recent attempt to analyze the orographic influences on precipitation is that by Spreen.[4] He correlated values of normal

[1] Alter, J. C., Normal Precipitation in Utah, *Monthly Weather Rev.*, Vol. 47, pp. 633-636, 1919.

Barrows, H. K., Precipitation and Runoff and Altitude Relations for Connecticut River, *Trans. Am. Geophys. Union*, Vol. 14, pp. 396-406, 1933.

Donley, D. E., and R. L. Mitchell, The Relation of Rainfall to Elevation in the Southern Appalachian Region, *Trans. Am. Geophys. Union*, Vol. 20, pp. 711-721, 1939.

[2] Lee, C. H., Precipitation and Altitude in the Sierra, *Monthly Weather Rev.*, Vol. 39, pp. 1092-1099, 1911.

[3] Henry, A. J., Increase of Precipitation with Altitude, *Monthly Weather Rev.*, Vol. 47, pp. 33-41, 1919.

[4] Spreen, W. C., A Determination of the Effect of Topography upon Precipitation, *Trans. Am. Geophys. Union*, Vol. 28, pp. 285-290, 1947.

seasonal precipitation with elevation, slope, orientation, and exposure, using the coaxial method (Appendix A). The parameters were defined as *elevation*, the station elevation in thousands of feet, mean sea level; *rise*, the difference in elevation between the station and the highest point within

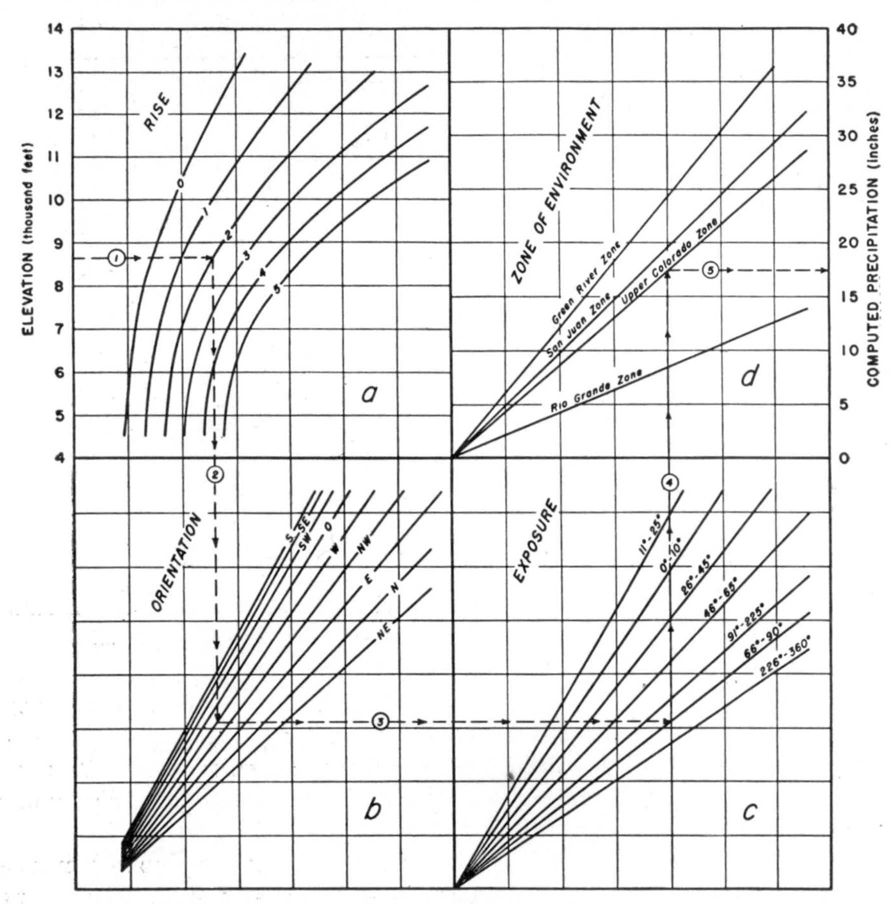

FIG. 6–21. Relation between normal October-April precipitation and topographic parameters for western Colorado. (After Spreen.)

a 5-mile radius, in thousands of feet; *exposure*, the sum, in degrees, of those sectors of a 20-mile-radius circle about the station not containing a barrier 1000 feet or more above the station elevation; and *orientation*, the direction, to eight points of the compass, of the greatest exposure defined above. Figure 6-21 shows the relation developed for western Colorado. It will be noted that, in this region, there are several distinct zones of environment, and a separate correction curve is provided for each. About 85 per cent of the original variation of precipitation was accounted for by the five parameters, while only 30 per cent was attributable to elevation. The process is extremely valuable in the construction of mean isohyetal maps in mountainous regions having relatively few precipitation stations.

TIME DISTRIBUTION OF PRECIPITATION

Although precipitation for a few years may be abnormal, there is usually a tendency to return to the mean pattern. Hence, a period of abnormally heavy precipitation is sooner or later balanced by a dry period so that the mean over a long interval does not change appreciably. Such variations in precipitation are of rather irregular occurrence. Many attempts have been made to find persistent regular cycles, but, with the exception of the diurnal and annual variation, none of any appreciable magnitude has been found in the data now available.[1]

Cycles. In a series of precipitation data, there appear fluctuations which are irregular in phase and amplitude. With sufficient smoothing, variations which appear to be cyclical may be detected. However, the available precipitation records are too short to reveal long-period fluctuations, and short-period variations are so irregular that numerous cycles can be found. Shaw[2] lists more than 100 apparent cycles, ranging in period from 1 to 744 years, which have been suggested by various investigators. Some investigators[3] have tried to associate variations in precipitation and other climatic factors with fluctuations in sunspots and solar radiation. Haurwitz[4] and Tannehill,[5] particularly, have tried to explain why weather should be affected by solar variations. Others have attempted to determine cycles in precipitation through analysis of tree rings[6] and geological formations.[7] As Landsberg pointed out, changes in precipitation regimes

[1] Landsberg, H., Climatology, Sec. XII in Berry, Bollay, and Beers (eds.), "Handbook of Meteorology," p. 964, McGraw-Hill, New York, 1945.

[2] Shaw, Sir Napier, "Manual of Meteorology," Vol. 2, 2d ed., pp. 320-325, Cambridge University Press, London, 1942.

[3] Clayton, H. H., "Solar Relations to Weather," 2 vols., Clayton Weather Service, Canton, Mass., 1943.

Abbot, C. G., Solar Radiation and Weather Studies, *Smithsonian Inst. Misc. Collections*, Vol. 94, No. 10, 1935.

[4] Haurwitz, B., Relations between Solar Activity and the Lower Atmosphere, *Trans. Am. Geophys. Union*, Vol. 27, pp. 161-163, 1946.

[5] Tannehill, I. R., "Drought," 1st ed., Princeton University Press, Princeton, N.J., 1947.

[6] Douglass, A. E., Climatic Cycles and Tree-growth, *Carnegie Inst. Wash. Pub.* 289, pp. 65-73, 1918.

Schulman, E., Centuries-long Tree Indices of Precipitation in the Southwest, *Am. Meteorolog. Soc. Bull.*, Vol. 23, pp. 148-161, 204-217, 1942.

Huntington, E., "The Climatic Factor as Illustrated in Arid America," Carnegie Institution, Washington, D.C., 1914.

[7] Gillette, H. P., Climatic Cycles Reflected in Geological Data, *Pan-Amer. Geol.*, Vol. 68, pp. 340-346, 1937.

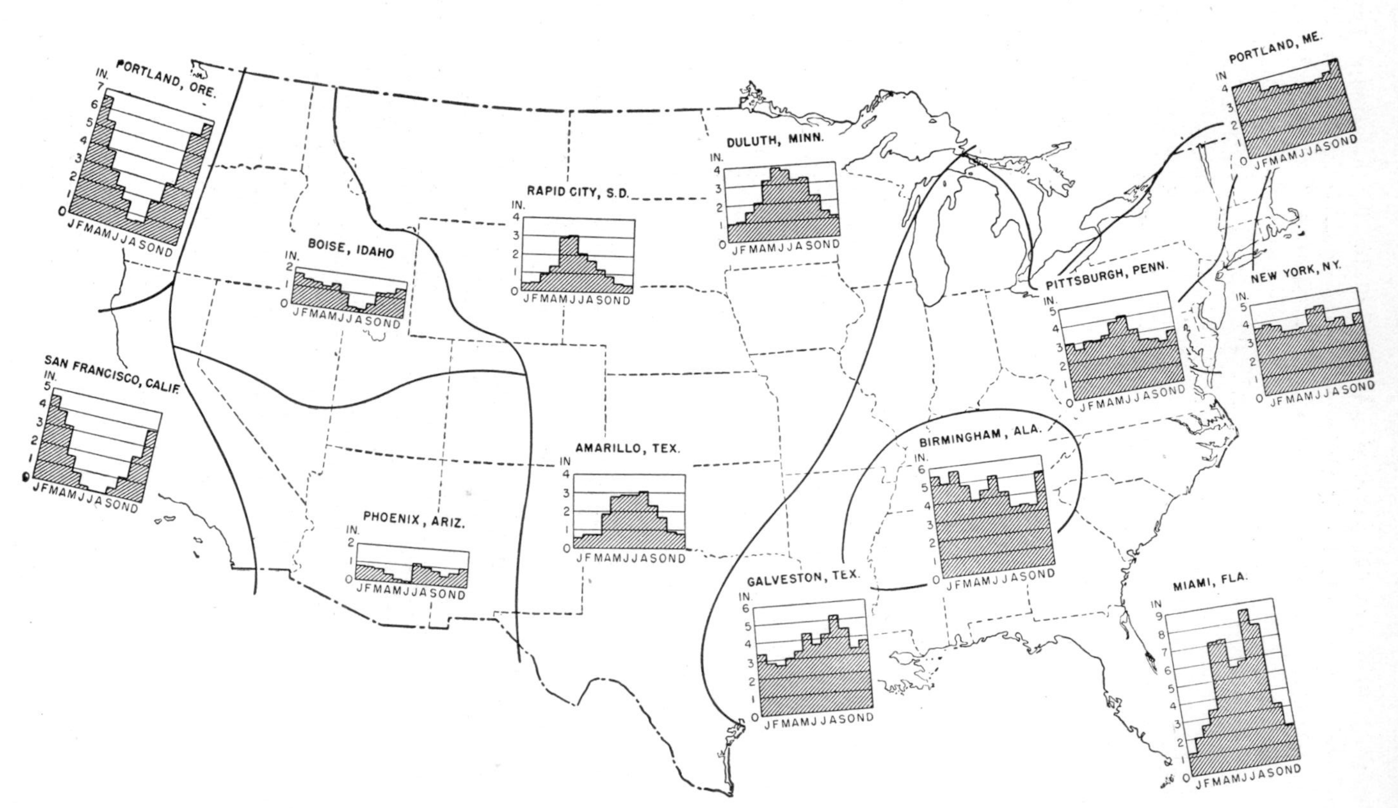

FIG. 6–22. Typical monthly distribution of precipitation in various climatic regions.

are usually noted in records of lake levels and river stages. These integrate rainfall effects over wide areas and are a statistically more reliable sample than a gage measurement which is supposed to represent the precipitation over many square miles. The Bruckner cycle,[1] which is apparently the result of superimposed basic fluctuations, was found in precipitation and lake-level data. Originally assumed to be a cycle of 35 years, it actually varies in length between 30 and 50 years. The mean deviation of precipitation from normal during the wettest and driest periods of the cycle is only 6 per cent.

Seasonal distribution. Because of the large size and heterogeneous physiography of the United States, the seasonal distribution varies widely from region to region.[2] Figure 6-22 shows typical seasonal-distribution graphs for stations in each of the precipitation regions defined by Kendrew.[3]

Much of the summer precipitation is of the convective, or thunderstorm type, while that in winter is cyclonic. In winter there is less difference between the dewpoint and air temperature, and the temperature decrease with increasing latitude is greater. Hence, precipitation may be induced in winter by feeble cyclones which would be inconsequential as rain producers in summer.[4]

Maps of mean annual precipitation and the average annual number of rainy days (0.01 in. or more) are shown in Figs. 6-20 and 6-23, respectively. Mean seasonal amounts of precipitation are shown in Figs. 6-24 to 6-27.

Diurnal variations. Few investigations of the diurnal variation in precipitation have been reported. The available material[5] deals with summer precipitation (April-September), which is largely from thunderstorms. The greatest contrast in the pattern of diurnal variation is to be found between the Central Plains states and the Southeastern states (Fig. 6-28). Slightly less than two-thirds of the precipitation in the Central Plains falls at night, as compared with about one-third in the Southeastern states. Elsewhere in the United States, the summer con-

[1] Marvin, C. F., Characteristics of Cycles, Supplement 15, *Geog. Rev.*, p. 666, 1923.

[2] Kincer, J. B., The Seasonal Distribution of Precipitation and Its Frequency and Intensity in the United States, *Monthly Weather Rev.*, Vol. 47, pp. 624-631, 1919.

[3] Kendrew, W. G., "The Climates of the Continents," 3d ed., pp. 340-348, Oxford, New York, 1937.

[4] Humphreys, W. J., "Physics of the Air," 3d ed., pp. 280-281, McGraw-Hill, New York, 1940.

[5] Kincer, J. B., Daytime and Nighttime Precipitation and Their Economic Significance, *Monthly Weather Rev.*, Vol. 44, pp. 628-633, 1916.

Means, L. L., "The Nocturnal Maximum Occurrence of Thunderstorms in the Midwestern States," *Misc. Rept.* 16, University of Chicago Press, Chicago, 1944.

"Thunderstorm Rainfall," *Hydrometeorolog. Rept.* 5, U.S. Weather Bureau and Corps of Engineers, Vicksburg, Miss., 1947.

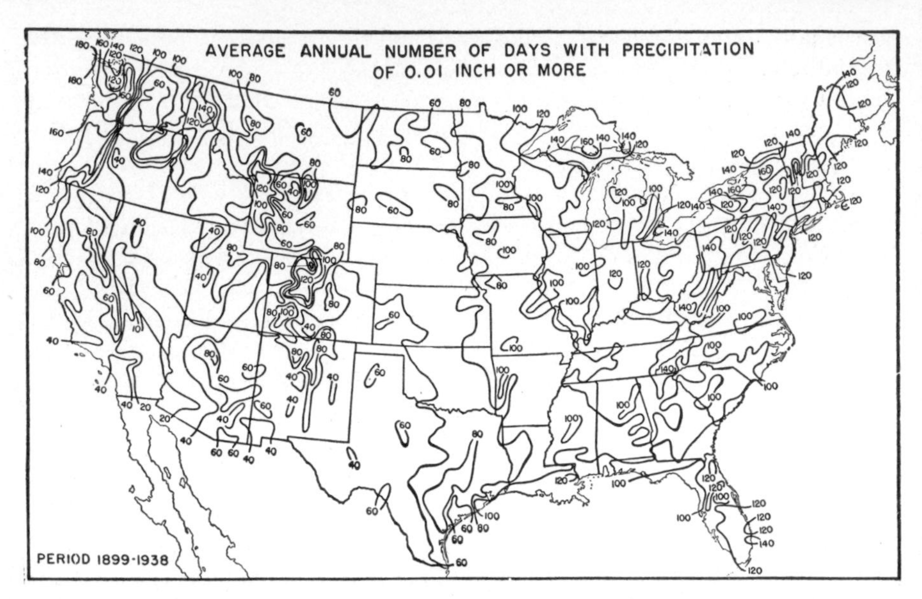

FIG. 6–23. Average annual number of days with precipitation of 0.01 in. or more. (*U.S. Weather Bureau.*)

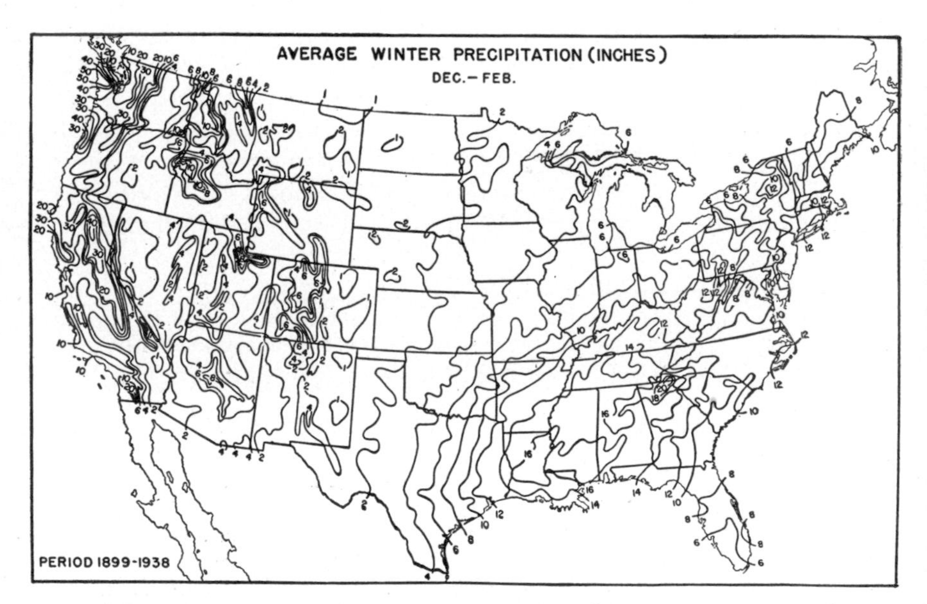

FIG. 6–24. Average winter precipitation. (*U.S. Weather Bureau.*)

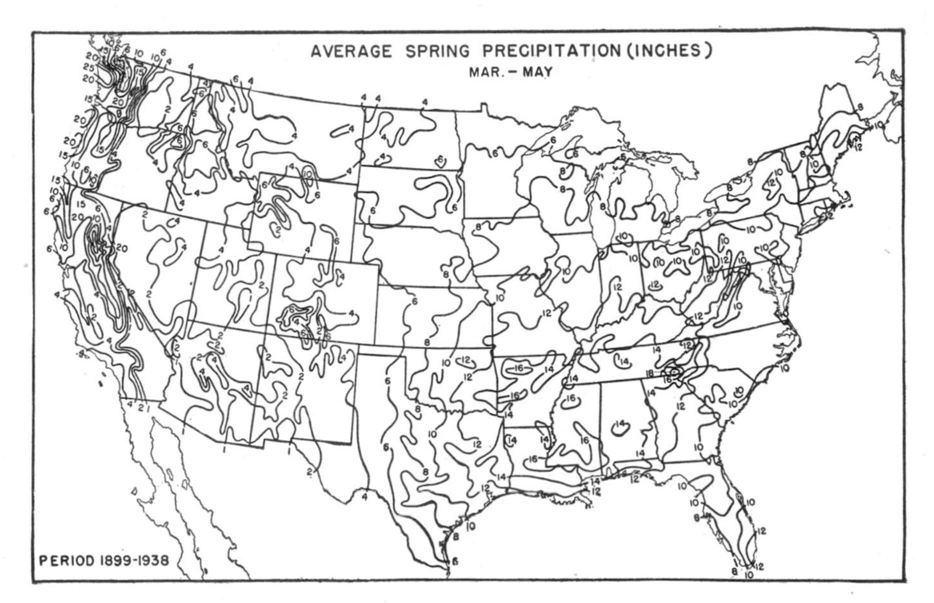

FIG. 6–25. Average spring precipitation. (*U.S. Weather Bureau.*)

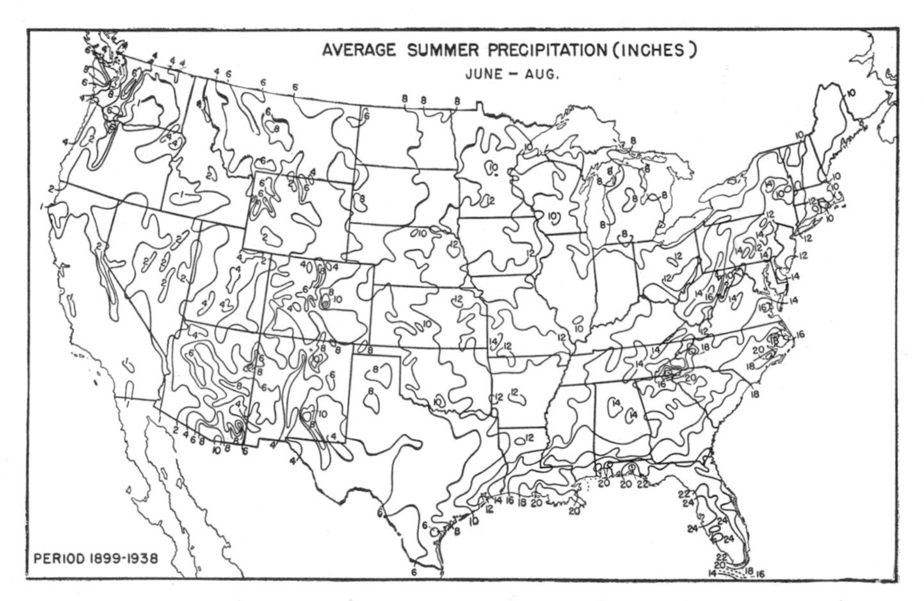

FIG. 6–26. Average summer precipitation. (*U.S. Weather Bureau.*)

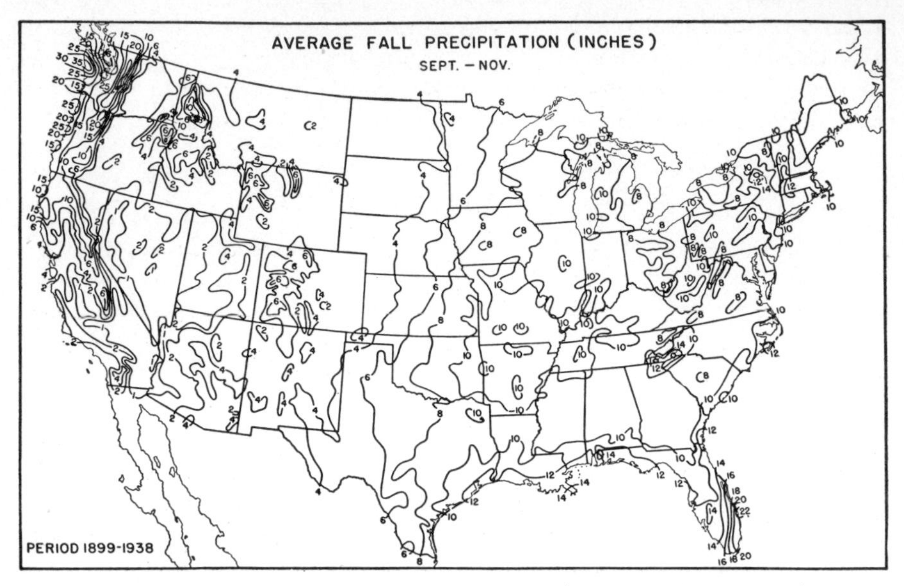

FIG. 6–27. Average fall precipitation. (*U.S. Weather Bureau.*)

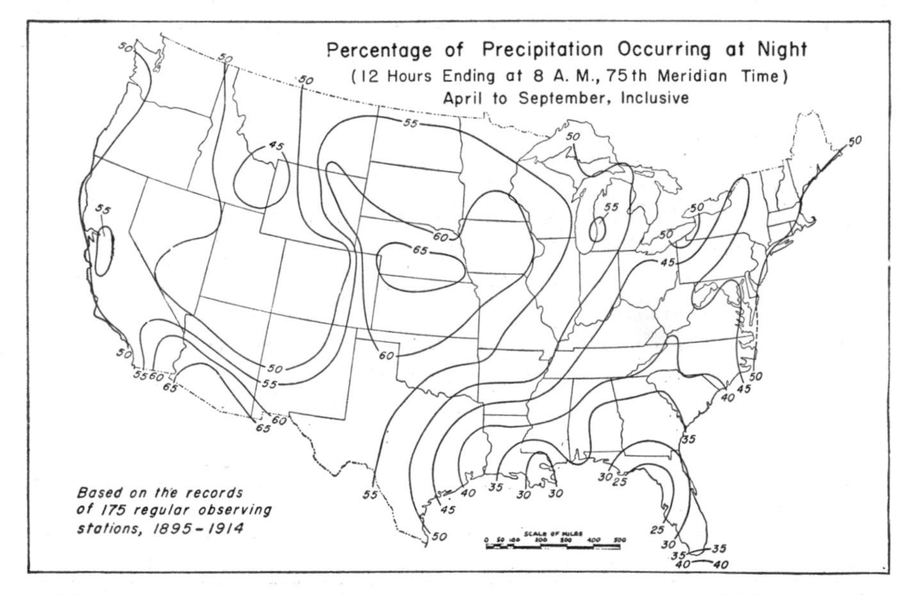

FIG. 6–28. Percentage of precipitation occurring at night. (*After Kincer.*)

trast between day and night precipitation, although less marked than in the areas just cited, can also be attributed mainly to the thunderstorm distribution. In general, it appears that the diurnal variation in amount and duration of precipitation corresponds with that of frequency.

PRECIPITATION VARIABILITY

In general, it may be said that the variability of precipitation decreases with increase in the time unit being considered. Thus, the range of annual precipitation values (in per cent normal) is less than the range of monthly data. Further, the variability of average precipitation over a river basin or other area is less than the variability at a point.

Another factor which must be considered in dealing with precipitation is the skewness of its frequency distribution. This skewness is most marked for periods so short that numerous zero entries occur in the record. In considering longer periods (months or years), zero totals are less frequent and the skewness is not so pronounced. About 60 per cent of the months have less than normal precipitation, and 40 per cent have more.

Annual precipitation variability. Lackey [1] made a rather thorough study of the variability of annual rainfall for over 2000 stations in the United States. Except in regions of low station density, the study was limited to records of 20 years or longer. Isohyetal maps showing the extreme, quartile, and median values of annual precipitation, in inches, are given in Figs. 6-29 to 6-33. Visher[2] also made a study of the variability of annual precipitation in the United States and presented his results in a series of charts.

MAXIMUM RAINFALL

Record rainfalls of the world. World record rainfalls are shown in Fig. 6-34 for their general interest. These records have not all been verified but are generally accepted as reasonable. It is of interest to note that these data, as plotted on logarithmic paper, define an enveloping curve which closely approximates a straight line.

Maximum rainfall at U.S. Weather Bureau first-order stations. Maximum point rainfall values[3] for about 200 first-order Weather Bureau stations with not less than 10 years of record are given in Table 6-2.

[1] Lackey, E. E., Annual Rainfall Variability Maps of the United States, *Monthly Weather Rev.*, Vol. 67, p. 201, 1939.

[2] Visher, S. S., Novel American Climatic Maps and their Implications, *Monthly Weather Rev.*, Vol. 71, pp. 81-97, 1943.

[3] Shands, A. L., and D. Ammerman, Maximum Recorded Point Rainfall, *U.S. Weather Bur. Tech. Paper* 2, 1947.

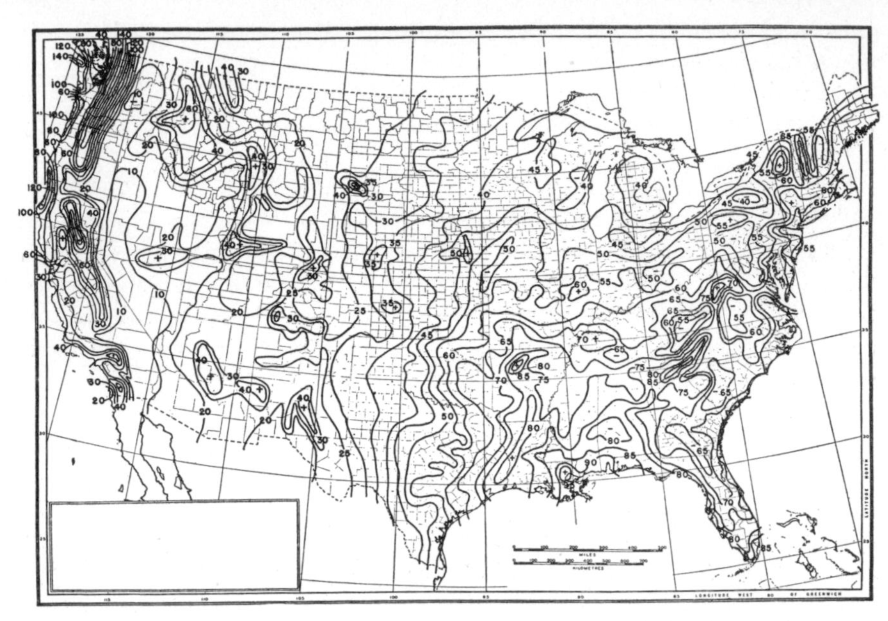

FIG. 6–29. Maximum annual precipitation. (*After Lackey.*)

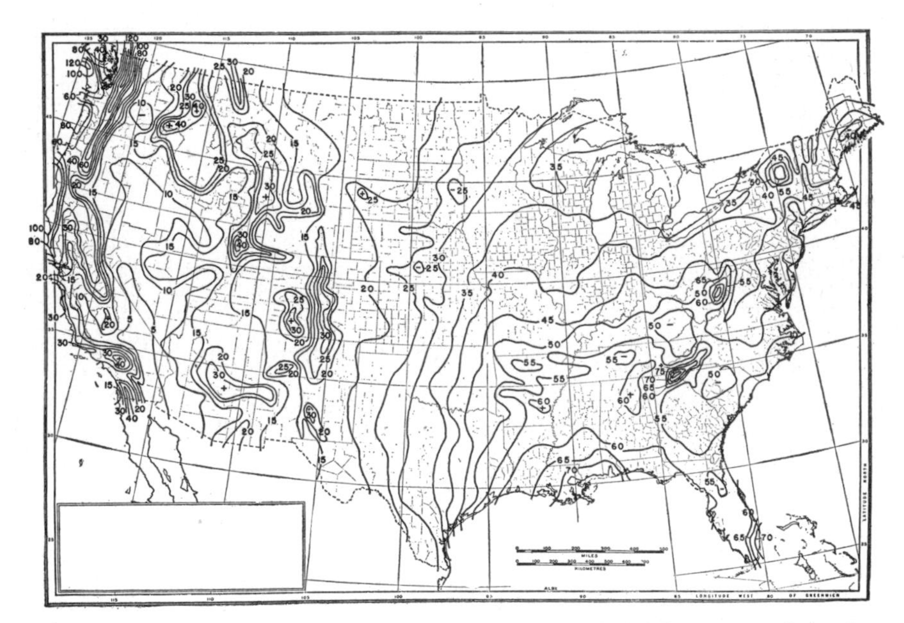

FIG. 6–30. Annual precipitation equaled or exceeded 25 per cent of the time. (*After Lackey.*)

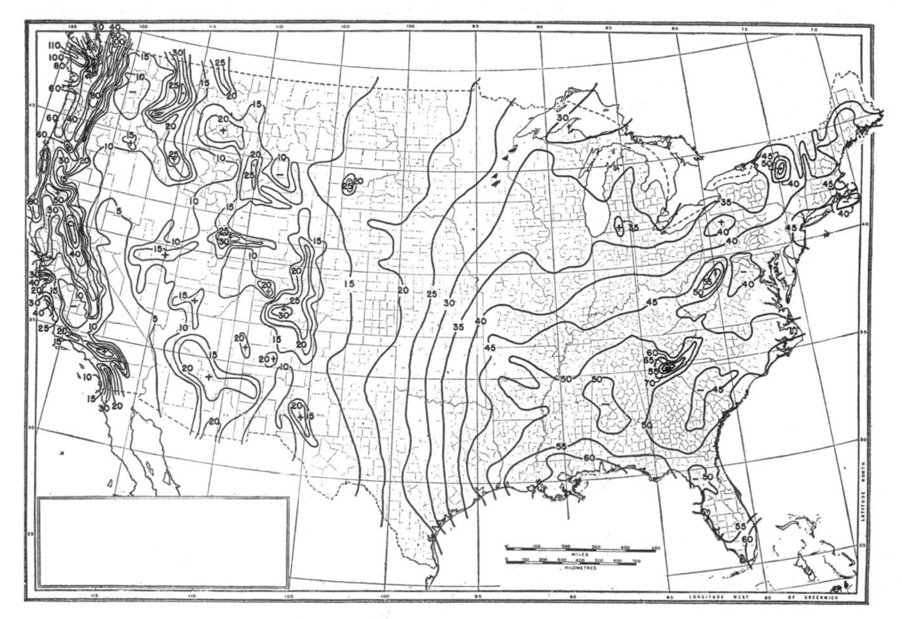

FIG. 6–31. Median annual precipitation. (*After Lackey.*)

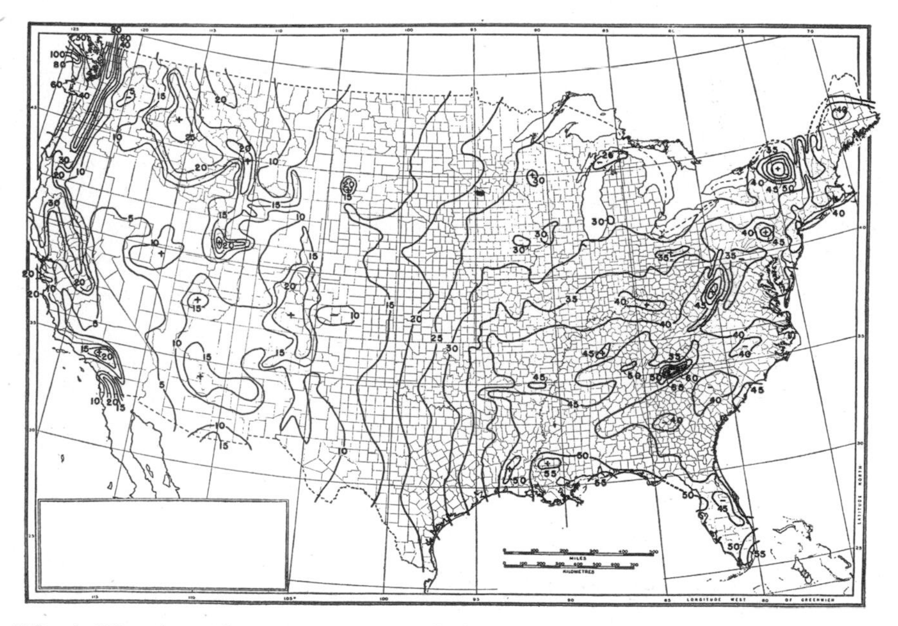

FIG. 6–32. Annual precipitation equaled or exceeded 75 per cent of the time. (*After Lackey.*)

Most of the data are from tipping-bucket gages. Prior to 1935, compilation of these data was often based only upon successive 5-min intervals of duration, beginning with the first indication of *excessive precipitation.*[1] As a result, the actual maximum intensity (not constrained to arbitrary 5-min

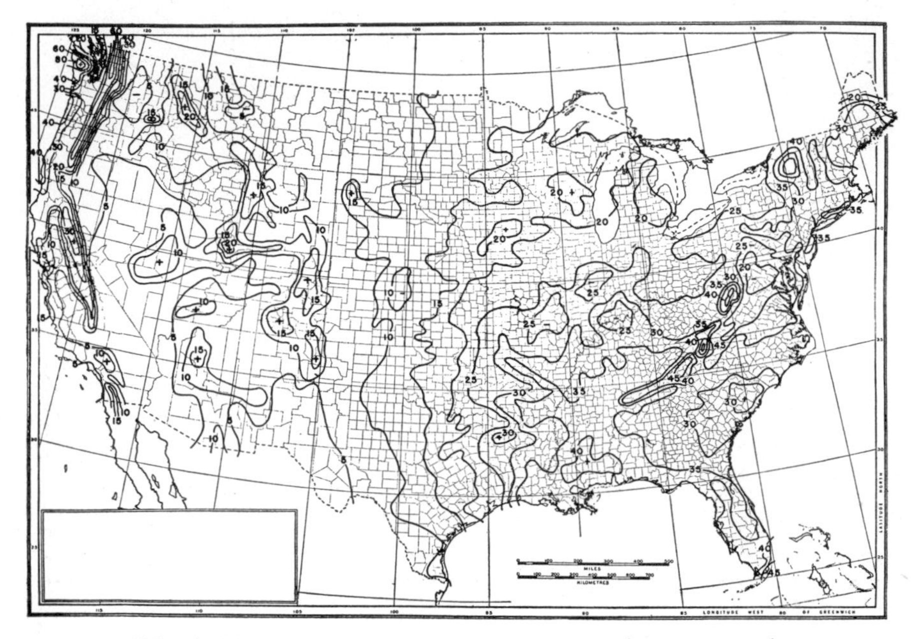

FIG. 6–33. Minimum annual precipitation. (*After Lackey.*)

intervals) may exceed the tabulated value by as much as 12 per cent[2] for the shortest durations. Similarly, maximum amounts for 6 and 12 hr have been obtained for some stations from hourly amounts by standard 1-hr clock intervals.

Figure 6-35 compares record rainfall amounts observed at first-order stations with corresponding values obtained from all available sources. It will be noted that the maximum amounts are about twice those recorded

[1] Excessive precipitation is defined by the U.S. Weather Bureau as precipitation falling at a rate which equals or exceeds that computed by the following formulas for durations of 5, 10, 15, 20, 25, 30, 35, 40, 45, 50, 60, and 80 min. The formula $A = 2t + 30$ is used to define the lower limit of excessive precipitation for the states of North Carolina, South Carolina, Georgia, Florida, Alabama, Mississippi, Tennessee, Arkansas, Louisiana, Texas, and Oklahoma. In all other states the formula $A = t + 20$ is used. In both formulas, A is the amount of precipitation which falls in time t.

[2] Meyer, A. F., "Elements of Hydrology," 2d ed., p. 165, Wiley, New York, 1928.

Yarnell, D. L., Rainfall Intensity-Frequency Data, *U.S. Dept. Agr. Misc. Pub.* 204, pp. 3-5. 1935.

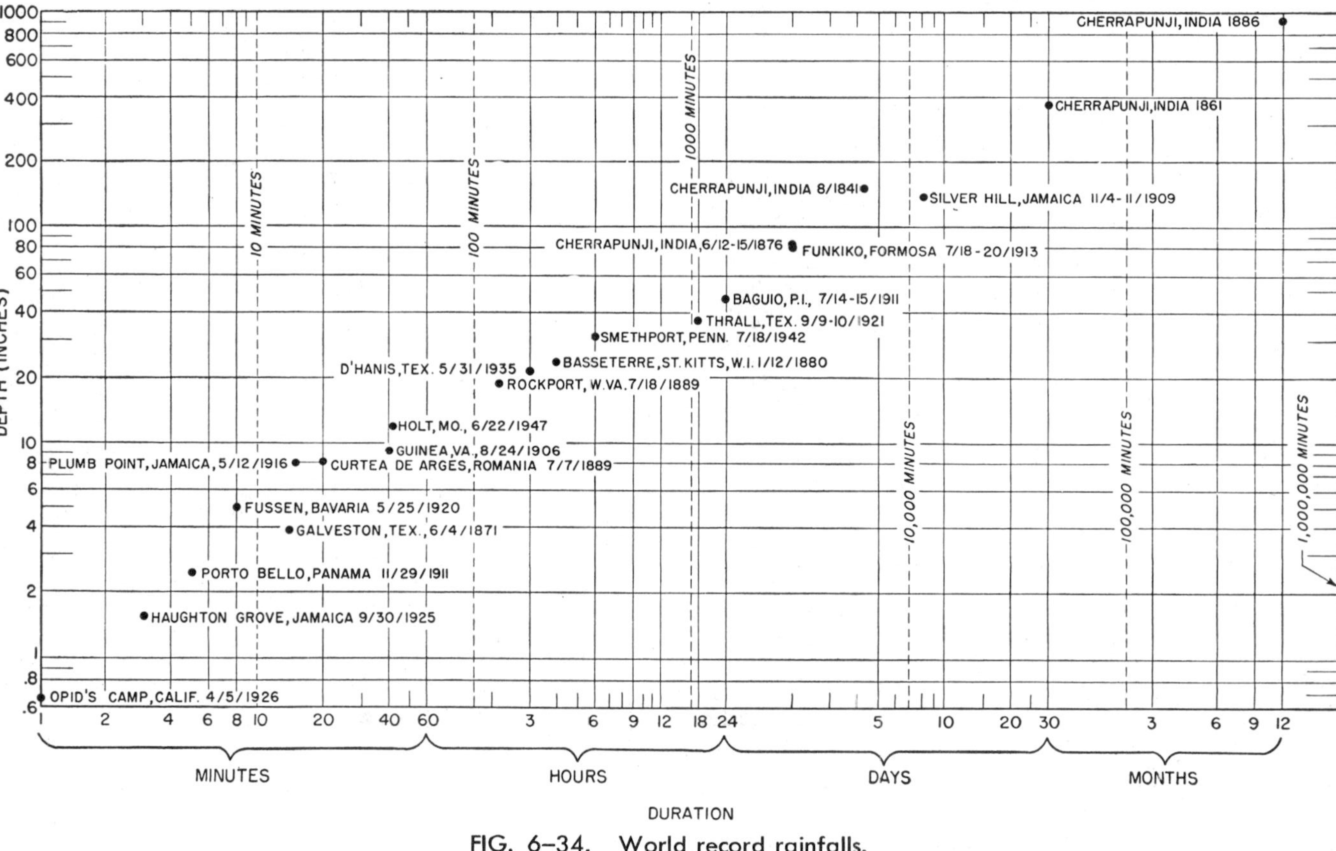

FIG. 6–34. World record rainfalls.

TABLE 6-2. Maximum Recorded Point Rainfall (Inches)

(Weather Bureau First-order Stations)

Station		Duration							
		Minutes				Hours			
		5	15	30	60	2	6	12	24
Alabama:									
Anniston	Amt.	0.66	1.81	3.04	3.62	3.69	4.54	5.13	6.26
	Date	9/5/06	9/5/06	9/5/06	9/5/06	9/5/06	6/7/06	3/6/30	3/6/30
Birmingham	Amt.	0.69	1.60	2.48	3.83	3.89	6.86	8.34	8.84
	Date	8/24/47	9/3/18	8/2/41	8/2/41	8/2/41	12/27/42	12/27/42	7/6/16
Mobile	Amt.	0.89	1.59	2.32	3.03	4.47	8.22	12.98	12.98
	Date	7/19/17	4/29/08	4/29/08	7/19/22	7/19/22	4/4/11	6/26/00	6/26/00
Montgomery	Amt.	0.65*	1.54	2.49	3.81	4.38	6.34	8.00	9.98
	Date	7/4/08	6/15/21	5/30/05	7/20/99	11/9/27	11/9/27	1/12/92	1/12/92
Arizona:									
Phoenix	Amt.	0.43	0.86	1.16	1.41	2.20	2.41	3.51	4.98
	Date	7/26/36	7/17/08	9/8/33	9/4/39	9/4/39	9/4/39	7/1/11	7/1/11
Arkansas:									
Bentonville	Amt.	0.75	1.58	1.84	2.31	3.56	5.07	5.21	5.64
	Date	4/23/08	4/23/08	7/4/16	10/8/19	9/9/37	9/9/37	9/9/37	9/9/37
Ft. Smith	Amt.	0.58	1.42	2.25	2.47	4.34	5.13	6.15	8.58
	Date	6/10/45	9/24/37	9/24/37	6/9/45	6/9/45	6/9/45	6/9/45	6/9/45
Little Rock	Amt.	0.63	1.35	1.92	2.42	3.23	5.14	8.16	9.58
	Date	7/2/39	5/10/30	7/11/03	6/27/10	4/9/13	4/9/13	4/9/13	4/8/13
California:									
Eureka	Amt.	0.29	0.51	0.74	1.04	1.30	2.73	3.52	5.10
	Date	1/1/31	11/11/26	11/15/41	11/15/41	12/10/39	12/10/39	12/10/39	1/20/03
Fresno	Amt.	0.48	0.88	1.22	1.36	1.70	1.70	2.07	2.86
	Date	2/24/41	6/14/39	6/14/39	6/14/39	4/8/26	4/8/26	10/6/04	11/16/00

Station									
Los Angeles	Amt.	0.44	0.81	1.12	1.51	1.99	2.97	4.16	7.36
	Date	1/14/08	2/18/14	2/18/14	2/18/14	2/18/14	2/18/14	12/31/33	12/31/33
Red Bluff	Amt.	0.48	0.76	1.21	2.14	3.73	5.50	5.94	6.12
	Date	6/23/23	6/23/23	9/14/18	9/14/18	9/13/18	9/13/18	9/13/18	9/13/18
Sacramento	Amt.	0.39	0.75	0.97	1.65	2.62	†	†	7.24
	Date	4/7/35	4/7/35	4/7/35	4/7/35	4/7/35	....	....	4/20/80
San Diego	Amt.	0.33	0.65	0.94	1.16	2.09	2.36	2.45	3.62
	Date	3/15/05	11/27/39	3/15/05	4/5/26	4/5/26	4/5/26	4/5/26	12/23/40
San Francisco	Amt.	0.33	0.65	0.83	1.07	1.29	1.70	2.83	4.67
	Date	11/25/26	11/4/18	3/4/12	3/4/12	9/23/04	1/13/14	12/3/15	1/29/81
San Jose	Amt.	0.18	0.34	0.50	0.85	1.11	2.14	2.72	4.56
	Date	3/6/11	11/18/13	1/23/42	1/23/42	9/12/18	12/3/15	1/13/11	1/13/11
San Luis Obispo	Amt.	0.29	0.53	0.72	1.07	1.77	3.15	4.75	5.98
	Date	2/2/26	2/2/26	2/12/26	2/12/26	3/7/11	3/7/11	3/7/11	3/6/11
Colorado:									
Denver	Amt.	0.91	1.54	1.72	2.20	2.54	2.91	3.90	6.53
	Date	7/14/12	7/14/12	7/14/12	8/23/21	8/23/21	8/23/21	8/23/21	5/21/76
Durango	Amt.	0.36	0.72	0.96	1.14	1.21	....	....	3.18
	Date	7/22/12	7/22/12	7/22/12	7/22/12	7/22/12	....	....	10/4/11
Grand Junction	Amt.	0.39	0.59	0.66	0.92	1.01	1.41	1.74	2.50
	Date	8/22/14	8/22/14	8/5/18	9/2/38	10/5/25	9/2/38	9/22/41	10/17/08
Pueblo	Amt.	0.47	1.15	1.92	2.29	2.31	2.78	2.88	2.93
	Date	8/26/46	8/26/46	8/26/46	8/26/46	8/26/46	6/3/21	6/3/21	6/3/21
Connecticut:									
Hartford	Amt.	0.71	1.43	2.32	2.93	2.96	3.29	4.50	6.72
	Date	8/1/29	8/1/29	8/1/29	8/1/29	8/1/29	9/20/38	9/20/38	9/20/38
New Haven	Amt.	0.84	1.96	2.34	2.38	3.12	4.09	7.01	8.73
	Date	7/24/28	7/24/28	7/24/28	7/24/28	6/12/36	6/12/28	6/12/28	8/8/74
District of Columbia:									
Washington	Amt.	0.80	1.51	2.43	3.42	3.91	5.38	6.20	7.31
	Date	8/11/97	7/30/13	9/12/34	9/12/34	9/4/39	8/11/28	8/11/28	8/11/28
Florida:									
Apalachicola	Amt.	0.78	1.65	2.27	2.73	3.75	5.67	7.37	11.71
	Date	5/2/23	5/2/23	5/2/23	10/12/27	4/23/28	9/14/32	9/14/32	9/13/32

TABLE 6-2. Maximum Recorded Point Rainfall (Inches) — *(Continued)*

(Weather Bureau First-order Stations)

Station		Duration							
		Minutes				Hours			
		5	15	30	60	2	6	12	24
Florida *(Continued)*:									
Jacksonville	Amt.	0.78	1.65	2.83	3.32	4.19	6.75	8.65	9.86
	Date	8/16/01	7/27/17	8/18/46	7/8/46	10/22/33	10/19/44	10/19/44	9/25/94
Miami	Amt.	0.71	1.89	2.92	4.53	6.11	10.64	13.86	15.10
	Date	6/14/33	10/11/47	10/11/47	6/14/33	11/30/25	11/30/25	11/30/25	11/29/25
Pensacola	Amt.	1.34	2.29	3.65	4.27	6.14	10.57	15.64	17.07
	Date	5/2/37	10/20/09	10/20/09	10/20/09	9/29/06	4/24/37	10/4/34	10/4/34
Tampa	Amt.	1.05	2.03	2.72	4.01	4.87	6.81	9.01	10.41
	Date	9/26/24	9/26/24	8/28/25	8/28/25	6/23/45	6/23/45	6/23/45	6/23/45
Georgia:									
Atlanta	Amt.	0.88	1.64	2.43	3.23	4.32	4.63	5.40	7.36
	Date	6/10/33	6/10/33	8/11/26	8/20/14	7/23/98	7/23/98	3/14/12	3/28/86
Augusta	Amt.	1.24	2.11	2.68	3.08	3.98	5.83	7.79	9.82
	Date	6/18/11	6/18/11	8/14/03	8/14/03	9/6/48	10/1/29	10/1/29	9/30/29
Macon	Amt.	0.72	1.57	2.41	4.28	6.55	6.71	7.92	8.36
	Date	6/1/46	7/18/16	6/10/23	6/10/23	6/10/23	6/10/23	8/10/28	8/10/28
Savannah	Amt.	0.72	1.50*	2.32	3.63	4.89	5.41	6.75	11.44
	Date	7/11/97	6/17/46	8/3/17	7/23/42	7/23/42	9/17/28	9/17/28	9/17/28
Thomasville	Amt.	0.71	1.83	3.05	4.15	4.47	5.58	6.72	9.00
	Date	6/27/09	6/27/09	6/27/09	6/27/09	6/27/09	4/7/30	9/14/24	9/14/24
Idaho:									
Boise	Amt.	0.34	0.43	0.67	0.98	1.16	....	....	2.72
	Date	5/22/42	6/27/41	5/18/21	7/30/12	7/30/12	....	....	3/5/71

Lewiston	Amt.	0.33	0.65	1.05	1.08	1.11	....	....	2.34
	Date	8/12/06	8/24/07	8/24/07	8/24/07	8/24/07	....	....	3/30/31
Pocatello	Amt.	0.38	0.82	0.96	1.24	1.26	....	....	2.60
	Date	7/1/25	7/31/36	8/2/20	8/2/20	8/2/20	....	....	9/29/26
Illinois:									
Cairo	Amt.	0.63	1.33	1.89	3.15	3.67	5.40	5.40	5.69
	Date	7/7/15	7/30/13	8/12/35	6/28/05	6/28/05	3/13/38	3/13/38	10/3/10
Chicago	Amt.	0.64	1.31	2.03	2.81	3.67	....	....	6.19
	Date	7/15/06	9/13/36	7/7/21	7/6/43	7/6/43	....	....	8/2/85
Peoria	Amt.	0.73	1.26	2.10	2.60	3.18	4.33	4.33	5.52
	Date	8/17/25	7/2/31	7/2/31	7/2/31	9/10/11	5/18/27	5/18/27	5/18/27
Springfield	Amt.	0.66	1.41	2.12	2.75	3.01	3.93	5.94	5.94
	Date	7/23/17	7/23/17	7/23/17	7/6/12	9/8/26	6/4/17	6/4/17	6/4/17
Indiana:									
Evansville	Amt.	0.51	1.19	1.96	2.79	3.11	4.40	4.82	6.94
	Date	9/15/34	8/10/08	6/26/43	7/20/16	7/20/16	9/19/24	10/5/10	10/5/10
Ft. Wayne	Amt.	0.81	1.27	2.10	2.27	2.94	3.53	4.92	4.93
	Date	7/14/16	7/21/28	7/14/16	7/14/16	5/17/28	8/1/26	8/1/26	8/1/26
Indianapolis	Amt.	0.83	2.00	2.65	3.20	3.27	6.55	6.80	6.80
	Date	9/30/02	8/12/44	8/12/44	8/12/44	8/12/44	9/4/95	9/3/95	9/3/95
Royal Center	Amt.	0.65	1.11	1.56	2.27	2.40	....	....	3.23
	Date	8/9/30	7/9/25	8/4/23	7/9/25	7/9/25	....	....	5/18/27
Terre Haute	Amt.	1.15	1.38	1.82	2.81	3.28	4.89	5.60	5.60
	Date	7/7/15	7/7/15	8/5/38	8/5/46	8/5/46	9/8/26	9/14/31	9/14/31
Iowa:									
Charles City	Amt.	0.57	1.16	1.92	2.48	3.09	5.17	6.43	6.74
	Date	9/26/16	6/22/30	6/21/30	6/21/30	7/26/40	7/26/40	7/26/40	7/25/40
Davenport	Amt.	0.64	1.43	1.88	2.71	2.74	5.14	5.18	5.18
	Date	7/17/39	7/17/39	7/7/15	7/7/15	7/7/15	7/13/89	7/13/89	7/13/89
Des Moines	Amt.	0.66	1.36	2.50	2.65	3.44	4.86	4.87	5.37
	Date	7/19/04	7/19/04	6/24/79	8/14/08	7/14/07	9/16/14	9/16/14	6/11/47
Dubuque	Amt.	0.80	1.54	2.23	2.84	3.24	4.55	5.48	5.48
	Date	7/9/19	7/9/19	7/9/19	6/14/38	6/14/38	7/4/76	9/8/27	9/8/27

TABLE 6-2. Maximum Recorded Point Rainfall (Inches) — (*Continued*)

(Weather Bureau First-order Stations)

Station		Duration							
		Minutes				Hours			
		5	15	30	60	2	6	12	24
Iowa (Continued):									
Keokuk	Amt.	0.69	1.33	1.95	2.56	3.11	4.39	4.99	5.88
	Date	5/26/39	8/1/32	8/1/32	8/1/32	8/1/32	6/28/33	6/28/33	6/28/33
Sioux City	Amt.	0.77	1.75*	2.73	2.94	3.20	4.02	5.11	5.12
	Date	7/21/28	6/13/30	6/13/30	7/21/28	7/21/28	6/3/40	6/3/40	6/3/40
Kansas:									
Concordia	Amt.	0.90	1.81	2.60	3.63	3.96	4.97	5.62	5.69
	Date	8/16/44	8/16/44	8/16/44	6/17/15	6/17/15	6/23/04	7/27/07	7/27/07
Dodge City	Amt.	0.58	1.35	2.34	3.47	3.52	....	....	6.03
	Date	8/19/33	8/1/27	6/30/44	9/16/06	7/24/44	....	....	6/7/99
Iola	Amt.	0.97	1.60	2.36	2.92	3.69	5.17	6.76	6.80
	Date	10/1/23	10/1/23	9/6/15	7/18/17	9/6/15	9/12/26	9/12/26	9/6/15
Topeka	Amt.	0.67	1.44	2.24	3.27	3.82	....	....	8.08
	Date	9/14/30	9/14/30	9/14/30	9/14/30	9/14/30	....	....	9/6/09
Wichita	Amt.	0.66	1.52	2.00	2.66	3.54	6.68	7.89	7.99
	Date	9/6/11	6/14/31	6/14/31	9/17/05	9/6/11	9/6/11	9/6/11	9/6/11
Kentucky:									
Lexington	Amt.	0.68	1.54	2.43	3.15	4.10	7.44	8.01	8.06
	Date	7/3/31	7/3/31	7/3/31	7/3/31	8/2/32	8/2/32	8/2/32	8/1/32
Louisville	Amt.	0.79	1.45	1.91	2.91	4.35	4.66	4.66	5.80
	Date	8/29/17	8/29/17	7/4/96	7/4/96	7/4/96	7/4/96	7/4/96	3/18/43
Louisiana:									
New Orleans	Amt.	0.90	1.89	2.38	3.66	5.71	7.95	12.76	14.01
	Date	3/27/46	3/27/46	9/30/05	4/9/20	9/7/29	4/15/27	4/15/27	4/15/27

Shreveport	Amt.	0.76	1.74	2.28	3.15	5.19	7.54	8.52	12.44
	Date	6/25/32	6/25/32	8/28/40	5/13/08	7/23/05	7/23/05	7/24/33	7/24/33
Maine:									
Eastport	Amt.	0.50	1.06	1.37	1.47	1.88	3.01	3.57*	5.48
	Date	7/22/43	7/22/43	7/22/43	7/22/43	7/24/48	8/26/22	8/13/43	5/16/81
Portland	Amt.	0.50	1.09	1.49	1.58	2.55	3.81	4.28	5.28
	Date	9/20/33	9/8/13	9/8/13	9/6/96	9/6/96	7/28/39	9/6/96	9/5/96
Maryland:									
Baltimore	Amt.	0.80	1.92	2.75	3.24	3.75	4.59	6.50	7.62
	Date	7/12/03	7/12/03	7/12/03	6/23/41	7/11/84	10/9/22	8/23/33	8/23/33
Massachusetts:									
Boston	Amt.	0.56	1.12	1.45	1.80	2.45	3.53	5.01	6.04
	Date	8/7/08	8/7/08	8/7/08	8/24/01	7/1/15	9/15/33	9/15/33	7/9/21
Michigan:									
Alpena	Amt.	0.65	1.14	1.58	1.90	2.34	....	....	4.40
	Date	5/29/14	7/12/15	6/6/15	6/6/15	8/24/22	....	....	9/2/37
Detroit	Amt.	0.86	1.86	2.44	3.09	3.86	4.51	4.56	4.75
	Date	8/17/26	8/17/26	8/17/26	8/17/26	8/17/26	7/31/25	7/28/09	7/31/25
Escanaba	Amt.	0.76	1.61	1.82	2.14	2.59	3.27	4.72	5.05
	Date	7/21/03	7/21/03	7/21/03	9/1/37	9/1/37	9/1/37	9/1/37	8/31/37
Grand Haven	Amt.	0.46	0.95	1.48	1.74	2.62	....	4.19	4.19
	Date	10/3/19	8/9/06	6/21/14	6/21/14	7/21/07	....	8/2/15	8/2/15
Grand Rapids	Amt.	0.59	1.10	1.71	2.21	2.77	2.96	4.17	4.58
	Date	9/10/15	6/26/09	6/26/09	6/26/09	6/26/09	6/5/05	8/19/39	6/5/05
Houghton	Amt.	0.48	1.01	1.44	1.62	1.81	3.07	3.07	3.70
	Date	4/25/21	7/3/29	7/3/29	7/3/29	7/3/29	9/19/07	9/19/07	9/2/05
Lansing	Amt.	0.70	1.22	1.58	2.06	2.23	2.58	4.08	5.08
	Date	8/17/21	8/10/37	7/7/23	7/7/23	8/29/32	9/5/17	6/5/05	6/5/05
Ludington	Amt.	0.54	1.13	1.54	2.50	3.26	3.76	4.21	4.22
	Date	7/24/21	6/26/31	8/26/21	8/26/21	9/13/31	9/13/31	9/13/31	9/13/31
Marquette	Amt.	0.74	1.23	1.70	2.93	3.79	....	....	5.14
	Date	9/20/34	9/3/39	6/23/07	6/23/07	6/23/07	....	....	6/20/78
Port Huron	Amt.	0.48	1.10	1.90	2.39	2.42	2.75	4.11	4.11
	Date	7/24/10	7/20/16	7/20/16	7/20/16	7/20/16	7/24/10	7/24/10	7/24/10

TABLE 6-2. Maximum Recorded Point Rainfall (Inches) — *(Continued)*

(Weather Bureau First-order Stations)

Station		Duration							
		Minutes				Hours			
		5	15	30	60	2	6	12	24
Michigan *(Continued)*:									
Saginaw	Amt.	0.65	1.16	1.23	1.26	1.29	2.18	2.18	3.97
	Date	7/5/23	7/5/23	7/5/23	7/5/23	7/5/23	7/5/23	7/5/23	8/9/13
Sault Ste. Marie	Amt.	0.65	0.94	1.10	1.37	1.75	3.62	5.10	5.64
	Date	8/7/16	7/29/41	7/7/21	8/25/41	9/4/16	9/4/16	9/4/16	9/3/16
Minnesota:									
Duluth	Amt.	0.59	1.30	1.61	2.37	2.68	2.97	3.97	5.35
	Date	8/18/08	8/12/10	7/21/09	7/21/09	7/21/09	7/21/09	7/21/09	7/21/09
Minneapolis	Amt.	0.81	1.17	1.98	2.29	2.63	4.30	4.56	7.80
	Date	9/1/26	6/26/14	8/22/14	6/12/99	8/22/14	10/19/34	10/19/34	7/26/92
Moorhead	Amt.	0.68	1.37	1.98	2.72	3.25	4.72	4.72	5.17
	Date	8/29/08	6/26/15	8/29/42	8/29/42	8/29/42	8/8/43	8/8/43	7/3/86
St. Paul	Amt.	0.61	1.33	2.13	2.60	3.00	3.15	5.67	5.69
	Date	6/14/24	6/14/24	6/14/24	6/14/24	6/14/24	6/14/24	7/26/92	7/26/92
Mississippi:									
Meridian	Amt.	0.71	1.57	2.64	3.66	3.77	5.49	6.73	9.50
	Date	5/12/22	3/15/38	3/15/38	8/13/06	8/13/06	2/3/36	2/3/36	4/16/00
Vicksburg	Amt.	0.83	1.41	2.32	3.11	4.17	7.10	7.55	7.99
	Date	4/12/09	8/19/18	8/19/18	8/19/18	2/17/27	7/13/07	7/13/07	7/13/07
Missouri:									
Columbia	Amt.	0.82	1.63	2.11	2.73	3.29	5.86	6.61	6.61
	Date	5/7/45	5/7/45	7/30/43	6/29/09	9/2/18	9/2/18	9/2/18	9/2/18
Hannibal	Amt.	0.56	1.39	1.91	2.95	4.67	4.98	5.19	5.83
	Date	7/7/15	8/18/06	6/19/30	6/19/30	6/19/30	6/19/30	6/19/30	9/3/26

Kansas City	Amt.	0.80	1.65	3.08	4.79	5.84	5.93	6.94	7.03
	Date	5/31/96	8/23/06	8/23/06	8/23/06	8/23/06	8/23/06	9/6/14	9/6/14
St. Joseph	Amt.	0.59	1.27	1.90	2.97	4.07	6.31	6.31	6.89
	Date	6/17/28	6/17/39	9/12/28	6/8/20	6/3/25	6/3/25	6/3/25	6/15/43
St. Louis	Amt.	0.60	1.39	2.56	3.47	3.68	3.72	5.38	8.78
	Date	7/9/42	8/8/23	8/8/23	7/23/33	7/23/33	7/23/33	8/19/15	8/15/46
Springfield	Amt.	0.85	1.74	2.22	2.26*	3.05	....	6.55	6.55
	Date	10/2/44	10/2/44	10/2/44	10/2/44	7/7/09	....	7/7/09	7/7/09
Montana:									
Havre	Amt.	0.52	1.12	1.46	1.60	1.80	2.71	2.88	3.71
	Date	6/22/38	6/22/38	6/22/38	7/26/16	7/26/16	6/16/87	6/16/87	6/15/87
Helena	Amt.	0.47	0.76	0.84	1.06	1.34	....	....	3.67
	Date	6/29/09	7/17/16	6/29/09	9/3/11	9/3/11	....	....	6/4/08
Kalispell	Amt.	0.44	0.90	1.00	1.03	1.04	....	....	2.20
	Date	8/10/20	8/10/20	8/10/20	8/10/20	8/10/20	....	....	6/6/24
Miles City	Amt.	0.78	1.14	1.26	1.26	1.26	....	....	3.74
	Date	7/27/40	8/1/37	8/1/37	8/1/37	8/1/37	....	....	5/19/08
Missoula	Amt.	0.23	0.47	0.67	0.76	0.97	1.40	2.32	2.32
	Date	6/30/43	5/16/39	5/16/39	5/16/39	6/21/38	6/21/38	11/5/27	11/4/27
Nebraska:									
Drexel	Amt.	0.59	1.19	1.60	2.08	2.89	3.20	3.22	5.31
	Date	4/22/19	9/28/23	6/28/19	6/28/19	7/8/25	7/8/25	7/8/25	9/28/23
Lincoln	Amt.	0.69	1.70	2.58	3.11	3.54	6.49	8.38	8.38
	Date	7/1/06	7/1/06	7/25/14	7/25/14	6/5/14	8/28/10	8/28/10	8/28/10
North Platte	Amt.	0.60	1.18	1.69	2.90	3.77	3.82	5.52	6.32
	Date	9/3/20	7/16/37	8/28/29	8/28/29	8/28/29	8/28/29	9/1/42	9/1/42
Omaha	Amt.	1.00	1.86	2.32	2.62	3.17	4.45	5.89	7.03
	Date	5/17/36	5/17/36	5/17/36	5/17/36	8/26/03	9/28/23	8/26/03	8/26/03
Valentine	Amt.	0.80	1.87	2.52	3.02	3.21	3.69	4.01	4.21
	Date	7/6/15	7/6/15	7/6/15	8/12/09	8/12/09	7/16/29	7/6/15	5/25/20
Nevada:									
Reno	Amt.	0.32	0.69	0.86	0.93	0.95	1.49	1.68	2.71
	Date	8/2/12	8/13/31	8/2/12	8/2/12	4/15/34	6/29/20	6/29/20	1/27/03

TABLE 6-2. Maximum Recorded Point Rainfall (Inches) — (*Continued*)

(Weather Bureau First-order Stations)

Station		Duration							
		Minutes				Hours			
		5	15	30	60	2	6	12	24
Nevada (*Continued*):									
Tonopah	Amt.	0.21*	0.39	0.47	0.51	0.72	....	....	1.97
	Date	9/12/23	9/12/23	7/19/22	7/19/22	7/19/22	....	....	4/29/15
Winnemucca	Amt.	0.40	0.77	1.02	1.04	1.06	....	....	1.56
	Date	6/23/45	6/23/45	6/23/45	6/23/45	6/23/45	....	....	6/19/14
New Hampshire:									
Concord	Amt.	0.66	1.60	2.53	2.71	2.73	3.82	5.53	5.97
	Date	7/15/27	7/7/07	7/7/07	7/7/07	7/7/07	6/20/44	9/16/32	9/16/32
New Jersey:									
Atlantic City	Amt.	0.87	1.45	2.66	3.98	5.15	6.04	8.08	9.21
	Date	5/31/06	8/21/33	8/21/33	8/21/33	8/21/33	8/13/19	8/13/19	10/8/03
Trenton	Amt.	0.64	1.36	1.93	2.34	2.78	3.09	3.36	5.42
	Date	9/16/25	8/18/39	8/18/39	6/30/39	6/30/39	9/17/34	9/16/34	10/8/03
New Mexico:									
Albuquerque	Amt.	0.33	0.80	1.03	1.56	1.96	2.13	2.14	2.26
	Date	8/27/33	8/2/35	8/2/35	6/17/33	6/17/33	6/17/33	6/17/33	9/27/93
Roswell	Amt.	0.55	1.22	1.47	2.22	2.88	4.51	5.19	5.65
	Date	6/6/30	6/6/30	9/14/23	9/14/23	9/16/23	8/8/16	8/8/16	10/31/01
Santa Fe	Amt.	0.46	0.77	1.03	1.16	1.65	1.88	2.81	2.83
	Date	6/27/37	8/12/22	8/12/22	9/3/09	9/22/29	9/22/29	9/22/29	9/22/29
New York:									
Albany	Amt.	0.60	1.19	2.12	2.97	4.10	4.12	4.12	4.75
	Date	7/9/38	7/20/45	7/29/38	7/9/38	7/9/38	7/9/38	7/9/38	10/8/03

Station									
Binghamton	Amt.	0.64	1.27	1.54	2.23	2.54	....	....	4.55
	Date	6/6/37	6/6/37	6/24/24	6/24/24	9/11/45	....	....	9/29/24
Buffalo	Amt.	0.82	0.96	1.34	2.22	2.40	3.54	3.64	4.28
	Date	3/20/97	8/6/05	8/1/22	7/19/11	7/19/11	8/17/44	8/17/44	8/28/93
Canton	Amt.	0.53	1.06	1.74	2.45	4.20	4.49	4.49	5.07
	Date	7/16/25	7/16/25	7/16/25	6/18/40	6/18/40	6/18/40	6/18/40	6/18/40
Ithaca	Amt.	0.63	1.46	2.34	2.70	2.72	4.26	6.64	7.90
	Date	7/24/18	7/24/18	7/24/18	7/24/18	7/24/18	7/7/35	7/7/35	7/7/35
New York	Amt.	0.75	1.63	2.34	2.48	3.50	4.09	6.15	9.40
	Date	8/12/26	7/10/05	8/12/26	8/12/26	6/14/17	10/9/03	10/8/03	10/8/03
Oswego	Amt.	0.74	1.28	1.32	1.33	1.95	2.38	2.88	3.76
	Date	7/3/15	7/3/15	7/3/15	7/3/15	6/8/19	6/8/19	7/16/11	8/28/93
Rochester	Amt.	0.56	1.25	1.98	2.54	2.88	3.37	3.65	4.19
	Date	6/14/99	7/7/35	7/7/35	7/11/97	7/11/97	7/11/97	8/28/93	8/28/93
Syracuse	Amt.	0.61	1.16	1.86	2.65	4.04	4.61	4.79	4.79
	Date	6/16/44	7/10/19	8/13/43	6/11/22	6/17/22	6/17/22	6/11/22	6/11/22
North Carolina:									
Asheville	Amt.	0.83	1.71	2.13	2.70	2.82	....	....	7.92
	Date	8/18/18	8/18/18	8/12/11	8/12/11	8/12/11	....	....	10/24/18
Charlotte	Amt.	0.63	1.56	2.33	2.81	3.29	5.18	6.59	6.59
	Date	8/15/28	8/23/34	8/23/34	7/1/44	9/13/33	7/1/44	7/1/44	7/1/44
Greensboro	Amt.	0.60	1.38	2.20	2.84	2.85	3.30	3.43	4.79
	Date	7/14/44	7/14/44	7/14/44	7/14/44	7/14/44	8/13/40	8/13/40	10/16/32
Hatteras	Amt.	0.65	1.72	3.04	5.35	5.86	....	....	12.46
	Date	9/5/28	9/5/28	9/5/28	9/5/28	9/5/28	....	....	10/13/42
Raleigh	Amt.	0.75	1.74	2.60	3.26	4.17	....	....	6.66
	Date	7/14/14	7/14/14	7/14/14	7/2/46	7/4/31	....	....	9/30/29
Wilmington	Amt.	0.66*	1.56	2.60	3.49	5.01	8.27	9.26	9.52
	Date	9/23/23	9/23/23	9/23/23	7/20/24	7/20/24	9/29/38	9/29/38	9/29/38
North Dakota:									
Bismarck	Amt.	0.75	1.40	2.31	3.07	3.35	3.56	3.60	3.76
	Date	9/11/30	9/11/30	8/9/09	8/9/09	8/9/09	8/9/09	8/9/09	6/26/14
Devils Lake	Amt.	0.93	1.84	2.44	2.70	4.31	4.76	4.82	4.82
	Date	6/8/29	6/8/29	6/14/20	6/14/20	7/14/05	7/14/05	7/14/05	7/14/05

TABLE 6-2. Maximum Recorded Point Rainfall (Inches) — *(Continued)*

(Weather Bureau First-order Stations)

Station		Duration							
		Minutes				Hours			
		5	15	30	60	2	6	12	24
North Dakota *(Continued)*:									
Ellendale	Amt.	0.62	1.40	1.85	2.66	3.42	5.25	5.54	5.58
	Date	6/18/21	7/2/21	6/22/25	6/22/25	8/30/26	8/30/26	8/30/26	8/30/26
Williston	Amt.	0.67	1.20	2.09	2.91	3.03	3.05	3.05	4.16
	Date	6/12/19	7/3/26	6/9/32	6/9/32	6/9/32	6/9/32	6/9/32	5/18/93
Ohio:									
Akron	Amt.	0.65	1.50	2.40	4.38	5.57	5.95	5.96	5.96
	Date	7/7/43	7/7/43	7/7/43	7/7/43	7/7/43	7/7/43	7/7/43	7/7/43
Cincinnati	Amt.	0.81	1.92	2.57	2.63	2.85	3.76	4.28	5.22
	Date	8/7/20	8/7/20	8/7/20	8/7/20	6/28/24	7/21/25	3/5/97	3/12/07
Cleveland	Amt.	0.78	1.46	2.09	2.21	2.45	3.74	4.09	4.97
	Date	8/29/03	8/19/01	6/16/46	6/16/46	6/16/46	9/1/01	9/1/01	9/1/01
Columbus	Amt.	0.67	1.31	2.22	2.83	3.02	3.79	3.91	3.91
	Date	7/15/47	6/23/01	7/11/97	7/11/97	7/11/97	7/11/97	9/12/38	9/12/38
Dayton	Amt.	0.57	1.13	1.75	2.26	2.66	3.50	3.51	4.56
	Date	7/6/39	8/14/47	9/5/16	7/21/31	7/21/31	9/5/16	9/5/16	9/12/25
Sandusky	Amt.	0.60	1.46	2.04	3.51	3.77	5.10	5.63	5.95
	Date	6/25/37	6/25/37	5/19/38	7/25/35	7/25/35	6/25/37	6/25/37	6/24/37
Toledo	Amt.	0.65	1.78	2.88	3.58	3.65	4.36	5.88	5.98
	Date	8/16/20	8/16/20	8/16/20	8/16/20	8/16/20	9/4/18	9/4/18	9/4/18
Oklahoma:									
Broken Arrow	Amt.	0.64	1.03	1.48	2.26	3.23	5.70	6.36	7.02
	Date	5/17/30	10/6/28	10/6/28	8/4/28	8/4/28	8/4/28	8/3/28	8/3/28

Oklahoma City	Amt.	0.74	1.49*	2.30	3.10	4.04	....	....	7.87
	Date	7/3/47	7/3/47	6/15/30	6/3/32	6/3/32	....	....	9/30/27
Oregon:									
Baker	Amt.	0.35	0.47	0.78	0.89	1.09	1.14	1.14	1.83
	Date	7/13/08	7/13/08	7/13/08	7/13/08	6/30/43	6/30/43	6/30/43	9/22/17
Portland	Amt.	0.40	0.93	1.10	1.31	1.74	....	....	7.66
	Date	8/8/00	8/8/00	8/8/00	6/7/27	6/7/27	....	....	12/12/82
Roseburg	Amt.	0.55	1.10	1.15	1.16	1.17	....	....	4.15
	Date	5/9/10	5/9/10	5/9/10	5/9/10	5/9/10	....	....	2/28/99
Pennsylvania:									
Erie	Amt.	0.98	1.41	2.02	2.97	4.75	4.83	5.71	5.77
	Date	7/21/43	7/22/47	7/22/47	7/22/47	7/22/47	8/3/15	8/3/15	8/3/15
Harrisburg	Amt.	1.04	1.50	2.20	2.42	2.84	4.36	4.92	6.16
	Date	8/8/25	8/8/25	8/8/25	8/18/20	8/21/15	9/10/07	9/14/16	5/31/89
Philadelphia	Amt.	0.65	1.35	2.24	3.81	5.48	5.48	5.63	5.89
	Date	5/22/08	8/6/05	8/3/98	8/3/98	8/3/98	8/3/98	8/3/98	8/3/98
Pittsburgh	Amt.	0.72	1.23	1.46	2.09	2.12	2.45	2.93	4.08
	Date	6/26/31	6/26/31	7/4/03	7/27/43	7/27/43	9/29/36	9/29/36	9/17/76
Reading	Amt.	0.61	1.41	2.05	2.68	4.89	5.26	5.28	5.45
	Date	6/25/24	8/7/32	8/7/32	7/21/16	7/21/16	7/21/16	8/17/19	8/17/19
Scranton	Amt.	0.67	1.12	1.83	2.36	2.67	....	....	5.09
	Date	7/28/22	7/24/33	7/24/33	8/16/35	7/24/33	....	....	9/29/24
Rhode Island:									
Providence	Amt.	0.46	1.11	1.62	2.46	3.33	4.69	5.32	6.17
	Date	7/28/48	6/20/19	6/20/19	8/24/27	7/23/22	9/14/44	9/16/32	9/16/32
South Carolina:									
Charleston	Amt.	0.63	1.51	2.42	4.11	6.64	8.62	9.03	10.57
	Date	9/6/33	9/6/33	9/6/33	9/6/33	9/6/33	9/6/33	9/5/33	9/5/33
Columbia	Amt.	0.74*	1.39	1.86	2.34	3.84	4.10	4.89	5.50
	Date	8/20/11	7/26/22	7/30/29	7/7/28	6/19/11	6/19/11	9/5/28	9/5/28
Due West	Amt.	0.61	1.58	2.54	3.46	4.66	4.95	4.95	6.53
	Date	7/27/26	7/27/26	7/27/26	7/27/26	7/27/26	7/27/26	7/27/26	9/30/29
Greenville	Amt.	0.58	1.38	2.30	3.43	3.59	3.74	5.34	8.20
	Date	8/6/31	8/6/31	7/9/28	7/9/28	7/9/28	8/15/28	8/15/28	5/7/10

TABLE 6-2. Maximum Recorded Point Rainfall (Inches) — (*Continued*)

(Weather Bureau First-order Stations)

Station		Duration							
		Minutes				Hours			
		5	15	30	60	2	6	12	24
South Dakota:									
Huron	Amt.	0.74	1.53	1.98	2.16	2.72	3.42	3.59	4.07
	Date	7/12/27	6/14/24	6/14/24	6/27/05	6/27/05	6/27/05	6/4/14	10/4/46
Pierre	Amt.	0.61	1.32	1.52	1.93	2.25	2.47	2.55	3.72
	Date	8/29/12	8/29/12	8/29/12	8/8/19	6/14/23	6/14/23	8/20/16	8/20/16
Rapid City	Amt.	0.47	1.13	1.93	2.43	2.76	3.49	4.44	5.57
	Date	5/14/25	7/29/44	7/29/44	7/22/10	7/22/10	5/27/26	5/27/26	5/27/26
Yankton	Amt.	0.52	1.27	1.71	2.34	3.14	....	....	6.28
	Date	5/26/12	5/26/12	5/26/12	9/15/27	9/15/27	....	....	9/20/02
Tennessee:									
Chattanooga	Amt.	0.80	1.62	1.96	2.52	2.76	4.62	5.59	7.61
	Date	6/12/22	6/15/24	8/17/12	8/22/12	8/22/12	4/4/11	4/4/11	3/29/86
Knoxville	Amt.	0.58	1.37	2.57	3.52	3.57	....	....	6.20
	Date	7/16/31	7/8/39	7/8/39	7/8/39	7/8/39	....	....	7/15/17
Memphis	Amt.	0.78	1.71	2.80	3.25	4.70	7.03	9.67	10.48
	Date	3/9/01	7/16/29	7/16/29	7/16/29	7/16/29	11/21/34	11/21/34	11/20/34
Nashville	Amt.	0.75	1.33	1.71	2.09	3.38	3.70	5.00	6.05
	Date	9/12/20	7/19/21	6/15/14	4/26/12	7/19/21	7/19/21	11/20/00	11/20/00
Texas:									
Abilene	Amt.	0.68	1.76	2.75	3.47	4.42	6.26	6.56	6.78
	Date	5/18/42	5/18/42	5/18/42	7/31/11	5/22/08	5/11/28	5/11/28	5/22/08
Amarillo	Amt.	0.65	1.58	2.57	3.36	3.56	4.08	4.08	4.42
	Date	7/8/43	7/8/43	6/24/48	6/24/48	7/8/43	7/8/43	7/8/43	6/20/39

Austin	Amt.	0.63	1.47	2.28	3.46	4.41	....	....	19.03
	Date	8/30/36	8/30/36	9/6/44	6/1/35	6/6/41	....	....	9/9/21
Brownsville	Amt.	0.69	1.82	3.00	5.00	5.82	6.11	6.17	11.91
	Date	4/27/32	4/27/32	4/27/32	4/27/32	4/27/32	4/27/32	4/27/32	9/22/86
Corpus Christi	Amt.	0.76	1.51	2.39	3.63	4.17	6.28	7.00	8.26
	Date	5/23/40	7/13/40	10/4/15	10/16/28	5/5/26	6/27/31	6/27/31	6/20/24
Dallas	Amt.	0.81	1.62	2.40	3.39	4.77	....	....	9.18
	Date	5/4/20	5/4/20	5/13/29	7/5/45	8/27/47	....	....	8/26/47
Del Rio	Amt.	1.15	2.08	2.88	4.82	5.16	6.76	6.86	8.88
	Date	3/21/35	3/21/35	2/27/21	2/27/21	2/27/21	6/13/35	6/13/35	6/13/35
El Paso	Amt.	0.90‡	1.95‡	3.09‡	4.80‡	6.50	6.50	6.50	6.50
	Date	7/9/81	7/9/81	7/9/81	7/9/81	7/9/81	7/9/81	7/9/81	7/9/81
Ft. Worth	Amt.	0.71	1.40	1.98	3.35	5.59	6.93	9.04	9.57
	Date	5/20/28	8/22/16	8/22/16	9/5/32	9/5/32	9/4/32	9/4/32	9/4/32
Galveston	Amt.	0.85	1.94	3.06	5.31	7.58	11.79	12.75	14.35
	Date	4/13/29	4/13/29	10/6/10	10/22/13	4/22/04	10/8/01	10/8/01	7/13/00
Groesbeck	Amt.	0.63	1.31	1.96	3.39	5.04	7.29	8.54	8.87
	Date	4/26/21	4/26/21	10/2/27	10/2/27	10/1/27	10/1/27	10/1/27	10/1/27
Houston	Amt.	0.84	2.00	2.92	4.36	6.05	8.67	9.92	10.83
	Date	8/11/26	8/11/26	12/10/23	11/1/43	11/1/43	11/1/43	11/1/43	11/1/43
Palestine	Amt.	0.61	1.56	2.47	3.24	4.31	....	....	12.06
	Date	3/6/35	5/9/21	6/4/26	5/9/21	11/23/40	....	....	11/22/40
Port Arthur	Amt.	0.72	1.60	2.76	3.97	5.81	10.72	12.67	17.76
	Date	5/11/30	5/11/30	12/11/22	6/8/46	7/28/43	7/27/43	7/27/43	7/27/43
San Antonio	Amt.	0.77	1.62	2.38	3.07*	4.60	5.41	5.91	7.08
	Date	4/29/19	5/9/35	5/9/35	9/25/46	4/18/15	4/18/15	4/18/15	10/1/13
Taylor	Amt.	1.30‡	2.53	2.89	4.25	7.51	14.16	17.91	23.11
	Date	4/29/05	4/29/05	4/29/05	9/9/21	9/9/21	9/9/21	9/9/21	9/9/21
Utah:									
Salt Lake City	Amt.	0.40	0.82	1.25	1.62	1.63	....	....	2.72
	Date	8/13/31	7/30/45	7/30/45	7/30/45	7/30/45	....	....	5/2/01

TABLE 6-2. Maximum Recorded Point Rainfall (Inches) — *(Concluded)*

(Weather Bureau First-order Stations)

Station		Duration							
		Minutes				Hours			
		5	15	30	60	2	6	12	24
Vermont:									
Burlington	Amt.	0.51	0.99	1.41	1.96	2.07	2.32	3.14	4.49
	Date	6/21/33	8/25/22	8/17/42	10/5/26	10/5/26	7/7/25	11/3/27	11/3/27
Northfield	Amt.	0.85	1.64	1.80	1.92	2.30	3.20	5.16	7.72
	Date	8/14/18	8/14/18	8/14/18	8/14/18	8/13/26	11/3/27	11/3/27	11/3/27
Virginia:									
Lynchburg	Amt.	0.56	1.51	2.21	3.49	3.65	4.72	5.88	7.59
	Date	6/24/05	8/29/03	8/29/03	9/3/07	9/3/07	9/3/07	8/11/28	8/10/28
Norfolk	Amt.	0.66*	1.51	2.69	3.34	4.80	4.81	4.82	6.84
	Date	7/10/39	8/19/40	7/10/39	7/10/39	7/10/39	7/10/39	7/10/39	8/11/42
Richmond	Amt.	0.75	1.79	2.60	4.07	6.33	7.24	7.24	7.26
	Date	6/3/20	7/14/48	8/19/08	7/30/23	7/30/23	7/30/23	7/30/23	7/30/23
Wytheville	Amt.	0.63	1.48	2.18	2.48	2.84	2.85	3.84	4.52
	Date	8/22/16	8/22/16	8/22/16	8/22/16	7/7/35	7/7/35	10/1/29	10/1/29
Washington:									
North Head	Amt.	0.33	0.58	0.85	1.00	1.15	....	....	4.29
	Date	8/8/47	8/8/47	11/13/41	11/13/41	11/13/41	....	....	1/2/95
Port Angeles	Amt.	0.27	0.30	0.41	0.49	0.62	....	....	3.30
	Date	8/1/18	8/1/18	8/15/30	8/15/30	8/15/18	....	....	2/16/49
Seattle	Amt.	0.29	0.52	0.61	0.80	0.98	....	....	3.52
	Date	8/24/21	6/23/17	9/11/07	9/11/07	9/11/07	....	....	12/11/21
Spokane	Amt.	0.46	0.81	0.83	1.02	1.09	....	1.62	2.22
	Date	8/21/43	8/21/43	8/21/43	6/6/41	6/6/41	....	5/20/25	6/7/88

Station									
Tacoma	Amt.	0.39	0.50	0.65	0.79	0.90	1.84	2.06	3.79
	Date	4/16/25	9/1/36	9/1/36	11/1/09	10/2/05	10/2/05	10/2/05	11/19/04
Walla Walla	Amt.	0.49	0.79	0.81	0.84	0.90	1.22	1.86	2.74
	Date	5/22/42	5/22/42	5/22/42	5/22/42	5/22/42	6/16/31	5/29/06	5/29/06
Yakima	Amt.	0.27	0.61	0.75	0.84	0.90	0.94	0.94	1.02
	Date	6/19/44	6/19/44	6/19/44	6/19/44	6/19/44	6/19/44	6/19/44	10/10/14
West Virginia:									
Elkins	Amt.	0.56	1.05	1.96	2.37	3.39	3.84	4.22	5.45
	Date	8/12/06	6/23/07	8/4/11	8/4/11	7/8/35	7/24/12	7/17/07	7/7/35
Parkersburg	Amt.	0.75	1.52	1.91	2.12	2.59	4.17	4.32	4.61
	Date	8/19/03	8/19/03	8/19/03	8/19/03	8/25/22	7/31/35	7/31/35	7/31/35
Wisconsin:									
Green Bay	Amt.	0.66	1.33	1.82	2.25	2.54	3.38	3.51	4.41
	Date	8/5/44	8/5/44	8/9/06	7/14/19	8/15/07	6/18/28	6/3/14	6/3/14
La Crosse	Amt.	0.73	1.79	1.99	2.61	3.26	3.27	4.85	7.23
	Date	7/21/37	7/5/34	7/5/34	7/5/34	7/5/34	7/5/34	10/27/00	10/27/00
Madison	Amt.	0.60	1.41	2.15	3.67	4.91	4.96	5.16	5.31
	Date	9/1/37	8/8/06	8/8/06	8/8/06	8/8/06	8/8/06	9/12/15	9/7/41
Milwaukee	Amt.	0.79	1.34	1.86	2.22	3.24	4.71	5.45	5.76
	Date	8/29/39	8/6/42	6/24/04	6/24/04	6/23/17	6/22/17	6/22/17	6/22/17
Wyoming:									
Cheyenne	Amt.	0.66	1.36	2.08	2.51	4.00	4.70	4.70	4.86
	Date	8/26/46	6/14/26	6/14/26	6/14/26	7/15/96	7/15/96	7/15/96	7/15/96
Lander	Amt.	0.54	1.15	1.34	1.44	1.46	....	....	3.66
	Date	7/31/31	7/31/31	7/31/31	7/31/31	7/31/31	....	....	5/29/24
Sheridan	Amt.	0.49	1.11	1.30	1.53	2.74	3.85	3.90	4.41
	Date	7/2/12	7/2/39	6/25/32	7/23/23	7/22/23	7/22/23	7/22/23	7/22/23
Yellowstone Park	Amt.	0.24	0.39	0.51	0.63	0.74	....	....	2.34
	Date	7/16/35	7/16/35	8/14/15	8/14/15	8/14/15	....	....	10/14/08

*Amount equaled on other dates. †4.58 in 8 hr 1/11/79; 6.35 in 16 hr 4/21/80. ‡Estimated.

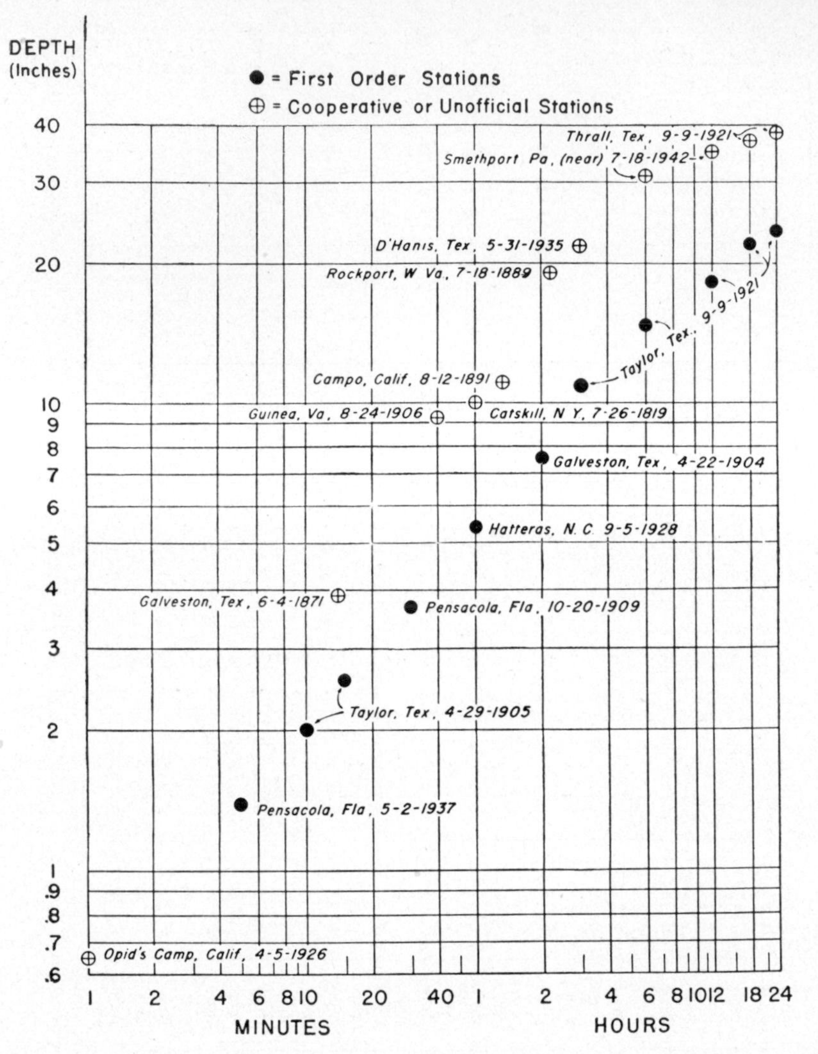

FIG. 6–35. **Maximum observed United States rainfalls.** (*U.S. Weather Bureau.*)

at first-order stations for comparable durations. This difference is caused by the relatively inadequate sample represented by the first-order stations. There are now roughly fifty cooperative and unofficial stations to each first-order Weather Bureau station, and the ratio was even less favorable in earlier years. It thus appears that, as a general rule, the maximum point rainfall in the vicinity of any first-order station is fairly well represented by the doubled station value. Naturally, this is not true for all regions and all records.

Most of the occurrences of maximum rainfall shown in Table 6-2 are associated with thunderstorms. Although the tabulations are of depth-duration values not necessarily occurring in one storm, at most stations the amounts up to durations of 1 hr have occurred in the same storm. The variation[1] of the depth-duration curve of rainfall with magnitude of the 1-hr total is shown in Fig. 6-36.

The frequency distribution of the data in Table 6-2 by seasons and quarter days is shown in Fig. 6-37. In this analysis,[1] the time of beginning of rainfall was taken as the time of occurrence. Summer is the dominant

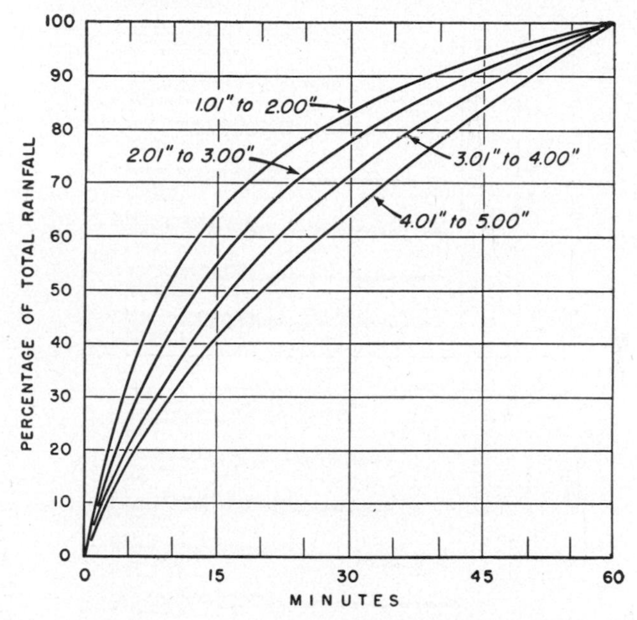

FIG. 6–36. Typical mass curves of 1-hr thunderstorm rainfall. (*U.S. Weather Bureau.*)

season, but there is a steady increase in the autumn frequency with increase of duration above 1 hr; the autumn frequency actually exceeds the summer frequency at the 24-hr duration. The greatest variation from this relationship is in California, where summer precipitation is rare and insignificant. An equalization of quarter-day frequencies with increasing duration is also evident.

Maximum depth-area-duration data. On the basis of storm studies by the Corps of Engineers, the Hydrometeorological Section of the U.S. Weather Bureau has compiled Table 6-3, showing maximum depth-area-duration data for the outstanding storms of record in the United States.

[1] Shands, A. L., and D. Ammerman, Maximum Recorded Point Rainfall, *U.S. Weather Bur. Tech. Paper* 2, 1947.

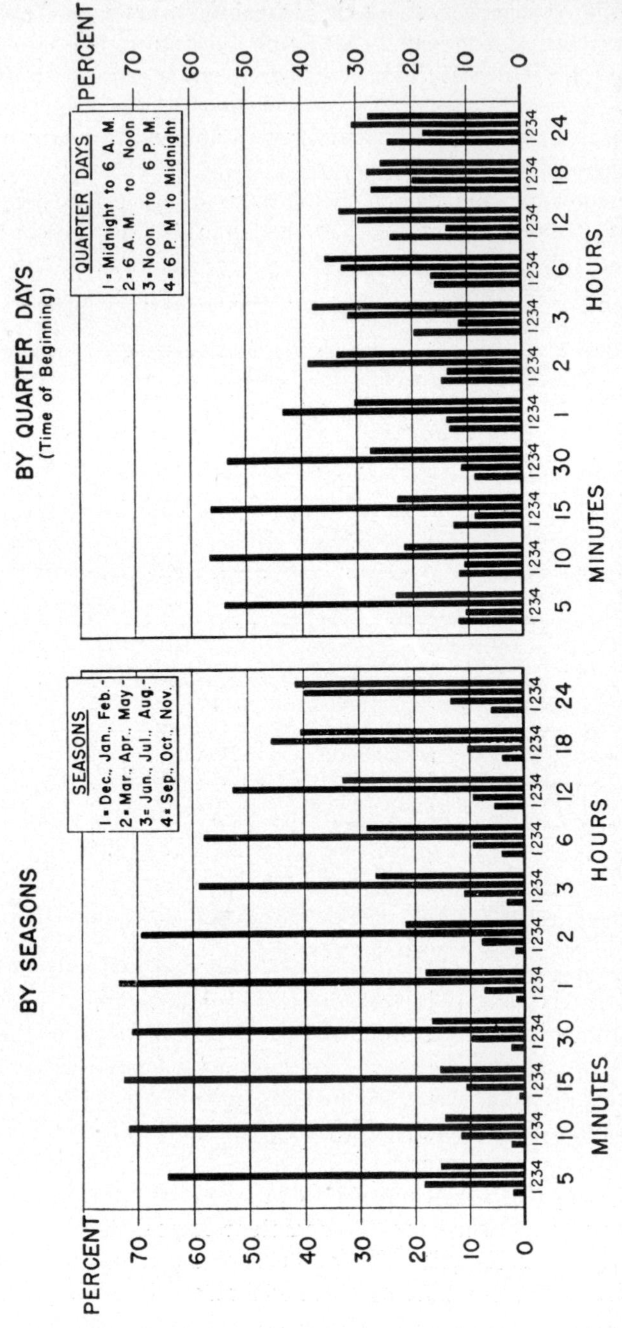

FIG. 6–37. Distribution of maximum rainfall occurrences at United States first-order stations. *(U.S. Weather Bureau.)*

TABLE 6-3. Maximum Depth-Area-Duration Data for the United States (Average precipitation in inches)

Area, square miles	Duration, hr								
	1	3	6	12	18	24	36	48	72
Point	12.0*a*	21.5*b*	30.7*c*	34.3*c*	36.4*d*	38.2*d*	39.7*d*	39.7*d*	39.7*d*
10	8.9*b*	17.8*b*	24.7*c*	29.8*d*	35.0*d*	36.5*d*	37.6*d*	37.6*d*	37.6*d*
100	6.0*d*	14.7*d*	19.6*d*	26.2*d*	30.7*d*	31.9*d*	32.9*d*	32.9*d*	35.2e
200	5.5*d*	13.7*d*	17.9*d*	24.3*d*	28.7*d*	29.7*d*	30.7*d*	31.9e	34.5e
500	4.7*d*	11.8*d*	15.4*d*	21.4*d*	25.6*d*	26.6*d*	27.6*d*	30.3e	33.6e
1,000	3.9*d*	10.0*d*	13.4*d*	18.8*d*	22.9*d*	24.0*d*	25.6*f*	28.8e	32.2e
2,000	2.9*d*	7.8*d*	11.2*d*	15.7*d*	19.5*d*	20.6*d*	23.1*f*	26.3e	29.5e
5,000	1.9*d*	5.1*d*	8.1*d*	11.1*d*	14.1*d*	15.0*d*	18.7*f*	20.7*f*	24.4*f*
10,000	.....	3.5*d*	5.6*d, g*	7.7*d, h*	10.1*g*	12.1*g*	15.1*f*	17.4*f*	21.3*f*
20,000	.....	.....	3.8*g*	5.7*i*	7.9*g*	9.6*g*	11.6*f*	13.8*f*	17.6*f*
50,000	.....	.....	2.5*g, j*	4.2*i*	5.3*g*	6.3*g*	7.9*g*	8.9*g*	11.5*h*
100,000	.....	.....	1.7*j*	2.5*j, k*	3.5*g*	4.3*g*	5.6*g*	6.6*h*	8.9*h*

Storm	Date	Location of center
a	June 22, 1947	Holt, Mo.
b	May 31, 1935	D'Hanis, Tex.
c	July 17–18, 1942	Smethport, Pa.
d	Sept. 8–10, 1921	Thrall, Tex.
e	Aug. 6–9, 1940	Miller Island, La.
f	June 27–July 1, 1899	Hearne, Tex.
g	Mar. 13–15,1929	Elba, Ala.
h	July 5–10, 1916	Bonifay, Fla.
i	Apr. 15–18, 1900	Eutaw, Ala.
j	May 22–26, 1908	Chattanooga, Okla.
k	Nov. 19–22, 1934	Millry, Ala.

7

SNOW, ICE, AND FROST

Snow as a form of precipitation is discussed in Chap. 6. Snow differs from other forms of precipitation, however, in that it may accumulate on the earth's surface for some time before it melts and runs off to the streams or is reevaporated to the atmosphere. Hence, in addition to measuring snow as it falls, the hydrologist is faced with the problem of measuring the accumulated amount on the ground and of determining those physical characteristics which control the rate of melting or evaporation. Snow is a deposit of ice crystals, in many ways analogous to soil, except that snow may undergo rapid changes in its crystal structure. Like soil, it has the capacity to retard the runoff from rainfall and to store a portion of such rainfall. These characteristics must eventually be accurately determined before the role of snow in the hydrologic cycle is completely understood.

MEASUREMENT OF SNOW ON THE GROUND

For determination of total seasonal precipitation or for forecasting long-period runoff volumes, the measurement of snow as it falls is usually satisfactory. For flood forecasting and other problems in short-period melt, it is far more important to know exactly how much snow is on the ground, *i.e.*, the seasonal catch to date minus runoff, basin recharge, and evaporation.

Depth of snow. A measurement of depth of snow on the ground has always been required of Weather Bureau cooperative observers. In regions of small accumulations these measurements are made with a ruler, yardstick, or rain-gage stick. The observer is instructed to average the results of several measurements in the general area of his station. Where large accumulations are expected, permanent *snow stakes*, posts graduated in feet and inches, are used to measure the total depth. Since the snow stake provides only a single point reading, care must be exercised to erect it on a representative site free from drifting and blowing snow.

Water equivalent. Snow-depth measurements serve many purposes but have limited use in quantitative hydrology because of variations in *snow density*, the ratio between the volume of melt water derived from a sample of snow and the initial volume of the sample. This is numerically equal to the specific gravity of the snow. Freshly fallen snow with a density of 0.004 was observed at Sodankylä, Finland, during the winter of 1917-1918, and a density of 0.005 was recorded at Charles City, Iowa, in 1904-1905. On the other hand, glacial ice formed from compacted snow has a maximum density of about 0.91. Freshly fallen snow usually has a density between 0.07 and 0.15, with an average of about 0.10. Although the practice is discouraged in the United States, the water equivalent of newly fallen snow was for many years computed on the assumption of a density of 0.10 and the practice is still standard in Canada. The packing action of wind and the weight of overlying snow result in an increase in density soon after the snow has fallen. In regions of considerable snow accumulation, densities between 0.4 and 0.6 are common by the time the spring thaws begin.

The *water equivalent* of the snow pack, *i.e.*, the depth of water which would result from melting, is dependent on the snow density as well as its depth. Water equivalent is usually determined by sampling with a snow tube (Fig. 7-1). While there are many types of snow tubes, the designs all follow that of the original Mt. Rose sampler designed by Church in 1909. This sampler consists of a steel or duralumin tube 1.485 in. in diameter, provided with a cutter section to aid in penetrating ice planes and dense snow. Additional sections of tube may be threaded into couplings in order to sample depths of 20 ft or more. Slots in the side of the tube and graduations on the outside permit determining the snow depth and length of core removed. The tube is driven vertically into the snow and is twisted when necessary to permit the cutter to move through the denser layers. When the cutter reaches the ground, the tube is withdrawn; soil or foreign material is removed from the cutter end; and the tube and contents are weighed to determine the amount of water in the sample. The diameter of the tube is such that 1 oz is equivalent to 1 in. of water. Slight errors introduced into the measurement by the soil collected in the cutter or by the possible loss of snow as the tube is withdrawn are probably small in the majority of measurements. Under unusual conditions, freezing of snow to the sampler tube may make it impossible to secure a measurement.

While snow samplers provide a satisfactory method for point measurement of water equivalent, sampling for large areas involves many problems. Snowfall may be quite uniform over fairly large areas, but drifting and nonuniform melting soon result in a highly variable snow cover. In order to allow for this variation, it is common practice to make a number of measurements along an established line, or *snow course*. In earlier years courses were sometimes as long as 1 mile, with samples taken at intervals of 50 or 100 ft, but it has been recognized that even at best such courses provide only an index to the snow cover of the basin and cannot be assumed to yield an accurate measure of water equivalent. Hence, the tendency is

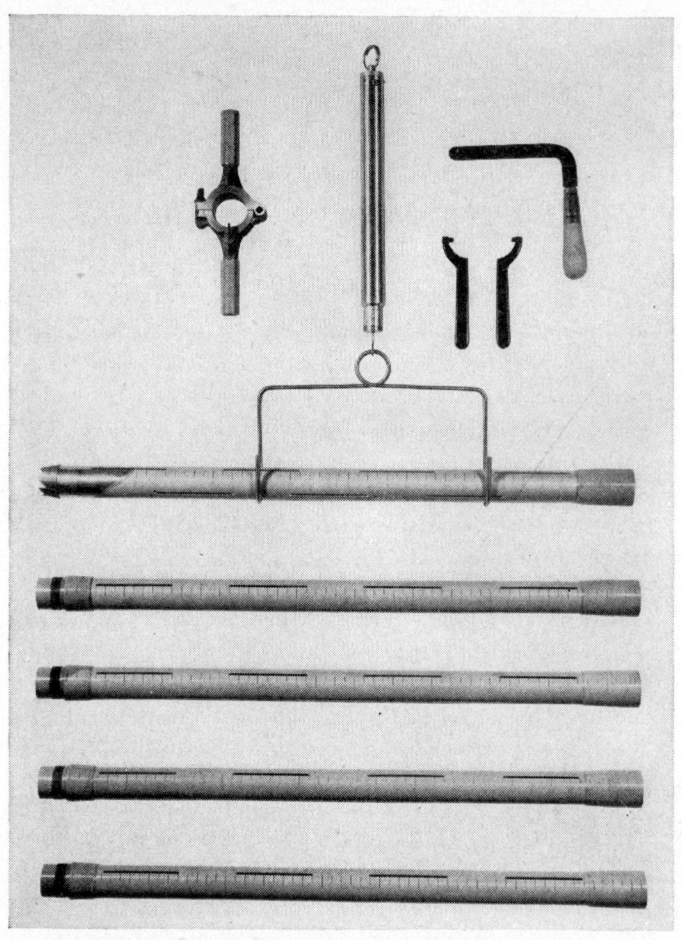

FIG. 7–1. Mt. Rose snow sampler with tubular scale, wrenches, driving handle, and cleaning tool. (*Leupold and Stevens Instrument* Co.)

now toward shorter courses, with 3 to 10 samples at intervals of 10 to 20 ft. Since a course yields only an index to snow cover, it is important that the survey be made along a carefully marked course under nearly similar conditions from survey to survey. A site free from extreme wind effect and lateral drainage of melt water should be selected.

A special problem is posed when measurements of water equivalent are required at frequent intervals. It is impossible to obtain accurate repetitive measurements at identically the same spot, since the sampling procedure disturbs the snow. Hence, a considerable area is required to make daily measurements throughout a season. Because of the variability of snow depth, daily readings vary so greatly that little significance can be attributed to differences between them, although a running plot of the data may define a seasonal trend. There is little to be gained, therefore, by making observations more frequently than once a week. A further difficulty is the time and effort required to reach a remote snow course by skis or snowshoes. While motorized snow vehicles and helicopters are now coming into use, surveys at intervals of less than 1 month are uncommon except in the immediate vicinity of inhabited areas.

Quality of snow. While snow is principally a deposit of ice crystals, there is usually some liquid water present, either as capillary water in the interstices between snow crystals or, more commonly, as molecular water around individual crystals. The term *water content* refers to the liquid water in a snow pack in contrast to the water equivalent, which is the total water present in both liquid and solid form. The *quality* of snow is the percentage by weight which is ice.

Most measurements of quality have been by a calorimetric process.[1] A sample of snow is inserted into a thermos bottle partly filled with hot water. From initial and final temperatures and known weights (or volumes) of water and snow, the quality Q_t can be computed by

$$Q_t = \frac{(T_1 - T_2)(W_1 + k) - (T_2 - 32)W_2}{1.44W_2} \tag{7-1}$$

where T_1 is the initial water temperature in degrees Fahrenheit, T_2 the final temperature of the mixture, W_1 the weight of hot water, W_2 the weight of the snow sample, and k the calorimeter constant. If the temperature of a snow sample is below 32°F, this equation will indicate quality in excess of 100 per cent because of the heat required to bring the snow to the melting point. The water content in per cent of the water equivalent is $(100 - Q_t)$. Since only very small samples can be introduced into thermos bottles of convenient size, accurate temperature measurement is important.

Gerdel[2] has reported the development of a meter which measures the variation in capacitance of a condenser consisting of two insulated stainless-steel plates inserted in the snow. Since the dielectric constant of snow depends on quality, the meter may be calibrated for direct determination.

[1] Bernard, M., and W. T. Wilson, A New Technique for the Determination of the Heat Necessary to Melt Snow, *Trans. Am. Geophys. Union*, Vol. 22, pp. 178-181, 1941.

[2] Gerdel, R. W., and A. R. Codd, "Snow Studies at Soda Springs, Calif.," pp. 15-16, *Ann. Rept. Coop. Snow Invest.*, U.S. Weather Bureau and University of Nevada, 1944-1945.

A simple test for the presence of free water in snow may be made with fuchsin dye (rosaniline). This dye is green when dry but turns brilliant red when moistened.

The vast majority of quality determinations reported to date have shown quality values of 90 per cent or more, but determinations as low as 50 per cent have been obtained. Much more observational work will be required to evaluate the factors controlling quality. The condition of low quality is necessarily transient, since it is indicative of snow during rapid melting. It is not surprising, therefore, that only a few measurements of low quality have been made.

Snow structure. Snow is largely a crystalline form of ice, and the great variety of crystal structures observed in snowflakes has been the subject of a great deal of micro-photography. The hydrologist usually is less interested in the crystal structure of snowflakes than in the ultimate structure attained by the snow just prior to melting. Snow which is in a condition to discharge melt water is loosely described as *ripe*. Such snow has a coarse, crystalline structure and a density near 0.5. When melting is under way, its quality is about 90 per cent and it is essentially isothermal at 32°F throughout its depth.

Seligman[1] has presented a detailed classification of snow and ice forms from the descriptive viewpoint, but there has been no successful classification of snow on an objective basis for quantitative hydrologic studies. The analogy between snow and soil suggests that a practical classification would be of considerable value.

VARIATIONS IN SNOWFALL AND SNOW DEPTH

Geographical variations. Figure 7-2 is a map of normal annual snowfall for the United States. Because of the relative scarcity of high-elevation stations and the variability of snowfall in the mountain regions of the West and to a lesser extent in the Northeast, the map may be considerably in error at some points. As would be expected, however, the areas of maximum snowfall coincide with areas where precipitation is high and temperatures relatively low. Thus, there is a pronounced increase in snowfall with latitude in the United States. Since high precipitation is often associated with orographic influences and since temperature decreases with elevation, mountain regions are also marked by high snowfall. In the Sierra Nevada and Cascade Range annual snowfall increases abruptly from nearly zero to more than 400 in. within an elevation range from 2000 to 10,000 ft—a horizontal distance of only a few miles. Maximum annual snowfall normally occurs at a slightly higher elevation than maximum

[1] Seligman, G., "Snow Structure and Ski Fields," pp. 26, 123-131, Macmillan, New York, 1936.

annual precipitation. If precipitation increases continuously toward the summit, snowfall will do likewise.

Figure 7-3 shows the number of days with 1 in. or more of snow on the ground. Like Fig. 7-2, this map is generalized on the basis of data from regular Weather Bureau offices and does not correctly display conditions in the higher elevations of the West, where snow cover may remain for 6 months or more.

Maps of normal depth on the ground or normal water equivalent for various dates are not available, except for small areas under special study.

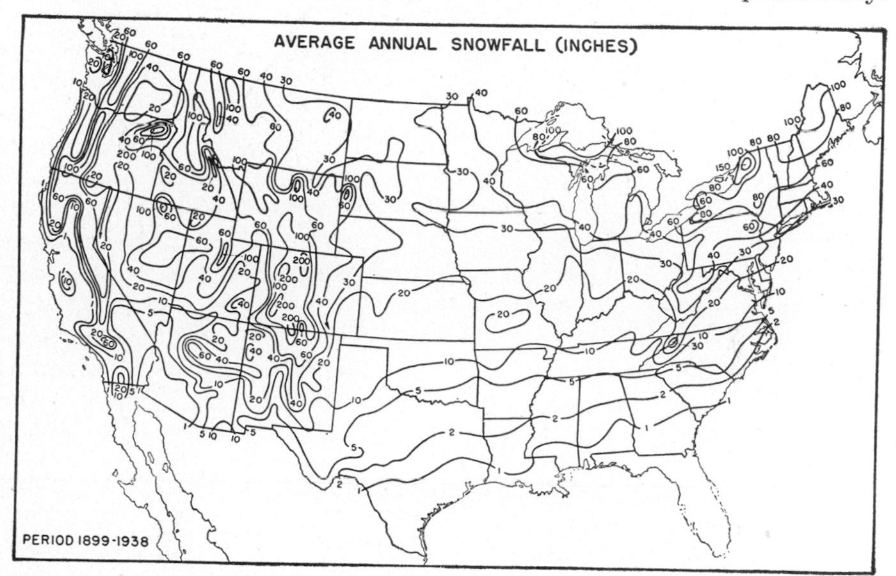

FIG. 7-2. Normal annual snowfall in the United States. (*U.S. Weather Bureau.*)

Snow depth usually builds up rapidly during the early portion of the season and then holds relatively constant as compaction of old snow compensates for new falls. Maximum depths on the ground are generally less than half the total annual snowfall at high elevations; and at low elevations, where intermittent melting takes place, the ratio is much lower. At high elevations the pack reaches a density of about 0.5 by the time spring thaws begin. Assuming an initial density of 0.1 and no losses, its depth will be only about one-fifth the total snowfall. If melting occurs during the season, the relative depths will be much less. The maximum water equivalent approaches 10 per cent of the annual snowfall in regions of semipermanent snow accumulation and is considerably less in areas of intermittent melting.

Small-scale variations. As a result of drifting, a considerable variation in depth and water equivalent of the snow pack may be observed within relatively short distances. After the melting season is under way, this variation is intensified by differences in melting rates. Snow on south slopes tends to melt more rapidly than that on shaded northern slopes. Snow in forests remains on the ground longer than snow in exposed meadows. Snow at lower elevations tends to melt more rapidly than that at high elevations. Croft[1] reports that on Apr. 1, 1943, a course on a

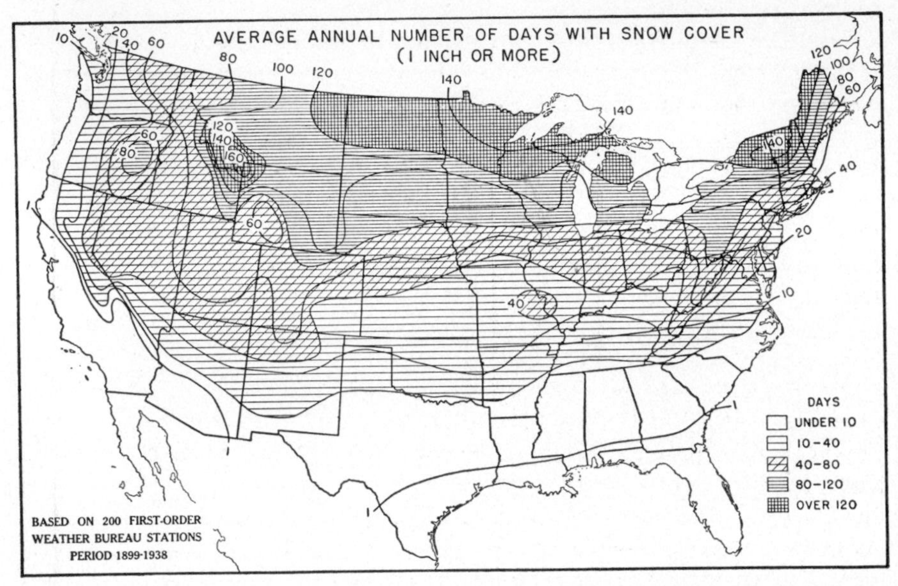

FIG. 7–3. Average number of days per year with 1 in. or more of snow on the ground. (*U.S. Weather Bureau.*)

north slope in the Wasatch Range showed a water equivalent of 20.3 in., while at the same elevation on a south slope the water equivalent was only 3.8 in. On May 1, 1946, surveys at 16 stations within Castle Creek Basin[2] (4 square miles) in the Sierra Nevada showed an average water equivalent of 39.3 in., with a standard deviation of 9.8 in.—a coefficient of variation of 25 per cent. The range in water equivalent was from 27.1 to 55.9 in. in little more than 1 mile. Variations between sampling points in a single survey course were as great as 28 in., with a mean of only 36 in.

Despite great variations in snow depth within short distances, there is a consistency in the distribution pattern from year to year. All factors affecting distribution—slope, aspect, elevation, forest cover, wind currents,

[1] Croft, A. R., Some Factors That Affect the Accuracy of Water-supply Forecasting in the Intermountain Region, *Trans. Am. Geophys. Union*, Vol. 27, pp. 375-388, 1946.

[2] "Hydrometeorological Log, Central Sierra Snow Laboratory, 1945-46," *Tech. Rept.* 5 *Coop. Snow Invest.*, Corps of Engineers and U.S. Weather Bureau, San Francisco, Calif., 1947.

etc.—are essentially unchanging. Aerial or terrestrial photographs show a consistent pattern from year to year, and the area covered by snow can be correlated with the water equivalent at a key station. Parshall[1] showed a good relation between per cent of snow-covered area on Comanche Peak, Colorado, and water equivalent at Cameron Pass.

The lower limit of the snow pack is called the *snow line*. The snow line follows the contours reasonably well as new snow is deposited at successively lower elevations during the accumulation season. During the melting season, however, the snow line fluctuates between wide limits of elevation. It is much higher on south slopes than on north slopes and is generally higher toward the southern end of a range. Again, however, there is a close correlation between index snow-line elevations and the area of the snow pack. This correlation can be used to advantage in empirical relations dealing with snowmelt. Index observations of snow line may be made along a fixed profile or other established route, such as a highway or trail.

THE PHYSICS OF SNOW

The basic problem of the hydrologist in regard to snow is twofold. First he must estimate the rates of snowmelt from his knowledge of the heat supplied to the snow, and second he must determine how the resulting melt water, perhaps in combination with concurrent rainfall, will reach the stream. The practical solution of these problems is discussed in subsequent chapters. This section discusses the theoretical aspects of snowmelt and the physical aspects of snow related to its water-holding capacity.

Heat-transmission characteristics of snow. The conductivity of snow has been the subject of much study. Jansson, in 1901, found that the conductivity K_c was related to snow density Ψ by

$$K_c = 0.012 + 0.46\Psi + 1.45\Psi^4 \qquad (7\text{-}2)$$

Jansson also noted that K_c varied with the crystal structure of the snow. Within practical limits K_c can probably be taken as 0.55Ψ in Btu per square foot per hour per Fahrenheit degree per foot when $\Psi < 0.4$.

The computation of the heat transferred through any medium is difficult if the temperature at the surface varies with time. In the simple case of a deep snow pack initially isothermal at temperature T_1 and having a temperature T_2 applied at its surface, the quantity of heat H transferred in t hr is[2]

$$H = \frac{2\,\Delta T\sqrt{K_c\rho\eta t}}{\sqrt{\pi}} \qquad (7\text{-}3)$$

[1] Parshall, R. L., Correlation of Streamflow and Snow-cover in Colorado, *Trans. Am. Geophys. Union*, Vol. 22, pp. 153-159, 1941.

[2] Churchill, R. V., "Modern Operational Mathematics in Engineering," pp. 106-112, McGraw-Hill, New York, 1944.

where $\Delta T = T_2 - T_1$, η is the specific heat (0.5), and ρ is the density in pounds per cubic foot (62.4 Ψ). Substituting for ρ and K_c in terms of Ψ and simplifying,

$$H = 4.68\,\Delta T\Psi\sqrt{t} \tag{7-4}$$

Taking $\Psi = 0.1$ and $\Delta T = 10$ F°, the transmission is

$$H = 4.68\sqrt{t} \tag{7-5}$$

Since 1 Btu/ft² is sufficient to melt only 0.0013 in. of water from the snow pack, it is evident that the heat transmission through snow is not significant. Within the range of air temperatures found in this country, temperatures only a few inches below the surface of the snow do not vary far from freezing.

The assumption of a constant value of T_2 is not the usual condition observed in nature where the temperature undergoes a diurnal fluctuation. Assuming this fluctuation to be sinusoidal, the amount of heat flowing through the snow surface in each direction during the two halves of the diurnal cycle is given[1] by

$$H = T'\sqrt{\frac{K_c\rho\eta t_0}{\pi}} = 2.33T'\Psi \tag{7-6}$$

where T' is one-half the diurnal range in temperature at the surface and t_0 is the length of the wave in hours.

Exchange of heat between air and snow. Heat may be transferred from the air to the snow pack by conduction or convection. The heat transferred by conduction from still air can be computed from Eq. (7-3). For air, $K_c = 0.01$, η is about 0.24, and ρ is approximately 0.08 lb/ft³ at 40°F.

The equation therefore reduces to

$$H = 0.015\,\Delta T\sqrt{t} \tag{7-7}$$

It can be seen that the transfer by conduction in still air is very small.

The exchange of heat between air and a snow surface by convection has been discussed by Light.[2] This transfer is accomplished by vertical transport of warm air effected by eddies near the earth's surface. The equation as derived by Sverdrup[3] is of the form

$$H = kv_w(T_a - T_s) \tag{7-8}$$

[1] Croft, H. O., "Thermodynamics, Fluid Flow, and Heat Transmission," pp. 205-206, McGraw-Hill, New York, 1938.

[2] Light, P., Analysis of High Rates of Snow Melting, *Trans. Am. Geophys. Union*, Vol. 22, pp. 195-205, 1941.

[3] Sverdrup, H. U., The Eddy Conductivity of the Air over a Smooth Snow Field, *Geofys. Publikasjoner*, Vol. 11, No. 7, 1934.

where v_w is the wind velocity, T_a is the air temperature, and k is a coefficient of turbulent exchange. The coefficient k depends on the specific heat and density of air, height of anemometer and thermometer above the snow surface, and a roughness parameter. There are certain assumptions in the formula concerning the logarithmic variation of temperature and wind with height above the ground which are still the subject of study. Placing Eq. (7-8) in terms of melt M,

$$M = cv_w(T_a - 32) \tag{7-9}$$

where c is the coefficient of turbulence converted to units of melt. Adopting reference elevations of 50 ft for the anemometer and 10 ft for the ther-

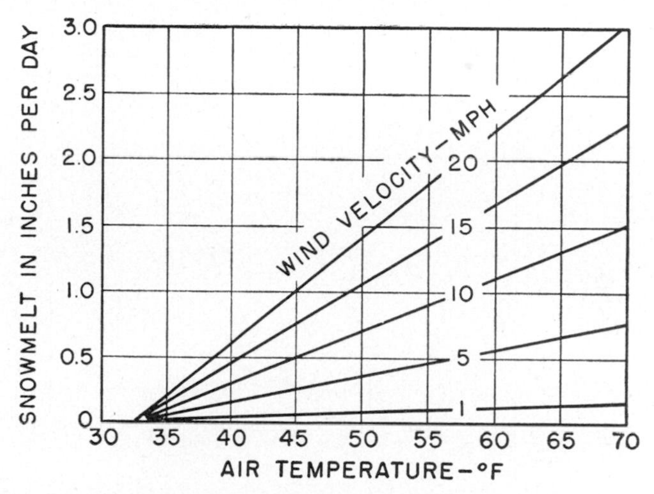

FIG. 7-4. Snowmelt by convective heat transfer from air. (*After Wilson.*)

mometer, the relation is shown graphically in Fig. 7-4, where c is taken as 0.004. It may be seen that convective transfer is far more effective than conduction.

Conduction from underlying soil. Since temperature at considerable depths in the soil lags behind surface temperature, there is normally an increase in temperature with depth during winter months. This results in a continuous transfer of heat from the soil to the snow pack above, which can be computed by use of Eq. (7-3). Assuming $K_c = 0.08$, $\eta = 0.25$, and $\rho = 65$ lb/ft³,

$$H = 1.29(T - 32)\sqrt{t} \tag{7-10}$$

where T is the initial temperature of the soil and where t is in hours. The assumption is made that the temperature of the upper soil layers is initially isothermal with depth. Matted vegetation supporting the snow slightly above the soil materially reduces heat transfer. The same is true if the surface soil is frozen. Assuming optimum conditions, the heat transfer would be sufficient to melt about 0.12 in. water equivalent on the first day, decreasing to 0.05 in. on the second day.

It is not likely that theoretical rates of transfer are attained under natural conditions, but observations verify that some heat transfer does take place. At Soda Springs, California, during the fall of 1944, the ground was observed to be frozen to a depth of 6 in., with a temperature of 27.5°F.

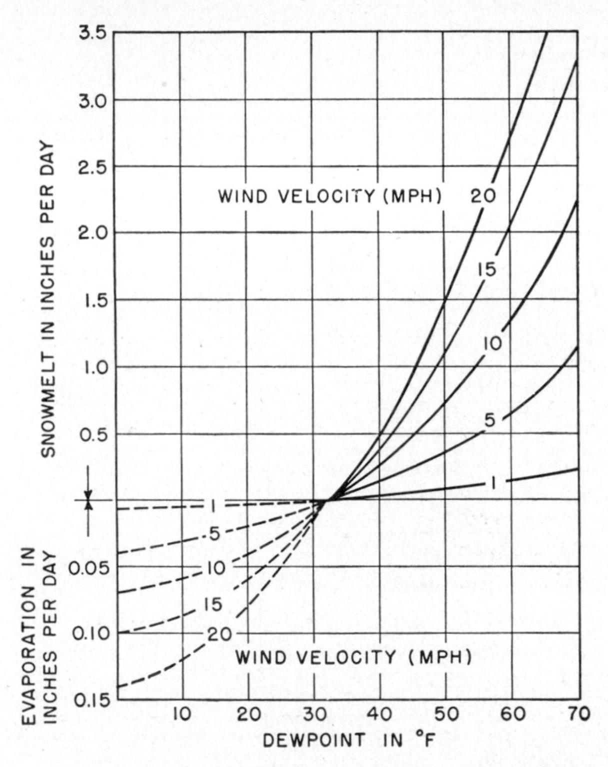

FIG. 7–5. Snowmelt by condensation of water vapor. (*After Wilson.*)

After the first permanent snow cover formed, the soil thawed completely and returned to 32°F. Soil moisture at the site was at field capacity all winter. Thus, while heat from underlying soil may not contribute substantially to the melting of snow after the pack has been on the ground for several weeks, it may be sufficient to thaw the soil and melt enough snow to bring the soil to field capacity early in the season. This provides opportunity for more prompt response of streamflow when melting from other causes takes place.

Effect of water vapor in the air. An important melting factor which is frequently overlooked in considerations of heat sources for melting snow is the condensation of water vapor. The heat of condensation at 32°F is about 1073 Btu/lb. Thus, the condensation of 1 in. of water vapor on a snow surface will melt about 7.5 in. of water from the snow in addition to the condensate. The water vapor is brought to the snow surface by turbulent exchange, following the laws discussed under convective transfer of heat from the air. Figure 7-5 shows the variation of melt corresponding to the equation[1]

$$M = av_w(e - 6.11) \tag{7-11}$$

where a is taken as 0.012, e is the vapor pressure of the air, and 6.11 is the saturation vapor pressure in millibars at 32°F. The figure is plotted in terms of dewpoint temperature, which is directly related to vapor pressure

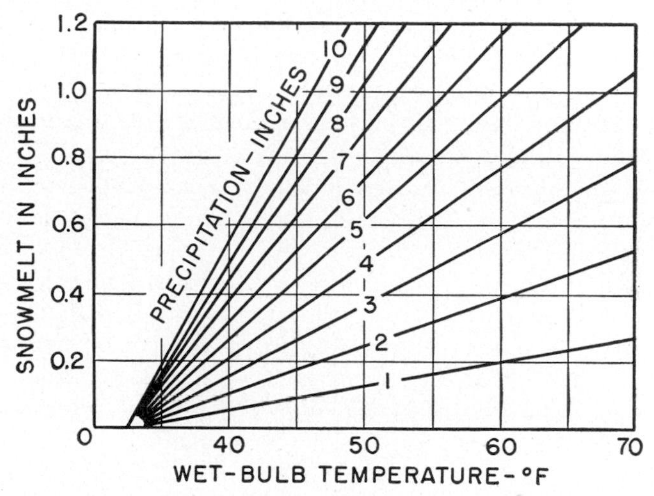

FIG. 7-6. Snowmelt by heat of rainfall. (*After Wilson.*)

(Chap. 4). It can be seen that the magnitude of the melt from this cause is of the same order as that from convective transfer.

Heat from rainfall. Rainfall is ordinarily considered to be an extremely important factor in snow melting. However, a simple calorimetric computation will show that the melt by rainfall is

$$M = \frac{P(T_w - 32)}{144} \tag{7-12}$$

where P is the depth of precipitation in inches and T_w is the wet-bulb temperature (assumed to be the temperature of the rain). Assuming T_w to be 50°F, 1 in. of rain would melt only 0.12 in. water equivalent from a snow cover. The relation is shown graphically in Fig. 7-6. It can be

[1] Wilson, W. T., An Outline of the Thermodynamics of Snow-melt, *Trans. Am. Geophys. Union*, Vol. 22, pp. 182-195, 1941.

seen that this factor is less important than convection or condensation. The misconception of its importance probably results from the fact that warm rains are accompanied by high humidity and temperature and often by moderate winds.

Undoubtedly, rainfall also has a mechanical effect on the snow cover which has not been evaluated theoretically. A driving rain acts to break down the snow structure and thus accelerates the release of any stored moisture. Heavy rains may also wash unmelted snow into the streams.

Insolation. Direct solar radiation is an important factor in melting snow and may under some conditions be the major factor. The amount of incoming radiation for a particular basin is a function of time of year and cloud cover. The amount which serves to melt snow is determined by its *albedo*, or reflecting power. The albedo is dependent on the condition of the snow surface. Clean, dry, freshly fallen snow has an albedo of about 90 per cent, *i.e.*, 90 per cent of the incident radiation is reflected and only 10 per cent absorbed. If the snow surface is dirty or wet, the albedo is considerably reduced. Recent determinations have shown that the albedo of reasonably clean, moist snow may be as low as 40 per cent. Snow almost completely covered with a thin layer of dirt or soot will have an albedo approaching zero.

The effect of radiation is dependent to some degree on depth of the snow pack. Evidence indicates that insolation penetrates only about 12 to 18 in. of snow. Thus, in a deep pack only the upper portion is directly affected by incident radiation. If the pack is shallow, radiation may penetrate to the soil, which is an effective absorption agent. Hence, a greater portion of the insolation is absorbed and can contribute to the liquefaction of the snow pack.

To some extent, the effect of insolation is offset by back radiation from the snow surface at night. This back radiation varies with the surface temperature of the snow and with the moisture content and cloudiness of the air. Snow emits long-wave radiation R_b in accord with the Stefan-Boltzman law

$$R_b = kT^4 \tag{7-13}$$

where T is the absolute temperature. The outgoing radiation amounts to about 0.012 Btu/in.^{2}/min, but a considerable portion of this radiation may be reflected back by clouds and water vapor in the atmosphere.

Figure 7-7 shows the incoming radiation between lat 40° and 48°N as a function of cloudiness. To determine the net gain from radiation, the values from this chart should be reduced by the estimated amount of reflection. The degree of cloudiness as observed by the U.S. Weather Bureau is not an entirely satisfactory parameter for such a chart. Although an overcast of thin, high cirrus clouds may be reported as ten-tenths cloudy, a large amount of radiation may still reach the surface. Hence, type and height of clouds should be considered in using the chart. If pyrheliometric data are available, Fig. 7-7 is unnecessary. However, only a small number of radiation stations are in operation in the United States.

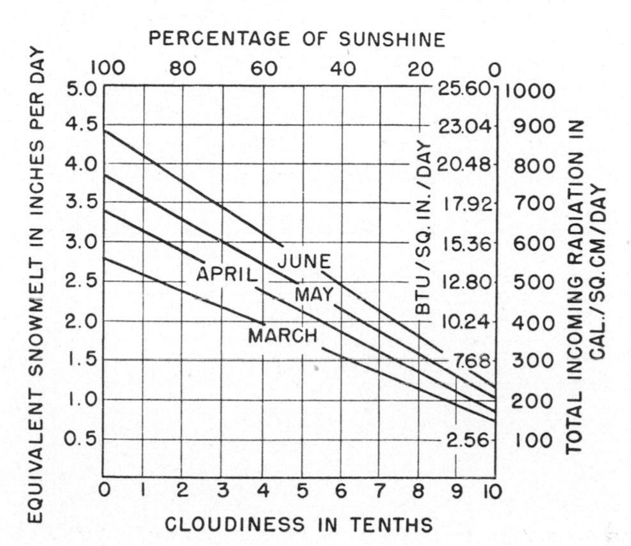

FIG. 7–7. Incoming solar radiation as a function of cloudiness. (*After Wilson.*)

Figure 7-8 is based on Wilson's estimates of outgoing radiation with degree of cloudiness and dewpoint as parameters. Dewpoint is used as a basis for estimating the moisture content of the air aloft from surface data, assuming saturated air and a pseudoadiabatic lapse rate. If upper-air soundings are available, the values of water vapor in inches may be used in lieu of dewpoint.

Water-holding capacity of snow. Numerous reports indicate that snow can retain a large volume of rainfall and release it suddenly. The effective duration of rainfall is thus considerably shortened—a matter of importance in design and forecasting problems. The available data on water retention and transmission are limited to studies of ripe snow. Gerdel[1] saturated 24-in. cores taken in an 8-in.-diameter tube with water at 32°F and allowed them to drain for several hours. Determination of the residual water content indicated that the water-holding capacity of ripe snow must be in the order of 5 per cent by weight, *i.e.*, 1 ft of snow at 50 per cent density can hold about 0.3 in. of water. Determination of the water content of snow at various heights above a free-water surface indi-

[1] Gerdel, R. W., Dynamics of Liquid Water in Deep Snow Packs, *Trans. Am. Geophys. Union*, Vol. 26, pp. 83-90, 1945.

cated that the moisture-tension curves (Chap. 12) for snow are quite similar to those for sand or gravel of comparable grain size.

Studies by the same investigator showed some snow samples to have moisture-holding characteristics more closely approximating those of loam than sand. It may be presumed that fine-grained new snow would have a relatively low transmission rate and correspondingly high retention. He reported an interesting case near Norden, California, in December, 1945. Six feet of new snow had brought the pack to a depth of 127 in. when rain began to fall on Dec. 26. Although 2.5 in. of rain fell in 60 hr ending about noon of the 29th, no increase in streamflow was noted until

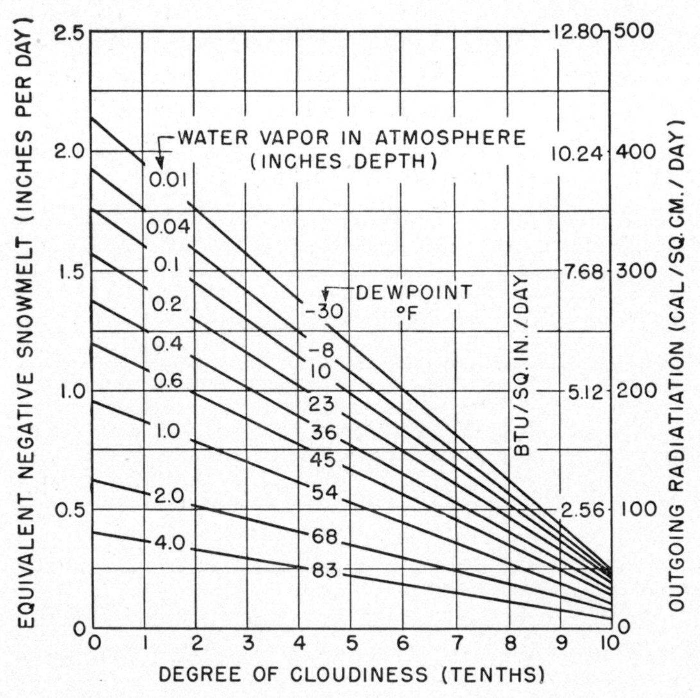

FIG. 7–8. Outgoing radiation from a snow surface at 32°F as a function of cloudiness and humidity. (*After Wilson.*)

10 A.M. of that date, when the stream rose rapidly, cresting at about 3 P.M. Actual discharge values are not available, but apparently most of the rain was discharged. Presumably, rain falling on the new snow was held as capillary moisture until the surface snow had ripened sufficiently to release this stored water. Cores taken after the rain had ended showed that the snow had become coarsely crystalline to a depth of 1 ft on steep slopes and 2 ft in relatively level areas. At lower depths the pack still had the characteristics of new snow. The snow surface was striated with channels,

apparently the result of collapse of subsurface channels eroded by rainwater discharged laterally through the upper portion of the pack.

In addition to the capillary capacity of snow, there remain other means of water storage which cannot be ignored. The intermittent deposition of snow layers permits the formation of ice planes separating layers of varying characteristics. Melt water can accumulate above these ice planes. Buried ice planes are rarely continuous so that their effect is more probably that of delaying the downward movement of melt water than of providing storage for any appreciable time. A snow pack resting on a fine-grained soil can transmit water more rapidly than the soil. Hence, a layer of water may build up at the interface between the snow and soil. Matted vegetation, ice dams, and the snow itself serve to prevent the rapid overland flow of this water, and a layer of slush is formed at the bottom of the pack. Depending on soil type, land slope, rate of melt, and other factors, a considerable volume of water might thus be stored for short periods.

Theoretical computation of snowmelt. Following the theory outlined earlier and utilizing experimental data on the coefficient of turbulence, Light[1] has suggested the following equation for the computation of snowmelt:

$$M = v_w[0.00736(T_a - 32)10^{-0.0000156Z} + 0.0231(e - 6.11)] \quad (7\text{-}14)$$

where M is the effective melt in 24 hr, v_w is the wind velocity 50 ft above the snow surface, T_a is the air temperature in degrees Fahrenheit 10 ft above the snow, e is the vapor pressure in millibars 10 ft above the snow, and Z is the station elevation in feet, mean sea level. The introduction of elevation corrects for the variation of atmospheric pressure with height. Ignoring this effect ($Z = 0$), the curves of Fig. 7-9 are a graphical expression of the equation. The curves have been constructed for both positive and negative vapor-pressure gradients. A temperature of 51°F without melt is possible if the humidity is sufficiently low. If the elevation factor were considered, this limiting temperature would be still higher. Table 7-1 gives correction factors to be applied to v_w, $T_a - 32°$, and $e - 6.11$ for various elevations of the instruments above the snow surface. Light was concerned with snowmelt during storm periods when the effect of radiation is small, and hence this factor is not included in Eq. (7-14). Moreover, conduction from air and soil is neglected. Melting by rainfall may be estimated from Eq. (7-12). There are only a few recorded cases of large volumes of snowmelt in short periods with adequate concurrent data by which Eq. (7-14) can be tested. Since this equation was derived for conditions over a smooth snow surface, it can be expected to indicate too much melt over natural basins. Where the formula has been compared

[1] Light, P., Analysis of High Rates of Snow Melting, *Trans. Am. Geophys. Union*, Vol. 22, pp. 195-205, 1941.

with observed conditions, it has been found that actual melt is about 55 to 65 per cent of the theoretical. The number of cases is too limited to establish whether or not these percentages are generally applicable. Determinations have been made for basins in western Pennsylvania, the Wasatch Range near Salt Lake City, and the southern Sierra Nevada.

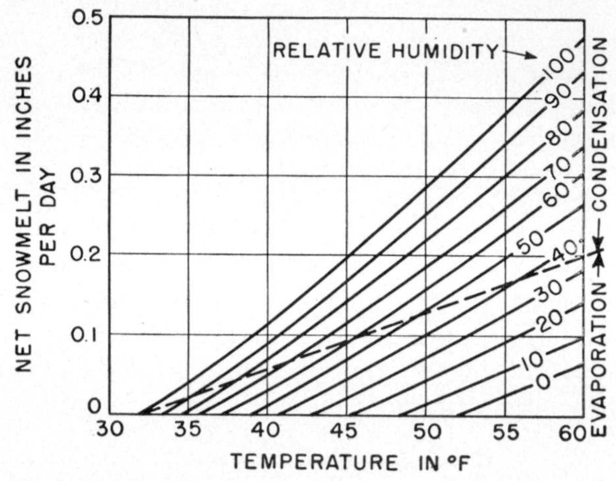

FIG. 7–9. Snowmelt by turbulent exchange per unit wind velocity. (*After Light.*)

The futility of theoretical computation is amply illustrated by observations of the Corps of Engineers–Weather Bureau Cooperative Snow Investigations Program during the 1945-1946 season in the Sierra Nevada. From Mar. 1 to May 9, 1946, approximately 460 Btu/in.², as determined from the difference between incident and reflected radiation, was absorbed

TABLE 7-1. Correction Factors to Be Applied to v_w, $T_a - 32$. and $e - 6.11$ of Eq. 7-14 to Adjust for Elevation of Instruments

Elev. of instruments above snow, ft	Adjustment factors	
	v_w (reference elev. 50 ft)	$T_a - 32$ and $e - 6.11$ (reference elev. 10 ft)
5	1.35	1.10
10	1.23	1.00
20	1.12	0.91
30	1.06	0.86
40	1.03	0.84
60	0.98	0.80
80	0.95	0.77
100	0.93	0.76

by the snow pack at the pyrheliometer site. Without considering any other sources of heat, this amount is more than twice that required to account for the 40 in. of water lost from the pack. Forest cover and aspect undoubtedly reduced the amount of insolation received in other portions of the basin. A large portion of the absorbed energy may have been returned by nocturnal back radiation or dissipated as latent heat of vaporization during periods of evaporation. Clearly, the problem of snowmelt computation from the theoretical viewpoint involves many complex relations. Even if the quantitative aspects of the many questions were known, present field instrumentation is probably inadequate to make use of the knowledge.

GLACIERS

Glaciers in the United States are limited to the northwestern portion of the country, and only a few large glaciers are to be found. They are, therefore, of far less economic importance in this country than elsewhere in the world. However, glaciers provide some interesting facts on long-term storage of snow and may provide a key to time trends in climate as revealed by their accretion and recession.

Source of glaciers. The term *glacier* is applied to all bodies of land ice formed from recrystallized snow accumulated on the ground. Glaciers may form where the annual accretion of snow is greater than ablation by runoff and evaporation. Broadly, glaciers fall into two classes, (1) *ice streams,* which form in mountain valleys and move downslope under the pull of gravity; and (2) *icecaps,* which cover large land masses and spread out radially because of the great pressures built up by their weight. The great glacier which covered much of the northern United States in the Pleistocene epoch was an icecap, but today icecaps are found only in the polar regions.

The glaciers remaining in this country today have their sources at high elevations where low temperatures prevent excessive runoff from melting and precipitation is sufficient to more than compensate for evaporation and melt. The accumulation of snow is further favored by the topography of the immediate glacier area. The great glacial cirques formed by erosion from narrow mountain valleys have the characteristics of large amphitheaters. Wind-blown snow collects in these hollows at the expense of adjacent mountain slopes, and as a result the annual accretion to the glacier may be several times the actual precipitation on its exposed surface.

During the course of its first year, snow deposited on a glacier undergoes the transformations characteristic of less permanent snow fields. Deposited with an initial density probably somewhat greater than 0.1 because of packing by wind, it gradually changes into a coarse crystalline structure with a density of about 0.5, called *névé,* or *firn,* by the glaciologist. As new snow is deposited on the firn, it is further compacted and much of the air expelled. Over a period of several years under the influence of upward of 100 ft of superimposed snow, the firn reaches a density near 0.90 but still retains its granular structure. Air bubbles in glaciers have been found to be under pressures as great as 10 atm. Finally, under strains imposed by glacier movement, a realignment of the crystal structure occurs. The process is aided by *regelation*, the pressure melting of crystals at points of contact and prompt refreezing as the pressure is thus relieved. This final transformation converts the firn into *glacier ice*, a tightly fitting crystal structure with a density of 0.9 or slightly higher.

Movement of glaciers. A glacier moves down its valley in a manner not far different from the flow of a stream. Velocity surveys across glaciers show that there is a definite central current, *i.e.*, velocities near the valley walls are much lower than in the center of the glacier. Vertical velocity surveys are more difficult, but the evidence indicates that on nearly horizontal or adverse slopes the greatest velocity is near the bottom of the ice mass, while on steep slopes the maximum velocity is near the surface. There remains little doubt that ice is plastic under stress. Surveys of old glacial valleys show that ice flows around and over obstructions much as any viscous fluid. Cracks and shear planes do develop in glaciers because ice is relatively weak in tension. Thus, as the ice moves over a convex surface, the upper surface is subject to stretching and crevasses appear. Similarly, as the motion of the lower layers is retarded by some obstacle, the upper layers of ice tend to override the lower ones and shear planes form parallel to the flow.

In temperate regions the minimum thickness of ice required to induce flow in glaciers appears to be between 100 and 150 ft. Both Matthes[1] and Demorest[2] have found evidence of glacial movement in valleys where the ice sheets were not much in excess of 150 ft thick. Valleys less than 100 ft deep showed no signs of glaciation.

ICE IN STREAMS

Closely akin to the problems of snow and glaciers is that of ice in streams. Ice affects the stage-discharge relation and makes discharge determinations more difficult. It creates operational problems when it collects on dams and appurtenances. It is an obstacle to navigation, and ice jams and gorges may be the cause of serious floods.

The ice-water system. Theoretically, the transfer from water to ice can be accomplished at 32°F by the removal of heat energy in the amount of 144 Btu/lb without any change in temperature. Actually, since water and ice are poor conductors of heat, a detectable temperature change takes

[1] Matthes, F. E., Glacial Sculpture of the Bighorn Mountains, Wyo., *U.S. Geol. Survey 21st Ann. Rept.*, Part 2, pp. 167-190, 1900.

[2] Demorest, M., Ice Flowage as Revealed by Glacial Striae. *J. Geol.*, Vol. 46, pp. 700-725, 1938.

place. When heat is applied to a mixture of water and ice, the ice cannot absorb the heat instantaneously, and the water is warmed slightly above 32° so that a gradient of heat from water to ice exists. When ice and water are present in a mixture in equal amounts, the system is most nearly balanced and the temperatures vary only by one- or two-thousandths of a degree from the freezing point. At the extreme, these deviations[1] from the freezing point do not exceed a few hundredths of a degree, but this delicate temperature balance is an important factor in ice formation and dissipation.

Water seems to be composed principally of double molecules called *dihydrol*, while ice consists of triple molecules, *trihydrol*. Trihydrol is present in water at all times, but at the freezing point the quantity of trihydrol reaches saturation (37 per cent), and with a sufficient temperature depression the necessary energy is removed and ice crystals are formed. The first ice precipitated is in the form of disklike, colloidal particles, which ultimately flocculate and grow rapidly into a crystalline form.

Ice formation in still water. Cooling of still water by transfer of heat to the air increases the density of the surface water, which sinks to the bottom and is replaced by upwelling of warmer water. Eventually the water body becomes essentially isothermal at 39°F throughout its depth. In lakes of sufficient depth, heat storage may be sufficient to prevent ultimate development of isothermal conditions prior to the rise of temperature on its annual march in the spring, and such lakes do not freeze. After a lake has reached 39°F throughout its depth, further cooling decreases the density of the surface layers and the cooled surface water remains at the top and is rapidly cooled to the freezing point. Atmospheric convection set up between land and water usually results in most rapid cooling of water near the shores, where ice crystals first begin to form. Thickening of ice continues by conduction of heat through the ice to the air. Frost and snow on the upper surface may also add to ice thickness. The rate of increase in thickness of an ice sheet diminishes as the sheet becomes thicker because of the poor conductivity of ice. The heat withdrawn from a unit area of water surface (32°F) in a short period of time is $K_c(32 - T_a)dt/x$, where x is the ice thickness, K_c the conductivity, and T_a the air temperature. This must equal the heat of formation of an ice layer dx, which is given by $H_f\rho_i\,dx$, where H_f is the latent heat of fusion and ρ_i the density of ice. Equating these terms and integrating,

$$x^2 = \frac{2K_c}{H_f\rho_i}\int_0^t (32 - T_a)\,dt \qquad (7\text{-}15)$$

and if T_a is constant,

$$x = \sqrt{\frac{2K_c t(32 - T_a)}{H_f\rho_i}} \qquad (7\text{-}16)$$

[1] Barnes, H. T., "Ice Engineering," Renouf Publishing Co., Montreal, 1928.

Table 7-2 is computed from Eq. (7-16) to give some idea of the possible growth of an ice sheet.

TABLE 7-2. Time Required for Ice Sheets of Various Thicknesses to Form

Thickness, in.	Air temperature, °F			
	30°	20°	10°	0°
1	10.3 hr	1.7 hr	0.9 hr	0.6 hr
2	1.7 days	6.9 hr	3.8 hr	2.6 hr
3	3.9 days	15.5 hr	8.5 hr	5.8 hr
6	15.5 days	2.6 days	1.4 days	23.2 hr
9	34.8 days	5.8 days	3.2 days	2.2 days
12	61.9 days	10.3 days	5.7 days	3.8 days
18	139.0 days	23.5 days	12.7 days	8.7 days

Frazil ice. The first type of ice to form in a flowing stream is usually frazil ice. In a turbulent stream, cooling proceeds both by thermal convection and turbulence within the water until the stream is isothermal at 39°F. Then, if the stream is sufficiently turbulent, continued cooling aided by turbulence brings the entire water body to 32°F. Tiny colloidal crystals form throughout the stream, giving the water a milky appearance. Several hundred colloidal particles may exist in 1 in.^{3} of water. These tiny particles rapidly coalesce into larger crystals, commonly spicular or needlelike in form, known as *frazil ice.* Although the density of frazil ice is the same as that of other forms of ice, its buoyancy is not sufficient to bring it to the surface against the turbulent action of the water.

Frazil ice forms in large quantities in rapids and is carried in the water until it reaches a quiet section of the stream, where it may freeze to the underside of sheet ice. The resulting spongy mass greatly accelerates the thickening of the ice sheet and may extend to considerable depths. Frazil ice is an important problem in the operation of dams and power plants. It will adhere tenaciously to any metal which extends above the water surface and is cooled below the freezing point. Trash racks can clog completely in only a few minutes, and sufficient frazil ice has been known to collect on a turbine runner to force the closing of the plant. A deep forebay with intakes located well below the water surface is the best protection against clogged racks.

Because of the delicate balance between ice and water, only very small temperature changes are required to dissipate frazil ice. The water temperature in a stream is never more than a small fraction of a degree below freezing. A small amount of heat supplied through perforated steam pipes or electrical heating of trash racks or turbine runners usually dissipates frazil ice rapidly. Such data as are available indicate that 0.12 to 0.25 kw/cfs is required for electrical heating.[1]

Anchor ice. *Anchor ice* forms on the bottom of a stream during clear, cold nights in the form of a cap or layer of ice as much as 2 in. thick. Anchor ice has not been observed on cloudy nights, under bridges, or under sheet ice. It forms only in clear, swift streams with dark rock bottoms. All evidence indicates that it is caused by the slight temperature depression resulting from heat loss by radiation. It is well recognized that water is opaque to most radiation and that temperatures at the stream bottom cannot be much lower than at the stream surface. However, only enough heat need be removed to bring the water a fraction of a degree below 32°F to accomplish the formation of ice. Anchor ice usually breaks free of the bottom shortly after sunrise and floats to the surface.

The annual ice cycle in streams. In those areas where a continuous ice cover builds up in streams and remains throughout the winter, a rather definite annual cycle[2] of streamflow can be observed. Large quantities of frazil ice represent a volume expansion and increase the viscosity of water, thus causing a slight rise in stage. Anchor ice forming on the channel bottom may also result in a small increase in stage, but its effect is never large. Sheet ice, however, forms an added friction surface on the stream and considerably reduces the discharge capacity. When the ice sheet first forms, the undersurface of the ice is usually rough. Some ice pans are tipped on edge, and masses of frazil ice adhere to the bottom of the sheet. As a result, the water surface in the stream must often rise several feet in order to discharge the same volume of flow that was being passed before the freeze-up. This rise in stage places a large volume of water into temporary storage and a consequent decrease in discharge is noted.

As time passes, the underside of the ice sheet is smoothed by the action of moving water, and the stage required to pass a given flow decreases. Hence, stages fall and a portion of the stored water is released so that a gradual increase in discharge takes place until the flow returns to approximately that occurring before the freeze. During the balance of the midwinter period, the streamflow normally recedes slowly as the groundwater contribution decreases (Chap. 15).

With the coming of spring, melting of the ice sheet begins. The melting is usually slow, but the ice sheet gradually loses its protective covering of snow, and under the effect of the sun and warm air the sheet becomes honeycombed with cracks and fissures. Although there may be little obvious change in the structure of the ice sheet, the first rise from the spring

[1] Gisiger, P. E., Safeguarding Hydroplants against the Ice Menace, *Civil Eng.*, Vol. 17, pp. 24-27, 1947.

[2] Parsons, W. J., Ice in the Northern Streams of the United States, *Trans. Am. Geophys. Union*, Vol. 21, pp. 970-973, 1940.

thaws breaks the ice free of the riverbanks and large cracks appear. Soon a weak section of ice breaks free and begins to move downstream. The water held in storage by the retarding effect of the ice is suddenly released and helps to break loose the next lower section of the sheet. The disintegration of the pack is rapid after the first breakup, and only a few hours are required to move the whole pack downstream except for occasional stranded ice floes.

Ice jams and gorges. Ice may be the indirect cause of serious flooding as the result of ice gorges or jams. Ice jams form after the spring breakup as floating pans of ice lodge against bridge piers, sand bars, or firm ice sheets. Frazil ice forming in the stream after the sheet ice has broken up may add to the jam. The result is a dam which may back up large volumes of water and flood the banks of the river for miles above. Jams tend to form at the same spots each year and hence may be prevented, in part at least, by removing the obstructions on which the ice lodges. The strategic use of explosives or thermit charges will break up a jam once formed. Barnes highly recommends thermit because the intense heat liberated causes shattering and cracking of ice over a large area. Calcium chloride can also be used to accelerate melting and aid in destroying the jam. Ashes, coal dust, or other materials scattered on the ice will absorb solar radiation and hasten melting. The latter techniques are particularly effective if the jam has formed behind an ice sheet which is still intact. Streams with northerly courses are more subject to jams because the breakup occurs in headwater areas to the south before it occurs in the lower reaches.

Stevens[1] has described ice gorges which are of frequent occurrence in the Madison River Valley in Wyoming and Montana. Here the stream flows through alluvial valleys with low banks and fairly steep gradients. During periods of sustained, moderately low temperatures (10 to 25°F), large volumes of frazil and anchor ice are formed. The decrease in discharge capacity caused by this ice forces the stream to overflow its low banks and spread out over the valley floor. As the velocity of flow is decreased in overbank flow, the ice is deposited much like sediment and begins to form an ice sheet over the flood plain. This action is aided by the freezing of water flowing over rocks and soil which have been cooled far below freezing. A broad ice sheet is thus formed in the flood plain, with the river flowing in a braided channel over the ice. It is reported that ice has covered the lower Madison Valley to a depth higher than the fence posts, providing clear stretches of ice more than 10 miles in extent which were suitable for iceboating.

It is interesting to note that extremely low temperatures (below 0°F) result in the formation of sheet ice, which puts an end to the formation of

[1] Stevens, J. C., Winter Overflow from Ice-gorging on Shallow Streams, *Trans. Am. Geophys. Union*, Vol. 21, pp. 973-978, 1940.

frazil and anchor ice and thus prevents extensive overflow gorges. Since such gorges are the result of large volumes of frazil ice brought into valley reaches from headwater streams, reservoirs which intercept this frazil ice aid in prevention of ice gorges.

Effect of ice on structures. Ice has been known to be particularly destructive to structures situated along banks and across rivers and lakes. Following the spring breakup, drift ice may jam behind a bridge or dam. Tremendous pressures are exerted by the water which builds up behind the jam. These pressures, aided by a lifting effect resulting from the buoyancy of ice, may move a bridge off its piers or cause the failure of a small dam. It should be noted that fairly high velocities of flow are required to cause a severe jam; hence, jams are not likely to form when a large reservoir is present above a dam. Damage to structures because of ice jams can be reduced by designing them so as to offer minimum opportunity for ice to jam up.

An ice sheet expands and contracts with temperature and thereby exerts considerable force on any structure in contact with it. The average coefficient of linear expansion for ice in the range from 0 to 32°F is about 0.00003 per Fahrenheit degree. However, the actual expansion is about one-half of that indicated by the coefficient as applied to air temperature, because the lower surface of natural ice is maintained consistently close to the freezing point of the water beneath it. Thus, an ice pack 1 mile in extent will expand about 2.5 ft during a temperature change of 30 F°. The pressure which this ice can exert is limited to its crushing strength. Under slowly applied loads, ice appears to have a crushing strength which varies with temperature from about 400 lb/in.^{2} at freezing to twice this amount at 0°F.

The actual pressure loading on dams is dependent on many factors. If the opposite shore of a lake is composed of yielding material, it may absorb the expansion and little thrust will be exerted on the dam. The same is true if the opposite shore is flat so as to permit the ice sheet to override the banks. If the dimensions of the ice sheet are great, it is more likely to buckle and form pressure ridges, which relieve the stress. If the ice sheet is free to expand laterally (parallel to the dam), the stress exerted on the dam will be less than if the sheet is restrained in this direction. Slanting the upstream face of a dam might be expected to relieve the ice thrust, but ice will adhere to concrete with a strength near 200 lb/in.^{2}, and the increased area exposed to adhesion by the slanting face may more than overcome the tendency of the ice sheet to slide up the sloping face.

The expansion of ice under temperature effects is augmented by a "ratchet" action resulting from cracking and refreezing. When an ice sheet contracts because of a drop in temperature, it contracts most in the upper surface. Because of the low tensile strength[1] of ice (approx. 200 lb/in.²), cracks will open in its upper surface. If these cracks are filled with water which subsequently freezes, the ice sheet is lengthened. Similarly, contraction may cause the sheet to crack near the shore line. These cracks immediately fill with water, which freezes, and with the next expansion the shore ice is pushed still farther inland. Ridges of soil and gravel sometimes form along riverbanks from this action.

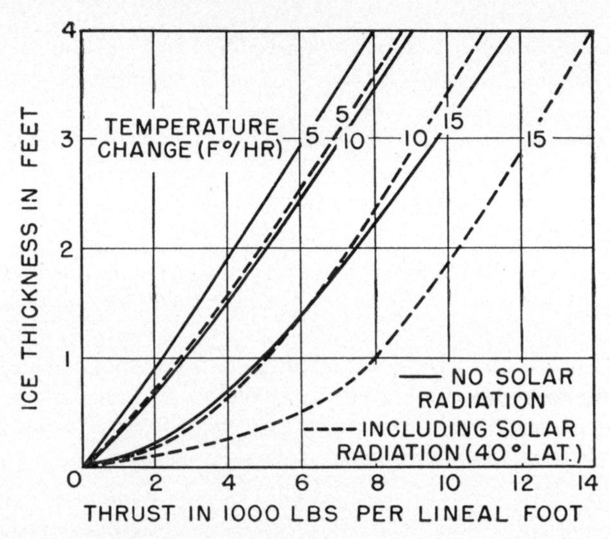

FIG. 7-10. Effect of temperature on ice thrust. (*After Rose.*)

Many dams in the northern United States have been designed for loads of 30,000 to 60,000 lb/lin ft applied at maximum winter water level. Recent evidence indicates that such stresses are unduly high. Because of the plastic properties of ice under stress, large pressures can be developed only under rapid changes in temperature. The curves in Fig. 7-10 show probable ice thrusts[2] for various ice thicknesses and rates of change of temperature, with and without solar radiation, assuming no lateral restraint. The temperature is assumed to rise at the indicated rate from -40 to $+32$°F and to remain constant until the ice sheet is essentially isothermal. For complete lateral restraint these values should be multiplied by 1.575 (assuming Poisson's ratio = 0.365). The absorption of solar radiation results in an added increase of temperature apart from the effect of air-temperature changes.

[1] "Report of Joint Board of Engineers on the St. Lawrence Waterway," Appendix F, Ottawa, 1927.

[2] Rose, E., Thrust Exerted by Expanding Ice Sheet, *Trans. ASCE*, Vol. 112, pp. 871-900, 1947.

Artificial heating which will prevent the formation of ice adjacent to a dam and maintain a lane of open water is the best protection against ice thrust. Compressed air released from small orifices 10 to 20 ft below the water surface will agitate it and carry warm water up with the bubbles. This is an effective and economical means of maintaining an open lane. Fluctuation of the water surface also tends to break up the sheet and reduce the pressures exerted. In extreme cases the water level may be lowered during winter months so that the ice thrust operates at a lower elevation, with correspondingly reduced overturning moment.

FROST IN THE SOIL

Frost in the ground is a matter of concern to hydrologists because it affects runoff phenomena. The occurrence of frost in the ground depends on a great number of complex interrelations between air temperature, soil type, moisture content, vegetal cover, snow, and other factors. Although some study has been given the subject, sufficient data covering a wide range of conditions are not currently available to permit reliable quantitative analysis.

Effect of soil type and condition. The type and condition of soil primarily influence the structure of the frost formation which occurs. Coarse-grained soils and soils with high humus content usually contain a honeycomb-type of frost which is relatively permeable and has little or no effect on infiltration. Dense, compacted, fine-grained soils, on the other hand, freeze into a dense mass, or "concrete" structure, which is highly impervious. This effect is interrelated with the moisture content of the soil, for, regardless of soil type, a soil containing a large amount of moisture will freeze into a denser mass than one which is relatively dry. Clay and compacted loam have a high capillary capacity and will hold more moisture following a given sequence of antecedent weather than will sand or soils with a high content of organic matter. It has been demonstrated, however, that litter placed on the soil surface, and not incorporated in the soil structure, is not particularly effective in controlling either frost penetration or frost structure. The humus content of soil appears to be a particularly effective factor[1] in preventing formation of the concrete type of frost.

In addition to its other influences on frost, moisture in the soil affects the rate of freezing because of its latent heat of fusion and its effect on the specific heat of the soil. A very wet soil will freeze more slowly than a dry soil, but as pointed out above, the ultimate frost structure will be much denser in the wet soil. Berggren[2] has shown by theoretical computation

[1] Lassen, L., and E. N. Munns, Vegetation and Frozen Soil, paper presented at the annual meeting of the *American Geophysical Union*, Washington, D. C., 1947.

[2] Berggren, W. P., Prediction of Temperature Distribution in Frozen Soils, *Trans. Am. Geophys. Union*, Vol. 24, pp. 71-77, 1943.

that dry soil (10 per cent moisture) initially at 50°F and cooled to 23°F will freeze to a depth of 4 in. in 24 hr, while soil having 45 per cent moisture by volume will require 54 hr to freeze to the same depth.

Effect of vegetal cover. Frost forms more slowly and the penetration is much less in areas with good forest cover than in plots with bare soil. This results from the compounding of several effects. First, the presence of vegetation, unless it is new growth, indicates a fairly high humus content of the underlying soil. The root channels of vegetation accelerate percolation, and the transpiration of water by plants reduces the moisture content of the soil and therefore reduces the density of the resulting frost structure. Finally, vegetation forms a protection against the loss of soil warmth by nocturnal radiation, and minimum temperatures within the forest cover are correspondingly higher. For the same reason, the amount of insolation received by forest soils is low, and, once frozen, they thaw more slowly than soil in open areas having the same amount of frost.

Effect of snow cover. A snow cover is an excellent insulating blanket if of sufficient depth. Atkinson and Bay[1] report tests in which plots with 0, 6, 12, and 24 in. of snow cover were observed. The plots with 12 and 24 in. of snow, although frozen before the snowfall, thawed completely in a few days after the snow cover formed. During subsequent periods, when the daily maximum temperatures were below 0°F, frost formed temporarily in the plot with 12 in. of cover, but never to the depth observed in plots with less snow. Berggren shows theoretical computations indicating that a 4-in. snow cover would reduce frost penetration to one-sixth that in a bare plot. Thawing of frost under a deep snow cover begins at the bottom and proceeds upward by transfer of heat from greater depths in the soil. It may be accelerated, however, by percolation of melt water from the snow above and consequent thawing at the soil surface.

Effect of air temperature. Sustained low temperatures over a considerable period of time are required for freezing to proceed to any considerable depth. Freezing of soil conforms to the laws of heat conduction discussed in connection with snow and river ice. The rate of penetration thus varies with the square root of time. Radiation received by the soil surface during the daytime may be sufficient to overcome freezing at night. Hence, cloudy days with maximum temperatures below freezing lead to maximum frost penetration. Because the humus content of the surface three or four inches is normally higher than that at greater depths, frost in the surface layers is relatively permeable. Consequently, intermittent freezing and thawing which affect only the surface soil is not greatly effective in controlling infiltration rates.

[1] Atkinson, H. B., and C. E. Bay, Some Factors Affecting Frost Penetration, *Trans. Am. Geophys. Union*, Vol. 21, pp. 935-951, 1940.

Areal extent of frost. Because of the great variation in factors influencing frost, it must be presumed that there may be a considerable variation in amount and type of ground frost over any large area. Such data as are available verify this presumption. Consequently, inferences as to runoff conditions in a basin should not be made on the basis of a few

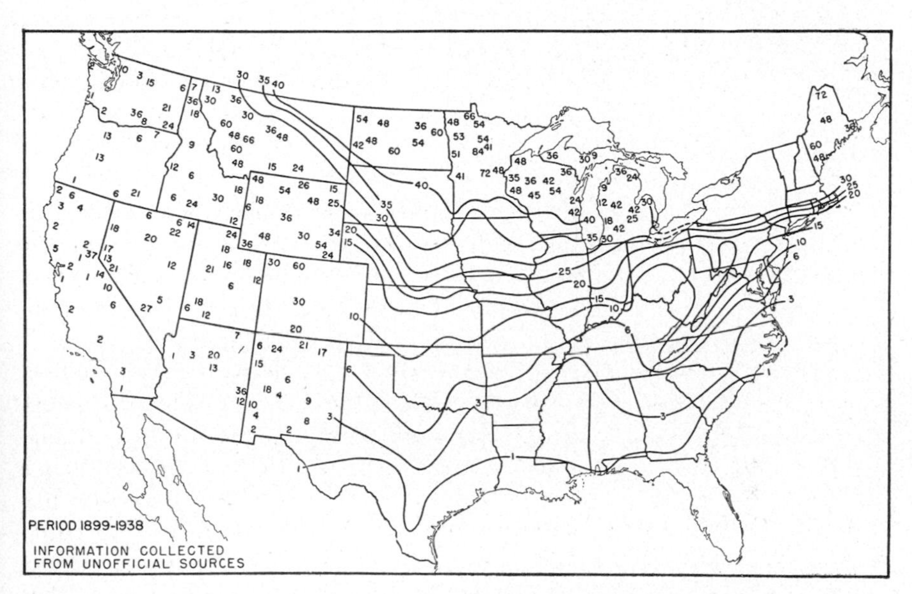

FIG. 7–11. Average maximum annual frost depth (inches) in the United States. (*U.S. Weather Bureau.*)

scattered observations without careful consideration of the possibility of differences in vegetal cover, soil type, etc., elsewhere in the basin. Frost observations are more likely to be made in open areas with light vegetal cover than in forested areas. Hence, available data probably indicate greater frost penetration and persistence than actually occur, on the average, within most river basins. Figure 7-11 shows average maximum annual depth of frost observed in the United States. It is undoubtedly subject to the criticisms mentioned above.

8
EVAPORATION AND TRANSPIRATION

Few phases of the hydrologic cycle have been so extensively investigated as *evaporation*, the process by which the precipitation reaching the earth's surface is returned to the atmosphere as vapor. The hydrologist is often concerned with total water losses and hence must consider evaporation from water surfaces, soil, and vegetation and also transpiration by plants. The combined evaporation from water, snow, and soil surfaces, including evaporation of intercepted precipitation and transpiration from vegetation, is termed *total evaporation*. It is also known as *evapo-transpiration, total loss, water losses*, and *fly-off*.

FACTORS AFFECTING EVAPORATION

Water molecules are in constant motion, and some have sufficient energy to break through a water surface and escape into the air as vapor. The molecules of water vapor in the air are also in constant motion, and some penetrate the water surface and remain within the liquid. The transformation from the liquid to the gaseous state is called vaporization, or evaporation. To the hydrologist, however, *evaporation* refers to the net rate at which liquid water is transferred to the atmosphere.

The factors controlling evaporation are known, but an accurate quantitative analysis of the relative effectiveness of each is difficult because of the interrelations. Evaporation is related to differences in vapor pressure at the water surface and in the air above, air and water temperatures, wind, atmospheric pressure, and quality of the water.

Vapor-pressure differences. The rate at which molecules leave the water depends on the vapor pressure of the liquid (Chap. 4). Similarly, the rate at which molecules enter the water depends on the vapor pressure of the air. The rate of evaporation, therefore, depends on the difference between the vapor pressure of the water e_w and the vapor pressure in the air e_a above the water surface. In other words, it depends on the difference between the saturation vapor pressures at the water temperature and at the dewpoint of the air. Evaporation is proportional to $e_w - e_a$ and continues until $e_a = e_w$.

When the air is warmer than the water, its saturation vapor pressure e_s is greater than that at the water surface ($e_s > e_w$) and evaporation continues until $e_a = e_w$, which will occur before the air becomes saturated. However, if the air is colder[1] than the water, then $e_s < e_w$; and when equilibrium conditions ($e_a = e_w$) are reached, a state of supersaturation ($e_a > e_s$) will exist, or condensation will take place in the air. Since condensation nuclei are generally present in abundance, the superfluous vapor usually condenses into fog. However, since the air is heated from below by the warmer water, it tends to be unstable and there is a tendency for the fog to be dissipated by convection. This probably accounts for the fact that evaporation has been observed to be at a maximum when the water was warmer than the air[2] and suggests the possibility that winter evaporation losses may be high.[3]

Temperature. The rate of emission of molecules from liquid water is a function of its temperature—the higher the temperature, the greater the energy of the molecules and the greater the rate of emission. Experiments with heated water show that evaporation does increase with the temperature of the water surface.[4] This is a direct result of the increase in vapor pressure with temperature. Empirical and theoretical equations which have been developed are not in agreement on the effect of air temperature [Eqs. (8-1) to (8-3)]. This disagreement probably results from differing fundamental approaches and differences in other factors included. While there is no experimental evidence to demonstrate a definite relation between air temperature and evaporation, the interrelation between temperature and other climatic factors results in a rather well-defined relation between monthly evaporation and temperature at a point (Fig. 8-1). This same relation between temperature and evaporation results in a general decrease in evaporation at higher latitudes, as shown on the map[5] of Fig. 8-2. It is evident, however, that other factors exert a controlling influence in some regions.

Wind. Since turbulence varies with wind speed, there must necessarily be a relation between evaporation and wind movement.[6] Experimental

[1] Pettersen, S., "Introduction to Meteorology," pp. 85-86, McGraw-Hill, New York, 1941.

[2] Rohwer, C., Evaporation from Free Water Surfaces, *U.S. Dept. Agr. Tech. Bull.* 271, p. 9, 1931.

[3] Hickman, H. C., Evaporation Experiments, *Trans. ASCE*, Vol. 105, pp. 807-817, 1940.

[4] Fortier, S., Evaporation Losses in Irrigation, *Eng. News*, Vol. 58, pp. 304-307, 1907.

[5] Horton, R. E., Evaporation-maps of the United States, *Trans. Am. Geophys. Union*, Vol. 24, p. 750, 1943.

[6] Fortier, S., and S. H. Beckett, Evaporation from Irrigated Soils, *U.S. Dept. Agr. Expt. Sta. Bull.* 248, pp. 68-70, 1912.

Rohwer, C., Evaporation from Free Water Surfaces, *U.S. Dept. Agr. Tech. Bull.* 271, pp. 15-27, 1931.

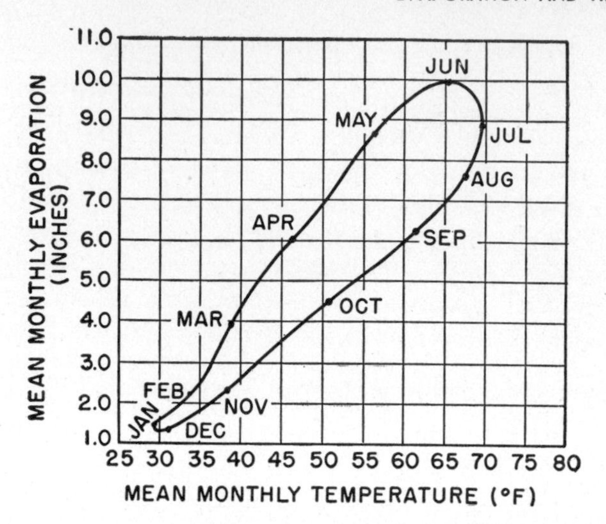

FIG. 8–1. Relation of evaporation to temperature, Sante Fe, New Mexico, 1919 to 1933.

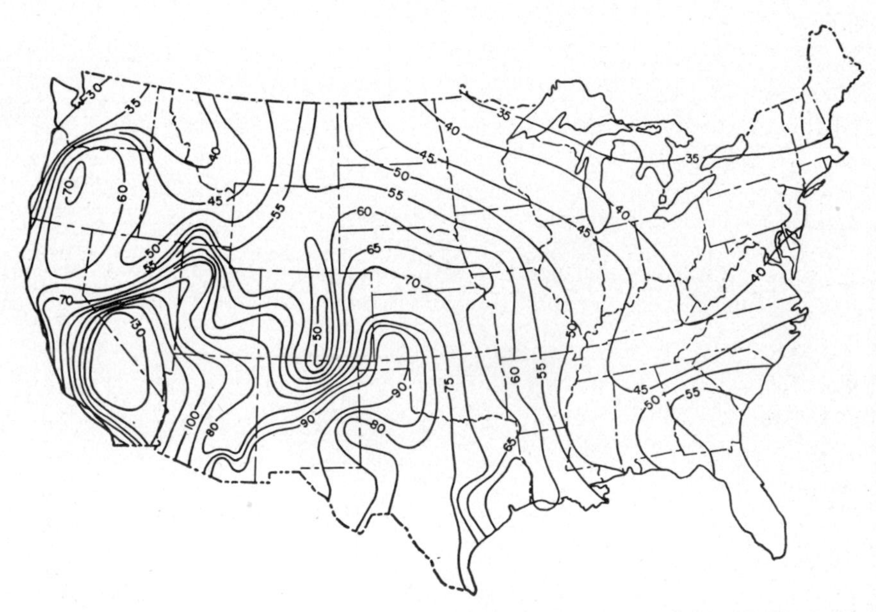

FIG. 8–2. Normal annual evaporation in inches from Class A land pans. *(After Horton.)*

data do not disclose the exact nature of this relation. It is commonly believed that the effect of increasing wind speed decreases as some high value is approached. The effect probably depends on surface roughness and the dimensions of the water body.

Atmospheric pressure. Atmospheric pressure is so closely related to other factors affecting evaporation that it is practically impossible to study the effects of its variations under natural conditions. The number of air molecules per unit volume increases with pressure. Consequently, with high pressures there is more chance that vapor molecules escaping from the water surface will collide with an air molecule and rebound into the liquid. Hence, evaporation would be expected to decrease with increasing pressure. Changes in other meteorological factors accompanying pressure changes at a station generally conceal the effect of pressure. The reduction in pressure with increase in elevation acts to increase evaporation at high elevations. This effect is offset by the general decrease in temperature with elevation, and hence the relation between elevation and evaporation is not clearly defined. Meyer[1] found that evaporation from water surfaces in mountains of the Coast Ranges increased with elevation. Evaporation-pan records[2] for Los Angeles County indicate a similar relationship from sea level to 4000 ft. Using six pans located at elevations ranging from 4500 to 14,500 ft on the east slope of Mt. Whitney, Adams[3] found that evaporation decreased with altitude to about 10,000 ft, above which there was little variation.

It has been shown also that evaporation at high altitudes is greatly influenced by the orientation of the slope.[4] Southern slopes receive more solar heat than northern slopes and consequently are subject to greater evaporation. Wagon Wheel Gap records showed that the mean June to October evaporation for 5 years was almost twice as great on the southern slope.

Quality of water. The rate of evaporation is less for salt water than for fresh and decreases as the specific gravity increases.[5] The evaporation rate decreases about 1 per cent for each 1 per cent increase in specific gravity until crusting takes place, usually at a specific gravity of about 1.30. Evaporation from sea water has been estimated to be about 2 to 3 per cent less than from fresh water when other conditions are the same. Turbidity appears to have no noticeable effect on the evaporation rate.

[1] Meyer, A. F., "Evaporation from Lakes and Reservoirs," p. 59, Minnesota Resources Commission, 1942.

[2] Evaporation from Water Surfaces in California, *Calif. Dept. Public Works Bull.* 54, pp. 22-23, 1947.

[3] Fortier, S., Evaporation Losses in Irrigation, *Eng. News*, Vol. 58, pp. 304-307, 1907.

[4] Follansbee, R., discussion of paper, Evaporation on United States Reclamation Projects, *Trans. ASCE*, Vol. 90, pp. 290-291, 1927.

[5] Lee, C. H., discussion of paper, Evaporation on United States Reclamation Projects, *Trans. ASCE*, Vol. 90, pp. 332-333, 1927.

Nature of the evaporating surface. The previous discussion has considered the factors affecting evaporation from a free-water surface. Evaporation from soil, vegetation, snow, and ice, which is affected by these same factors, requires special consideration.

Soil surfaces. An important factor affecting the volume of evaporation from a soil surface is the *evaporation opportunity*, or the availability of water. As long as the soil surface is saturated, the evaporation rates are probably not greatly different from those which would be observed from a water surface at the same temperature. However, if the soil surface is not saturated, the rate of evaporation may be limited by the rate at which moisture is transferred to the surface from below, even though existing meteorological conditions might favor greater rates. Because the specific heat of soil is lower than that of water, the temperature of the soil surface varies through a wider range than does that of the water surface of a lake or reservoir. This difference is further emphasized because surface cooling of a water body sets up convection currents which act to stabilize surface temperature. Consequently, both the diurnal and the annual range of the evaporation rate are greater for land surfaces than for water bodies. The diurnal variation is emphasized by the formation of dew or frost when nighttime soil temperatures drop below the dewpoint. Similarly, evaporation from soil during the summer months would be expected to exceed that from an adjacent lake provided that adequate soil moisture were available.

The difficulties of measuring evaporation from natural soils have discouraged experimental work on the subject. While it is presumably feasible to expose soil samples in pans to determine their loss in weight through evaporation, such an exposure is probably no better index to evaporation from soil *in situ* than the measured loss from an exposed water surface. The movement of soil moisture and the thermal characteristics of soils are discussed in Chap. 12. The total loss from soil through combined evaporation and transpiration is discussed in a later section of this chapter.

Vegetation. A portion of all precipitation is retained on the exposed surfaces of vegetation (Chap. 11). The water thus retained is returned to the atmosphere by evaporation. Like evaporation from soil, this loss is greatly dependent on the evaporation opportunity. It is doubtful that the evaporation rate from a leaf surface is materially different from that from an equal area of water surface exposed under similar conditions. Because of the large leaf area in a bush or tree, however, the rate of evaporation per unit of projected area is well in excess of that from a water surface so long as water is available for evaporation. Water on the leaves of trees and bushes normally evaporates rapidly because of the favorable exposure, which permits the vapor to be removed readily even in the slightest breeze. On the other hand, moisture retained in dense grass cover may evaporate slowly because air movement within the cover is limited and the vapor-pressure difference rapidly approaches zero. The evaporation of water released by growing plants is discussed in connection with transpiration later in this chapter (page 169).

Snow and ice. The maximum temperature which a snow surface can attain is 32°F, and hence evaporation cannot take place unless the dewpoint is below 32°. The evaporation at low temperatures is also reduced by the increase in heat of vaporization with decrease in temperature (Appendix C). Thus, at low temperatures, when the heat available for vaporization or sublimation is low, the heat requirement is increased. Furthermore, at low temperatures the increment of vapor pressure per degree decreases so that extremely low dewpoints are required to produce vapor-pressure differences comparable with those normally experienced in the usual range of summer temperatures. Thus, under most conditions evaporation from snow and ice is much less than from water surfaces. Only under chinook and similar conditions is high evaporation from snow favored.

The problem of measuring evaporation from snow is more difficult than from water, for several reasons. Church,[1] Croft,[2] Clyde,[3] and others have reported data on evaporation from snow as determined by exposing samples in small pans and determining their loss in weight. The melting of snow in small pans is accelerated by the radiative absorption of the pan, and since the melt water cannot drain, the sample has a higher water content than natural snow. Since evaporation from ice is less than that from water, the excessively wet sample must be presumed to indicate evaporation which is too large in comparison with natural losses. Croft attempted to overcome this by changing his snow samples frequently.

Other experiments[4] have attempted to measure evaporation from a snow pack over a shallow pan about 20 ft in diameter. Runoff from the pan is collected in a drain, and the water equivalent of the snow in the pan is estimated from depth measurements on slender snow stakes erected in the pan and density measurements made outside its perimeter. The problem of adequately determining the water equivalent of the snow and the hazard of lateral drainage into or out of the pan area offer the principal objections to this technique.

[1] Church, J. E., "Climate and Evaporation in Alpine and Arctic Zones," report of the Greenland Expedition, Part II, University of Michigan, Ann Arbor, 1941.

[2] Croft, A. R., Evaporation from Snow, *Am. Meteorolog. Soc. Bull.*, Vol. 25, pp. 334-337, 1944.

[3] Clyde, G. D., Snow-melting Characteristics, *Utah Agr. Expt. Sta. Bull.* 231, 1931.

[4] Wilm, H. G., and E. G. Dunford, Effect of Timber Cutting on Water Available for Stream Flow from a Lodgepole Pine Forest, *U. S. Dept. Agr. Tech. Bull.* 968, 1948.

Croft's data, though covering only a short period, show some interesting facts concerning exposures. Evaporation from pans in the open sun was not significantly higher than from pans shaded from all insolation. More important than insolation was the effect of wind. Although velocities were only about 2 mph at 0.5 ft above the snow, shielding a pan from the wind reduced evaporation by 50 per cent. Evaporation during the day was three to four times as great as sublimation losses at night. The evaporation from water averaged about 20 per cent more than that from snow.

The data reported by various investigators are surprisingly consistent. Most of the experiments indicate that evaporation during the spring months averages about 1 in./month or less. While the evaporation losses from snow are not negligible, it is probable that an equal or greater loss occurs from the saturated soil around the edge of patches of melting snow. Parshall[1] found evaporation from tanks of saturated soil to be about 5 in./month at Ft. Collins, Colorado.

Assuming that Eq. (7-11) applies, the curves of Fig. 7-5 extended below 32° dewpoint may be used as an approximation to evaporation loss. For evaporation to take place at these rates, the necessary heat must be supplied from convection, radiation, or other sources. It should be noted that a must be divided by approximately 8 to account for the difference between the latent heats of fusion and vaporization, or sublimation. Figure 7-5 has been adjusted to compensate for this.

MEASUREMENT OF EVAPORATION

Because evaporation plays such an important role in the hydrologic cycle, a great deal of effort has been expended in attempts to find a means of measuring it directly. Obviously, the most direct approach to determination of evaporation from lakes and reservoirs would be the direct computation from observed values of inflow, outflow, precipitation, and seepage.[2] However, seepage cannot be measured, and the errors in measurement of the other factors may exceed the evaporation. Therefore, this procedure is rarely satisfactory. The difficulties in direct measurement of evaporation from soil are far more formidable. Consequently, measurement of evaporation has been restricted to the use of instruments which measure the evaporative power of the air and not the actual evaporation.

The *evaporative power* is a measure of the degree to which a region is favorable or unfavorable to evaporation. Thus, the evaporative power is greater over a hot desert than near a humid coastline. A suitable correc-

[1] Parshall, R. L., Experiments to Determine Rate of Evaporation from Saturated Soils and River Bed Sands, *Trans. ASCE*, Vol. 94, pp. 961-999, 1930.

[2] Harding, S. T., Evaporation from Large Water Surfaces Based on Records in California and Nevada, *Trans. Am. Geophys. Union*, Vol. 16, pp. 507-512, 1935.

tion must be applied to adjust measured evaporative power to the actual evaporation from a specified surface.

Instruments for measuring the rate of evaporation are called *atmometers, evaporimeters, evaporometers,* or *atmidometers.* The terms are synonymous, but the first is most generally used. Atmometers may be segregated into three classes, (1) tanks or pans, (2) porous porcelain bodies, and (3) wet paper surfaces.

Evaporation tanks or pans. Evaporation tanks or pans, commonly used for ordinary measurements, are made of galvanized iron, zinc, or copper, are usually circular, and are made in various sizes. They may be unpainted or painted in various colors, and their tops may or may not be screened. They may be installed above or in the ground or may float on a water surface. Because of these variations, the exact type and exposure of the pan must be specified before any measurements can be evaluated.[1] Since evaporation is related to atmospheric changes, meteorological data should be collected at each pan site. The more important elements are (1) wind movement, (2) air temperature, (3) water-surface temperature, (4) atmospheric humidity, and (5) precipitation.

One of the chief causes of variations in the ratio of evaporation from a pan to that over a relatively deep body of water is the difference in the heat storage. Some of the heat received at the surface of a deep lake or reservoir during the spring and summer serves to warm the water to considerable depths and is not immediately available as a source of energy for evaporation (Fig. 8-3). This stored heat provides additional energy for evaporation during the fall and winter months. The small amount of water in the pans has little capacity for heat storage, with the result that measurements are more directly related to the heat supply. Floating pans are often used to minimize this discrepancy. Although their measurements are considered to be somewhat more accurate, they still require adjustment. An element of uncertainty in floating-pan measurements is the possible splashing of water into or out of the pan by wave action.

Evaporation from pans is greater than from adjacent water bodies. The difference usually varies inversely as the size of the pans, so that small pans require larger adjustments. The ratio of evaporation from a large body of water to that from a pan is known as the *pan coefficient.* It is used to estimate evaporation from a lake or reservoi[illegible] plication t[illegible]

[1] Sleight, R. B., Evaporation from the Surfaces of Water [illegible] River-bed Materials, *J. Agr. Research,* Vol. 10, pp. 209-259, 1917.

Houk, I. E., Evaporation on United States Recl[illegible] Projects, *Trans. ASCE,* Vol. 90, pp. 266-378, 1927.

Rohwer, C., Evaporation from Free Water S[illegible] U. S. Dept. Agr. Tech. Bull. 271, pp. 1-96, 1931.

Rohwer, C., R. Follansbee, and ot[illegible]oration from Water Surfaces, *Trans. ASCE,* Vol. 99, pp. 673-747, 1934.

nearby pan measurements. The coefficient is variable and is usually higher in winter than in summer. Coefficients for monthly evaporation are naturally more variable than those for annual evaporation. Since the determination of pan coefficients requires the estimation of actual reservoir evaporation from inflow and outflow data, these coefficients are approximate at best.

The depth of water in the pan and the height of the pan rim above the water surface apparently have some effect on the rate of evaporation, but the results of investigations are at variance. It appears that deep-buried

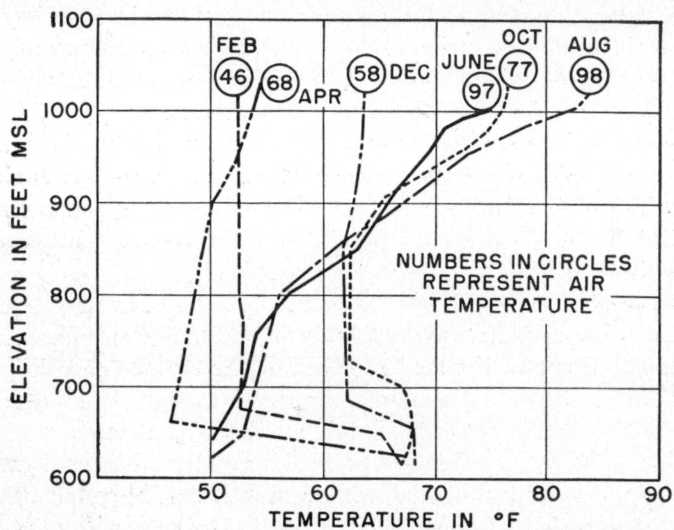

FIG. 8–3. Temperature profiles in Lake Mead, June, 1936, to April, 1937. *(After Houk.)*

pans have more evaporation than shallow pans, especially during winter months. For surface pans, there seems to be little effect in the usual range of depths. The influence of pan colors on rates of evaporation depends on their relative heat absorption. The evaporation from dark pans is greater than from unpainted, galvanized pans, while light-colored pans show the least evaporation. Painting of the pan interior below the water surface apparently has little effect on the evaporation rate. It is theoretically possible to reduce pan evaporation to the equivalent of that from a lake by the use of a scr[illegible] over the water surface in the pan. By keeping the water temperature mor[illegible]arly uniform throughout the day and night, the screen maintains a [illegible]ably uniform rate of evaporation, which is less than that from unscree[illegible]ns. The screen also acts to reduce turbulence at the water surface.[1]

[1] Hickox, G. H., Evaporation [illegible] Free Water Surface, *Trans. ASCE*, Vol. 111, pp. 1-66, 1946.

Class A evaporation pan. The standard pan used by the U.S. Weather Bureau,[1] known as the Class A land pan (Fig. 8-4), is 4 ft in diameter and 10 in. deep, and the depth of water is maintained between 7 and 8 in. It is made of galvanized iron and is unpainted. In order to standardize installations, it has been the practice to place the pan in a level spot open to the maximum possible sunshine. The pan is placed on timbers so that

FIG. 8-4. Class A land pan showing hook gage and anemometer. *(U.S. Weather Bureau.)*

its bottom is about 6 in. above the ground, in order that air may circulate beneath the pan. The depth of water is measured with a hook gage in a stilling well. A coefficient of 0.7 has been recommended for this pan, but values ranging from 0.6 to 0.8 or greater have been reported. Although having a coefficient considerably less than unity, the use of the Class A pan has been recommended[2] because (1) more data are available from this type of pan, (2) its coefficient has relatively little geographic variation, and (3) it is reasonably free from drifting dirt and debris.

[1] Instruction for the Installation and Operation of Class A Evaporation Stations, *U.S. Weather Bur. Circ. L*, 1919.

[2] Standard Equipment for Evaporation Stations, final report Subcommittee on Evaporation of the Special Committee on Irrigation Hydraulics, *Trans. ASCE*, Vol. 99, pp. 716-718, 1934.

Colorado "sunken" pan. The Colorado sunken pan, which has been used a great deal in the West, is 3 ft square and 18 in. deep. It is made of unpainted galvanized iron and is usually sunk into the ground to within 4 in. of its rim. The water surface is maintained near the ground level. A hook gage is used to make the water measurements. Its coefficient ranges generally between 0.75 and 0.85, with a mean value of slightly less than 0.8. The evaporation from a pan of this type agrees closely with that from a floating pan of the same dimensions.

Floating pans. Attempts have been made to simulate reservoir evaporation by floating a pan in water. Such pans are usually supported in the water by floats so that the rim is about 3 in. above the water surface. The water surface inside the pan is kept at the same level as that outside. The amount of evaporation is determined by the number of cups of water required to bring the water level up to a fixed index point in the center of the pan. Surging in the pan may be reduced by perforated baffle plates or screens below the water line, and the pan is surrounded by a raft to protect it from waves. Being located in the water, this type of pan is not affected by drifting soil and snow and is subject to conditions which are very similar to those over and in the lake or reservoir. This type of pan is subject to splashing during high winds and is less accessible for measurement than a land pan. A coefficient of 0.80 has been recommended for a floating pan of the Colorado type.

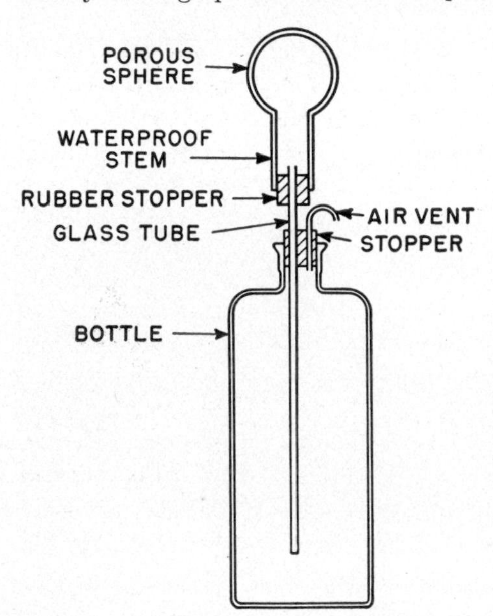

FIG. 8–5. Porous-cup atmometer of the Livingston type.

Porous porcelain bodies. Porous porcelain spheres, cylinders, or blocks are commonly used by plant physiologists for measuring evaporation, because evaporation from their surfaces is considered to be quite representative of that from plants. The Livingston sphere (Fig. 8-5), which is frequently used in botanical investigations, is about 2 in. in diameter and about 0.1 in. in thickness. It is filled with distilled water and connected to a supply reservoir so that atmospheric pressure on the water surface in the container acts to keep the sphere full. Since the characteristics of the porous material cannot be absolutely controlled, each sphere must be compared with a standard and a correcting coefficient determined. For field use, a valve[1] must be provided to prevent intake of rainwater.

Wet paper surfaces. The Piche atmometer[2] is probably the best known of the wet paper type. It consists of a graduated glass tube, about 9 in. in length and 0.4 in. in internal diameter, with one end closed, and with a disk of filter paper held against the open end by a spring and metal disk. The tube is filled with distilled water, and after the filter and disk are in place, it is inverted.

EVAPORATION FORMULAS

Evaporation formulas may be broadly classified into two types, (1) formulas based on theoretical considerations of energy exchange, and (2) empirical relations developed by correlation of atmometer data with weather elements. Most of the formulas of the first type involve assumptions based on experimental evidence or contain coefficients which must be evaluated empirically. Hence, any classification is somewhat academic. Because of the difficulty of evaluating actual evaporation from natural surfaces, formulas of all types are subject to much the same limitations as are atmometer observations.

Formulas based on turbulent exchange. Since eddy motion is the principal mechanism by which water vapor is removed from the vicinity of an evaporating surface, numerous investigators[3] have attempted to derive formulas by considering the mass transport by turbulent exchange. Thornthwaite and Holzman[4] investigated the vertical distribution of moisture in the turbulent layer and the intensity of turbulence by simultaneous observations at two levels (Z_1 and Z_2) to compute evaporation by the following equation:

$$E_a = \frac{833\mathbf{k}^2(e_{a_1} - e_{a_2})(v_{w_2} - v_{w_1})}{(T + 459.4)[\log_e (Z_2/Z_1)^2]} \tag{8-1}$$

where E_a is the evaporation in inches per hour; $\mathbf{k}$ is von Kármán's constant (0.4); e_a is the vapor pressure in inches of mercury; v_w is the wind speed in

[1] Weaver, J. E., and F. E. Clements, "Plant Ecology," 2d ed., pp. 350-354, McGraw-Hill, New York, 1938.

[2] Abbe, C., The Piche Evaporometer, *Monthly Weather Rev.*, Vol. 33, pp. 253-255, 1905.

[3] Sutton, O. G., Wind Structure and Evaporation in a Turbulent Atmosphere, *Proc. Roy. Soc. (London)*, Series *A*, Vol. 146, pp. 701-722, 1934.

Montgomery, R. B., Observations of Vertical Humidity Distribution above the Ocean Surface and Their Relation to Evaporation, *Mass. Inst. Technol. Meteorol. Papers*, Vol. 7, No. 4, pp. 1-30, 1940.

Sverdrup, H. U., On the Evaporation from the Oceans, *J. Marine Research (Sears Foundation)*, Vol. 1, No. 1, pp. 3-14, 1937.

[4] Thornthwaite, C. W., and B. Holzman, Measurement of Evaporation from Land and Water Surfaces, *U.S. Dept. Agr. Tech. Bull.* 817, 1942.

miles per hour; and T is the mean temperature of the layer in degrees Fahrenheit. The subscripts 1 and 2 refer to the lower and upper levels, respectively. This formula assumes an adiabatic atmosphere and a logarithmic distribution of wind speed and moisture in the vertical. Under conditions of temperature inversion or light winds, the computed evaporation may be too high. The chief disadvantage of this formula is that it requires meteorological observations not ordinarily available, *e.g.*, simultaneous observations of vapor pressure and wind speed at two levels over a point. For this reason, it cannot be used to determine evaporation from past meteorological records.

Hickox[1] considered evaporation to be a process of mass transport analogous to heat transfer. Representing vapor transfer by dimensionless moduli as for heat transfer through convection, he obtained the following proportionality for evaporation into air in motion:

$$E_a \propto \frac{\Delta c_v v_w^{0.75} T^{0.375}}{d^{0.25} p^{0.25}} \tag{8-2}$$

where Δc_v is the vapor-concentration difference in pounds per cubic foot, d is the diameter of the evaporation pan in feet, p is the air pressure in pounds per square foot, T is the absolute temperature in degrees Fahrenheit, and v_w is the wind velocity in feet per second.

Formulas based on the transformation of energy. The transformation of a liquid to vapor is a process which requires heat. For water to remain at constant temperature while evaporating, it is necessary that heat be supplied to it at a rate equal to the cooling by evaporation. Thus, if there is no change in water temperature, the rate at which heat is being supplied is a measure of the evaporation rate. In nature, however, the temperature of the evaporating body may change so that the net gain or loss of heat during the evaporation process must also be considered. Since heat may be added to or removed from a body of water by several methods, few of which can be reliably evaluated, the computation of evaporation by the heat-balance method is difficult.

Bowen,[2] McEwen,[3] Richardson,[4] and Cummings[5] have used formulas based on the heat-balance method. While developed on a sound basis,

[1] Hickox, G. H., Evaporation from a Free Water Surface, *Trans. ASCE*, Vol. 111, pp. 1-33, 1946.

[2] Bowen, I. S., The Ratio of Heat Losses by Conduction and by Evaporation from Any Water Surface, *Phys. Rev.*, Vol. 27, pp. 779-787, 1926.

[3] McEwen, G. F., Results of Evaporation Studies, *Scripps Inst. Oceanog. Tech. Ser.*, Vol. 2, pp. 401-415, 1930.

[4] Richardson, B., Evaporation as a Function of Insolation, *Trans. ASCE*, Vol. 95, pp. 996-1019, 1931.

[5] Cummings, N. W., Evaporation from Water Surfaces, *Trans. Am. Geophys. Union*, Vol. 17, pp. 507-509, 1936.

such formulas have relatively little practical usefulness because of the difficulty in obtaining measurements of some of the parameters, especially back radiation to the sky. The paucity of solar-radiation observations usually restricts the use of this type of formula to a few localities.

The general heat-balance equation is

$$E_a = \frac{R_i - (R_b + S_H + c)}{H_v(1 + R_B)} \tag{8-3}$$

where E_a is in centimeters, R_i is the incoming radiation on a horizontal surface, R_b is the back radiation to the sky, S_H is the heat consumed in warming the water (heat storage), c is a correction for leakage through the walls of the container, expansion of the water, and heat carried by flowing water, H_v is the latent heat of vaporization of water in calories per cubic centimeter, and R_B, known as *Bowen's ratio*, is computed by Eq. (8-4). All quantities in the numerator are expressed in calories per square centimeter of open water surface for the same time period as that used for E_a.

$$R_B = \frac{0.46p}{760}\frac{(T_s - T_a)}{(e_w - e_a)} \tag{8-4}$$

where T_s is the water-surface temperature and p is the barometric pressure. Temperatures are in degrees centigrade and pressures in millimeters of mercury.

In connection with Eq. (8-3), it should be noted that the incoming radiation R_i varies from 0 to 80 cal/cm²/hr. The back radiation to the sky R_b is always positive and varies from near zero to about 10 cal/cm²/hr. The heat storage S_H, positive when the water is warming up and negative for cooling, varies from about -10 to about $+10$ cal/cm²/hr. The correction c is usually negligible for a lake but may be as great as 10 cal/cm²/hr for pans. Bowen's ratio R_B is introduced to correct for heat lost by diffusion and convection. For a short period it may vary from -1 to $+1$, but for 24-hr intervals it is seldom greater than 0.30 and is frequently less than 0.20.

Formulas based on Dalton's law. Evaporation is expressed as a function of various atmospheric elements, such as temperature, pressure, humidity, and wind speed, in many empirical formulas based on observations of evaporation from pans, reservoirs, and lakes. Dalton[1] first recognized the relationship between evaporation and vapor pressure expressed by

$$E_a = b(e_w - e_a) \tag{8-5}$$

[1] Dalton, J., Experimental Essays on the Constitution of Mixed Gases; on the Force of Steam or Vapor from Waters and Other Liquids, Both in a Torricellian Vacuum and in Air; on Evaporation; and on the Expansion of Gases by Heat, *Mem. Proc. Manchester Lit. & Phil. Soc.*, Vol. 5, pp. 535-602, 1802.

where b is an empirical coefficient. This relationship has been the basis of a variety of formulas[1], many of which merely introduce a wind-correction factor. Only a few of the better known formulas are discussed here.

The Meyer[2] formula is

$$E_a = c(e_s - e_a)\left(1 + \frac{\overline{v_w}}{10}\right) \tag{8-6}$$

where E_a is monthly evaporation in inches; e_s is the saturation vapor pressure, in inches of mercury, corresponding to the monthly mean air temperature; e_a is the average monthly vapor pressure of the air (usually computed from monthly mean air temperature and relative humidity); $\overline{v_w}$ is the monthly mean wind speed in miles per hour; and c is an empirical constant having a value of about 15 for pans, puddles, shallow ponds, or vegetation. For computing evaporation from deeper lakes or reservoirs, e_w should be used in place of e_s, and c should be given a value of about 11.

Horton[3] adapted the Dalton formula by introducing wind speed as a power function to give an expression for daily evaporation (in inches) in the form

$$E_a = c[(2 - \mathbf{e}^{-0.2v_w})e_w - e_a] \tag{8-7}$$

where pressures are in inches of mercury and wind velocity is in miles per hour. Horton suggested a value of 0.36 for c in the case of a pan 12 in. square.

As a result of extensive investigations, Rohwer[4] derived a formula for daily evaporation (in inches) which includes a pressure term to compensate for differences in altitude:

$$E_a = 0.771(1.465 - 0.0186p)(0.44 + 0.118v_w)(e_w - e_a) \tag{8-8}$$

where pressures are in inches of mercury, v_w is in miles per hour, and the coefficient 0.771 is inserted to make the formula applicable to reservoirs.

Coaxial graphical correlation (Appendix A) provides a convenient means for establishing the relation between evaporation and meteorological parameters. Figure 8-6 shows such a relation for monthly evaporation

[1] Fitzgerald, D., Evaporation, *Trans. ASCE*, Vol. 15, pp. 581-646, 1886.

Russell, T., Depth of Evaporation in the United States, *Monthly Weather Rev.*, Vol. 16, pp. 235-239, 1888.

Bigelow, F. H., Studies of the Phenomena of Evaporation over Lakes and Reservoirs, *Monthly Weather Rev.*, Vol. 35, pp. 311-316, 1907; Vol. 36, pp. 24-39, 1908; Vol. 38, pp. 307-313, 1910.

Folse, J. A., A New Method of Estimating Stream-flow, Based upon a New Evaporation Formula, *Carnegie Inst. Wash. Pub.* 400, 1929.

[2] Meyer, A. F., Computing Run-off from Rainfall and Other Physical Data, *Trans. ASCE*, Vol. 79, pp. 1056-1224, 1915.

[3] Horton, R. E., A New Evaporation Formula Developed, *Eng. News-Record*, Vol. 78, pp. 196-199, 1917.

[4] Rohwer, C., Evaporation from Free Water Surfaces, *U.S. Dept. Agr. Tech. Bull.* 271, p. 78, 1931.

at Yuma, Arizona. Evaporation and wind data are from the Yuma Citrus Station, while temperature and dewpoint data are from the Weather Bureau Office. This relation can be expressed by the equation

$$E_a = c(e_s - e_a)(b + av_w^n) \tag{8-9}$$

where, for Yuma, $a = 0.54$ and $b = 7.14$. The coefficient c is unity for the data based on the evaporation pan but should, of course, be lower for reservoirs. The data suggest that the exponent n should have a value greater than unity, but, because of the small range in monthly wind travel at Yuma, the use of $n = 1$ does not introduce appreciable error.

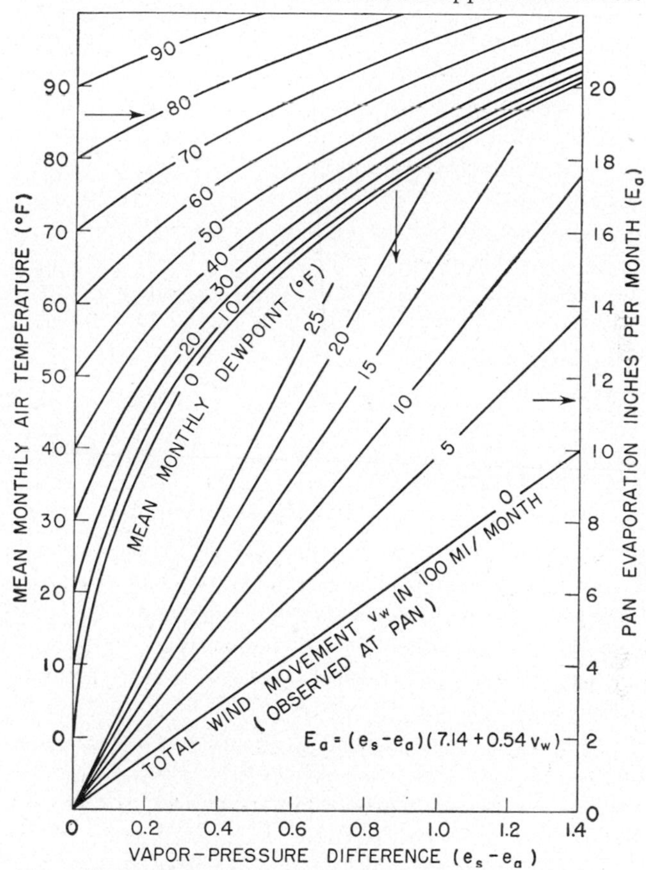

FIG. 8-6. The relation between evaporation and meteorological parameters for Yuma, Arizona, as determined by graphical correlation.

THE TRANSPIRATION PROCESS

Direct evaporation from soil is often exceeded in importance by *transpiration*—the process by which water in plants is transferred to the atmosphere as water vapor. Whether transpiration is beneficial or harmful to plant life has long been a source of controversy among students of plant physiology. Regardless of its net effect on plant life, it is a very wasteful process in so far as water is concerned and must not be neglected by the hydrologist in studies of the hydrologic balance.

Absorption of soil moisture. Except for aquatic vegetation, most plants obtain their water supply from the soil through their roots. Conditions favorable for the absorption of atmospheric moisture by plant leaves and stems are seldom observed in nature, and the amount of moisture acquired by this method is generally considered insignificant. Transpiration rates may be greatly reduced, however, by showers, dew, and even moist air. Soil water passes into the plant through the root system, which may penetrate the soil to relatively great depths. Depth of root penetration is determined to a considerable extent by the distribution of water in the soil. Root systems of most annuals are confined to the upper foot of the soil, but close-growing perennials, such as alfalfa, may have roots extending downward 40 ft. Shrubs and trees that form taproots, such as pine and oak, penetrate 10 to 20 ft in fine soil, but such trees as cottonwood and spruce rarely reach below 5 ft.

Water is absorbed into the root system near the growing ends of the rootlets through root hairs, which are outgrowths of epidermal cells. The absorption is accomplished by the attraction of colloidal cell material for water, a process called *imbibition.* Although forces of imbibition may amount to many atmospheres, plant roots are never able to remove all water from the soil. The amount remaining after the plant reaches its wilting point is expressed by the wilting coefficient (Chap. 12) and depends mostly on soil type. Experiments indicate that there is little difference in the ability of young plants to remove moisture from soil.[1]

The rate at which plants absorb moisture from soil depends on (1) the capacity of the soil to provide water to the root systems and (2) the degree to which atmospheric conditions favor transpiration. The capacity of the soil to deliver water to the root systems is limited by the slow rate at which soil water moves at low moisture contents.[2] Hence, plants will reach the wilting point much more quickly when transpiration rates are high because the soil cannot supply moisture at a sufficient rate. Actually, soil moisture may be depleted to a greater degree when transpiration rates are low.

Movement of water in the plant. The penetration of watery solutions from the outer cell wall to the cell sap within and to the inner, or endodermal, cells, is accomplished by osmosis. Osmosis and imbibition always act jointly, with a tendency for equalization, in the absorption of

[1] Alway, F. J., Studies of the Relation of the Non-available Water of the Soil to the Hygroscopic Coefficients, *Nebraska State Research Bull.* 3, pp. 5-122, 1913.

[2] Veihmeyer, F. J., Evaporation from Soils and Transpiration, *Trans. Am. Geophys. Union,* Vol. 19, pp. 612-615, 1938.

water by the root system and its progress through it. When imbibitional forces exceed osmotic forces, water moves into imbibing matter, such as protoplasm or cell wall; and it moves from imbibing matter into cell sap whenever osmotic forces become greater.

The forces effecting the movement of water or sap through the stem from the roots to the leaves of plants are not thoroughly understood. Of the many theories advanced, only the cohesion theory seems adequate to explain the process within a tall tree. A column of water in a thin capillary tube can transmit a considerable tension because of cohesion or the attraction of water particles for one another. The tensile strength of a small-diameter column of water may exceed 300 atm.[1]

These conditions are met in plants by the tubes, or *lumina*, within the stem. Tension, induced by transpiration from cell walls exposed to intercellular air spaces in the leaves, is transmitted through the stem to endodermal cells of the root, where it creates a water deficit. With abundant water supply and low transpiration rates, absorption and movement of water in the root system can be explained by imbibition and osmosis. These processes, however, act too slowly to replace water transpired at high rates. Under such conditions, the imbibitional and osmotic forces are exceeded by those pulling from the region above the endodermal cells, the root cells become passive, and their chief function is to prevent the absorption of air.

Leaves. Leaves are composed largely of thin-walled cells (*mesophyll*) and thousands of fine, open-ended veins. An external cell layer, the *epidermis*, is relatively impervious to moisture and gases but contains numerous pores called *stomata*. Many air spaces are present in the loosely-constructed mesophyll, and these spaces unite with large air spaces beneath the stomata. Thus, the area of moist cell surfaces is many times greater than the external leaf surface. Water moistening the mesophyll cell walls exposed to these intercellular cavities vaporizes and escapes from the leaf through the stomata.

Guttation. Guttation is a process for disposing of water absorbed by the roots in excess of transpiration. It occurs when conditions are unfavorable for transpiration and is accomplished through specialized organs called *hydathodes*. Water of guttation usually collects at the edges and tips of leaves, but under unusual conditions the entire leaf may be covered. Guttation is caused by pressure in the plant system, called *root pressure* because of its supposed source in root cells. Considerable water may be lost by guttation and sometimes may be felt as a fine mist under such trees as willow and cottonwood. Guttation usually occurs at night but may occur in the daytime if proper conditions prevail. Warm, humid weather and cool nights preceded by warm days are both favorable.

[1] Miller, E. C., "Plant Physiology," 2d ed., p. 867, McGraw-Hill, New York, 1938.

FACTORS AFFECTING TRANSPIRATION

Physiologic factors. The principal physiologic factors affecting transpiration are density and behavior of stomata, extent and character of protective coverings, leaf structure, and plant diseases.

The density of stomata is a characteristic of the plant species but is influenced by environmental conditions, such as atmospheric and soil moisture and light intensity. It may vary from 50,000 to about 800,000 stomata per square inch and is about three times as great on the lower side of the leaf as on the upper. Stomata are usually smallest where their density is greatest.

Stomata have the ability to open or close. In all plants, they open with light and close with darkness or when the moisture supply to the leaf is deficient. The temperature of the air affects their speed of opening and closing, and high humidity permits them to open wider and to remain open longer. Stomata exercise only a limited control on the transpiration rate. They close after wilting begins and not in anticipation of it. When stomata are fully opened, the transpiration rate is determined by the same factors that control evaporation alone; and it is not until they are almost closed that stomatal regulation exerts a controlling influence. It is not known to what degree transpiration is affected by the complete closure of the openings, but cuticular transpiration has been estimated to account for about 10 per cent of the total water loss from leaves and stem.

Environmental factors. Since transpiration is essentially the evaporation of water from leaf cells, its rate is materially influenced by the same factors as those which control evaporation from a water surface. Thus, high temperature, low humidity, and strong winds all tend to increase transpiration unless wilting takes place. Solar radiation, in addition to providing a source of heat energy for evaporation, acts to make the leaf more permeable to water movement and also influences the opening of the stomata.

Since soil moisture is the source of water for transpiration, the rate of transpiration is limited to the rate at which soil moisture is supplied to the root system (Chap. 12). It has been shown that the transpiration rate is at a maximum for a certain soil-water content and that increasing moisture above this amount does not increase transpiration. Any decrease in moisture content below this amount, however, lowers the transpiration rate until the water content has been depleted to the wilting point.

DETERMINATION OF TRANSPIRATION

It is not possible to measure the transpiration loss from a large stand of plants under natural conditions, and hence determinations are limited to studies of small samples under laboratory conditions. The methods in use can be grouped into two classes, (1) measurement of water vapor transpired and (2) measurement of change in weight due to loss of water.

Measurement of water transpired. If a small plant is placed in a closed container, the transpiration can be computed from changes in humidity. Because of the high humidity which develops in the container, this method is not too satisfactory. An alternate method is to draw air through the container and through absorption tubes containing a drying agent and to compute the transpiration from the gain in weight of the tubes corrected for atmospheric moisture. The use of these methods is limited to short-period tests on small plants or portions of plants.

Measurement of change in weight due to loss of water. The simplest method in this class consists in cutting the plants and determining the rate at which they lose weight prior to wilting. The assumption inherent in the method, that there is no change in transpiration rate after cutting, is questionable, and the method is not in general use.

Most practicable determinations of transpiration are made with instruments called potometers and phytometers. A *potometer* is a small vessel containing water and sealed so that the only escape of moisture is by transpiration from a leaf, twig, or small plant with its cut end inserted in the water. A *phytometer* is a larger vessel filled with soil in which one or more plants are rooted. Since the only escape of moisture from either device is by transpiration, the loss in weight of plant and container is a measure of the transpiration by the specimen being tested. The potometer is limited to small specimens to be observed over short periods of time, but tests show that the results are applicable to normal plants rooted in soil. The phytometer, on the other hand, is limited only by the practicable size and weight of container for handling and weighing. Aeration and additional water must be provided for long tests, but phytometers permit studies of transpiration loss through the entire life cycle of plants. Their use is limited to relatively shallow-rooted plants; and care must be taken that the soil in the container simulates natural conditions, that plant density is comparable with that found under usual growing conditions, and that general exposure with regard to wind, light, humidity, etc., is close to that encountered in the field.

Interpretation of transpiration data. Data on transpiration are expressed in a number of different ways. Agricultural research workers have defined the *transpiration ratio*, or *water-use ratio*, of a plant as the ratio of the weight of water transpired by the plant during its growing season to the weight of dry matter produced (exclusive of roots). Although the term *water requirement* is sometimes used in the same sense, this usage conflicts with that of irrigation engineers, who use the same term to describe the total quantity of water required to mature a specified crop under field conditions. The data obtained by the use of phytometers or similar methods are most useful as a measure of the relative water use by plants; for phytometers rarely perfectly simulate natural conditions, and furthermore the actual water transpired may vary widely depending on climatic conditions, soil characteristics, and nature of special treatments, such as fertilization. In order to apply experimental data to large areas, it is necessary to estimate the total dry weight of crops produced. Hence, some investigators have expressed the transpiration ratio in terms of harvested dry matter instead of total dry matter. Thus, figures on actual crop production can be used as the basis for transpiration estimates.

In order to apply experimental data to trees, bushes, and other vegetation where crop-yield data are not available, the transpiration is sometimes expressed in terms of unit leaf area. This requires an estimate of the total leaf area of a forest stand if total transpiration is to be determined. Such estimates may be extremely unreliable. An alternate method is to determine the dry weight of leaves per unit area of forest by actually stripping and weighing the leaves and applying a transpiration ratio determined experimentally.

TABLE 8-1. Mean Transpiration Ratios of Crops

Plant Species	Ratio Based on Dry Matter
Grain sorghum	304
Corn	349
Sugar beets	443
Barley	518
Buckwheat	540
Common wheat	557
Cotton	568
Potatoes	575
Oats	583
Rye	634
Rice	682
Legumes	750
Flax	783

TABLE 8-2. Mean Transpiration Ratios of Trees

Tree	Ratio Based on Dry Matter
Birch	375
Ash	244
Alder	227
Oak	220
Larch	220
Plains pine	213
Beech	209
Mountain pine	208
Spruce	193
Fir	145

Most transpiration investigations in this country have been concerned with field crops. Data showing transpiration ratios for selected crops[1] are given in Table 8-1. Similar data[2] for selected forest trees are given in Table 8-2.

CONSUMPTIVE USE AND TOTAL EVAPORATION

The hydrologist studying the hydrologic balance for a given area or basin is less concerned with the magnitudes of the individual elements such as transpiration and soil evaporation than with their total. *Total evaporation*, or *evapo-transpiration*, is considered to include all water losses from a given area by transpiration and by evaporation from water surfaces, soil, snow, ice, and vegetation. The term *consumptive use*[3] has been widely used by irrigation engineers to describe the total amount of water taken up by vegetation for transpiration or building of plant tissue plus the evaporation of soil moisture, snow, or intercepted precipitation. The *duty of water*, as used in irrigation work, describes the total volume of water required to mature a crop, including, in addition to consumptive use, the water lost by evaporation from canals and ditches and the water eventually returned to the streams by percolation or surface runoff. All terms are expressed in units of depth (feet or inches) for a specified period, usually a growing season or water year.

Measurement of consumptive use. The measurement or computation of consumptive use may be approached in three ways, (1) by the use of tanks or lysimeters, (2) by the use of field plots, and (3) by studies of groundwater fluctuations.

Tanks and lysimeters. Tanks are watertight containers set into the ground with their rims approximately flush with the surface. They vary in size from a 50-gal oil drum to over 30 ft square and 10 ft deep. The larger tanks are to be preferred because they permit more nearly natural root development. In addition, soil within the tank should simulate field conditions as closely as possible, and plant density and environment should be representative. Consumptive use is determined by measuring the quantity of water required to maintain constant moisture conditions within the tank. The moisture conditions to be maintained depend on the character of the vegetation being studied. For marsh plants, such as tules, a free-water surface is maintained. For plants which obtain their

[1] Shantz, H. L., and L. N. Piemeisel, The Water Requirement of Plants at Akron, Colo., *J. Agr. Research*, Vol. 34, pp. 1093-1190, 1927.

[2] Raber, O., Water Utilization by Trees with Special Reference to the Economic Forest Species of the North Temperate Zone, *U.S. Dept. Agr. Misc. Pub.* 257, pp. 1-97, 1937.

[3] "The Rio Grande Joint Investigation in the Upper Rio Grande Basin," Vol. 1, National Resources Committee, Washington, D. C., 1938.

moisture from the capillary fringe, the water table is kept at a constant level by an auxiliary supply reservoir.[1]

Tank measurements are considered reasonably reliable, provided that the tanks are properly designed and care is taken to ensure representative exposure. Tank data have been collected under a variety of conditions; consequently, the experimental procedures must be investigated before the data are applied to field problems.

Lysimeters are essentially the same as tanks, with the exception that they have pervious bottoms. Consumptive use is equal to the difference between the amount of water applied at the surface and that draining through the pervious bottom, adjusted for changes in moisture content. Although lysimeters probably provide more nearly natural growing conditions, surface tension at the bottom of the soil column tends to form a capillary fringe which may not occur at the same depth in natural soils.

Field plots. Consumptive use may also be determined from selected test plots under actual field conditions. Water input to the plot is determined from measurements of precipitation and irrigation water, while water losses include surface runoff and deep percolation in addition to consumptive use. Since deep percolation cannot be measured, irrigation must be applied in small quantities to minimize this factor. Furthermore, the water table must be at such a depth that the plants cannot obtain water from the capillary fringe. Consumptive use can be computed as the difference between total input and surface runoff, adjusted for changes in soil moisture. Systematic measurements of soil moisture must be taken for some distance below the root zone.

This method has the advantage that the determinations are made under natural conditions, and it is therefore considered to be more reliable than the use of tanks and lysimeters. However, the assumption that there is no deep percolation introduces an error which may be considerable under some conditions.

Water-table fluctuations. Where vegetation obtains its moisture from the capillary fringe or zone of saturation, the height of the water table is influenced by the amount of water absorbed by the plants and its fluctuations can be used as a basis for computing consumptive use. On the basis of studies of the diurnal fluctuations of shallow water tables, White[2] developed the formula

$$U_c = Y_s(24a + b) \tag{8-10}$$

where U_c is the consumptive use in inches per day, Y_s is the specific yield of the soil (Chap. 14), a is the rate of rise of the water table in inches per

[1] Parshall, R. L., Laboratory Measurements of Evapo-transpiration Losses, *J. Forestry*, Vol. 35, p. 1033, 1937.

[2] White, W. N., Method of Estimating Ground-water Supplies Based on Discharge by Plants and Evaporation from Soil, *U.S. Geol. Survey Water Supply Paper* 659-A, 1932.

hour from midnight to 4 A.M., and b is the net change in water-table elevation during the day in inches. Values of a and b can be determined from water-stage recorder charts for wells in the area of interest. The method is applicable only in areas where the water table is near the surface.

Application of experimental data on consumptive use. To simplify the interpretation of experimental consumptive-use data, each test is generally limited to a single plant species. The actual volume of water required for consumptive use by a specified area with mixed cover is the sum of the products of consumptive use and area for each type of vegetation. The probable duty of water can be determined by adding estimated deep percolation and surface runoff to the consumptive use.

Consumptive use is highly dependent upon environmental factors such as weather, soil moisture, and groundwater. To apply experimental data to regions with environment different from that under which the tests were conducted, allowances must be made for the effects of the various factors. Probably the two most important factors are available moisture and available heat. While it is known that, within limits, consumptive use increases as additional water is made available to the plants, little has been done to determine the quantitative nature of this relation. Several methods have been proposed to account for the effect of variations in heat supply. Hedke[1] proposed the use of the formula

$$U_c = kH \tag{8-11}$$

where H is the available heat expressed in degree days and k is an empirical coefficient. The base temperature for computing degree days depends upon the minimum growing temperature for the particular type of vegetation under consideration (Table 8-3). Considerable judgment is required in the selection of k, since only limited data are now available. A value of about 0.0004 was determined by Hedke for the Cache la Poudre Valley in Colorado and by the Bureau of Agricultural Engineering for the Mesilla Valley in New Mexico.

TABLE 8-3. Minimum Growing Temperatures for Various Crops (After the Bureau of Agricultural Engineering)

Crop	Temperature, °F
Alfalfa	33
Cotton	48
Forage	44
Fruits	46
Grains	44
Pasture	38
Vegetables	40

[1] Harding, S. T., and others, Consumptive Use of Water in Irrigation, progress report of the Duty of Water Committee of the Irrigation Division, *Trans. ASCE*, Vol. 94, pp. 1349-1399, 1930.

A more recent study by Lowry and Johnson[1] based on data from 20 areas distributed throughout the United States indicated that the consumptive use can be closely approximated by the equation

$$U_c = 0.00015H + 0.9 \tag{8-12}$$

in which H is the accumulated degree days during the growing season computed from the maximum temperature above 32°F. The data developed by Lowry and Johnson are shown in Fig. 8-7. The plotted points represent average values for a period of years. A much wider scatter results when individual years are plotted instead of means.

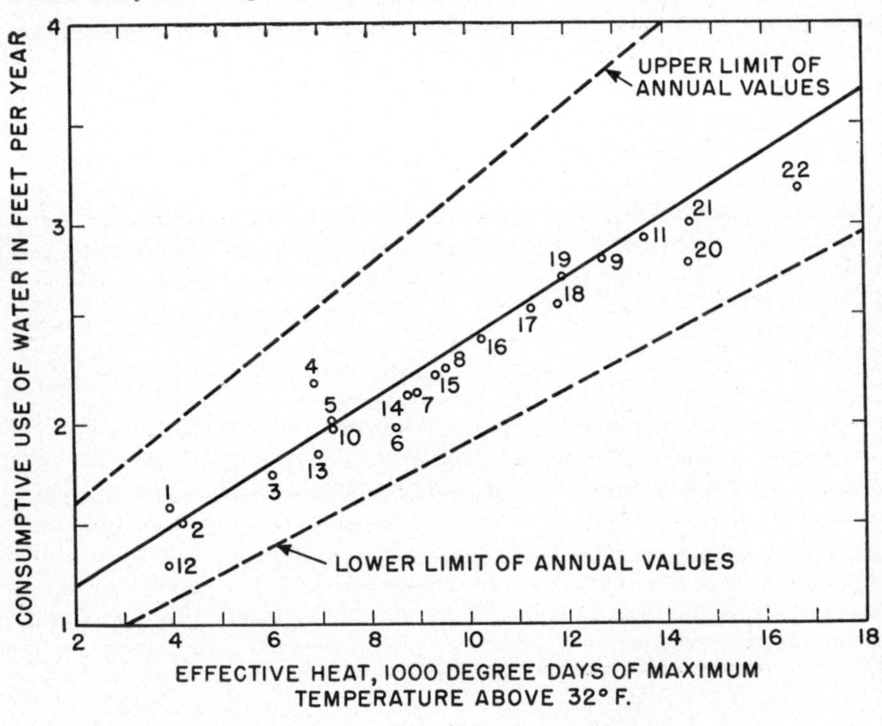

List of areas

1	New Fork, Wyo.	12	Wagon Wheel Gap, Col.
2	Michigan R., Col.	13	Black R., Wisc.
3	S.W. San Luis Valley, Col.	14	Mad R., Ohio
4	West Tule Lake, Calif.	15	Skunk R., Iowa
5	Garland Div., Shoshone Proj., Wyo.	16	Sangamon R., Ill.
6	N. Platte R., Wyo.-Nebr.	17	N.Fk., White R., Mo
7	Mason Cr., Ida.	18	Green R., Ky.
8	Uncompahgre R., Col.	19	Tallapoosa R., Ga.
9	Mesilla Valley, N.Mex.-Tex.	20	E.Fk., Trinity R., Tex.
10	Greenfields Div., Sun R. Proj., Mont.	21	Cypress Cr., Tex.
11	Pecos R., N.Mex.	22	San Jacinto R., Tex.

FIG. 8-7. Relation between average annual consumptive use and effective heat. *(After Lowry and Johnson.)*

[1] Lowry, R. L., and A. F. Johnson, Consumptive Use of Water for Agriculture, *Trans. ASCE,* Vol. 107, p. 1252, 1942.

Determination of total evaporation. As previously defined, total evaporation includes all water losses from a given area by transpiration and by evaporation from water surfaces, soil, snow, ice, and vegetation. While water used in building plant tissue is excluded by this definition, it is usually included in total evaporation because it is difficult to evaluate. Thus, from a practical viewpoint, total evaporation is generally considered as the difference between the inflow and outflow of liquid water to and from the basin, adjusted for changes in storage. In the general case, the items of inflow are precipitation, surface flow, and groundwater; the items of outflow are surface flow and groundwater; and the storage items are groundwater, soil moisture, and channel storage. In a particular case, one or more of the items may be negligible. Total evaporation is frequently assumed to equal the difference between precipitation and streamflow.[1] This assumption results in reasonable long-term averages but may lead to serious errors when applied to small basins for short periods of time.

TIME VARIATIONS IN EVAPORATION PHENOMENA

The evaporative power, as discussed previously, is closely related to various meteorological elements, notably temperature, wind, and humidity. The first two factors show marked diurnal and seasonal fluctuations, which are reflected in the variations of evaporation.

Diurnal variations. Generally speaking, there is little diurnal variation in the vapor pressure of the air. Exceptions to this arise from the occurrence of precipitation, land or sea breezes, or changes of air mass. Consequently, no regular diurnal variation in evaporation can be expected because of changes in the vapor pressure of the air, except where land and sea breezes prevail. There is usually a marked diurnal variation in air temperature and, in so far as this affects the temperature of the evaporating surface, a corresponding diurnal fluctuation in evaporation results. The water temperature in Class A land pans has been observed to agree very closely with the air temperature. Consequently, the maximum rate of evaporation from such pans may be expected to occur in midafternoon when the vapor-pressure difference is greatest. The temperature range in soil may exceed that in air, while the variation in buried or floating pans or in large reservoirs may be somewhat less because of the heat-storage effect. The maximum wind speed is ordinarily observed in the afternoon, and its effect, therefore, further emphasizes the temperature influence. Since transpiration is essentially evaporation from plants, it naturally has a diurnal fluctuation corresponding to that of evaporation. It has been estimated that 75 to 90 per cent of the daily evaporation occurs between

[1] Williams, G. R., and others, Natural Water Loss in Selected Drainage Basins, *U.S. Geol. Survey Water Supply Paper* 846, 1940.

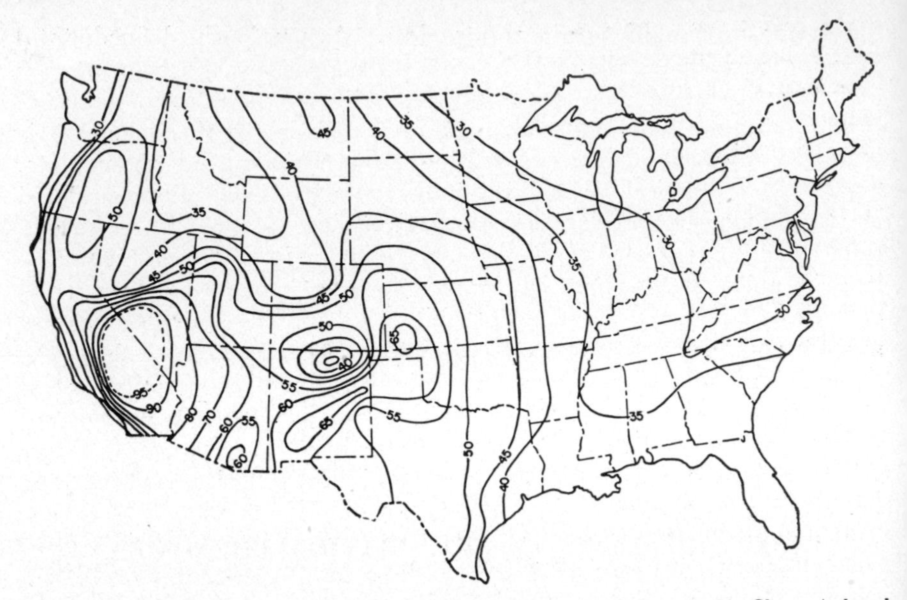

FIG. 8–8. Normal May to October evaporation in inches from Class A land pans. *(After Horton.)*

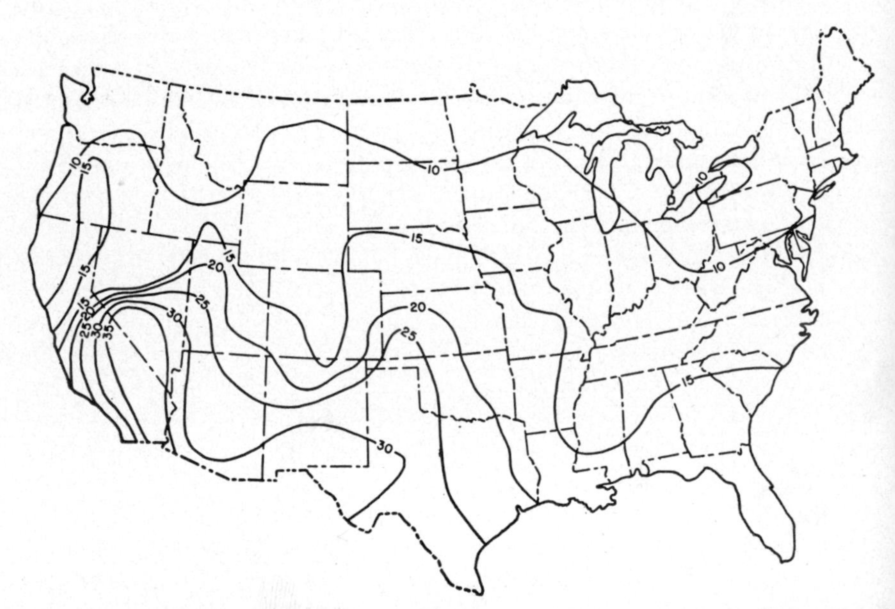

FIG. 8–9. Normal November to April evaporation in inches from Class A land pans. *(After Horton.)*

6 A.M. and 6 P.M.[1] and that about 95 per cent of the daily transpiration occurs during the daylight hours.[2]

Seasonal variations. Seasonal fluctuations are caused by the same meteorological factors responsible for diurnal fluctuations. In addition, however, there may be marked seasonal fluctuations of humidity. In general, evaporative power is much greater during summer than in winter (Figs. 8-8 and 8-9). While the annual variations of temperature and dewpoint are essentially in phase, their effects on evaporation are opposite. However, the annual range in temperature exceeds that of dewpoint so that maximum vapor-pressure differences ($e_w - e_a$) occur during summer months. Generally speaking, wind speeds are greatest during winter and spring months and least during late summer (Chap. 5). Consequently, the effect of wind tends to dampen and shift the annual march of evaporation which would be expected from temperature and humidity. The nature of the evaporating surface probably has a more important effect on seasonal variations than on diurnal fluctuations. While evaporative power is at a maximum during summer months, there are many portions of the country where little or no evaporation occurs from the soil during this period because of the low evaporation opportunity. The heat-storage effect in deep reservoirs tends to minimize seasonal variations in evaporation resulting from fluctuations in the meteorological factors. The annual march of transpiration is in phase with that of evaporation, but its amplitude is greater because of the cessation of plant activity when the temperature falls below the minimum growing temperature.

[1] Landsberg, H., "Physical Climatology," p. 136, Pennsylvania State College, State College, Pa., 1941.

[2] Lee, C. H., Transpiration and Total Evaporation, Chap. VIII, p. 280, O. E. Meinzer (ed.), in "Hydrology," McGraw-Hill, New York, 1942.

9

STREAMFLOW

The discussion of the hydrologic cycle (Chap. 1) pointed out that moisture evaporated from oceans and other water surfaces is carried over the land and deposited as precipitation. A considerable portion of this water is returned as *streamflow*, the movement of water under the force of gravity through well-defined, semipermanent surface channels. The measurement, analysis, and interpretation of streamflow data are therefore important phases of hydrology. Streamflow is the only portion of the hydrologic cycle in which moisture is so confined as to make possible reasonably accurate measurements of the volumes involved. All other measurements in the hydrologic cycle are, at best, only inadequate samples of the whole. While the myriad of channels, large and small, crossing the earth's surface make it virtually impossible to measure the total volume of water involved in streamflow on a world-wide basis, it is feasible within a specific basin to make a reasonably complete inventory. The U.S. Geological Survey operates approximately 5000 gaging stations on the important streams in the United States.

RIVER STAGE

Measurement of flow in natural streams cannot ordinarily be accomplished by the use of recording flowmeters such as are used in the measurement of flow in pipes. It is quite simple, however, to obtain a record of *river stage*, the height of the water surface above some arbitrary datum. If a relation between stage and rate of discharge can be developed, the flow volume can be determined from a known stage sequence. This two-step procedure is the method almost universally adopted for the measurement of streamflow. River stages are, in themselves, useful hydrologic data and can be used for the solution of many problems without knowledge of the actual flows involved.

Gage datum. Stage has been defined as the height of the water surface at a given point along the river above any arbitrary datum, or *gage zero*.

Stage is customarily expressed in feet and hundredths, although some early gages were graduated in feet and inches. In countries using the metric system, stages are usually recorded in meters. Many gages, particularly those on reservoirs and on the lower reaches of coastal streams, are referred to a zero at mean sea level. However, the greater number of gages are set at a zero selected at or slightly below the lowest low-water elevation known or anticipated at the time the gage was established. At some points scouring has lowered the channel bottom far below the gage zero, and negative stage readings result. The actual elevation of the gage zero should always be determined with reference to suitable permanent benchmarks in the vicinity so that it can be reestablished if damaged by floods and to permit the determination of relative water-surface elevations along the stream. In the absence of a convenient benchmark, a suitable reference mark should be established.

Staff gages. The simplest form of river gage is a vertical staff graduated in suitable units and placed so that some portion of it will be in the water at all stages. It may consist of a board with painted markings or of enameled plates fastened to a board. Occasionally, graduations are painted on a bridge, pier, or other suitably located structure. On streams with considerable sediment load, raised numerals and graduations or a series of saw-tooth notches on one edge of the staff may be necessary for legibility after a coat of silt has covered painted markings.

Staff gages must be attached to some solid structure or be otherwise adequately supported so that there will be no change in datum as a result of settlement. Gages should be shielded as much as possible from floating debris or ice. It is not always practicable to place a long staff gage in such a position that it is accessible throughout the entire range of stage. In this case, a *sectional staff gage* or an *inclined gage* may be used. Sectional staff gages consist of a series of overlapping sections placed in positions up the bank such that each section is easily read throughout the range of stage it covers. The inclined staff consists of a sloping gage graduated so that stages can be read directly.

Wire-weight gages. The *wire-weight gage* (Fig. 9-1) makes use of a thin stainless-steel cable wound on a drum of such diameter that one turn about the drum contains 1 ft of cable. As the weight is lowered, a counter indicates the number of turns of the drum (feet of cable released), while graduations on the circumference of the drum indicate, with reference to a fixed mark, the hundredths of a foot. Numerous other versions of the suspended-weight gage have been devised, including gages using a graduated steel tape instead of wire or chain and gages equipped with indicators to show when the weight is at the water surface. All such gages are subject to damage from floating debris and, without automatic indication, are difficult to place on the water surface at night.

Automatic recording gages. Manual gages are most economical in first cost but require regular attendance. It is extremely difficult to obtain readings accurate to less than tenths of feet from manual gages under good conditions. Errors of 1 ft or more are not uncommon and are frequently undetectable. Perhaps the most serious disadvantage of the manual gage

FIG. 9–1. Wire-weight gage. *(Leupold and Stevens Instrument Co.)*

is that, without frequent observations, large changes in stage may be inadequately reported. On many small streams a major flood may develop, rise to a peak, and drop back to low stages within 24 hr. Daily readings are insufficient to define such an event. Even on larger streams, where a greater time is involved, the readings may prove inadequate, and it is fortuitous indeed for a flood crest to occur exactly at observation time. Many streams are subject to marked diurnal fluctuations as the result of operations at a power dam or to diurnal variation in rates of snowmelt or transpiration. Here again, one or even two daily readings are inadequate. Because of these facts, automatic water-stage recorders should be used whenever their cost can be justified. Several years are required to build up a good streamflow record, and needs should be anticipated and justified well in advance.

There are many types of float or pressure-actuated water-stage recorders. Most recorders now in use are float actuated. In the continuous water-stage recorder of the type shown in Fig. 9-2, the vertical motion of a float,

FIG. 9–2. Stevens continuous water-level recorder, type A35b. *(Leupold and Stevens Instrument Co.)*

FIG. 9–3. Corrugated-steel gage well and cableway. *(U.S. Geological Survey.)*

as it rises and falls with changes in water level, is transmitted to a pen or pencil and causes this marker to move back and forth across a long chart, which is turned past the scriber by clockwork. In the drum-type recorder, the float motion is transmitted to a drum on which the chart is placed, and the pen or pencil is moved parallel to the axis of the drum by clockwork.

The float and float cable of a recording gage must be protected from drift,

FIG. 9–4. Diagram of typical water-stage recorder installation in reinforced-concrete shelter. *(U.S. Geological Survey.)*

and the instrument itself must be sheltered from the weather. Accordingly, a gage well and shelter house are standard features of an automatic recording station. These may be of many types of construction, but the corrugated-steel-pipe well and shelter (Fig. 9-3) and the concrete well and shelter (Fig. 9-4) are the most common. The well serves to reduce surge and wave action, as well as to protect the float.

The chart of most drum-type recorders is free to revolve as many times as necessary to record the stage. The trace is a continuous line when the chart is on the drum, but when the chart is opened, the trace is broken at

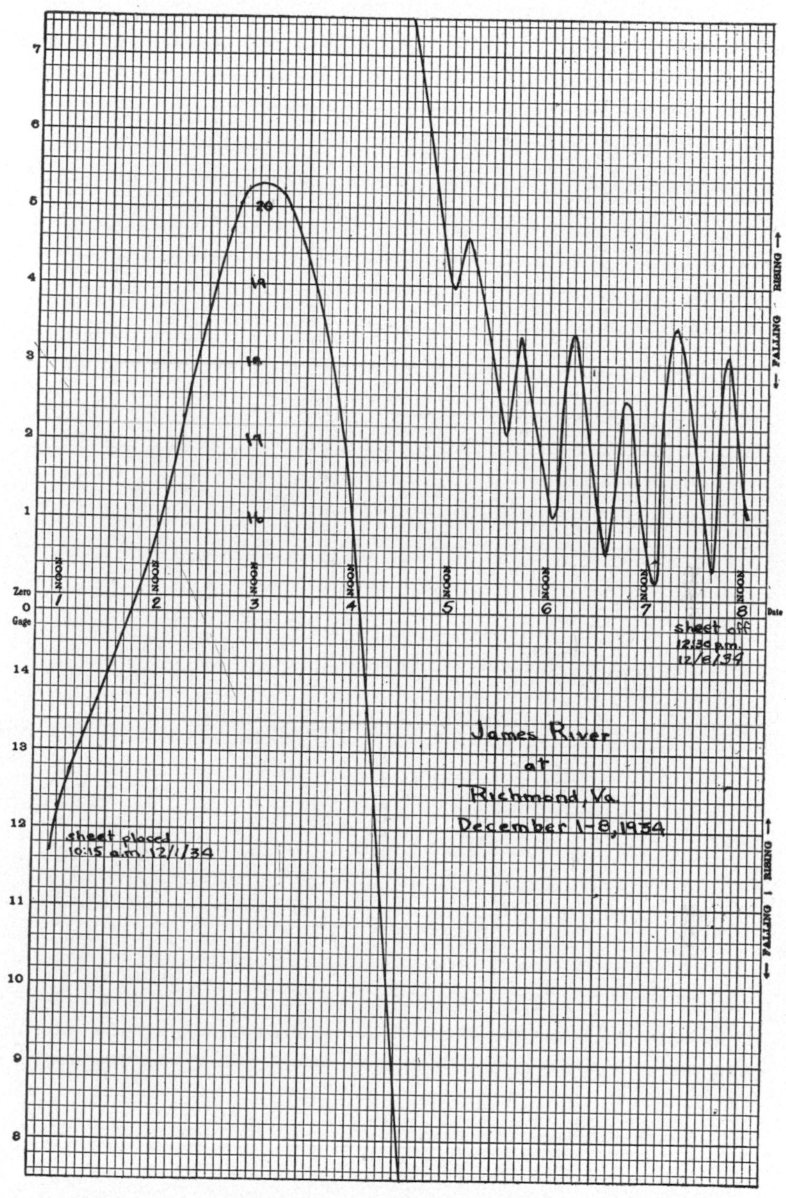

FIG. 9–5. Chart from a drum-type water-stage recorder.

the top of the chart and resumed at the bottom each time the stage passes through the range of the chart (Fig. 9-5). Continuous-strip charts are usually 10 in. wide, and a scale of 1 or 2 in. to the foot is generally adopted. This limits the range of the recorder on a single traverse, and a recorder expected to exceed this limitation must be equipped with a reversal mechanism which causes the pen to reverse its direction (Fig. 9-6).

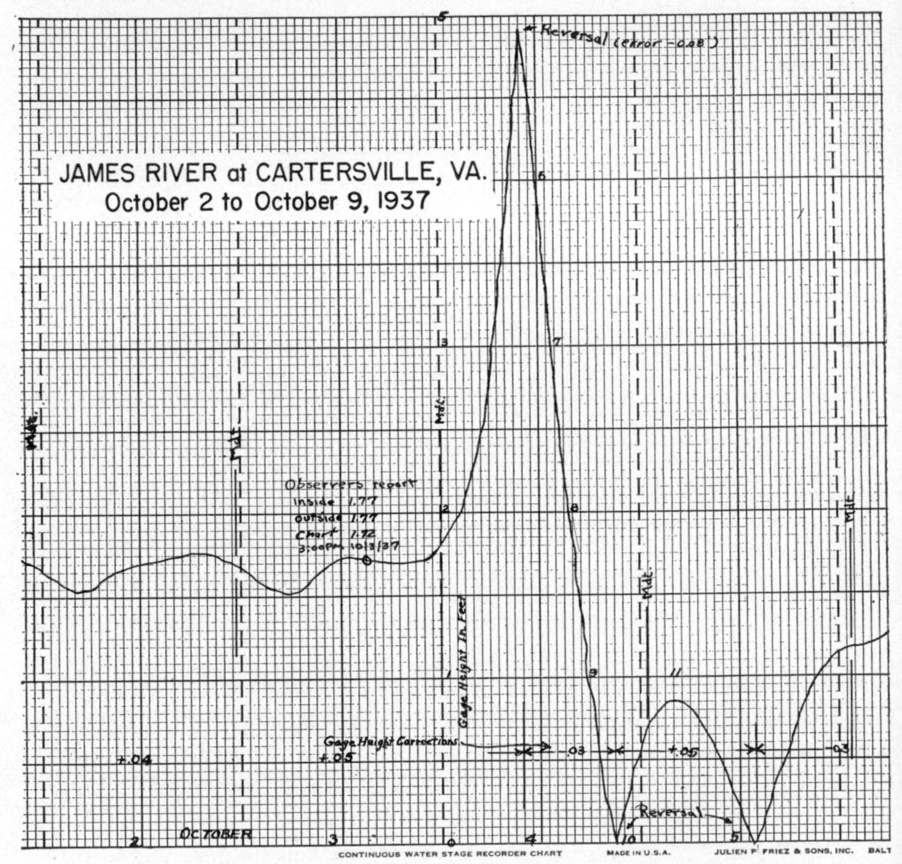

FIG. 9–6. Chart from a continuous-type water-stage recorder.

The selection of equipment and establishment of a recording gage are complex problems and are not discussed in detail in this text. Those readers who are interested in the matter of gage equipment and installation are referred to the several instrument manufacturers, to the U.S. Geological Survey, or to other agencies with experience in the work. Grover and Harrington[1] have prepared an extensive text on the subject of streamflow measurement.

[1] Grover, N. C., and A. W. Harrington, "Stream Flow," 1st ed., Wiley, New York, 1943.

Crest gages. An important defect of nonrecording gages is the frequent failure to obtain crest readings. The observer must be on the alert to secure frequent readings at or near crest or must estimate the crest stage from high-water marks visible at the time of his first observation subsequent to the crest. On large streams where changes in stage are slow, this may prove wholly adequate, but on flashy streams it is far from satisfactory. Numerous types of crest gages which automatically register the highest stage which occurs at the station between observations have been devised. A series of small bottles mounted at intervals of elevation so that the observer may note the highest one containing water,[1] a panel painted with water-soluble paint such as yellow dextrin,[2] float-type gages free to move upward but prevented from dropping by friction catches,[3] and tubes containing a solution of powder[4] to record a high-water line have been proposed. Such gages provide an economical means of obtaining crest-stage records at a large number of points for intensive flood studies or for reporting of crests by unskilled observers. They cannot replace the recording gage where continuous discharge records are necessary.

Floodmarks. A discussion of stage measurement would be incomplete without mention of floodmarks. Data on floods occurring prior to the beginning of systematic records can be secured only from a careful search for floodmarks. Such marks are frequently found as inscriptions, painted marks, or monuments erected by inhabitants after extreme floods. Written accounts of early floods may refer to the height of water on a particular building, bridge, or other landmark, and older inhabitants may be able to indicate the flood height or some reference point from memory. This latter source of information must, of course, be corroborated by independent testimony before it can be given a great deal of weight.[5]

Immediately after a flood, much valuable data can be collected by floodmark surveys. For a short period after each flood, high-water marks may be determined by inspection of grass, brush, debris deposits on trees and fences, sediment deposits, and other evidence. All evidence must be reviewed to make certain that the high-water level defined is actually due to the flow of the main stream. Flow from tributaries and overland flow sometimes leave traces which appear to be high-water marks of the main river. Survey parties dispatched immediately after a flood should set

[1] Guy, L. T., Unique Method of Gaging High Water, *Civil Eng.*, Vol. 12, p. 397, 1942.

[2] Doran, F. J., High Water Gaging, *Civil Eng.*, Vol. 12, pp. 103-104, 1942.

[3] Collet, M. H., Crest-stage Meter for Measuring Static Heads, *Civil Eng.*, Vol. 12, p. 396, 1942.

Stevens, J. C., Device for Measuring Static Heads, *Civil Eng.*, Vol. 12, p. 461, 1942.

[4] Ferguson, G. E., Gage to Measure Crest Stages of Streams, *Civil Eng.*, Vol. 12, pp. 570-571, 1942.

[5] Larson, G. E., Research for Flood Control Data, *Civil Eng.*, Vol. 12, p. 131, 1942.

semipermanent marks by paint on bridges or other structures and by stakes or other reference points which can be mapped and tied in to a level circuit at a later date.

DISCHARGE

Any quantitative analysis of hydrologic problems requires the determination of the quantity of water flowing in a stream. In itself, stage provides nothing more than a qualitative index to streamflow. It is possible, however, to establish a relation between stage and discharge on most streams, which permits the computation of discharge if stages are known.

Theory. If the cross-sectional area and mean velocity of a stream of flowing water are known, the discharge can be computed from the formula $q = a_c v$. A cross section of a stream may be plotted from data collected by sounding or leveling and a relation between stage and area established. For streams with permanent rock channels the stage-area curve is permanent for all practical purposes, but in channels subject to scour or sedimentation the area must be determined at the time of each measurement.

The determination of mean velocity is a more difficult task since velocity is not uniform throughout a channel and a single velocity reading is not practicable for accurate work. Instead, the channel must be subdivided, and the velocity measured in each subarea. The measurement of velocity is accomplished with a *current meter,* of which the Price meter (Fig. 9-7) is now the most common type. Six conical cups mounted around a vertical axis rotate under the action of the moving water. Every revolution (or every fifth revolution, if desired) causes a click in a set of headphones. The operator merely counts the number of clicks in a fixed time or measures the time required for a specified number of clicks. The velocity can be computed from a rating curve for the meter. Tail vanes keep the meter pointing into the current, and a heavy weight helps to keep it vertically under the point of measurement.

The modern Price meter is the result of many years of development and improvement by the U.S. Geological Survey. It will measure velocities from 0.1 to 20 fps. It is rugged, easily dismantled for cleaning, does not lose its rating readily under rough treatment, and can be used in turbid water without damage from silt entering the bearings. Vertical motion, which may occur when measurements are made from a boat or in turbulent flow, does affect its accuracy. Screw-type meters, which employ a propeller mounted on a horizontal axis to indicate the velocity, are not subject to errors from vertical motions, but such meters cannot be protected from silt and are therefore not satisfactory for turbid water. They are also unsatisfactory for measurement of low velocities.

Current meters can be mounted on a staff for wading measurements or can be supported by a cable for measurements in deep water. When cable is used, measurements can be made from a bridge, cableway, or boat. Measurement from a bridge avoids the initial cost of a cableway and is faster than from boats. Frequently, however, bridges are not situated at sections suitable for velocity measurements. Furthermore, bridge piers may cause crosscurrents, which make for an undesirable measuring section. For boat measurements, a cable must be placed across the stream to hold the boat in position, or successive positions of the boat must be determined by ranges on landmarks on the shore. A cable for boat measurements

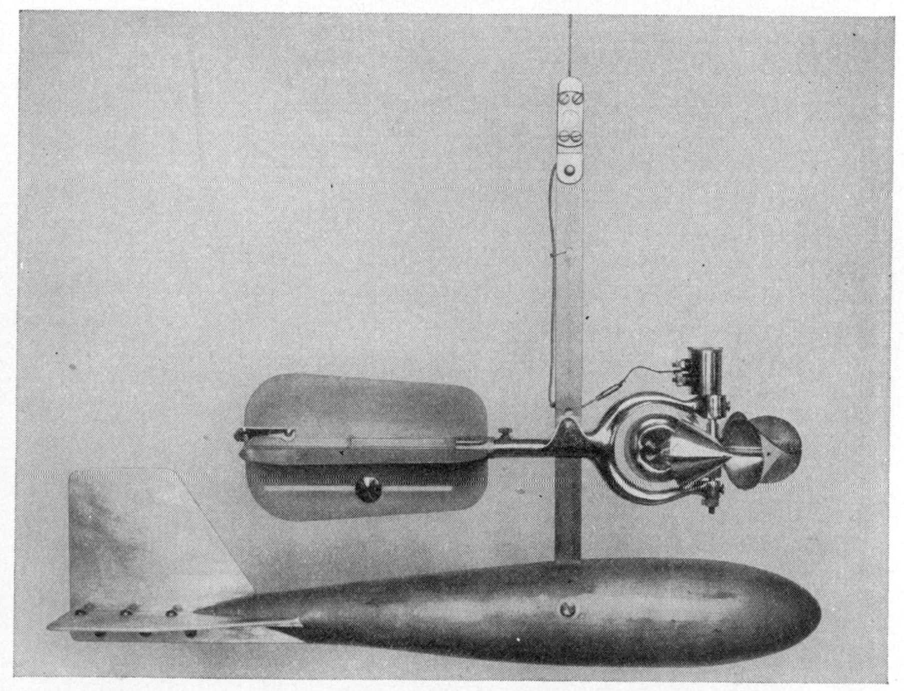

FIG. 9–7. Price current meter and 30-lb C-type sounding weight. *(U.S. Geological Survey.)*

can rarely be left in place permanently since it would interfere with navigation, and even a temporary cable may lead to difficulties in this regard. Generally speaking, a permanent cableway (Fig. 9-3) is found to be most satisfactory.

Considerably more thought must be given to the selection of a site for discharge measurements than is necessary where stage data alone are to be collected. Ideal conditions for a measuring section require a fairly long, straight stretch of channel. The flow should be confined to a single channel with little overbank discharge at high stages, and the measuring section should be accessible at all stages. The measuring section may be located at any suitable site either upstream or downstream from the point at which the stage record is obtained. However, the water-stage recorder must be located above a control if a stable stage-discharge relation is to be obtained. The ideal control is a rock ledge at the head of a reach of rapids or a falls with a pool above it. On many streams, particularly in the Middle West, such controls cannot be found or do not act as controls except at low water. A *channel control* must be accepted in such cases, *i.e.*, a control established by the flow characteristics of the channel. Inasmuch as the channel shape is rarely permanent in sandy streams, the rating will vary considerably from time to time and more frequent discharge measurements are necessary. When the expense is justified, an *artificial control*[1] consisting of a low dam or weir may be built across the stream. A V notch is frequently provided to increase the accuracy of low-flow measurements.

The discharge measurement. In theory, the measurement of discharge appears to be quite simple, but in actual practice there are numerous difficulties which must be overcome. In the interests of an adequate mean discharge, as many individual point measurements should be made in the section as is practicable. However, since the objective is the establishment of a relation between stage and discharge, it is important to complete the measurement in a minimum of time during periods of rapidly changing stage.

Experience has shown that the vertical distribution of velocity in most stream cross sections is approximately parabolic and that an average of velocity determinations at 0.2 and 0.8 of the depth will define the mean velocity in the vertical quite closely. A single observation at 0.6 of the depth below the surface is only slightly less accurate. It is customary to divide the channel into vertical sections and compute the total discharge as the sum of the discharges in the several sections. In general, no less than 20 verticals should be used on the narrowest streams and a larger number on wider streams. The width of the vertical sections may be varied, depending on the nature of the velocity distribution across the channel and the shape of the cross section. No more than 10 per cent of the total discharge should be included in a single vertical section. At new stations, it is usually advisable to make several intensive velocity surveys of the stream to determine the horizontal velocity distribution which, together with the section profile, determines the proper spacing of the verticals. These data will also indicate whether the 0.2- and 0.8-depth method is adequate for determination of the mean velocity in the vertical. Such surveys should include conditions at several different stages.

The first step in the actual measurement is the determination of the depth. This is done by lowering the meter so that the bottom of the

[1] Corbett, D. M., and others, Stream-gaging Procedure, *U.S. Geol. Survey Water Supply Paper* 888, pp. 117-118, 1945.

weight is at the water surface and noting the length of additional line required to lower the weight to the channel bottom. Special reels which indicate the length of line paid out are available for this purpose, or the meter cable may be fitted with foot markers. Despite the use of a heavy weight, it is rarely possible to get true vertical depth by sounding in swift water because the weight and meter are carried downstream by the current. The meter line is straight from the reel to the water surface and forms a catenary curve under water (Fig. 9-8). If the angle of the sounding line with the vertical is measured, the corrections to obtain true vertical depth can be determined from Tables 9-1 and 9-2.

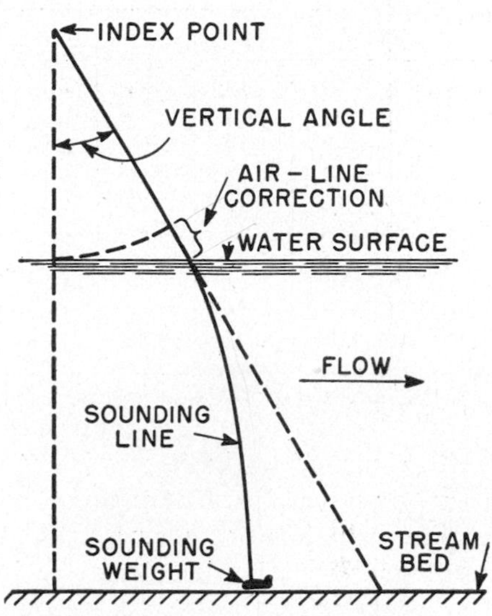

FIG. 9–8. Position of sounding line in swift water.

After the true vertical depth has been determined, the meter is raised until it is at 0.2 of the depth above the bottom. Its position must be computed again in terms of the vertical angle, which may change as the meter and weight are lifted to a region of higher velocity. Since the bottom of the weight has heretofore been the reference for depth, allowance must also be made for the distance from the bottom of the weight to the center line of the meter.

TABLE 9-1. Air-line Correction Table *

(Difference in feet between vertical length and slant length of sounding line above water)

Vertical length, ft	Vertical angle								
	4°	8°	12°	16°	20°	24°	28°	32°	36°
10	0.02	0.10	0.22	0.40	0.64	0.95	1.33	1.79	2.36
20	0.05	0.20	0.45	0.81	1.28	1.89	2.65	3.58	4.72
30	0.07	0.29	0.67	1.21	1.93	2.84	3.98	5.38	7.08
40	0.10	0.39	0.89	1.61	2.57	3.79	5.30	7.17	9.44
50	0.12	0.49	1.12	2.02	3.21	4.73	6.63	8.96	11.80
60	0.15	0.59	1.34	2.42	3.85	5.68	7.95	10.75	14.16
70	0.17	0.69	1.56	2.82	4.49	6.62	9.28	12.54	16.52
80	0.20	0.79	1.79	3.22	5.13	7.57	10.61	14.33	18.89
90	0.22	0.88	2.01	3.63	5.78	8.52	11.93	16.13	21.25
100	0.24	0.98	2.23	4.03	6.42	9.46	13.26	17.92	23.61

*Adapted from *U.S. Geol. Survey Water Supply Paper* 888, 1945, Table 1, pp. 46-47.

TABLE 9-2. Wet-line Correction Table *

(Difference in feet between wet-line length and vertical depth)

Wet-line length, ft	Vertical angle								
	4°	8°	12°	16°	20°	24°	28°	32°	36°
10	0.01	0.03	0.07	0.13	0.20	0.30	0.41	0.54	0.70
20	0.01	0.06	0.14	0.26	0.41	0.59	0.82	1.09	1.40
30	0.02	0.10	0.22	0.38	0.61	0.89	1.22	1.63	2.09
40	0.02	0.13	0.29	0.51	0.82	1.18	1.63	2.18	2.79
50	0.03	0.16	0.36	0.64	1.02	1.48	2.04	2.72	3.49
60	0.04	0.19	0.43	0.77	1.22	1.78	2.45	3.26	4.19
70	0.04	0.22	0.50	0.90	1.43	2.07	2.86	3.81	4.89
80	0.05	0.25	0.58	1.02	1.63	2.37	3.26	4.35	5.58
90	0.05	0.29	0.65	1.15	1.84	2.66	3.67	4.90	6.28
100	0.06	0.32	0.72	1.28	2.04	2.96	4.08	5.44	6.98

*Adapted from *U.S. Geol. Survey Water Supply Paper* 888, 1945, Table 2, pp. 50-51.

If the current in the stream is not normal to the measuring section, the meter will be carried off at an angle. The true vertical angle in the measuring line will thus be somewhat greater than the actual measured angle. Corrections for this effect are given in Table 9-3.

TABLE 9-3. Horizontal-angle Correction *

(Degrees to be added to observed vertical angle to get true vertical angle)

Measured vertical angle	Horizontal angle					
	8°	12°	16°	20°	24°	28°
8°	0.1	0.2	0.3	0.5	0.8	1.0
16°	0.1	0.4	0.6	1.0	1.4	2.0
24°	0.2	0.5	0.8	1.4	2.0	2.8
32°	0.2	0.6	1.0	1.6	2.4	3.3
40°	0.2	0.6	1.1	1.8	2.6	3.5

*Adapted from *U.S. Geol. Survey Water Supply Paper* 888, 1945, Table 4, p. 59.

When the meter has been placed in the proper position, it is allowed to run for a few seconds to become adjusted to the current and then the number of revolutions of the rotor in a period of about 1 min is observed. A stop watch is started on a click of the meter (count zero) and stopped at a signal approximately 1 min later. For velocities under 1 fps, a longer time interval is frequently required. The number of revolutions observed, together with distance from the bank, depth of meter, and depth of water, are recorded (Fig. 9-9). The velocity at the point can then be computed from the meter rating. If the current is not normal to the section, a meter

9-275
September 1943

UNITED STATES
DEPARTMENT OF THE INTERIOR
GEOLOGICAL SURVEY
WATER RESOURCES BRANCH

Date 5-4, 1945 DISCHARGE MEASUREMENT NOTES

Antietam River at Sharpsburg

Angle coefficient	Dist. from initial point	Depth	Observation depth	Revolutions	Time in seconds	Velocity: At point	Velocity: Mean in vertical	Velocity: Mean in section	Area	Mean depth	Width	Discharge
	52	3.4	.2	50	44	2.50	2.28					
			.8	40	43	2.05		2.21	6.8	3.4	2	15.0
	50	3.4	.2	50	45	2.44	2.14					
			.8	40	48	1.84		2.20	6.7	3.35	2	14.7
	48	3.3	.2	50	43	2.55	2.26					
			.8	40	45	1.96		2.16	9.7	3.25	3	21.0
	45	3.2	.2	50	46	2.39	2.06					
⊙			.8	40	51	1.73		1.90	9.6	3.2	3	18.2
	42	3.2	.2	40	43	2.05	1.74					
			.8	30	46	1.44		1.65	9.5	3.15	3	15.7
	39	3.1	.2	40	48	1.84	1.56					
			.8	25	43	1.29		1.46	8.9	2.95	3	13.0
	36	2.8	.2	30	42	1.58	1.36					
			.8	20	39	1.14		1.01	7.7	2.55	3	7.8
	33	2.3	.6	15	51		.66					
								.33	3.5	1.15	3	1.2
	30	0					0					
	LEW @	10:20 a.m.										
	Total								257.4		75	456.4
								Susp. Coef.				1.005
												458.6

No. 4 of 4 Sheets. Comp. by P.W.B. Chk. by E.M.W.

U. S. GOVERNMENT PRINTING OFFICE 16—26076-2

FIG. 9–9. Record sheet for current-meter measurement. (*U.S. Geological Survey.*)

supported on a cable will, in effect, measure the velocity in a vertical section greater in width than the measuring section. It is usual practice to compensate for this error by multiplying the measured velocity by the cosine of the horizontal angle. This cosine is the *angle coefficient* shown in protractor form on the margins of the sheet (Fig. 9-9) for use in direct measurement.

When the measurement at 0.8 depth has been completed, the meter is raised to a position 0.2 of the depth below the surface and a second velocity determination is made and entered on the second line of the form. The average of these two is the mean velocity in the vertical from which the discharge in the vertical can be computed. The average of the mean velocities in adjacent verticals gives the mean velocity in the intervening area. If the 0.6-depth method is used, only a single entry is made for each vertical.

Figure 9-10 shows the form used by the U.S. Geological Survey to record all necessary data required at each discharge determination, in addition to the actual meter notes of Fig. 9-9. To prevent serious errors, the discharge for the station should be computed and plotted on the rating curve before the engineer leaves the site. If considerable deviation is evident, a check measurement should be made immediately.

Other methods of measuring discharge. It is sometimes impossible to make a current-meter measurement by the method just outlined because of insufficient time, lack of equipment, excessive drift, or other causes. Several other procedures are used, although none is comparable in reliability to use of a current meter. The simplest procedure is to time the interval required for a float to travel a measured distance. To determine the velocity distribution, several float measurements across the stream are necessary. A surface float moves with the surface velocity of the water, and, assuming parabolic velocity distribution in the vertical, the mean velocity is 0.85 of the float velocity. If actual meter measurements at other times have defined the vertical velocity curve, this adjustment factor can be computed more exactly.

TABLE 9-4. Coefficients for Rod-float Velocity Measurements

Ratio of Length of Submerged Rod to Depth of Channel	Ratio of Mean Velocity to Float Velocity
0.90	1.00
0.75	0.95
0.50	0.92
Surface float	0.85

A weighted rod floating with a considerable portion submerged indicates more nearly the true mean velocity in the vertical. Table 9-4 lists appropriate coefficients for various ratios of submerged length of rod to total

9-275 c
(July 1935)

UNITED STATES
DEPARTMENT OF THE INTERIOR
GEOLOGICAL SURVEY
WATER RESOURCES BRANCH

DISCHARGE MEASUREMENT NOTES

Meas. No. 147
Checked by EMW
Date 5-24-45

Antietam Creek near Sharpsburg, Md.

Date May 4, 1945 Party P. W. Brewer

Width 75 Area 257 Vel. 3.40 G. H. 3.40 Disch. 459

Method 2 & .8 No. secs. 32 G. H. change +0.04 in 1 1/3 hrs. Susp. 30# C

Method coef. 1.00 Hor. angle coef. 1.00 Meter No. 1378 Susp. coef. 1.005

GAGE READINGS				
Time		Recorder	Inside	Outside
8:45a		3.37	3.37	3.35
9:00a	Start	3.38		
	Finish			
10:20		3.42		
10:25		3.42	3.42	3.40
Weighted M. G. H.		3.40	3.40	
G. H. correction				
Correct M. G. H.		3.40	3.40	

Date rated 10-21-42 Used rating for rod susp. Meter 0.5 ft. above bottom of wt. Tags checked
Spin before meas. O.K. after O.K.
Meas. plots % diff. from rating
Wading, cable, ice, boat, upstr., downstr., side bridge 60 feet, mile, above, below gage, and
Chain, wire, found , changed to at
Correct length
Levels obtained

Measurement rated excellent (2%), good (5%), fair (8%), poor (over 8%), based on following conditions: Cross section Fairly smooth
Flow Smooth Weather cloudy, cool
Other
Gage Operating O.K.
Record removed Yes Intake flushed Yes
Observer

Control Clean. Removed small log @ 8:40 a.m. no change in gage-height. Log caused no B.W.
Remarks

Sheet No. 1 of 4 sheets. G. H. of zero flow —— ft.

U. S. GOVERNMENT PRINTING OFFICE 6—7440

FIG. 9–10. Supplemental data sheet for current-meter measurement. *(U.S Geological Survey.)*

depth. The length of the float reach must be such as to permit a reasonably accurate velocity determination and in general should be at least 500 ft.

Discharge may also be computed from theoretical considerations following the principles of steady flow in open channels. The selected reach should be straight and the cross section reasonably uniform. Cross sections, slope of water surface as indicated by floodmarks, and data for estimating **n** can be determined by field surveys. Slope reaches should rarely be less than 1000 ft and preferably long enough so that the drop in water surface is at least 1 ft. However, it must be recognized that high-water marks represent, not points on an instantaneous profile, but simply the highest stages attained as the flood crest passed through the reach.

If uniform flow is assumed, the measured water-surface slope may be taken to equal the energy gradient and either the Chezy or the Manning formula applied. If the flow is not uniform, an application of Bernoulli's principle is necessary. If velocities measured during other floods are available, **C** or **n** can be computed by reversing the procedure for computing q.

Discharge of small streams. Shallow depths, floating debris, moving bedload, or large boulders in the channel may make the use of meters for discharge measurements in small streams impracticable. Depths can be increased by blocking off part of the channel to permit use of meters. However, weirs or flumes, which can be rated theoretically, are more commonly used. An adequate pool should be provided above a weir to reduce velocity of approach to a negligible value, and the approach channel should be straight and uniform to eliminate irregular velocity distributions. The weir crest should be short so that changes in head can be accurately measured and high enough to avoid submergence at any stage. Unusual conditions may cause the weir rating to deviate from that obtained under laboratory conditions, and a few check measurements with a current meter may be desirable. Head on the weir can be measured by a staff, hook, or recording gage.

The *Parshall flume*,[1] which can operate with very small loss in head, was designed for measuring flow in irrigation canals. Debris-laden water passes through a Parshall flume without depositing material in the upstream pool. In this respect, it has a decided advantage over weirs, since their ratings change as the pool fills and velocity of approach becomes significant.

Figure 9-11 depicts the general design of the Parshall flume, while Table 9-5 gives the dimensions corresponding to the letters of the figure for various sizes of flumes. The larger flumes consist of a converging section with level floor, a throat with floor inclined downward on a slope of 3:8, and a divergent section with adverse floor slope of 1 : 6. Flumes under 1-ft throat width depart from the proportions of the larger flumes.

[1] Parshall, R. L., The Parshall Measuring Flume, *Colo. Expt. Sta. Bull.* 423, 1936.

Two conditions of flow may exist in a Parshall flume. Free-flow conditions are most common with critical depth occurring at the crest and a hydraulic jump often forming in the exit section. Tests indicate the discharge equation for free flow in flumes 1 ft or more in width to be

$$q = 4Bh_a^{1.522B^{0.026}} \tag{9-1}$$

where B is the throat width and h_a is the depth at the upstream stilling well.

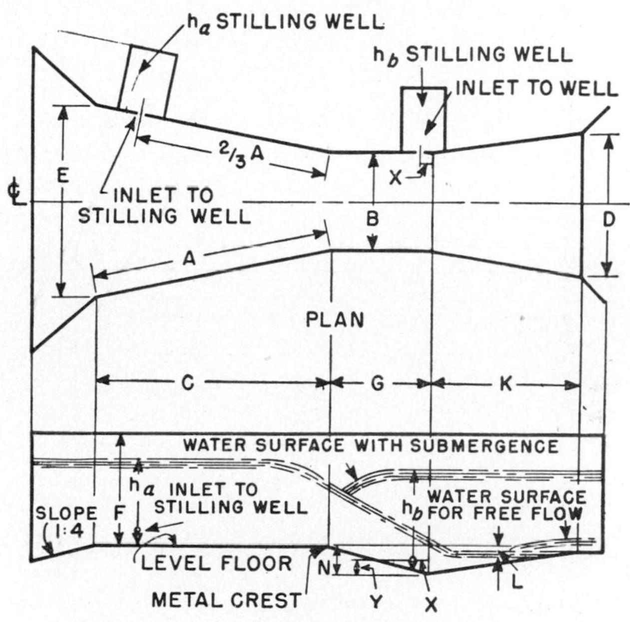

FIG. 9–11. Plan and elevation of the Parshall measuring flume. *(After Parshall.)*

Table 9-6 summarizes the rating characteristics of flumes of different sizes. The equations for the smaller flumes are

$$q = 0.992h_a^{1.547} \quad \text{(3-in.)} \tag{9-2}$$

$$q = 2.06h_a^{1.58} \quad \text{(6-in.)} \tag{9-3}$$

$$q = 3.07h_a^{1.53} \quad \text{(9-in.)} \tag{9-4}$$

When the stage h_b reaches $0.7h_a$, submergence is effective in reducing discharge of the larger flumes. Submergence of 50 per cent may prove critical on flumes of less than 1-ft throat width. Discharge under conditions of submergence is computed by subtracting a correction from the free-flow discharge. Values of the correction for the 1-ft flume are given in Table 9-7. When multiplied by $B^{0.815}$ (Table 9-8), they are applicable to larger flumes.

TABLE 9-5. Dimensions and Capacities for Parshall Measuring Flumes of Various Sizes

(All dimensions in feet and inches)

Throat width											Free-flow capacity, cfs	
B	A	C	D	E	F	G	K	L	N	X	Y	Max	Min
0-3	1-6 3/8	1-6	0-7	0-10 3/16	1-4	0-6	1-0	0-1	0-2 1/4	0-1	0-1 1/2	1.1	0.03
0-6	2-7/16	2-0	1-3 5/8	1-3 5/8	2-0	1-0	2-0	0-3	0-4 1/2	0-2	0-3	3.9	0.05
0-9	2-10 5/8	2-10	1-3	1-10 5/8	2-6	1-0	1-6	0-3	0-4 1/2	0-2	0-3	8.8	0.09
1-0	4-6	4-4 7/8	2-0	2-9 1/4	3-0	2-0	3-0	0-3	0-9	0-2	0-3	16.1	0.35
1-6	4-9	4-7 7/8	2-6	3-4 3/8	3-0	2-0	3-0	0-3	0-9	0-2	0-3	24.6	0.51
2-0	5-0	4-10 7/8	3-0	3-11 1/2	3-0	2-0	3-0	0-3	0-9	0-2	0-3	33.1	0.66
3-0	5-6	5-4 3/4	4-0	5-1 7/8	3-0	2-0	3-0	0-3	0-9	0-2	0-3	50.4	0.97
4-0	6-0	5-10 5/8	5-0	6-4 1/4	3-0	2-0	3-0	0-3	0-9	0-2	0-3	67.9	1.26
6-0	7-0	6-10 3/8	7-0	8-9	3-0	2-0	3-0	0-3	0-9	0-2	0-3	103.5	2.63
8-0	8-0	7-10 1/8	9-0	11-1 3/4	3-0	2-0	3-0	0-3	0-9	0-2	0-3	139.5	4.62

TABLE 9-6. Free-flow Discharge in Cubic Feet per Second for Parshall Flumes of Various Sizes

h_a, ft	Throat width B									
	3 in.	6 in.	9 in.	1 ft	1.5 ft	2 ft	3 ft	4 ft	6 ft	8 ft
0.1	0.03	0.05	0.09							
0.2	0.08	0.16	0.26	0.35	0.51	0.66	0.97	1.26		
0.3	0.15	0.31	0.49	0.64	0.94	1.24	1.82	2.39	3.52	4.62
0.4	0.24	0.48	0.76	0.99	1.47	1.93	2.86	3.77	5.57	7.34
0.5	0.34	0.69	1.06	1.39	2.06	2.73	4.05	5.36	7.94	10.5
0.6	0.45	0.92	1.40	1.84	2.73	3.62	5.39	7.15	10.6	14.1
0.7	0.57	1.17	1.78	2.33	3.46	4.60	6.86	9.11	13.6	18.0
0.8	0.70	1.45	2.18	2.85	4.26	5.66	8.46	11.3	16.8	22.4
0.9	0.84	1.74	2.61	3.41	5.10	6.80	10.2	13.6	20.3	27.0
1.0	0.99	2.06	3.07	4.00	6.00	8.00	12.0	16.0	24.0	32.0
1.1	.....	2.40	3.55	4.62	6.95	9.27	13.9	18.6	27.9	37.3
1.2	.....	2.75	4.06	5.28	7.94	10.6	16.0	21.3	32.1	42.9
1.3	.....	3.12	4.59	5.96	8.99	12.0	18.1	24.2	36.5	48.8
1.4	.....	3.51	5.14	6.68	10.1	13.5	20.3	27.2	41.1	55.0
1.5	.....	.....	5.71	7.41	11.2	15.0	22.6	30.3	45.8	61.4
1.6	.....	.....	6.31	8.18	12.4	16.6	25.1	33.6	50.8	68.1
1.7	.....	.....	6.92	8.97	13.6	18.2	27.6	37.0	56.0	75.1
1.8	.....	.....	7.54	9.79	14.8	19.9	30.1	40.5	61.3	82.3
1.9	.....	.....	8.20	10.6	16.1	21.6	32.8	44.1	66.8	89.8
2.0	.....	.....	.....	11.5	17.4	23.4	35.5	47.8	72.5	97.5
2.1	.....	.....	.....	12.4	18.8	25.3	38.4	51.6	78.4	105.4
2.2	.....	.....	.....	13.3	20.2	27.2	41.3	55.5	84.4	113.6
2.3	.....	.....	.....	14.2	21.6	29.1	44.2	59.6	90.6	122.0
2.4	.....	.....	.....	15.2	23.0	31.1	47.3	63.7	97.0	130.7
2.5	.....	.....	.....	16.1	24.6	33.1	50.4	67.9	103.5	139.5

TABLE 9-7. Submergence Corrections in Cubic Feet per Second for 1-ft Parshall Flume

Head, h_a, ft	Submergence ratio h_b/h_a					
	0.70	0.75	0.80	0.85	0.90	0.95
0.3	0.07	0.08	0.10	0.13	0.20	0.33
0.5	0.08	0.10	0.14	0.22	0.37	0.65
1.0	0.13	0.21	0.35	0.59	1.00	1.80
1.5	0.25	0.42	0.70	1.20	2.00	3.40
2.0	0.44	0.73	1.25	2.00	3.30	5.40
2.5	0.69	1.10	1.90	2.90	4.70	7.50

Parshall flumes will operate successfully under 95 per cent submergence. Far less head loss is therefore necessary than in the case of weirs. In free-flow conditions, head loss is about one-fourth that for a weir.

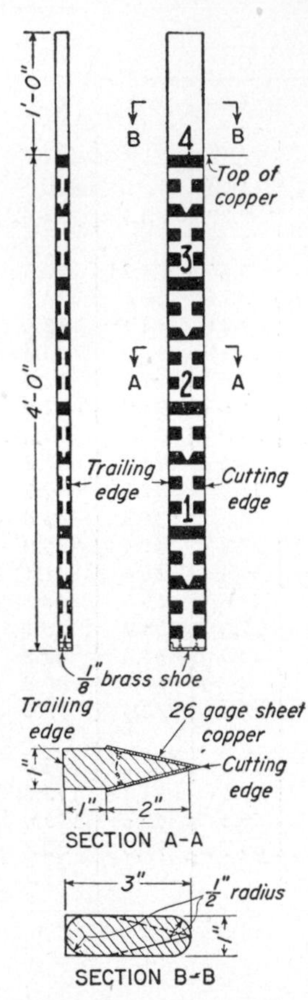

FIG. 9–12. Velocity-head rod. (*After Wilm and Storey.*)

Table 9-8. Values of $B^{0.815}$

B	$B^{0.815}$
1	1.0
1.5	1.4
2	1.8
3	2.4
4	3.1
6	4.3
8	5.4

Wilm and Storey[1] devised a simple *velocity-head rod* for the approximate measurement of flow in small streams (Fig. 9-12). In use, the rod is set on the channel bottom with the sharp edge upstream and the depth of water noted (neglecting the ripple at the rod). The rod is then turned 180° so that the flat edge is upstream. The obstruction to flow causes an increase in height of water surface at the face of the rod essentially equal to the velocity head h_v. The velocity is therefore given by

$$v = \sqrt{2gh_v} = 8.02\sqrt{h_v} \qquad (9\text{-}5)$$

Data presented indicate that the rod may be expected to have an average error of 2 to 3 per cent and to be accurate within 10 per cent under adverse conditions. It is difficult to read with velocities under 1 fps and hard to handle at velocities above 8 fps. It can, however, be used in a stream carrying considerable bed load or debris.

Discharge over dams and embankments. Dams often afford convenient points for discharge determination. For most satisfactory results, the features of the dam should conform to the conditions applicable to the general case of weirs. That is:

1. The axis of the dam should be normal to the direction of flow, and the crest should be straight and level.

[1] Wilm, H. G., and H. C. Storey, Velocity-head Rod Calibrated for Measuring Streamflow, *Civil. Eng.*, Vol. 14, pp. 475-476, 1944.

2. The velocity of approach should be small, and the distribution of velocities above the dam should be reasonably uniform.
3. Submergence should be negligible.

Dams equipped with flashboards are not satisfactory because of uncertainties relative to the effect of the boards from day to day. Discharge through turbines or over dams equipped with crest or sluice gates is best determined by current-meter measurements below the dam or by model tests. It is difficult to rate such structures because of the variable conditions which may be encountered. For example, the discharge per gate at a given head often depends on whether the gate is operating singly or whether adjacent gates are open. Old dams, cofferdams, or other structures in the pool above the dam may also affect the discharge.

Values of the weir coefficient can be determined from discharge measurements or may be selected from reported experimental data.[1] The discharge over highway or railroad embankments[2] may be considered analogous to the flow over broad-crested weirs.

STAGE-DISCHARGE RELATIONS

Measurements by customary methods provide only occasional determinations of discharge, which must be correlated with stage in order that a continuous discharge record may be computed. This correlation is customarily expressed in the form of a curve or table called a *stage-discharge relation*, or *rating*.

Simple rating curve. If measured discharge is plotted against simultaneous stage, the data will normally define a curve which is approximately parabolic. For the great majority of stations in the United States, such a curve is an adequate stage-discharge relation. If a station possesses a permanent control, the rating will be essentially permanent but should be confirmed by occasional measurements and extended by measurements at each new record-high stage. Scour above or below the control or changes in conditions downstream from the control which alter its effect may cause changes in the rating.

Some stations have two or more controls, each serving in a different range of stage. This condition may result in a rather abrupt break in the rating at the stage corresponding to a change in the control. Submergence of a control such as a ledge or weir begins when the tailwater below the control rises above the lowest point of the control. The *submergence ratio* is defined as the ratio of the depth of tailwater on the control to the head

[1] Horton, R. E., Weir Experiments, Coefficients, and Formulas, *U.S. Geol. Survey Water Supply Paper* 200, 1907.

[2] Yarnell, D. L., and F. A. Nagler, Flow of Floodwater over Railway and Highway Embankments, *Public Roads*, Vol. 11, pp. 30-34, 1930.

upstream from the control. Rather high submergence ratios may occur before the discharge features of the control are materially affected. Occasionally, ratings are well defined by measurements at low and high stages but show a considerable divergence of points at medium stages. Such a condition exists when a well-defined low-water control is subjected to submergence at medium stages, above which a high-water control becomes effective. If the conditions causing submergence are not always constant, a scatter of measurements may be observed in the range of stage subject to submergence.

On streams having steep slopes and adequate, permanent controls not subject to varying backwater from a dam or downstream tributary, the simple rating will prove satisfactory. Most of these conditions can be satisfied in the Appalachian Highlands in the East and in the western mountains.

Shifting control. A station is subject to a *shifting control* when the stage-discharge relation changes, either gradually or rapidly, as a result of physical changes in the control. There are numerous causes of shifting controls. In most cases, a simple rating is applicable between changes in the control. Because of the changing control, it is necessary to make measurements so closely spaced in time that sufficient points are always available to define the rating in an interval between shifts. Some further facts as to the time or nature of the shift may be deduced if its cause is known.

Two procedures are used to adjust for shifting control. Separate ratings can be drawn for each specific interval between shifts and the applicable dates clearly indicated (Fig. 9-13). The curve appropriate for any date is used in determining discharge for that day. This procedure is most satisfactory where the control shifts abruptly and then remains unchanged for some period of time. Scour induced by floods and man-made changes, such as dredging or construction work, are the most common causes of such shifts. The date of such a change can be rather closely defined, and the qualitative effect of the change can be deduced from inspection of the station. Subsequent measurements will serve to define the changed rating. In each case, however, there will be a period of time during a flood or during the construction period, in the case of artificial changes, in which the control will shift gradually and the rating can be defined only by frequent measurements.

A gradual change in the control may occur as the result of silting or other channel changes in streams moving through soft erosible channels. The growth of brush or aquatic plants in the channel or the development of an ice cover on a stream may also cause a gradual change in control. Under such conditions, it is not possible to prepare separate ratings for definite periods, and it is necessary to assume a mean curve. Each measurement is then compared with this curve to determine the stage correction necessary to adjust to the measured discharge. A continuous plot of correction against date of measurement is maintained, interpolating between gagings by following the time trend of the data. Since the conditions which favor gradual shift in a control also favor abrupt changes during floods, the stage-correction curve may change sharply during periods of rapid rise. To compute the discharge on any particular day, the indicated stage cor-

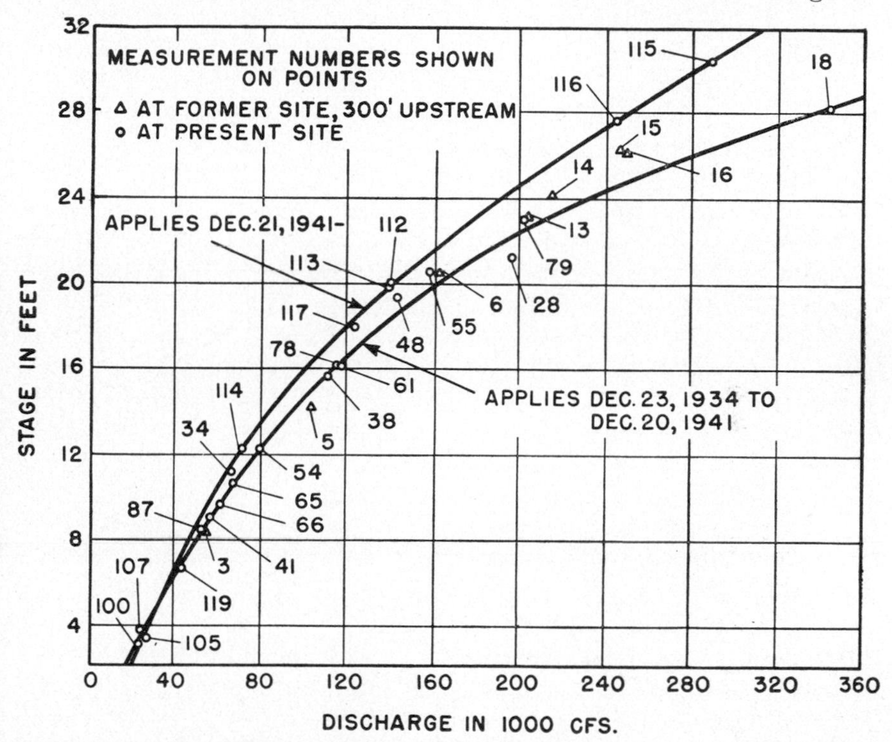

FIG. 9–13. Stage-discharge relation for the Willamette River at Salem, Oregon, showing the effect of shifting control.

rection is applied to the observed stage and the discharge read from the mean stage-discharge relation.

The inaccuracies of the shifting-control rating can be avoided only by providing an adequate control, which may be impossible in many cases without construction of an expensive artificial control. Shifting-control ratings are used on most streams with flat slopes and unstable channels, such as are found in the Middle West and the Intermountain Region, and on many coastal streams of the country.

Effect of ice on the stage-discharge relation. The types of river ice and their causes are discussed in Chap. 7. Ice in any form at a control results in a condition of shifting control. Anchor ice on the control raises it by an amount equal to the ice thickness and necessarily displaces the rating by about the same amount. Also, a control may be submerged by backwater from an ice jam downstream.

Sheet ice, perhaps the most common type of ice, must be present at the control to affect discharge materially. It provides a new friction surface and hence reduces the channel capacity from that for a corresponding open-river stage. Ice formation may be slow or rapid and its effect, especially during the period of formation, may change rapidly. The continuity of discharge records can be maintained only by interpolation between frequent discharge measurements. Fortunately, ice effect is usually important only during periods of low and relatively steady flow so that interpolation is not too difficult.

The presence of drift ice or frazil ice seriously hampers discharge measurements, endangers equipment, and makes reliable measurements almost impossible. Continuous sheet ice capable of supporting the hydrographer permits reasonably accurate measurements, although considerably more work is involved than for open-water conditions. Measurements must be made through holes cut in the ice, and the two-point procedure or the 0.5-depth method is used, depending on the depths. Ice cover distorts the vertical velocity curve, and it is desirable to determine the velocity distribution at one or two sections by measurements at several depths. On the average, the velocity under ice at middepth is about 1.14 of the mean and at 0.6 depth about 1.09 of the mean.[1] The meter must be moved from one vertical to the next as rapidly as possible to prevent ice from forming on it. Stages of frozen streams should be measured to the free-water surface, not the top or bottom of ice.

Slope-stage-discharge relations. A careful study of the discharge measurements at most gaging stations indicates a tendency for points obtained during rising stages to show more discharge than measurements at comparable falling stages. A consideration of the water-surface slopes during rising and falling stages shows that steeper slopes exist during the rise. For stations located on steep channels, these differences are small compared with the channel slope, and the errors introduced by assuming constant slope are normally insignificant in comparison with the usual errors of discharge measurement.

Where channel slopes are flat, important differences in discharge are usually observed between rising and falling stages. Stations having channel control may also have variable slopes as a result of backwater conditions from a reservoir or intersecting stream below the station. These conditions require a special type of rating called a *slope-stage-discharge*

[1] Barrows, H. K., and R. E. Horton, Determination of Stream Flow during the Frozen Season, *U.S. Geol. Survey Water Supply Paper* 187, 1907.

relation. From the Manning formula, it is evident that, for a section where all factors are constant but the slope of the energy gradient,

$$\frac{q_a}{q_m} = \sqrt{\frac{s_a}{s_m}} \tag{9-6}$$

where q_a and q_m are discharges at a given stage with slopes of s_a and s_m, respectively. If an auxiliary gage is installed downstream from the station being rated, Eq. (9-6) can be used to calculate discharge from observed stages and slopes. The distance between gages must be such that the difference in elevation can be determined with necessary precision after due allowance for the usual errors in gage reading. In general, the average difference in water-surface elevation between the two gages should not be less than 1 ft.

Certain practical aspects of flow in natural channels preclude a precise measurement of the slope of the energy gradient, or even of actual water-surface slope, by use of an auxiliary gage. The characteristic backwater curve is concave upward. Thus, the slope measured between any two points is the slope of the chord between those points and not the true surface slope at either place. Variations in velocity head along the channel, breaks in bottom slope, and superelevation of flow on curves further complicate the situation. If the slope reach is straight and uniform, these effects will be minimized, but in any event the measured fall can be considered no more than an index to the true slope of the water surface. Velocity-head gradients are not usually large with respect to other elements of energy slope. Velocities are generally quite low under conditions where variable slope may affect the stage-discharge relation significantly. A study by the U.S. Geological Survey on the Tennessee River at Chattanooga indicated that velocity-head gradients ranged from 0.1 to 4 per cent of the water-surface slope. Velocity surveys at each end of a reach permit calculation of the velocity-head gradient, and such a check should be made before the velocity head is omitted from further consideration. The effect of nonuniform velocity distribution should not be neglected in this check.

The actual solution of the variable-slope rating is based on a modification of Eq. (9-6),

$$\frac{q_a}{q_m} = \left(\frac{F_a}{F_m}\right)^n \tag{9-7}$$

where F_a and F_m are the observed fall and mean fall for steady flow, respectively. The procedure requires that a rating be drawn for those points where the observed fall equals F_m. Practical considerations suggest the selection of $F_m = 1.00$ ft, if possible. Equation (9-7) can then be modified to

$$q_a = q_m F_a^{\,n} \tag{9-8}$$

The approximate position of the desired rating may be evident from the plotted measurements if a sufficient number are available. Otherwise, all available points can be adjusted to the approximate position of the constant-fall rating by use of the equation

$$q_m = q_a \sqrt{\frac{F_m}{F_a}} \tag{9-9}$$

After the constant-fall rating has been drawn, values of the ratio q_a/q_m can be plotted against corresponding values of F_a/F_m (Fig. 9-14) to determine the slope-adjustment curve. The discharge for a given stage and

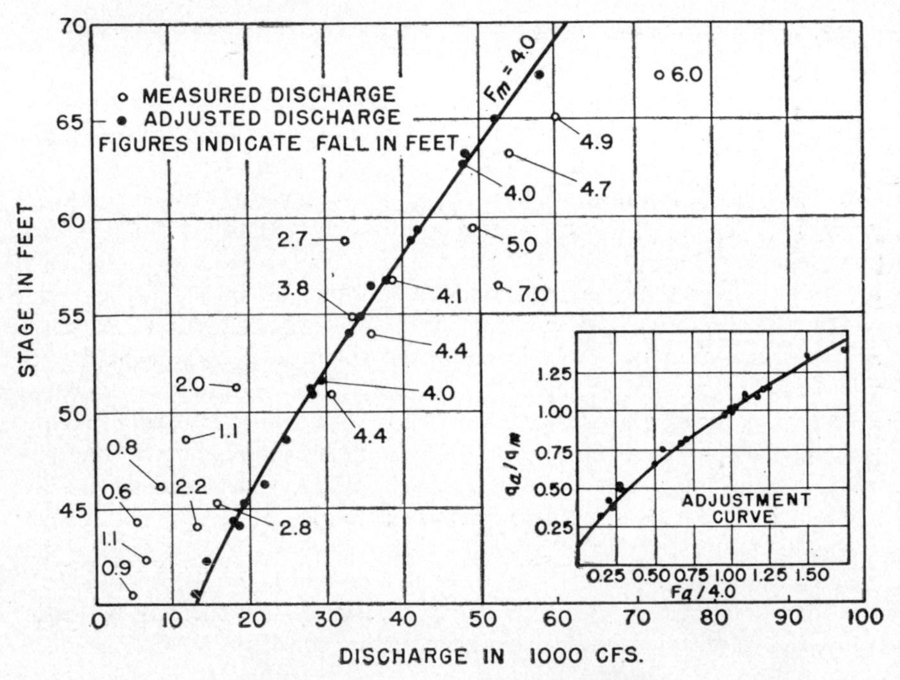

FIG. 9–14. Constant-fall rating curve for the Kootenai River at Copeland, Idaho.

fall can be computed by multiplying the value of q_m corresponding to the given stage (from the constant-fall curve) by the correction factor corresponding to the ratio F_a/F_m. A family of curves expressing this relation may be constructed to reduce the work required to compute discharge.

A second approximation may be desirable as a refinement of the rating developed as outlined above. This is accomplished by dividing each measured discharge by the correction factor corresponding to the observed fall. The adjusted points should be evenly distributed about the first approximation of the selected constant-fall curve. If they are not, a revised curve should be drawn and the correction curve redetermined, using new values of q_m from the adjusted constant-fall rating.

In some reaches a condition may exist in which a section control becomes effective as backwater decreases. This means that for any stage there is a value of fall marking the beginning of backwater at that stage. Backwater is effective for falls less than this critical value, while with higher falls the section control governs. Under these conditions a constant-fall rating cannot be used. Instead, a curve defining the *normal fall*, F_n, as a function of stage must be constructed (Fig. 9-15). Conditions requiring the use of a normal-fall rating will be disclosed by a grouping of points

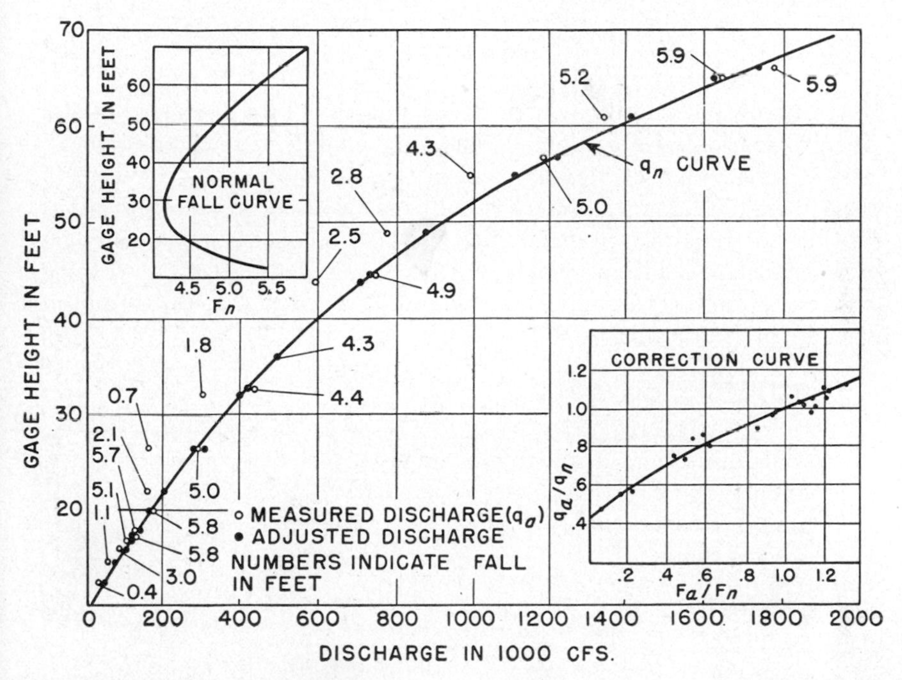

FIG. 9-15. Normal-fall rating curve for the Ohio River at Metropolis, Illinois.

defining the curve of no backwater effect at the extreme right of the plotted data. This is a simple stage-discharge relation and may be used as such when backwater is not effective. Inspection of the data falling along this curve will permit selection of the least value of fall indicated at any stage. If these falls are plotted against stage, the resulting curve shows the fall at which backwater begins at any stage. The balance of the rating can be constructed by following the technique outlined for constant-fall ratings but substituting the appropriate value of F_n for each stage in place of the constant F_m and using q_n in place of q_m.

The correction curves which express Eq. (9-7) graphically usually represent a function of the fall ratio to approximately the 0.5 power. Variation in flow conditions from stage to stage may result in a variable exponent. In any case, the curve must pass through the point at which both ratios have the value of unity but may not pass through the origin if the gages are at different datums or if a break in the bed slope exists.

Variable slope due to change in stage. Stations not subject to variable slope because of backwater may still be materially affected because of change in stage with time. If s_m is the slope of the water surface during periods of steady flow, then the slope s of the water surface when the stage is changing is

$$s = s_m + \frac{1}{u}\frac{dg}{dt} \tag{9-10}$$

where u is wave celerity (Chap. 18) and dg/dt is rate of change of stage. The problem of variable slope because of changing stage can be treated in several ways. Direct measurement of the fall and the development of a slope-stage-discharge relation as outlined in the preceding section is possible but requires the installation and maintenance of an auxiliary gage.

An alternate solution, which requires an auxiliary gage only during a preliminary period, assumes the slope to conform to Eq. (9-10) and uses the correction formula

$$\frac{q_a}{q_m} = \sqrt{\frac{s_m + (1/u)dg/dt}{s_m}} \tag{9-11}$$

A curve defining s_m as a function of stage may be determined by a period of preliminary observations using an auxiliary gage.

Assuming that the energy gradient slope s_e is equal to $s_m + (1/U)dg/dt$, Eq. (9-11) becomes

$$\frac{q_m}{q_a} = \sqrt{1 - \frac{1}{us_e}\frac{dg}{dt}} \tag{9-12}$$

In application, the value of s_e is determined from Manning's formula. The wave celerity u in the preceding equations may be determined from Eqs. (18-3), (18-8), or (18-20). Within the accuracy ordinarily required for the adjustment, u may be assumed to equal 1.3 times the mean velocity in the section. In using Eq. (9-11) or (9-12) to derive a rating, the curve of q_m is determined by correcting measured discharges with the selected equation. To determine discharge the procedure can be reversed, or a family of curves may be constructed to permit the direct reading of discharge by entering with values of stage and dg/dt.

Theoretical computations of the effect of changing stage may not always prove satisfactory. In such cases, the station rating can be developed empirically in a manner similar to that described for slope ratings. A rating curve for steady-flow conditions is first constructed by use of measurements made when dg/dt was zero (Fig. 9-16). A correction curve is constructed by plotting the ratio q_a/q_m as a function of dg/dt. If a second approximation is indicated, the q_m curve is adjusted by correcting all measurements with the first approximation to the correction curve and a second correction curve is derived by using a new steady-flow rating. Discharge for any combination of stage and dg/dt is determined by multiplying

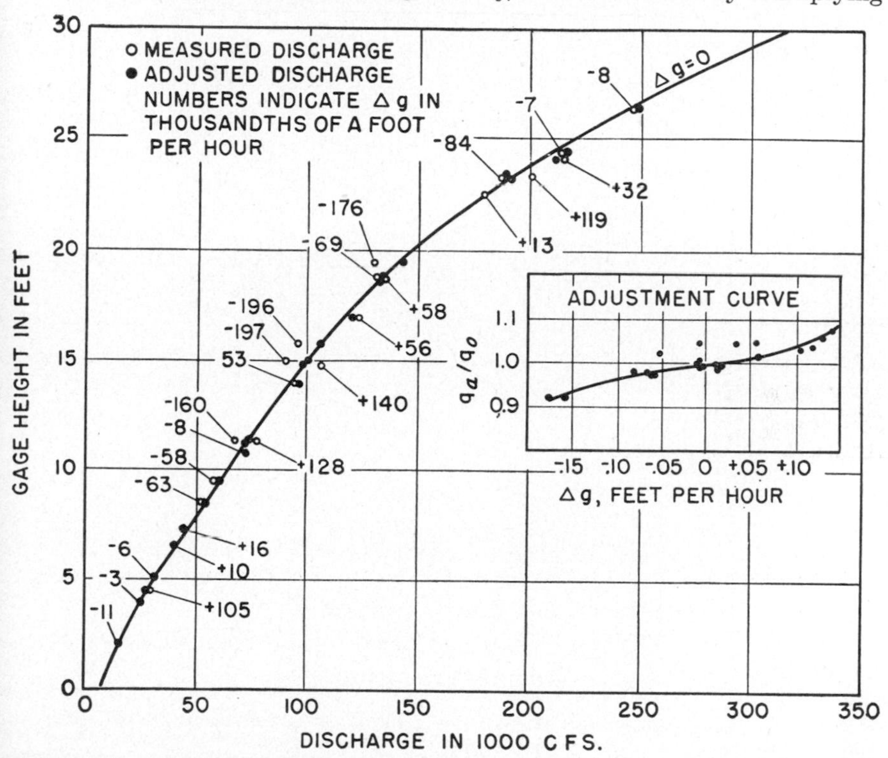

FIG. 9–16. Change-in-stage rating curve for the Tennessee River near Scottsboro, Alabama.

the value of q_m corresponding to the given stage by the correction factor indicated for the observed value of dg/dt.

The rate of change of stage dg/dt is the instantaneous slope of the stage hydrograph. This value is difficult to determine, and for practical reasons the change in stage during the hour preceding the gage reading is ordinarily used. For certain purposes, *e.g.*, in river forecasting, where hourly data are rarely available, time increments of 6 or 12 hr may be used. As long as there is no marked change in slope of the stage hydrograph during the period selected, adequate ratings may be derived using the longer time increments.

Loop ratings. If the requirements of the project at hand do not justify the effort to develop complex ratings of the type outlined in the previous paragraphs, approximate determination of discharge may be made through the use of a *loop rating* (Fig. 9-17). Here the discharge measurements during the course of a flood have been plotted, and their sequence has been noted. A smooth loop conforming to the measured data provides a method

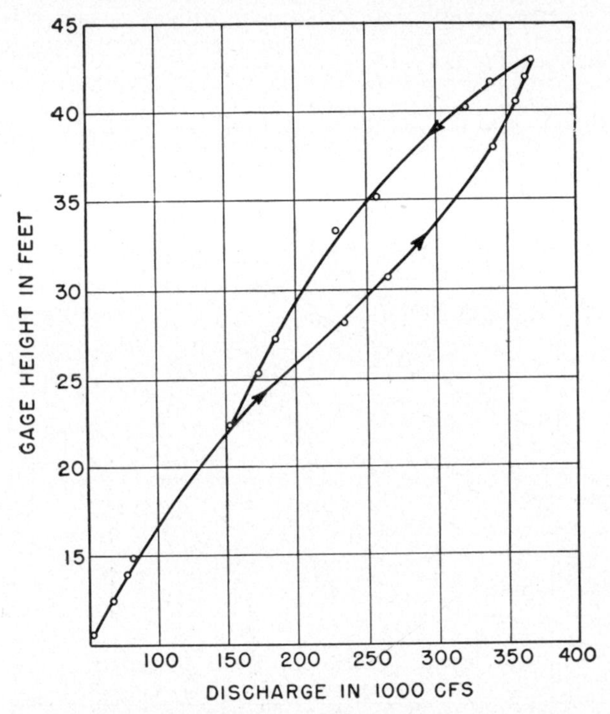

FIG. 9-17. Stage-discharge loop for the Ohio River at Wheeling, West Virginia, during the flood of March 14-27, 1905.

for interpolating flow within the flood for which it is drawn. With judgment, it may be used for an approximation on other floods of about the same magnitude. The loop ratings from any two floods cannot coincide exactly unless the peak discharges are identical, and even then variations in conditions during rise and fall cause differences. Floods of different magnitudes may have similar loops provided that their general development and recession are comparable. Discharge loops for floods having two or more individual crests often become quite complex. In general, loop ratings should not be used except for reconstructing the hydrograph of a flood for which sufficient discharge measurements are available to define the loop.

Extension of rating curves. For river forecasting or design problems, it is frequently necessary to have stage-discharge relations extended above the limit of the highest previous measurement. Several techniques have been developed as the result of experience and study of a large number of stage-discharge relations. In many cases, these procedures will lead to a reasonably adequate estimate of the extensions. It must be emphasized

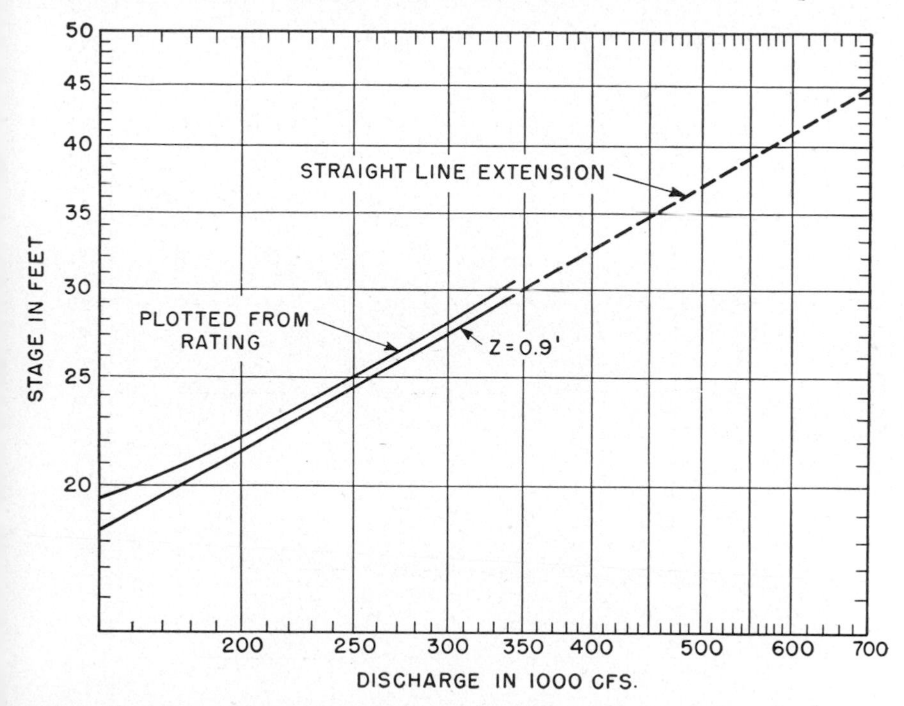

FIG. 9–18. Logarithmic extension of a rating curve for the Willamette River at Salem, Oregon.

that any extrapolation is open to possible serious error, and a field survey to establish the probable trend of the rating should be made if possible. The possibility of acute breaks in slope of the rating as a result of changes from one control to another have already been discussed. If no material change in control is probable within the range of extension, then any one of several techniques may be adopted with fair assurance that no gross errors will result. In addition to the specific procedures for extension of ratings which follow, the high-water stage-discharge relation may also be computed by use of the hydraulics of open-channel flow.

A study of numerous rating curves indicates that, in general, they conform to the equation

$$q = a(g - Z)^b \tag{9-13}$$

where g is the gage height, Z is the elevation of zero flow above gage datum, and a and b are station constants. If Eq. (9-13) holds, then a plotting of q vs. $(g - Z)$ on logarithmic paper should yield a straight line, which can be extended. It is often difficult to determine Z for stations lacking a clearly defined control, and in this case values of q vs. g may be plotted. If

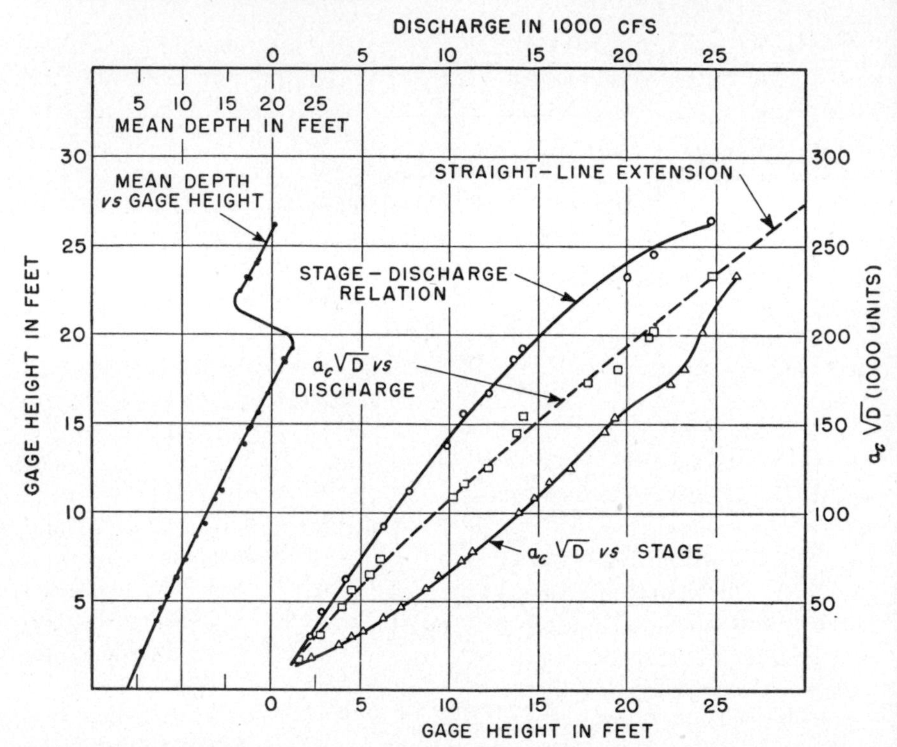

FIG. 9-19. Stage, depth, area, and discharge functions on the Tennessee River near Scottsboro, Alabama.

the resulting curve is concave upward, Z is positive; if it is concave downward, Z is negative. Having determined the sign of Z, successive assumptions may be made until a value which results in a straight-line plotting is determined (Fig. 9-18).

Stevens[1] has proposed a method which is based on an adaptation of the Chezy formula ($q = a_c\mathbf{C}\sqrt{Rs}$). If $\mathbf{C}\sqrt{s}$ is assumed to be a constant for the station and the mean depth D_m is assumed to be a suitable substitute for R,

$$q = f(a_c\sqrt{D_m}) \tag{9-14}$$

Since both a_c and D_m are subject to determination by field survey, a curve

[1] Stevens, J. C., A Method of Estimating Stream Discharge from a Limited Number of Gagings, *Eng. News-Record*, July 18, 1907.

of q vs $a_c\sqrt{D_m}$ may be constructed. This curve should approximate a straight line, which may be extended as required. Since the relation between $a_c\sqrt{D_m}$ and stage is known, the stage-discharge relation may be extended (Fig. 9-19).

INTERPRETATION OF STREAMFLOW RECORDS

Units. Rate of discharge is usually expressed in terms of *cubic feet per second* (cfs), often shortened to *second-feet.* The volume discharged by one cubic foot per second flowing for 24 hr is called a *second-foot-day* (sfd). In other words, the average discharge in cubic feet per second during a 24-hr period is numerically equal to the discharge volume expressed in second-foot-days. An alternate unit of volume is the *acre-foot,* the volume required to cover one acre to a depth of one foot. The acre-foot contains 43,560 ft^3, while the second-foot-day equals 86,400 ft^3. It is common practice to use the convenient though not precise conversion ratio of 2 acre-ft : 1 sfd.

A convenient unit for comparing flows from different basins is the *second-foot per square mile* (csm). It is simply the rate of discharge divided by the drainage area of the contributing basin. The second-foot per square mile permits comparison of flow data between basins by eliminating the variable element of area. Another unit which is useful in many problems, particularly those in which rainfall and runoff are compared, is the *inch of runoff.* An inch of runoff is equivalent to the volume of water which would cover a level surface (equal in area to the particular basin) to a depth of one inch. The actual volume of flow is not apparent from data expressed in inches until the contributing area is stated. Other less frequently used units, conversion factors between the several units, and conversion tables are given in Appendix C.

Accuracy. The accuracy of streamflow measurement is decidedly variable and depends largely on the physical features of the station site (particularly the control), the frequency of measurements, and the type and adequacy of the stage-measuring equipment. The adjective classification applied by the U.S. Geological Survey to its measurements and published records is given in Table 9-9.

TABLE 9-9. Accuracy of Streamflow Data

(Probable errors in per cent)

Adjective classification	Individual measurements	Published records
Excellent	<2	<5
Good	<5	<10
Fair	<8	<15
Poor	>8	>15

Limitations of basic data must always be considered in working with streamflow records. Intensive study to reduce errors in correlations below the limits of error in basic data is hardly warranted. In dealing with differences in flow between two stations, errors of considerable magnitude may be encountered, especially if the errors at the upper and lower stations should happen to be of opposite sign.

Accumulated flow volumes over long periods, such as a year, are more likely to be reliable than short-period values because of the opportunity for compensation of errors. Low-flow data for stations lacking a permanent and well-defined control may be subject to large percentage errors as the result of rather small shifts in the control. Very high flows may be subject to large absolute errors because of the difficulties of measurement and the lack of numerous confirming measurements. If the question of accuracy of records within accepted tolerances is important, a field survey of the station site and discussion with the hydrographer maintaining the station is recommended. Over and above the errors of measuring and computing discharge, there remain other factors which may introduce errors into correlations involving streamflow. These factors are discussed in some detail in subsequent chapters which deal with the development of such relations.

Correlations between the volume of water deposited on a basin in the form of precipitation and that volume discharged as streamflow are materially influenced by any diversion or storage of water upstream from the gaging station. Diversion for irrigation or water supply, natural diversion through surface or underground by-pass channels, and storage of water in natural lakes and ponds or man-made reservoirs may adversely affect such relations. Addition of water by diversion from another basin or by groundwater movement from a distant source may be equally troublesome. Pumping of groundwater may also influence surface-water flows. Man-made diversion or storage works usually introduce the most serious problems since the operation of such works is determined by the operator, while natural diversion or storage generally acts in the same manner from one occurrence to the next. These influences generally vary in importance inversely with the size of the basin. Small diversions may introduce large percentage errors into analyses of very small basins, but comparable percentage errors from either natural or artificial causes are less probable in large basins.

Adjustment of streamflow records. The need for adjustment of a streamflow record may arise from several causes, each requiring special techniques of adjustment. The most common problems are:

1. Computation of *full natural flow, i.e.,* the correction of observed flow volumes for storage and diversion of water above the station.

2. Adjustment of hydrograph shape to correct for the controlling effect of regulation works.
3. Combination of records from two or more stations to synthesize one long-period record.
4. Adjustment of *time trend* to correct early records to measurement and runoff conditions prevailing at the present time.

In order to compute full natural flow, it is necessary to have a complete inventory of all reservoirs having significant storage capacities and of all important diversions of water within the basin. While any single item of storage or diversion may be negligible in comparison with the total flow, the aggregate of a number of such items may be significant. The adjustment is made by adding to the observed flow the amount of diversions and the net increase in storage. If storage volumes decrease during a particular period, the amount of the decrease is subtracted from the observed flow. If volumes are to be adjusted, it is not usually necessary to consider travel time. As the time period is reduced, the effect of travel time may become important, reaching its maximum importance for item 2, where the shape of the hydrograph is under adjustment. Corrections being made to observed flows for diversions or changes in storage must be applied to that portion of the hydrograph affected by the control operations. If travel times are important, an adjustment for the effect of channel storage on the water in transit is quite likely to be necessary (Chap. 19). It is often difficult to estimate the true effect of diversion or storage. A considerable portion of irrigation water eventually returns to the stream by surface or underground channels. Observed flows should be adjusted, not by the gross amount of diversion, but by gross diversion less *return flow*. The amount of return flow depends on the method of irrigation, soil type, underlying geological formations, topography, and other factors.

Between 20 and 50 per cent of diverted water may be lost by seepage through the bed and banks of unlined canals. Only a portion of the irrigation water reaching a field is consumed by evapo-transpiration (Chap. 8), the balance percolating to groundwater or the streams. Reports of the California Division of Water Resources[1] show the average return flows in the Sacramento Valley to be slightly less than 50 per cent of the diversions, with a variation between 33 and 64 per cent in individual years. In general, the percentage of return flow appears to be higher during years of high runoff. In the San Joaquin Valley, a much greater portion of the diversions remains in the basin to replenish badly depleted groundwater storage, and return flows average about 20 per cent of the diversion, ranging from 16 to 29 per cent in individual years.

[1] "Report of Sacramento–San Joaquin Water Supervision (1938)," pp. 78-106, State of California, Department of Public Works, Sacramento, 1939.

Similar complications are involved in the storage correction. Seepage into channel banks, evaporation, and unrecorded diversion continually extract water from a stream. Thus, the full amount released from a reservoir rarely reaches a station at any great distance downstream. When a net gain in reservoir storage is added to an observed flow, the resulting estimate of full natural flow is usually too high. Conversely, subtracting a net decrease in storage results in an underestimate of full natural flow—in the extreme case, zero or negative flow. The evaporation opportunity is greater from the large area of a reservoir than from the smaller natural channel. To compute full natural flow, it is necessary to include among the corrections the estimated evaporation loss from a water-surface area equal to the difference between the reservoir area and the channel area.

The combination of records from two or more stations or the adjustment for time trend is best accomplished by the use of the double-mass-curve procedure outlined in Chap. 6. One or more long discharge records from adjacent stations may serve as a base for combination of records or adjustment of records after a station move. However, if the time trend is to be eliminated, a streamflow base is not usually adequate. The time trend can be treated only on a relative basis, because there is no base of comparison which is free oı time trends. Since hydrology is most frequently interested in the relation between precipitation and runoff, a precipitation base is usually most satisfactory. The use of such a base implies, in effect, that today a given *observed* precipitation yields a certain amount of runoff and that the record for earlier years should be adjusted to show a comparable yield. Thus, any time trend between precipitation and runoff is eliminated, but we cannot be sure that either item is independently freed of time trend.

The technique for double-mass adjustment of streamflow is described in Chap. 16. Final adjustment curves for several stations are shown in Fig. 9-20. In every case, the adjustment reduces the observed streamflow of the earlier record. This trend can be supported by the increased consumptive use of water and by changes in streamflow-measurement techniques which have, in general, acted to lower measured flows. As has been pointed out, this trend is relative with respect to precipitation and therefore reflects also the general improvement in precipitation measurements in recent years.

To reduce the possibility of errors in streamflow determination, it is the practice of the U.S. Geological Survey to examine its records for consistency between stations before publication. This is accomplished by comparison of flows between stations on a stream or in nearby or similar drainage basins, on the basis of drainage areas, precipitation variation, and other factors. One purpose of such comparison is to isolate errors in computation or errors in the base data not previously detected. Estimates of flow during periods when base data are missing or unreliable are often made by comparison with nearby stations or from meteorological data. However, estimated figures are qualified in published reports, as it is recognized that arbitrary adjustments of discharge to achieve consistency between stations may obscure local losses or gains in streamflow.

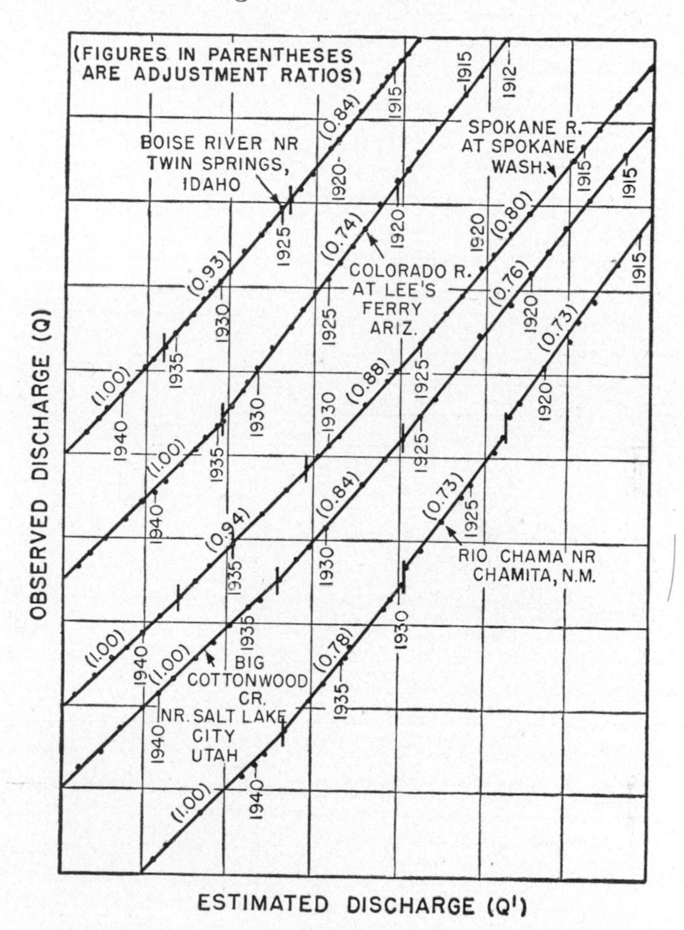

FIG. 9-20. Typical double-mass curves of streamflow.

The hydrograph. A hydrograph is a plotting of discharge or stage against time (Fig. 9-21). A discharge hydrograph may show either mean daily flows or instantaneous discharges. A great deal of graphical analysis is performed directly on the hydrograph, and a judicious selection of scales and care in plotting are essential to satisfactory results. Hydrographs of mean daily flow plotted on a relatively condensed time scale provide an effective visual reference for selection of time periods for analysis. Where volume of flow is the important element of the analysis, such hydrographs are also suitable. Where studies involve analysis of hydrograph shape, particularly of peaks, hydrographs should be plotted from instantaneous flows, using an open scale.

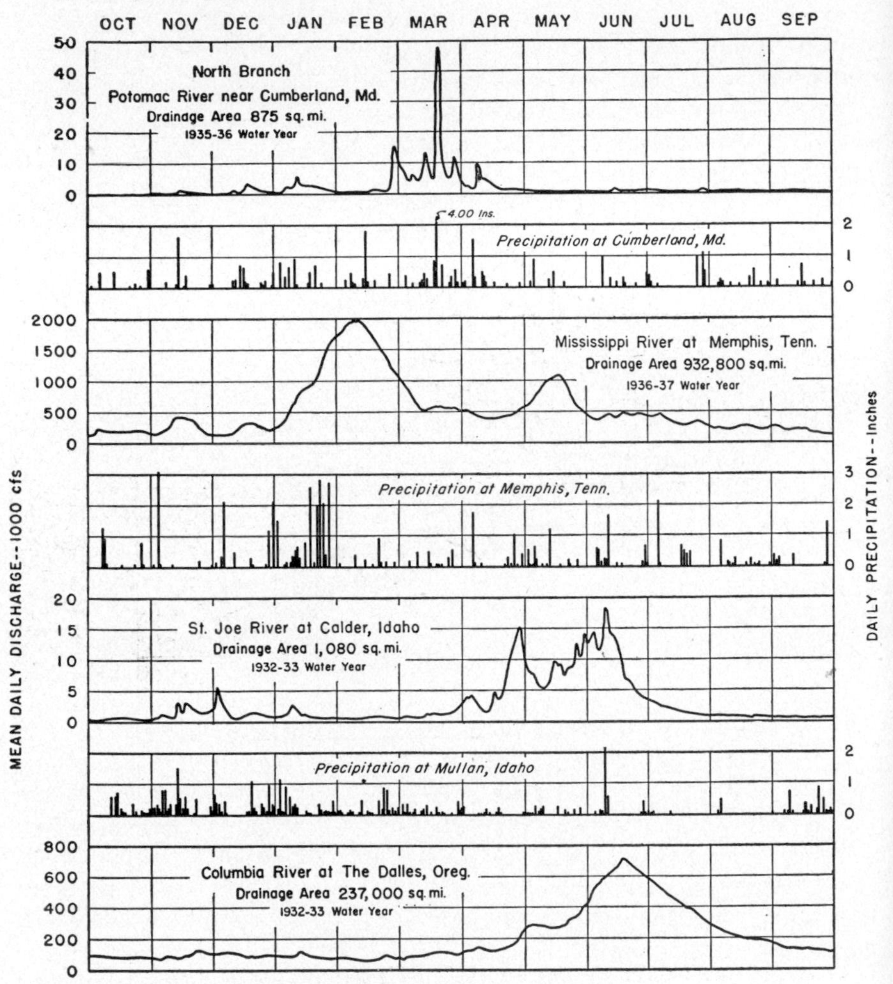

FIG. 9–21. Typical hydrographs.

The apparent shape of the hydrograph is established by the selection of scales, and it is easily possible to distort the visual impression of a stream's characteristics by a poor selection of scales. In operations requiring personal judgment as to hydrograph shape or where hydrographs are to be used for purposes of comparison, it is a wise policy to adopt standard scales for time and discharge.

Most hydrographs are plotted on arithmetically graduated paper. For occasional needs, a logarithmic discharge scale is useful. Logarithmic discharge scales tend to suppress extremes of flow, making it possible to plot very high discharges while retaining an open scale at low flows. However, a disadvantage in some work is the fact that zero discharge cannot be shown. The shape distortion resulting from logarithmic plotting prevents the use of logarithmic hydrographs for analysis of hydrograph shape.

Stage hydrographs are frequently used in hydrologic problems where discharge is not a factor. The chart from a water-stage recorder is itself a gage-height hydrograph. Because of the typical parabolic stage-discharge

FIG. 9–22. Discharge integrator. *(U.S. Geological Survey.)*

relation, a stage hydrograph tends to suppress extremes in the same way as does a logarithmic discharge plotting.

Mean daily flows. Most published streamflow data are given in terms of the *mean daily flow*. Such data permit a year of record to be condensed to a fairly small table. Any more detailed summarizations would make publication costs prohibitive.

Because of the curvature of the usual rating, mean daily flow cannot be determined from mean daily stage if the range in stage is at all large. It is necessary, instead, to subdivide the gage-height record for the day into a number of shorter periods, determine the flow during each period, and sum these values to obtain the total volume for the day.

Where a great deal of integration is necessary, *e.g.*, on streams where there is a diurnal fluctuation because of operation of a hydroelectric plant, the mechanical discharge integrator (Fig. 9-22) may be used to advantage. This device is a planimeter operating from a fixed base line and provided with a means of varying the speed of the dial rotation as the distance from the base line increases. This variation is accomplished by means of a flexible bar which can be set to conform to the rating of the station.

Inspection of Fig. 9-23 reveals certain practical deficiencies of mean daily flows. The maximum mean daily flow never equals the peak flow, and only occasionally will the maximum 24-hr period coincide with a calendar day. The maximum mean daily flow rarely, therefore, represents the

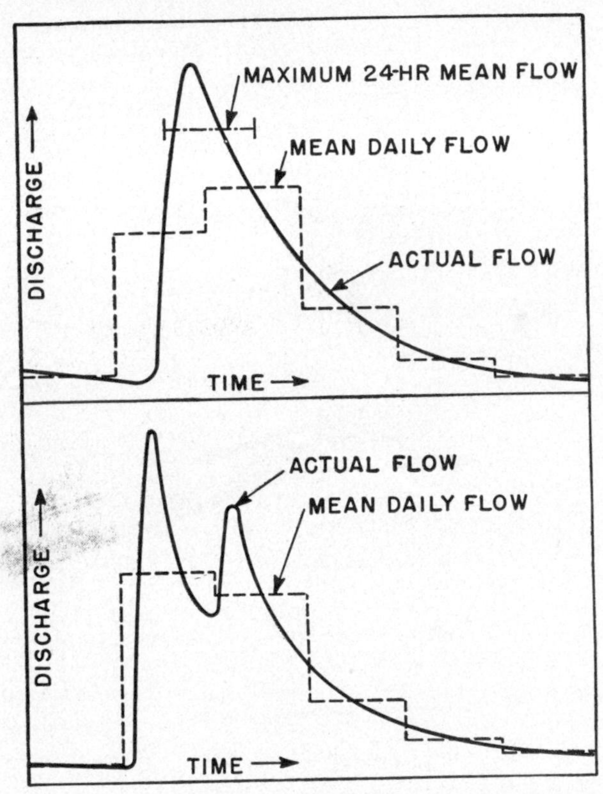

FIG. 9-23. Relation between actual flows and period averages.

maximum 24-hr flow. Random timing of a hydrograph with respect to calendar days frequently results in a maximum mean daily flow on a day other than that on which the actual instantaneous peak flow occurred. Secondary flood peaks may be completely masked by the averaging of flow to compute mean daily values.

The deficiencies outlined above are most serious when small, flashy streams are involved. The following paragraph discusses some approximate methods for reconstructing detailed hydrographs from mean daily data. Such solutions can never be wholly satisfactory, and it is far better to secure copies of the water-stage recorder charts to develop the necessary data than to resort to empirical adjustment of mean daily flow.

Water Supply Paper 771[1] presents a large amount of data on peak discharges and on maximum calendar-day and maximum 24-hr flows and concludes that the data do not permit generalized conclusions. The

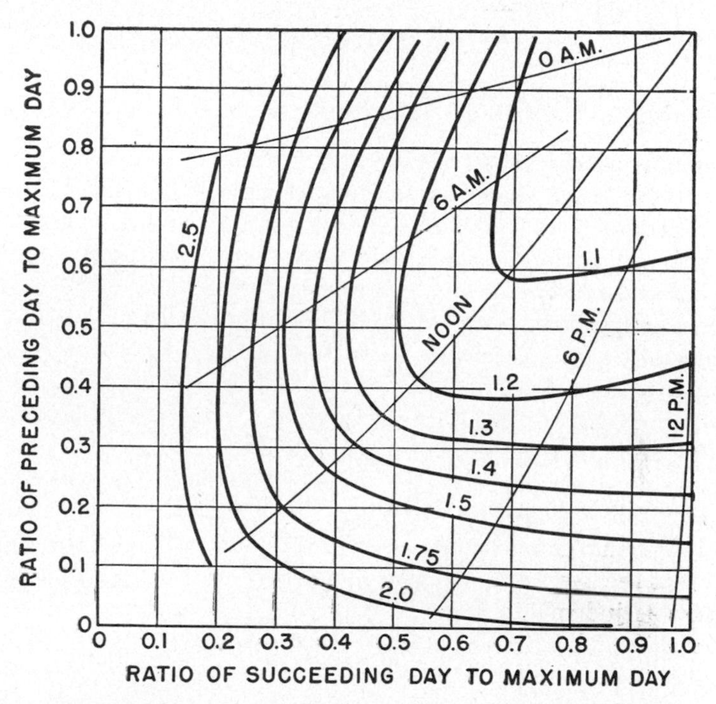

FIG. 9–24. Peak discharge and time of crest in relation to daily mean discharges. Labels on curves indicate clock time of crest on maximum day and ratio of instantaneous peak flow to maximum mean daily discharge. *(U.S. Geological Survey.)*

bulletin suggests that a fair approximation to the peak can be made by plotting the mean daily discharge and sketching a hydrograph in such a manner that the correct daily volumes are maintained. Langbein[2] derived the chart of Fig. 9-24 from reported data on peaks and corresponding mean daily flows. The ratio of peak flow to maximum daily flow and the time of peak are shown as functions of the ratios of mean flow on the maximum

[1] Jarvis, C. S., and others, Floods in the United States, *U.S. Geol. Survey Water Supply Paper* 771, pp. 90-96, 1936.

[2] Langbein, W. B., Peak Discharge from Daily Records, *U.S. Geol. Survey Water Resources Bull.*, Aug. 10, 1944, p. 145.

day to the average flow on the days immediately preceding and following the maximum day. Points falling near the upper or right-hand edges of the chart indicate crests on the days preceding or following the maximum day, respectively. Generalized charts of this type are of necessarily limited accuracy and should be used with caution. More reliable results can undoubtedly be obtained by developing a similar chart from data for the basin under consideration or from basins of similar size and topography.

MEANS AND EXTREMES OF STREAMFLOW

Normal annual runoff. Figure 9-25 is a map of normal (mean) annual runoff in the United States as developed by the U.S. Geological Survey. The preparation of such a map is difficult because of the dearth of data in some areas and because a streamflow record is a record of runoff, not at a point, but rather from an area. The runoff generation over a large river basin is usually not uniform, and measured runoff must be apportioned by some means if a reliable map is to be constructed.

In order to construct Fig. 9-25, values of average annual runoff in inches for the period 1921 to 1945 were computed for gaged streams and for increments of area between gages on the stream. All possible streamflow records were used, and short records were adjusted to the standard period by comparison with nearby stations. The computed averages were then entered on a map as values for specific areas and isolines drawn by inspection so that the average for each area corresponded to the computed value. Considerable judgment was required in interpreting precipitation, topography, and vegetal cover as indices to the shape and position of the isolines. Over large areas, the indicated runoff is probably quite representative of the average, but substantial errors may exist for small, ungaged areas, particularly in the mountain regions.

Median and extremes of runoff. Table 9-10 supplements the map of Fig. 9-25 by presenting the median annual and monthly runoff for selected stations. The median value is that which falls at the mid-point of the array in order of magnitude. In the distribution of runoff values it is somewhat lower than the mean. The maximum and minimum runoff for each month and for the year are also given. These data give some idea of the frequency distribution of runoff and of the seasonal distribution of flow in various parts of the country.

Figure 9-26 displays graphically the frequency distribution and seasonal variation of maximum monthly stages. The chart was prepared from an analysis of the highest stages occurring in each month of record. In most cases a distinct seasonal trend of median values is evident, but the maximum values of record are more erratic, indicating the possibility of occurrence of extremely high stages in almost every month of the year.

FIG. 9–25. Normal annual runoff in inches. *(U.S. Geological Survey.)*

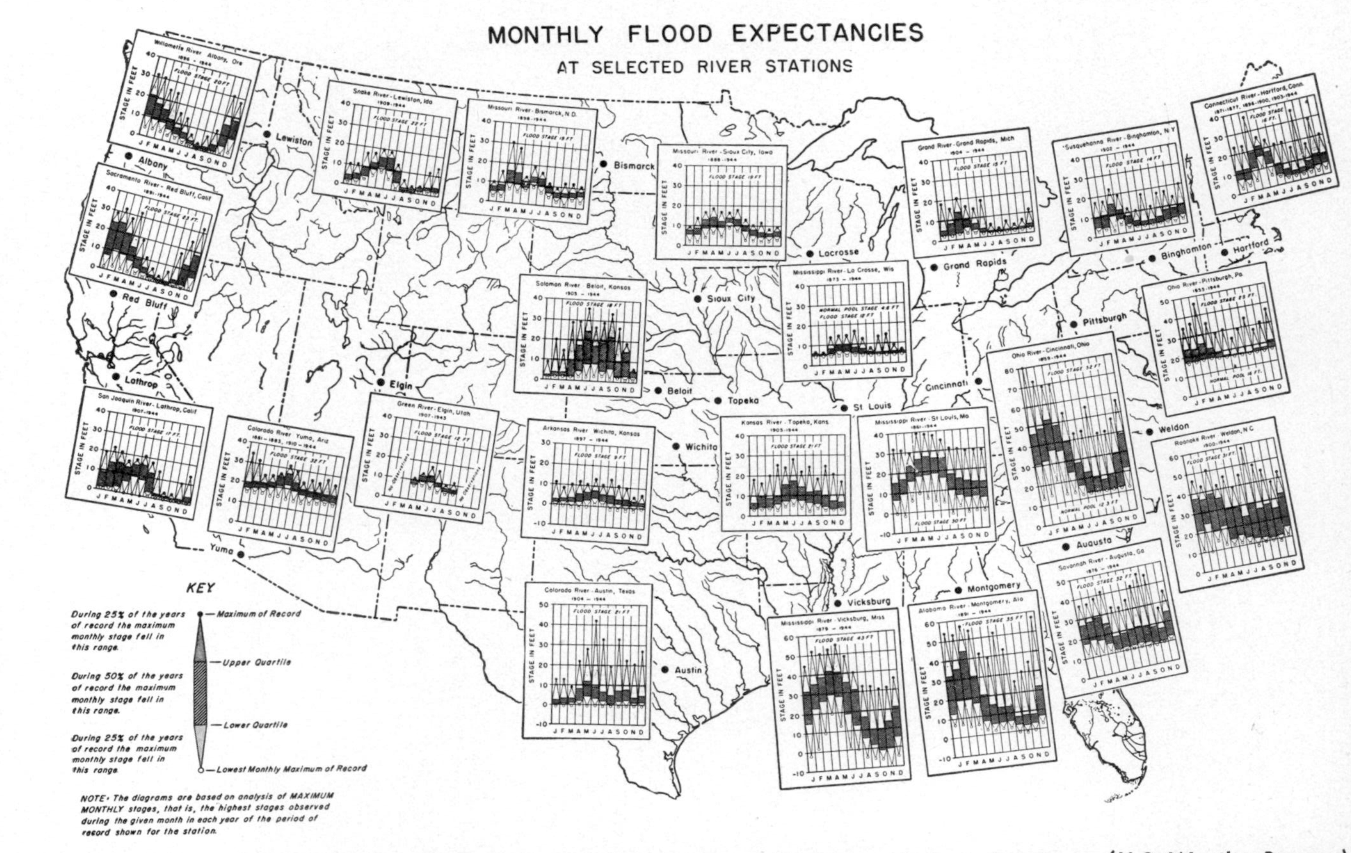

FIG. 9–26. Frequency and seasonal distribution of maximum monthly stages at selected stations. (*U.S. Weather Bureau.*)

Record peak flows. Table 9-11 summarizes record maximum instantaneous discharges and their dates of occurrence for selected stations throughout the United States. The table includes flows in second-feet per square mile and values of the Myers rating (Chap. 20) for comparative purposes. Most of these data were selected from the 1945 *Water Supply Papers* of the U.S. Geological Survey.

TABLE 9-10. Variation in Monthly and Annual Flows at Selected Stations

(All flows shown in cubic feet per second per square mile)

	Oct.	Nov.	Dec.	Jan.	Feb.	Mar.	Apr.	May	June	July	Aug.	Sept.	Water year
White R. at West Hartford, Vt., drainage area 690 square miles, record 1915-1946													
Maximum	3.50	3.14	3.38	3.08	2.41	10.40	8.82	6.85	2.88	1.92	1.76	4.01	2.22
Year	1945	1926	1938	1937	1925	1936	1933	1940	1917	1945	1943	1938	1937
Median	0.56	1.13	1.09	1.07	0.82	2.12	5.80	2.52	1.09	0.70	0.40	0.42	1.68
Minimum	0.31	0.44	0.34	0.29	0.24	0.32	2.12	0.92	0.32	0.20	0.15	0.19	1.03
Year	1930	1922	1922	1925	1940	1940	1946	1941	1921	1933	1934	1921	1941
South Br., Raritan R. nr. High Bridge, N.J., drainage area 65 square miles, record 1919-1946													
Maximum	3.94	5.14	4.25	3.00	4.61	7.15	4.27	3.31	2.94	3.98	4.36	2.62	3.26
Year	1927	1927	1927	1936	1925	1936	1940	1924	1940	1928	1942	1933	1928
Median	1.03	1.35	1.62	1.84	2.10	2.80	2.44	1.88	1.24	0.91	0.84	0.85	1.69
Minimum	0.37	0.49	0.64	0.61	0.83	1.59	1.45	0.83	0.70	0.49	0.36	0.38	0.89
Year	1941	1931	1946	1940	1934	1931	1935	1941	1932	1944	1944	1941	1932
Coosa R. at Childersburg, Ala., drainage area 8390 square miles, record 1914-1946													
Maximum	2.25	5.61	7.55	6.71	7.00	7.86	7.41	4.67	2.28	2.03	2.82	1.23	2.81
Year	1934	1929	1932	1937	1946	1929	1920	1929	1922	1920	1920	1920	1920
Median	0.42	0.50	1.07	1.97	2.62	2.62	2.21	1.19	0.87	0.73	0.74	0.72	1.55
Minimum	0.19	0.27	0.37	0.96	0.80	0.76	0.89	0.50	0.37	0.39	0.24	0.17	0.87
Year	1931	1931	1939	1942	1938	1914	1915	1941	1925	1925	1925	1925	1941
Allegheny R. at Franklin, Pa., drainage area 5982 square miles, record 1918-1946													
Maximum	3.42	4.15	5.56	6.92	5.29	8.33	8.35	4.99	2.91	1.59	1.19	1.91	2.51
Year	1926	1926	1927	1937	1938	1936	1940	1943	1928	1942	1937	1926	1943
Median	0.40	1.20	1.91	1.88	1.87	3.52	3.10	1.92	0.76	0.36	0.34	0.24	1.64
Minimum	0.09	0.13	0.72	0.41	0.51	1.56	1.41	0.47	0.18	0.09	0.07	0.07	1.08
Year	1930	1930	1930	1925	1934	1937	1935	1934	1934	1934	1930	1930	1931

French Broad R. at Asheville, N.C., drainage area 945 square miles, record 1895-1946

Maximum	6.35	3.95	6.32	6.42	5.91	10.31	7.96	6.02	6.11	12.18	9.94	6.15	4.70
Year	1906	1906	1901	1938	1899	1899	1899	1901	1909	1916	1901	1906	1901
Median	1.19	1.29	2.04	2.06	2.48	2.70	2.54	2.16	1.72	1.63	1.49	1.39	2.17
Minimum	0.46	0.43	0.66	0.91	1.09	1.32	1.26	0.98	0.77	0.62	0.35	0.39	1.28
Year	1904	1904	1904	1941	1898	1898	1896	1941	1925	1925	1925	1925	1926

East Fk., White R. at Shoals, Ind., drainage area 4940 square miles, record 1903-1946

Maximum	2.53	2.44	3.63	9.65	4.19	6.94	4.02	4.33	2.44	1.46	1.19	1.85	1.97
Year	1910	1925	1927	1937	1916	1945	1939	1933	1945	1915	1915	1926	1933
Median	0.17	0.31	0.46	0.93	1.40	1.90	1.75	0.88	0.47	0.32	0.27	0.20	1.10
Minimum	0.05	0.06	0.08	0.09	0.12	0.11	0.21	0.11	0.14	0.08	0.05	0.06	0.17
Year	1940	1914	1943	1909	1931	1941	1915	1941	1936	1930	1936	1940	1941

Yellowstone R. at Corwin Springs, Mont., drainage area 2630 square miles, record 1910-1946

Maximum	0.89	0.78	0.53	0.46	0.43	0.47	1.12	5.16	7.06	4.77	2.06	1.08	1.59
Year	1918	1927	1927	1912	1925	1916	1946	1928	1918	1943	1913	1917	1928
Median	0.58	0.45	0.38	0.34	0.34	0.36	0.53	1.92	4.06	2.25	1.06	0.69	1.04
Minimum	0.36	0.27	0.21	0.17	0.16	0.16	0.22	1.05	1.61	0.77	0.50	0.39	0.72
Year	1931	1936	1936	1937	1937	1937	1937	1912	1934	1919	1919	1934	1934

Smoky Hill R. at Enterprise, Kans., drainage area 19,200 square miles, record 1905-1946

Maximum	0.46	0.093	0.064	0.13	0.069	0.068	0.30	0.33	0.55	0.41	0.44	0.38	0.16
Year	1941	1941	1909	1910	1937	1919	1944	1944	1935	1915	1928	1946	1942
Median	0.020	0.012	0.010	0.010	0.013	0.017	0.020	0.050	0.112	0.052	0.044	0.031	0.042
Minimum	0.002	0.001	0.003	0.002	0.002	0.005	0.005	0.006	0.008	0.005	0.001	0.002	0.011
Year	1913	1913	1912	1912	1917	1935	1913	1907	1933	1913	1913	1913	1913

North Platte R. at Saratoga, Wyo., drainage area 2880 square miles, record 1904-1906, 1911-1946

Maximum	0.35	0.25	0.19	0.16	0.15	0.35	1.17	2.62	4.48	1.80	0.49	0.35	0.77
Year	1925	1927	1927	1928	1926	1916	1926	1928	1909	1909	1909	1909	1917
Median	0.14	0.12	0.10	0.09	0.09	0.14	0.52	1.30	1.72	0.42	0.15	0.10	0.42
Minimum	0.045	0.055	0.064	0.052	0.049	0.088	0.17	0.40	0.097	0.020	0.029	0.023	0.12
Year	1934	1934	1934	1933	1933	1924	1935	1934	1934	1934	1934	1934	1934

TABLE 9-10. Variation in Monthly and Annual Flows at Selected Stations — (*Concluded*)

(All flows shown in cubic feet per second per square mile)

	Oct.	Nov.	Dec.	Jan.	Feb.	Mar.	Apr.	May	June	July	Aug.	Sept.	Water year
Grand R. nr. Gallatin, Mo., drainage area 2250 square miles, record 1921-1946													
Maximum	2.90	3.83	0.96	1.87	0.88	2.41	3.52	3.43	3.68	2.74	0.83	5.16	1.35
Year	1926	1928	1931	1932	1937	1929	1927	1945	1935	1922	1944	1926	1929
Median	0.13	0.056	0.062	0.060	0.30	0.30	0.21	0.26	0.93	0.11	0.13	0.12	0.39
Minimum	0.002	0.004	0.003	0.002	0.003	0.008	0.033	0.034	0.027	0.006	0.003	0.005	0.052
Year	1938	1938	1938	1940	1939	1938	1938	1939	1933	1936	1936	1939	1934
Manistee R. near Sherman, Mich., drainage area 900 square miles, record 1903-1946													
Maximum	1.42	1.51	1.58	1.36	1.62	2.01	2.44	1.93	1.77	1.23	1.33	1.44	1.40
Year	1911	1945	1911	1916	1938	1913	1916	1904	1943	1905	1903	1912	1912
Median	1.08	1.20	1.11	1.16	1.10	1.32	1.68	1.36	1.19	1.06	1.00	1.05	1.21
Minimum	0.93	0.99	0.99	0.84	0.67	0.90	1.23	1.12	0.92	0.82	0.82	0.92	0.99
Year	1946	1938	1939	1936	1936	1940	1946	1937	1936	1936	1941	1936	1936
Red R. of the North at Grand Forks, N.D., drainage area 30,100 square miles, record 1882-1946													
Maximum	0.19	0.15	0.091	0.061	0.053	0.30	1.01	0.48	0.40	0.38	0.22	0.15	0.19
Year	1900	1900	1900	1901	1906	1945	1897	1883	1896	1916	1897	1905	1916
Median	0.016	0.015	0.012	0.009	0.010	0.033	0.120	0.065	0.052	0.030	0.014	0.015	0.038
Minimum	0.0004	0.001	0.0006	0.0006	0.0001	0.0014	0.032	0.012	0.005	0.003	0.001	0.0007	0.008
Year	1936	1936	1936	1937	1937	1937	1938	1934	1934	1936	1934	1936	1934
Neches R. at Evadale, Tex., drainage area 7908 square miles, record 1904-1906, 1923-1946													
Maximum	0.62	2.77	5.62	3.60	4.35	3.94	4.24	6.30	4.37	1.29	0.67	0.48	1.61
Year	1946	1941	1940	1932	1932	1932	1945	1944	1929	1905	1933	1942	1941
Median	0.063	0.140	0.42	1.16	1.29	1.25	0.99	0.89	0.49	0.21	0.12	0.072	0.72
Minimum	0.024	0.026	0.098	0.25	0.27	0.18	0.13	0.102	0.051	0.036	0.023	0.026	0.13
Year	1939	1904	1924	1928	1925	1925	1925	1925	1925	1925	1925	1925	1925
Roaring Fork at Glenwood Springs, Colo., drainage area 1460 square miles, record 1905-1909, 1910-1946													
Maximum	1.02	0.58	0.38	0.40	0.32	0.42	1.09	4.82	7.53	4.27	1.48	1.29	1.75
Year	1911	1929	1927	1933	1917	1916	1936	1914	1914	1914	1912	1929	1914
Median	0.45	0.38	0.31	0.28	0.25	0.28	0.63	2.20	3.94	1.82	0.69	0.50	0.95
Minimum	0.28	0.25	0.23	0.20	0.18	0.19	0.32	0.95	0.83	0.29	0.20	0.26	0.47
Year	1934	1934	1939	1935	1935	1935	1944	1915	1934	1934	1934	1934	1934

Salt R. nr. Roosevelt, Ariz., drainage area 4310 square miles, record 1913-1946

Maximum	0.33	0.50	1.07	3.01	2.09	1.94	1.40	1.17	0.32	0.76	0.84	0.43	0.70
Year	1916	1919	1919	1916	1920	1916	1915	1941	1941	1919	1921	1923	1916
Median	0.059	0.058	0.061	0.064	0.14	0.33	0.41	0.18	0.065	0.061	0.11	0.089	0.16
Minimum	0.036	0.037	0.046	0.045	0.053	0.092	0.074	0.046	0.025	0.030	0.061	0.046	0.076
Year	1938	1938	1939	1931	1925	1921	1921	1934	1946	1939	1944	1924	1934

Santa Ana R. nr. Mentone, Calif., drainage area 189 square miles, record 1896-1946

Maximum	0.58	0.63	1.68	1.27	4.39	7.43	2.92	2.37	1.30	0.93	0.66	0.57	1.24
Year	1916	1907	1922	1907	1927	1938	1907	1922	1922	1922	1922	1906	1938
Median	0.31	0.24	0.24	0.24	0.37	0.39	0.51	0.45	0.39	0.39	0.39	0.36	0.37
Minimum	0.140	0.102	0.105	0.127	0.164	0.159	0.161	0.172	0.167	0.137	0.132	0.127	0.180
Year	1931	1929	1929	1902	1930	1931	1934	1931	1931	1902	1902	1902	1931

Kings R. at Piedra, Calif., drainage area 1694 square miles, record 1895-1946

Maximum	1.14	0.81	1.67	2.50	2.82	3.59	4.45	7.50	9.99	9.61	2.59	0.67	3.18
Year	1904	1900	1937	1914	1937	1938	1916	1897	1906	1906	1906	1906	1906
Median	0.12	0.15	0.27	0.35	0.68	0.98	2.09	4.19	3.60	1.26	0.31	0.14	1.22
Minimum	0.064	0.066	0.080	0.12	0.17	0.20	0.73	1.37	0.31	0.12	0.062	0.045	0.32
Year	1934	1929	1929	1926	1924	1924	1912	1934	1924	1924	1924	1924	1924

Umpqua R. nr. Elkton, Ore., drainage area 3680 square miles, record 1905-1946

Maximum	1.60	6.19	10.10	8.53	8.91	7.19	5.57	4.29	2.50	1.36	0.44	0.95	3.29
Year	1920	1924	1942	1909	1907	1938	1937	1921	1917	1913	1916	1920	1921
Median	0.35	1.31	2.68	3.75	3.54	2.92	2.36	1.60	0.93	0.41	0.30	0.29	1.87
Minimum	0.23	0.23	0.37	0.60	0.91	0.94	0.66	0.52	0.28	0.20	0.19	0.20	0.86
Year	1929	1929	1936	1937	1931	1941	1926	1934	1926	1926	1931	1931	1931

Kootenay R. at Wardner, B.C., drainage area 5200 square miles, record 1914-1946

Maximum	1.57	1.05	0.66	0.70	0.47	0.50	2.83	5.25	6.60	5.27	2.06	2.13	2.25
Year	1927	1927	1941	1919	1928	1934	1934	1934	1933	1916	1916	1927	1916
Median	0.62	0.46	0.35	0.31	0.29	0.29	0.79	2.54	4.61	2.52	1.28	0.79	1.35
Minimum	0.39	0.28	0.26	0.21	0.22	0.16	0.29	1.75	1.87	1.30	0.70	0.60	0.80
Year	1936	1936	1922	1937	1931	1914	1945	1920	1926	1926	1926	1936	1926

TABLE 9-11. Record Peak Flows at Selected Stations

Stream	Station	Peak flow		Drainage area, square miles	Myers rating	Date
		Cfs	Csm			
The North Atlantic Slope Drainage						
Indian Run	Nr. Long Level, Pa.	4,050	1,940	2.1	28	7/–/14
Strong's Brook	Nr. Smithville Flats, N.Y.	6,650	1,040	6.4	26	7/–/35
Saw Kill	Nr. Shady, N.Y.	9,180	966	9.5	30	7/–/35
Salem Cr.	At Woodstown, N.J.	22,000	1,508	14.6	58	9/1/40
Merrill Cr.	Nr. Upper Lisle, N.Y.	15,100	726	20.8	33	7/–/35
Ellis R.	Nr. Jackson, N.H.	14,800	529	28	28	11/–/27
Dudley Cr.	Nr. Lisle, N.Y.	16,200	547	29.6	30	7/–/35
Middle Br., Westfield R.	At Goss Heights, Mass.	19,900	378	52.6	27	9/21/38
Cancadea Cr.	At Hornell, N.Y.	21,000	354	59.4	27	7/–/35
Rondout Cr.	Nr. Lackawack, N.Y.	26,700	267	100	27	8/26/28
Westfield R.	At Knightsville, Mass.	37,900	234	162	30	9/21/38
Robertson R.	Nr. Locust Dale, Va.	44,000	244	180	33	10/15/42
Octoraro Cr.	Nr. Rising Sun, Md.	35,000	183	191	25	8/9/42
Esopus Cr.	At Coldbrook, N.Y.	55,000	286	192	40	8/24/33
Sherman R.	At Shermandale, Pa.	37,000	185	200	26	7/22/27
North Fk., Shenandoah R.	At Cootes Store, Va.	50,000	232	215	34	10/15/42
Farmington R.	At Riverton, Conn.	37,100	172	216	25	9/21/38
Schoharie R.	At Prattsville, N.Y.	45,000	191	236	29	9/21/38
South Fk., South Br., Potomac R.	Nr. Moorefield, W. Va.	43,000	152	283	26	3/17/36
Hazel R.	At Rixeyville, Va.	60,000	210	286	35	10/15/42
Lackawaxen R.	At Hawley, Pa.	50,000	173	290	29	5/23/42
Frankstown Br., Juniata R.	At Williamsburg, Pa.	47,600	164	291	28	3/18/36
West R.	At Newfane, Vt.	52,300	170	308	30	9/21/38
Swatara R.	At Harper Tavern, Pa.	53,000	159	333	29	6/1/89
Deerfield R.	At Charlemont, Mass.	56,300	156	362	30	9/21/38

Shetucket R.	Nr. Willimantic, Conn.	52,200	130	401	26	9/21/38
Rapidan R.	Nr. Culpeper, Va.	58,100	125	465	27	10/16/42
Rappahannock R.	At Remington, Va.	90,000	146	616	36	10/16/42
Pemigewasset R.	At Plymouth, N.H.	65,400	105	622	26	3/19/36
Cacapon R.	Nr. Great Cacapon, W. Va.	87,600	129	677	34	3/18/36
White R.	At West Hartford, Vt.	120,000	174	690	46	11/4/27
Raystown Br., Juniata R.	At Saxton, Pa.	80,500	106	756	29	3/18/36
North Fk., Shenandoah R.	Nr. Strasburg, Va.	100,000	130	772	36	10/16/42
Frankstown Br., Juniata R.	At Huntingdon, Pa.	81,000	99	816	28	3/18/36
North Br., Potomac R.	Nr. Cumberland, Md.	89,000	102	875	30	6/1/89
South Br., Potomac R.	Nr. Springfield, W. Va.	143,000	97	1,471	37	3/18/36
Rappahannock R.	Nr. Fredericksburg, Va.	140,000	88	1,599	35	10/16/42
South Fk., Shenandoah R.	At Front Royal, Va.	130,000	79	1,638	32	10/16/42
Schuylkill R.	At Philadelphia, Pa.	135,000	71	1,893	31	10/4/69
West Br., Susquehanna R.	At Renovo, Pa.	236,000	79	2,975	43	3/18/36
Shenandoah R.	At Millville, W. Va.	230,000	76	3,040	42	10/16/42
Juniata R.	At Newport, Pa.	209,000	62	3,354	36	6/1/89
Potomac R.	At Hancock, Md.	340,000	83	4,073	53	3/18/36
West Br., Susquehanna R.	At Williamsport, Pa.	264,000	46	5,682	35	3/18/36
Delaware R.	At Riegelsville, N.J.	275,000	43	6,328	35	10/10/03
Potomac R.	At Point of Rocks, Md.	480,000	50	9,651	49	3/19/36
Connecticut R.	At Thompsonville, Conn.	282,000	29	9,661	29	3/20/36
Susquehanna R.	At Harrisburg, Pa.	740,000	31	24,100	48	3/19/36

South Atlantic and Eastern Gulf of Mexico Drainage

Morgan Cr.	Nr. Chapel Hill, N.C.	30,000	1,110	27	58	8/4/24
Yadkin R.	At Patterson, N.C.	16,200	563	29	30	8/13/40
Linville R.	At Branch, N.C.	39,500	608	65	49	8/13/40
Henry Fk.	Nr. Henry River, N.C.	31,300	391	80	35	8/13/40
Prairie Cr.	Nr. Gallion, Ala.	39,000	230	170	30	12/28/42
Yadkin R.	At Wilkesboro, N.C.	160,000	324	493	72	8/14/40
Rocky R.	Nr. Norwood, N.C.	155,000	113	1,370	42	9/18/45

TABLE 9-11. Record Peak Flows at Selected Stations — (*Continued*)

Stream	Station	Peak flow		Drainage area, square miles	Myers rating	Date
		Cfs	Csm			
South Atlantic and Eastern Gulf of Mexico Drainage — (*Continued*)						
Catawba R.	At Catawba, N.C.	177,000	115	1,535	45	8/14/40
Cape Fear R.	At Lillington, N.C.	192,000	56	3,440	33	9/19/45
Choctawatchee R.	At Caryville, Fla.	206,000	59	3,490	35	3/17/29
Escambia R.	Nr. Century, Fla.	315,000	85	3,700	52	3/–/29
Black Warrior R.	At Tuscaloosa, Ala.	215,000	45	4,830	31	4/18/00
Broad R.	At Richtex, S.C.	228,000	47	4,850	33	10/3/29
Pee Dee R.	Nr. Rockingham, N.C.	270,000	39	6,870	33	9/18/45
Roanoke R.	At Clarkesville, Va.	280,000	38	7,320	33	8/17/40
Savannah R.	At Augusta, Ga.	350,000	47	7,508	40	10/3/29
Ohio River Basin						
Elk Cr.	Nr. Elk Park, N.C.	27,500	655	42	42	8/13/40
South Toe R.	At Newdale, N.C.	29,400	484	61	38	8/13/40
Watauga R.	Nr. Sugar Grove, N.C.	50,800	560	91	54	8/13/40
White Cr.	At Glen Alice, Tenn.	35,500	261	136	30	3/2/34
Tuckaseegee R.	At Tuckaseegee, N.C.	40,800	286	143	34	8/30/40
Twin Cr.	Nr. Germantown, Ohio	66,000	240	275	40	3/25/13
North Fk., New R.	At Crumpler, N.C.	79,400	286	277	48	8/14/40
New R.	At New R., Tenn.	70,000	224	312	40	3/23/29
Tuckaseegee R.	At Dillsboro, N.C.	52,600	152	347	28	8/30/40
Watauga R.	At Butler, Tenn.	71,500	168	427	35	8/13/40
Nolichucky R.	At Poplar, N.C.	74,500	122	608	30	8/13/40
Collins R.	Nr. McMinnville, Tenn.	75,300	121	624	30	3/23/29
Mad R.	Nr. Dayton, Ohio	75,700	120	632	30	3/25/13

Stillwater R.	At Englewood, Ohio	85,400	132	646	34	3/–/13
Gauley R.	Nr. Summersville, W. Va.	92,000	135	680	35	7/4/32
Conemaugh R.	At Seward, Pa.	90,000	126	715	34	3/18/36
Emory R.	At Oakdale, Tenn.	195,000	256	764	71	3/23/29
French Broad R.	At Asheville, N.C.	110,000	117	945	36	7/16/16
Cheat R.	At Rowlesburg, W. Va.	125,000	129	972	40	7/6/1844
Miami R.	At Taylorsville, Ohio	127,000	110	1,155	37	3/–/13
South Fk., Cumberland R.	At Nevelsville, Ky.	160,000	127	1,264	45	3/23/29
Gauley R.	Above Belva, W. Va.	105,000	80	1,315	29	7/5/32
New R.	At Ivanhoe, Va.	155,000	116	1,340	42	8/14/40
Scioto R.	At Columbus, Ohio	138,000	85	1,624	34	3/25/13
Caney Fk.	Nr. Rock island, Tenn.	210,000	128	1,640	52	3/23/29
Kiskiminetas R.	At Vandergrift, Pa.	185,000	101	1,825	43	3/18/36
New R.	At Radford, Va.	218,000	79	2,748	42	8/14/40
Miami R.	At Hamilton, Ohio	352,000	97	3,639	58	3/26/13
Scioto R.	At Chillicothe, Ohio	260,000	68	3,847	42	3/26/13
New R.	At Hinton, Va.	246,000	39	6,257	31	8/15/40
Muskingum R.	At McConnelsville, Ohio	270,000	36	7,411	31	3/27/13
Kanawha R.	At Kanawha Falls, W. Va.	320,000	38	8,367	35	9/14/78
Allegheny R.	At Natrona, Pa.	365,000	32	11,410	34	3/18/36
Ohio R.	At Sewickley, Pa.	574,000	29	19,500	41	3/18/36
Ohio R.	At Pomeroy, Ohio	633,000	16	40,500	31	3/30/13
Ohio R.	At Cincinnati, Ohio	894,000	12	76,580	32	1/26/37
Ohio R.	At Owensboro, Ky.	1,210,000	12	97,200	39	1/28/37
St. Lawrence Basin						
Glen Cr.	Nr. Townsend, N.Y.	7,330	2,530	2.9	43	7/–/35
Trumansburg Cr.	At Trumansburg, N.Y.	17,800	1,550	11.5	52	7/–/35
Glen Cr.	At Watkins Glen, N.Y.	27,900	1,310	21.3	61	7/–/35
Lamoille R.	At Cays Falls, Vt.	36,600	125	293	21	11/–/27
Winooski R.	At Montpelier, Vt.	57,000	144	397	29	11/3/27
Lamoille R.	At Fairfax Falls, Vt.	66,900	120	559	28	11/4/27
Missisquoi R.	At Sheldon Springs, Vt.	62,900	78	812	22	11/4/27
Winooski R.	Nr. Essex Junction, Vt.	113,000	108	1,044	35	11/4/27

TABLE 9-11. Record Peak Flows at Selected Stations — *(Continued)*

Stream	Station	Peak flow		Drainage area, square miles	Myers rating	Date
		Cfs	Csm			
Hudson Bay and Upper Mississippi Basins						
Panther Cr.	Nr. Viele, Iowa	7,300	520	14	19	6/10/05
Little Devils Cr.	Nr. Viele, Iowa	10,700	560	19	24	6/10/05
Dry Run	At Decorah, Iowa	16,000	720	22.3	34	3/15/19
Little Maquoketa R.	Nr. Durango, Iowa	23,500	181	130	21	6/13/47
Salt Cr.	Nr. Elberon, Iowa	34,000	170	200	24	6/–/44
Big Eau Pleine R.	Nr. Stratford, Wis.	41,000	183	224	27	9/9/38
North R.	Nr. Norwalk, Iowa	30,000	86	348	16	6/13/47
South R.	Nr. Ackworth, Iowa	32,000	67	475	15	6/5/47
Jump R.	At Sheldon, Wis.	46,000	90	510	20	8/31/41
Black R.	At Neillsville, Wis.	48,800	65	756	18	9/10/38
Cuivre R.	Nr. Troy, Mo.	120,000	133	903	40	10/5/42
Sangamon R.	At Riverton, Ill.	68,700	27	2,560	14	5/19/43
Chippewa R.	At Chippewa Falls, Wis.	102,000	18	5,600	14	9/1/41
St. Croix R.	At St. Croix Falls, Wis.	35,800	6	5,930	5	3/26/20
Des Moines R.	Nr. Tracy, Iowa	168,000	14	12,400	15	6/14/47
Mississippi R.	At Keokuk, Iowa	360,000	3	119,000	10	6/6/1851
Missouri Basin						
Magpie Gulch	Nr. Golden, Colo.	1,900	1,270	1.5	16	7/26/23
Missouri Canyon	Sec 26, T6N, R70W	4,350	1,810	2.4	28	6/15/23
Sand Coulee	Nr. Dubois, Wyo.	6,700	515	13	19	7/24/34
Bayou Gulch	Nr. Parker, Colo.	8,670	456	19	20	7/28/22
Waubonsie Cr.	Nr. Bartlett, Iowa	9,450	315	30	17	6/4/47
Cherry Cr.	Nr. Parker, Colo.	17,000	195	87	18	7/28/22

Blue R.	Nr. Kansas City, Mo.	26,400	141	188	19	4/23/44
Little Piney Cr.	At Newburgh, Mo.	30,000	150	200	21	8/20/15
Medicine Cr.	Nr. Galt, Mo.	24,200	108	225	16	6/6/47
Vermilion Cr.	Nr. Wamego, Kans.	38,500	169	228	26	–/–/15
Weldon R.	Nr. Mercer, Mo.	24,600	100	246	16	6/5/47
Marmaton R.	Nr. Ft. Scott, Kans.	34,200	83	411	17	5/18/43
Lamine R.	At Clifton City, Mo.	60,000	100	598	25	5/18/43
Pomme de Terre R.	At Hermitage, Mo.	70,000	107	655	27	8/8/27
Medicine Cr.	At Cambridge, Neb.	100,000	125	800	35	6/22/47
Delaware R.	At Valley Falls, Kans.	45,900	50	922	15	6/16/45
Blackwater R.	At Blue Lick, Mo.	54,000	48	1,120	16	11/18/28
Sac R.	Nr. Stockton, Mo.	120,000	104	1,160	35	5/19/43
Gasconade R.	Nr. Hazelgreen, Mo.	76,400	61	1,250	22	4/14/45
Osage R.	Nr. Ottawa, Kans.	75,000	60	1,260	21	11/17/28
South Fk., Republican R.	At Newton, Colo.	103,000	81	1,270	29	5/31/35
South Grand R.	Nr. Brownington, Mo.	63,900	38	1,660	16	11/19/28
Thompson R.	At Trenton, Mo.	95,000	57	1,670	23	6/5/47
South Fk., Republican R.	Below St. Francis, Kans.	150,000	68	2,200	32	5/–/35
Gasconade R.	At Jerome, Mo.	120,000	42	2,840	23	1/6/97
Osage R.	At Trading Post, Kans.	120,000	41	2,910	22	11/18/28
North Loup R.	Nr. St. Paul, Neb.	90,000	24	3,720	15	6/6/96
Republican R.	At Max, Neb.	190,000	33	5,840	25	5/31/35
Grand R.	Nr. Sumner, Mo.	160,000	23	6,880	19	6/8/47
Osage R.	Nr. Bagnell, Mo.	220,000	16	14,000	19	5/19/43
Republican R.	Nr. Bloomington, Neb.	260,000	14	19,000	19	6/1/35

Lower Mississippi Basin

Council Cr.	Nr. Stillwater, Okla.	18,000	596	30.2	33	8/14/42
West Fk., White R.	Nr. Fayetteville, Ark.	53,000	450	118	49	4/14/45
Sallisaw Cr.	Nr. Sallisaw, Okla.	110,000	608	181	82	4/15/45
South Fourche La Fave R.	Nr. Hollis, Ark.	54,400	254	214	37	3/30/45

TABLE 9-11. Record Peak Flows at Selected Stations — (*Continued*)

Stream	Station	Peak flow		Drainage area, square miles	Myers rating	Date
		Cfs	Csm			
Lower Mississippi Basin, *Continued*						
Middle Fk., Little Red R.	At Shirley, Ark.	60,700	206	294	35	5/11/43
Cypress Cr.	Nr. Pittsburg, Tex.	58,500	175	334	32	3/30/45
Little Missouri R.	Nr. Murfreesboro, Ark.	120,000	316	380	62	3/30/45
Mountain Fork R.	Nr. Eagletown, Okla.	88,500	113	784	32	3/29/45
Elk R.	Nr. Tiff City, Mo.	137,000	162	848	47	4/19/41
St. Francis R.	Nr. Patterson, Mo.	100,000	105	956	32	8/–/15
Black R.	At Leeper, Mo.	125,000	130	957	40	3/–/04
Buffalo R.	Nr. Rush, Ark.	164,000	150	1,091	50	8/19/15
Ouachita R.	Nr. Mountain Pine, Ark.	123,000	112	1,100	37	3/30/45
Ouachita R.	Nr. Malvern, Ark.	140,000	89	1,570	35	5/15/23
Spring R.	Nr. Quapaw, Okla.	190,000	74	2,580	37	5/19/43
White R.	Nr. Reeds Spring, Mo.	196,000	54	3,617	33	4/16/45
White R.	Nr. Flippin, Ark.	240,000	40	6,067	31	4/16/27
White R.	Nr. Calico Rock, Ark.	310,000	31	9,973	31	4/16/45
Neosho R.	Nr. Choteau, Okla.	400,000	34	11,650	37	5/20/43
Arkansas R.	Nr. Muskogee, Okla.	700,000	7	96,800	23	5/21/43
Western Gulf of Mexico Drainage						
Red Bank Cr.	Nr. San Angelo, Tex.	2,490	3,280	0.8	29	9/17/36
Seven Mile Draw	At Ames, Tex.	5,140	2,140	2.4	33	9/26/36
Bunton Br.	Nr. Kyle, Tex.	13,800	3,370	4.1	68	6/30/36
Dry Cr.	Nr. San Angelo, Tex.	24,600	1,760	14	66	9/17/36
Alazan Cr.	Below Martinez Cr., Tex.	25,900	1,510	17.1	63	9/9/21
Atacosa R.	Nr. Benton City, Tex.	25,900	1,220	21.3	56	6/22/24

Sabinal R.	At Vanderpool, Tex.	52,300	1,140	45.7	78	7/2/32
East Fk., James R.	At Old Noxville, Tex.	105,000	1,730	61	135	7/1/32
South Fk., Guadalupe R.	Nr. Hunt, Tex.	84,300	1,290	65.3	104	7/1/32
East Fk., Frio R.	Nr. Leakey, Tex.	89,500	1,190	75	104	7/1/32
North Fk., Guadalupe R.	Nr. Hunt, Tex.	108,000	982	110	103	7/1/32
Johnson Cr.	Nr. Ingram, Tex.	138,000	1,240	111	131	7/2/32
West Fk., Copperas Cr.	Nr. Roosevelt, Tex.	98,900	838	118	91	9/16/36
Salado Cr.	Nr. Salado, Tex.	143,000	966	148	117	9/10/21
Seco Cr.	Nr. D'Hanis, Tex.	230,000	1,500	153	185	5/31/35
West Nueces R.	Nr. Brackettville, Tex.	580,000	1,440	402	290	6/14/35
Llano R.	Nr. Junction, Tex.	319,000	181	1,762	76	6/14/35
Nueces R.	Below Uvalde, Tex.	616,000	317	1,947	140	6/14/35
Devils R.	Nr. Juno, Tex.	370,000	135	2,733	71	9/1/32
Little R.	At Cameron, Tex.	647,000	92	7,034	77	9/10/21

Colorado River Basin

Skyrocket Cr.	At Ouray, Colo.	2,000	2,000	1	20	7/20/23
Sonoita Cr.	Nr. Patagonia, Ariz.	20,000	95	210	14	8/–/34
San Juan R.	At Pagosa Springs, Colo.	25,000	84	298	14	10/5/11
Clear Cr.	Nr. Winslow, Ariz.	50,000	82	607	20	4/4/29
San Pedro R.	At Charleston, Ariz.	98,000	80	1,220	28	9/28/26
Agua Fria	Nr. Glendale, Ariz.	105,000	74	1,420	28	11/27/19
San Pedro R.	Nr. Redington, Ariz.	90,000	31	2,940	17	9/28/26
Salt R.	Nr. Roosevelt, Ariz.	117,000	27	4,310	18	3/14/41
Bill Williams R.	At Planet, Ariz.	200,000	39	5,140	28	2/21/91

The Great Basin

Rock Cr.	Nr. Valyermo, Calif.	8,300	361	23	17	3/2/38
Donner Cr.	Nr. Truckee, Calif.	1,800	62	29	3	12/11/37
Little Rock Cr.	Nr. Little Rock, Calif.	17,000	347	49	24	3/2/38
Markleeville Cr.	At Markleeville, Calif.	3,500	66	53	5	12/11/37
West Fk., Carson R.	At Woodfords, Calif.	3,500	52	68	4	12/11/37
West Fk., Mojave R.	Nr. Hesperia, Calif.	26,100	348	75	30	3/2/38

TABLE 9-11. Record Peak Flows at Selected Stations — (*Continued*)

Stream	Station	Peak flow		Drainage area, square miles	Myers rating	Date
		Cfs	Csm			
	The Great Basin, *Continued*					
Coal Cr.	Nr. Cedar City, Utah	2,910	32	92	3	7/9/36
Palm Canyon Cr.	Nr. Palm Springs, Calif.	3,850	41	94	4	2/6/37
Deep Cr.	Nr. Hesperia, Calif.	46,600	340	137	40	3/2/38
Little Truckee R.	At Boca, Calif.	6,200	41	150	5	12/11/37
Weber R.	Nr. Oakley, Utah	4,010	25	163	3	7/6/07
Martin Cr.	Nr. Paradise Valley, Nev.	9,000	52	172	7	1/21/43
West Walker R.	Nr. Coleville, Calif.	5,800	32	182	4	12/11/37
Deep Cr.	Above Adel, Ore.	5,030	20	249	3	12/11/37
East Fk., Carson R.	Nr. Gardnerville, Nev.	12,000	33	360	6	12/11/37
Weber R.	At Gateway, Utah	7,980	5	1,610	2	5/31/96
Bear R.	Nr. Collinston, Utah	11,600	2	6,000	1	6/7/09
	Pacific Slope Basins in California					
Cucamonga Cr.	Nr. Upland, Calif.	10,300	1,020	10.1	32	3/2/38
San Antonio Cr.	Nr. Claremont, Calif.	21,400	1,267	16.9	52	3/2/38
Lytle Cr.	Nr. Fontana, Calif.	25,200	527	47.9	36	3/2/38
Santa Ysabel Cr.	Nr. Mesa Grande, Calif.	21,000	362	58	28	1/27/16
West Fk., San Gabriel R.	At Camp Rincon, Calif.	34,000	334	102	34	3/2/38
Tujunga Cr.	Nr. Sunland, Calif.	50,000	471	106	49	3/2/38
Santa Ysabel Cr.	Nr. Ramona, Calif.	28,400	258	110	27	1/27/16
San Jacinto R.	Nr. San Jacinto, Calif.	45,000	322	140	38	2/16/27
Ventura R.	Nr. Ventura, Calif.	39,200	210	187	29	3/2/38
Santa Ana R.	Nr. Mentone, Calif.	52,300	277	189	38	3/2/38
San Gabriel R.	Nr. Azusa, Calif.	65,700	311	211	45	3/2/38
Sespe Cr.	Nr. Fillmore, Calif.	56,000	220	254	35	3/2/38
Nacimiento R.	Nr. San Miguel, Calif.	50,800	143	354	27	1/21/43
Los Angeles R.	At Los Angeles, Calif.	67,000	131	510	30	3/2/38
South Fk., Eel R.	Nr. Miranda, Calif.	69,200	127	547	30	1/21/43
Smith R.	Nr. Crescent City, Calif.	91,400	149	613	37	12/31/42

Los Angeles R.	Nr. Downey, Calif.	79,700	130	614	32	3/2/38
Putah Cr.	Nr. Winters, Calif.	70,500	115	614	28	2/27/40
Middle Fk., American R.	Nr. Auburn, Calif.	62,000	100	619	25	3/25/28
North Fk., American R.	At Rattlesnake Br., Calif.	95,000	95	999	30	1/21/43
American R.	At Fair Oaks, Calif.	140,000	73	1,921	32	3/25/28
Eel R.	At Scotia, Calif.	345,000	112	3,070	62	12/11/37
Feather R.	Nr. Oroville, Calif.	230,000	64	3,611	38	3/19/07
Sacramento R.	Nr. Red Bluff, Calif.	291,000	31	9,300	30	2/28/40
Pacific Slope Basins in Washington and Upper Columbia Basin						
North Fk., Skokomish R.	Nr. Hoodsport, Wash.	23,300	388	60	30	11/5/34
Wynoochee R.	Nr. Aberdeen, Wash.	18,000	277	65	22	1/22/35
South Fk., Skokomish R.	Nr. Union, Wash.	21,600	267	81	24	1/22/35
Soleduck R.	Nr. Fairholm, Wash.	24,300	290	84	27	12/21/33
Sultan R.	Nr. Sultan, Wash.	24,600	280	88	26	12/12/21
Wynoochee R.	Nr. Montesano, Wash.	25,000	238	105	25	2/11/24
Soleduck R.	Nr. Beaver, Wash.	23,500	212	111	22	12/12/21
South Fk., Stillaguamish R.	Nr. Granite Falls, Wash.	26,700	224	119	24	2/26/32
Clearwater R.	Nr. Clearwater, Wash.	29,200	209	140	25	10/28/37
Baker R.	Nr. Concrete, Wash.	36,800	200	184	27	12/29/17
Hoh R.	Nr. Spruce, Wash.	40,000	207	193	29	11/5/34
North R.	Nr. Raymond, Wash.	35,000	160	219	24	12/10/33
Green R.	Nr. Palmer, Wash.	33,600	145	231	22	12/9/33
South Fk., Stillaguamish R.	Nr. Arlington, Wash.	35,000	138	254	22	2/26/32
Quinault R.	At Quinault Lake, Wash.	37,000	140	264	23	12/12/21
Satsop R.	Nr. Satsop, Wash.	52,500	167	315	30	1/22/35
South Fk., Skykomish R.	Nr. Index, Wash.	57,000	161	355	30	12/18/17
Queets R.	Nr. Clearwater, Wash.	100,000	220	454	47	1/22/35
Skykomish R.	Nr. Gold Bar, Wash.	79,000	148	535	34	12/21/33
Sauk R.	Nr. Sauk, Wash.	68,500	96	714	26	2/26/32
Skagit R.	Nr. Concrete, Wash.	147,000*	54	2,700	28	2/27/32
Skagit R.	Nr. Sedro Wooley, Wash.	220,000	74	2,970	40	11/30/09
Flathead R.	At Columbia Falls, Mont.	150,000	34	4,440	23	6/–/94
Columbia R.	At Kettle Falls, Wash.	700,000	11	64,500	28	6/–/94
Columbia R.	At Grand Coulee, Wash.	725,000	10	74,100	27	6/–/94

* A flood about 1815 is believed to have attained a peak of 500,000 cfs.

TABLE 9-11. Record Peak Flows at Selected Stations — (*Concluded*)

Stream	Station	Peak flow		Drainage area, square miles	Myers rating	Date
		Cfs	Csm			
Snake River Basin						
Squaw Cr.	Nr. Gross, Idaho	1,010	48	21	2	6/8/27
Lake Fk., Payette R.	Nr. McCall, Idaho	2,520	46	55	3	6/9/33
North Fk., Payette R.	At McCall, Idaho	4,260	30	144	4	6/10/33
Johnson Cr.	At Yellow Pine, Idaho	5,150	24	213	4	6/9/33
Snake R.	At Moran, Wyo.	15,100	18	816	5	6/12/18
South Fk., Salmon R.	Nr. Warren, Idaho	23,000	20	1,160	7	5/28/48
Lochsa R.	Nr. Lowell, Idaho	34,800	30	1,180	10	6/10/33
Selway R.	Nr. Lowell, Idaho	48,900	26	1,510	13	5/29/48
North Fk., Clearwater R.	Nr. Ahsanka, Idaho	100,000	41	2,440	20	12/23/33
Clearwater R.	At Kamiah, Idaho	99,000	20	4,850	14	5/29/48
Clearwater R.	At Spalding, Idaho	177,000	18	9,570	18	5/29/48
Snake R.	Nr. Clarkston, Wash.	409,000	4	103,200	13	6/5/94
Pacific Slope Basins in Oregon and Lower Columbia River Basin						
Balm Cr.	Nr. Heppner, Ore.	36,000	1,800	20	80	6/14/03
Siletz R.	At Siletz, Ore.	40,800	202	202	29	11/20/21
Sandy R.	Nr. Bull Run, Ore.	58,000	132	440	28	3/31/31
South Santiam R.	At Waterloo, Ore.	70,000	109	640	28	3/31/31
Lewis R.	At Ariel, Wash.	129,000	176	731	48	12/22/33
Santiam R.	At Jefferson, Ore.	176,000	98	1,790	42	11/21/21
Cowlitz R.	At Castle Rock, Wash.	139,000	62	2,240	29	12/23/33
Umpqua R.	Nr. Elkton, Ore.	172,000	47	3,680	28	2/21/27
Willamette R.	At Albany, Ore.	340,000	70	4,840	49	12/4/61
Willamette R.	At Salem, Ore.	500,000	69	7,280	59	12/4/61

10

THE BASIN

The practical hydrologist engaged in problems of design or forecasting deals individually with each river and with the drainage area which is its water source. The theoretical hydrologist studying the water balance of the hydrologic cycle is also forced to seek an area of such dimensions as to make a rational accounting reasonably practical. His selection is usually also the river basin. The physical characteristics of the river basin thus become important factors in hydrology. The role of the streams in shaping the physical features of their basins is naturally of considerable interest to the hydrologist, although these changes are, for the most part, of little importance in the direct application of hydrology as it is described in this book. Hydrology does, however, play an important role in the study of short-term erosion processes.

The purpose of this chapter is twofold: (1) It explains the terminology with which the hydrologist describes a river basin and the measurement of the physical features which affect its hydrologic characteristics. (2) It serves as a brief introduction to the broad field of geomorphology. If any reader wishes to learn more of the formation of landscapes than can be included here, he is referred to detailed texts[1] on the subject.

River basins. A *river*, or *drainage, basin* is the entire area drained by a stream or system of connecting streams such that all streamflow originating in the area is discharged through a single outlet. Multiple channels through alluvial delta deposits constitute a single outlet. Subsurface flow may or may not conform to surface drainage boundaries. In large basins it is usually assumed that all groundwater originating from precipitation on the area is ultimately discharged from the basin as streamflow, with the exception of that moisture which is returned directly to the atmosphere by evapo-transpiration. In small basins, *stream piracy* may result in ultimate

[1] Hinds, N. E. A., "Geomorphology: The Evolution of Landscape," Prentice-Hall, New York, 1943.

Lobeck, A. K., "Geomorphology: An Introduction to the Study of Landscapes," McGraw-Hill, New York, 1939.

discharge of groundwater in adjacent basins and, with favorable geologic structure, into basins far removed from the original source area.

The basin is necessarily completely bounded by a *divide*, which separates it from adjacent basins. The divide follows the ridge line around the

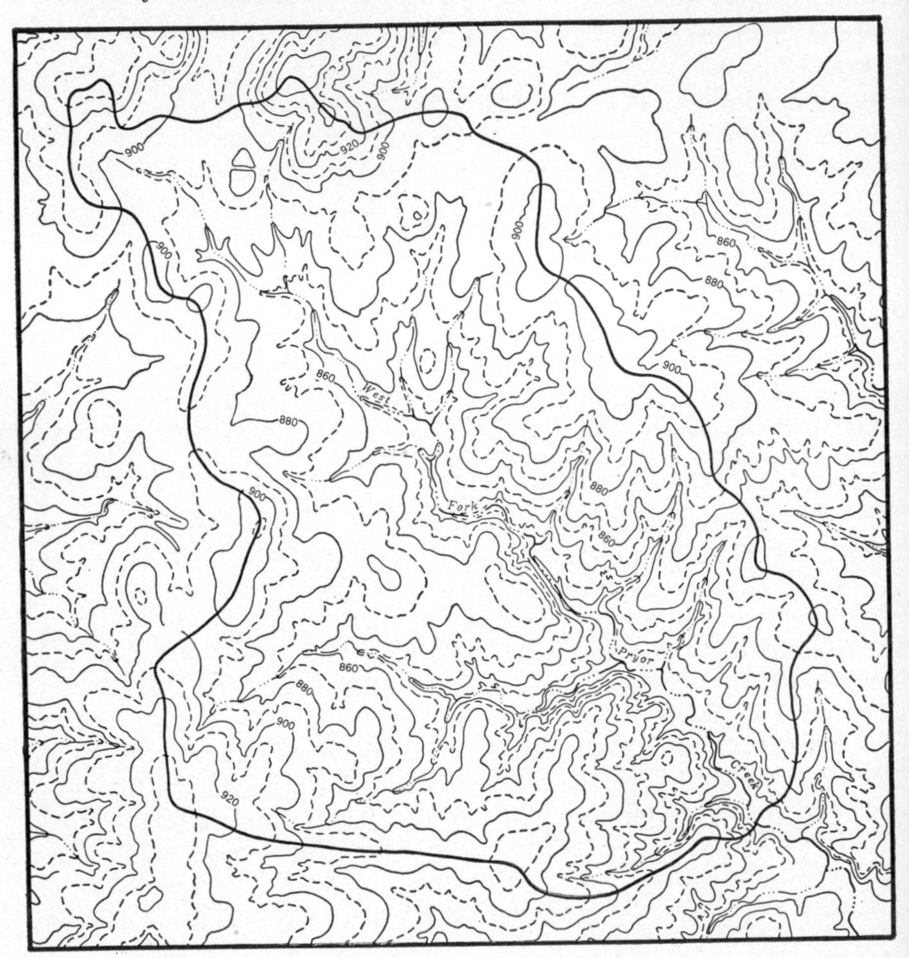

FIG. 10–1. Topographic map showing location of a divide.

basin, crossing the stream only at the outlet point (Fig. 10-1). It marks the highest points between basins, but isolated peaks within a basin may reach greater elevations than any point on the divide. Large river basins have a tendency to be fan- or pear-shaped, but small basins vary widely in shape, depending on the geological structure of the terrane.

Within some basins, areas containing *closed*, or *blind*, drainage are found, *i.e.*, areas in which surface flow collects in sinks or lakes not connected by surface channels to other streams in the basin. Such areas are often designated as *noncontributing* to streamflow, although groundwater connections may exist.

It is frequently necessary to subdivide larger basins in order to obtain working units of practical size. The subareas, or *tributary basins*, are defined by interior divides exactly as is the larger basin. It is customary, however, to select the outlet points of working basins at stream-gaging stations, which are generally located at some distance upstream from the mouth. Hence, when all tributary divides have been drawn, there remain areas below each gaging station which are not included in any tributary basins (Fig. 10-2). These *local areas* must be treated as separate sub-basins of the major basin. They include numerous small ungaged streams and *reaches*, or segments, of the major stream and one or more tributaries. They are bounded by a divide which crosses the major stream twice and each gaged tributary once.

Streams are commonly classed according to three types on the basis of constancy of flow. *Perennial*, or *continuous, streams* contain water at all times, except during extreme droughts. *Intermittent streams* carry water most of the time but cease to flow occasionally because evaporation and seepage into their bed and banks exceed the available streamflow. *Ephemeral streams* carry water only after rains or periods of snowmelt. Perennial streams receive their low-water flow from groundwater, while the channels of ephemeral streams are above the groundwater table at all times. Many streams have sections of all three types, depending on the varying geologic structure along their course, and it is difficult to catalogue them clearly by types. Most large rivers are perennial, while the majority of definitely ephemeral streams are quite small.

Physical description of the basin. The physical features of any river basin are important factors in its hydrologic characteristics and have been expressed in many ways. The more commonly used physical measures are discussed below.

The *drainage area* of a basin is the plane area enclosed within its divide, *i.e.*, the area of its horizontal projection. Noncontributing area is customarily deducted from the total. Drainage area is usually determined by planimetry from reasonably large-scale maps and is expressed in square miles except for basins under 10 square miles, for which the area is sometimes given in acres.

Stream order is a classification reflecting the degree of branching, or bifurcation, within a basin. Horton[1] has classified stream order by assigning order 1 to small, unbranched, finger-tip tributaries, order 2 to those streams which have branches of the first order only, order 3 to streams with

[1] Horton, R. E., Erosional Development of Streams, *Geol. Soc. Am. Bull.*, Vol. 56, pp. 281-283, 1945.

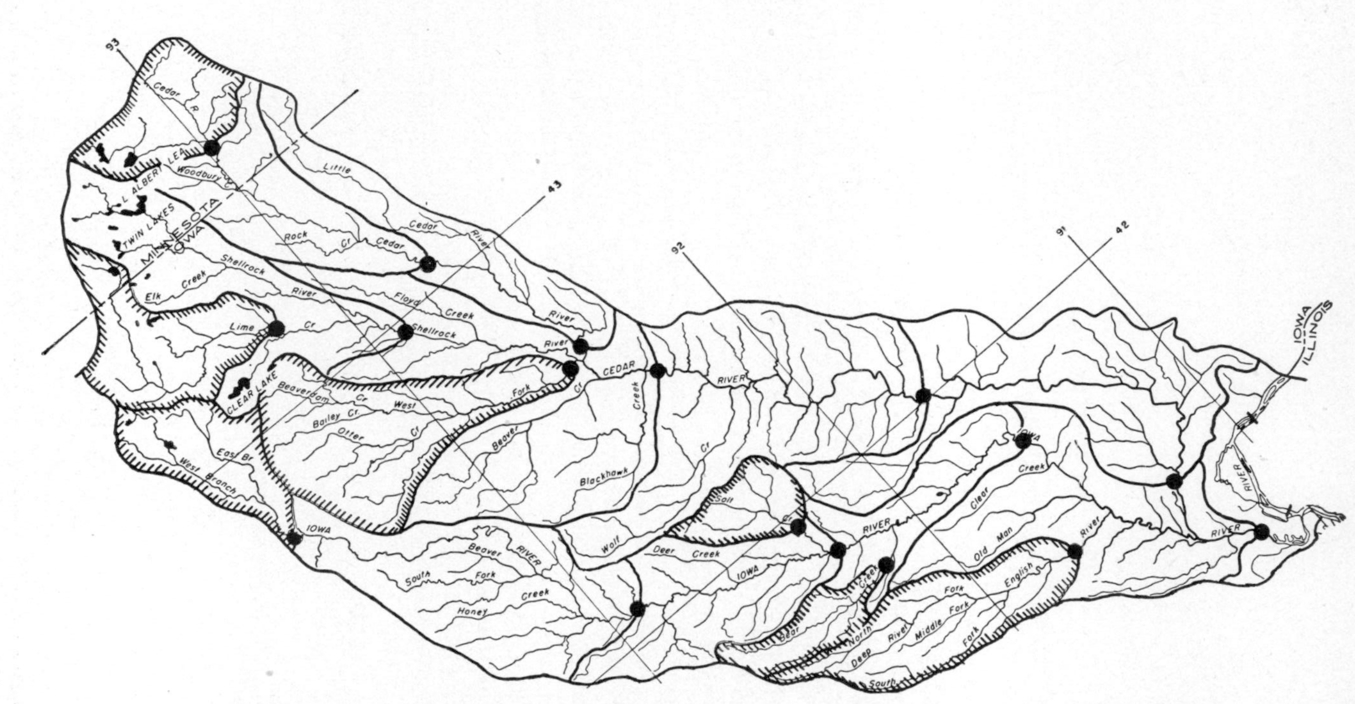

FIG. 10–2. Gaged tributaries (hatched divides) and ungaged local areas in a river basin.

branches of second and lower orders, etc. Thus, the order of the main stream indicates the extent of branching in the basin. This classification is the inverse of the European system, in which the main stream is always classified as first order and the extreme tributaries as the highest order.

The *drainage density*, D_D, is the average length of streams per unit area within the basin, *i.e.*,

$$D_D = \frac{\Sigma L}{A_d} \tag{10-1}$$

where ΣL is the total length of streams in the basin and A_d is the drainage area. If D_D is to be determined accurately, the length of streams must be measured from detailed maps showing all stream channels. Since factors

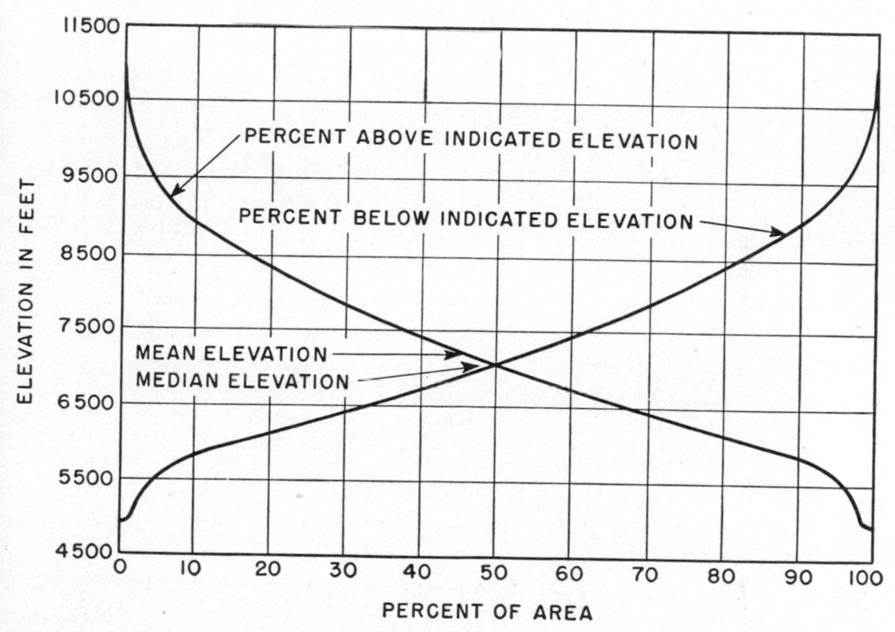

FIG. 10–3. Area-elevation curves for Teton River Basin above St. Anthony, Idaho.

such as this are used most frequently in connection with flood flows, intermittent and ephemeral channels should be included in computing ΣL.

In any discussion of drainage density, it is pertinent to discuss the use of the word "stream" in hydrology. A hydrologist discussing the hydraulics of surface runoff will refer to streams in connection with the small rills and rivulets which cross the landscape and are evident only during rains or periods of snowmelt. Such channels are far too small to be shown on any ordinary topographic map; yet they do represent the beginning of channel flow as distinct from surface, or overland, flow. In describing a river basin or area in excess of a few acres, we are primarily concerned with those aspects which affect hydrograph shape and need not be concerned with the virtually impossible task of computing lengths for these minute channels. Drainage density is, however, indirectly an inverse measure of the extent of such rivulets, since a low drainage density necessarily indicates relatively long overland travel of surface water.

Published figures on drainage density are too scarce to permit any summarization for the country. However, it may be said that values of drainage density ordinarily range from well below 1 mile/square mile in poorly drained basins, upward to 5 miles/square mile in exceptionally well-drained basins.

The *area-elevation distribution* in a basin is usually displayed by plotting elevation against area, or percentage of area, above or below a given elevation (Fig. 10-3). The use of percentage of area is convenient in comparing the elevation distribution in basins of different sizes. The area-elevation curve is, in a sense, the basin profile, and its mean slope (in feet per square mile) is a useful statistic in comparing basins.

Area-elevation data are usually assembled by planimetering on topographic maps the area enclosed within each contour and the basin divide. Equally satisfactory results may be obtained by use of a transparent grid laid over a topographic map. The number of intersections falling within various elevation ranges can be counted, and the resulting tally (Fig. 10-4) gives a frequency distribution of elevation of grid intersections which, if based on a sufficient number of points, is also a reasonably close approximation to the area-elevation distribution. In general, at least 100 points should be used.

The *median elevation* of the basin may be determined from the area-elevation curve as the elevation at 50 per cent area. A *mean elevation* can be computed by multiplying each increment of area by its mean elevation and dividing the sum of these products by the drainage area.

The *stream profile* is usually presented as a plotting of horizontal distance along the main stream vs. elevation. The *slope* of a stream between any two points is frequently taken as the total fall between the points divided by the stream length (line *ab*, Fig. 10-5). A more realistic definition of slope is given by line *cb*, which is drawn so as to have the same area under it as does the profile. This latter definition is used throughout this text. Neither the profile nor the mean slope describes the over-all basin slopes, but only those of the stream channel.

The first step in the determination of land slope is the establishment of a grid on a contour map of the basin. The grid is customarily laid off on north-south and east-west lines, but this is not essential. For basins of 100 square miles or less, at least four grid lines should cross the basin in each direction, while for larger basins the number should be increased. On very large basins, there should be one grid in each direction for each 100

AREA-ELEVATION COMPUTATION

Basin Teton River above St. Anthony, Ida. Drainage area 920 sq mi

Maps Grand Teton Quadrangle USGS Scale 1:125000 Grid 4 mi

Pocatello Aeronautical Chart Scale 1:500,000 Grid 4 mi

Elev. 100 ft	Tally	Total tally	Acc. tally	% area below elev.	Mean zonal elev.	Moment about msl
45				0		
50	III	3	3	1.3	4750	14,250
55	卌 I	6	9	3.9	5250	31,500
60	卌 卌 卌 卌 II	22	31	13.4	5750	126,500
65	卌 卌 卌 卌 卌 卌 卌 卌 IIII	44	75	32.4	6250	275,000
70	卌 卌 卌 卌 卌 卌 卌 IIII	39	114	49.4	6750	263,250
75	卌 卌 卌 卌 卌 II	27	141	61.1	7250	195,750
80	卌 卌 卌 卌 卌	25	166	72.0	7750	193,750
85	卌 卌 卌 卌 IIII	24	190	82.3	8250	198,000
90	卌 卌 卌 IIII	19	209	90.5	8750	166,250
95	卌 卌 II	12	221	95.7	9250	111,000
100	卌 I	6	227	98.4	9750	58,500
105	IIII	4	231	100.0	10250	41000
110						
115						
Totals		231	231	100	—	1,674,750

Maximum elev. 11075′ Minimum elev. 4990′ Mean elev. 7250′

FIG. 10–4. Computation form for area-elevation data.

square miles of drainage area. After the grid is completed, the length of each line within the basin boundaries is measured, and the contours crossing or tangent to each line are counted. The land slope s in either direction is then

$$s = \frac{N\,\Delta Z}{l} \tag{10-2}$$

where N is the total number of contour crossings for all lines in one direction, l the total length of lines in that direction, and ΔZ the contour interval.

Horton[1] suggested that the mean basin slope could be determined by

$$s = \frac{N \, \Delta Z \sec \theta}{l} \tag{10-3}$$

where l and N are the total length and total number of contours in both directions and θ is the angle between the contours and the grid lines. The

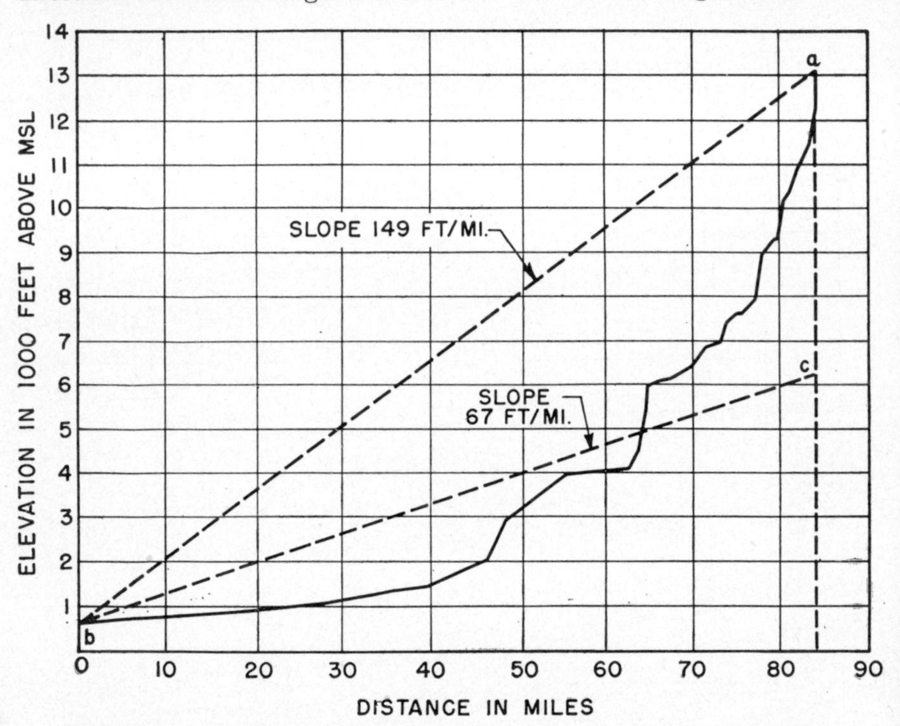

FIG. 10–5. Profile of Merced River above Exchequer Dam, California.

introductions of sec θ is an attempt to compute the slope along a normal to the contours. Because of the work involved in computing sec θ for each contour intersection, Horton suggested the use of an average value of 1.571. Any attempt to determine an average secant for this purpose is at best uncertain, and for comparative purposes it seems equally effective to ignore sec θ.

A more effective measure of basin slope can be obtained by determining the frequency distribution of slope normal to the contours at grid inter-

[1] Horton, R. E., discussion of paper, Flood Flow Characteristics, *Trans. ASCE*, Vol. 89, p. 1084, 1926.

sections. For this purpose, a grid with at least 50, and preferably 100, intersections within the basin should be used. The resulting frequency distribution (Fig. 10-6) can be analyzed to determine the mean, median, and modal slopes and at the same time to display the entire distribution

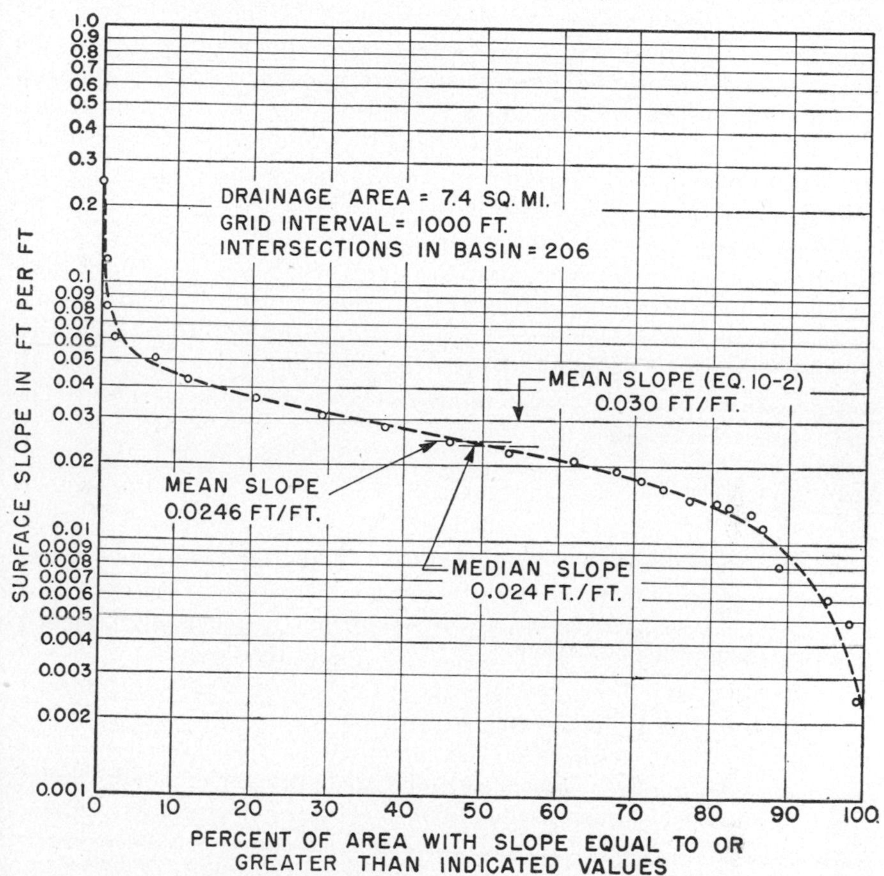

FIG. 10–6. Distribution of land slope in West Fork, Pryor Creek, Missouri.

of slope in the basin. It is thus a far better picture of the basin slope than is given by the mean value computed from Eq. (10-3).

The distribution of area with distance from the outflow station is important in establishing the time distribution of runoff. It can be shown as a histogram (area by zones vs. distance) or as an accumulation curve (area or per cent area within or beyond the indicated distance from the outflow point). If distances from the outflow station are marked off along each stream and isopleths of distance drawn, the data for the area-distance diagram may be obtained by use of the frequency-distribution method.

The *aspect* of a slope is defined as the compass direction normal to the slope contour and pointing downslope. It defines the direction toward which the slope is exposed. In large basins a detailed aspect analysis made by determining the frequency distribution of points with various aspects will generally yield a circular or nearly circular diagram if plotted on polar coordinates, *i.e.*, the distribution of aspect is largely uniform. Hence, the aspect of large basins is necessarily defined in broad terms as the compass direction (downslope) toward which the major valley of the basin opens. In small basins it is often possible to find a definite distribution of aspect favoring a limited range of direction. Such information may be of value in problems involving snowmelt.

The water-surface area of the streams within a basin is difficult to determine because of (1) the wide variation in area with stage and (2) the difficulties of representation on ordinary maps, where most streams appear only as lines without areal significance. An approximation to the stream area A_w may be made by assuming that stream width decreases uniformly with distance, from B_t at the outlet to zero at the extreme headwater. The area would then be given by

$$A_w = \frac{B_t L}{2} \tag{10-4}$$

where L is the length of the main channel. While Eq. (10-4) is obviously an oversimplification, there seems to be no basis for any more involved approach because local variations in width due to topography play an important role. Any error will usually be small with respect to the total drainage area.

Evolution of drainage patterns. All landscape forms may be broadly classified as either constructional or destructional. *Constructional landscapes* are the result of volcanism, folding, faulting, and other factors, which form such features as mountains, plains, and plateaus. *Destructional landscape* forms result from the action of weather, streams, glaciers, wind, waves, and organisms. Streams are one of the most important factors in the formation of destructional landscapes. Features resulting from the action of streams can be separated into three classes, *erosional* features such as valleys and canyons, *residual* features such as mountains and divides, and *depositional* features such as deltas, alluvial fans, and flood plains.

The development of a drainage system depends on many factors. The initial landforms to a great extent determine the direction of flow, the stream pattern, and the general nature of the streams. Climate cannot be ignored, however, for identical landforms yield different drainage systems in arid and humid climates. Evolution is slow in an arid climate, since the most important changes take place during floods, which occur only infrequently in desert regions. On the other hand, wind may become a very important geophysical agent in arid climates, where there is little vegetation to protect the dry soil. The type of basic soil and rock material and its distribution within the earth's crust also determine the nature and rate of landscape development. Finally, the works of man cannot be ignored as factors in the development of river systems. The construction of dams and levees, deforestation and reforestation, cultivation, and many other activities of man now act to affect the present and future development of river systems.

More than a century ago, Playfair stated a law which has come to bear his name.

> Every river appears to consist of a main trunk, fed from a variety of branches, each running in a valley proportioned to its size, and all of them together forming a system of valleys, communicating with one another, and having such a nice adjustment of their declivities that none of them join the principal valley either on too high or too low a level.

This law, based wholly on observation, is important to hydrologists. Many empiricisms in hydrology are possible because nature has made a careful adjustment of the stream systems to satisfy the multitude of factors which affect streamflow.

The hydrophysical evolution[1] of a stream system may be outlined briefly by considering the case of a simple rectangular drainage basin having uniform surface slope and structure. On such a basin, runoff must occur initially as surface flow, also called *sheet*, or *overland*, flow. At some line downslope from the divide, this sheet flow attains sufficient velocity and volume to cause erosion and, hence, to develop a system of small channels or rills wherever small surface irregularities are sufficient to cause a concentration of flow.

Once a rill has started, it causes flow concentration, which results in self-enlargement. The result is a system of roughly parallel rills crossing the basin. During the course of excessive storms when runoff exceeds the capacities of the rills, caving may destroy the ridge between adjacent rills, and the flow from one rill may be diverted into another. The rill carrying the greatest volume of water has the greatest opportunity for erosion and is therefore deeper than others. Cross grading diverts flow from adjacent rills to the largest rill, which grows in size until a small valley is cut, with the basin surface sloping to it from three directions. This gully is now a first-order stream. Repetition of the process on a larger scale results in the development of connecting channels, and the order of the stream system is raised. Cross grading initially produces channels with sharp bends. On

[1] Horton, R. E., Erosional Development of Streams, *Geol. Soc. Am. Bull.*, Vol. 56, pp. 331-350, 1945.

steep slopes the erosive action of the water tends to scour a fairly straight channel through these bends, but on flat slopes centrifugal forces acting at the bends tend to lengthen them and, hence, to develop a system of meanders. Meanders on large, reasonably mature streams are not the result of meanders formed in this initial development.[1]

The development continues until a system of channels is established such that no point in the basin is farther from a channel than the distance required to develop erosion by overland flow. The process would theoretically cease at this point, with the end of erosion opportunity. Actually, such is not the case. Surface irregularities, man-made changes in land use and cover, and erosion by raindrop impact all act to continue the development.

The ultimate trend in valley development is toward an S-shaped valley slope normal to the stream. In the zone of no erosion near the divides, slopes are relatively flat remnants of the original surface. In the intermediate zone, erosion is most effective, and the steepest slopes occur. Since main-stream slopes are generally lower than those of the tributaries, the erosive power of the main stream fixes the level of the valley bottom. Tributary channels are cut to the same level as the main channel, and sediment is deposited in the flood plain as the slope and carrying power of the tributaries decrease.

The life history of a river. In geological terms, a river is *young* when it is actively eroding its channel. Young streams are normally clear and swift. They are capable of transporting all the sediment load delivered by their tributaries. Because of this, the young stream is always cutting its channel deeper. Consequently, the valleys of young streams are steep-sided, and the streams occupy all of the narrow valley floor. Waterfalls and rapids develop where the stream crosses rocks which are particularly resistant to erosion. The steep valleys of young streams are usually ideal for the construction of high dams.

Erosion gradually reduces the slope of the stream until the water velocities are just sufficient to carry the debris delivered by the tributaries, which have steeper slopes than the main stream. The stream is then said to be *mature.* It is no longer able to erode its channel deeper, and lateral erosion begins, resulting in the development of a narrow flood plain. The valley slopes are gentle, and the channel profile is regular, without rapids or waterfalls.

Maturity of the trunk stream marks the early maturity of the stream system. As the tributary streams reach maturity, the river system as a whole is in an advanced stage of maturity. When all channels, including wet-weather rills, are graded, the stream system is said to be *old.* Old

[1] Friedkin, J. F., "Meandering of Alluvial Streams," U.S. Waterways Experiment Station, Vicksburg, Miss., 1945.

streams have a wide flood plain, a broad meander belt, and gentle slopes. The Mississippi is a typical old stream. It must be pointed out that the terms young and old do not necessarily signify age in the usual sense of the word. Some of the youngest basins in this country are found in the Southwest, in part because the arid climate retards erosion. Young basins are the type usually classified as *flashy* by the hydrologist, because flows collect rapidly from the steep slopes and flood peaks occur soon after the end of rain. As the age of the stream system advances, the slopes decrease, the flood peaks form more slowly, and the stream is termed *sluggish*.

Some writers have suggested that a stream be called mature when its flood plain is the same width as its meander belt and old when its flood plain is wider than its meander belt. The meander belt of most streams is usually 10 to 20 times their mean channel widths. Characteristic of old streams are the oxbow-lake remnants of old meanders. Natural levees are often formed by the deposit of sediment at the edge of the low-water channel. Often a tributary may flow in the same flood plain, separated from the main stream by the natural levees. The Yazoo River in Mississippi is a typical example, and tributaries of this type are called *Yazoo-type tributaries*.

Some mature or old streams have a *braided* channel instead of a meander belt. A study of typical braided streams such as the Platte River will show that their channel slopes are much steeper than those of meandering channels.[1] Moreover, the sediment load of braided streams is much coarser than in meandering streams. It is this coarse load which is responsible for the formation of the braided channel and the relatively steep slopes, since the streams could not carry their load of coarse material on lesser slopes. However, even with the steep slopes, such streams can do no more than move their load and have no excess energy to form meanders.

Genetic types of streams. The geologist classifies streams into several genetic types on the basis of their geologic history. When the location of a stream is the result of the initial slope of the land, it is called a *consequent* stream (Fig. 10-7). Typical consequent streams are found in the Atlantic Coastal Plain. A *subsequent* stream is one which has developed its valley along a belt of relatively erosible rock. The Shenandoah River and others in the Appalachians have developed along weak belts of rock and, hence, are subsequent streams. A stream which flows in the direction opposite to the initial consequent streams and the slope of the original landforms is said to be an *obsequent* stream. Obsequent streams are usually short and are also usually tributary to subsequent streams which are responsible for the valley gradients contrary to the original constructional landforms.

[1] Lobeck, A. K., "Geomorphology: An Introduction to the Study of Landscapes," pp. 224-225, McGraw-Hill, New York, 1939.

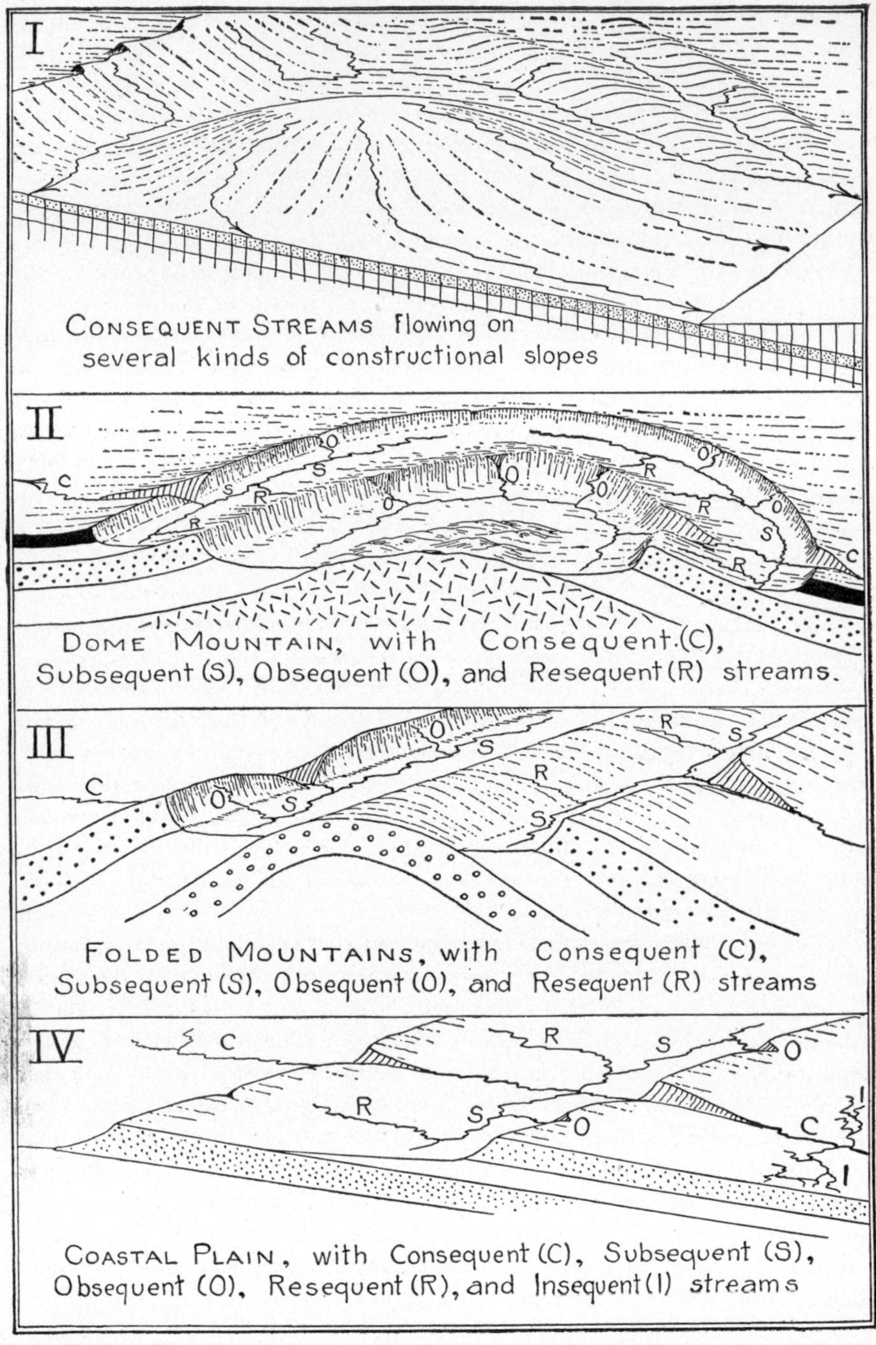

FIG. 10–7. Several kinds of constructional land forms showing the different genetic types of streams. *(After Lobeck.)*

A stream which flows in the same direction as the original consequent streams, but at a lower level on a stripped surface, is said to be *resequent*, a combination of recent and consequent. Resequent streams are frequently tributary to subsequent streams which have eroded the original surface strata. A stream which does not have any obvious geologic control is called *insequent*. Such streams do not follow the dip, or strike, of the beds, nor do they follow cracks or joints in the rocks. Large numbers of the smaller streams are properly classified as insequent.

A stream which develops its course in alluvial deposits over rock is said to be *superimposed* (Fig. 10-8). Eventually, the alluvium may be removed, and the stream will cut a channel through the underlying rock without any regard for the rock structure. The Delaware Water Gap is explained as the result of a superimposed stream on a coastal plain which was initially higher than the present ridge. As the coastal plain was eroded, the stream cut its way through the underlying ridge to form the Water Gap. A stream which has maintained its course across a subsequent uplift is said to be *antecedent*. The Sevier River, Utah, has cut a gorge entirely across a block mountain, which presumably was lifted across the stream channel slowly enough so that stream erosion exceeded the lifting rate and the river's course remained essentially unaltered. A *reversed* stream is one which has had its course reversed by the lifting or tilting of a region.

Stream patterns. In a region where the rock structure is homogeneous, there is no variation in the resistivity of the rocks to influence the stream pattern. The resulting streams run in all directions and are called *dendritic*, or treelike (Fig. 10-9). Typical dendritic patterns are found in the granite mountains of the Sierra Nevada. In contrast, the many rectangular joints and faults of the Adirondack region in New York result in a system of valleys joining at nearly right angles. Such a pattern is called a *rectangular* drainage system.

When the underlying rock is strongly folded or sharply dipping, a *trellis* drainage pattern develops. The longer streams are subsequent and follow the weaker rock strata, while the short tributaries are either obsequent or resequent. Trellis-type drainage is found throughout the Appalachian Mountains. The drainage from dome mountains and volcanoes usually radiates outward from a central focus, and the pattern is described as *radial*. Occasionally, the drainage into a depression is radial in form, but with flow converging toward the center rather than diverging outward. Such a pattern is said to be *centripetal*. The subsequent streams which form in the weaker strata of a dome mountain define a roughly circular, or *annular*, pattern. The tributaries are both obsequent and resequent. The annular pattern is simply a special form of the trellis pattern.

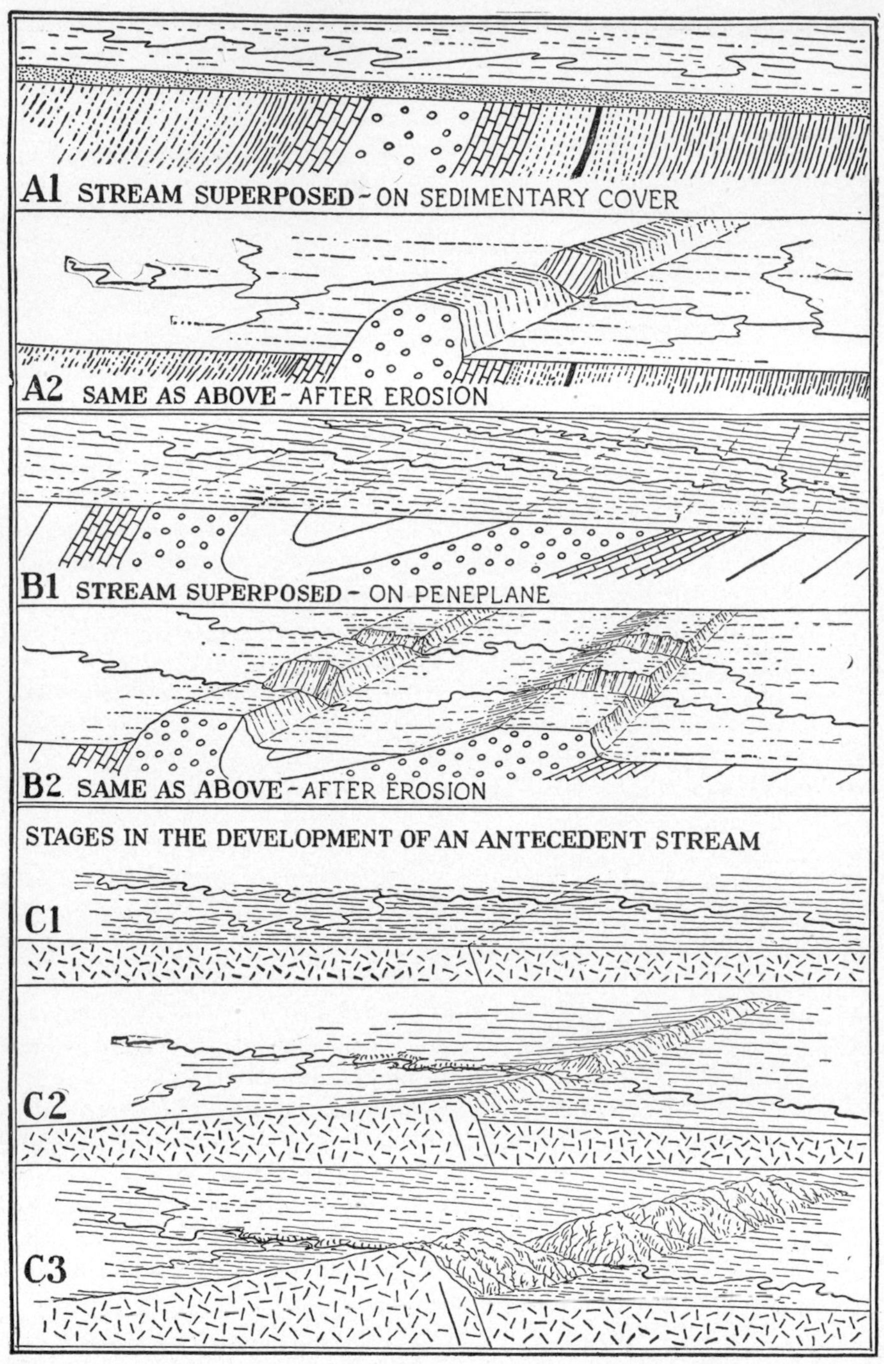

FIG. 10–8. Stages in the development of superimposed and antecedent streams. (*After Lobeck.*)

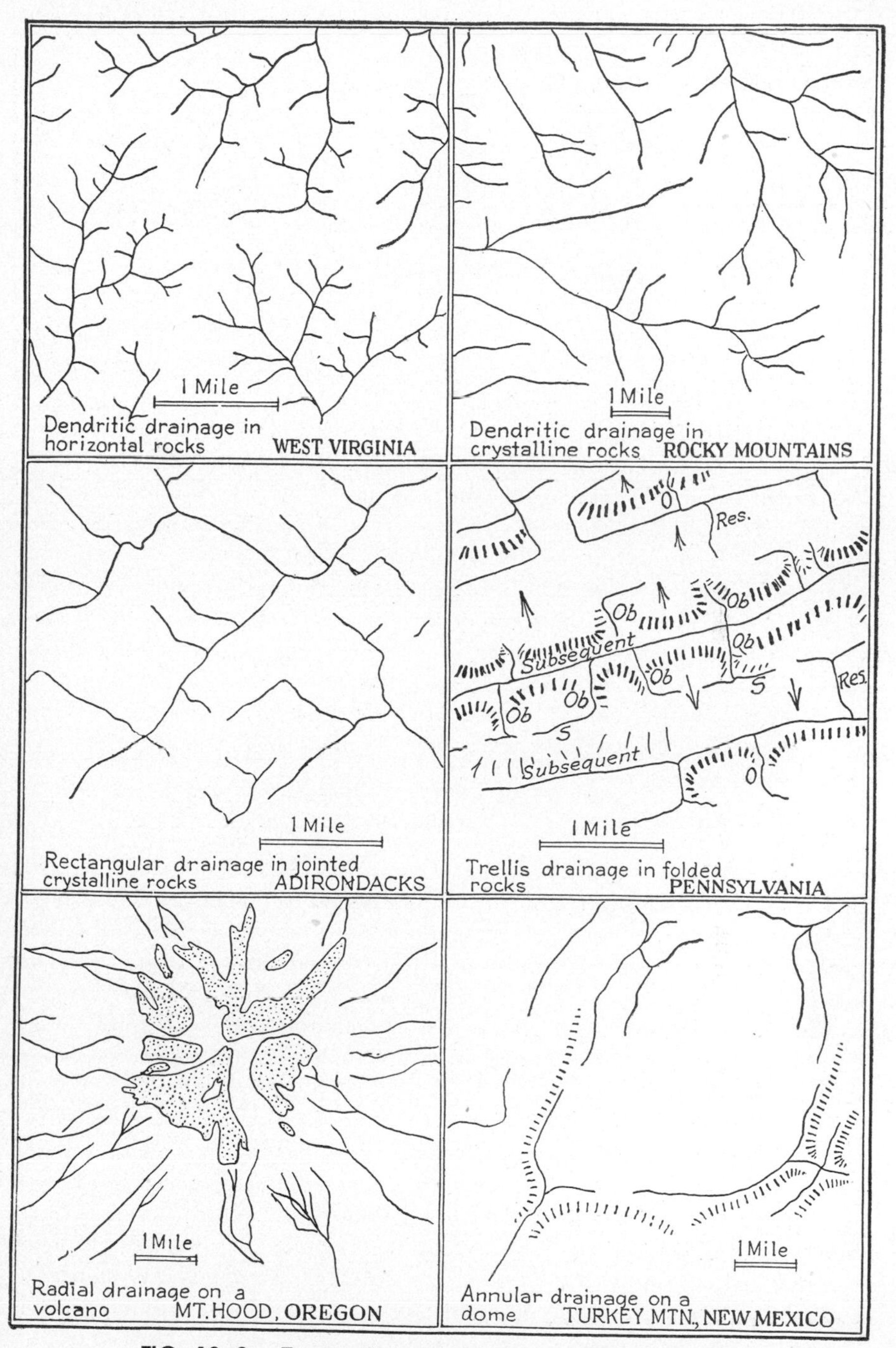

FIG. 10–9. Types of stream patterns. *(After Lobeck.)*

11

SURFACE RETENTION AND DETENTION AND OVERLAND FLOW

Precipitation falling to the earth's surface is either retained where it falls, passes through the soil surface as infiltration, or finds its way into the surface-channel system of the basin, whence it becomes surface runoff. This chapter considers that portion of the hydrologic cycle between incident precipitation and subsequent surface runoff or infiltration.

A considerable portion of the rain at the beginning of a storm is stored on the vegetal cover as *interception* and in surface puddles as *depression storage*. As rain continues, the soil surface becomes covered with a film of water, known as *surface detention*, and flow begins downslope toward an established surface channel. En route to a channel, the water is designated as *overland flow;* upon entering the channel, it becomes *surface runoff*.

SURFACE RETENTION

Surface retention, variously known as *surface storage* and *initial detention*, refers to that part of the precipitation which does not appear either as infiltration or as surface runoff during the period of precipitation or immediately thereafter. Thus, surface retention includes (1) interception by vegetal cover, (2) depression storage, and (3) evaporation during precipitation. It does not include that water which is temporarily stored en route to the stream system. The combined elements of surface retention may be of sizable magnitude, ranging from 0.5 to 1.5 in. for cultivated fields, grasslands, and forests.

Interception. The effect of vegetal cover in reducing the amount of precipitation reaching the ground is usually insignificant in studies of major floods. However, interception by some types of cover amounts to a considerable portion of the annual rainfall. Since interception is essentially satisfied out of the first part of the rain in an average storm and since most storms yield only small amounts of precipitation, interception by forest or other dense cover commonly amounts to 25 per cent of the annual precipitation.

While a large amount of experimental interception data have been accumulated through the works of numerous investigators, in many cases the problems were not carefully analyzed before the experiment was undertaken and, consequently, many of the data cannot be readily correlated. Further, because of the nature of the subject, reliable experimental data are extremely difficult to determine.

Another factor which renders some of the data difficult to compare is the method of computing the interception. Sometimes the difference between the catch in the open and that under the vegetal cover has been considered as the interception, while in other cases this difference has been adjusted for water transmitted down the tree trunks and/or for the per cent of the area actually covered by the designated type of vegetation.

Physical aspects of interception. When the first drops of rain in any storm strike the leaves of vegetation, they are almost completely retained as droplets or as a thin film over the surface of the leaves. Only a small portion of the rain reaches a point on the ground until such time as all the leaves overhead have retained their maximum amount of stored water. Probably a considerable portion of the water which does spatter earthward as the drops disintegrate upon impact is evaporated before it reaches the ground because of the extremely small size of the resulting particles. When a leaf has acquired its maximum surface storage, added water causes drops to form on the lower edge. In the absence of wind, each of these drops grows in size, and when gravity overbalances surface-tension forces, the drops fall to the ground or to a lower leaf. Usually, however, drops are jarred free from the leaf by wind or by impact of rain before the gravitational force exceeds surface tension. Nevertheless, raindrops falling from interception storage are, on the average, larger than the original raindrops.

After the vegetation is completely saturated, the net interception would be zero, were it not for the fact that even during rain there is considerable evaporation from the enormous wet surface of the foliage. Thus, after interception storage has been filled, the amount of water reaching the soil surface is equal to the rainfall less the evaporation from the vegetal cover. At the cessation of rain, the vegetation still retains the interception storage. This water is eventually returned directly to the atmosphere through evaporation.

Wind affects interception in two distinct ways. (1) It reduces the maximum storage. (2) It increases the rate of evaporation from storage. These effects act in opposite directions, and the net effect of wind for the storm as a whole may increase or decrease the total interception, depending upon the wind velocity throughout the storm, the duration of rain, and the humidity of the air. In a steady rain with no wind, the rate of interception is relatively rapid until the storage is filled, and then it diminishes to the slow rate of evaporation experienced under calm conditions. In a shower with wind, the initial rate of interception is much less because the wind blows water from the leaves during the time the storage is being filled and, at the same time, the interception capacity is reduced. However, even after the amount of water stored on vegetation reaches its maximum, wind causes a high rate of interception by its effect on evaporation. Thus, it can be said that wind generally tends to increase total interception during a long storm and to decrease it for a short storm. The amount of precipitation remaining in interception storage after a rain is a function of the wind velocity experienced only during the last portion of the storm, while evaporation depends upon the velocity throughout the storm. The evaporation rate per unit of surface during a period of rainfall is normally very small as compared with fair-weather evaporation because of smaller vapor-pressure differences. However, low evaporation rates, when multiplied by the ratio of foliage area to the projected area of the tree, become significant.

The total interception throughout a storm consists of two parts, (1) that required to satisfy the surface storage of the vegetation and (2) that which evaporates during the period of rainfall. The total-storm interception V_i can be expressed[1] as

$$V_i = S_i + C_P E_a t_R \tag{11-1}$$

where S_i is the storage capacity per unit of projected area, C_P is the ratio of the vegetal surface area to its projected area, E_a is the evaporation rate per unit of surface area, and t_R is the duration of rainfall. The value of S_i varies with plant growth or leaf development, with rain intensity and drop size, and with wind velocity. Leaves of different plants vary greatly in the manner in which they retain falling rain. Some retain water in the form of a thin film, while others store it in droplets or blotches. Hence, for different vegetative types, S_i may vary even though the values of C_P are the same. Logically, drops would be expected on the leaves which appear "waxy," and the soft, dull leaves would be expected to become thoroughly wetted. However, this is not the case—there is no apparent relation between the form of moisture deposit and the appearance of the foliage.

Equation (11-1) yields a value of interception which is independent of the amount of precipitation. Actually, this equation assumes that the rainfall in each storm completely fills interception storage. Hence, for light rainfalls, computed values of interception may exceed observed precipitation. Any adequate equation must relate interception to amount of precipitation as well as storm duration. Equation (11-1) is essentially correct provided that rainfall is sufficient throughout the storm to permit maximum interception, *i.e.*, the storage must be at capacity. If we

[1] Horton, R. E., Rainfall Interception, *Monthly Weather Rev.*, Vol. 47, pp. 603-623, 1919.

assume that the interception given by Eq. (11-1) is approached exponentially as the amount of rainfall is increased from zero to some high value (for a specified duration), then

$$V_i = (S_i + C_P E_a t_R)(1 - \mathbf{e}^{-kP}) \tag{11-2}$$

where $\mathbf{e}$ is the Napierian base, P is the amount of rainfall, and k is a constant. When only that portion of the area actually covered by vegetation is considered, the interception should approach the rainfall for very small storms. Therefore, dV_i/dP must be equal to unity when P is near zero. Differentiating Eq. (11-2) and equating to unity, $k = 1/(S_i + C_P E_a t_R)$. Assuming reasonable values for the constants ($S_i = 0.20$ in., $C_P = 100$, and $E_a = 0.0001$ in./hr), Eq. (11-2) is shown graphically in Fig. 11-1.

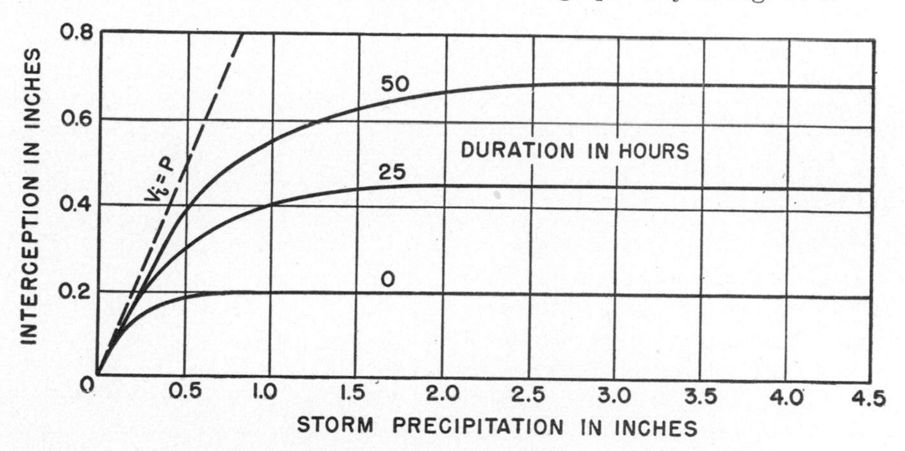

FIG. 11-1. Theoretical relation between interception, precipitation, and duration.

Measurement of interception. Most available interception data have been observed by placing one or more rain gages (interceptometers) on the ground under the vegetation and comparing their catch with that of gages in the open. The difference in catch, adjusted for water running down the trunk or stalk, is the interception. Riegler's data, cited by Harrington[1] and shown in Table 11-1, were based on a single gage equal in area to that of the tree crown and so arranged that the flow down the trunk was included in the gage catch.

The observation of flow down a tree trunk is not too difficult and may be accomplished by attaching a metal trough around the tree near the ground, making certain of a watertight joint between the metal and the trunk. Stem flow for weeds and crops, however, is much more difficult to measure, and consequently very little is known in this regard. Some attempts have been made toward the measurement of interception by herbaceous vegeta-

[1] Forest Influences, *U.S. Forest Service Bull.* 7, 1893.

tion by comparing the runoff from plots with and without vegetal cover. Since it is necessary to estimate the difference in infiltration rates on the two plots, this method yields only approximate results for large storms and is of no value for small storms.

TABLE 11-1. Average Interception by Trees in Per Cent of Rain Falling in the Open

(After Riegler)

Vegetal type	Rain falling through crown on soil	Rain running down trunk	Total interception
Beech	65.4	12.8	21.8
Oak	73.6	5.7	20.7
Maple	71.5	6.0	22.5
Spruce*	39.8	1.4	58.8

*According to Harrington, the data for spruce are in error because a portion of the rain ran off the ends of outward-inclined branches and was not caught in the interceptometer.

In the subsequent discussion of the variation of interception with such factors as vegetal type and amount and duration of precipitation, trunk flow is not considered as a separate item. Some idea of the range in variation of this factor may be gained from Table 11-1 and from the results of Horton's experiments[1] shown in Fig. 11-2. In general, it can be stated that the quantity of water running down the trunk varies inversely with the roughness of the bark. Some of Horton's data may be slightly too high because of direct rainfall on the tree trunks. Most of the trees in his experiments were more openly exposed than would be the case in a forest; consequently, for storms with driving wind, the direct rainfall on the trunks may have been significant. Through comparing results for storms with and without wind, Horton concluded that the effect of direct rainfall was inconsequential for average results.

Variations in interception. For a specific storm, the type and density of vegetal cover determine the quantity of precipitation intercepted, provided that there is no water in storage on the foliage prior to the rain. The variation of interception with vegetal type is demonstrated in Figs. 11-2 to 11-4 and Tables 11-1 and 11-2. While these variations are chiefly the result of differences in total surface area of vegetation, the physical properties of the foliage play an important part through their effect on surface tension.

[1] Horton, R. E., Rainfall Interception, *Monthly Weather Rev.*, Vol. 47, pp. 603-623, 1919.

The seasonal variation of interception for crops results from changes in surface area of the foliage. Interception by deciduous trees varies in a similar manner, except in regions where a considerable portion of winter precipitation falls as snow. The horizontal movement of falling snow is relatively greater than that of rain, and thus the tendency for snow to

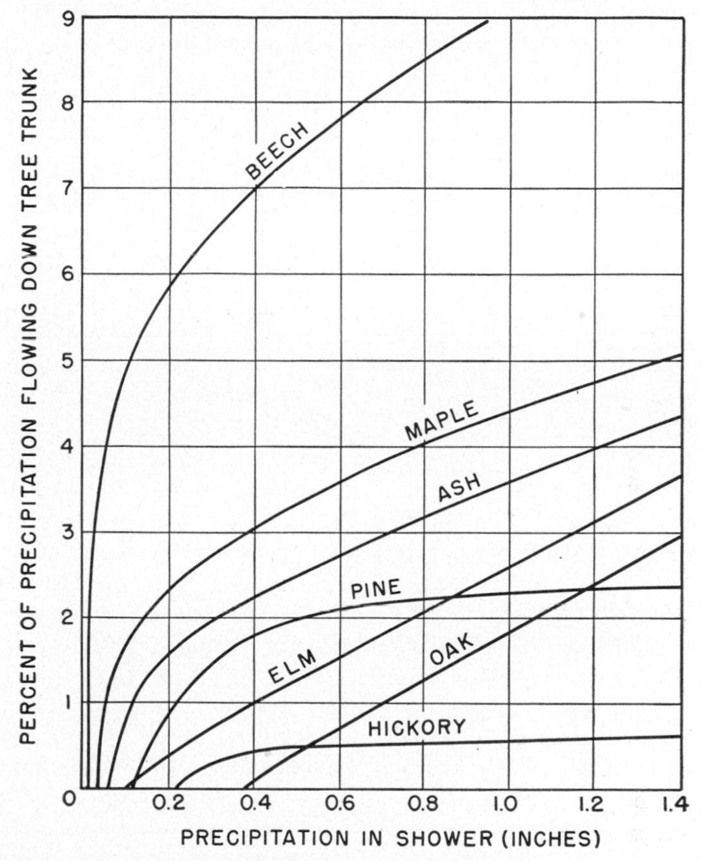

FIG. 11–2. Trunk flow in per cent of total precipitation on tree crown. *(After Horton.)*

collect on the side of trees near a clearing is more pronounced than for rain. The capacity of twigs, branches, and trunks for storing freezing rain or snow may approach or even exceed the storage capacity of summer foliage. Further, unlike summer rain, snow and freezing rain do not immediately begin to flow down the trunk and therefore are more susceptible to evaporation. The variation of storm duration and intensity also tends to increase winter interception with respect to that during summer. Views presented in the literature are widely divergent in their conclusions regarding the seasonal variation of interception by forest cover.[1] Variations in climate, type and age of cover and experimental technique are probably responsible for the inconsistent conclusions expressed. Although the available experimental data are inadequate for quantitative analysis, it seems probable that evergreens are about equally good interceptors in summer and in winter, while broad-leaved trees intercept relatively more during summer.

The variation of interception with duration and amount of precipitation per storm period as shown in Figs. 11-3 and 11-4 is based on the data collected by Horton. These figures show interception for single trees of

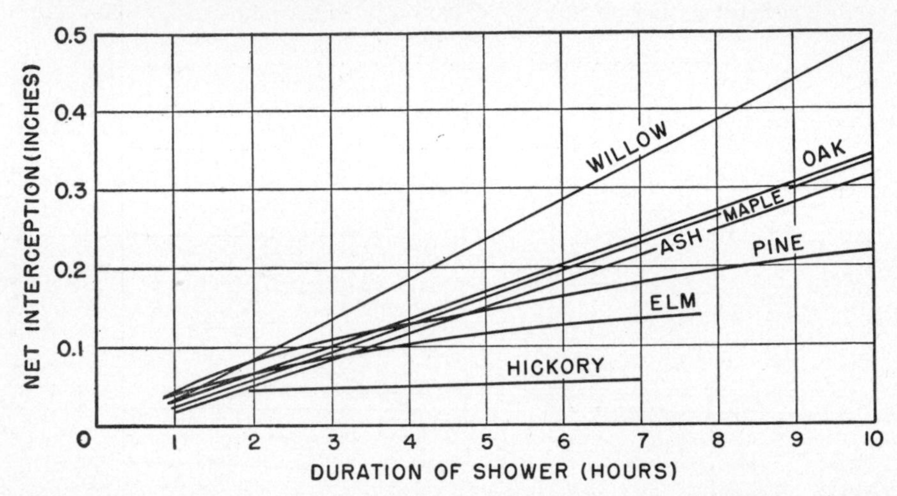

FIG. 11–3. Variation of interception with duration of precipitation. (*After Horton.*)

various species adjusted for trunk flow. Since rainfall amount and duration are intercorrelated, the true effect of either upon interception is difficult to determine from natural storms. The curves shown are based on averages of groups of storms classified by increments of rainfall amount. Consequently, some of the variation shown with respect to duration may be due to storm magnitude, and vice versa. Because of this intercorrelation and the limited range of Horton's relatively small samples, his relations are not reliable for extreme conditions of rainfall amount, duration, or intensity. Data are not available to determine accurately the

[1] Zon, R., "Forests and Water in the Light of Scientific Investigation," pp. 205-273, final report of the National Waterways Commission, Washington, D. C., 1912.

Forest Influences, *U.S. Forest Service Bull.* 7, 1893.

Alter, J. C., Where the Snow Lies in Summer, *Monthly Weather Rev.*, Vol. 39, pp. 758-761, 1911.

Johnson, W. M., The Interception of Rain and Snow by a Forest of Young Ponderosa Pine, *Trans. Am. Geophys. Union,* Vol. 23, pp. 566-569, 1942.

joint relation between interception, rainfall amount, and storm duration for various species of trees and other vegetation. However, graphical correlation of an adequate sample of reliable data should produce a curve family similar to that shown in Fig. 11-1.

Secondary interception. Most hydrologic studies involve interception by two or more levels of vegetation, such as trees, underbrush, and grass. Unfortunately, most experimental data for forests have been collected by placing interceptometers free of underbrush, grass, etc.; consequently, little is known of total interception. It is obvious, however, that on a long-period basis total interception is less than the sum of that which each type

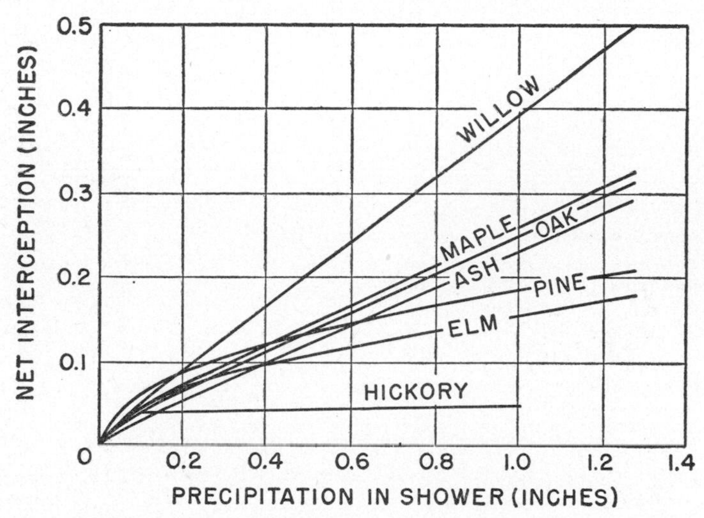

FIG. 11-4. Variation of interception with amount of precipitation. (*After Horton.*)

of vegetation would retain if standing alone, since the lower layer can intercept only that water which falls through from the upper layers. Thus, in light showers, the lower layers may receive practically no rain. For long, heavy storms all storage becomes filled, but the water on the lower layers of vegetation is subjected to a shorter period of evaporation than the upper layer.

Empirical interception formulas. In view of the scarcity of interception data, a list of empirical relations for determining approximate values of interception under specified conditions is given in Table 11-2. These formulas were suggested by Horton[1] and are to be applied to individual storms rather than to monthly or annual periods. They are for primary

[1] Horton, R. E., Rainfall Interception, *Monthly Weather Rev.*, Vol. 47, pp. 603-623, 1919.

interception, in inches, directly under the designated vegetal cover. Average interception over an area is determined by applying a projection factor to the computed interception in order to adjust for that portion of the area not covered by vegetation. Where no projection factor is listed, it must be estimated on the basis of cover density for existing conditions. The equations are based on limited experimental data from relatively small storms and should be used with caution. They are not applicable for large storms.

TABLE 11-2. Working Formulas for Primary Interception per Shower on Projected Areas of Trees and Plants

(After Horton)

Vegetal cover	Interception $= a + bP^n$			Projection factor
	a	b	n	
Orchards	0.04	0.18	1.00	
Chestnut, hedges and open	0.04	0.20	1.00	
Chestnut, in woods	0.06	0.15	1.00	
Ash, hedges and open	0.015	0.23	1.00	
Ash, in woods	0.02	0.18	1.00	
Beech, hedges and open	0.03	0.23	1.00	
Beech, in woods	0.04	0.18	1.00	
Oak, hedges and open	0.03	0.22	1.00	
Oak, woods	0.05	0.18	1.00	
Maple, hedges and open	0.03	0.23	1.00	
Maple, woods	0.04	0.18	1.00	
Willow, shrubs	0.02	0.40	1.00	
Elm, hedges and open	0.03	0.23	0.50	
Elm, woods	0.04	0.18	0.50	
Basswood, hedges and open	0.03	0.13	0.50	
Basswood, woods	0.05	0.10	0.50	
Hemlock and pine, hedges and open	0.03	0.20	0.50	
Hemlock and pine, woods	0.05	0.20	0.50	
Beans, potatoes, cabbage, and other small hilled crops	$0.02h$	$0.15h$	1.00	$0.25h$
Sorghum, kaffir corn, etc., sowed in drills	$0.007h$	$0.006h$	1.00	1.00
Clover and meadow grass	$0.005h$	$0.08h$	1.00	1.00
Forage, alfalfa, vetch, millet, etc.	$0.01h$	$0.10h$	1.00	1.00
Small grains, rye, wheat, barley	$0.005h$	$0.05h$	1.00	1.00
Tobacco	$0.01h$	$0.08h$	1.00	$0.20h$
Cotton	$0.15h$	$0.10h$	1.00	$0.33h$
Corn	$0.005h$	$0.005h$	1.00	$0.10h$

Note: These equations give interception in inches for values of precipitation P in inches. The symbol h refers to the height of the plants in feet.

Depression storage. Water retained in puddles, ditches, and other depressions in the soil surface is known as *depression storage*. These depressions, closed drainages, are of all sizes and depths, ranging from micro-depressions of the order of magnitude of soil particles to flooded flats of many acres.

As soon as rainfall intensity at the soil surface exceeds the infiltration capacity, the rainfall excess begins to fill surface depressions. An understanding of the sequence of events which takes place after the beginning of rainfall excess requires recognition of the following facts:

1. Each depression has its own capacity or maximum depth.
2. As each depression is filled to capacity, further inflow is balanced by outflow plus infiltration and evaporation.
3. Depressions of various sizes are both superimposed and interconnected. In other words, every large depression encompasses many interconnected smaller ones.
4. Each depression, until such time as it is filled, has a definite drainage area of its own.

Almost immediately after the beginning of rainfall excess, the smallest depressions become filled and overland flow begins. Most of this water in turn fills larger depressions, but some of it follows an unobstructed path to the stream channel. This chain of events continues, with successively larger portions of overland flow contributing water to streams, until such time as all depression storage within the basin is filled. Water held in depressions at the end of rain is either evaporated or absorbed by the soil through infiltration. The process is repeated each time a runoff-producing storm occurs, and several inches of water may be added to the soil as a direct result of depression storage during the course of a year.

In small basins on steep slopes, most depressions are undoubtedly filled to capacity by only 1 or 2 in. of rainfall excess. On the other hand, closed drainages with capacities for many feet of rain over their drainage area are not uncommon. Generally speaking, the capacity of depressions within a unit area varies inversely with surface slope. The capacity also tends to increase with drainage area up to a certain point. Cultivation tends to destroy natural depressions but replaces them to a considerable extent by tillage marks.

The rate at which depression storage is extracted from rainfall excess is a function of the volume of excess up to the time under consideration. The first small increment of rainfall excess is almost entirely lost to the depressions, while greater portions of later increments contribute to runoff. The volume of water in depression storage V_s at any time throughout a storm can be approximately expressed in terms of the accumulated rainfall excess P_e by an equation of the type

$$V_s = S_d(1 - \mathbf{e}^{-kP_e}) \tag{11-3}$$

where S_d is the total depression-storage capacity of the basin and k is a constant. This equation neglects evaporation from depressions during the storm —a factor which is certainly inconsequential. Assuming that the initial increment of rainfall excess is completely absorbed by depressions, dV_s/dP_e is unity when P_e is near zero. Then, by differentiation, k is found to equal the reciprocal of S_d.

The rate at which depression storage is depleted by evaporation and infiltration during periods between storms determines the available capacity at the beginning of any storm. While evaporation from the soil surface is relatively unimportant during rain periods, it can be of considerable magnitude immediately following the end of rain. Because of the difficulties involved in making experimental observations, little is known of actual variations in depression storage. The volume rate at which storage is depleted by evaporation and infiltration probably recedes logarithmically with time, since the area covered tends to decrease in this fashion. This assumes that the basin has depressions of all sizes, including ponds which never completely dry up. It is probably safe to assume that V_s drops to less than half of S_d within 24 hr after the end of a major storm.

Throughout the above discussion, depression storage was considered in relation to rainfall in excess of interception and infiltration. Therefore, variables influencing interception and infiltration rates were not involved. However, since depression storage is rarely completely filled, the amount of water withheld from storm runoff through depression storage is a function of the infiltration characteristics of the soil. Since seasonal fluctuations in interception and infiltration tend to be in phase, there is a seasonal variation in the ratio of depression storage to total-storm precipitation. However, the amplitude of this fluctuation is somewhat reduced by snow accumulations. Factors such as soil type and rainfall intensity, affecting rates of infiltration, are discussed in Chap. 12.

Since the greater portion of depression storage is filled soon after the ground rainfall rate exceeds infiltration, the existence of such storage effectively reduces the duration of surface runoff. Figure 11-5 illustrates the effect of varying amounts of depression storage upon surface runoff[1] for two selected storm intensities and durations. Two simplifying assumptions were made in this analysis. (1) All depression storage is filled before surface runoff begins. (2) The infiltration rate is constant throughout the storm. Nevertheless, certain valid conclusions regarding the effect of depression storage upon runoff can be drawn from the charts. In the case of the 4-hr storm, since the runoff did not attain equilibrium, the maximum runoff intensity was reduced as a direct result of depression storage. Furthermore, the total volume of runoff was reduced by about the same ratio. In the case of the 10-hr storm, the runoff essentially reached the limiting intensity before the end of the storm so that there was no sub-

[1] Horton, R. E., "Surface Runoff Control," Chap. II, Headwaters Control and Use, Government Printing Office, Washington, D.C., 1937.

stantial reduction in the peak flow. As before, however, there was a reduction in the total volume of runoff.

It is evident that natural storage of water on the ground surface during rain reduces surface-runoff volumes and intensities. Unfortunately, natural surface depressions, while highly effective on flat areas, diminish rapidly in volume and effectiveness as the surface slopes increase, and it is

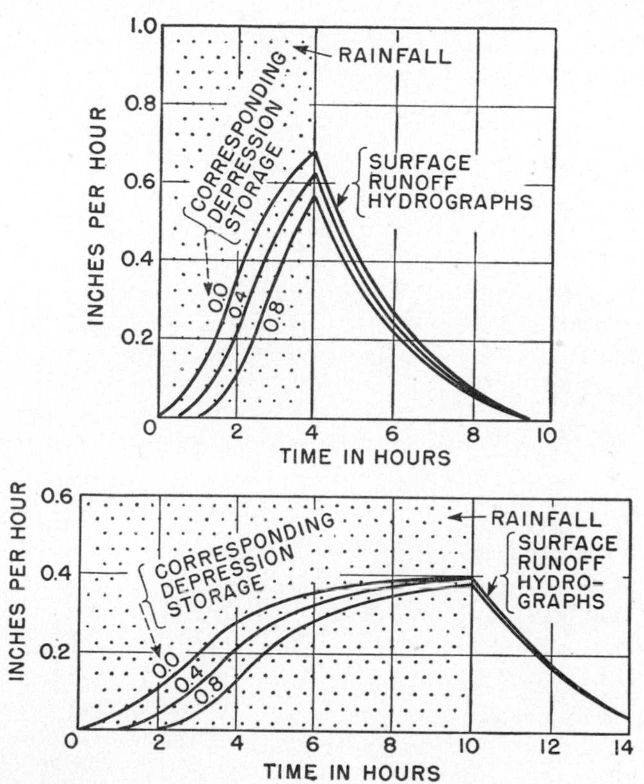

FIG. 11–5. Effect of depression storage on surface-runoff intensity and distribution. *(After Horton.)*

on these steeper slopes that they are most needed. Decreasing surface slopes not only increases depression storage but also reduces velocities of overland flow for given depths of surface detention. Stock ponds, terraces, and contour farming all tend to moderate the runoff cycle in this manner.

SURFACE DETENTION AND OVERLAND FLOW

Soon after rainfall excess begins, a thin sheet of water builds up over the soil surface and overland flow takes place. Water in temporary storage as a sheet over the basin, known as *surface detention*, is not to be confused with depression storage, which in no way contributes to surface runoff. Detention depths increase until discharge reaches equilibrium with the rate of supply to surface runoff. In experimental work and theoretical discussions, it is found convenient to deal with a slope of unit width and uniform surface. Unless otherwise stated, the subsequent discussion assumes these conditions.

Types of overland flow. The type of flow occurring at any given point within an area of overland flow depends upon such factors as viscosity, discharge, and degree of roughness. If detention depths are sufficient to

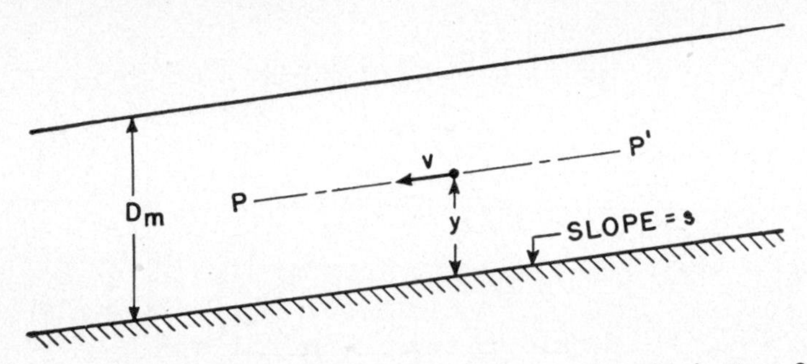

FIG. 11-6. Diagram showing symbols used in equation for laminar flow.

produce persisting eddies, then the flow is turbulent and the velocity can be expressed in terms of the Manning formula,

$$v_m = \frac{1.486}{\mathbf{n}} R^{2/3} s^{1/2} \tag{11-4}$$

where v_m is the mean velocity in feet per second, $\mathbf{n}$ is a roughness factor, R is the hydraulic radius, and s is the slope. In the case of overland flow, R becomes identical with the mean depth D_m of the cross section, and since the rate of discharge q per unit width is equal to the product $v_m D_m$,

$$q = bD_m^{5/3} \tag{11-5}$$

where b is a coefficient involving slope and roughness.

If velocities and depths of flow are relatively slight, the viscosity of the fluid becomes a controlling factor and the flow is viscous or laminar. In the case of uniform laminar sheet flow, the component of the gravitational force parallel to the flow is balanced by the frictional force. Therefore, using the symbols shown in Fig. 11-6 and considering the forces acting on a liquid column of unit area above the plane PP',

$$\rho \mathbf{g}(D_m - y)s = \mu \frac{dv}{dy} \tag{11-6}$$

where ρ is the fluid density and μ the absolute viscosity. This equation assumes that the slope is so slight that the sine and tangent are essentially equal. Since μ/ρ is equal to the kinematic viscosity ν,

$$dv = \frac{gs}{\nu} (D_m - y)dy \tag{11-7}$$

Integrating, and noting that $v = 0$ when $y = 0$,

$$v = \frac{gs}{\nu} \left(yD_m - \frac{y^2}{2} \right) \tag{11-8}$$

Integrating from $y = 0$ to $y = D_m$, the average velocity is

$$v_m = \frac{gsD_m^2}{3\nu} \tag{11-9}$$

and the discharge per unit width is

$$q = cD_m^3 \tag{11-10}$$

where c is a coefficient involving slope and viscosity.

Overland flow entering along a channel may change from turbulent to laminar, or vice versa, within a short distance. Any natural soil surface is uneven, and consequently detention depth and slope change from point to point. Flow is apparently always laminar close to the divide, but the portion of the area covered by turbulent flow increases downslope toward the channel because of increased depth and velocity. Thus, except on very uniform surfaces, the flow past any cross section of significant length is quite apt to be mixed between laminar and turbulent. If the area over which flow is occurring is covered with dense vegetation such as grass, the flow may be *superturbulent*, or *subdivided*.[1] Part of the energy is expended on the vegetation, and the quantity so expended increases with detention depth until this depth exceeds the height of the vegetation. Vegetation also reduces the effective cross-sectional area. The exponent of D_m for subdivided flow is even less than that indicated for turbulent flow in Eq. (11-5). Horton and others have presented data for which this exponent varies between 1.0 and 3.0, apparently verifying the possible existence of superturbulent flow as well as mixed flow.

Flow criteria. In applying Reynolds' criterion ($\mathbf{R} = vl/\nu$) to sheet flow, the mean depth of flow is used for l. The boundary between laminar and turbulent flow in open channels is generally considered to be represented by a Reynolds number of about 500. The published values for

[1] Horton, R. E., Erosional Development of Streams and Their Drainage Basins, *Geol. Soc. Am. Bull.*, Vol. 56, pp. 275-370, 1945.

sheet flow, however, vary considerably—Jeffreys[1] gives 310; Hopf[1] 300 to 330; and Horton[2] 550 to 770.

Horton concluded that Reynolds' criterion is not applicable to sheet flow over relatively rough surfaces and devised another which depends upon a roughness factor. He reasoned that the energy for both types of flow must be the same at the transition point. From an analysis of velocity distribution in channels, he concluded that, when the velocities for laminar and turbulent flow are equal, the translational and nontranslational energy for turbulent flow is nearly identical with the translational energy for laminar flow (per unit volume). Hence, the point of equal velocities represents the minimum amount of energy capable of maintaining turbulent flow. Thus, equating the right-hand members of Eqs. (11-4) and (11-9) (noting that $R = D_m$) and simplifying,

$$\frac{7.214\mathbf{n}D_m^{4/3}s^{1/2}}{\nu} = 1 \qquad \text{(ft-lb-sec units)} \tag{11-11}$$

Solving this equation for $D_m^{2/3}s^{1/2}$ and substituting in Eq. (11-4),

$$v_m = \frac{\nu}{4.86\mathbf{n}^2D_m^{2/3}} \tag{11-12}$$

According to Horton, the flow cannot be turbulent if the velocity is less than that computed by Eq. (11-12). His experiments did not indicate the existence of an upper limit for laminar flow.

Profile of overland flow. The general equation of flow is

$$q = \kappa D^m \tag{11-13}$$

where D is the depth at the point of outflow. At equilibrium, the discharge from a strip of unit width at a point x distance below the drainage divide is

$$q = xP_e \tag{11-14}$$

where P_e is the rainfall excess, or supply rate, per unit area. Combining Eqs. (11-13) and (11-14) and simplifying,

$$D_x = \left(\frac{xP_e}{\kappa}\right)^{1/m} \tag{11-15}$$

While this equation for the profile of overland flow is not strictly correct because the retarding effect of raindrop impact has been neglected, it is sufficiently accurate for most practical purposes, except at the extremities

[1] Jeffreys, H., The Flow of Water in an Inclined Channel of Rectangular Section, *Phil. Mag.*, Series 6, Vol. 49, No. 293, 1925.

[2] Horton, R. E., H. R. Leach, and R. Van Vliet, Laminar Sheet-flow, *Trans. Am. Geophys. Union*, Vol. 15, pp. 393-404, 1934.

of the strip.[1] The value of κ depends upon the characteristics of the slope, type of flow, and the viscosity (for laminar flow). The value of m depends only on the type of flow, *i.e.*, $\frac{5}{3}$ for turbulent and 3 for laminar.

It is sometimes desirable to relate the discharge at the base of a slope of length L_o to the average detention depth over the slope. The relation between depth D at the point of outflow and the average depth over the slope (detention volume V_d divided by the length L_o) can be found by integrating Eq. (11-15) and determining the average ordinate between the limits $x = 0$ and $x = L_o$. Thus,

$$\frac{V_d}{DL_o} = \frac{m}{m+1} \tag{11-16}$$

The ratio of average to outflow depth is therefore $\frac{5}{8}$ for turbulent flow and $\frac{3}{4}$ for laminar. Since the two depth measurements are directly proportional, average detention depth can be substituted in the flow equations [Eqs. (11-5) and (11-10)] after making proper adjustments to b and c.

Hydrograph of overland flow. The broad principles of the analysis outlined here were introduced by Horner and Jens[2] and Hicks.[3] However, the technique discussed is essentially that developed by Izzard[4] through analysis of data from cooperative experiments conducted by the Public Roads Administration and the Soil Conservation Service. The experiments were conducted in such a manner that the flow was laminar at all times. The relations expressed below apply for laminar flow only and, according to Izzard, should not be used when the product of the supply rate (in./hr) and the slope length (ft) exceeds 500. While some of the runs were made on a surface of dense bluegrass turf, conditions were such that infiltration and retention could be neglected. Consequently, the equations are written in terms of rainfall intensity rather than supply rate. The subscript e on the various symbols denotes equilibrium conditions.

The dimensionless hydrograph. Analysis of hydrographs resulting from simulated rainfall at a constant rate showed that the rising limb could be adequately represented by the dimensionless chart (q/q_e) of Fig. 11-7. The maximum ordinate indicates a discharge q equal to the product of rainfall intensity i and length of overland flow L_o, and a value of unity on the abscissa denotes the time required for flow to reach equilibrium. Since equilibrium conditions are approached asymptotically, the time t_e must be

[1] Izzard, C. F., The Surface-profile of Overland Flow, *Trans. Am. Geophys. Union*, Vol. 25, pp. 959-968, 1944.

[2] Horner, W. W., and S. W. Jens, Surface Runoff Determination from Rainfall without Using Coefficients, *Trans. ASCE*, Vol. 107, pp. 1039-1117, 1942.

[3] Hicks, W. I., A Method of Computing Urban Runoff, *Trans. ASCE*, Vol. 109, pp. 1217-1268, 1944.

[4] Izzard, C. F., Hydraulics of Runoff from Developed Surfaces, *Proc. Highway Research Board*, Vol. 26, pp. 129-150, 1946.

determined in a somewhat arbitrary manner. In this study, t_e was defined as the time when q/q_e reached 0.97. From the figure it is seen that this definition is such that $t_e/2$ corresponds to a q/q_e value of 0.55. Since this is the best-defined portion of the hydrograph, values of t_e were determined as twice the time required for q/q_e to reach 0.55. The relation for t_e was found to be

$$t_e = \frac{2V_{de}}{60q_e} \tag{11-17}$$

where V_{de} is in cubic feet, q_e is in cubic feet per second, and t_e is in minutes. The constant 60 is a conversion factor, and 2 is an empirical coefficient. Thus, the volume of water in detention at equilibrium is equal to the volume

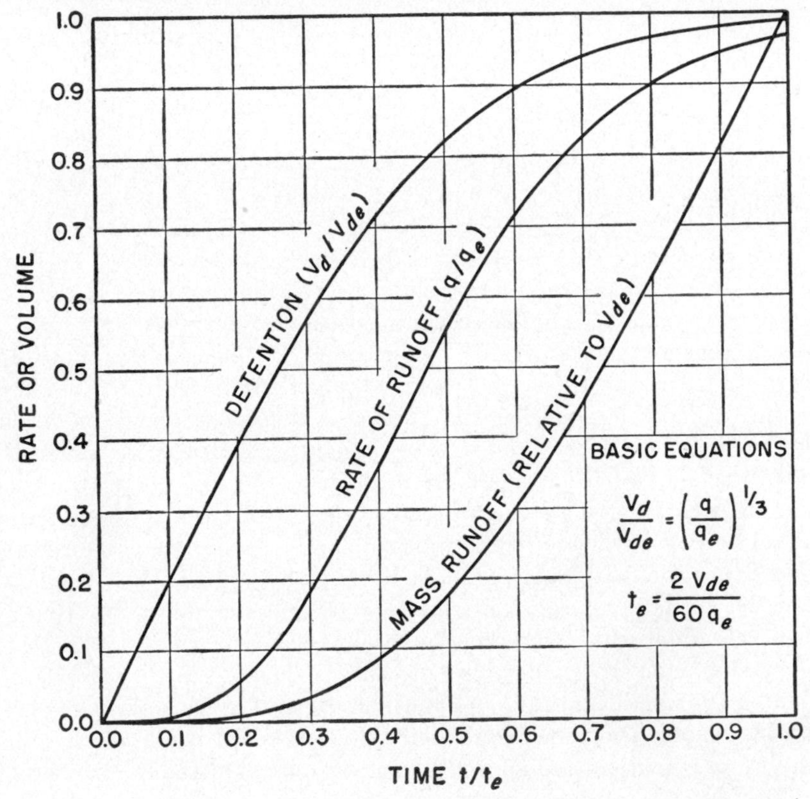

FIG. 11–7. Dimensionless hydrograph of overland flow. *(After Izzard.)*

discharged during the time required to reach equilibrium. That is, the area above the q/q_e curve in Fig. 11-7 is equal to the area below the curve. The three curves of the figure are based on Eq. (11-17) and

$$\frac{V_d}{V_{de}} = \left(\frac{q}{q_e}\right)^{1/3} \tag{11-18}$$

Both equations were derived empirically. Actually, values of the exponent in Eq. (11-18) varied from about 0.2 for very smooth pavement to nearly 0.4 for turf.

The volume of detention in overland flow at any time t is equal to the product of V_{de} and V_d/V_{de} as determined from Fig. 11-7 at time t/t_e. Similarly, the volume of runoff up to time t is equivalent to the ordinate of the mass-runoff curve at time t/t_e multiplied by V_{de} (since runoff equals detention at t_e).

If i is the rainfall intensity in inches per hour and L_o the length of overland flow in feet, then the discharge in cubic feet per second is

$$q_e = \frac{iL_o}{43{,}200} \tag{11-19}$$

where the constant 43,200 is a conversion factor. Substituting average depth on the strip for outflow depth, Eq. (11-10) may be written in the form

$$\frac{V_{de}}{L_o} = kq_e^{1/3} \tag{11-20}$$

Combining Eqs. (11-19) and (11-20),

$$V_{de} = \frac{kL_o^{4/3}i^{1/3}}{35.1} \tag{11-21}$$

It was determined experimentally that k could be represented by

$$k = \frac{0.0007i + c}{s^{1/3}} \tag{11-22}$$

where s is the slope of the surface in feet per foot and c is a retardance coefficient having the following values:

Very smooth asphalt pavement	0.007
Tar and sand pavement	0.0075
Crushed-slate roofing paper	0.0082
Concrete pavement	0.012
Tar and gravel pavement	0.017
Closely clipped sod	0.046
Dense bluegrass turf	0.060

The nomograph shown in Fig. 11-8 affords a convenient solution of Eqs. (11-21) and (11-22). The steepest slopes represented by the data utilized in the development of Eq. (11-22) were of the order of 0.04, and the equation should be used with caution for steeper slopes.

Recession limb of the hydrograph. Raindrops entering the surface-detention film must be given a horizontal component of velocity in the direction of flow. The necessary energy is supplied by the flowing water. The impact of the falling drops also creates resistance to flow over the entire surface. Hence, the depth of detention required to effect a given discharge is less on the receding limb of the hydrograph than on the rising side, because of the fact that rainfall has ceased. The effect of concurrent rainfall upon the detention-discharge relation is shown in Fig. 11-9. This effect is responsible for the intensity term in Eq. (11-22).

If V_{d0} is the detention corresponding to q_e after the end of rainfall [*i.e.*, $i = 0$ in Eq. (11-22)] and t_a is the time from the beginning of recession to

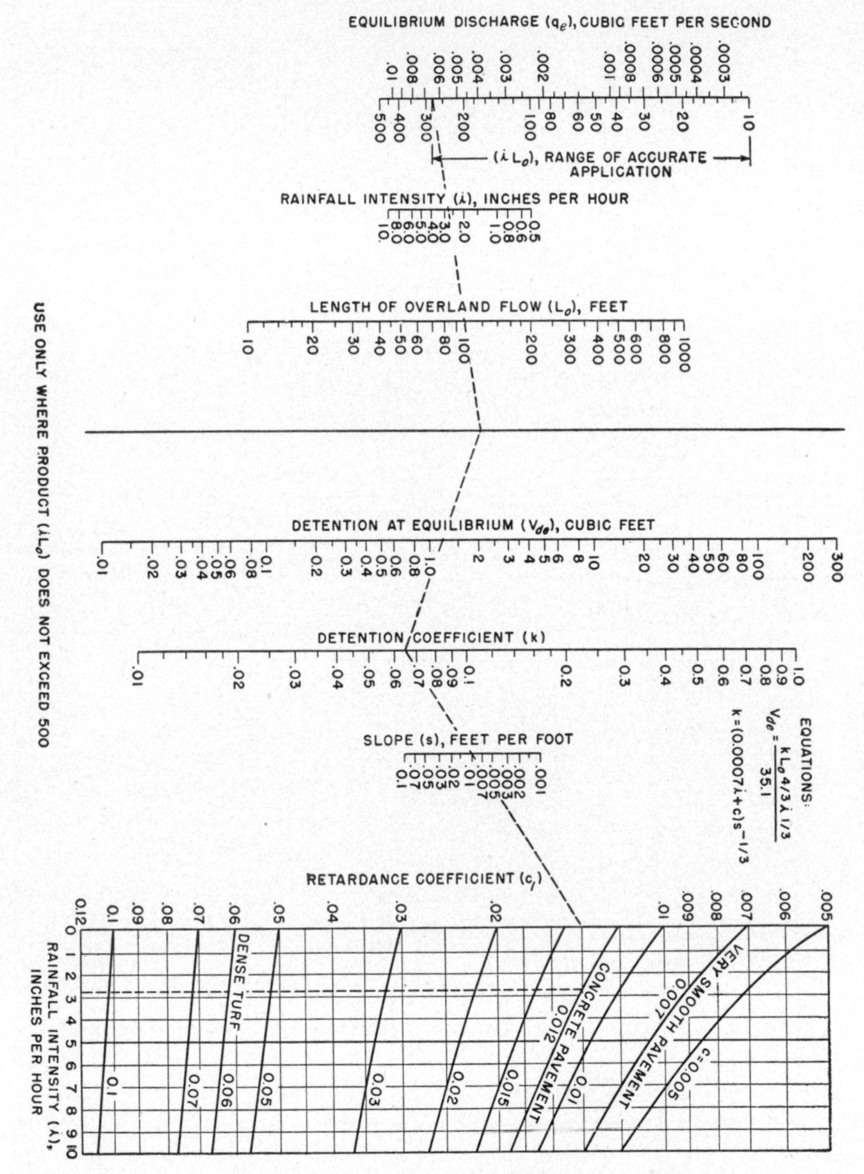

FIG. 11–8. Overland-flow detention on unit strip. (*After Izzard.*)

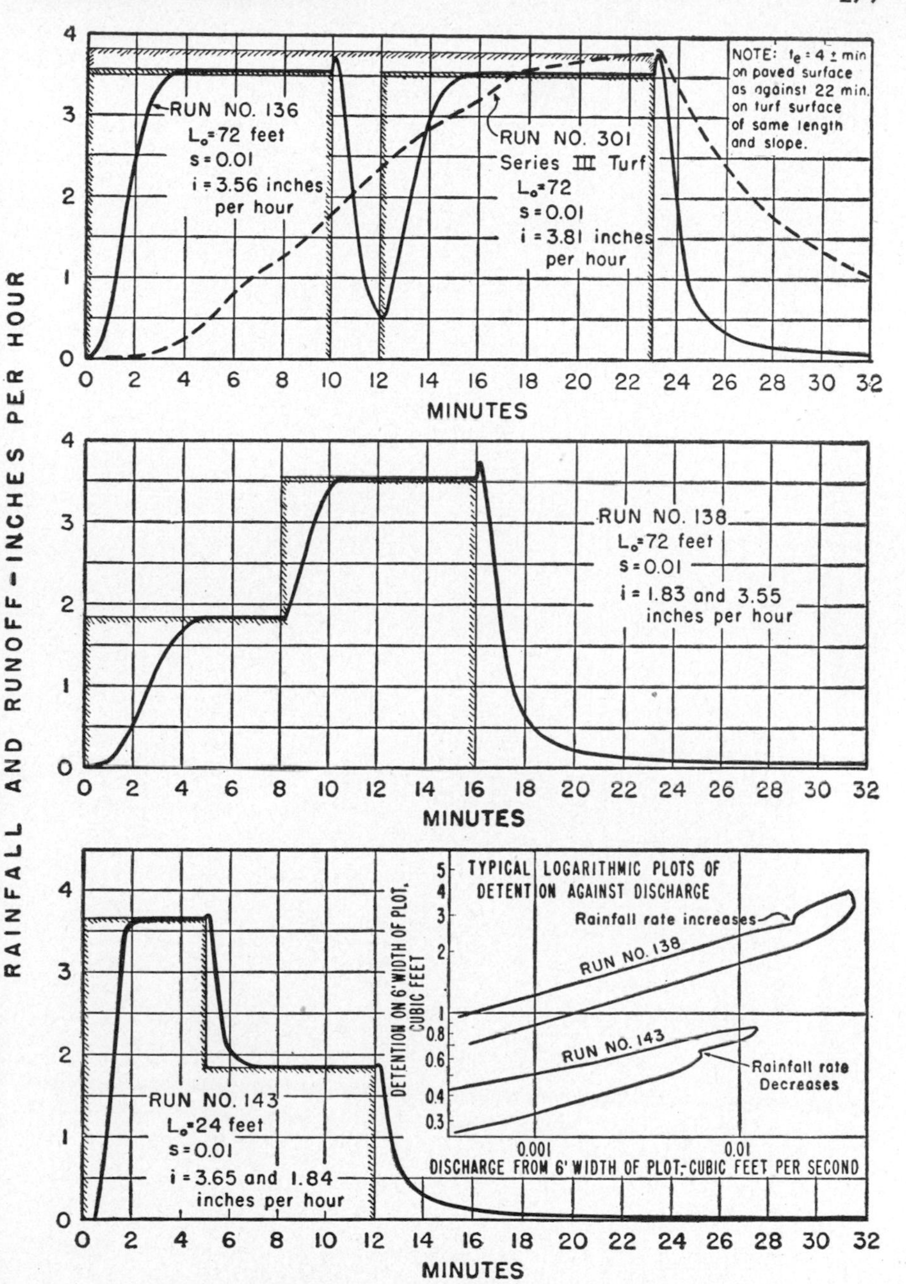

FIG. 11–9. Typical hydrographs and detention vs. discharge curves. (*After Izzard.*)

the point where $q/q_e = a$, then from Eq. (11-18), remembering that $q\,dt = dV_d$,

$$t_a = \frac{V_{d0}\,f(a)}{60q_e} \tag{11-23}$$

in which

$$f(a) = 0.5(a^{-2/3} - 1) \tag{11-24}$$

For convenience, the relation between a and $f(a)$ is given in graphical form in Fig. 11-10.

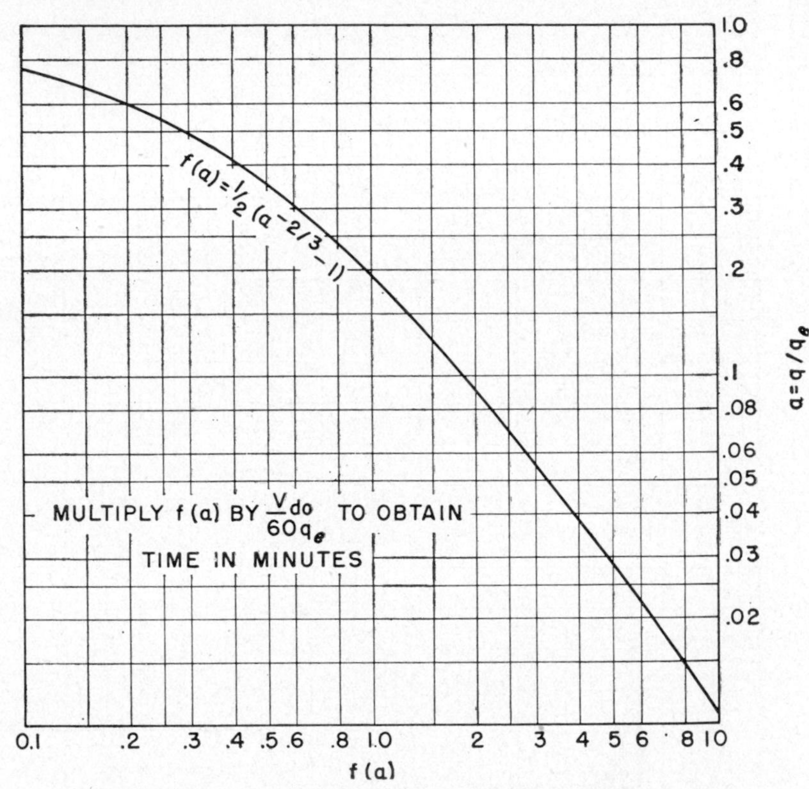

FIG. 11-10. Dimensionless recession curve. *(After Izzard.)*

Application of technique. To illustrate the application of the dimensionless hydrograph, nomograph, and recession relation, let us consider the complex rainfall sequence shown in Fig. 11-11, which, incidentally, is an observed experimental run. A tabulation of the required computations is shown in the accompanying tables.

First, values of q_e, k, V_{de}, and t_e are computed from given values of L_o, s, c, and i through the use of the nomograph (Fig. 11-8). For the first 2 min, each assumed value of t is divided by 5.30 min, which is the computed value

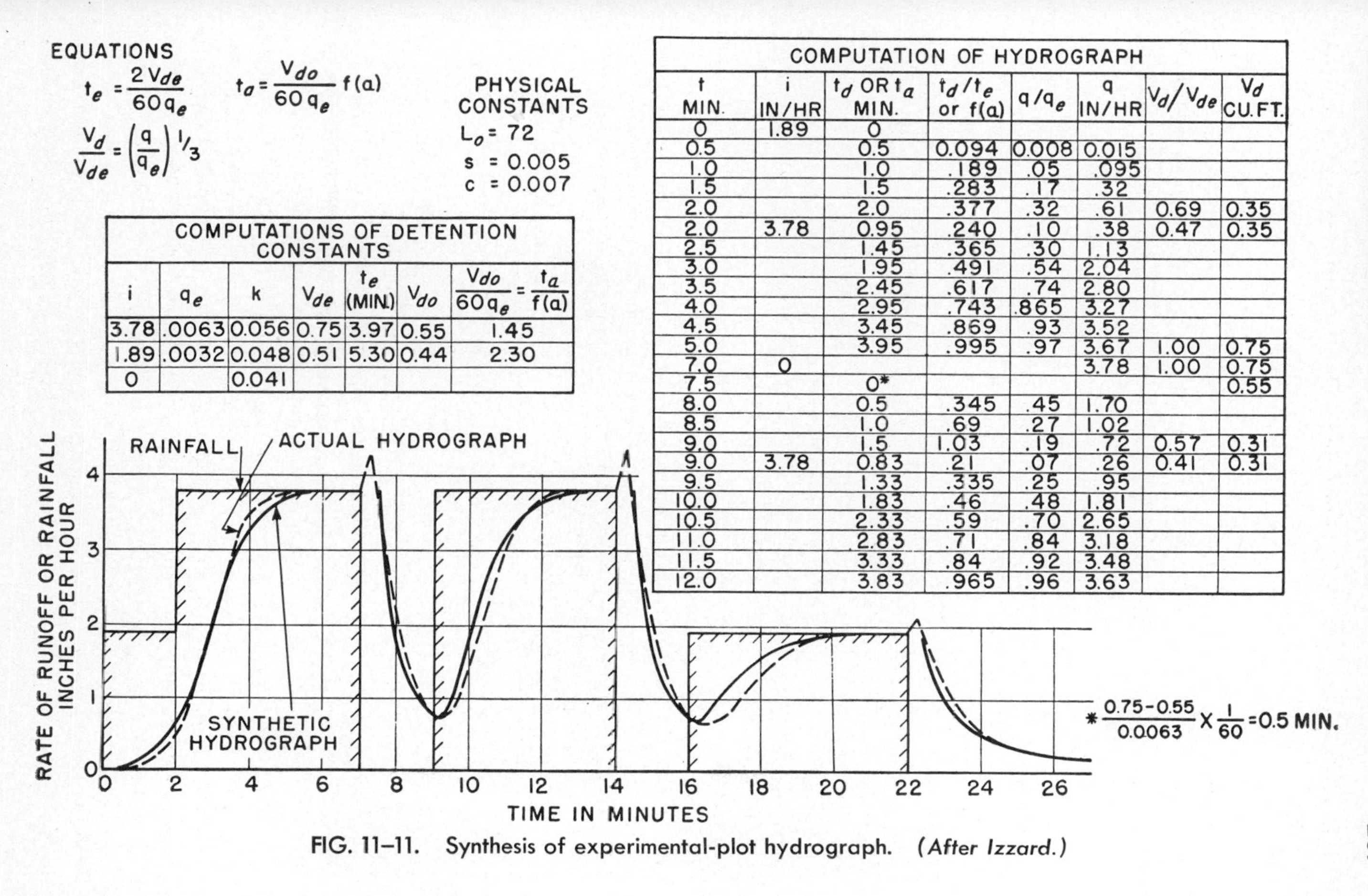

COMPUTATIONS OF DETENTION CONSTANTS

i	q_e	k	V_{de}	t_e (MIN)	V_{do}	$\frac{V_{do}}{60q_e} = \frac{t_a}{f(a)}$
3.78	.0063	0.056	0.75	3.97	0.55	1.45
1.89	.0032	0.048	0.51	5.30	0.44	2.30
0		0.041				

COMPUTATION OF HYDROGRAPH

t MIN.	i IN/HR	t_d OR t_a MIN.	t_d/t_e or f(a)	q/q_e	q IN/HR	V_d/V_{de}	V_d CU.FT.
0	1.89	0					
0.5		0.5	0.094	0.008	0.015		
1.0		1.0	.189	.05	.095		
1.5		1.5	.283	.17	.32		
2.0		2.0	.377	.32	.61	0.69	0.35
2.0	3.78	0.95	.240	.10	.38	0.47	0.35
2.5		1.45	.365	.30	1.13		
3.0		1.95	.491	.54	2.04		
3.5		2.45	.617	.74	2.80		
4.0		2.95	.743	.865	3.27		
4.5		3.45	.869	.93	3.52		
5.0		3.95	.995	.97	3.67	1.00	0.75
7.0	0				3.78	1.00	0.75
7.5		0*					0.55
8.0		0.5	.345	.45	1.70		
8.5		1.0	.69	.27	1.02		
9.0		1.5	1.03	.19	.72	0.57	0.31
9.0	3.78	0.83	.21	.07	.26	0.41	0.31
9.5		1.33	.335	.25	.95		
10.0		1.83	.46	.48	1.81		
10.5		2.33	.59	.70	2.65		
11.0		2.83	.71	.84	3.18		
11.5		3.33	.84	.92	3.48		
12.0		3.83	.965	.96	3.63		

FIG. 11–11. Synthesis of experimental-plot hydrograph. (After Izzard.)

of t_e for $i = 1.89$ in./hr. Values of q/q_e for corresponding values of $t/5.30$ are obtained from Fig. 11-7 and multiplied by 1.89 to get the ordinates of the hydrograph in inches per hour. The detention at the time the rainfall rate changes is also computed from the detention curve (Fig. 11-7) at $t/t_e = 0.377$.

The value of V_{de} for the new rainfall intensity (3.78 in./hr) is 0.75 ft³, and since the detention built up at the old rate is 0.35, V_d/V_{de} at 2 min is 0.47. The time ratio (0.24) corresponding to this detention ratio multiplied by the new t_e, 3.97, gives 0.95 min. This means that the absolute volume of detention built up in 0.95 min with $i = 3.78$ is the same as that built up in 2.0 min with $i = 1.89$ in./hr. By adding assumed increments of time to this initial value of $t_d = 0.95$, values of t_d/t_e are computed, and the corresponding values of q are derived as before. It will be noted that there are two values of q given in the table for 2.0 min. The computed hydrograph should pass through the first value, 0.61 in./hr, and fade into the curve computed for the second intensity.

When the rainfall ceases at 7 min, there is a momentary increase in the discharge due to the fact that during rainfall the amount of detention is greater than the amount required to cause the same rate of runoff after cessation of rainfall. In the table in the upper left portion of Fig. 11-11, it is seen that $V_{d0} = 0.55$. This value is computed from Eq. (11-21), using $i = 3.78$, but with k based on $i = 0$ in Eq. (11-22). The excess detention ($0.75 - 0.55 = 0.20$ ft³) is discharged at a rate slightly greater than the corresponding value of q_e. Incomplete experimental evidence indicates that the peak discharge is about $1.15q_e$. The time in seconds required to discharge the excess may therefore be assumed as about 0.20/0.0063, or roughly 0.5 min. The time of beginning of the actual recession is therefore assumed to be $7.0 + 0.5 = 7.5$ min, at which time $q = 3.78$ in./hr and $V_{d0} = 0.55$ ft³.

The recession constant, $t_a/f(a) = 1.45$, is computed as indicated in the table of detention constants (Fig. 11-11). In the other table, t_a is taken as zero at 7.5 min. At 8 min, $t_a = 0.5$, which, divided by the recession constant, gives $f(a) = 0.345$. The corresponding value of a from Fig. 11-10 is 0.45, and consequently $q = 0.45 \times 3.78 = 1.70$ in./hr. Discharges at other times along the recession are computed in a similar manner.

At 9 min the rainfall resumes. At this time $V_d/V_{d0} = a^{1/3} = 0.19^{1/3} = 0.57$, from which $V_d = 0.57 \times 0.55 = 0.31$ ft³. This is $0.41V_{de}$ relative to an intensity of 3.78 in./hr. The procedure from this point is the same as that at 2 min, namely, to find the corresponding t/t_e from which q/q_e and q are computed. The rest of the synthetic hydrograph to 27 min is computed in a similar manner.

12

SOIL PHYSICS

The term *soil*, as applied to engineering, usually designates earth material, whether lying in its original undisturbed state or in a structure such as an earth-fill dam. In agriculture, soil refers to that part of the earth's crust which is penetrated by the roots of plants.

A superficial consideration of the composition and structure of soils will reveal wide variations within relatively limited areas. However, there are certain groups of constituents which are common to all soils, namely, *mineral* and *organic matter*, *soil moisture*, and *soil air*. The composition and amount of soil moisture and soil air are dependent upon the mineral and organic components. These components are in unstable equilibrium, resulting from variations in temperature, water content, chemical and physical actions, activities of micro-organisms, and the drain of nutrients by plants. The soil profile may show many layers, which are generally considered to fall in two classes, *topsoil* and *subsoil*.

Soil solids are composed of rock which has been disintegrated and decomposed by physical and chemical action and mixed with organic matter. Their composition varies considerably within relatively short distances and depends upon many factors, such as quantity and type of organic matter and composition of the parent rock. Soil water may fill all or part of the spaces between soil particles. Its quantity and chemical composition vary considerably with time, location, and rate of movement. Soil air occupies the pore space which is not filled with liquid, and it also is subject to marked changes in composition and quantity. *Soil physics* is the study of the physical properties and interrelations of the soil components and atmospheric phenomena. The field of soil physics has expanded rapidly of recent years, especially in its application to agriculture. Only those aspects of soil physics of direct interest in the general field of hydrology are covered in this chapter.

MECHANICAL COMPOSITION OF SOILS

Surface area and particle size. The *internal surface* of a mass of soil is the sum of the surface areas of each particle within the mass. When expressed as units of area per unit of volume or weight, the internal surface becomes *specific surface.* It varies between wide limits, ranging from 200 or 300 ft^2/lb for sand to as much as 20,000 to 30,000 ft^2/lb for clay. This great difference of specific surface is an important factor in creating dissimilarities in the physical properties of clay and sandy soils.

Classification of soil particles. Soil particles are classified according to size by a number of different classifications, none of which is accepted by all soil physicists. Classifications adopted as standard by the Bureau of Chemistry and Soils, U.S. Department of Agriculture, and by the International Society of Soil Science are given in Table 12-1.

TABLE 12-1. Classification of Soil Particles

Designation	Diameter of particle, mm	
	U.S. Department of Agriculture	International Society of Soil Science
Fine gravel (grit)..........	2 to 1	
Coarse sand.............	1 to 0.5	2.0 to 0.2
Medium sand...........	0.5 to 0.25	
Fine sand................	0.25 to 0.10	0.2 to 0.02
Very fine sand...........	0.10 to 0.05	
Silt.....................	0.05 to 0.005	0.02 to 0.002
Clay....................	0.005 or less	0.002 or less

MECHANICAL ANALYSIS OF SOILS

The *mechanical analysis* of soils, the determination of the distribution of particle size, is perhaps the most important laboratory examination to which soil is subjected.[1] The first step in the analysis is the separation of the coarser fractions by the use of sieves. The finer particles are then separated by a wet analysis, usually based on the fact that the speed of sedimentation is a function of particle size. Before an accurate wet analysis can be performed, however, the sample must be pretreated to obtain complete dispersion.

Classification of soils. Soils are composed of various mixtures of gravel, sand, silt, clay, and organic matter and are classified according to the proportions of these substances. The three basic classes are sand, loam, and clay. By using various combinations of these three terms and

[1] Baver, L. D., "Soil Physics," Wiley, New York, 1940.

"silt," such as sandy clay or silty clay loam, the possible number of classes is multiplied. Davis and Bennett[1] have outlined a system of classification which has become widely recognized (Table 12-2).

Soil classes are further subdivided into types based on texture, color, structure, character of subsoil, and source. Some examples are Muskingum silt loam, Houston black clay, Vernon fine sandy loam, yellow sandy silt loam, and brown silt loam.

TABLE 12-2. Mechanical Composition of the Principal Soil Classes

Soil class	Per cent		
	Sand	Silt	Clay
Sand	80–100	0–20	0–20
Sandy loam	50–80	0–50	0–20
Silt loam	0–50	50–100	0–20
Loam	30–50	30–50	0–20
Silty clay loam	0–30	50–80	20–30
Sandy clay loam	50–80	0–30	20–30
Clay loam	20–50	20–50	20–30
Silty clay	0–20	50–70	30–50
Sandy clay	50–70	0–20	30–50
Clay	0–50	0–50	30–100

Experiments have demonstrated that many of the physical characteristics of soils are attributable principally to the clay in the soil (*clay fraction*). This is due in part to the relatively large specific surface of clay and is further emphasized by the difference in the chemical and mineralogical nature of clay as compared with sand and silt. Sand and silt are quartz or unweathered primary minerals, which display only slight chemical or physical activity. They may, therefore, be considered as the soil skeleton, while clay and humus materials make up the active portions.

PHYSICAL CHARACTERISTICS OF SOIL COLLOIDS

It has been pointed out earlier in the chapter that the finer fractions of the soil are responsible for its major chemical and physical activities, principally because they possess such a large portion of the total internal surface. In most soils, the colloidal fraction is primarily inorganic. However, depending upon such factors as climate, vegetation, and methods of cropping, organic colloids may be relatively significant.

[1] Davis, R. E., and H. H. Bennett, Grouping of Soils on the Basis of Mechanical Analysis, *U.S. Dept. Agr. Circ.* 419, 1927.

Shape of clay particles. The shape of the clay particles in soil is an important physical property, since the specific surface and amount of contact per unit surface are each a function of particle shape. Although most theoretical concepts of soil behavior are based on the assumption that the particles are spherical, virtually all experimental evidence indicates that they are plate-shaped. Consideration of soil properties, such as plasticity, crusting, and compaction, supports experimental evidence.

True and apparent density. The densities of the inorganic soil constituents which occur in appreciable quantities fall within a fairly narrow range. Therefore, the *true density* depends principally upon the relative proportions of organic and inorganic matter present. While the specific gravity of the organic matter in soil varies from 1.2 to 1.7, the principal mineral constituents (quartz, clay, and feldspar) are such that the average specific gravity of soils is generally taken as 2.65. The *apparent density* is that value obtained by weighing a unit volume of soil and hence depends on the degree of compaction and moisture content.

Hygroscopicity of clay particles. Materials which possess the property of collecting moisture from a nonsaturated atmosphere are *hygroscopic.* Soils are hygroscopic, and therefore a sample of perfectly dry soil placed in an atmosphere containing water vapor will adsorb water molecules until such time as the system reaches a state of equilibrium. In equilibrium with a saturated atmosphere the hygroscopic moisture is at a maximum, while in perfectly dry air the soil eventually loses all its moisture. The relation between hygroscopic soil moisture and atmospheric vapor pressure has been studied extensively.[1] The relation, as determined by Alexander and Haring, is shown for several typical soil colloids in Fig. 12-1. The degree of saturation of the atmosphere is generally controlled during such experiments by placing the soil sample and a solution of sulfuric acid in a closed chamber. A solution of 3.3 per cent sulfuric acid (by weight) yields a relative humidity of 99.8 per cent, while 10 per cent and 30 per cent solutions result in humidities of 94.3 per cent and 74.9 per cent, respectively. In view of the inflection point near 50 per cent humidity, it has been proposed[2] that all comparative observations be made with a sulfuric acid solution of density 1.3321 (relative humidity 50 per cent). Under these conditions, the moisture content determined does not differ greatly from air-dried soil, since the rate of change of moisture content

[1] Puri, A. N., E. M. Crowther, and B. A. Keen, The Relation between the Vapor Pressure and Water Content of Soils, *J. Agr. Sci.*, Vol. 15, pp. 68-88, 1925.

Thomas, M. D., Aqueous Vapor Pressure of Soils, *Soil Sci.*, Vol. 11, pp. 409-434, 1921; Vol. 17, pp. 1-18, 1924.

Alexander, L. T., and M. M. Haring, Vapor Pressure–Water Content Relations for Certain Typical Soil Colloids, *J. Phys. Chem.*, Vol. 40, p. 199, 1936.

[2] Puri, A. N., E. M. Crowther, and B. A. Keen, The Relation between the Vapor Pressure and Water Content of Soils, *J. Agr. Sci.*, Vol. 15, pp. 68-88, 1925.

with degree of saturation is relatively small for a considerable range about this point.

Under given conditions, the amount of hygroscopic moisture in soils is principally determined by the relative amounts of clay they contain, since it is this fraction which supplies the major portion of the internal surface. The amount of water adsorbed under specific conditions increases with clay content. Other factors which affect hygroscopic-moisture content

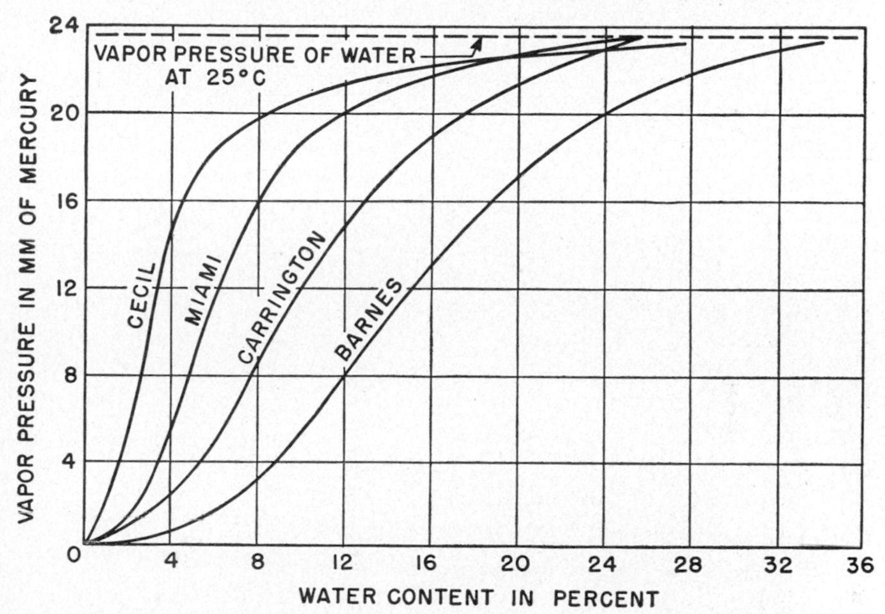

FIG. 12–1. Water-content relation for soil colloids at 25° C. *(After Alexander and Haring.)*

are the nature of the colloidal fraction and temperature of the soil. At soil temperatures between 20 and 40°C, adsorption of moisture is practically independent of temperature when the relative humidity is near 100 per cent but decreases with increasing temperatures when the humidity is low.

Heat of wetting. Hygroscopic moisture is separated from soil only at the expense of energy supplied to the soil. Heat must be applied to hygroscopic material to free the water molecules and convert them into vapor. Conversely, heat is evolved when dry, hygroscopic soil is placed in water. Heat released under these conditions, termed *heat of wetting*, represents the loss in kinetic energy of water molecules during adsorption.

The heat of wetting decreases as the initial moisture content of the soil increases. Like most other soil properties, it is a function of the specific surface, nature of the clay colloids, and type of exchangeable cations.

The effect of variations in internal surface is of considerable magnitude, the heat of wetting for heavy clay at zero moisture content being about 15 cal/g and only about 2 cal/g for sandy loam.

Swelling and shrinking of soils. The fact that soils shrink as they dry out and swell as they become wet is evidenced by the large cracks appearing in the earth's surface during extended drought periods and disappearing with the first succeeding heavy rain. Shrinking and cracking are most pronounced in the heaviest clays, since the phenomenon is closely related to the internal surface of the substance. The terms "swelling" and "shrinking" refer only to the soil solids. For example, if 10 cc of water is added to 100 cc of dry soil, the total volume will be less than 110 cc but greater than the original volume of soil.

SOIL WATER

When precipitation falls upon soil, a portion of the water passes through the surface, enters the pores, and begins to move downward under the pull of gravity. Because of the absorption of water in the surface layers through surface tension, hygroscopicity, etc., there is a progressive decrease in the amount of water passing through successively lower levels until such time as the intervening layers become saturated. Thus, it is evident that the disposition of the infiltered water is dependent on the character of the soil pore space.

From a theoretical point of view, there are two concepts of soil-water relationships. The older (and still prevailing) concept, the *capillary-tube hypothesis,* pictures the soil as consisting of numerous capillaries of varying dimensions, with water retention explained as resulting from the tension of water films around the particles and through the pores. In recent times, thinking has followed the lines of energy relationships, considering the flow of water through soil to be analogous to the flow of heat or electricity through a conductor. The distinction is principally academic, and there is essentially no conflict between the two schools of thought.

The capillary-tube hypothesis. If a tube with a porous stopper at the bottom is filled with dry soil and the bottom of the tube placed in contact with a water surface, the soil becomes gradually moistened from below. The upper surface of the rising moisture is practically horizontal at all times as if the moisture were moving in parallel, thin tubes of approximately equal diameter. According to the *capillary-tube hypothesis,* the height to which the moisture would eventually rise under these conditions is

$$h_c = \frac{2F_s \cos \theta}{g\rho_w r} \tag{12-1}$$

where h_c is the height of the meniscus above the level of the liquid, F_s is the surface tension of the water, θ is the angle between the meniscus and the wall of the capillary, ρ_w is the density of water, and r is the radius of the capillary. Substituting average values for F_s, $\mathbf{g}$, and ρ_w and assuming θ equal to zero, Eq. (12-1) becomes (in cgs units)

$$h_c = \frac{0.15}{r} \tag{12-2}$$

If we consider the extremely small diameter of the pores in fine clay, this equation yields a very large capillary rise, the validity of which has been questioned by numerous investigators. Keen[1] has concluded, on the basis of experimental data, that capillary rise is ineffective above 35 cm for coarse sand, 70 cm for fine sand, and 80 cm for heavy loam. Although some scientists have considered the limit of capillary rise to be somewhat greater, recent studies have adequately demonstrated that the estimates of earlier investigators were in general much too high.

Concept of ideal soil. Recent investigators have attempted to explain moisture distribution by assuming the soil to consist of uniform spheres in close hexagonal packing. Under these conditions, with low moisture content, water exists as separate rings around the contact points of the spheres. With increasing moisture the rings become larger until eventually they become connected, forming a continuous system which is permeated by a network of air passages. It is obvious that natural soils cannot be expected to approximate the "ideal soil" even closely, but the hypothesis, which must be considered a marked advance over the capillary-tube theory, has been of assistance in explaining the distribution and movement of soil water.

Classifications of soil water. Briggs,[2] in 1897, proposed that soil water be classified as:

1. Hygroscopic water—that which is adsorbed from the atmosphere as a thin film on the surface of soil particles, held with considerable force, and unavailable to plants.
2. Capillary water—that which is held by surface tension in the capillary spaces and as a continuous film around the particles, free to move under the influence of capillary forces, and available to plants.
3. Gravitational water—that which drains through the soil under the influence of gravity.

Zunker[3] has proposed an elaborate scheme of classification which is essentially an expansion of the capillary-tube hypothesis. His classification

[1] Keen, B. A., The Limited Role of Capillarity in Supplying Water to Plant Roots, *Proc. Intern. Congr. Soil Sci.*, Vol. 1, pp. 504-511, 1928.

[2] Briggs, L. J., The Mechanics of Soil Moisture, *U.S. Dept. Agr. Bur. Soils Bull.* 10, 1897.

[3] Zunker, F., Das Verhalten des Bodens zum Wasser, "Handbuch der Bodenlehre," Vol. VI, pp. 66-220, Berlin, 1930.

does not differ materially from that of Briggs, except that he gives place to the vapor phase.

Soil-moisture energy relationships. As early as 1907, Buckingham[1] introduced the idea of characterizing soil-moisture phenomena by energy relationships. He visualized the flow of water through soil as being comparable to the flow of heat or electricity through a conductor and proposed the term *capillary potential* (analogous to electric potential) to designate the attraction of soil for water at a given point. The *potential* at any point in a conservative field is, by definition, the potential energy of a unit quantity at that point. Accordingly, the *capillary potential* is the potential energy per unit mass of water. Potential, or potential energy, is purely relative and must therefore be measured with respect to some reference point, such as sea level in gravitational problems. Thus, the potential becomes equivalent to the amount of work required to move unit quantity from the reference point to the point under consideration. With a free-water surface (the groundwater level) as reference, the *capillary potential* is defined as the work required to move a unit mass of water from the free-water surface to the specified point, against capillary forces in the column of soil. It will be seen that, because of the choice of reference, capillary potential is negative in sign, since water will move upward from groundwater by capillarity. Work is required, however, to move water in the soil downward to the reference plane against capillary action. The negative sign is frequently ignored.

In a column of soil of which the base is in contact with a free-water surface and the top and sides are sealed off to prevent evaporation, the moisture distribution will eventually reach equilibrium. Then, neglecting gravity, the energy E required to move an incremental mass of water $d\mathbf{m}$ from height y to $(y + dy)$, the respective capillary potentials being ψ and $\psi + (\partial\psi/\partial y)\,dy$, is

$$dE = \psi\,d\mathbf{m} - \left(\psi + \frac{\partial\psi}{\partial y}\,dy\right)d\mathbf{m} = -\frac{\partial\psi}{\partial y}dy\,d\mathbf{m} \tag{12-3}$$

In the process, the mass $d\mathbf{m}$ was raised through the distance dy; hence the work done against the force of gravity is $\mathbf{g}\,dy\,d\mathbf{m}$. Since the system is in equilibrium, the total amount of work done for infinitesimal displacement is zero. Therefore,

$$-\frac{\partial\psi}{\partial y}dy\,d\mathbf{m} + \mathbf{g}\,dy\,d\mathbf{m} = 0 \tag{12-4}$$

and

$$\frac{\partial\psi}{\partial y} = \mathbf{g} \tag{12-5}$$

[1] Buckingham, E., Studies on the Movement of Soil Moisture, *U.S. Dept. Agr. Bur. Soils Bull.* 38, 1907.

The capillary potential, however, is a function of moisture content M_c as well as height; consequently,

$$\frac{\partial\psi}{\partial M_c} = \frac{\partial\psi}{\partial y}\frac{\partial y}{\partial M_c} \tag{12-6}$$

Combining Eqs. (12-5) and (12-6),

$$\frac{\partial\psi}{\partial M_c} = \mathbf{g}\frac{\partial y}{\partial M_c} \tag{12-7}$$

From this equation it is seen that the rate of change of capillary potential with respect to moisture content is equal to **g** divided by the rate of change of moisture with height. Integration of either Eq. (12-5) or (12-7) yields (noting that $\psi = 0$ when $y = 0$)

$$\psi = \mathbf{g}y \tag{12-8}$$

Consequently, if the variation of moisture content with height is determined experimentally, the relation between moisture content and capillary potential can be computed. Buckingham made numerous experiments with soil columns and found the moisture-height relation to be

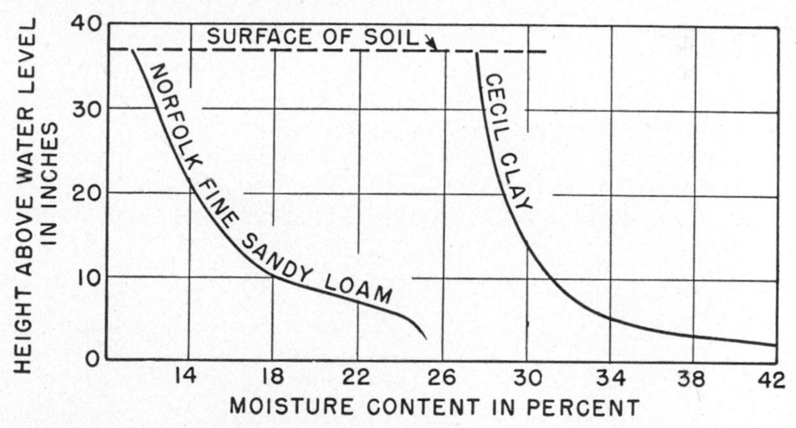

FIG. 12–2. Moisture-content vs. height curves. *(After Buckingham.)*

roughly hyperbolic, with moisture content at corresponding heights being greater the finer the soil (Fig. 12-2). His investigations demonstrated that the energy required to remove water from soil is a continuous function; therefore, any classification of soil water is necessarily arbitrary.

Measurement of capillary potential. Various methods have been employed to determine capillary potential, including use of moisture absorption by seeds, depression of freezing point, centrifugation, and vapor pressure. Perhaps the most widely known method, however, measures the "suction force" of the soil for water, using an instrument called a *ten-*

siometer (Fig. 12-3). The porous cup A and a portion of the manometer tube B are filled with water through opening C, which is then sealed with a stopper. The porous cup is then placed in the soil in such a manner as to ensure close contact. When the soil moisture and the water in the cup are in equilibrium, the potential of the soil is that corresponding to the manometer reading. A detailed discussion of several types of tensiometers may be found in a paper presented by Richards[1] and others.

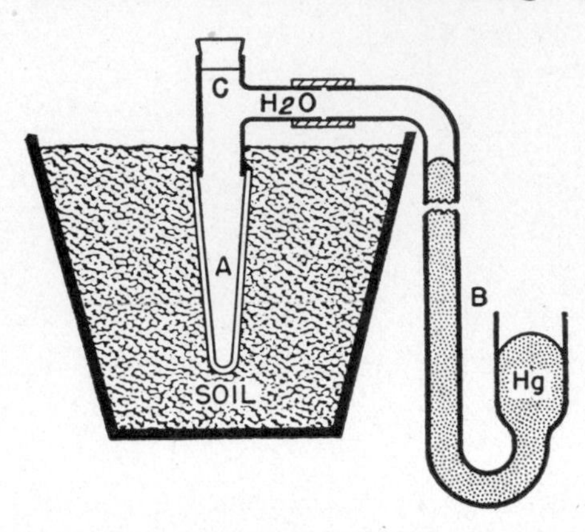

FIG. 12-3. A simple tensiometer used to determine tension-moisture relations of soils.

A troublesome factor in the use of the tensiometer is the hysteresis effect, *i.e.*, different manometer readings are obtained for the same moisture content, depending on whether the soil is drying or is being wetted. Being limited to tensions of less than 1 atm, the tensiometer can be used to determine only the wet end of the energy-moisture curve.

Vapor-pressure measurements provide data from which the capillary potential can be computed from Eq. (12-8) and

$$\log_e \left(\frac{e}{e_w}\right) = -\frac{gy}{R_w T} \qquad (12\text{-}9)$$

where e is the vapor pressure at height y, e_w is the vapor pressure at the free-water surface, T is the absolute temperature (°C), and R_w, the gas constant for water vapor, equals 4.61×10^3 for pressures in millibars. Figure 12-4 shows the relation between the vapor pressure and corresponding capillary potential for a temperature of 20°C.

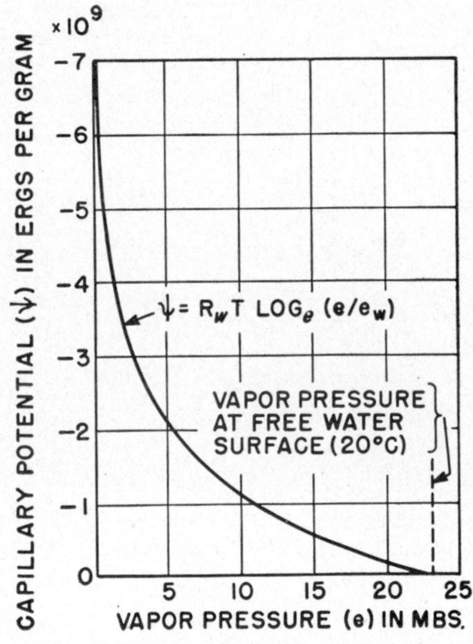

FIG. 12-4. Relation between vapor pressure and capillary potential at 20° C.

[1] Richards, L. A., M. B. Russell, and O. R. Neal, Further Developments on Apparatus for Field Moisture Studies, *Proc. Soil Sci. Soc. Am.*, Vol. 2, pp. 55-64, 1937.

The pF of soil water. In 1935 Schofield[1] suggested the use of the logarithm of the capillary potential pF to express energy relations of soil water. By analogy with pH, the letter p signifies a logarithm and the letter F represents "free energy." Schofield defined pF as the common logarithm of the head in centimeters of water necessary to produce the suction corresponding to the capillary potential. The use of pF considerably reduces the extreme range in the values of the potential, thus facilitating graphical presentation, tabulation, etc. Figure 12-5 shows the relation between pF

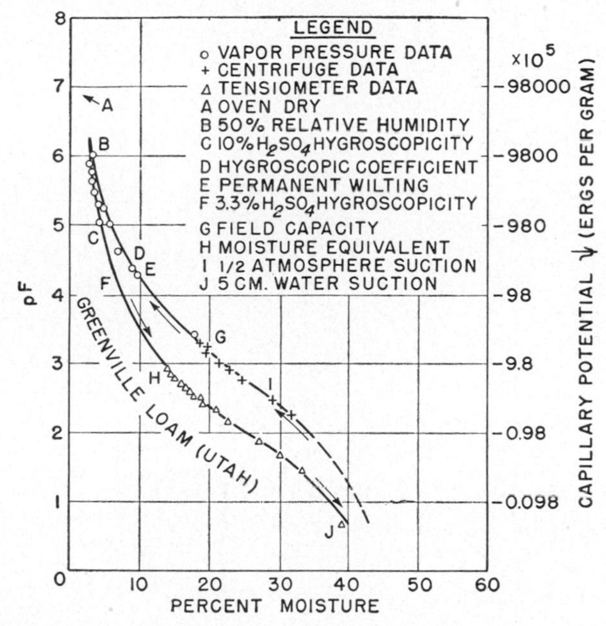

FIG. 12–5. Energy relations for Greenville loam. *(After Schofield.)*

and soil moisture for Greenville loam. Considerable hysteresis will be noted, and therefore a series of data cannot be expected to plot on a single curve unless they are all based on observations from the same phase (either wetting or drying).

Soil constants and equilibrium points. According to the capillary-tube hypothesis, soil water is considered to be of three types, hygroscopic, capillary, and gravitational. Early investigators sought equilibrium points which would define the limits of the three classes. Various so-called "soil constants" or "equilibrium points" were suggested, but the arbitrary nature of their definitions precludes their having a definite physical meaning. Figure 12-6 displays schematically the relations of pertinent soil-

[1] Schofield, R. K., The pF of the Water in Soil, *Trans. 3d Intern. Congr. Soil Sci.*, Vol. 2, pp. 37-48, 1935.

water constants and relative moisture content. The approximate pF values of the constants are shown in Fig. 12-5. While the so-called "soil-water constants" are convenient for comparative purposes, they represent nothing more than arbitrarily defined points along the continuous vapor-pressure–moisture curve.

The *hygroscopic coefficient* was originally defined as the maximum percentage of moisture which could be taken up by a dry soil in contact with an atmosphere saturated with water vapor. However, it was later discovered that, in a saturated atmosphere, soil will continue to take up moisture until it is itself saturated. To have any particular significance, therefore, the original definition must be altered to the extent that the

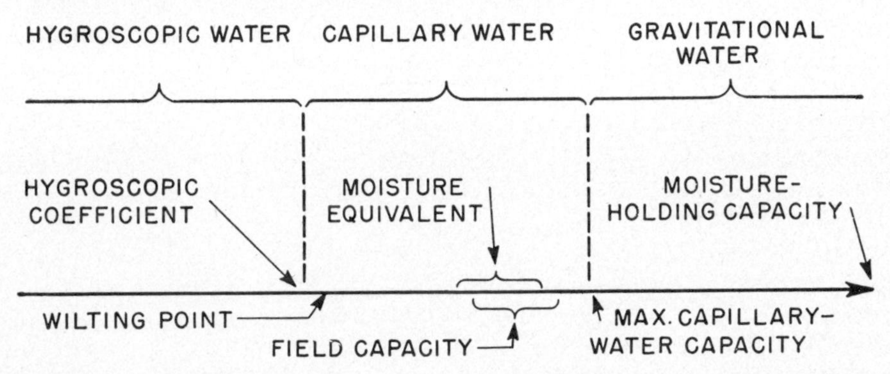

FIG. 12–6. Schematic diagram of the relative moisture content of soil-moisture constants or equilibrium points.

atmosphere have a definite relative humidity less than 100 per cent. In Europe, the measurement is quite generally made over a 10 per cent solution of sulfuric acid (94.3 per cent relative humidity at 25°C). The U.S. Department of Agriculture uses both a 30 per cent and a 3.3 per cent solution (relative humidity 74.9 per cent and 98.2 per cent, respectively). Many investigators prefer to use an atmosphere of 50 per cent humidity, since the change in moisture content with vapor pressure is least under these conditions (Fig. 12-1).

The *wilting point* is defined as the moisture content at which permanent wilting of plants occurs. Briggs, who introduced the concept, found the observed values to be largely independent of the kind of plant and concluded that the constant was a measure of quantity of water which soil could hold against a given extractive force. However, it has subsequently been demonstrated that the wilting point depends upon the physiological behavior of the plant, atmospheric conditions, expanse of the root system, and quantity of soil used in the test, as well as upon the soil-water relationships.

The *field capacity* is the amount of water held in the soil after excess gravitational water has drained away and the rate of downward movement has materially decreased. The arbitrary nature of this factor is self-evident. Nevertheless, the field capacity is widely used for comparative purposes.

The *maximum capillary-water capacity* is the maximum water content which a soil retains when subjected to the force of gravity. This term and field capacity were both devised to represent the upper limit of "available water" with respect to plant growth and are approximately equal. Since the wilting point marks the lower limit for plant growth, *available water* is the quantity of water represented by the difference between the wilting point and the maximum capillary-water capacity. Therefore, the slope of the tension-moisture curve between these two points is an important factor in determining the feasibility of raising specified crops in a given soil.

The *moisture equivalent* is the water retained by soil (initially saturated) when centrifuged under specified conditions. The usual procedure is to centrifuge a sample of 10 mm depth for a period of 40 min at a speed corresponding to a force of 1000**g**. Russell and Burr[1] investigated the effect of speed, period of centrifuging, and depth of soil layer on the moisture equivalent for 16 widely differing soils in an attempt to arrive at a less arbitrary definition of moisture equivalent or a better appreciation of the necessity of strict adherence to the adopted procedure. They found the observed values to be inversely proportional to the nth power of the centrifugal force, where n is positive, is greater than unity, and varies with soil characteristics. The moisture equivalent was found to decrease about 1 per cent when the depth was increased from 10 to 12 mm and about 0.6 per cent for each 20-min increase in the period after the first 20 min. For most heavy soils the moisture equivalent closely approximates the field capacity; however, for sands the moisture equivalent is relatively lower.

The *moisture-holding capacity*, or *maximum water capacity*, is the water content when the soil voids are completely filled, *i.e.*, the quantity of water required to saturate the soil. The moisture-holding capacity is determined by gently packing a shallow layer of soil in a small container and saturating it from below (to permit the escape of entrapped air). The arbitrary nature of this equilibrium point is obvious, since the degree of packing and the initial condition of the soil exert considerable influence on the results.

Determination of soil moisture. In laboratories the soil-moisture content is usually determined by observing the weight of a sample before

[1] Russell, J. C., and W. W. Burr, Studies on the Moisture Equivalent of Soils, *Soil Sci.*, Vol. 19, pp. 251-266, 1922.

and after heating to a temperature of slightly over 100°C. The *moisture content* expressed as a percentage is the ratio of the weight of the water driven off by heating to that of the dry soil. While many valid reasons may be advanced for expressing moisture content in percentage by volume, most measurements are made on the basis of weight, principally because of the inaccuracies of volume measurements of small, disturbed soil samples.

Many hydrologic problems are concerned principally with moisture content or time changes in it at a given point under field conditions. Where numerous observations are required, the difficulty of obtaining comparable samples and the time required for analysis make the laboratory method impractical. Consequently, the development of a simpler and more efficient method of determining moisture content has long been the goal of soil scientists. As early as 1897, Gardner[1] proposed a method based on the measurement of electrical resistance between two electrodes buried in the soil. This method was found to be unsatisfactory because of variable contact resistance between the electrodes and the soil. Moreover, small changes in salt content of the soil solution were found to cause resistance variations comparable with those resulting from changes in moisture.

Shaw and Baver[2] have shown that the heat conductivity of soil is a reliable index of its moisture content. In their method, insulated copper wire wound around a piece of glass tubing is placed in the soil and connected through a Wheatstone bridge with a micro-ammeter. The bridge is balanced, and a current is then passed through it for a predetermined period of time. With a fixed initial current, the observed current at the end of the specified time is a function of the temperature increase in the soil element, which is in turn related to the heat conductivity and moisture content of the soil. The readings of such an apparatus are not affected by changes in soil temperature or changes in concentration of electrolytes, and measurements can be made over the entire moisture range (air dry to saturation) to an accuracy of about 1 per cent. However, the relation of moisture content to heat conductivity changes from one soil type to another, and the element must be calibrated for the particular soil under observation.

Of recent years, many types of electrical moisture meters have been developed in which the changing properties of a porous block are observed and correlated to changes in moisture content. It has been found that, when a porous dielectric block is buried in soil, its moisture content changes with that of the soil. Also, the block's moisture content determines its heat conductivity, electrical resistance, and capacitance.

[1] Gardner, F. D., Electrical Method of Moisture Determination in Soils, *U.S. Dept. Agr. Div. Soils Bull.* 12, 1898.

[2] Shaw, C. F., and L. D. Baver, Heat Conductivity as an Index of Soil Moisture, *J. Am. Soc. Agron.* Vol. 31, pp. 886-891, 1939.

One of the many types of such meters is that recently developed by the U.S. Forest Service.[1] The soil unit is a disk-shaped, methacrylate-type plastic base, upon which are mounted two monel screen electrodes separated by several layers of fiberglas fabric, which serve as the porous dielectric. Since the observed resistance is dependent on temperature, a coil of copper wire is embedded in the rim of the disk to serve as a resistance thermometer.

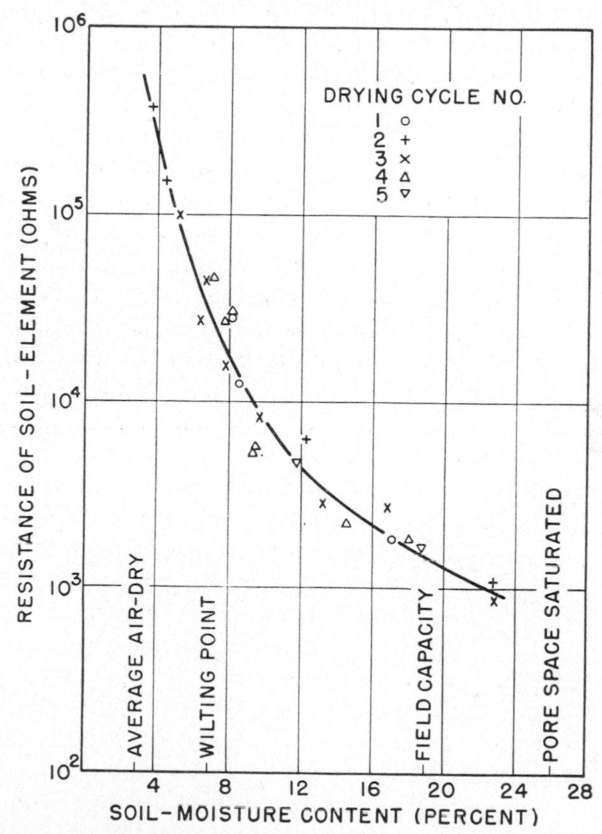

FIG. 12–7. Relation between resistance of soil element and soil-moisture content in a field plot. *(After Colman.)*

An alternating-current ohmmeter is used to measure the resistance between the electrodes of the soil unit. A battery-operated vacuum-tube oscillator generates low-frequency alternating current which passes between the electrodes. The measuring current is rectified by a selenium oxide bridge-type rectifier, and its magnitude is indicated on the dial of a micro-ammeter. The dial readings are directly related to resistance. The temperature of

[1] Colman, E. A., The Place of Electrical Soil-moisture Meters in Hydrologic Research, *Trans. Am. Geophys. Union*, Vol. 27, pp. 847-853, 1946.

the element is measured by using a separate circuit in the same meter unit. Figure 12-7 shows moisture content and corresponding resistance of the soil unit for a series of observations taken over a period of 7 months, during which the test plot was periodically irrigated and allowed to dry. There appears to be no significant time trend in the calibration curve during the relatively short test period. This calibration curve is not applicable when all or a portion of the soil water is frozen. Because of the great difference in resistivity between water and ice, electric moisture meters utilizing porous blocks may be effectively used to detect freezing and melting, depth of frost, etc.

Movement of soil water. The flow of moisture through soils is governed by a complex combination of forces created by gravity, capillarity, vapor-pressure gradients, soil temperatures, etc. Moisture may be transported either as vapor or as liquid. From a theoretical viewpoint, it is convenient to classify the liquid phase according to whether the flow is in saturated or unsaturated soil. In the first case, the water moves primarily through the larger pores under the influence of gravity, while in unsaturated soils capillary forces dominate and movement is confined to the smaller pores. Since a portion of the voids in unsaturated soils are filled with air, the transport of water takes place in both the liquid and the vapor phase. Only moisture transport in unsaturated soils is considered in this section; flow in saturated soils is discussed in Chap. 14.

Movement of liquid water in unsaturated soils. In unsaturated soil, the movement of water may take place in any direction since gravity is not necessarily the controlling force. If we consider the flow of water through soil to be analogous to the flow of heat or electricity through a conductor, the quantity of water passing through a unit cross section is proportional to the potential gradient, or

$$q_x = -K_w \frac{\partial \Lambda}{\partial x} \tag{12-10}$$

where q_x is the mass of water passing in unit time through unit cross section perpendicular to the direction of flow, x is distance along the line of flow, K_w is the conductivity, or transmission, constant, and Λ is the potential. In the general case, the potential gradient $\partial\Lambda/\partial x$ is the algebraic sum of capillary and gravitational gradients; however, for horizontal flow, $\partial\Lambda/\partial x = \partial\psi/\partial x$. The capillary potential and conductivity of soil are dependent upon the moisture content and consequently vary both with time and distance. Equation 12-10 can have little significance until both quantities K_w and ψ can be expressed as functions of a measurable factor (for example, the moisture content). Buckingham showed that capillary conductivity increases with moisture content and decreases with the pore size. Gardner[1]

[1] Gardner, W., A Capillary Transmission Constant and Methods of Determining It Experimentally, *Soil Sci.*, Vol. 10, pp. 103-126, 1920.

has presented data on the effect of packing upon conductivity for Greenville soil (Table 12-3). In view of the extreme variations of conductivity and the difficulties involved in determining a function relating it to moisture content and other measurable factors, Eq. (12-10) must be considered of only qualitative value.

TABLE 12-3. Effect of Packing on Capillary Conductivity

Degree of Packing	Capillary Conductivity (Cgs Units)
Extremely loosely packed	1.8×10^{-3}
Well packed (by previous wetting and drying)	5.4×10^{-3}
Packed dry by tapping of tube	7.4×10^{-3}
Field soil in natural structure	8.7×10^{-3}

Movement of water vapor. Because of experimental difficulties, relatively little is known of the magnitude and time distribution of the transport of water vapor in soil under field conditions. It is known that the transport of vapor in soil is the result of a vapor-pressure gradient, the transport being from regions of high vapor pressure to those of low. Vapor-pressure differences in soil are created by temperature gradients or by variations in soil-moisture content. Experimental data presented by Lebedeff[1] indicate that the relative humidity is always 100 per cent in soils of moisture content greater than the hygroscopic coefficient. Consequently, vapor transport at moisture contents greater than the hygroscopic coefficient is essentially the result of temperature gradients alone, and it is probable that temperature differences account for most of the transport even at lower moisture contents.

While the mean annual range of soil temperature is considerably greater near the surface than in the lower layers (Fig. 12-11), the mean annual temperature at all depths tends to equal the mean annual temperature in the surface layers of the atmosphere. Consequently, soil temperature increases with depth during winter and decreases in summer. This results in a net transport of water vapor to the surface during winter and downward during summer. Superimposed on the seasonal fluctuations are diurnal variations. In experiments conducted by Lebedeff at Odessa, U.S.S.R., it was found that 66 mm of water was transported to the surface as vapor from Oct. 26 to Mar. 1. In a single test, he found that the moisture content of the surface layer of soil increased from 1.99 to 5.26 per cent during a 12-hr period between 4 P.M. and 4 A.M. (in July). While available data on transport of soil moisture in the vapor phase are extremely limited, the experiments of Lebedeff and others demonstrate that vertical transport can be of considerable magnitude. One condition that favors rapid

[1] Lebedeff, A. F., The Movement of Ground and Soil Waters, *Proc. 1st Intern. Congr. Soil Sci.*, Vol. 1, pp. 459-494, 1927.

upward transport is that of a frozen surface layer overlying relatively warm layers.[1] In this case, the vapor-pressure difference is accentuated because the vapor pressure over ice is less than over water. Thus, when dry surface soil is frozen, there is a considerable upward transport of moisture and subsequent thawing renders the surface muddy, even though no precipitation has fallen in the meantime.

THE SOIL ATMOSPHERE

The soil is a porous medium, the voids around and between the soil particles being filled with air and water. The air is the lighter of the two fluids and acts as a cushion, filling pores as they become void of water and retreating to the atmosphere above when water flows into the pores. Thus, the soil-air relationships depend not only upon soil texture and structure but also upon soil moisture.

Capacity of soils for air. The pore space of soils ranges generally between 30 and 50 per cent by volume. This total pore space naturally represents the maximum air content. However, the capillary pores are not readily accessible to soil air, and consequently it has been found that noncapillary porosity is a better index to aeration, especially with respect to plant growth. In view of this fact, the *air capacity* of a soil is generally considered to be equivalent to its noncapillary porosity.

Many factors influence soil-air relationships through their effect on noncapillary porosity. In general, the finer the texture of the soil, the smaller the air capacity. Thus, with respect to plant growth, clays tend to have too little aeration, while sandy soils are so porous that they have a tendency to lose moisture rapidly. As would be expected, porosity and air capacity can be considerably reduced by compaction. Compression has been found to reduce the noncapillary porosity of specific clay samples by as much as 60 per cent. On the other hand, the air capacity of heavy soils can be materially increased by adding cinders, sand, or organic matter. It should be emphasized that the noncapillary porosity of the surface soil is not static—tillage operations and weather conditions exert a profound influence upon this soil property.

Mechanism of gas exchange. Variations in meteorological elements play an important role in the gas exchange between the soil and the atmosphere. As pressure systems pass over the soil, air is alternately forced into and out of the surface layers, since the mass of gas in a given volume is directly proportional to pressure. In addition to the succession of highs and lows which move across the country, a diurnal variation of pressure occurs with maxima about 10 A.M. and 10 P.M. and minima about 4 A.M. and 4 P.M. The amplitude of these diurnal fluctuations varies with latitude,

[1] Anderson, H. W., The Effect of Freezing on Soil Moisture and Evaporation from Bare Soil, *Trans. Am. Geophys. Union*, Vol. 27, pp. 863-870, 1946.

amounting to about 0.1 in. of mercury in equatorial regions and only about one-fourth this amount at 50° lat. The depth of penetration of atmospheric air is proportional to the depth of unsaturated soil and the total change in pressure. From Boyle's law, the theoretical penetration for a pressure change of 1 in. of mercury in a uniform soil column 10 ft deep is slightly less than 4 in. However, the decrease with depth of porosity and amplitude of pressure wave and the absence of any sharp separation between soil air and the atmosphere result in a rinsing action far less than would be anticipated from theoretical reasoning. It has been estimated that not more than about 1 per cent of the normal aeration of soils can be ascribed to fluctuations of barometric pressure. *Normal aeration* is defined as the complete renewal of the soil air to a depth of 20 cm about once each hour.

Temperature gradients within the soil layers or between the soil and the atmosphere tend to produce convection currents within the soil. The transport of soil air is greatest when the temperature decreases upward because of the inverse relation between temperature and density. Were the soil column open at the bottom to permit cool air to enter, become heated, and rise, an appreciable convection current could be created by a moderate temperature gradient. However, under natural conditions the cool air must settle through the same pores in which the warm air rises. Because of this dampening of convection and because of the relatively low heat conductivity of soil, the diurnal temperature range diminishes rapidly with depth below the soil surface. While the temperature gradient established by seasonal variations extends to considerably greater depths, the noncapillary porosity at these depths is generally so small as to render convective circulation almost completely ineffective. That portion of the normal aeration which results from temperature gradients is probably less than 1 per cent of the total.

The infiltration of precipitation into the soil contributes to gas exchange by forcing air out of the soil and by carrying dissolved oxygen into the soil. Conversely, evaporation results in a corresponding increase in the volume of soil air. It should be pointed out that even large amounts of rainfall cannot drive all air from the soil, since some of the pores are so constructed that downward-moving water entraps air. In loam, the normal noncapillary porosity is about 10 per cent by volume. Thus, if the infiltration during a storm were 1 in., soil air would be replaced to a depth of 10 in. Considering the normal aeration rate, it is seen that the effect of precipitation is also relatively unimportant.

While the combined effects of variations in meteorological elements may under some conditions be of material magnitude, the major portion of the normal aeration rate must be attributed to other factors. If a partition separating two gases in a vessel be removed, the molecules of each gas immediately begin to penetrate the space occupied by the other. This mixing process, known as *diffusion*, continues until a uniform mixture prevails throughout. Diffusion tends to equalize the composition of the soil air and the atmosphere by transporting CO_2 from the soil to the atmosphere and O_2 from the atmosphere into the soil. Buckingham[1] defined the *diffusion constant*, Θ, as the average number of cubic centimeters of two gases which pass in opposite directions through a centimeter of soil per second per square centimeter, when the partial pressure of each gas is one millimeter of mercury greater on its respective side of the layer than on the other. He found that this constant was directly proportional to the square of the free pore space V_p, expressed as a fraction of the total volume.

$$\Theta = kV_p^2 \tag{12-11}$$

The value of the coefficient k varies inversely with total pressure and directly with the square of the absolute temperature. Within the range of his data, Buckingham found it to be 2.16×10^{-4}. He concluded that the rate of diffusion is not materially affected by the texture, structure, and moisture content of the soil except as they change the free pore space. It follows, then, that heavy and close-textured soils are not necessarily badly aerated, provided that the free pore space is not too restricted.

Buckingham used air and carbon dioxide on opposite sides of a soil layer. Under natural conditions nitrogen constitutes about 80 per cent of the soil atmosphere, and the rate of diffusion is about 12 per cent higher than shown by his experiments. For some time after Buckingham's original work, the true importance of diffusion was not generally recognized because the difference between the carbon dioxide content of soil air and that of the atmosphere was considered to be insufficient to promote significant transport. Diffusion is now recognized to be the most important factor in gas exchange between the soil and the atmosphere.

SOIL TEMPERATURE

Micro-biological activity in soil and processes related to the growth of plants are controlled to a considerable extent by soil temperatures. Temperature gradients within the soil profile also result in transport of soil moisture from regions of high temperature to those of low. Variations in soil temperature, especially as they indicate frozen or frost-free conditions, also influence such factors as surface runoff, evaporation and transpiration, groundwater flow, infiltration, and snowmelt. Thus, it becomes immediately evident that soil temperature must be considered in any comprehensive study of the hydrologic cycle.

Sources of heat. The soil receives heat by radiation from the sun, conduction from the interior of the earth, and chemical and biological

[1] Buckingham, E., Contributions to Our Knowledge of the Aeration of Soils, *U.S. Dept. Agr. Bur. Soils Bull.* 25, 1904.

processes within the soil. The latter two sources are inconsequential as compared with the sun. For the earth as a whole, the *solar constant* is about 1.94 cal/min/cm². The soil temperature at any point at a specific time depends upon many factors such as position, cloudiness, season, vegetative cover, and soil composition and color.

The amount of radiation received per unit area is proportional to the cosine of the angle of incidence. Thus, considerably less radiation is received by the soil of the polar regions than by that of the tropics. Similarly, local variations result from differences in land slope and aspect. Shreve[1] made comparative temperature observations in alluvial clay on 30° slopes near Tucson, Arizona. He found the average weekly maximum temperatures at a depth of 3 in. on the south slope to be about 11 F° higher than on the north slope in April and May. Since soil temperatures are affected by air temperature, it is obvious that factors which control air temperature (Chap. 3) will also influence soil temperatures.

Thermal characteristics of soil. The chemical composition and texture of soil influence its specific heat and color and, hence, the amount of radiation absorbed. In general, dark soils are warmer than light soils in summer and cooler in winter and experience greater diurnal variations in temperature. However, these contrasts between light and dark soils are not of practical significance because they are partly compensated by differences in heat conductivity and specific heat, which are to some extent intercorrelated with color.

The absorption and transmission of heat by soil are influenced, not only by surface conditions, but also by the nature of the material itself. *Specific heat* is normally defined on a weight basis, *i.e.*, the number of calories required to raise the temperature of one gram of a substance one centigrade degree. The *heat capacity* of a given amount of a substance is equal to its specific heat times its weight. In considering soils we are concerned with the heat capacity of a given volume (or depth) rather than a given weight. Therefore, it is found convenient to use the *specific heat by volume*, or the number of calories required to raise the temperature of one cubic centimeter of soil one centigrade degree. Thus, light humus has a high specific heat by weight; but, because of its low apparent specific gravity, humus soil has relatively low specific heat by volume[2] (Table 12-4). While differences in specific heat are observed from soil to soil, variations with moisture content in a given soil are even more striking, owing to the high specific heat of water. Experimental data determined by Mitscherlich (Table 12-5) show that the specific heat of saturated humus is more than

[1] Shreve, F., Influence of Slope Exposure on Soil Temperature, *Carnegie Inst. Yearbook*, Vol. 23, pp. 140-141, 1924.

[2] Ulrich, R., Untersuchungen über die Wärmekapazität der Bodenkonstituenten, *Forsch. Geb. Agrik-Phys.*, Vol. 17, pp. 1-31, 1894.

six times as great as that of dry humus. The data presented in this table point to the need of adequate drainage in order that soils will warm up earlier in the spring. Observed temperatures within the soil profile also depend upon the heat conductivity of the soil, which is interrelated with the specific heat.

TABLE 12-4. Comparison of Specific Heat by Weight and by Volume for Sand, Clay, and Humus

Soil material	Apparent specific gravity	Specific heat	
		By weight	By volume
Sand	1.52	0.191	0.290
Clay	1.04	0.224	0.233
Humus	0.37	0.443	0.164

TABLE 12-5. Variation in Volume Specific Heat of Soils with Their Moisture Content

(After Mitscherlich)

Soil	Specific heat, cal/cc		
	Dry	50 per cent saturated	Saturated
Sand	0.302	0.510	0.717
Clay	0.240	0.532	0.823
Humus	0.148	0.525	0.902

Flow of heat in a conducting material. The flow of heat through a porous material of ever-changing properties is much more complicated than that through homogeneous solids; however, the fundamental principles are much the same in both cases. Consider the application of heat to the upper horizontal surface of a vertical soil column of unit cross section. The quantity of heat flowing in unit time through an imaginary horizontal plane at distance x below the surface is $-K_c\,dT/dx$, where dT/dx is the temperature gradient at surface x and K_c is the *heat conductivity* of the soil (the quantity of heat which will flow through a cube of unit dimensions in unit time when a unit temperature difference is maintained between two opposite faces). The fact that T decreases as x increases accounts for the negative sign. The temperature a small distance below x will be $T - (dT/dx)\,\Delta x$, and the heat flowing through this surface in unit time will be $-K_c \frac{d}{dx}\left(T - \frac{dT}{dx}\Delta x\right)$. The rate at which heat is being stored in the incremental volume is the difference between inflow and outflow, or

$$\Delta H = \frac{K_c\, d^2T}{dx^2}\Delta x \tag{12-12}$$

The heat which is being stored in the soil element raises its temperature. This being the case,

$$\Delta H = \frac{\eta_v\, dT}{dt}\Delta x \tag{12-13}$$

where η_v is the specific heat by volume. Combining Eqs. (12-12) and (12-13),

$$K_c \frac{d^2T}{dx^2} = \eta_v \frac{dT}{dt} \tag{12-14}$$

and letting $K_d = K_c/\eta_v$,

$$K_d \frac{d^2T}{dx^2} = \frac{dT}{dt} \tag{12-15}$$

The constant K_d, called *diffusivity*, is the rate of change of temperature with time when the rate of change of temperature gradient with distance is unity. It is widely used in soil studies in preference to η_v and K_c.

If the heat supply at the soil surface were constant, then, at equilibrium, dT/dt and consequently d^2T/dx^2 would be zero [Eq. (12-15)]. Under these conditions it can be shown that soil temperature is proportional to depth. This case has little value, however, since the heat supply is extremely variable.

If we assume, for simplicity, that the time variation of temperature at the surface of the soil is sinusoidal, then the solution of the derived differential equation yields

$$T = T_0 \mathbf{e}^{-2\pi x/\lambda} \sin 2\pi\left(\frac{t}{t_o} - \frac{x}{\lambda}\right) \tag{12-16}$$

where t_o is the period of oscillation (24 hr for a diurnal wave) and λ is the wave length, related to the diffusivity by the equation $\lambda = \sqrt{4\pi t_o K_d}$. An analysis of the above equation reveals that the fluctuation of temperature at any depth x is sinusoidal; respective maximum and minimum points on the temperature wave are delayed progressively more as depth increases; and the amplitude of the temperature wave decreases exponentially as depth increases.

Heat conductance in natural soils. In the theoretical analysis of heat propagation, it was assumed that (1) the fluctuations of temperature at the soil surface were of simple harmonic type and (2) the conducting material was uniform throughout. Neither of these assumptions is strictly true, since the daily temperature wave is of a complex nature, the composition of soil material varies from layer to layer, and the moisture content varies with time. However, the assumption that the temperature wave is a simple harmonic variation or, if necessary, a series of superimposed harmonic fluctuations is adequate for most purposes. Variations in the mechanical composition, moisture content, and degree of compaction are of major proportions and render the simple theoretical case of qualitative significance only. Consequently, variations in soil temperatures must be treated experimentally.

With the exception of discontinuities created by plowing and cultivation, the values of K_c and η_v, although variable with depth, do not commonly display any abrupt changes. Observations have shown that, except in the case of organic matter, the conductivity of soil constituents varies but little from one soil to another. The degree of packing and the porosity are the principal factors determining thermal transfer. In general, heat conductivity decreases as porosity increases because of the poorer contact between soil particles and the low conductivity of air.

Moisture affects heat transfer in soil by changing the specific heat and conductivity of the material. The variation of specific heat by volume with moisture content is illustrated in Table 12-5. While the conductivity of soil material in continuous form averages about seven times that of water, it drops to only about one-third that of water in natural soils. Thus, the conductivity of soil is increased by the addition of water, not only because of the high conductivity of water, but also because water in the form of ringlets around the points of contact of the particles considerably improves their thermal contact.

The difficulties encountered in attempting to determine the relations between moisture and conductivity or diffusivity cannot be overemphasized. The experimental technique necessarily involves a flow of heat, *i.e.*, a temperature gradient must be established in the soil column. This naturally disturbs the original moisture equilibrium, since vapor pressure, viscosity, and surface tension are all functions of temperature. The net effect is the transport of moisture from regions of high temperature to those of low. The process tends to be of a progressive nature, owing to the fact that moisture transfer changes the conductivity and specific heat throughout the profile, which in turn influence thermal transfer. Therefore, K_c and η_v [Eq. (12-14)] are not independent of dT/dt and d^2T/dx^2, as was assumed.

Patten[1] carried out extensive experiments on the conductivity and diffusivity of soils in which he attempted to minimize the effect of moisture transport by making observations at some distance from the heat source as soon as possible after heat was applied. He filled a well-insulated box with soil of known moisture content. One end of the box was brought into close contact with a vessel containing boiling water, and periodic tempera-

[1] Patten, H. E., Heat Transference in Soils, *U.S. Dept. Agr. Bur. Soils Bull.* 59, 1909.

ture readings were obtained at specified distances along the soil profile (Fig. 12-8). The slope of these curves is equal to dT/dt. The value of d^2T/dx^2 was estimated from a plotting of T vs x, and, knowing η_v, the conductivity K_c and the diffusivity K_d were computed from Eqs. (12-14) and (12-15). By making a series of such observations based on varying moisture contents, Patten obtained relations of the type shown in Fig. 12-9. At high moisture contents, the effective specific heat η_v increases much more rapidly because of the decrease in specific volume, while at the same time the rate of increase

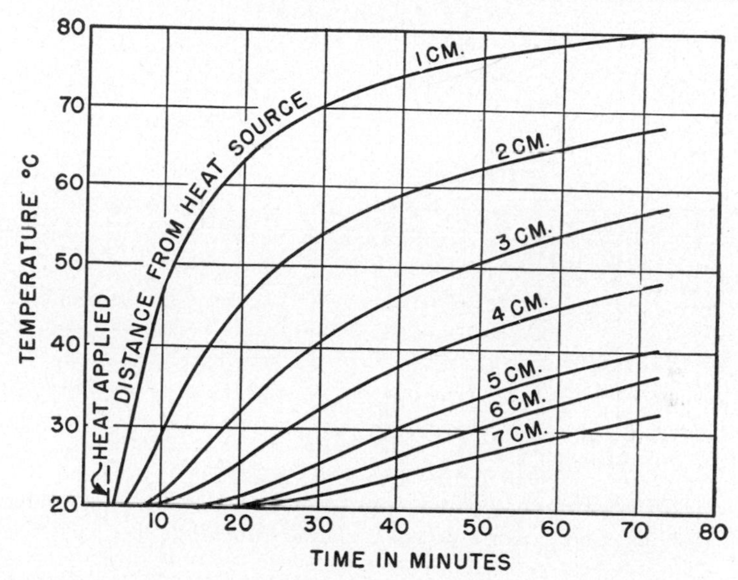

FIG. 12–8. Temperature-time curves for air-dry coarse quartz powder. *(After Patten.)*

in the conductivity K_c slackens off; consequently, the diffusivity K_c/η_v begins to decrease. Thus, while more heat may be transported downward through wet soils, their high specific heat results in relatively small temperature changes.

Seasonal and diurnal temperature waves. The amplitude of the diurnal temperature wave increases from winter to summer as a result of the increasing elevation of the sun. These diurnal waves are superimposed on the annual temperature cycle. The period and amplitude of the diurnal waves are so small that diurnal temperature variations in the soil are rarely observed at depths below 3 ft (Fig. 12-10). However, significant seasonal variations in soil temperature are observed at depths in excess of 10 ft (Fig. 12-11). While field conditions deviate from the assumptions made in the relatively simple theoretical analysis, the conclusions based on such analysis are essentially verified by the curves in these figures.

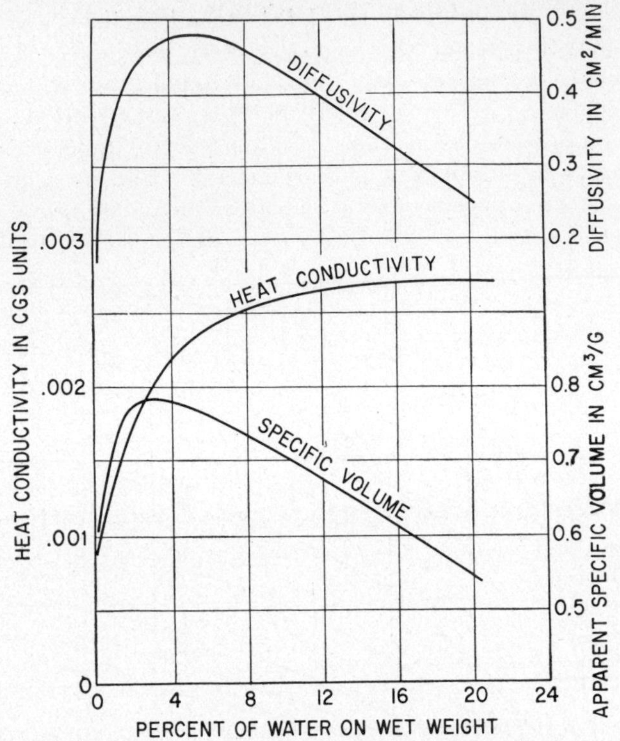

FIG. 12–9. Effect of moisture on the apparent specific volume, heat conductivity, and diffusivity of coarse quartz powder. *(After Patten.)*

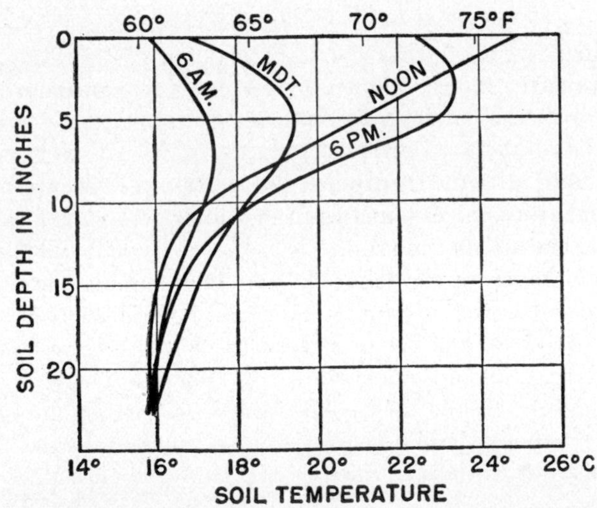

FIG. 12–10. Temperature gradients existing in a sandy soil at four different times throughout a summer day. *(From data by Mutterich.)*

INFILTRATION THEORY OF RUNOFF

The role of infiltration in the hydrologic cycle was first discussed by Horton[1] in 1933. As conceived by Horton, *infiltration* is the passage of water through the soil surface into the soil. It is to be distinguished from *percolation,* which is the movement of water within the soil. The two phenomena are closely related, however, in that infiltration cannot continue unimpeded unless percolation provides sufficient space in the surface layer for infiltered water.

The infiltration theory has been given many different interpretations. The concept presented by Sherman[2] is considered quite adequate in dealing

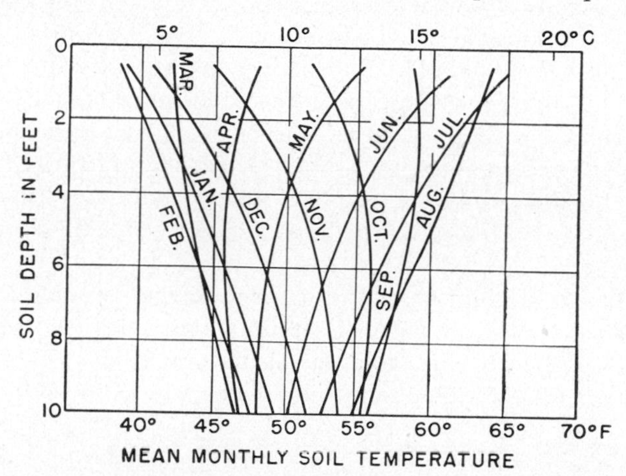

FIG. 12–11. Mean monthly temperature gradients in grass-covered soil. *(From Radcliffe Observations, Vol. 51.)*

with most hydrologic problems. He considered a column of soil of 1 in.^{2} cross section extending into or through the zone of aeration. The soil column is penetrated by channels, capable of carrying gravity water through the soil. The channels extend downward and laterally in all directions, and although they are constricted at numerous points, infiltration water finds its way downward along the lines of least resistance. Assuming that the soil has a noncapillary porosity of 30 per cent, there is an average of 0.30 in.^{3} of noncapillary channels in each cubic inch of soil. In addition to the larger gravity-water channels, the soil column is permeated with small capillary pore spaces, which have a stronger affinity for water than for air. The force of capillarity acts in all directions and fre-

[1] Horton, R. E., The Role of Infiltration in the Hydrologic Cycle, *Trans. Am. Geophys. Union,* Vol. 14, pp. 446-460, 1933.

[2] Sherman, L. K., Infiltration and the Physics of Soil-moisture, *Trans. Am. Geophys. Union,* Vol. 25, pp. 57-71, 1944.

quently exceeds the force of gravity. Capillary water always moves from the wet zones toward drier zones in accord with well-established laws of capillary movement. When the soil is dry, infiltration into the surface layer takes place, not only through large gravity channels, but also through direct capillary action over the entire surface. This surface capillary movement decreases as the water penetrates deeper. The capillary potential declines so that capillary intake of surface water proceeds at a slower rate. The water in gravity channels, however, continues to penetrate deeper and at a fairly uniform rate. This gravity water now furnishes a supply, at relatively high potential, for lateral capillary absorption into the soil. The gravity channels are the water mains, and the capillary pores are the local supply feeders. Suppose that infiltration at capacity rates is stopped after 3 hr, and it is found that water has penetrated to a depth of 20 in. The surface soil has been subjected to a 3-hr supply period for capillary absorption, but at a depth of 20 in. the soil has just begun to receive an additional supply of capillary moisture. Although infiltration has ceased, the gravity channels are full of water. Capillary action continues to draw upon this gravity water until the capillary pores are filled or until the gravity storage is depleted.

While the basic concept of infiltration is quite simple, practical applications are limited by the difficulty of determining quantitative relationships which are applicable to all conditions on natural basins. Further, since the concept is still relatively new, discussions which are quite diverse in their conclusions, definitions, and symbols abound in the literature. The material presented in this section deals mostly with theoretical aspects of infiltration. Applications of the theory to the calculation of surface runoff are discussed in Chap. 16.

Definitions. Horton defined *infiltration capacity*, f_p, as the maximum rate at which a given soil in a given condition can absorb rain as it falls. Thus, the infiltration capacity is equal to the observed infiltration rate f_i only when the rainfall intensity i equals or exceeds f_p. The value of f_p is found to start at a maximum f_0, decrease rapidly at first, and then approach a constant rate f_c. Horton suggested that the relation between f_p and the duration of rainfall t_R can be expressed by the equation

$$f_p = f_c + (f_0 - f_c)\mathbf{e}^{-kt_R} \tag{12-17}$$

where k is a positive constant. While Eq. (12-17) was developed empirically, it can also be derived from the assumption that the processes which reduce f_0 to f_c are of the nature of exhaustion processes. Some of the exhaustion processes influencing infiltration rates are rain packing, inwashing, swelling of colloids, closing of sun checks, and breaking down of the crumb structure of the soil. Infiltration rates are also reduced as the duration of rainfall increases because of increasing resistance to flow as the moisture front moves downward through the soil profile. This resistance results from increasing friction because of increased channel length and decreased permeability with depth.

The relation between infiltration capacity and duration of rainfall is commonly shown either as a direct function or as a mass curve[1] (Fig. 12-12).

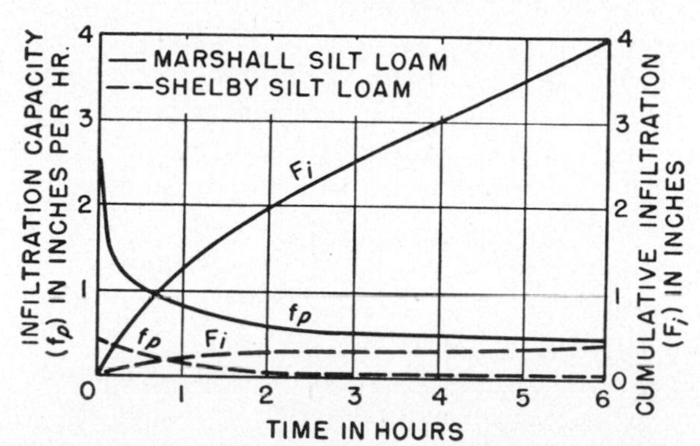

FIG. 12-12. Infiltration curves for Marshall and Shelby silt loam. *(After Musgrave.)*

Determination of infiltration rates. Methods of determining infiltration rates are of five general types:

1. Laboratory experiments using artificial rainfall.[2]
2. Field experiments using artificial rainfall.[3]
3. Field determinations with natural rainfall on isolated runoff plots.[4]
4. From rainfall and runoff records for small drainage basins with homogeneous soils.[5]

[1] Musgrave, G. W., The Infiltration Capacity of Soils in Relation to the Control of Surface Runoff and Erosion, *J. Am. Soc. Agron.*, Vol. 27, pp. 336-345, 1935.

[2] Neal, J. H., The Effect of the Degree of Slope and Rainfall Characteristics on Runoff and Soil Erosion, *Univ. Missouri Research Bull.* 280, 1938.

Wilm, H. G., The Application and Measurement of Artificial Rainfall on Types FA and F Infiltrometers, *Trans. Am. Geophys. Union*, Vol. 24, pp. 480-487, 1943.

[3] Free, G. R., G. M. Browning, and G. W. Musgrave, Relative Infiltration and Related Physical Characteristics of Certain Soils, *U.S. Dept. Agr. Tech. Bull.* 729, 1940.

[4] Kohnke, H., F. R. Dreibelbis, and J. M. Davidson, A Survey and Discussion of Lysimeters and a Bibliography on Their Construction and Performance, *U.S. Dept. Agr. Misc. Pub.* 372, 1940.

Harrold, L. L., and F. R. Dreibelbis, An Accounting of the Daily Accretion, Depletion, and Storage of Soil-water as Determined by Weighing Monolith Lysimeters, *Trans. Am. Geophys. Union*, Vol. 26, pp. 283-297, 1945.

[5] Horton, R. E., and R. Van Vliet, "Determination of Areal Average Infiltration Capacity from Rainfall and Runoff Data," *U.S. Department of Agriculture*, Soil Conservation Service, 1940 (mimeo.).

Zingg, A. W., The Determination of Infiltration Rates on Small Agricultural Watersheds, *Trans. Am. Geophys. Union*, Vol. 24, pp. 476-480, 1943.

5. From rainfall and runoff records for heterogeneous basins—the determination of an average equivalent infiltration capacity.[1]

In this classification, the distinction between field and laboratory methods is based on whether or not the soil profile is disturbed.

Since it is impossible to measure directly the quantity of water penetrating the soil surface, infiltration is generally computed by assuming it to equal the difference between rainfall and runoff. In many techniques where the soil surface is flooded, it is common practice to apply water at such a rate that runoff is zero and the infiltration capacity is equal to the rate at which water is applied. In addition to difficulties inherent in simulating raindrop size and velocity of fall with sprinklers, experiments using artificial rainfall have other features generally tending to cause higher rates in tests than under natural conditions. Among these may be noted the opportunity for lateral flow into areas beyond the limits of the test plots and the opportunity for escape of soil air around the periphery of the plot or cylinder. On natural basins of significant size, allowance should be made for surface storage and detention.

Variations in infiltration capacity. Infiltration capacity under specified initial conditions decreases with duration and rainfall (Fig. 12-12). However, the total volume of infiltration F_i for a specified duration varies from soil to soil and with initial conditions in the same soil.

Physical characteristics. Porosity determines the storage available for infiltered water and also affects resistance to flow. Both these effects are such that infiltration increases with porosity. Correlation coefficients[2] between infiltration and various factors from data collected at 68 sites throughout the country are shown in Table 12-6. The correlations between characteristics other than infiltration are such that one cannot be certain which factors directly affect infiltration rates.

Initial moisture content. Neal[3] observed that initial soil moisture content had a greater effect on infiltration capacity during the first 20 min. than any other factor. His relation between infiltration (for the first 10 min.) and initial moisture content is shown in Fig. 12-13. The effect of initial moisture content upon the entire infiltration-duration curve[2] is

[1] Horton, R. E., Determination of Infiltration Capacity for Large Drainage Basins, *Trans. Am. Geophys. Union*, Vol. 18, pp. 371-385, 1937.

Sherman, L. K., Comparison of F-curves Derived by the Methods of Sharp and Holtan and of Sherman and Mayer, *Trans. Am. Geophys. Union*, Vol. 24, pp. 465-467, 1943.

Cook, H. L., The Infiltration Approach to the Calculation of Surface Runoff, *Trans. Am. Geophys. Union*, Vol. 27, pp. 726-747, 1946.

[2] Free, G. R., G. M. Browning, and G. W. Musgrave, Relative Infiltration and Related Physical Characteristics of Certain Soils, *U.S. Dept. Agr. Tech. Bull.* 729, 1940.

[3] Neal, J. H., The Effect of the Degree of Slope and Rainfall Characteristics on Runoff and Soil Erosion, *Univ. Missouri Research Bull.* 280, 1938.

illustrated in Fig. 12-14. It will be noted that the curve for the wet run is not simply the last portion of the curve for the dry run. It follows, then, that a capacity curve must be developed for each value of initial moisture content before surface runoff can be accurately computed. Extremely fine, very dry soil may actually repel water until it is thoroughly

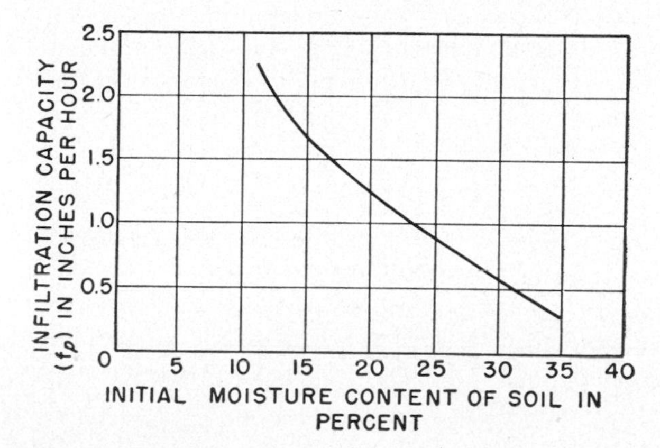

FIG. 12-13. Effect of initial soil-moisture content on rate of infiltration during the first 10 min. of rain. *(After Neal.)*

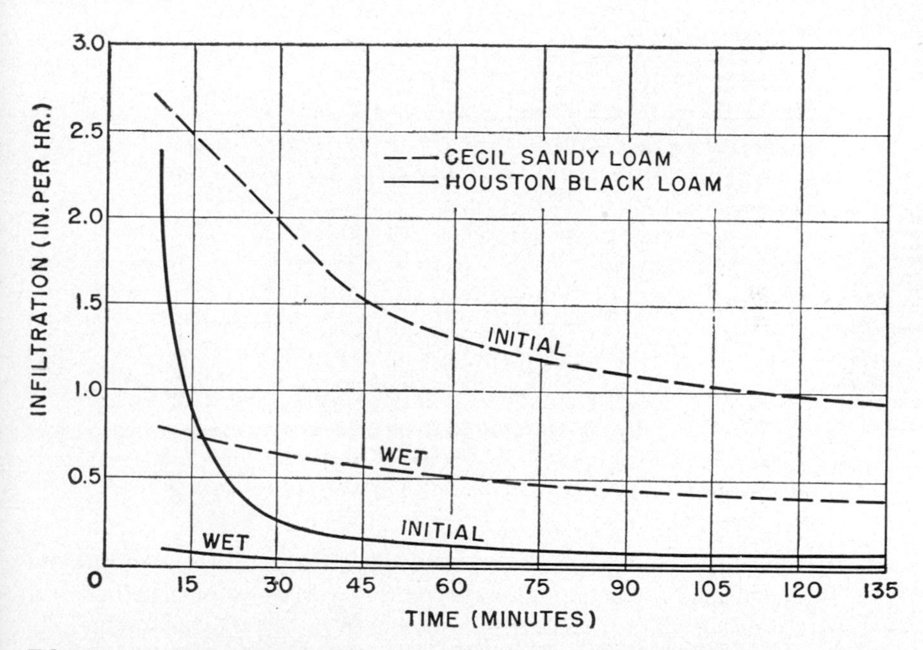

FIG. 12-14. Comparative infiltration rates during initial and wet runs. *(After Free, Browning, and Musgrave.)*

wetted, and under such conditions initial infiltration rates may be very low, increasing as the soil is wetted.

Drop size and rainfall intensity. The effect of drop size on infiltration capacity is mostly due to its effect on the rate of rain packing and breaking down of soil structure. Therefore, excessively large drops tend to reduce the amount of infiltration during the first few minutes of rainfall until such time as a sheet of water collects over the soil surface. The rate of infiltration varies directly with rainfall intensity when intensity is less than the infiltration capacity. However, the intensity has little noticeable effect on the rate of infiltration when it exceeds the capacity rate.

TABLE 12-6. Correlation Coefficients of Certain Characteristics of Soils

(After Free, Browning, and Musgrave)

Characteristics	Infiltration*	Clay content	Volume weight	Total porosity	Noncapillary porosity	Organic matter	Moisture equivalent
Infiltration*		− 0.16	− 0.24	0.24	0.36	0.50	0.02
Clay content	− 0.42		− 0.36	0.36	0.10	0.12	0.50
Volume weight	− 0.33	− 0.04		− 0.99	− 0.75	− 0.63	− 0.81
Total porosity	0.36	0.03	− 0.97		0.76	0.62	0.82
Noncapillary porosity	0.54	− 0.39	− 0.79	0.80		0.38	0.30
Organic matter	0.40	0.15	− 0.59	0.55	0.39		0.62
Moisture equivalent	− 0.30	0.74	− 0.37	0.36	− 0.24	0.32	

Surface soils (above diagonal); Subsoils (below diagonal)

*Rate of infiltration as measured for the third hour of the wet run by the tube method.

Slope. Neal made laboratory experiments with an overhead sprinkling system on Putnam silt loam and observed that variations in slope between 1 and 16 per cent had little effect on infiltration rates. For zero slope, the infiltration was increased slightly owing to the increased pressure head which built up on the soil surface.

Season. Horton[1] made a study of the seasonal variation of maximum, minimum, and average apparent infiltration capacities for the North Concho River Basin in Texas (Fig. 12-15). The seasonal variation is readily explained by variations in such factors as temperature, evaporation, vegetation, farming practices, and biological activity.

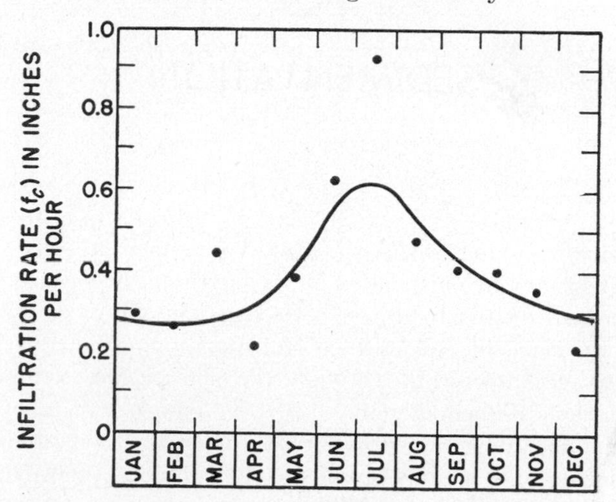

FIG. 12–15. Seasonal variation of apparent minimum infiltration capacity, North Concho River Basin. *(After Horton.)*

Vegetation. The effect of vegetation on infiltration capacity is difficult to determine directly, for vegetation also exerts an influence on interception. Nevertheless, vegetation does increase infiltration as compared with that for barren soil because (1) it retards surface flow, thus giving the water additional time to enter the soil surface, (2) the root systems of plants make the soil more pervious to infiltrating water, and (3) it shields the soil from raindrop impact and hence reduces rain packing.

[1] Horton, R. E., An Approach toward a Physical Interpretation of Infiltration Capacity, *Proc. Soil Sci. Soc. Am.*, Vol. 5, pp. 399-417, 1940.

13
SEDIMENTATION

Geologically speaking, *sediment* may be defined as any fragmental material transported by, suspended in, or deposited by water or air. Only sedimentation as related to water is discussed in this text. While water infiltrating through the soil surface transports minor quantities of very fine soil particles downward through the soil profile, sedimentation is essentially a surface phenomenon.

The impact of falling raindrops breaks down the clods and aggregates at the soil surface into a single-grained soil structure. These fine particles are in turn thrown into suspension by the energy of the falling drops and are carried along with the overland flow toward established channels. Furthermore, the force of the flowing water tends to loosen additional particles, and they, too, may be transported toward the stream channel. Upon entering the channel, the flow velocities may decrease and thereby cause some of the heavier suspended particles to fall to the bottom. If conditions are such that the velocity of the water increases after it enters the stream, bottom material in the channel will be picked up and transported downstream. The size of particles which remain in suspension varies approximately as a power of the velocity. In addition to the soil particles transported in suspension, some of the heavier particles roll and bounce along the channel bottom. The construction of a dam across a stream results in an increased cross-sectional area and a resulting decrease in velocity of flow. This is why reservoirs are, in effect, "sediment traps," inevitably losing their storage space to the encroaching sediment. Similar deposits, known as *deltas*, are formed where streams issue into a sea or lake. During flood periods when streams overflow their banks, the velocities in the overflow section are usually very small, and consequently a part of the load carried by the water is dropped and forms a flood plain

Deposits left by running water are generally finer the farther they are from the source of supply. Consequently, particles brought by a stream to the sea or a lake are, as a rule, relatively fine-grained and settle very slowly to form marine deposits. Soils formed through the action of running water are known as *alluvial*, or water-laid, soils. In the field of hydrology, sedimentation is broadly considered to comprise the study of the interactions of water and soil particles from the raindrop impact to outflow to the sea through all the various phases described above. In other words, sedimentation covers erosion, transport, and deposition of soil material by water.

EROSION OF SOIL MATERIAL

The life cycle of a basin as developed through geologic processes which slowly but continuously transport the material comprising the surface of the lithosphere is discussed in Chap. 10. The discussion in this chapter is limited to a brief description of the erosive effects of water as related to the initial phase of sedimentation. The rate at which the processes of erosion proceed is dependent upon three factors, (1) the energy of the erosive agents; (2) the erosibility of the soil, or its susceptibility to erosion; and (3) the protective influence of vegetal cover. The erosive agents to be considered with respect to water erosion are precipitation (raindrops) and runoff or overland flow.

Resistance to erosion. Water erosion is generally considered to be of two types, (1) *sheet erosion,* the process of removing the surface layer of the soil over a tract or field more or less evenly as a sheet; and (2) *gully erosion,* the development of relatively deep, steep-sided channels through the action of running water. Sheet erosion is caused by raindrop impact and storm runoff, which develop countless rills and fine channels of an unstable nature. These rills and watercourses are eradicated by tillage operations and natural weathering phenomena from time to time, and thus the soil tends to be removed from the area as a sheet. Gully erosion is caused by a concentration of storm runoff, which results in large volumes of high-velocity flow. By the very nature of erosion, any classification must be arbitrary and relative. In the first place, gullies or definable channels are of all sizes—from small rills to large ravines. A field which may be considered to display severe gully erosion as viewed from the ground will appear more like an area with severe sheet erosion from a considerable altitude. Each gully starts as a rill—therefore, the size and density of channels which form the boundary between the two classes must be arbitrary.

The *erosibility* of soils, their susceptibility to erosion, depends upon many factors, most of which are highly interrelated. Some of the more important factors influencing the resistance of soil to erosion are (1) structure, (2) stratification, (3) permeability, (4) moisture content, (5) texture, (6) mechanical composition, (7) type and extent of vegetal cover, and (8) land slope. Although the erosibility of a particular type of soil material varies inversely with particle size, fine sandy soil erodes much more readily than cemented hardpan or tough clay. Since cohesion is reduced by lack of moisture, soils are generally more erosible when dry than when moist. A soil with a crusted top layer is much less susceptible to erosion than the same soil immediately after cultivation. The presence of colloidal material, especially that of vegetal origin, tends to increase the coherence of the soil particles and thus decrease the erosibility. In addition to the fact that vegetation dissipates much of the energy of falling raindrops, it also tends to increase the resistance of the soil to erosion. Fine particles adhere to the root systems near the soil surface and act as a soil binder. Furthermore, a dense cover such as grass restricts the velocity of flow and at the same time acts as a protective carpet covering the underlying soil. Observations have shown that the extent to which erosion occurs is almost proportional to the slope up to about 20°, is a maximum at about 40°, and decreases thereafter.

Effect of raindrops. The disintegration of aggregates and clods and the transport of the particles produced are directly related to the energy of the falling raindrops. Consequently, the energy of raindrops is of prime concern to the soil conservationist. Even in storms sufficiently intense to produce surface runoff, the energy expended by rain falling on a slope of average length usually exceeds that expended by overland flow. The kinetic energy of a single raindrop as it strikes the soil surface is equal to one-half the product of its mass and the square of its velocity. Since its mass is proportional to the cube of its diameter and its terminal velocity also increases with diameter (Table 6-1), the energy of a single drop increases rapidly as its size increases. Limited available evidence indicates that the average drop size increases only slightly with rainfall intensity for a given locality. The effect of this variation, coupled with the increased mass, however, causes the erosive power of rain to increase relatively more rapidly than rainfall intensity.

The energy of a raindrop can be computed in a straightforward manner if the size and velocity are known. However, the computation of the total energy of the falling rain within a storm is not so simple, even if the total mass of the rain is known. Since the drops falling concurrently vary considerably in size and since energy is not directly proportional to size, some estimate of the size distribution must first be made. Some idea of the magnitude of the energy involved can be gained, for example, by assuming all the droplets of a 4-in. rain to be about 0.1 in. in diameter. The terminal velocity of such drops is in the order of 23 fps. It can be shown that the energy of the raindrops in the assumed storm is sufficient to raise the top 4 in. of the soil to a height of more than 6 ft.

In considering the amount of soil thrown into suspension, it is necessary to determine the energy of the drops as they strike the soil. This is a far more complex problem than that of computing the energy of falling rain.

Some energy is dissipated before the water reaches the soil, since some drops are intercepted by vegetation, stones, and plant residue. These factors are highly variable from point to point and from time to time. In addition to variations in vegetative cover, any comparison between identical storms must consider variations in wind direction and velocity. The amount of rain intercepted by drilled crops is far greater when the wind blows across the rows than when it blows parallel with them. Also, a tall, open canopy will intercept much less rain when the drops are falling vertically than when a driving wind causes the rain to fall at a low angle. If the vegetative cover or plant residue is extremely dense, variations in wind, drop size, and velocity of fall are of little consequence—the energy is essentially dissipated before the water reaches the soil.

FIG. 13–1. A sampler designed to measure the quantity of soil transported by raindrop splash. *(After Ellison.)*

In studies of aggregate breakdown conducted at Coshocton, Ohio, by the Soil Conservation Service,[1] soil plots 5 by 6 ft were exposed to artificial rainfall. The rainfall intensity and drop size and velocity were varied one at a time to determine the effect of each. Results of the experiments are shown in Tables 13-1 to 13-4. The percentages of the different aggregate sizes carried in the raindrop splash and in the surface runoff were determined at various times during rainfall. Aggregate analysis of the soil (eroded Muskingum silt-loam) was made before rainfall was applied, and material scraped from the soil surface after rainfall had ceased was also analyzed. Since the wet-sieve method was used in the analysis, it was assumed that the percentage differences (before and after rain) should reflect only the effects of raindrop impact in breaking down the soil aggregates. The quantities of soil carried in the raindrop splash were determined by use of a specially designed interceptor (Fig. 13-1). While the quantities are purely relative (grams of soil intercepted in splash samplers

[1] Ellison, W. D., Studies of Raindrop Erosion, *Agr. Eng.*, Vol. 25, pp. 131-136, 181-182, 1944.

Ellison, W. D., Some Effects of Raindrops and Surface-flow on Soil Erosion and Infiltration, *Trans. Am. Geophys. Union*, Vol. 26, pp. 415-429, 1945.

during a 30-min period), they clearly demonstrate the effect of small changes in drop size and velocity. Through analysis of the data in Table 13-4 it was found that the quantity of soil caught in the sampler was approximately proportional to the fourth power of drop velocity, first power of drop diameter, and two-thirds power of rainfall intensity.

In experiments related to those described above, it was found that the sizes of particles carried by the raindrop splash and the distances they were transported depended on the size and velocity of the raindrops. With drops 5.1 mm in diameter having a velocity of 19 fps, 4-mm stones were splashed as much as 8 in., 2-mm particles as much as 16 in., and some

TABLE 13-1. Aggregate Analysis of Soil Materials Contained in Raindrop Splash

(After Ellison)

Raindrop size, mm	Height of fall, ft	Velocity, fps	Size of grain, mm					
			>2	1–2	0.5–1	0.25–0.5	0.105–0.25	<0.105
			Per cent of soil materials					
5.1	6.7	19.2	2.40	3.89	5.07	5.24	11.38	71.98
5.1	3.9	15.0	1.41	3.68	4.98	5.12	11.53	73.25
5.1	2.3	12.0	1.04	2.87	5.74	6.56	12.11	71.65
3.5	6.7	18.0	0.74	2.87	5.24	6.65	10.83	73.66
3.5	3.9	14.5	0.94	2.81	5.66	5.85	10.81	73.91
3.5	2.3	12.0	0.44	2.31	6.25	8.22	13.86	68.89

TABLE 13-2. Aggregate Analysis of Soil Materials Contained in Runoff

(After Ellison)

Raindrop size, mm	Height of fall, ft	Velocity, fps	Size of grain, mm					
			>2	1–2	0.5–1	0.25–0.5	0.105–0.25	<0.105
			Per cent of soil materials					
5.1	6.7	19.2	0.40	1.68	2.39	2.85	5.27	87.26
5.1	3.9	15.0	0.41	0.91	1.71	2.25	6.25	88.45
5.1	2.3	12.0	0.61	0.56	1.27	1.55	3.95	92.04
3.5	6.7	18.0	0.47	1.13	1.99	2.14	6.03	88.21
3.5	3.9	14.5	0.08	0.66	1.35	1.91	3.02	92.88
3.5	2.3	12.0	0.23	0.80	1.47	1.41	3.64	92.43

TABLE 13-3. Aggregate Analysis of Original Soil Materials and of Those Scraped from Surface of Plot Following Rainfall

(After Ellison)

Raindrop size, mm	Height of fall, ft	Velocity, fps	Size of grain, mm					
			>2	1–2	0.5–1	0.25–0.5	0.105–0.25	<0.105
			Per cent of soil materials					
Original material.			13.34	6.33	6.69	8.01	12.05	53.55
Soil material scraped from surface following rainfall								
5.1	6.7	19.2	19.85	4.38	4.47	4.09	12.62	54.56
5.1	3.9	15.0	22.13	5.52	4.33	3.47	7.89	56.62
5.1	2.3	12.0	18.91	4.53	4.62	3.92	7.61	60.37
3.5	6.7	18.0	18.32	4.77	4.32	4.17	10.23	58.16
3.5	3.9	14.5	19.45	5.11	4.63	3.89	10.07	56.36
3.5	2.3	12.0	25.29	4.15	3.39	3.29	7.12	56.73

TABLE 13-4. Quantities of Soil Contained in Raindrop Splash for Various Values of Drop Size and Velocity and Rainfall Intensity

(After Ellison)

Drop size, d = 3.5 mm				Drop size, d = 5.1 mm			
Experiment	v, fps	i, in./hr	Erosion, g	Experiment	v, fps	i, in./hr	Erosion, g
A	18.0	4.8	223	M	19.2	4.8	446
B	18.0	6.6	245	N	19.2	6.6	543
C	18.0	8.1	368	P	19.2	8.1	690
D	18.0	14.8	492	Q	19.2	14.8	786
E	14.5	4.8	67.1	R	15.0	4.8	203
F	14.5	6.6	96.3	S	15.0	6.6	233
G	14.5	8.1	138	T	15.0	8.1	295
H	14.5	14.8	232	U	15.0	14.8	329
I	12.0	4.8	15.3	V	12.0	4.8	35.7
J	12.0	6.6	20.5	W	12.0	6.6	61.7
K	12.0	8.1	33.2	X	12.0	8.1	67.3
L	12.0	14.8	47.8	Y	12.0	14.8	157

smaller particles thrown a maximum of 5 ft. With 3.5-mm drops having a velocity of 17 fps, 2-mm soil aggregates and stone fragments were carried as far as 8 in., and the maximum distance for any particle was 3.5 ft. In the absence of wind and on a level surface the outgoing splash from any point should normally be balanced by incoming. However, by experiment on a 10 per cent slope, it was found that more than three times as much soil was caught by samplers facing uphill as by those facing downhill. If the soil is bare, great amounts of material are apparently transported downhill by raindrop splash, especially when augmented by a downslope wind.

Effect of overland flow. Much of the soil thrown into suspension by the impact of falling raindrops is carried to the channel system of the basin by overland flow. In addition, the flowing water may possess sufficient energy to break up aggregates and produce further erosion. The erosive power of surface runoff is derived principally from the turbulence of the fluid motion. Strictly speaking, laminar flow is streamline flow and is free of turbulence. If the flow past any section is in agreement with that determined by Eq. (11-9), then the flow is said to be laminar. This means, not that there are no eddies at any point upstream, but rather that any eddy or turbulence created by surface projections is rather quickly damped out by viscous forces. Thus, in considering the areal distribution of overland flow, it is entirely possible that the discharge-depth relation for the flow through a section indicates laminar flow when at the same time eddies exist at various points upstream. In other words, turbulence and erosion can take place in laminar overland flow.

For the usual slight depths of surface detention, translational energy is a much greater portion of the total in the case of overland flow than in the usual type of channel flow experienced. Also, the relative roughness is decidedly different in the two cases. Particles of sand of 0.01 in. diameter submerged in overland flow of 0.10 in. depth are relatively comparable in roughness with boulders 1 ft in diameter in a channel 10 ft deep. For these and other reasons, the application of experimental results and analyses for open-channel flow to problems of overland flow is certainly open to question. Except in the case of lakes and reservoirs, channel flow is usually turbulent. On the other hand, overland flow on natural surfaces may range from laminar to turbulent within short distances—laminar flow through depressions interconnected with channelized turbulent flow.

SEDIMENT TRANSPORT

The study of the laws governing the transport of sediment by flowing water has been intensified in recent years because of the increased rate of construction of river-control works. In addition to the fact that more and larger projects are now being built, sediment calculations are becoming more and more an integral part of the design phase for structures of all sizes. Also, with the initiation of the expanded soil-conservation program by the Federal government (1935), it became immediately evident that the current knowledge of sedimentation processes was inadequate to permit the accurate planning of balanced conservation practices.

Sedimentation problems are encountered in several fields—hydrologic and hydraulic engineering, geology, fluid mechanics, etc.—and as a result the theories, empirical relations, and definitions which appear in the literature are somewhat confused. In an attempt to standardize definitions, a Subcommittee on Sediment Terminology was organized by the Section of Hydrology, American Geophysical Union, in 1941. In the interests of clarity, the definitions reported by this subcommittee[1] have been adopted throughout this chapter, even though the terms used may not conform with reference material. Those definitions recommended and considered pertinent are as follows:

Contact load is the material rolled or slid along the bed in substantially continuous contact with the bed. . . .

Saltation load is the material bouncing along the bed, or moved, directly or indirectly, by the impact of the bouncing particles. . . .

Suspended load can be used for either (1) the material moving in suspension in a fluid, being kept up by the upward components of the turbulent currents or by colloidal suspension, or (2) the material collected in or computed from samples collected with a suspended-load sampler. (A suspended-load sampler is a sampler which attempts to secure a sample of the water with its sediment load without separating the sediment from the water.) Where it is necessary to distinguish between the two meanings given above, the first may be called the *true suspended load*. . . .

Bed load may be used to designate either coarse material moving on or near the bed or material collected in or computed from samples collected in a bed-load sampler or trap. . . .

Bed-material load is that part of the sediment load of a stream which is composed of particle sizes found in appreciable quantities in the shifting portions of the stream bed. . . .

Wash load is that part of the sediment load of a stream which is composed of particle sizes smaller than those found in appreciable quantities in the shifting portions of the stream bed. . . .

Nominal diameter is the diameter of a sphere of the same specific gravity and the same terminal uniform settling velocity as the given particle in the same sedimentation fluid.

Methods of transport. The transport of bed and soil materials in natural watercourses and the resulting changes in the configuration of the bed are important problems to the designer of projects for the improvement, regulation, and economic development of river systems. In the first place, the transport is accomplished by three different processes, which may occur singly or in combination. Furthermore, a portion of the material is intermittently moved by first one process and then another. Conse-

[1] Report of the Subcommittee on Sediment Terminology, *Trans. Am. Geophys. Union*, Vol. 28, pp. 936-938, 1947.

quently, accurate observation of the total transport under natural conditions by sampling techniques is virtually impossible. Even approximate measurement requires a combination of at least two different types of observations.

Methods of sediment transport are generally classified in accordance with the corresponding definitions given above as (1) suspension; (2) contact, or traction; and (3) saltation. Generally speaking, the suspended load consists of the smaller particles, while the larger grains are moved in contact with the bed by traction forces. The third class of movement, saltation, is hard to distinguish from suspension (in water), but the particles so transported are generally smaller than those in contact with the bed and larger than the suspended particles. Since even suspended particles bounce against the bottom with a frequency proportional to their mass, the distinction between suspension and saltation is difficult to define. According to recent studies,[1] saltation is of little importance in hydrology because of the relatively minor quantities of material moved in this manner. In the case of sediment transport by air, however, it is sometimes of major importance.

In most streams, sediment is transported concurrently by two or all three methods. Large particles move along in contact with the stream bed. Within a thin layer immediately above the bed, materials are relatively coarse and their concentration is relatively high, and they are transported either in suspension or by saltation, or both. Above this and extending to the water surface is a thick layer in which the concentration decreases with height, the grains are relatively fine, and the material is carried along in suspension. The suspended load comprises the greatest part of the total load in most streams and, therefore, is the most important in considering reservoir silting, etc. However, the coarser material is generally of greater importance in the formation of the bed and banks.

Theory of distribution and transportation of suspended material. Material suspended in still water settles at a rate approximately in accordance with Stokes' law.[2] In the case of steady laminar flow, the rate at

[1] Kalinske, A. A., Criteria for Determining Sand Transport by Surface Creep and Saltation, *Trans. Am. Geophys. Union*, Vol. 23, pp. 639-643, 1942.

[2] Stokes' law states that the velocity of fall of a particle through a liquid is a function of the radius of the particle. The equation is:

$$v = \frac{2(\rho_g - \rho)gr^2}{9\mu}$$

where v is the velocity of fall, ρ_g and ρ are densities of the particle and liquid respectively, r the radius of the particle, and μ the absolute viscosity of the liquid. The equation assumes (1) that the particles are large as compared with the molecules of the liquid but small enough so that viscosity is the only source of resistance to their fall; (2) that the particles are rigid, smooth, and spherical; and (3) that the velocity of fall is not impeded by adjacent particles. It is generally considered applicable to particles between 0.0002 mm and 0.2 mm in diameter.

which a particle settles with respect to the water around it is the same as in still water because the elements of water encounter no vertical displacement with respect to each other. In either case, the concentration of suspended material decreases with time (as does the size of the particles in suspension) until such time as the suspension is depleted. That is, the suspension is unstable, and equilibrium conditions cannot occur. In turbulent flow, however, the gravitational settling of the suspended material is counteracted by eddy or turbulent motion. Since gravitational settling produces a concentration gradient, eddies transporting water upward to a given layer carry more suspended material than do those moving downward. Thus, transportation in suspension is a continuous process of scouring and settling-out. If the two processes act at equal rates, the bed configuration is unchanging with time and suspension conditions are said to be in equilibrium. If velocity of flow and roughness of bed are such that turbulent transfer exceeds gravitational settling, then the bed is being scoured, or eroded. Conversely, if gravity predominates, sediment is being deposited on the stream bed and the concentration in the overlying water is being correspondingly decreased.

Equilibrium conditions. The mathematical derivation of the basic theory of turbulent transport is considered beyond the scope of this text. For such a discussion, the reader is referred to a review of the subject by O'Brien[1] or to some of the earlier discussions.[2] It will suffice to begin the discussion here with a general equation for the vertical distribution of a suspension of uniform particles with settling velocity v_s. This relation is

$$c_s v_s = -\epsilon \frac{dc_s}{dy} \qquad (13\text{-}1)$$

where c_s is the average concentration at depth y above the bottom and ϵ is a mixing coefficient variously known as *eddy conductivity, diffusion coefficient, mechanical viscosity,* or *eddy viscosity.* Theoretically, the coefficient ϵ is supposedly of the same value whether one is considering the distribution and transport of momentum, sediment, or any other form of turbulent transfer. Actually, however, there is reason to believe that it may be different, even for simultaneous observations of momentum and sediment.[3]

[1] O'Brien, M. P., Review of the Theory of Turbulent Flow and Its Relation to Sediment Transportation, *Trans. Am. Geophys. Union,* Vol. 34, pp. 487-491, 1933.

[2] Leighly, J. B., Toward a Theory of the Morphologic Significance of Turbulence in the Flow of Water in Streams, *Univ. Calif. Pub. Geog.,* Vol. 6, 1932.

Taylor, G. I., Eddy-motion in the Atmosphere, *Trans. Roy. Soc. (London),* No. 215, 1915.

Schmidt, W., Der Massenaustausch in freier Luft und verwandte Erscheinungen, *Wasserwirt.,* No. 5-6, 1932.

[3] Vanoni, V. A., Some Experiments on the Transportation of Suspended Load, *Trans. Am. Geophys. Union,* Vol. 22, pp. 608-621, 1941.

Upon integration, Eq. (13-1) becomes

$$\log_e\left(\frac{c_s}{c_{sa}}\right) = -v_s \int_a^y \frac{dy}{\epsilon} \tag{13-2}$$

where c_{sa} is the concentration at some reference depth a.

If ϵ can be expressed as a function of y, then the integral in the right-hand member of Eq. (13-2) can be evaluated. Various assumptions have been made by different investigators regarding this relationship, with varying degrees of experimental success. Any assumed function must necessarily be considered approximate in a general sense, since the variations and irregularities inherent in any natural channel preclude the possibility of a simple, exact function. The assumption is generally made that the mixing coefficient ϵ for sediment transfer is the same as that for momentum, in which case it can be shown from turbulence theory that the unit shear τ at any point is

$$\tau = \rho\epsilon \frac{dv}{dy} \tag{13-3}$$

where v is the velocity of flow at depth y above the bottom and ρ is the fluid density.

The Prandtl-von Kármán[1] equation for vertical velocity distribution in a wide stream is

$$\frac{v}{v_m} = 1 + \frac{\sqrt{\mathbf{g}\,Ds}}{\mathbf{k}v_m}\left(1 + \log_e \frac{y}{D}\right) \tag{13-4}$$

where v_m is the mean velocity in the section. From Manning's formula, and noting that von Kármán's constant $\mathbf{k} = 0.4$, it will be seen that $\sqrt{\mathbf{g}\,Ds}/\mathbf{k}v_m$ is equivalent to $1.70\mathbf{n}\sqrt{\mathbf{g}}/D^{1/6}$.

Near the center of a wide stream (two-dimensional flow) the unit shear increases approximately linearly from zero at the surface to τ_0 at the bottom, where τ_0 is equal to $\rho\, D\mathbf{g}s$. In other words, $\tau = \rho\mathbf{g}\,Ds[1 - (y/D)]$. Hence, differentiating Eq. (13-4) and substituting for dv/dy in Eq. (13-3),

$$\epsilon = \mathbf{k}y\sqrt{\mathbf{g}\,Ds}\left(1 - \frac{y}{D}\right) \tag{13-5}$$

Equation (13-5) shows that ϵ is maximum at mid-depth and approaches zero at the top and bottom.

Combining Eqs. (13-2) and (13-5), and integrating,[2]

$$\frac{c_s}{c_{sa}} = \left[\frac{a(D - y)}{y(D - a)}\right]^{v_s/\mathbf{k}\sqrt{\mathbf{g}\,Ds}} \tag{13-6}$$

[1] Von Kármán, T., Some Aspects of the Turbulence Problem, *Proc. 4th Intern. Congr. Applied Mech.*, Cambridge, England, 1934.

[2] Rouse, H., Modern Conceptions of the Mechanics of Fluid Turbulence, *Trans. ASCE*, Vol. 102, pp. 463-543, 1937.

Thus, having values of the readily measurable quantities in Eq. (13-6), the concentration of sediment with settling velocity v_s need be found only at depth a to determine the vertical distribution. The equation is applicable down to some small depth a above the bottom, below which suspension becomes mixed with the contact load. The relation between relative concentration and depth for selected values of the exponent [Eq. (13-6)] is

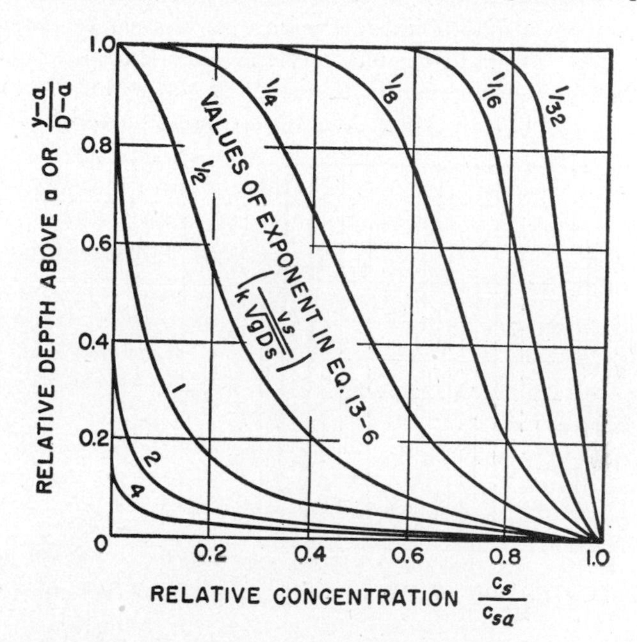

FIG. 13-2. Distribution of suspended sediment according to Eq. (13-6), letting $a = 0.05D$. *(After Vanoni.)*

shown in Fig. 13-2, assuming $a = 0.05D$. Experimental data collected at the California Institute of Technology[1] agree quite closely with Eq. (13-6).

The total sediment transport in a stream is the summation of all point values of the product of velocity and concentration. A combination of Eqs. (13-4) and (13-6) is not convenient to handle in practical problems. Lane and Kalinske[2] made the further assumption that ϵ is constant with depth. This is equivalent to assuming a parabolic velocity distribution, instead of logarithmic as used in previous derivations. However, data on sediment distribution in wide rivers indicate that the assumption is suffi-

[1] Vanoni, V. A., Some Experiments on the Transportation of Suspended Load, *Trans. Am. Geophys. Union*, Vol. 22, pp. 608-621, 1941.

[2] Lane, E. W., and A. A. Kalinske, Engineering Calculations of Suspended Sediment, *Trans. Am. Geophys. Union*, Vol. 22, pp. 603-607, 1941.

ciently precise for practical problems. From Eq. (13-5) the average value of ϵ is found to be $D\sqrt{\mathbf{g}\,Ds}/15$. Therefore, Eq. (13-2) may be written

$$\frac{c_s}{c_{sa}} = \mathbf{e}^{-15\chi[(y-a)/D]} \tag{13-7}$$

where $\chi = v_s/\sqrt{\mathbf{g}\,Ds}$ for wide streams.

From the equation it is seen that the concentration of particles with settling velocity v_s at any point in a vertical section can be determined by plotting the known concentration c_{sa} on semilogarithmic paper and drawing a straight line through the point with a slope of -15χ (note that 6.5 should be used instead of 15 if the log scale is to the base 10 instead of to base $\mathbf{e}$).

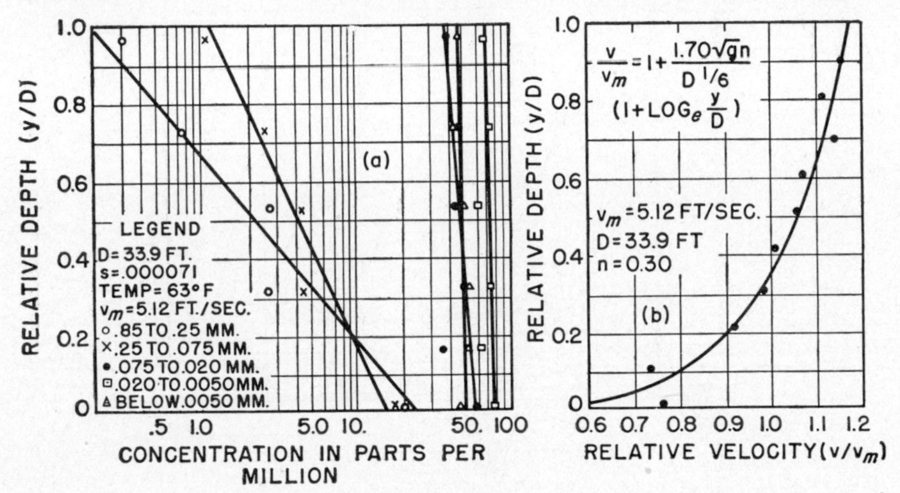

FIG. 13-3. Suspended-sediment (*a*) and velocity (*b*) distribution in the Mississippi River at Muscatine, Iowa. (*After Lane and Kalinske.*)

Figure 13-3*a* shows a plotting of observed data for samples taken at a point in the center of the Mississippi River at Muscatine, Iowa, during the flood of September, 1938. The slope of the lines is -6.5χ, using the depth and river slope shown and a settling velocity corresponding to the average value for the size range considered. Figure 13-3*b* shows the velocity distribution corresponding to the sediment distribution of Fig. 13-3*a*.

The total suspended load M_i carried through the section per unit of time per unit of width is equal to $\int_0^D vc_s\,dy$. Combining Eqs. (13-4) and (13-7),

$$M_i = v_m c_{sa} \int_0^D \frac{v}{v_m}\,\mathbf{e}^{-15\chi[(y-a)/D]}dy = qc_{sa}\,\xi\,\mathbf{e}^{+15\chi a/D} \tag{13-8}$$

where q is the water discharge per unit width, and ξ is a function of χ and the relative roughness $(\mathbf{n}/D^{1/6})$. It can be shown that ξ is actually equal to the ratio of the average concentration to that at the bottom. Values of ξ

for various values of χ and $\mathbf{n}/D$ can be determined from the chart of Fig. 13-4.

Nonequilibrium conditions. Equilibrium suspension conditions are often approached in natural watercourses but are never actually attained. For example, if the velocity at a section is less than that in the reach upstream, the sediment concentration at that section will be in excess of the equilibrium capacity. If steady uniform flow prevails for a considerable distance

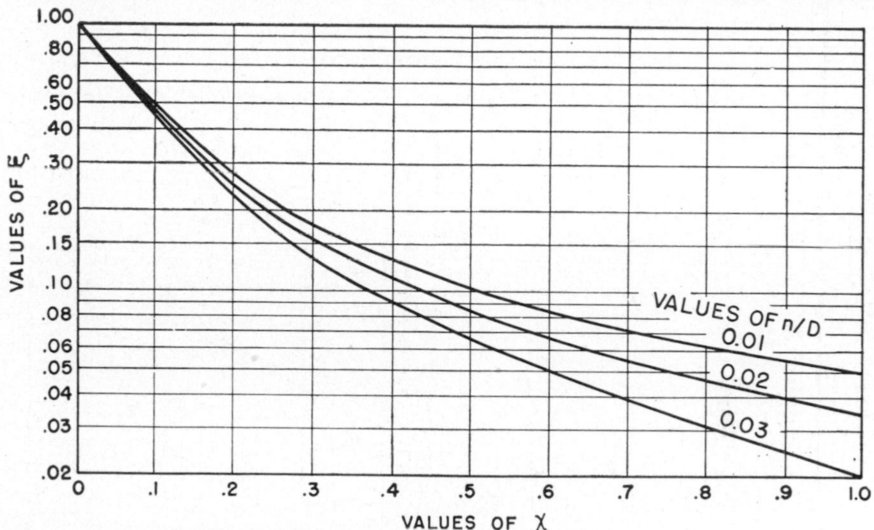

FIG. 13-4. The relation between χ and ξ in Eq. (13-8) for various values of relative roughness. *(After Lane and Kalinske.)*

equilibrium conditions will be approached exponentially as one proceeds downstream. Obviously, the resulting differential deposition along the channel bottom gradually alters the hydraulic features of the bed and thus further delays equilibrium.

As would naturally be expected, the turbulent theory of suspensions under nonequilibrium conditions requires considerably more involved mathematics than does the case of equilibrium conditions.[1] For the case of two-dimensional flow (steady uniform flow near the middle of a wide channel), it can be shown that the general differential equation for the transport of material in suspension is

$$v\frac{\partial c_s}{\partial x} = v_s\frac{\partial c_s}{\partial y} + \frac{\partial \epsilon_x}{\partial x}\frac{\partial c_s}{\partial x} + \frac{\partial \epsilon_y}{\partial y}\frac{\partial c_s}{\partial y} + \epsilon_x\frac{\partial^2 c_s}{\partial x^2} + \epsilon_y\frac{\partial^2 c_s}{\partial y^2} \tag{13-9}$$

[1] Kalinske, A. A., Suspended-material Transportation under Non-equilibrium Conditions, *Trans. Am. Geophys. Union*, Vol. 21, pp. 613-617, 1940.

Dobbins, W. E., Effect of Turbulence on Sedimentation, *Trans. ASCE*, Vol. 109, pp. 629-678, 1944.

where ϵ_x and ϵ_y are the turbulent-transfer coefficients in the direction of flow and in the vertical, respectively. The solution of this equation requires that v, ϵ_x, and ϵ_y be expressed as functions of y. Needless to say, no solution has yet been obtained for this two-dimensional case. By making certain assumptions, however, the equation can be greatly simplified.

One assumption generally made is that the turbulence coefficients in the x and y directions are equal or at least proportional. If parabolic velocity distribution is assumed,

$$v = v_d - b(D - y)^2 \tag{13-10}$$

where v_d is the surface velocity and b is a constant. Differentiating Eq. (13-10),

$$\frac{dv}{dy} = 2b\,D\left(1 - \frac{y}{D}\right) \tag{13-11}$$

From Eq. (13-3), assuming $\tau = \tau_0[1 - (y/D)]$,

$$\epsilon_y = \frac{\tau_0[1 - (y/D)]}{\rho\, dv/dy} \tag{13-12}$$

Combining Eqs. (13-11) and (13-12),

$$\epsilon_y = \frac{\tau_0}{2b\,D\rho} \tag{13-13}$$

Thus, it is seen that assuming a parabolic velocity distribution is equivalent to assuming that ϵ_y is constant throughout depth. If it is further assumed that $\partial\epsilon_x/\partial x$ and $\partial^2 c_s/\partial x^2$ are negligible,

$$[v_d - b(D - y)^2]\frac{\partial c_s}{\partial x} = \epsilon_y \frac{\partial^2 c_s}{\partial y^2} + v_s \frac{\partial c_s}{\partial y} \tag{13-14}$$

If, instead, it is assumed that the concentration is constant along the direction of flow x (no diffusion in that direction), then both the first and second partial derivatives of c_s with respect to x will be zero and Eq. (13-9) becomes

$$\epsilon_y \frac{\partial^2 c_s}{\partial y^2} + v_s \frac{\partial c_s}{\partial y} = 0 \tag{13-15}$$

In the case of a confined liquid with uniform turbulence imposed throughout, y and t become the only independent variables and Eq. (13-9) becomes

$$\frac{\partial c_s}{\partial t} = \epsilon_y \frac{\partial^2 c_s}{\partial y^2} + v_s \frac{\partial c_s}{\partial y} \tag{13-16}$$

This is the only form of the differential equation which has been solved analytically (Dobbins). The simplifying assumptions required to reduce the general equation to this form, however, probably render it of little or no value in the case of natural streams. Kalinske has demonstrated that Eqs. (13-14) and (13-15) can be solved by numerical integration with an accuracy satisfactory for many problems. The assumed parabolic velocity distribution does not introduce serious error in v, but this is not true with respect to ϵ. The errors introduced by other assumptions may or may not be significant, depending upon the specific case.

Sediment-discharge ratings. While there are many and varied factors affecting the suspended load of a stream, observations indicate that a rather well defined relation exists between the load and the concurrent

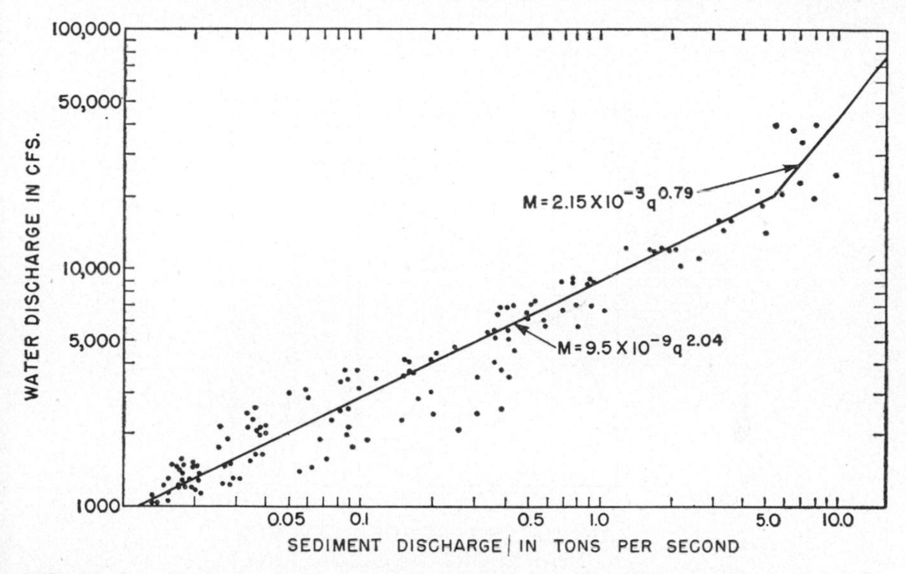

FIG. 13–5. Sediment rating for the Red River near Denison, Texas. *(After Campbell and Bauder.)*

discharge for some rivers. An example[1] of a *sediment-discharge rating* is shown for the Red River in Fig. 13-5. The form of the sediment-discharge rating is generally considered to be

$$M_t = kq^n \tag{13-17}$$

in which M_t is the rate of sediment transport, q is the discharge, and k and n are constants. The same equation appears to apply as well to water-year flow volumes and suspended load, as shown for the Green River in Fig. 13-6. For instantaneous or daily data, the value of n is sometimes found to be less for extremely high flows than for moderate flows. Thus, in Fig. 13-5 the value of the exponent is apparently greater than 2 for moderate flows, while it is less than unity when the discharge is extremely high. Although the number of observations is insufficient to reach any definite conclusion in this case, the possibility of a more complex relation

[1] Campbell, F. B., and H. A. Bauder, A Rating-curve Method for Determining Silt-discharge of Streams, *Trans. Am. Geophys. Union*, Vol. 21, pp. 603-607, 1940.

is certainly indicated. It appears that n is a function of the availability of transportable material in the bed for maintaining the sediment load.

While the rating-curve method of estimating suspended transport is so inaccurate as to be of little value for many rivers, it can be used to great advantage in some cases, especially when the problem involves only the total transport over an extended period of time. The value computed for any one day may be considerably in error, depending upon variations in such factors as tendency of the river, location of principal contributing area, relative portions of groundwater and surface runoff, etc.

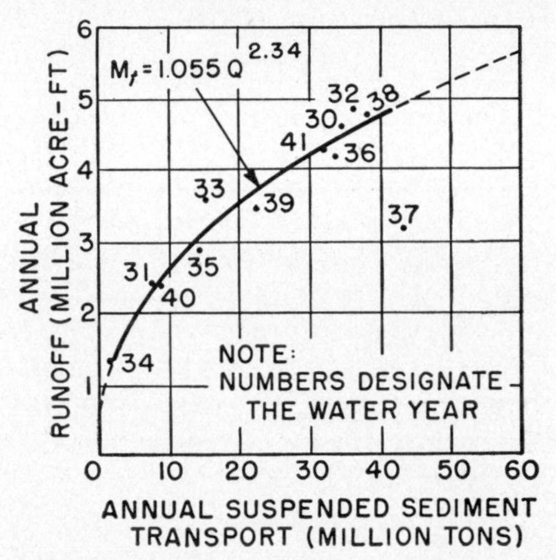

FIG. 13–6. Sediment rating for Green River at Greenriver, Utah, based on water-year data. *(From U.S. Geological Survey Water Supply Paper 998.)*

Bed-load movement. Until quite recently, the detailed mechanism by which sediment is transported along the bottom of stream channels was only vaguely known. While present-day engineering knowledge is still rather limited, especially for the complicated conditions existing in natural channels, many features of the processes involved can be explained now that our knowledge of turbulent flow is more advanced. Many attempts toward a rational approach have been made through the years, but most formulas which have been applied to practical problems in the past are more or less of an empirical nature. A number of such formulas are discussed briefly later in the section.

Theoretical approach. In 1879 du Boys[1] presented a formula for the rate of bed-load transport which he derived by making the assumption that sand is moved in layers subject to uniform tractive force and that the

[1] Straub, L. G., Missouri River: H. Doc. No. 238, 73d Cong., 2d Sess. (1935), 1032-1245, App. 6.

vertical velocity gradient in the moving sand is linear. His formula may be written

$$G_i = \Upsilon \frac{\tau_0}{w} (\tau_0 - \tau_c) \tag{13-18}$$

in which G_i is the rate of transport of sediment along the stream bed per unit width, Υ is a coefficient depending upon size, shape, etc., of the sediment particles, w is the unit weight of water, and τ_c is the value of unit shear at which transport begins. This formula admittedly omits any direct consideration of the mechanism of turbulent flow. While oversimplified, it has been utilized in conjunction with Manning's formula, with moderate success. Furthermore, it has been found to fit experimental data collected by Chang[1] and others reasonably well.

Of recent years, emphasis has been directed toward a theoretical approach based on established concepts of turbulent flow.[2] The following derivation of the equation for bed-load movement is essentially that presented by Kalinske, which is based in part on the work of White.[3] In any analysis of bed-load movement, there are two basic concepts which must be considered, (1) that there is a minimum fluid force F_t which must be exerted on any particle before it will start to move and (2) that the force to which a particle on the channel bed is subjected is not constant but fluctuates about some mean value. Since all particles do not rest identically, the required force will vary slightly, even for uniform particles. The second concept follows directly from the theory of turbulent flow. Should the flow be laminar, the fluctuations are considerably diminished but nevertheless are of importance.

The forces acting upon a particle of noncohesive material, resting on similar particles (Fig. 13-7), are buoyancy, gravity, and fluid force. The relative torque exerted by the fluid force is dependent upon the Reynolds number of the grain, $d\sqrt{\tau_0/\rho}/\nu$, where d is the diameter of the grain, τ_0 is the unit shear on the bottom, and ρ and ν are the fluid density and kinematic viscosity, respectively. If the Reynolds number is greater than 3.5, as is usually the case in most practical problems, then the resultant of the fluid forces may be assumed to pass through the center of gravity of the particle and the critical force is

$$F_t = \frac{\pi \rho' g d^3 \tan\theta}{6} \tag{13-19}$$

[1] Chang, Y. L., Laboratory Investigation of Flume Traction and Transportation, *Trans. ASCE*, Vol. 104, p. 1268, 1939.

[2] Kalinske, A. A., Movement of Sediment as Bed Load in Rivers, *Trans. Am. Geophys. Union*, Vol. 28, pp. 615-620, 1947.

Einstein, H. A., Formulas for the Transportation of Bed Load, *Trans. ASCE*, Vol. 68, pp. 561-597, 1942.

[3] White, C. M., Equilibrium of Grains on Bed of Stream, *Proc. Roy. Soc. (London)*, Series *A*, Vol. 174, pp. 322-334, 1940.

in which ρ' is the difference in density of the particle and the fluid and θ is the angle of repose. The relation between F_t and τ_0 depends on the number of grains per unit area which in combination absorb the shear. If j is the portion of the bed taking the shear, then there are $j/(\pi\, d^2/4)$ spherical grains per unit area and the critical shear is

$$\tau_c = \frac{2\rho' jg\, d \tan \theta}{3}. \tag{13-20}$$

Data obtained by White indicate that τ_c is only about half that given by the equation. Evidently, the turbulence in the wake of the particle causes the force to fluctuate in such a manner that the maximum value approaches twice the mean. Only meager data are presently available regarding the values of j and θ. Those determined by White are $j = 0.35$ and $\theta = 45°$. Thus, assuming the specific gravity of the particle to be 2.65 and introducing a factor of 0.5 to agree with White's findings, Eq. (13-20) becomes

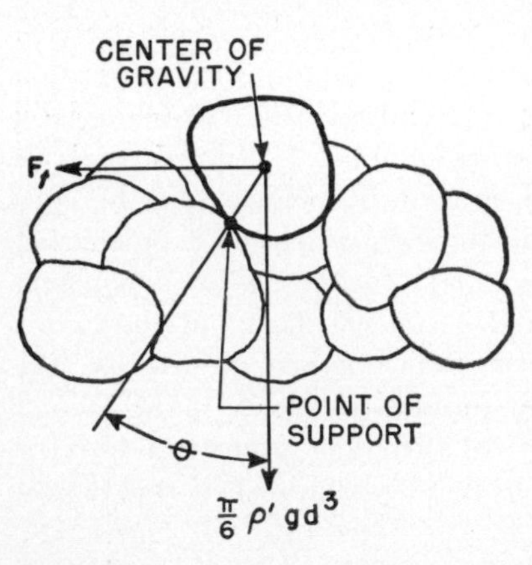

FIG. 13–7. Forces acting on a sand grain in a river bed.

$$\tau_c = 12d \tag{13-21}$$

where d is in feet and τ_c is in pounds per square foot.

It should be remembered that τ_c in this equation is the actual critical tractive force required to start movement. However, Kalinske has shown that the standard deviation σ of the velocity is about 25 per cent of the mean value for fully developed turbulent flow. Since the time variations in velocity follow the normal-error law, the instantaneous value will exceed the mean by more than 3σ about 0.1 per cent of the time. The shear being proportional to the square of the velocity, it is then evident that the instantaneous shear may be expected to reach three times the average value. In other words, a mean shear force of $4d$ may be expected to start movement.

The rate of transport of bed-load material depends upon the mean velocity of the grains and the mass of material in motion. The velocity of a single grain v_g at any instant may be considered proportional to the difference between the existing flow velocity v and the critical velocity v_c for the grain. That is,

$$v_g = k(v - v_c) \tag{13-22}$$

Experimental data indicate that the constant of proportionality k is, for all practical purposes, unity. In the case of uniform particles, the mean rate of movement in weight per unit width of channel is

$$G_i = \frac{4\pi w_g\, d^3 \bar{v}_g j}{6\pi d^2} = \frac{2}{3}\, \bar{v}_g w_g j d \tag{13-23}$$

in which $\bar{v}_g$ is the time average of velocity for any particle and w_g is the specific weight of the material being moved. Rearranging this equation

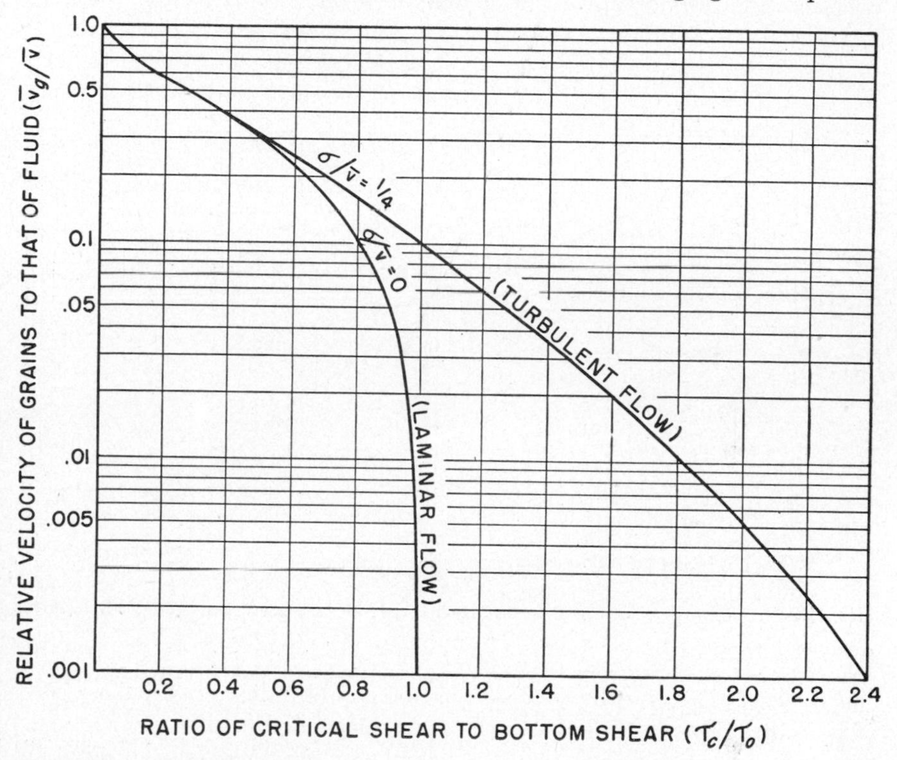

FIG. 13–8. The relation between ($\bar{v}_g/\bar{v}$) and (τ_c/τ_0) for laminar and turbulent flow. *(After Kalinske.)*

and dividing both members by the time average of fluid velocity $\bar{v}$ at the grain level,

$$\frac{G_i}{j\bar{v}\, dw_g} = \frac{2}{3}\frac{\bar{v}_g}{\bar{v}} \tag{13-24}$$

By assuming that the time variations in v follow the normal-error law, which has been essentially verified by experiment, it can be shown that the ratio $\bar{v}_g/\bar{v}$ is a function of τ_c/τ_0 and the relative intensity of turbulence $\sigma/\bar{v}$, where σ is the standard deviation of the time variations in v. Figure 13-8 shows this function for two values of $\sigma/\bar{v}$. Since boundary-layer theory indicates that $\bar{v} = c\sqrt{\tau_0/\rho}$, where c is about 11, Eq. (13-24) may be written

$$\frac{G_i}{j\,dw_g\,\sqrt{\tau_0/\rho}} = \frac{2}{3} f\left(\frac{\tau_c}{\tau_0}\right) \tag{13-25}$$

where $f(\tau_c/\tau_0)$ is that shown in Fig. 13-8. Equation (13-25) is the basic bed-load equation for approximately spherical uniform material. This equation and supporting experimental data are shown in Fig. 13-9, using Eq. (13-20) for τ_c, $j = 0.35$, $\sigma/\bar{v} = \frac{1}{4}$, and assuming a specific gravity of 2.65 for the bed-load material. When the bottom shear is high as compared with the critical shear for movement, the measured values of G_i are

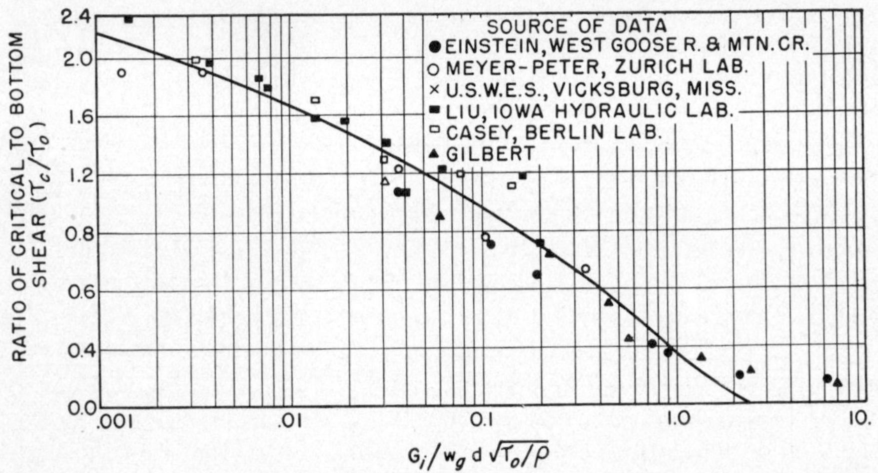

FIG. 13–9. Comparison between bed-load data and Eq. (13-25). *(After Kalinske.)*

much larger than the theoretical equation would indicate. In these cases it is quite probable that there was some suspended-load movement, part of which was measured as bed load. Some of the points shown represent mean values of a number of observations, and, in a few cases, data for nonuniform sand are plotted using the median diameter.

By use of a summation process, as discussed by Kalinske, Eq. (13-25) can be made to apply to sand mixtures. However, for any specified mixture, there is some diameter which, when used in the equation, will give the same rate of movement as does the summation process. This size will vary to some extent with τ_0, but for practical purposes the median diameter has been found satisfactory.

Experimental formulas. The more important of the bed-load formulas have been adequately summarized by Chang.[1] Some of the formulas are

[1] Chang, Y. L., Laboratory Investigation of Flume Traction and Transportation, *Trans. ASCE*, Vol. 104, pp. 1246-1313, 1939.

strictly empirical, while others were derived in a more or less rigorous manner but contain coefficients determined from experimental data. For an extensive summary of experimental data relative to laboratory investigations of bed-load transportation, the reader is referred to the compilation published by the Soil Conservation Service.[1]

The Schoklitsch formula was developed by analyzing experimental flume data for which the bed-load material was uniform quartz grains. It may be written

$$G_i = \frac{437}{\sqrt{d}} s^{1.5}(q - q_c) \tag{13-26}$$

in which G_i is the rate of bed-load transport in pounds per second per unit width, s is the slope, d is the particle diameter in millimeters, and q and q_c are the observed and critical discharges, respectively, in cubic feet per second per unit width. The value of q_c is given by $0.00021\ d/s^{4/3}$.

The Meyer-Peter bed-load formula, developed by Swiss engineers, considers the grain diameter, slope, and discharge. It may be written

$$G_i = (bsq^{2/3} - cd)^{3/2} \tag{13-27}$$

where b and c are constants to be experimentally determined.

Through analyzing data collected at Massachusetts Institute of Technology, MacDougall[2] reported the equation of best fit to be of the form

$$G_i = cs^m(q - q_c) \tag{13-28}$$

in which the coefficients c and m are interrelated and depend upon d.

The experimental data obtained by Chang were found to best fit an equation of the du Boys type,

$$G_i = \frac{k\mathbf{n}}{\tau_c^{\,2}} \tau_0(\tau_0 - \tau_c) \tag{13-29}$$

where $\mathbf{n}$ is Manning's roughness factor and k is a constant. Assuming that the grains are spherical with specific gravity of 2.65, the value of τ_c is given by $0.0175(1.65d)^x$, in which d is in millimeters and x is either unity or one-half, depending upon whether $1.65d$ is greater or less than unity, respectively.

By combining Manning's formula with that of du Boys, Straub[3] developed the empirical formula

$$G_i = \frac{\mathbf{n}^{1.2} s_c^{\,1.4} q^{0.6}}{1.609} \Upsilon(q^{0.6} - q_c^{\,0.6}) \tag{13-30}$$

in which s_c is the critical slope corresponding to q_c.

[1] Johnson, J. W., Laboratory Investigations on Bed-load Transportation and Bed Roughness, *U.S. Dept. Agr. Soil Conservation Service Tech. Bull.* 50, 1943.

[2] MacDougall, C. H., Bed-sediment Transportation in Open Channels, *Trans. Am. Geophys. Union*, Vol. 14, pp. 491-495, 1933.

[3] Straub, L. G., Effect of Channel-contraction Works upon Regimen of Movable Bed-streams, *Trans. Am. Geophys. Union*, Vol. 15, p. 455, 1934.

Sediment observations. From the previous discussion of bed and suspended load, it is evident that it would be impossible to design a single sampling instrument which would supply an accurate observation of total sediment load, even in a single vertical in the cross section. The amount of material being carried in suspension can be determined by obtaining a group of samples or a single representative sample of the flow and determining the weight of sediment per unit volume. The total suspended transport in weight per unit of time is then computed as the summation of concentration multiplied by the rate of discharge. Bed load does not move at the same velocity as the water, however, and this procedure is not applicable. For bed material, it is necessary to measure the sediment transport (per unit of time for a known width of channel) at enough points to compute

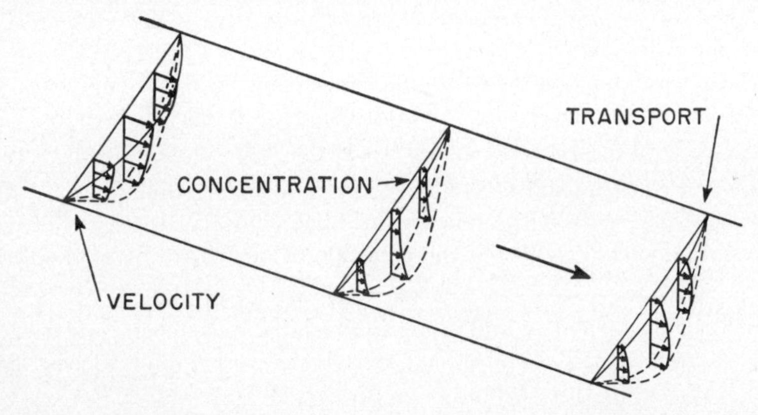

FIG. 13–10. Distribution of velocity, suspended sediment, and sediment transport in a flowing stream.

the total transport. It is virtually impossible to measure directly the amount of material moved by saltation in natural streams. By current methods of observation, this material is unavoidably included in the samples of bed and suspended load. By virtue of this fact and because saltation is relatively unimportant, no attempt is made to distinguish this type of transport from the total.

Observations of suspended transport. Considerable study has been given the problem of selecting the best points in the stream cross section at which to take suspended-sediment observations. The problem is similar to that of measuring the water discharge (Chap. 9), but inasmuch as the vertical distribution is somewhat the reverse in the two cases, the best sampling points are necessarily different. The distribution throughout the cross section of velocity, concentration of suspended material, and the product of the two are shown schematically in Fig. 13-10. The number of verticals at which samples are taken depends upon the accuracy required and the economic aspects of the problem. Usually, arbitrary points are selected, such as the middle and quarter or sixth points from the ends of the section, which may or may not be assumed to give samples of equal weight. For greatest accuracy, however, the verticals should be selected to represent equal portions of the total discharge or, better yet, total transport. Except in the case of depth-integrating samplers (Fig. 13-11), the selection of measuring points in the verticals must also be considered. Obviously, the simplest method involves a single sample taken at a representative depth. Such samples are frequently taken at 0.6 of the depth below the surface, but the proper depth should preferably be determined on the basis of surveys to establish the true vertical distribution of sediment. In some cases, samples are taken at the surface, bottom, mid-depth, or a combination of any two or all three. By integrating the product of suspended-load and velocity-distribution curves in river verticals, Straub[1] developed the formula

$$M_i = (\tfrac{3}{8}c_a + \tfrac{5}{8}c_b)q \qquad (13\text{-}31)$$

in which M_i is the suspended-sediment discharge per unit width of channel, c_a and c_b are the concentrations at the 0.8 and 0.2 depths below the surface, respectively, and q is the water discharge per unit width.

Many and varied types of suspended-sediment samplers have been developed, most of which have features which are more or less objectionable. Considerable progress has been made in determining qualitatively the errors from defects common to many types of samplers,[2] but much remains to be done in this regard. In general, samplers fall into two classes, instantaneous and integrating. Since this classification is based on the elapsed time during which the sample is taken, there is naturally no definable boundary between the two classes. However, if the orifice of inflow is relatively large and the entire sample is collected within a very few seconds, the sampler is considered to be of the instantaneous type.

Most recent developments in sampling devices have been directed toward an integrating technique. If integrating samplers are held at a constant depth while the sample is being collected, a time-integrated measurement of concentration is obtained. On the other hand, if the sample is collected while the instrument is moved throughout the vertical, a depth-integrated measurement results. If the problem at hand is that of determining the total suspended transport of a stream, then integration over depth is the most logical type of observation, since fewer samples are required for the same degree of over-all accuracy. The ideal type of instrument in this case is one which will take in water continuously while being lowered at a uni-

[1] Straub, L. G., Missouri River: H. Doc. No. 238, 73d Cong., 2d Sess. (1935), 1032-1245, App. 6.

[2] Lane, E. W., Measurement of Sediment Transportation, *Proc. 2d Hydraulics Conf., Univ. Iowa Studies Eng. Bull.* 27, pp. 83-94, 1942.

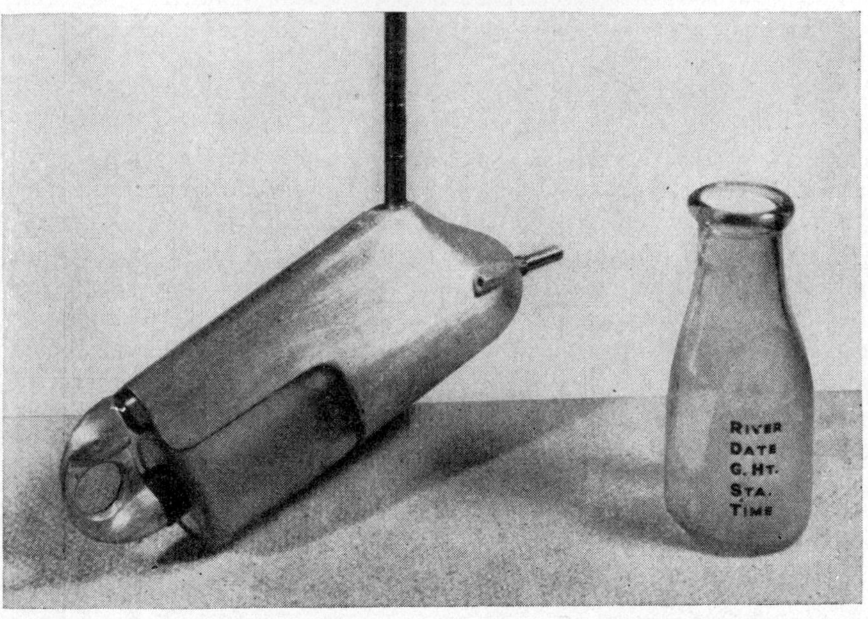

FIG. 13–11. Depth-integrating sediment samplers (upper) U.S. D-43 for large streams and (lower) U.S. DH-48 hand sampler for small streams.

form rate from the surface to the bottom of the stream, with the intake rate at all times being proportional to the flow velocity.

Observations of bed-load transport. Little has been done regarding the scientific location of sampling points for bed-load transport observations. Customarily, observations are taken at a sufficient number of points across a channel to determine the variations in load between points with reasonable accuracy. Transport per unit width is then plotted against the position of the observation point and a curve fitted. The total bed-load transport of the stream is equivalent to the area under the curve.

Bed-load observations are much more common in Europe than in this country, and consequently much of the instrumental development work has been accomplished by European investigators. The simplest type of sampler consists of a framework covered with screening and open at the upstream end so as to catch the coarse material swept into it by the current. The bottom of the sampler is of a heavy, flexible material which settles snugly against the stream bed when the box is lowered into place.

In the pressure-difference sampler (Fig. 13-12), the intake is connected to an expansion section, which is in turn fastened to a wire-mesh bag. The expansion section is of dimensions such that it creates a suction sufficient to balance the resistance to flow through the entire mechanism, thus enabling the water and bed-load material to approach and enter the filtering bag unobstructed. While more complex, these instruments have an advantage in that they need not be calibrated.

SEDIMENT MOVEMENT AND DEPOSITION IN STREAMS

The previous section deals principally with methods by which flowing water transports granular materials, without placing any particular emphasis on the over-all mechanics of streams. The interrelations between the hydraulic features of the channel, such as slope, width, depth, and roughness, and the geological and climatological characteristics of a region prevent the existence of rivers which may be treated alike in all respects. The complexity of the joint relations existing between the numerous physical characteristics defies independent considerations of such elements as slope and bed erosibility. While changes in channel shape are exceedingly gradual for streams traversing areas of cohesive material which is essentially nonerosible, equilibrium conditions do not exist in natural watercourses. Superimposed on the long-term trend in channel changes are short-period fluctuations produced by alternate wet and dry periods as they are related to stream discharge.

River mechanics. Near their source, rivers generally flow through steep, rugged terrane; and as a result the high-velocity flow is capable of transporting detritus of considerable diameter. Here, however, the quantities of flow are limited and intermittent, and while large amounts of material are moved, significant transport occurs only during freshets. Proceeding downstream, the slopes become flatter, and the competence for transporting detritus diminishes as a result of the decreased velocity. This decrease in concentration, however, is usually more than compensated by the increased volume of flow, so that the total quantity of sediment transport generally increases downstream. In other words, the quantity of sedi-

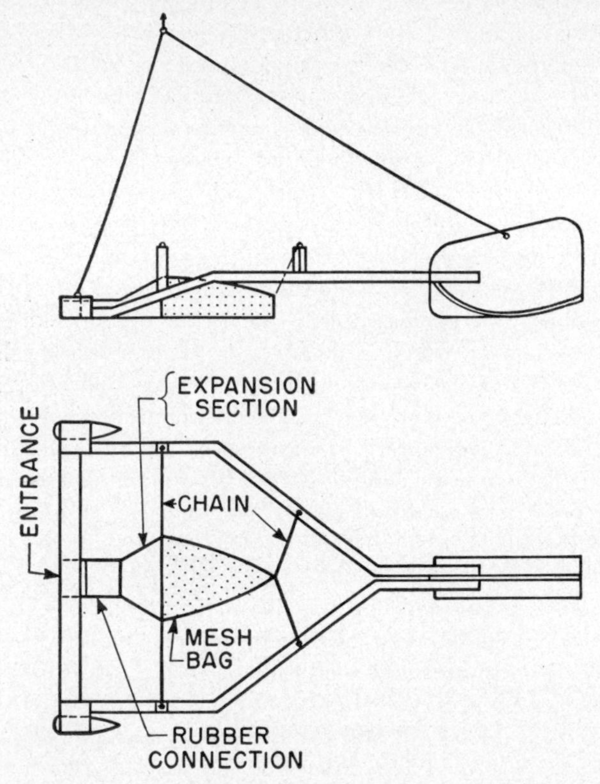

FIG. 13–12. Bed-load sampler of the pressure-difference type developed by the Dutch government.

ment transported is a function of drainage area. This generalized picture is sometimes greatly modified by lakes or reservoirs. The outflow from a large natural or artificial lake is usually clear, even though the inflow contains a high concentration of suspended and bed-load sediment. If the bed material in the channel below is not readily susceptible to erosion, the lake will effectively reduce the concentration for some distance downstream. In easily erosible channels, however, clear water rapidly regains the greater portion of its original load except for the finer grains, which may not be available in the bed material.

Alluvial rivers. Although the terms erosible and nonerosible are purely relative, the experimental study of river mechanics has been confined principally to a consideration of rather highly erosible channel material as found in alluvial streams. Among other things, the relative ease with which adequate models can be constructed and the short period required to observe significant changes in channel shape are important factors contributing to this limited scope of experimental study. Since our knowledge of the mechanics of alluvial streams is based on well-founded experimental evidence, this phase is given most emphasis in this section—the discussion of other types of rivers is limited to those features which distinguish them from alluvial streams.

The Mississippi River Commission has studied the meandering of alluvial rivers for many years. Numerous misconceptions regarding the source and route followed by particles of sediment, causes of meandering, etc., have been dispelled by experiments conducted at its Waterways Experiment Station at Vicksburg, Mississippi. The discussion which follows is based in great part upon published results of these studies.[1]

The meandering of streams has been attributed to many causes—Coriolis acceleration, excessive energy, changes in stage, flow disruption by a tree or irregular bankline, etc. Moreover, many have believed that meanders could not develop within a reach of river unless there was an inflow of sediment from above. Figure 13-13 illustrates the results of an experiment in which the flow was maintained at a constant rate with sufficient velocity to erode the banks. The channel, cut in uniform sandy material, was initially straight. There was no inflow of sand at the upper end of the stream. The photographs show that the stream developed meanders, and it will be noted that the meanders were smaller at the head of the reach—a direct result of the fact that the inflow was clear water. Meandering was initiated by a local disturbance created by a sand bar which resulted from bank erosion. Caving banks overloaded the stream, and deposition took place. The path of flow in the middle and lower portions of the channel shifted continuously throughout the experiment. The stream deepened its channel in the upstream section until the decreased velocity resulting from the flattened slope was insufficient to move material and erode the banks. From this experiment it was concluded that bank erosion is the only requisite for meandering.

Other tests showed that, under ideal conditions of uniformity, an initial bend is perfectly transmitted downstream, forming a series of uniform meanders (Fig. 13-14). As is characteristic of meandering rivers, the cross sections show that the channel is deep along the concave banks of bends and shallow in the crossings between bends, so that the talweg (line joining

[1] Friedkin, J. F., "Meandering of Alluvial Rivers," U.S. Waterways Experiment Station, Vicksburg, Miss., 1945.

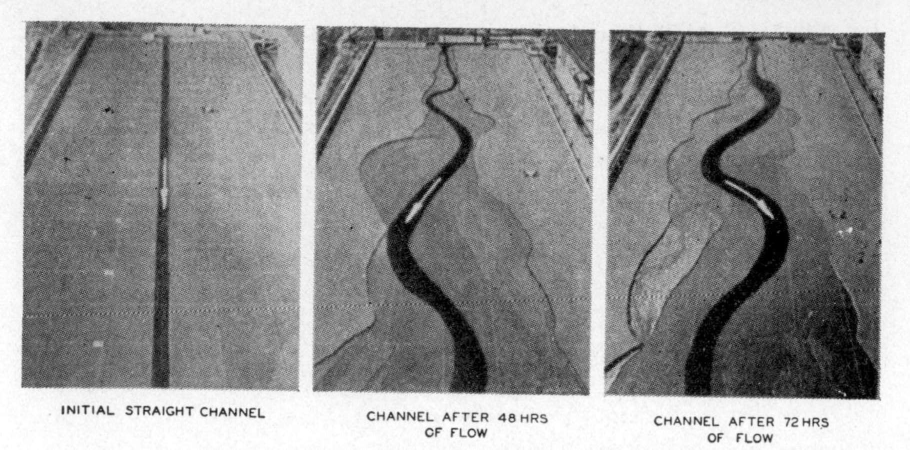

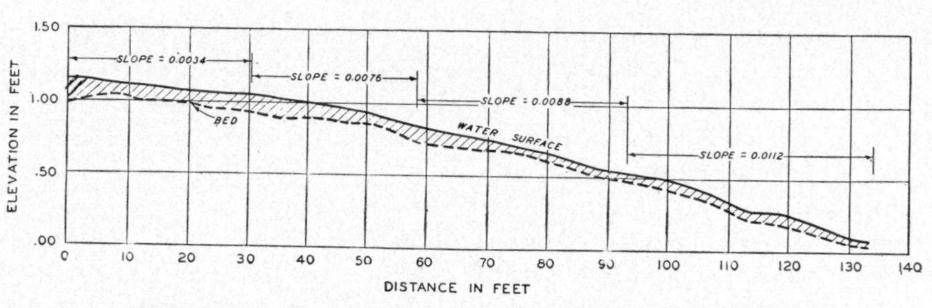

LONGITUDINAL PROFILE OF SINUOUS CHANNEL AFTER 72 HOURS OF FLOW
NO SAND WAS FED AT ENTRANCE

TEST DATA

BED MATERIAL .... MISSISSIPPI RIVER SAND (KINGS POINT)
DISCHARGE .... 0.30 CFS (CONSTANT)
VALLEY SLOPE 0.009
INITIAL CROSS SECTION 2.0 0.30 1.70

MISSISSIPPI RIVER COMMISSION
U. S. WATERWAYS EXPERIMENT STATION
LABORATORY STUDY OF THE
MEANDERING OF ALLUVIAL RIVERS

FIG. 13–13. Development of a meandering channel from a straight channel in uniform material. *(Mississippi River Commission.)*

points of greatest depth in successive cross sections) profile consists of a series of alternating deeps and shoals. Observation clearly indicated that the channel is deeper at the bends because of the impingement of flow against the concave banks, which results in greater turbulence and erosive power.

In an attempt to determine the source, route of travel, and deposition of sand in meandering rivers, a series of tests was made with rapidly eroding

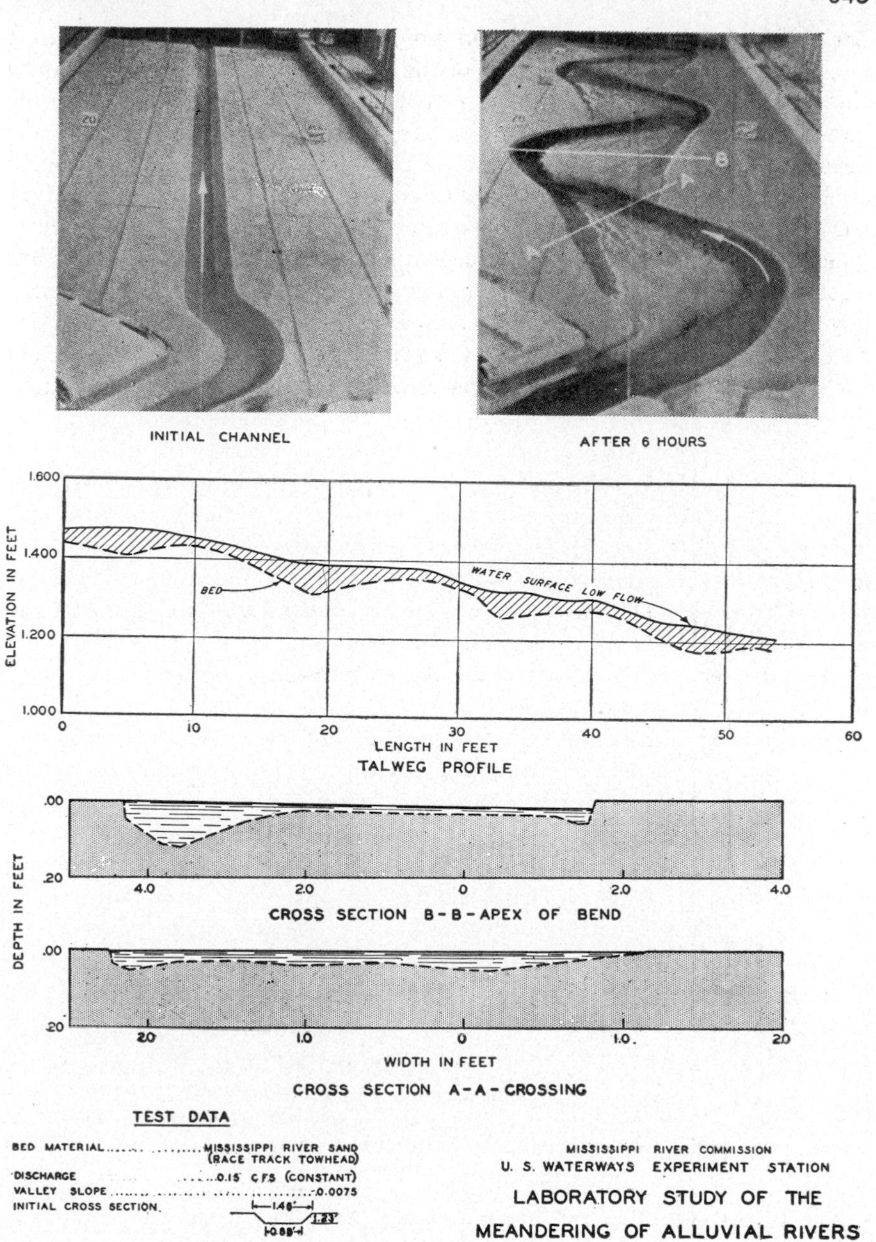

FIG. 13–14. Development of meandering channel from an initial channel in uniform material. *(Mississippi River Commission.)*

banks, slowly eroding banks, and no bank erosion. With nonerosible banks, sand entering at the head of the reach passed nearly continuously through the channel. The sand passed over the talweg at each crossing between the bends and moved along the convex side of the channel in the bends. In the case of highly erosible banks, it was found that the sand eroded from the concave bank was essentially all deposited at the convex bar immediately downstream on the same side of the channel. Only minor quantities of sand eroded from a concave bank were deposited on the bar directly opposite. With slowly eroding banks, part of the sand entering any bend was deposited on the convex bar below, and the remainder passed on through the bend. These tests showed conclusively that the source of the sand in a meandering river is the caving banks. There is a continuous interchange of sand—erosion from the concave banks and deposition on the convex bars. The rate of interchange is directly related to the rate of bank caving. While there was evidence of helical flow, the cross component was insufficient to carry the eroded particles across the talwag before the downstream currents carried them to the crossing or bar below.

Figure 13-15 demonstrates the effect of changes in stage on the source, path of travel, and points of deposition of sand as a result of changes in direction of flow along the channel. In the normal cycle of flow, bends are scoured deeper and deposition takes place at crossings or bendways during high flows, while at low stages sand is eroded from the crossings and deposited in the bends below. In other words, high flows tend to deteriorate the low-water channel of meandering streams. The figure also shows the tendency toward uniform surface slope during high flows. At times of low water, slopes are relatively steep at crossings and flat through bends.

A series of tests in which discharge and slope were varied independently indicated that these factors have a direct bearing on the size of the bends (Fig. 13-16). The illustrated effect of discharge bears out the general relation observed in nature between large and small rivers and also explains the changes in direction of flow and the downstream shifting of the attack against the concave banks with increasing stage (Fig. 13-15). The effect of slope is similar to that of discharge in that they both affect the velocity and energy of flow. Thus, the greater the velocity or momentum of the flowing water, the less able it is to make sharp changes in direction.

In all experiments discussed above, uniform bank materials were used throughout the length of the channel. In all cases, the bends which developed were essentially of uniform dimensions. In nature, however, the bends of a meandering river are by no means uniform. Tests conducted with heterogeneous bank material demonstrated that local variations cause varying rates of erosion and thus result in dissimilar bends. The shape of each bend and the direction of flow into the bend below depend on the rate of erosion within the bend. Therefore, there is a tendency for changes in

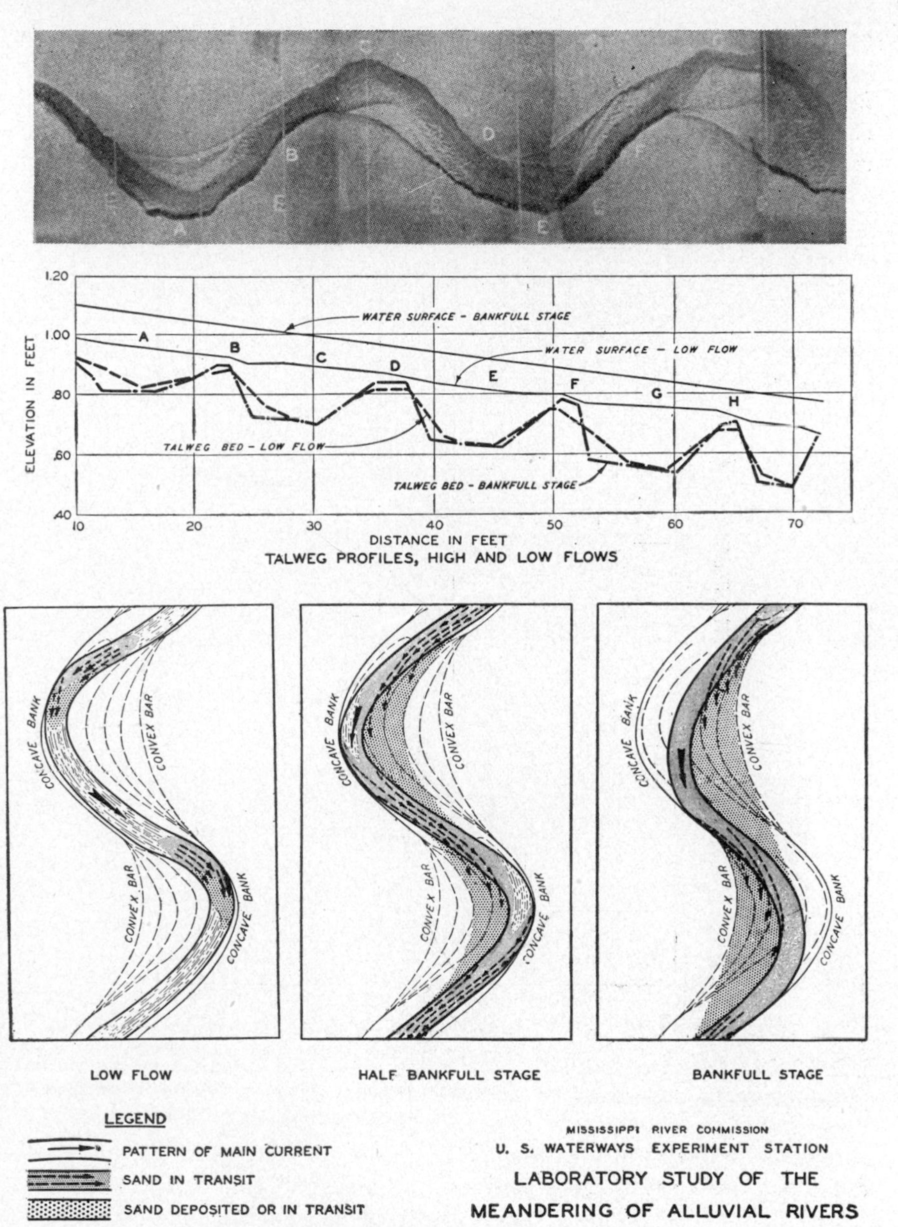

FIG. 13–15. Change in source, path of travel, and deposition of sand with changing stage. *(Mississippi River Commission.)*

one bend to affect the alignment of several downstream bends. In uniform bank material, all bends tend to migrate down the valley at the same rate, *i.e.*, the upper arm of a bend never catches up with the lower arm. A natural cutoff can occur only if the downstream bank of the lower arm erodes more slowly than that of the upper arm. While chutes formed

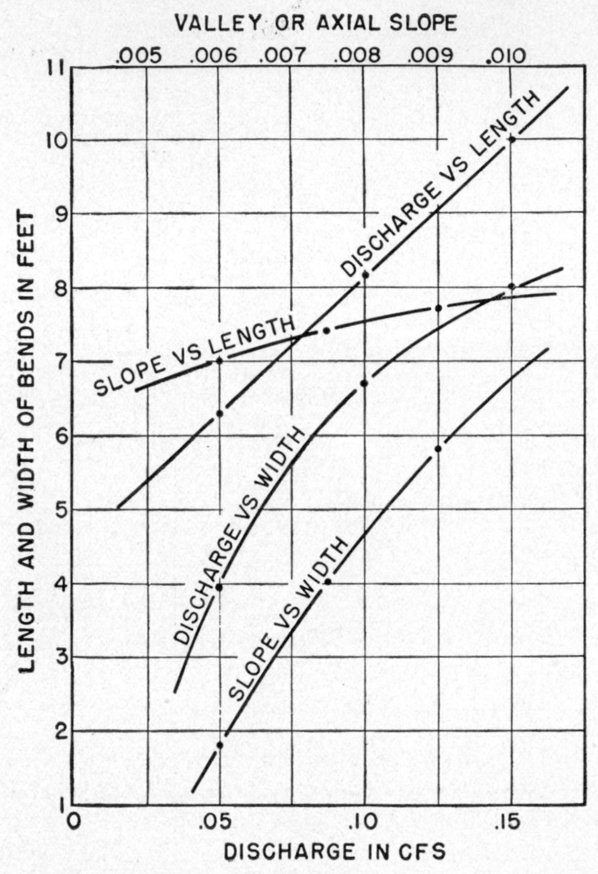

FIG. 13–16. Effect of discharge and slope on size of bends in model studies. ***(Mississippi River Commission.)***

through practically all bends during periods of overbank flow, no cutoffs developed during the tests with uniform bank material.

Although the experiments were controlled in such a manner that the effects of each factor were studied singly, the tests showed that every phase of a meandering river depends upon the relation between (1) the discharge and hydraulic properties of the channel, (2) the amount of sand to be transported, and (3) the rate of bank erosion. A change in discharge, slope, amount of sand entering a bend, or rate of bank erosion tends to bring about definite changes in the channel cross sections and pattern of a meandering river. The extent of such changes is virtually impossible to determine, however, because changes in one variable produce changes in another.

Erosion-resistant channels. In many respects, the behavior of a river with essentially nonerosible banks differs only in degree from that of an alluvial river. The changes in channel configuration of erosible-bank

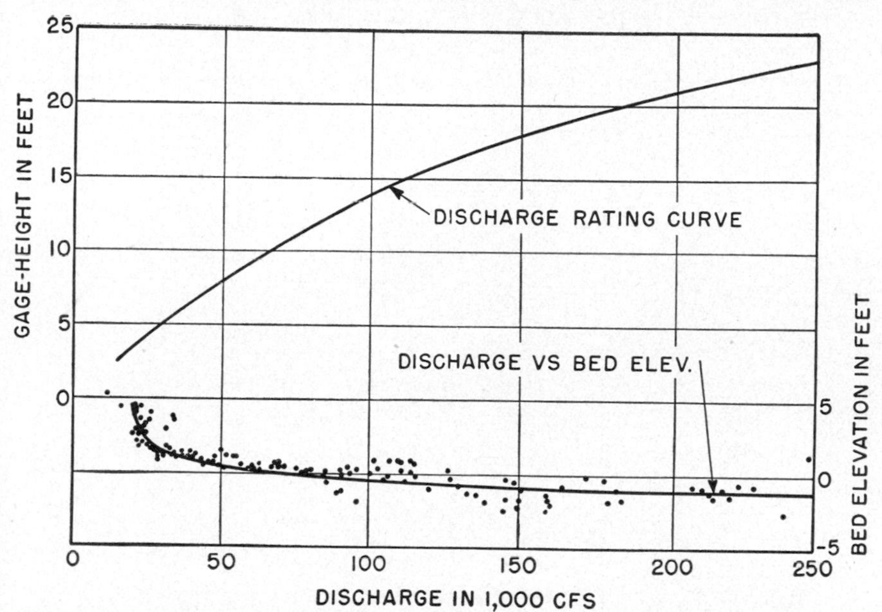

FIG. 13–17. Variation of bed elevation with discharge (1929–1930) for Missouri River at Kansas City, Missouri. *(After Straub.)*

streams are relatively greater than in those stable channels where the process of channel realignment is extremely slow. The filling of the crossings during high flows and their scouring during low flows (Fig. 13-15) are common to all streams. In cases where the crossing is composed of relatively coarse material, however, its erosion during low water is extremely slow, and as a result the variations in water-surface slope along the talweg are accentuated. Observations on natural streams[1] show that a constricted reach of straight channel with erosible bed has a tendency to scour during high flows and to fill during low-water periods (Fig. 13-17). It is these short-term changes in bed elevation that are most significant in streams with nonerosible banks.

Reservoir sedimentation. As water enters a reservoir, its velocity diminishes because of the increased cross-sectional area of the channel. If

[1] Straub, L. G., Effect of Channel-contraction Works upon Regimen of Movable Bed-streams, *Trans. Am. Geophys. Union*, Vol. 15, pp. 454-463, 1934.

the water stored in the reservoir is clear and the inflow is muddy, the two fluids have different densities and the heavy, turbid water flows along the channel bottom toward the dam under the influence of gravity (Fig. 13-18). This condition is known as *stratified flow*, and the underflow is called a density current. In a general sense, a *density current* may be defined as a gravity flow of a fluid under, over, or through a fluid or fluids of approximately equal density. In the field of hydrology we are concerned only with masses of water of different turbidity and temperature. From Fig. 13-18 it is seen that the depth of the turbid flow increases to the point where the density current is established, after which it tends to decrease again. The

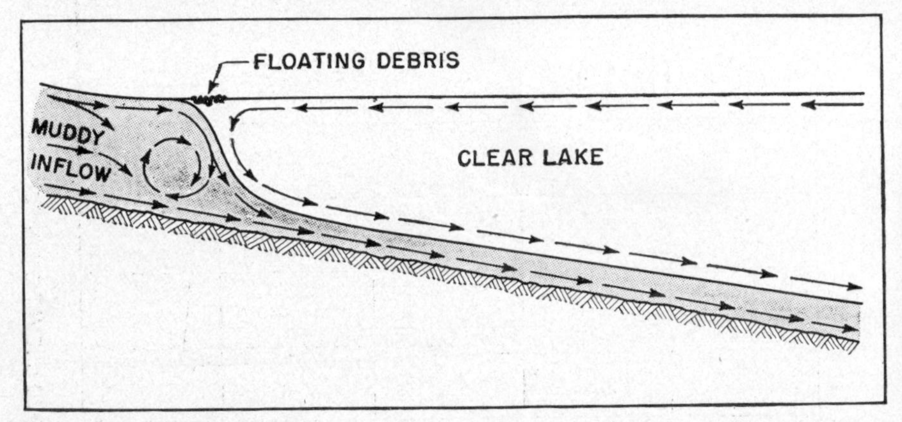

FIG. 13–18. Schematic flow pattern of muddy inflow to a clear reservoir or lake. (*After Bell.*)

magnitudes of these relative changes and their effects upon sediment deposition depend on many factors such as reservoir shape, channel slope, relation of outflow to inflow, and density differences. As a rule, however, conditions are such that density currents move very slowly. In Lake Mead, for example, maximum observed velocities are near 2 mph, while the average velocity is somewhat less than 1 mph.

The history of a turbid density flow is illustrated schematically[1] in Fig. 13-19. The velocity decrease above the point where the density flow begins results in delta deposits near the head of reservoirs. As the density flow hits the dam, it is forced upward; if the lake is shallow, it may rise to the surface and some muddy water may flow over the spillway. Usually, however, it settles back to form a static, submerged, turbid lake from which the suspended particles settle very slowly over a period of days or weeks. During the settling process, the density of the submerged lake may increase in such a manner that subsequent density flows may be forced along the interface as interflows.

[1] Brown, C. B., The Control of Reservoir Silting, *U.S. Dept. Agr. Misc. Pub.* 521, 1943.

BANK STABILIZATION AND SEDIMENT CONTROL

Most hydrologic problems related to sediment control fall into two general classes, (1) bank stabilization and (2) sediment deposition in reservoirs. Bank stabilization becomes important in natural streams when it must be considered for protection of bridges, levees, and other structures. It is also of importance in the design and maintenance of canals and other waterways. The problem of reservoir sedimentation has gained prominence rapidly of recent years, probably owing in great part to the construction of many

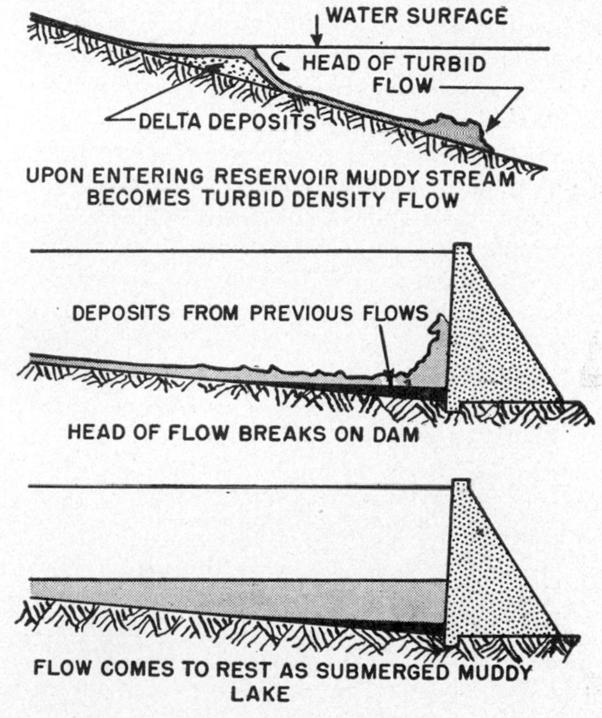

FIG. 13–19. Life history of a density flow. *(After Bell.)*

large reservoirs on the silt-laden streams of the West. Impounding reservoirs are the most important of all types of water-utilization developments in the United States, in terms of both capital investment and annual service value.

Bank stabilization. In alluvial rivers such as the Lower Mississippi, where costly levees are continually threatened by the downriver advance of meanders, channel and bank stabilization presents a major problem. In general, levees are constructed quite close to the meander belt so as to protect as much of the rich bottom land as possible and also to take advantage of the off-river slope created by differential deposition (sometimes called *natural levees*). Although due allowances are made for normal changes in channel configuration during the economic life of the structures, excessive bank caving presents a problem requiring immediate attention. Moreover, experiments have shown that, under some conditions, stabilization by revetment increases the channel capacity and thus may be considered a direct flood-control measure.

In model tests conducted at the U.S. Waterways Experiment Station,[1] eroding banks were stabilized by revetment after meanders had been fully developed by a series of high and low flows simulating natural conditions. After stabilization, the same cycles of flow were continued until no further channel changes were evident. In all cases the talweg depths were increased when the banks were made resistant to erosion. Other tests verified the conclusion that talweg depths increase as the erosibility of the banks decreases. Although low-water depths increased or remained unchanged, stages for maximum flows were lowered after stabilization in channels with moderate curvature and were unchanged in cases where the sinuosity was relatively low or high. When the sinuosity was either very high or very low, the higher flows tended to cross the convex bars instead of taking full advantage of the deep channel along the concave bank. The degree of curvature required for bank stabilization to result in lowering the stages for high flows cannot be determined from these experiments. The results are considered to have qualitative significance only.

Measures for prevention of bank caving are few and extremely costly. Dredging of a channel to divert the water from the concave bank sometimes provides temporary relief. Deflecting dikes of various types are effective and reasonably permanent where foundation conditions are adequate. The most common method of stabilization is the use of bank revetments. Mats of willows, lumber, asphalt, or articulated concrete are laid on the concave bank to prevent erosion. While all such revetments have been found reasonably effective, the articulated-concrete mats are believed to be the most economical in the long run. With costs of labor and materials at 1946 levels, however, the installation of this type of revetment for the Lower Mississippi was only slightly less than three-quarters of a million dollars per linear mile.[2]

A problem of channel stabilization is also met in the design and maintenance of canals. Because the discharge in canals can be controlled between relatively narrow limits, they can be designed to minimize bank caving, even in erosible material. To prevent scouring or filling of the channel, the velocity must be great enough at all points to prevent settling of the sus-

[1] Friedkin, J. F., "Meandering of Alluvial Rivers," U.S. Waterways Experiment Station, Vicksburg, Miss., 1945.

[2] Senour, Charles, New Project for Stabilizing and Deepening Lower Mississippi River, *Trans. ASCE*, Vol. 112, pp. 277-297, 1947.

pended sediment and yet insufficient to attack the subgrade of the canal. Such conditions can be met, of course, only when the subgrade material is relatively coarse as compared with the inflowing sediment.

Reservoir sediment control. The various methods of controlling silt deposition in reservoirs may be divided into four general classes, (1) proper selection of the reservoir site, (2) design features of the dam and reservoir, (3) control of sediment inflow, and (4) removal of sediment deposits. Wherever possible, the advantages and disadvantages of all the various methods should be weighed to determine the most economical combination of measures to be taken before the reservoir is definitely located. A complete discussion of the methods of sediment control is beyond the scope of this text. The material presented is essentially a summary of that given by Brown.[1]

Selection of reservoir site. In many water-storage projects, alternate reservoir sites are available, and in such cases the quantity and type of sediment produced by the respective drainage basins should be given careful consideration. In America, unfortunately, too little emphasis has been given this factor in selecting the most economical site. Although available data are rather meager for most sections of the country, every attempt should be made to arrive at an adequate appraisal through analysis of (1) reservoir-sedimentation surveys in the surrounding region, (2) suspended and bed-load observations, and (3) soil-erosion surveys.

The Soil Conservation Service has conducted numerous reservoir surveys, the published results of which can be obtained upon request to this agency. No single agency has attempted to gather and publish suspended-load data. Many of the earlier records have been summarized by Stevens.[2] The Sedimentation Section of the Soil Conservation Service maintains a tabulation of station locations and periods of record, but no attempt is made to collect and publish all measurements. Bed-load measurements are practically nonexistent—limited observations at the sites under consideration generally provide the only basis for an adequate estimate of this factor. While erosion surveys conducted by the Soil Conservation Service cannot at present be used to make quantitative estimates of the sediment transport from a particular drainage basin, they are of value in estimating the relative extent of erosion above alternate dam sites.

Design of the reservoir. Factors determining the useful life of a reservoir as it is limited by sediment deposition are (1) the rate at which sediment is delivered to the reservoir, (2) the efficiency of the reservoir as a sediment trap, and (3) the storage capacity of the reservoir relative to the rate at which sediment is trapped. The rate of sediment delivery increases with

[1] Brown, C. B., The Control of Reservoir Silting, *U.S. Dept. Agr. Misc. Pub.* 521, 1943.

[2] Stevens, J. C., The Silt Problem, *Trans. ASCE,* Vol. 101, pp. 207-288, 1936.

the volume of discharge, which in turn may be assumed to be approximately proportional to the drainage area within a limited region. Similarly, the efficiency[1] of a reservoir as a sediment trap increases as the storage-capacity–drainage-area ratio increases, as shown in Fig. 13-20. This figure also illustrates the fact that the portion of the inflowing sediment trapped by the reservoir decreases with time, approaching zero as the reservoir becomes completely filled with sediment. While the per cent of sediment

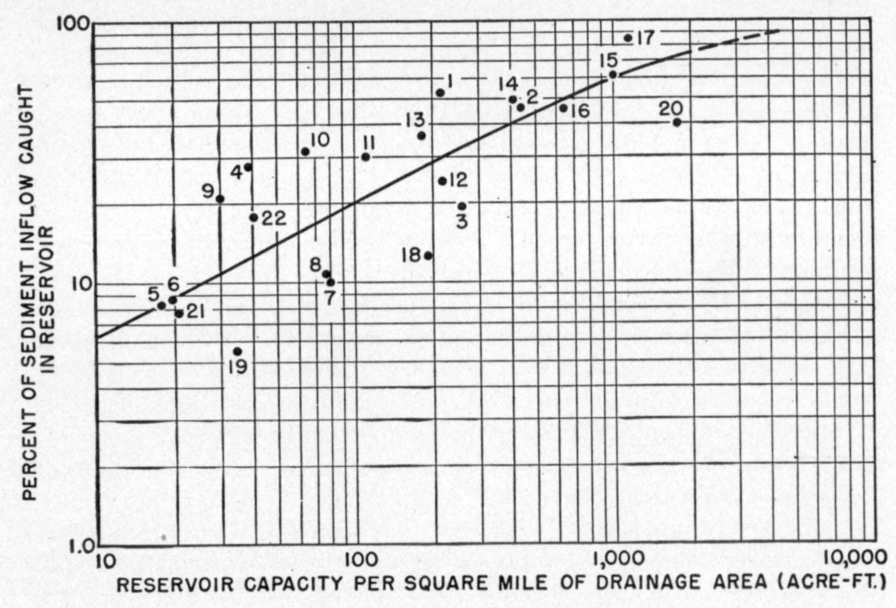

FIG. 13–20. Percentage of sediment inflow trapped by reservoirs of various capacity–drainage-area ratios. *(After Brune and Allen.)*

trapped by a reservoir with a given drainage area increases with increased capacity, the useful life nevertheless increases because of the additional space which may be allotted to sediment. In other words, doubling the size of the reservoir does not double its trapping efficiency.

The useful life of many reservoirs has been severely reduced because they were built without regard for the potential sediment inflow. In 1936 a water-supply reservoir was constructed on the Solomon River at Osborne, Kansas. The drainage area was approximately 2100 square miles, and the storage capacity was about 300 acre-ft, or only 0.14 acre-ft/square mile. The reservoir was completely filled by sediment within a year after completion, the total cost of $150,000 being chargeable to one year's operation.

[1] Brune, G. M., and R. E. Allen, A Consideration of Factors Influencing Reservoir-sedimentation in the Ohio Valley Region, *Trans. Am. Geophys. Union*, Vol. 22, pp. 649-655, 1941.

While this is an extreme example, more than a dozen similar failures have been recorded, and there are many cases in which the useful life has been reduced to relatively few years.

The question of increasing the size of a reservoir to prolong its useful life is one of economics. The minimum expected life must necessarily equal the period of amortization—usually between 20 and 50 years in this country. From a long-term viewpoint, however, it would seem desirable that the design call for a much longer useful life in the interests of conserving reservoir sites since they are a very real natural resource. It is not to be gathered from the foregoing discussion that increasing the size of the reservoir is the solution to all sediment problems. Increasing the capacity naturally increases the water-surface area when filled and thus increases the evaporation losses. Especially in the semiarid West, such losses may be so great that the value of the water evaporated may far outweigh the saving through increased useful life. The question of evaporation is not particularly important if the reservoir banks are steep, but in wide, flat valleys it must be considered.

Designing the dam so that sediment may be passed through or over it is an effective method of silt control. By placing a series of outlets at various elevations, density currents of turbid water can be discharged before the suspended material has had time to settle to the reservoir bottom. Although observations indicate that density currents probably occur in most reservoirs under proper conditions, few quantitative data are yet available. Nevertheless, it is probable that as much as 20 per cent of the sediment inflow could be passed through many reservoirs by venting density currents through outlets properly designed and controlled. For most projects, proper operation for minimizing sediment deposition within the reservoir will necessarily result in the loss of water. In many western reservoirs which seldom spill, water is extremely valuable, and the venting of turbid density currents can be tolerated only when the water released can be used below. However, in reservoirs which waste water a considerable portion of the time, releasing water from the level of greatest concentration should be well worth while.

Control of sediment inflow. The recognized methods of controlling the inflow of sediment to impounding reservoirs are (1) erosion control, (2) use of settling basins, and (3) establishment of vegetative screens. Settling basins and vegetative screens are essentially types of erosion control, except that they are designed primarily to protect the reservoir by retaining the soil materials in transit to it and are therefore located near the reservoir.

Removal of sediment deposits. A variety of mechanical and hydraulic methods, such as excavation, dredging, siphoning, draining, and sluicing, have been suggested and used for the removal of sediment deposits from reservoirs. It is generally agreed that the redemption of lost storage by sediment removal is economically feasible only as a last resort, because of the nature of sediment, its distribution throughout the reservoir, and the tremendous mass of material involved. The most practical means of maintaining storage capacity are those designed to prevent the accumulation of permanent deposits—removal operations are extremely expensive, unless the material removed is usable and can be sold. Generally speaking, the construction of a new reservoir is more economical than removing the sediment from an existing one.

14

GROUNDWATER

Groundwater wells and springs are important sources of water for irrigation, domestic, and industrial uses. Moreover, during protracted spells of dry weather the groundwater is the sole source of streamflow in unregulated streams. The study of groundwater is thus a very important branch of hydrology but, because of the geological aspects of the groundwater problem, is very specialized and complex. The location and movement of groundwater are largely determined by the local geological formation. The complexity and variety of such formations make a detailed discussion of the problems of groundwater hydrology very lengthy. Complete textbooks[1] are available in the field, and the U.S. Geological Survey has recently published an excellent bibliography[2] on the subject.

ORIGIN AND OCCURRENCE OF GROUNDWATER

Figure 14-1 is a cross section of a slope tributary to a lake. It is divided into two areas by a line called the *water table,* or *phreatic surface.* Below the water table the soil is saturated, and this zone is called the *zone of saturation.* Above the water table the pore spaces are partly filled with air, and this region is called the *zone of aeration.* Water in the zone of aeration follows the laws of soil physics (Chap. 12). In this chapter we are primarily interested in water in the zone of saturation.

Origin of groundwater. Numerous estimates of the available groundwater supply have been made. These estimates range upward from a figure of an equivalent depth of 96 ft over the entire surface of the earth.[3] Whatever the true amount may be, we can be certain that it represents an immense volume of water. The origin of this water was a subject of debate for many years (Chap. 1), but it is now generally accepted that the greater

[1] Tolman, C. F., "Ground Water," McGraw-Hill, New York, 1937.

[2] Waring, G. A., and O. E. Meinzer, Bibliography and Index of Publications Relating to Ground Water Prepared by the Geological Survey and Cooperating Agencies, *U.S. Geol. Survey Water Supply Paper* 992, 1947.

[3] Fuller, M. L., Underground Water Papers, *U.S. Geol. Survey Water Supply Paper* 160, 1906.

portion of this water is *meteoric, i.e.*, water which originated in the atmosphere and reached the zone of saturation through infiltration and percolation. Small amounts of *connate water*, water incorporated in the pores of rocks at the time of their deposition on old ocean floors, are to be found. Some *magmatic*, or *juvenile*, water has also been brought to the earth's surface from great depths in the upward movement of intrusive igneous rocks.

Meteoric water reaches the zone of saturation largely by percolation from precipitation and by influent seepage from streams. Many European hydrologists believe that a significant amount of recharge occurs through condensation of water vapor entering soil and rock interstices from the atmosphere, but this theory does not seem to be supported by data. Some

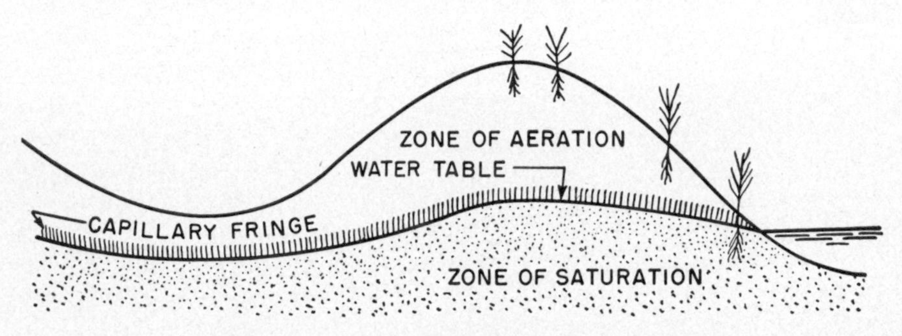

FIG. 14–1. The location of the water table.

water from almost any rainfall reaches the groundwater through rock crevices and channels left by decayed roots, but significant recharge from precipitation can be expected only when the soil mantle above the water table is brought to field capacity. Hence, isolated rainfalls of small magnitude and short, intense rains yielding considerable surface runoff cannot be expected to result in important recharge of groundwater. For the most part, groundwater recharge by percolation from precipitation can be significant only during extended rainy periods. Since snowmelt rates are relatively low as compared with rainfall intensities, sustained periods of snowmelt may be expected to yield a high contribution to groundwater. Sandy soils having rather low field capacities are particularly favorable recharge areas.

In some areas seepage from streams is an important source of groundwater. Mountain streams flowing out over an alluvial fan are quite generally above the groundwater table in the fan, and considerable quantities of water may percolate downward through the permeable alluvial material. Since any dry stream bed is above the water table, streamflow which enters such channels is subject to depletion through seepage. Floods of considerable magnitude have been dissipated in very short distances because of such channel losses. Babcock and Cushing[1] report percolation rates averaging 2 ft of water per day during floods and 4 ft during periods of sustained flow in a typical desert wash. The higher rates occurred when the water was fairly clear. White[2] in a study of the Mimbres River, New Mexico, observed losses as great as 4.5 per cent of the flow per mile. Local conditions control seepage, and general factors should not be used to estimate possible losses. Where data on seepage losses are required, it is advisable to make actual tests by measurement of discharge at two points.

In many areas artificial recharge of groundwater is being accomplished through spreading streamflow in ditches or shallow basins. Under favorable conditions seepage rates as high as 10 ft/day have been observed immediately after spreading, decreasing to about 3 ft after a period of 1 or 2 months.

Most sedimentary rocks and many lava deposits were laid down under oceans. It is natural that these deposits incorporated water and, when later elevated above sea level, retained a portion, if not all, of this water. If the deposits became associated with circulating groundwater, the salty water was probably removed but many deposits of salty water still remain. Such deposits are usually horizontally stratified and are found well below the water table and often below sea level. They are frequently associated with oil or natural-gas deposits.

The water table. As shown in Fig. 14-1, the water table normally coincides with the free surface of lakes and streams. Between such open-water bodies, a water table, not confined by overlying impermeable strata, follows in modified form the contours of the land. It is higher under the hills than under the adjacent valleys. The contours of the water table do not show as pronounced variations as does the land surface, because of the tendency of water to seek its own level. The water table, since its position is dependent on the continued accretion of groundwater, fluctuates with annual variations in rainfall, being both lower and flatter after dry spells than after rainy periods. For various reasons the water table in some areas intersects the land surface, and *springs*, or *seeps*, result. Wet-weather seeps occur when a water table, raised by protracted rains, cuts the land surface. Occasionally a body of groundwater will be found above a bed of impervious or relatively impervious material (Fig. 14-2). Such a locally anomalous condition is called a *perched water table*. A water table confined from above by an impermeable layer so that the water is under pressure represents *artesian* conditions.

[1] Babcock, H. M., and E. M. Cushing, Recharge to Groundwater during Floods in a Typical Desert Wash, Pinal County, Ariz., *Trans. Am. Geophys. Union*, Vol. 23, pp. 49-56, 1942.

[2] White, W. N., Preliminary Report on the Groundwater Supply of the Mimbres Valley, N.M., *U.S. Geol. Survey Water Supply Paper* 637, p. 79, 1930.

The shape of the upper surface of the water table is dependent on the flow conditions within the zone of saturation. Where the water can move rapidly, it naturally flows from the higher spots and a more nearly level water table results. It is entirely possible for a perched water table to be present above an impermeable stratum and for artesian water to occur below the same stratum. A stream flowing over an alluvial fan may be

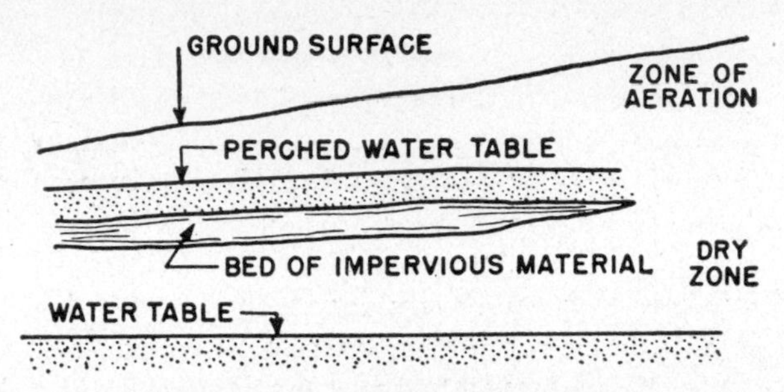

FIG. 14–2. Perched water table.

entirely above the water table. Under such conditions the stream is said to be *influent*, and water is continually percolating through the stream bed to the groundwater. In such cases a ridge of groundwater may form under the stream (Fig. 14-3).

Water-bearing formations. A formation which transmits water in sufficient quantity to support wells or springs is called an *aquifer*. In contrast, an *aquiclude* may contain large volumes of water but does not permit its movement at rates sufficiently large for economical development by pumping or to support large springs. An *aquifuge* is a formation which has

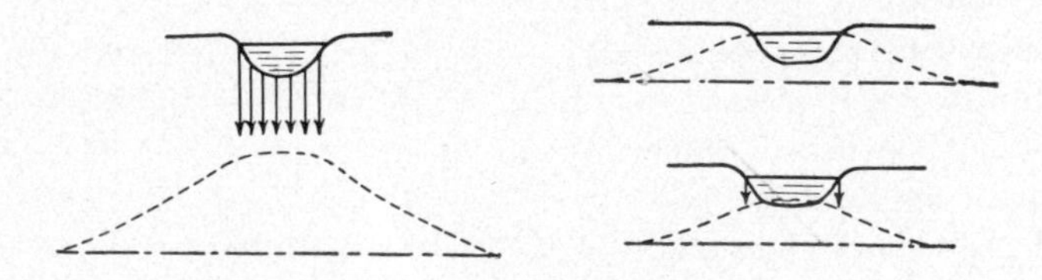

FIG. 14–3. Groundwater ridges under influent streams. *(After Tolman.)*

no interconnected openings and hence cannot absorb or transmit water. In addition to the geologic description of an aquifer in terms of its constituents and history, the groundwater hydrologist is interested in its *porosity*, its *yield*, or the volume of water it will yield by gravity drainage, and its *permeability*, or capacity to transmit water.

The porosity of an aquifer is expressed as a percentage by volume of the interstices in the material. These interstices vary from enormous limestone caverns to pore spaces of molecular size. Interstices may be classified as *original,* those formed at the time the rock was laid down, and *secondary,* the joints and solution cavities developed later. In this section we shall consider only sedimentary deposits. Although limestone and lava deposits are important sources of groundwater, their special features demand separate consideration.

The porosity of sedimentary rocks depends on the nature and assortment of the basic particles and on the degree of cementation and fracturing which the rock has undergone. It is generally true that deposits of irregularly

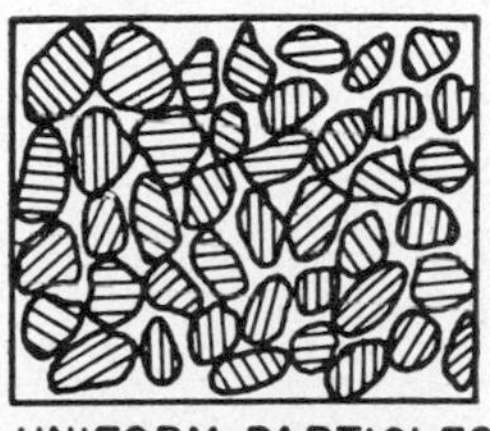

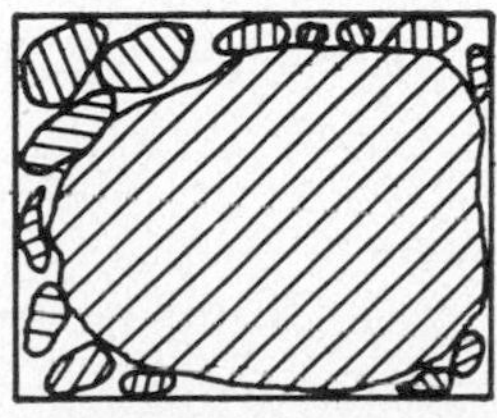

FIG. 14–4. Factors influencing porosity.

shaped particles are most porous because the irregular particles do not fit together as well as more regular grains would. The degree of assortment of the particles is particularly important in fixing porosity. A completely uniform particle size will result in the greatest porosity, while a well-graded sediment will have low porosity because the smaller grains fill the interstices between the larger grains. Size of grains has little effect on porosity of uniform deposits. Considering spherical grains, the volume of interstices in uniform deposits is entirely independent of grain size. In nonuniform deposits it is generally true that very large cobbles or boulders reduce the porosity (Fig. 14-4). The arrangement of the particles is also an important factor in establishing porosity. Flat plates of mica in haphazard arrangement may have high porosity, while the same material oriented in parallel planes will have very low porosity. Spheres arranged in a regular rectangular pattern will have a porosity of 47 per cent, but if the spheres are shifted to a rhombic pattern, the porosity is immediately reduced to 26 per cent (Fig. 14-5).

The subsequent cementation of sedimentary rocks and the openings created by solution channels or fractures contribute materially in determining the porosity of such rocks. Porosity varies widely, ranging from as low as 1 per cent in some internal rocks to as high as 80 per cent in fresh delta deposits. Porosities higher than 40 per cent are quite rare in undisturbed natural deposits. Table 14-1 lists average porosities for various types of rock and uncemented deposits.

TABLE 14-1. Average Porosity of Various Materials *

Material	Porosity, per cent
Granite	1.2
Sandstone	15.9
Quartzite	0.8
Shale	4.0
Limestone	4.8
Uniform sand	35.0
Clay	45.0

* Fuller, M. L., Underground Water Papers, *U.S. Geol. Survey Water Supply Paper* 160, 1906.

The total water content of an aquifer may be computed by multiplying its volume by its porosity. However, some of this water is not available for springs and wells but is permanently retained in the aquifer by molecular forces. The quantity of such dead storage depends largely on the dimensions of the interstices. The volume of water free to drain from the rocks,

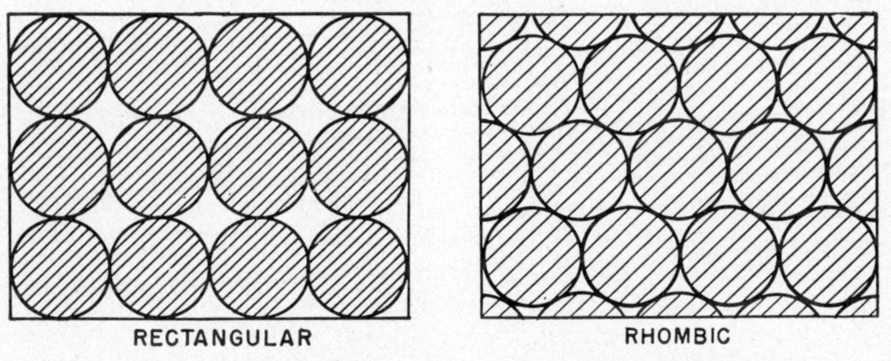

FIG. 14–5. Effect of arrangement of particles on porosity.

expressed as a percentage of the total volume of the aquifer, is called the *specific yield*. Conversely, that volume which is not available is called the *specific retention*. The specific retention is approximately equal to the moisture equivalent of soils (Chap. 12). In coarse sands the specific retention is not large but in fine sands may equal the specific yield, and in clays and silts the specific yield may be nearly zero.

The *permeability* of an aquifer is its ability to transmit water. Permeability is closely related to yield since those fine-grained deposits which have small interstices do not release water readily and hence do not transmit large volumes of water. Large, interconnected interstices result in high permeability.

The best aquifers are unconsolidated material—*alluvium*, stream deposits; *till*, glacial deposits; and *loess*, wind deposits. Of the sedimentary rocks, sandstone is perhaps the most consistently good aquifer if not too densely cemented, while limestone is a prolific producer in areas where considerable solution has taken place. Of the volcanic rocks, basalt is usually an excellent aquifer, while rhyolite is usually of low permeability. Least productive aquifers are the clay and silt deposits, which, while having a high porosity, have a low yield and permeability.

The groundwater provinces of the United States. Four broad groundwater regions can be outlined within the United States (Fig. 14-6). Within these regions several subdivisions or provinces can be delineated. *Water Supply Paper* 836-*D*,[1] from which Fig. 14-6 is taken, describes the provinces in summary as follows:

East-Central Region of Paleozoic and other old rocks. Province C is underlain by igneous and metamorphic rocks (chiefly pre-Cambrian) and Triassic sandstone. These rocks yield many small supplies of good water. Province D is mountainous and is underlain by folded and faulted Paleozoic strata, pre-Cambrian metamorphic rocks, and associated igneous rocks. These rocks supply water of good quality to numerous springs, spring-fed streams, and shallow wells. In province B the bedrocks (chiefly metamorphic) are overlain by glacial drift. The bedrock and boulder clay yield many small supplies of good water, and glacial sand and gravel yield large supplies in some places.

Provinces E, F, and G are underlain by Paleozoic rocks. The sandstones and limestones yield good water to shallow wells, but deep wells strike mineralized water, much of which is unfit for use. The shales yield meager supplies. The glacial drift in province F yields many supplies, both large and small. The outwash sand and gravel in valleys in province G and the northern part of province E yield large supplies.

In province H glacial drift yields many water supplies, but where the drift is thin only meager supplies are obtained from the underlying granite or other pre-Cambrian rocks. The water ranges in quality from soft and good in the eastern part of the province to highly mineralized and even unfit for use in the western part.

Atlantic and Gulf Coastal Plain Region. In province A Cretaceous, Tertiary, and younger strata of sand and limestone yield many small and many large water supplies. Much of the water is of good quality, but some is salty.

Great Plains Region. Provinces I, J, K, N, O, and Q′ are in general underlain by Cretaceous formations—chiefly unproductive shale with interbedded or underlying sandstone that yields highly mineralized artesian water. Flowing wells are especially abundant in province I. In large areas in province Q′ and in most of province J, except in the Black Hills, thick Cretaceous shales occur at the surface and are barren of water or yield only meager supplies of poor water. In province O and the eastern part of province N the Cretaceous strata are overlain by strata of early Tertiary and perhaps in part late Cretaceous age, which include sand, gravel, and coal that in most places yield small to moderate supplies. In provinces I and N the glacial drift generally yields supplies of hard but otherwise fairly good water.

[1] Meinzer, O. E., Ground Water in the United States, *U.S. Geol. Survey Water Supply Paper* 836-*D*, 1939.

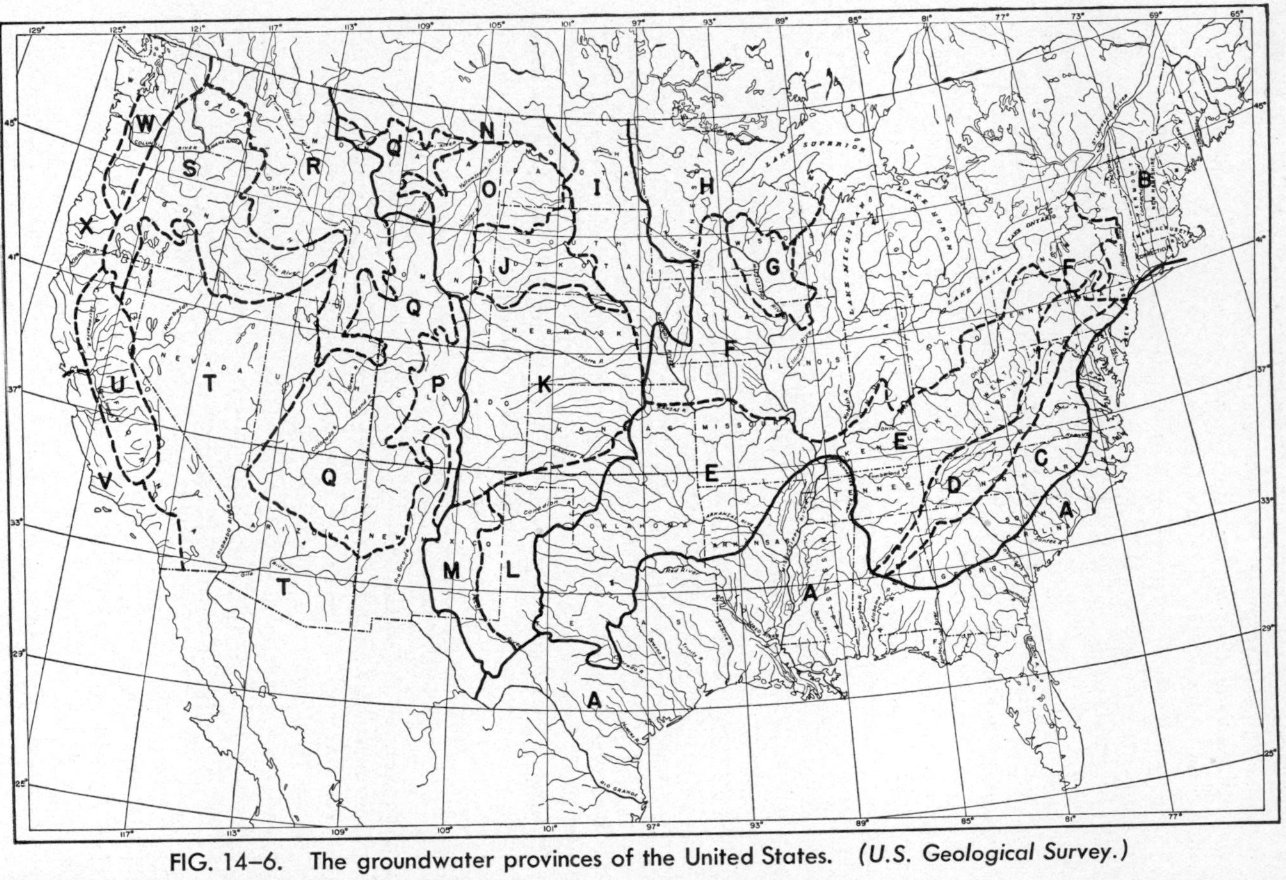

FIG. 14–6. The groundwater provinces of the United States. *(U.S. Geological Survey.)*

In provinces K and L Tertiary and Quarternary sand and gravel yield abundant supplies of somewhat hard but otherwise good water in most places. The underlying Cretaceous formations in province K and the underlying Permian or Triassic "Red Beds" in province L furnish water supplies in some places but generally are not of much value, and where they occur at or near the surface, water may be scarce.

In the Roswell artesian basin, in province M, Permian limestone yields large supplies of hard but usable water. Elsewhere the Carboniferous rocks underlying this province generally yield only meager supplies of poor quality, but in certain areas alluvial sand and gravel furnish abundant supplies.

Western Mountain Region. In the Rocky Mountains (provinces P and R) and the Sierra Nevada (part of province U), water supplies are furnished by springs, streams, and shallow wells. In province Q more or less flat-lying Paleozoic, Mesozoic, and younger strata form dissected plateaus with generally meager water supplies. In province S extensive lava beds and associated gravel give rise to very large springs and in some places yield large supplies of good water to wells. In provinces T, U, V, W, and X, sand and gravel in the broad valleys between mountain ranges yield numerous supplies of generally good water, at many places in large quantities. In parts of these provinces water supplies are obtained also from lava beds, glacial outwash, and other formations.

It should be emphasized that any outline of provinces must necessarily be generalized. Special local variations within the provinces must be expected, both in geological structure and in groundwater resources. Ample water may be obtained in some areas within a province generally unsatisfactory for groundwater supply, and dry wells may be driven in areas which have, on the whole, fully adequate subsurface water.

MOVEMENT OF GROUNDWATER

With the exception of the flow in cavernous limestone or in large fractures in other rocks, the flow of groundwater is usually in the laminar state. Velocities are low as the water follows an irregular path through the interstices of the rocks. Its movement may be under the effect of gravity following the slopes of the water table or under pressure along a path controlled by the undulations of the confining strata.

The equation of flow. The flow of water in capillary tubes was first studied by Hagen and Poiseuille. Darcy later verified their results and demonstrated them to be applicable to movement of water in filter sands. Their findings showed that the rate of flow is directly proportional to the hydraulic gradient, *i.e.*,

$$v = \frac{kh}{l} \tag{14-1}$$

where h is the difference in head over the distance l and k is a constant depending on the physical features of the aquifer. After the publication of

Darcy's formula, much debate developed concerning its validity and applicability to the problem of flow in permeable media. Subsequent experiments have definitely confirmed Eq. (14-1). It is significant to note that this formula is analogous to the laws of conductivity of heat and electricity.

The measurement of groundwater velocities is obviously not a simple matter. One method involves the measurement of time of travel of dyes or salts between two wells. Although effective in measurements of rather definite underground streams, such techniques[1] are less satisfactory for measuring the three-dimensional flow of the usual aquifer. In laboratory tests of more than 2000 rock samples under hydraulic gradients of 100 per cent, the observed range of velocities was from a minimum of 1 foot in 10 years to a maximum of 60 ft per day.[2] Field tests have reported velocities as high as 420 ft per day, but in most of the aquifers subject to economic development the velocity range is probably between 5 ft per day and 5 ft per year.

Permeability determinations. The rate of discharge q of an aquifer may be expressed by a variation of Darcy's law [Eq. (14-1)],

$$q = \frac{K_p a_c h}{l} \tag{14-2}$$

where K_p, the *coefficient of permeability,* is the rate of discharge per unit cross section per unit gradient and a_c is the cross-sectional area. The coefficient K_p has been expressed in a variety of units, but the standard definition of the U.S. Geological Survey is the rate of flow of water at 60°F in gallons per day through a cross section of 1 ft^2 under a hydraulic gradient of 1 ft/ft. This definition is convenient for laboratory purposes, but for field use the *field coefficient of permeability* is defined as the flow in gallons per day per foot of thickness for an aquifer 1 mile wide under a gradient of 1 ft/mile. The *coefficient of transmissibility* is equal to the field coefficient multiplied by the thickness of the aquifer in feet. Laboratory tests have revealed coefficients of permeability ranging from 0.0002 to 90,000, but for most natural aquifers they range between 10 and 5000.

Laboratory determinations of permeability are made with instruments called *permeameters.* Many different types of permeameters have been used, but the essential features are about the same. Most models consist of a U tube filled with the sample, through which water can percolate down one leg and up the other. The various types differ in whether or not a constant head is maintained on the supply reservoir and whether the seepage is discharged or held in a receiving reservoir.

[1] Schlichter, C. S., Field Measurements of the Rate of Movement of Underground Water, *U.S. Geol. Survey Water Supply Paper* 140, 1905.

[2] Stearns, N. W., Laboratory Tests on Physical Properties of Water Bearing Materials, *U.S. Geol. Survey Water Supply Paper* 596, 1927.

Field determination of permeability may be accomplished by velocity measurements, using salts or dyes. Two different velocities should be recognized. The average velocity of flow v (in feet per day), assuming all groundwater in the aquifer to be moving, is

$$v = \frac{K_p h}{7.48 V_p l} \tag{14-3}$$

where V_p is the porosity and $K_p/7.48$ is the permeability in cubic feet per day. The velocity so computed will not agree with the *effective velocity*, v', as measured by experimental techniques. Using Y_s as the specific yield,

$$v' = \frac{K_p h}{7.48 Y_s l} \tag{14-4}$$

When salt or dye velocities are measured in the field, Eq. (14-4) should be used to compute K_p.

Field measurement of permeability is also accomplished by means of pumping tests. Formulas relating permeability to the rate of discharge from a well, drawdown of the water table, and dimensions of the aquifer are discussed later in this chapter.

Head and storage. The principles of flow in permeable media as outlined in the previous sections are relatively simple and straightforward. Their application to practical problems is made difficult by the irregular variations in groundwater conditions which occur in nature. Two types of aquifers can be noted, those in which little if any flow takes place and those with pronounced circulation. The first type may be likened to reservoirs and the second to conduits. Deep aquifers with salty water are generally evidence of the first type, except where local salt deposits may provide the dissolved minerals. Aquifers near the surface, subject to recharge from rain and snow and discharging freely, are of the second type. Even in water-bearing formations where a strong circulation exists, storage plays an important role in groundwater hydraulics. Recharge is rarely uniform over a large area. It is controlled by the availability of water and by intake conditions. Little groundwater recharge can be expected in an area where impervious rock is at the surface. On the other hand, the most permeable intake area will be ineffective without precipitation or streamflow to provide the necessary water. Hence, a three-dimensional system of gradients is developed with groundwater mounds forming under areas of favorable recharge conditions and with water moving outward from these mounds. Shifting of the conditions may change the direction of flow from time to time. These adjustments cannot take place instantaneously, for, like flow in surface channels, a movement of water must take place from regions of high head to regions of low head. Since the movement is dependent on head, the rate must decrease as the adjustment proceeds and the difference in head decreases.

These facts have been generally accepted when a free-water table exists, but only recently has it been recognized that artesian systems are subject to the same sort of effects. It was thought that flow in artesian aquifers was analogous to flow in pipes, *i.e.*, that changes in head were transmitted almost instantaneously and that the only water which need be transferred to transmit the effect of an increase in pressure was that required to satisfy the small volume elasticity of the water. Meinzer[1] in studying the Dakota artesian system noted evidence of a storage effect resulting from compression of the aquifer. He found evidence that much of the water which had been discharged by flowing wells had come from storage released by compression of the aquifer as the head was lowered. This phenomenon is supported by evidence from several sources. In the Dakota aquifer, despite pumpage in excess of recharge, the drop in head had not affected the intake area, indicating that the excess volume was being taken from storage in the vicinity of the wells. The opening or closing of a valve in a rigid conduit under pressure causes almost immediate adjustments of the pressure gradient. In an artesian field such adjustments take place slowly, indicating that storage is playing a role in the adjustment.

Actual subsidence of the ground surface has been observed in many areas. Depressions of as much as 4 ft were measured in the vicinity of San Jose, California, between 1920 and 1933, with a drop in water levels of about 45 ft during the same period. The data leave little doubt that this subsidence results from a compaction of the aquifer underlying the valley, but data are not yet sufficient to establish definitely whether or not the aquifer is elastic and will return to its original dimensions if adequate water is available. Although the San Jose field is not artesian, the pronounced subsidence observed leaves little doubt that compaction of an artesian aquifer is possible.

Under water-table conditions, the water level in a well corresponds to the elevation of the water table if the well is not being pumped. The slope of the water table, or *phreatic surface*, is directly proportional to the velocity of flow and inversely proportional to the permeability. Ridges or mounds in the water table occur in areas of recharge, but the energy gradient is essentially at the water table since velocity heads are generally negligible. The upper surface of an artesian aquifer, as defined by the confining stratum, is not considered to be a water table. However, a water table usually exists in permeable material above the confining bed. Wells bored into the artesian aquifer will contain water to some height above the upper level of the aquifer. If the wells are uncapped, water may rise far above the surface of the ground. When first drilled, wells in the Dakota artesian basin shot columns of water over 200 ft into the air. One

[1] Meinzer, O. E., Compressibility and Elasticity of Artesian Aquifers, *Econ. Geol.*, Vol. 23, No. 13, pp. 263-291, 1928.

well at Woonsocket, South Dakota, had a static pressure of 130 lb/in.[2] and was used to drive a Pelton wheel. Such high-pressure flows can be expected only in large, sheetlike aquifers, such as the Dakota sandstones, where the intake area is considerably above the discharge point. In the alluvial cones and valley fills of the Southwestern states, high-pressure flows do not have opportunity to develop, but because of the relatively high permeability of the alluvial material as compared with sandstone the volume of flow is much greater. Depending on the general topography of a region, it is quite possible to tap a confined aquifer in which the water will not rise above the ground surface. As long as the water rises above the general water table in the area, the well may be considered artesian.

The pressure head, or height to which artesian jets will rise, marks a piezometric surface, or *static level*, which is the artesian counterpart of the water table in unconfined groundwater. Velocity head may be neglected because of the low velocities to be found in the usual aquifer. If there is no flow, the pressure gradient is horizontal at the level of the water in the intake area. This is the theoretical static level, which is rarely if ever attained in a natural artesian basin because of leakage from the aquifer. With leakage, a gradient develops, the slope depending on the relative amount of leakage and reaching a maximum if the aquifer actually discharges. Variations in permeability result in variations in the pressure gradient. In regions of low permeability, the energy loss is greatest and the gradients proportionally steeper. It is reasonable to assume that the increased velocity in constricted sections of aquifers results also in an accelerated energy loss and a corresponding steepening of gradients, but no detailed studies of this phenomenon have been reported.

If the head on the intake of the aquifer is low, the pressure gradient may be lowered until at some point along the conduit it falls below the upper surface of the aquifer (Fig. 14-7). In the region AB artesian conditions exist, while between B and C water-table conditions exist. This condition probably occurs only where withdrawal from a well at a rate in excess of replenishment reduces the amount of stored water sufficiently to drain the upper levels of the aquifer near the well. Overpumping may reduce the levels at the intake area sufficiently to convert the whole aquifer to water-table conditions.

In areas of considerable leakage from confined aquifers, the water table is found near the surface, and little or no pressure head will be found in a shallow well. If the depth of the well is increased until it enters the aquifer, an increase in pressure head is noted (Fig. 14-8). This has led to the fallacious generalization that pressure head increases with depth. Actually, this condition is subject to the same analysis outlined in earlier paragraphs. The shallow well measures conditions in what is virtually unconfined water with all pressure head expended in percolating upward, whereas the deep well is tapping an artesian aquifer under pressure.

Hydraulics of wells. If a line of wells is driven as shown in Fig. 14-9 and the central one is pumped, a drawdown of the water level in the other

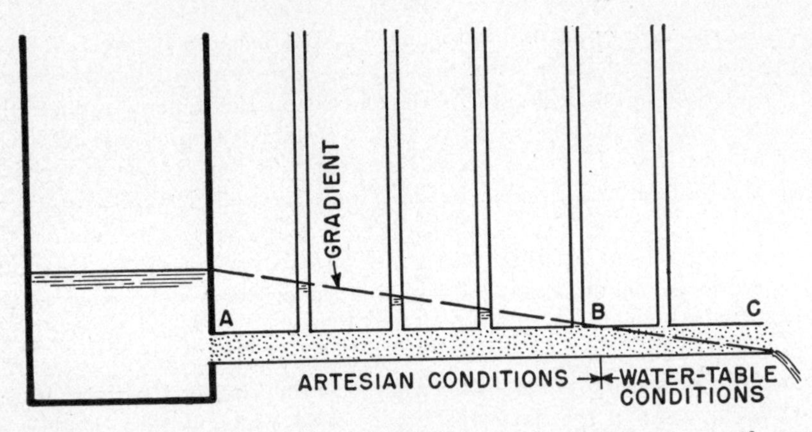

FIG. 14-7. Change from artesian to water-table conditions in an aquifer under low heads.

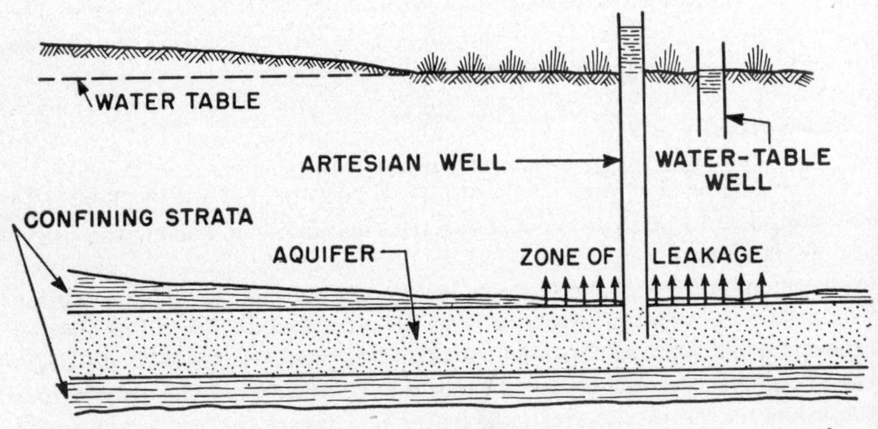

FIG. 14-8. Pressure conditions in zone of leakage over an artesian aquifer.

wells will be noted. In homogeneous material with a level water table this *cone of depression* will be symmetrical around the pumped well. The depression represents the withdrawal of water from storage around the well and a consequent steepening of the hydraulic gradient to accelerate the replacement of this withdrawn water. A similar cone of pressure relief is observed around a discharging artesian well.

Considering Fig. 14-9, the cross-sectional area through which water is flowing to the well is $2\pi xy$, and the slope of the water table at any point x distance from the well is dy/dx. From Eq. (14-2),

$$q = 2\pi K_p xy \frac{dy}{dx} \tag{14-5}$$

Integrating with respect to x from r to r_d and y from h_1 to h_2,

$$q = \frac{\pi K_p(h_1^2 - h_2^2)}{\log_e r_d - \log_e r} \tag{14-6}$$

Equation (14-6) is the Dupuit formula for water-table conditions. By a similar analysis it can be shown that under artesian conditions the formula becomes

$$q = \frac{2\pi \,\Delta Z\, K_p(h_1 - h_2)}{\log_e r_d - \log_e r} \tag{14-7}$$

where ΔZ is the thickness of the artesian stratum and h is the elevation of the pressure surface.

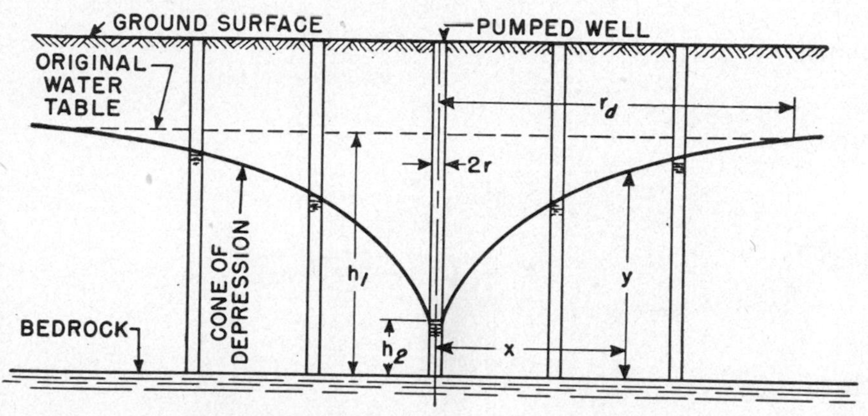

FIG. 14-9. Drawdown of water table in the vicinity of a pumped well.

The Dupuit formula has probably never been used for practical problems because of the vast difference between assumed and actual field conditions. The initial water table is rarely horizontal except in trapped formations where no flow can take place. Actual conditions are more frequently like those shown in Fig. 14-10. The contours of the initial water table define a fairly uniform slope, but when pumping begins, a depression is formed, creating a groundwater divide downslope from the well and causing a diversion of the flow, as shown by the arrows. Other conditions within the aquifer are rarely uniform, with variations in permeability and thickness in all directions. Finally, equilibrium conditions can be attained only by uniform pumpage over a long period of time.

Thiem[1] modified the Dupuit formula to determine K_p on the basis of the

[1] Thiem, G., "Hydrologische Methoden," J. M. Gebhardt's Verlag, Leipzig, 1906.

drawdowns D_{d1} and D_{d2} in two wells, at distances l_1 and l_2 from the pumped well, to the form

$$K_p = \frac{q(\log_e l_2 - \log_e l_1)}{2\pi \Delta Z(D_{d1} - D_{d2})} \tag{14-8}$$

where ΔZ for artesian conditions is the thickness of the aquifer and for water-table conditions is the average thickness of the saturated stratum at l_1 and l_2.

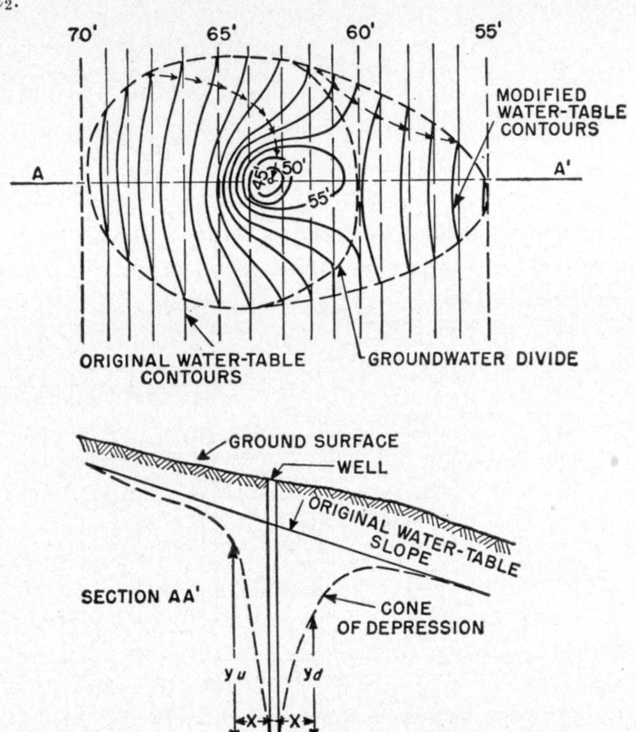

FIG. 14–10. Effect of drawdown on sloping water table.

Since the water table normally has a slope which distorts the cone of depression, the true gradient causing flow toward the well can be measured only along a line normal to the contours existing when the well is not pumping (section AA', Fig. 14-10). Data collected in pumping tests at Grand Island, Nebraska, show that the hydraulic gradient causing flow is approximately equal to the average of the gradients upslope and downslope from the well. The gradient formula[1] developed on this basis is

$$K_p = \frac{2q}{\pi x(y_u + y_d)(s_u + s_d)} \tag{14-9}$$

[1] Meinzer, O. E., and L. K. Wenzel, "Ground Water," Chap. X, Hydrology, O. E. Meinzer (ed.), pp. 469-470, McGraw-Hill, New York, 1942.

where y_u and y_d are the saturated thicknesses of water-bearing material at a distance x upstream and downstream from the well and s_u and s_d are the slopes of the gradient at these two points. For artesian conditions, the term $y_u + y_d$ should be replaced by $2\Delta Z$.

In areas where withdrawal by pumping is almost continuous, it is difficult to ascertain the location of the static water level. Under these conditions the formulas can be applied in modified form if the well or wells can be pumped at a uniform rate for a considerable time and then changed to another rate for a like period. The difference in drawdown and the change in discharge during the two periods are used in the formulas.

The cone of depression around pumped wells may be extensive. In the Grand Island tests a measurable drawdown was observed 1050 ft from the pumped well after 48 hr of pumping, but for practical purposes equilibrium conditions had been reached only within a radius of about 200 ft from the well. Fluctuations in levels as far as 7 miles from a well being pumped have been reported. Time is a very real factor in the interpretation of any pumping tests. Formulas of the equilibrium type depend on the use of r_d, the distance at which the effect of pumping is negligible. Many writers have suggested limiting values of r_d ranging from 500 to 1000 ft. Such values must be interpreted, not as indicating the limiting distance at which the effect of pumping may be noted, but rather as empirical approaches to a practical application of the formulas. A moderate variation in the value of r_d does not make a great difference in the determination of q or K_p.

Equation (14-6) shows that q is inversely proportional to $\log_e(r_d/r)$. Assuming r_d to be 1000 ft, a variation of well radius r from 3 to 6 in. will increase the discharge about 11 per cent, and an increase from 6 to 18 in. will add another 13 per cent. Doubling the well diameter will, however, double the intake area and reduce the intake velocity by one-half. This reduction in intake velocity reduces both friction loss and the amount of material transported into the well casing. Reduced friction loss decreases the drawdown and, hence, the power requirements of the pump.

LOCATION AND DEVELOPMENT OF GROUNDWATER SUPPLIES

The development of groundwater supply can be an expensive operation, particularly if the water is at considerable depth. To get maximum benefit from the outlay, it is important that the site be carefully selected and that the wells be properly developed.

Test holes. Perhaps the most direct method of prospecting for water is the driving of small-diameter test holes in the area of interest. The area tested should be selected on the basis of geological reconnaissance. The test holes serve to refine the geologic interpretation by providing data on specific conditions beneath the ground. Test wells are particularly efficient where drilling conditions are favorable and depths to water not likely to be large. The data obtained are more accurate and do not require so much interpretation as do data obtained from geophysical surveys. A test well which is successful in locating water can often be enlarged into a producing well without excessive additional cost.

Small-diameter soil piezometers[1] may provide a useful tool for certain groundwater exploration problems. While such piezometers may vary in design, they are usually of ¼- or ⅜-in. pipe and are driven into the ground by a pneumatic hammer or a weighted driver. A rivet placed under the lower end of the pipe will prevent the entry of dirt during the driving and may be punched out with a small-diameter rod after the pipe is at the desired depth. The depth of water in the piezometer can be measured by use of a weighted insulated wire connected through a small battery and milliammeter to indicate when the weight is at the water surface. Such piezometers may be used to determine water-table gradients or drawdown and to locate artesian aquifers at depths as great as 30 ft.

Geophysical exploration. Broadly speaking, any method of exploring the earth's crust may be classified as geophysical exploration. In the more limited sense in which the term is ordinarily used, geophysical exploration depends on the determination of gravimetric, magnetic, seismic, or electrical-conductivity anomalies. The first two of these methods rely on measurements of local variations of gravity or of the earth's magnetic field by such instruments as the torsion balance and the magnetometer. In the hands of an experienced geophysicist, the resulting map of local anomalies may be interpreted to provide a description of the stratigraphic features of the area. Faults, fissures, troughs, and other geologic features favoring the presence of water may be located, but the methods do not indicate definitely the presence of groundwater. Test holes or other exploration techniques must be resorted to for confirmation of the presence of water and for data as to its quality and quantity. Gravimetric and magnetic determinations of the geologic structure are widely used in petroleum surveying. Recent magnetometer surveys from airplanes have proved the value of this instrument for high-speed reconnaissance work.

For groundwater prospecting the seismic and electrical methods are more satisfactory. The velocity of an elastic wave is greater in moist deposits than in dry ones. Hence, under favorable conditions, seismic surveys may be interpreted directly as to the presence or absence of groundwater; but, except as used in conjunction with data from nearby well fields, such surveys give no indication of the quality or quantity of water which can be obtained from the aquifer. Geophones have been used to pick up the sound

[1] Donnan, W. W., and J. E. Christiansen, Ground Water Determinations, *Western Construction News*, Vol. 19, pp. 77-79, November, 1944.

of water escaping from leaky pipes and can be applied to the location of underground channels of freely flowing water. In the usual seismic survey, however, the travel of shock waves created by the detonation of small explosive charges is timed by a battery of 6 to 12 sensitive detectors dispersed through the area being surveyed. Since the velocity of such shock waves is dependent on the density of the materials through which they pass, the travel-time data may be analyzed to provide an estimate of the geologic structure in the survey area.

Electrical-resistivity methods have been most frequently used in prospecting for water. In principle, two electrodes are inserted in the ground,

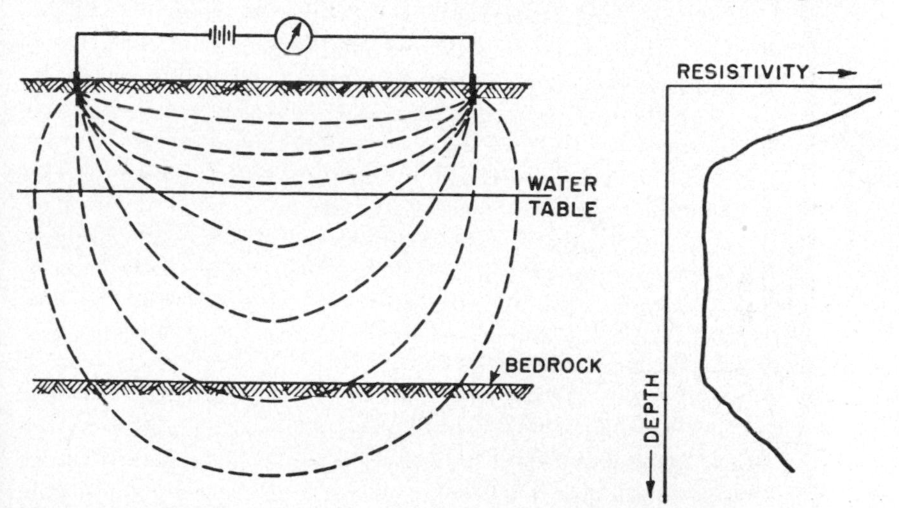

FIG. 14–11. Schematic diagram of the electrical-resistivity method of groundwater prospecting.

and the resistance between them is measured. The depth of penetration of the current is approximately equal to the electrode spacing (Fig. 14-11). Hence, by placing the electrodes at successively greater distances, measurements of total resistance through comparable depths are obtained. The resistivity of soil materials[1] is largely dependent on the amount of water they contain, and the resistances show variations with depth, wherever a water-bearing formation is present. Porous unconsolidated materials with

[1] Wenner, F., A Method of Measuring Resistivity, *U.S. Bur. Standards Bull.*, Vol. 12, 1916.

Jakosky, J. J., and C. H. Wilson, "Electrical Conductivity of American Ores and Minerals," University of Utah, Salt Lake City, 1928.

Edge, A. B., and T. H. Laby, "Principles and Practices of Geophysical Prospecting," Cambridge University Press, London, 1931.

Jakosky, J. J., and C. H. Wilson, Geophysical Studies in Placer and Water Supply Problems, *AIME Tech. Pub.* 515, 1933.

high water content show much lower resistance than do solid rocks with low water content.

Numerous variations of the electrical method have been employed, each designed to refine the determination of depth to the critical horizons. Much depends on the experience of the person directing the survey and interpreting the resistivity curves. Entirely false conclusions may be drawn by inexperienced analysts. The general success attained with geophysical methods has been such that they now have a very definite place in groundwater prospecting. Their use is probably not economical unless a relatively large well field is contemplated. Electrical methods are generally cheaper and more satisfactory, although seismic methods, in the proper hands, will give very reliable results at costs not greatly exceeding those of the electrical methods.

FIG. 14–12. Well point with continuous V slot for a driven well. *(E. E. Johnson, Inc.)*

Development of a groundwater supply. The most successful type of well in a given area is determined largely by the distribution of water and the geologic structure. Although the various types of wells vary considerably in initial cost, the best type for a particular case may not necessarily be the one with the lowest first cost.

Dug wells. The simplest and cheapest well is usually the dug well, which consists simply of a pit entering the aquifer. The water may be removed from the well by a pump or bucket and hoist. Dug wells are practicable only in unconsolidated material where water is reached at relatively small depths. They should be lined with rock, timber, or metal to prevent collapse, and for domestic use the upper portion of the lining should be impervious, to prevent entrance of contaminated surface waters. Unless caissons are used, dug wells cannot penetrate an aquifer for any great distance because of the difficulty of digging with water seeping into the pit. Hence, overdraft of the groundwater may result in lowering of the water table below the well bottom.

Bored wells. Wells may be bored in unconsolidated material by use of a large auger. Although bored wells have reached depths of 500 ft and diameters as large as 30 in., this method is more frequently used for shallow wells in diameters up to about 12 in. In clay soils the loosened material is brought to the surface by the auger, but loose sand must be removed with a bailer.

Driven wells. Shallow, small-diameter wells may be constructed economically by driving a well point and casing (Fig. 14-12) into the ground until an aquifer is reached. The well point is slightly larger in diameter than the tubing, and the combination is driven with a wooden maul or power ram. New sections of casing are coupled as the driving progresses. The perforated section of the casing must be screened if the shaft penetrates fine sand. Driven wells are usually under 100 ft in depth and 6 in. in

FIG. 14–13. Truck-mounted cable-tool rig for well drilling. *(Bucyrus-Erie Co.)*

diameter. Because such wells can be placed rapidly and easily pulled for redriving, they are useful in prospecting for water near the surface or for development of temporary supplies.

Cable-tool wells. The most common method of percussion well drilling in this country utilizes cable tools. A heavy bit is raised and lowered in the hole, crushing the material at the bottom. Sufficient water is introduced into the hole to permit the removal of the crushed material by a bailer or sand pump. The cable tools are usually suspended from an A frame at one end of a portable rig (Fig. 14-13), and the reciprocating motion of the drill is obtained by an eccentric crank or walking beam. A long tube, smaller in diameter than the hole and with a flap valve at the bottom, is used as a bailer. As the tube is lowered into the hole, the flap valve permits entry of sand or other broken material into the tube and prevents its escape as the tube is raised.

Hydraulic rotary wells. In the hydraulic rotary method, which originated in the oil fields, the hole is drilled by the rapid rotation of a bit on the end of a drill pipe. A mud fluid is circulated down through the drill pipe and up on the outside to bring the drilling debris to the surface. While portable rigs have been used, the most common procedure involves the erection of a drilling derrick. The hydraulic rotary process can be used to drill larger holes than the cable-tool method, but the latter is usually cheaper for shallow holes, is more portable, and requires less water in the operation.

SPRINGS

Natural discharge of groundwater occurs through effluent streams, springs, seeps, and transpiration by plants. A study by the U.S. Geological Survey[1] on the Pomperaug River in Connecticut indicated an average annual recharge of about one-third the annual precipitation of 45 in. About 60 per cent of this water is discharged as streamflow and about 40 per cent by evapo-transpiration. In the more arid regions of the country, the relative recharge is less and the discharge as streamflow much less. Thus, in the Tarkio Basin of Iowa, only about 2 per cent of the total precipitation is returned to the streams as groundwater runoff.

Most of the streams of the Eastern states receive groundwater as effluent seepage over virtually their entire course. In poorly drained basins much groundwater is lost by evaporation and transpiration from swamps. Groundwater runoff in streams and the phenomena of evaporation and transpiration are discussed in other chapters of this text. This section deals largely with discharge of groundwater through springs.

Gravity springs. Bryan[2] has divided springs into two broad classes, (1) those resulting from gravitational forces and (2) those flowing as the result of forces other than gravity. A *spring* is concentrated groundwater flow issuing at the surface as a current of flowing water. In contrast, *effluent seepage* is a diffuse percolation over a large area directly into a stream or lake or on an open slope, and *capillary seepage* is the discharge of water brought to the surface by capillary action from the water table. Both effluent and capillary seepage are evaporated quickly unless discharged into a water body.

When the water-bearing formation is thick and pervious, stratification is

[1] Meinzer, O. E., and N. D. Stearns, A Study of Groundwater in the Pomperaug Basin, Conn., *U.S. Geol. Survey Water Supply Paper* 597-*B*, 1929.

[2] Bryan, K., Classification of Springs, *J. Geol.*, Vol. 27, pp. 522-561, 1919.

unimportant and springs are formed wherever the water table cuts the surface. Such springs, variously called *depression springs* and *water-table springs*, are usually not large, for the hydraulic gradients upslope are ordinarily relatively flat, and the flow is controlled by the permeability of the material. Desert water holes are often depression springs formed where a surface depression extends below the water table.

Contact springs form where the boundary between a permeable water-bearing formation and a less permeable formation cuts the earth's surface. Such springs form at the toe of talus slopes and landslides as well as at the contact zone between pervious deposits on an impermeable basement elevated above the general valley level. Contact springs are generally small because the thickness of the pervious deposit and the area drained by the spring are usually small.

Where a permeable formation is between relatively impermeable strata, *artesian springs* may be expected. Since the water is under pressure, the velocity of discharge may be large, and since artesian aquifers often drain substantial areas, springs of this type may be particularly large. A fourth type of gravity spring is that formed in fractures and solution channels in impermeable rock. Such springs are called *tubular* and *fracture springs*. They are usually fed by subsurface streams, and many of the largest known springs are in this class.

Nongravity springs. Nongravity springs are caused by heat and subterranean gases. Thermal springs are probably the most numerous and most interesting of the springs in this class. Springs yielding water at temperatures above 70°F are usually classified as *thermal springs*, of which something over 1000 are known to exist in this country (Fig. 14-14). The most spectacular of the thermal springs are the *geysers*, which periodically discharge hot water. The classic explanation by Bunsen is that water from near the surface enters the geyser tube, where temperatures exceed the boiling point. The water at great depths is temporarily prevented from boiling by the pressure of water above it. Finally, the boiling point is reached at the bottom of the column, and steam is formed, which causes an overflow and a rapid reduction in pressure. Water in the lower portion of the column is then superheated with respect to the reduced pressure, and violent eruption follows.

Where gases such as hydrogen sulfide, carbon dioxide, or any of the hydrocarbons are present, they may collect in pockets in such a way as to build up a pressure forcing water to the surface. In solution with water, they may also decrease the average density of the mixture so as to allow it to rise above the surface under action of hydrostatic or gas pressure.

Exterior features of springs. Springs are only one of the aspects of groundwater as an agent acting to shape the landscape. Many springs appear to have carved large canyons by erosion or solution of the basic rock material. The erosional features of springs are of two types, (1) channels eroded by the runoff water and (2) pools formed around the point of discharge. Because the flow of springs does not vary through such ranges as the flow of streams, the depositional features are probably more outstanding than the erosional. Many springs are highly mineralized, and the mineral matter is frequently deposited around the point of discharge as the result of rapid cooling of water from thermal springs and chemical precipitation or

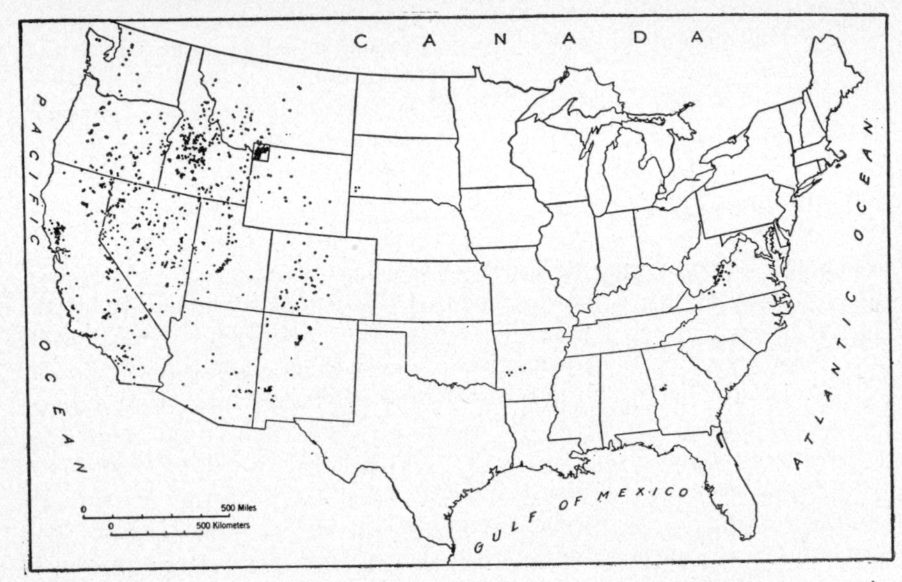

FIG. 14–14. Thermal springs in the United States. *(U.S. Geological Survey.)*

evaporation of water from nonthermal springs. In arid regions, a spring may support vegetation in its immediate vicinity, which will serve to trap windblown debris and hence result in the formation of a mound around the spring.

Size of springs. Meinzer[1] has proposed classification of springs into eight magnitudes based on their discharges (Table 14-2). According to a study by this writer,[2] there are 65 springs of the first magnitude in the United States. There are probably several hundred second-magnitude springs, and thousands of the third magnitude. Of the first-magnitude springs, 38 rise in volcanic rocks, 24 in limestone, and 3 in sandstone. The springs in volcanic rock are found in Idaho, Oregon, and California, while those in limestone are in the Ozarks, in the Balcones fault area in Texas, and

[1] Meinzer, O. E., Outline of Ground-water Hydrology, *U.S. Geol. Survey Water Supply Paper* 494, 1923.

[2] Meinzer, O. E., Large Springs in the United States, *U.S. Geol. Survey Water Supply Paper* 557, 1927.

in Florida and the adjacent area. The three sandstone springs are in Montana and are believed to be associated with faults. The largest known spring in the world is the Fontaine de Vaucluse in France, which has a discharge often exceeding 4000 cfs. This spring drains limestone terrane and is estimated to discharge 60 per cent of the precipitation in the area.

TABLE 14-2. Classification of Springs according to Discharge

Magnitude	Discharge
First	In excess of 100 cfs
Second	Between 10 and 100 cfs
Third	Between 1 and 10 cfs
Fourth	100 gpm (0.22 cfs) to 1 cfs
Fifth	Between 10 and 100 gpm
Sixth	Between 1 and 10 gpm
Seventh	Between 1 pt/min and 1 gpm
Eighth	Less han 1 pt/min

Variation in the flow of springs. Nearly all springs fluctuate considerably in discharge. In most cases, the fluctuations are in response to recharge. Thus, the discharge of springs in pervious material of low yield varies widely, with highest flows occurring during the rainy season. Such springs often also respond to variations in transpiration by showing a diurnal variation in flow. Many limestone springs are essentially outlets of underground streams. Consequently, their discharge may vary with recharge almost as rapidly as that of surface streams.

Springs issuing from thick pervious formations with a moderate or low permeability are relatively constant in flow because such material acts as a stabilizing reservoir. Similarly, the discharge of artesian springs is relatively stable, varying only slightly with recharge and probably also with barometric pressure. Springs which discharge throughout the year are classed as *perennial,* while those which discharge only during a portion of the year as the result of rainfall or high water table are said to be *temporary,* or *intermittent.*

Springs which fluctuate at intervals not directly related with rainfall are called *periodic springs.* Periodic flow may result from variations in transpiration or barometric pressure and, in aquifers near the seacoast, from the effect of tides on the head in elastic artesian systems. About 20 *ebbing and flowing springs* are known to exist in the United States. These springs resemble geysers in their periodic variations, but their temperatures are normal. The cause is generally ascribed to a natural siphon effect. The siphon presumably empties an underground storage basin, after which flow ceases until the basin is refilled by supply from an underground channel. During periods of very heavy precipitation, the flow may be constant. Springs of this type occur primarily in limestone formations where solution channels can develop into the necessary siphon.

SPECIAL GROUNDWATER CONDITIONS

Limestone terranes. Although they do not represent a major portion of the topography of this country, limestone terranes furnish an interesting study in groundwater hydrology because of their special and sometimes dramatic features. The classic limestone terrane is the *karst* region of the western Balkan plateau, and this name is commonly used to describe any characteristic limestone physiography. Karsts are regions where the basement rocks are almost exclusively calcareous. Their surface features are controlled by the weathering characteristics of these rocks. Typical features of karst topography are sinkholes, caverns, "lost" rivers, large springs, barren uplands, and thin soil.

The extensive beds of Mississippian limestone reaching from central Indiana through Kentucky into Tennessee constitute one of the largest karst areas in the United States. Extensive limestone deposits are found in the Florida Peninsula and the adjacent area. Limestone valleys occur throughout the Appalachian Mountains from Alabama to New England, the outstanding example being the Shenandoah Valley of Virginia. Many of the characteristics of the Roswell artesian basin in New Mexico are evidence of the effect of an ancient karst development in that area.

Limestones may have either primary or secondary porosity or both. The oolitic limestones of Florida, formed from cemented grains of precipitated calcium carbonate, are extremely porous and permeable. Wells in this area yield large flows with extremely small drawdowns, and artesian conditions exist throughout the region. Groundwater problems here are essentially those of any pervious area. In contrast, limestone of the Kentucky-Tennessee area is quite impervious except along fractures and solution channels. Large volumes of water exist in the great caverns, but the success of a well depends on its intersecting a water-bearing channel. In limestones where secondary porosity dominates, the water-table concept has little significance. Water in interconnected channels stands at essentially the same level, but a clear-cut surface defining the upper level of the zone of saturation exists only as a theoretical concept.

Limestone terranes of moderate and high relief are often marked by scrubby or weak vegetation and an almost complete lack of surface streams because the high permeability permits the rapid downward percolation of rainwater to subsurface storage. In the absence of headwater rivulets, which are characteristic of other geologic regions, the streams of limestone areas frequently rise from large springs. More than one-third of the first-magnitude springs of the country are in limestone areas. The reduced opportunity for evaporation and transpiration in areas of such high permeability results in relatively high percentages of the precipitation appearing as runoff; but, because of the retarding effect of the groundwater storage, the maximum flows are relatively smaller and the runoff is more uniformly distributed throughout the year than in less permeable regions.

The permeability of limestone areas is considerably enhanced by the frequent *sinkholes* encountered. More than 1000 sinkholes have been counted in 1 square mile of the limestone country in southern Indiana. Sinkholes vary in size and shape from small, nearly conical depressions, *dolines*, to large, elongated valleys, *uvalas*. Many factors contribute to their formation, but probably the most frequent causes are the solution of the limestone by surface waters percolating downward through a joint or fracture and the collapse of thin, surface layers over a cave. In many cases a combination of these two factors may be responsible. Larger sinks may result from the combination of two or more sinks as their margins are extended by continued erosion. The sinks may appear as open holes but more commonly are partly filled with soil, plant litter, and debris from the collapse of their own top and side walls. Frequently, the sinks contain water, which stands at or near the level of the water table.

Groundwater from limestone terranes may naturally be expected to be hard, *i.e.*, to contain a high percentage of dissolved minerals, chiefly carbonates. Despite its discharge as groundwater, the runoff from areas of high secondary porosity may be rather turbid because its travel through large underground channels does not provide the natural filter obtained through other materials. By the same token, groundwater from areas of high secondary porosity may show high bacterial contamination. Such groundwater shows a marked response to rainfall, indicating a rapid inflow to the groundwater reservoir. Groundwater springs with constant flow and wells in artesian aquifers are less likely to suffer from bacteria or turbidity.

Volcanic terranes. Large areas of the western United States have volcanic rocks at or near the surface (Fig. 14-15). These rocks are important factors in the groundwater (and surface-water) hydrology of the area. The significant feature of volcanic rocks as a source of groundwater is their variability, which is so great that it is difficult in some ways to generalize their characteristics. The principal controlling factors which determine the water-holding characteristics of volcanic rocks are (1) their chemical composition, (2) the mode of deposition, and (3) the initial landforms on which they were deposited.

The two extremes of chemical composition are *basalt* and *rhyolite*. Basalt rocks are rich in ferromagnesian minerals and low in silica content. Rhyolite is rich in silica and low in ferromagnesian minerals. Between these two extremes, there is a series of rocks, such as andesite and trachyte, of intermediate chemical composition. Rocks high in silica tend to be more viscous than basalt and, consequently, are more often erupted in fragments which form steep volcanoes, while the basaltic rocks are more fluid and form broad deposits such as the Modoc lava beds in California and the Snake River Plain of Idaho. Basaltic lavas often display a ropy or billowy surface known as *pahoehoe*. A jumbled surface of basaltic lava is known as *aa*, while the rhyolites sometimes form a rough, jumbled mass known as *block lava*.

The viscous rhyolite lavas, when cooled rapidly at the surface, develop into a hard, glassy form. The more fluid basaltic lavas develop a grainy

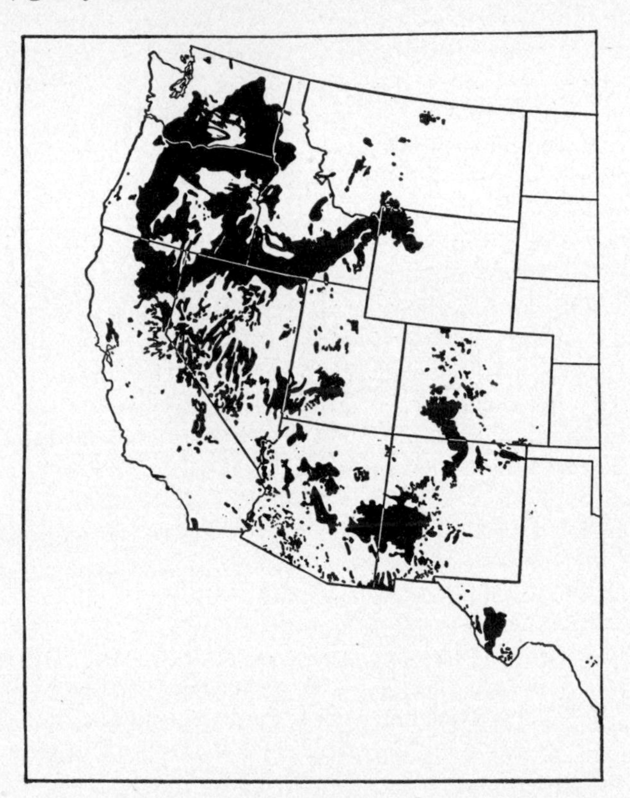

FIG. 14–15. Map of Western United States showing areas where Tertiary or Quaternary volcanic rocks are at or near the surface. No such rocks are exposed in the Eastern states. *(U.S. Geological Survey.)*

structure and also large numbers of shrinkage cracks, tubes, and other passageways. As a general rule, basaltic lavas are extremely permeable, while silica-rich lavas are relatively impermeable. There are notable exceptions to this rule, for example, the springs at Obsidian Cliff in Yellowstone Park, which issue from a glassy deposit sufficiently fractured to permit relatively large movement of water. Rocks of either type when blown from a volcano are known as *pyroclastic* rocks. These deposits are highly fragmented, and their permeability depends largely on their compaction and the extent to which interstices have been subsequently filled by ash or other material.

Highly permeable basaltic lava flows are often laid down in thick sheets over a wide area. These flows vary in thickness from a few feet over the higher points of the original land surface to more than a thousand feet in some of the original valleys. The flow may have occurred at one time or may be interstratified with sedimentary deposits formed during periods cf quiescence. Generally, the basalt is more permeable than the basement material, and groundwater tends to collect above the original land surface. The water table tends to be flat because of the high permeability, and as a

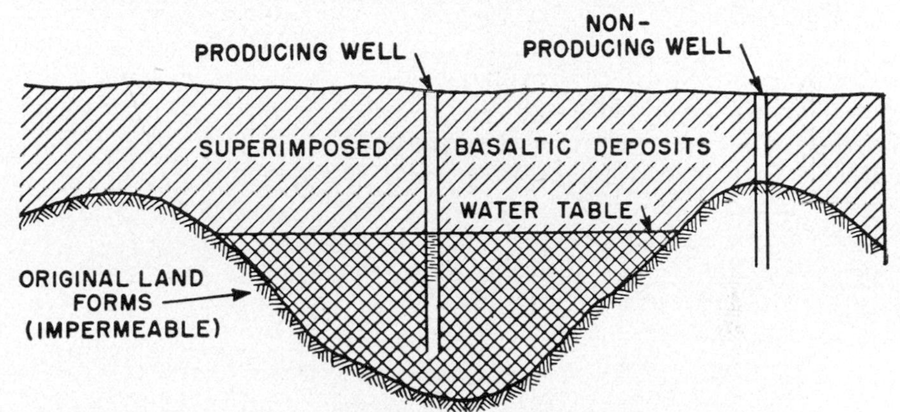

FIG. 14–16. Variations in availability of water under volcanic terrane.

result large volumes of water may be stored in the basalt of a buried river valley, with little or none occurring in the deposits covering original ridges. The present surface contours of the area may in no way resemble those of the original landforms. Drilling for wells has often been undertaken a short distance from a producing well in the belief that there would be ample water, only to strike a buried ridge of basement rock before water was reached (Fig. 14-16). Because of the tendency to a nearly flat water table, depth to water can be predicted with much assurance from the data of existing wells. Occasionally, however, when the lava is interstratified with other materials, steep gradients in the water tables called *groundwater cascades* are observed. Because of the high permeability of basaltic lavas, water tables are usually close to the basement rock, and hence depths to water usually great.

Artesian flows from lava beds are obtainable when the beds are interstratified with clay or other impermeable material and subsequently warped. The same result occurs if the beds were initially dipped so as to provide artesian head. Artesian developments in volcanic terrane are not extensive in the United States.

Fluctuations in the water table in volcanic terrane are usually slow because of the extremely high porosity ordinarily encountered. Tremendous volumes of water are required to effect a change in level of only a few feet. Because of the great depth of some of the volcanic deposits, they have an enormous capacity for storage. Ten thousand square miles of the Snake River Valley in southern Idaho have no surface runoff, and most of the mountain streams disappear as they reach the plain. A few streams have scoured channels across the lava plains by silting the crevices in the channel bottom so that leakage is reduced sufficiently to permit perennial flow. However, since Big Wood River was dammed in 1920, losses have increased by about 145 cfs in a 45-mile stretch because the silt is allowed to dry out when the flow is being diverted for irrigation and is subsequently eroded as water is again released to the channel.[1] Many streams flowing through lava are relatively uniform in flow. The Deschutes River of Oregon has a more uniform flow than any stream of its size in the United States. It receives much of its flow from springs.

The immense capacity of the basalt reservoir is sometimes ignored in planning irrigation projects. In the South Side Twin Falls tract in Idaho, groundwater levels rose as much as 37 ft/year during the first few years of irrigation, which began in 1905. In 1928, the average rate of rise for the previous 15 years was found to be about 4 ft/year. Outflow from this area is restricted, and a drainage problem may eventually arise. On the North Side tract across the Snake River, many deep canyons exist in the basement rock, and although 600,000 acre-ft of water is contributed annually to groundwater, the water table fluctuates only slightly.

Many lakes are found in volcanic terrane as a result of lava dams laid down in old stream valleys. Where these lakes have been silted, the principal escape for the water is by evaporation. Depressions in lava beds extending below the water table also permit escape of a considerable volume of water by evaporation.

The quality of groundwaters from volcanic areas is usually good. Soluble minerals are scarce, and the water is soft. Long storage in the large deposits usually ensures low bacterial contamination.

[1] Stearns, H. T., L. Crandall, and W. G. Steward, Geology and Groundwater Resources of the Snake River Plain in Southeastern Idaho, *U.S. Geol. Survey Water Supply Paper* 774, 1938.

15
HYDROGRAPH ANALYSIS

The hydrograph of outflow from a river basin is an irregular graph showing fluctuations of varying magnitude and shape (Fig. 9-21). Except where the outflow is regulated by a reservoir, each significant rise is the result of a period of rainfall or snowmelt. Previous chapters have discussed the factors which determine the volume of inflow to a stream. Before a relationship between these factors and runoff volume for a particular basin can be established, it is necessary to segregate the continuous hydrograph into those portions associated with particular storm periods. The hydrograph of discharge from a basin is a unique expression of many features of a river basin which are rarely replicated in the same combination in any other basin. Hence, the hydrographs from two basins are rarely alike, and the analysis of the hydrograph is, therefore, a study of the particular characteristics of a basin.

COMPONENTS OF THE HYDROGRAPH

Runoff from rain and/or melting snow reaches the stream channels by several routes. Logic and qualitative analysis of observed data indicate the existence of four hydrograph components, each of which reaches the stream by a different path. It is practically impossible to measure the volumes of water following each path or to identify the water once it reaches the channel.

Surface runoff. That water which reaches the streams by traveling over the soil surface is called *surface runoff*. It is important to emphasize in this connection that the term "stream" includes, not only the larger permanent streams, but also the tiny rills and rivulets which carry water only during and immediately after rains or periods of snowmelt. Surface runoff involves, therefore, not long distances of overland flow, but only the relatively short distances to the nearest minor channels.

Surface runoff is the residual after infiltration, interception, and surface storage have been extracted from precipitation. It can occur only when rainfall or snowmelt rates exceed the infiltration rate. Hence, many small and moderate stream rises may contain little or no surface runoff. Few basins are, however, completely without some impermeable area, and small amounts of surface runoff can be expected. Surface runoff is generally considered to be the most important component of flow in major floods. Its importance is accentuated by the fact that it is the first element of runoff to reach the streams. The bulk of the surface runoff is discharged into the streams during the period of rain, while other components of flow reach the streams much later and are spread over a longer period of time. Surface runoff may therefore be assumed to be the major contributor to flood peaks.

Interflow. A portion of the water which infiltrates the soil surface moves laterally through the upper soil horizons until its course is intercepted by a stream channel or until it returns to the surface at some point downslope from its point of infiltration. This component is known as *subsurface flow*, or *interflow*. Some interflow may be expected in all basins, but the relative portion of total runoff following this route depends materially on the soil structure. The presence of a relatively impermeable soil horizon just below the surface is the most favorable condition for interflow. Such a condition limits the rate of percolation to groundwater and forces a large portion of the infiltrate to move laterally above this horizon. Wet-weather seeps and springs are the result of interflow.

Like surface runoff, interflow is also a residual—infiltration less soil moisture recharge and deep percolation. An estimate of the amount of interflow can be made indirectly by comparing runoff from infiltrometer plots and natural basins. Values of the average infiltration rate f_{av} in excess of 1.00 in./hr are not uncommon in infiltrometer tests. Analysis of runoff from natural basins indicates values of the **W**-index (Chap. 16), which are commonly in the order of 0.20 in./hr or less. Since interflow is not included in the runoff from test plots but is included in the runoff from actual basins, the difference between these two values is an index to the magnitude of interflow. Hertzler[1] reports that the interflow from 10 experimental basins in the Coweeta Forest, North Carolina, averages 85 per cent of the total annual runoff. While this value is not representative of the country as a whole, large contributions from interflow may be expected in Middle Western basins where a plow bed exists at depths of 1 ft or less.

Groundwater flow. Whenever the soil in the zone of aeration contains sufficient moisture to permit the passage of gravity water downward, a portion of the rainfall reaches the groundwater table. The amount of water which takes this path is limited to that which can percolate through the least permeable soil horizon during the period that free water is available in the soil. Accretion to groundwater from light rains on relatively dry soil is obviously slight.

[1] Hertzler, R. A., Engineering Aspects of the Influence of Forests on Mountain Streams, *Civil Eng.*, Vol. 9, pp. 487-489, 1939.

Groundwater flow follows a more devious route to the stream than any of the other components. Its movement is restricted by the low percolation rates ordinarily experienced. As a result, the water volume represented by the groundwater accretion from a particular storm is discharged into the stream over a long period of time. The amount of lag depends on the geology of the river basin under consideration. However, the accretion from a specific storm is discharged over a period of months for the average basin, and there is evidence of groundwater carry-over for 2 years or more in some areas such as the volcanic terrane of the Klamath River Basin in Oregon and portions of the Snake River Basin in Idaho. Since groundwater flow is distributed over a long period of time, its changes are gradual and groundwater does not represent an important contribution to flood peaks.

Channel precipitation. A fourth source of streamflow is that precipitation which falls directly on the water surfaces of lakes and streams. Streamflow from this source may be computed by multiplying the average rainfall by the percentage of basin area covered by water surfaces connected with the stream system. This percentage varies from basin to basin and from time to time for a given basin, depending on the level of the streams. The percentage of water-surface area at low flows may be multiplied many times at high stages. It is probable that the percentage of water-surface area for most basins does not exceed 5 per cent at fairly high stages. Table 15-1 classifies the states on the basis of percentage of water area. These percentages represent low-water conditions.

TABLE 15-1. Percentage of Water-surface Area by States

Per Cent	States
Less than 0.5	Arizona, Colorado, Kansas, New Mexico, Wyoming
0.5 to 1.0	Georgia, Idaho, Indiana, Michigan, Montana, Nebraska, Nevada, North Dakota, Ohio, Oklahoma, Pennsylvania, South Dakota, Tennessee, West Virginia
1 to 2	Alabama, Arkansas, California, Illinois, Iowa, Kentucky, Mississippi, Missouri, Oregon, Rhode Island, South Carolina, Texas, Wisconsin
2 to 5	Connecticut, Massachusetts, Minnesota, New Hampshire, New York, Utah, Vermont, Washington
5 to 10	Florida, Louisiana, New Jersey, North Carolina, Virginia
10 to 20	Maine
Over 20	Maryland, Delaware

Channel precipitation is not ordinarily treated as a separate component of the hydrograph. It is the first water from a storm to reach a stream, but since it is a relatively small amount, it is usually included with surface runoff. Precipitation falling directly on the water surface of large reservoirs can account for significant inflow, and a detailed analysis of inflow hydrographs for reservoirs may well include consideration of this factor. A family of curves for computing reservoir inflow from direct rainfall is easily constructed from the known area-elevation curve (Fig. 15-1). Given the average rainfall over the reservoir and the water-surface elevation, the equivalent inflow rate may be read from the curves. These values should be subtracted from the total inflow to obtain a hydrograph of net inflow from streams tributary to the lake.

Although channel precipitation need not ordinarily be considered as a separate component of runoff, the hydrologist should be aware of its occurrence. Except when the channels are completely dry, channel precipita-

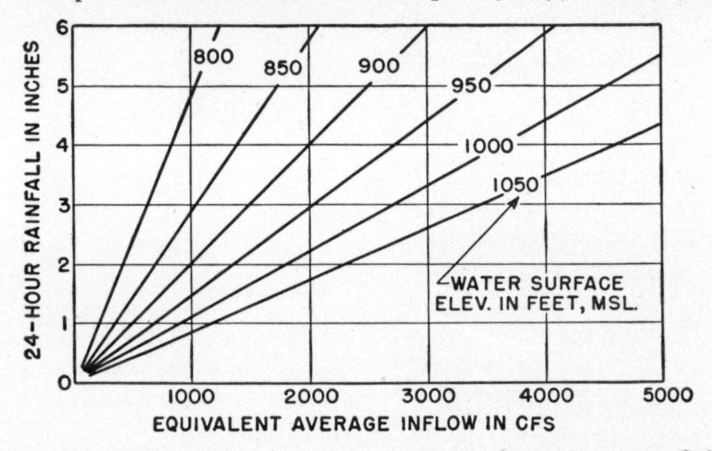

FIG. 15–1. Curves for converting rainfall to inflow to Shasta Reservoir, California.

tion from any rain, no matter how small, will affect streamflow. In determining such factors as "days to the last runoff-producing rain" for the development of rainfall-runoff relations, one cannot be sure that surface runoff or interflow occurred simply because the streamflow increased. Hence, in defining a "runoff-producing rain" it should be specified that the runoff must exceed some fixed percentage of the average rainfall, the percentage being the ratio of water surface to land area in the basin.

THE SHAPE OF THE HYDROGRAPH

An inspection of the hydrograph of a typical natural basin (Fig. 15-2) will show that it may be considered to consist of three parts, the *concentration curve*, or *rising limb*, the *crest segment*, and the *recession*, or *falling limb*. Each of these parts has certain inherent properties which, within limits, fix its shape.

The factors determining hydrograph shape. A consideration of a hypothetical basin and of the possible hydrographs it might produce (Fig. 15-3) is helpful in understanding the features of natural-basin hydrographs. It is assumed that the basin is impermeable and semicircular in shape and that the surface slopes are such that isochrones of equal travel time to the outlet enclose equal areas. The *time of concentration*, t_c, for the basin, *i.e.*, the time required for water to travel from the most remote portion of the basin to the outlet, is 4 hr. Let us assume a uniform rainfall of 1 in. in 1 hr on all zones of the basin [case (*a*)]. Runoff from zone A will begin with the rain and will increase uniformly until, at the end of the first hour, all of zone A is contributing at the rate of 1 in./hr. Since the rainfall ends at this time, runoff from the area immediately adjacent to the gage ceases and at the end of the second hour all flow from zone A has passed the outlet. We

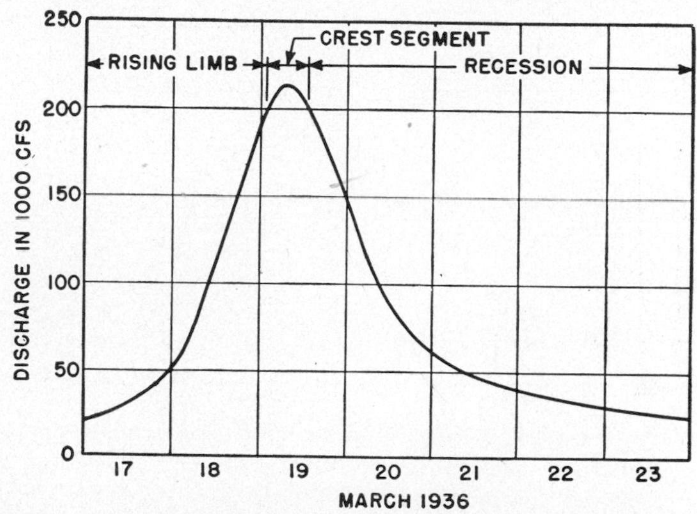

FIG. 15–2. Hydrograph for the Juniata River at Newport, Pennsylvania.

have, therefore, a triangular hydrograph with a base equal to the travel time through zone A plus the duration of rain, and a maximum ordinate equal to the rate of rainfall. Each of the four zones will produce identical hydrographs, each beginning 1 hr later than the one next downstream. The four combine to yield a trapezoidal hydrograph with a base equal to the time of concentration plus the duration of rain t_R, and with a maximum ordinate equal to the rainfall rate.

In case (*b*) the same volume of rainfall is assumed to occur over a 4-hr period. The resulting outflow graph can be constructed following the same reasoning applied in case (*a*), and again the time base of the hydrograph equals $t_c + t_R$. Since the rainfall is uniform with respect to time and area, the outflow hydrograph is symmetrical. The longer base results in a slower rate of rise and fall than in the first case. Case (*c*) is similar except that the duration is assumed to be ⅓ hr. Hence, only one-third of the area in any zone can contribute simultaneously, and the maximum ordinate is only one-third of the maximum rainfall rate. The shorter time base causes a more rapid rate of rise or fall than in either (*a*) or (*b*).

Uniform areal distribution of rainfall is rarely observed in nature. Cases (*d*) and (*e*) show the hydrographs which would result from the same volume of rainfall as assumed in the first three cases (1-in. average over the basin), but with this volume distributed unevenly between zones.

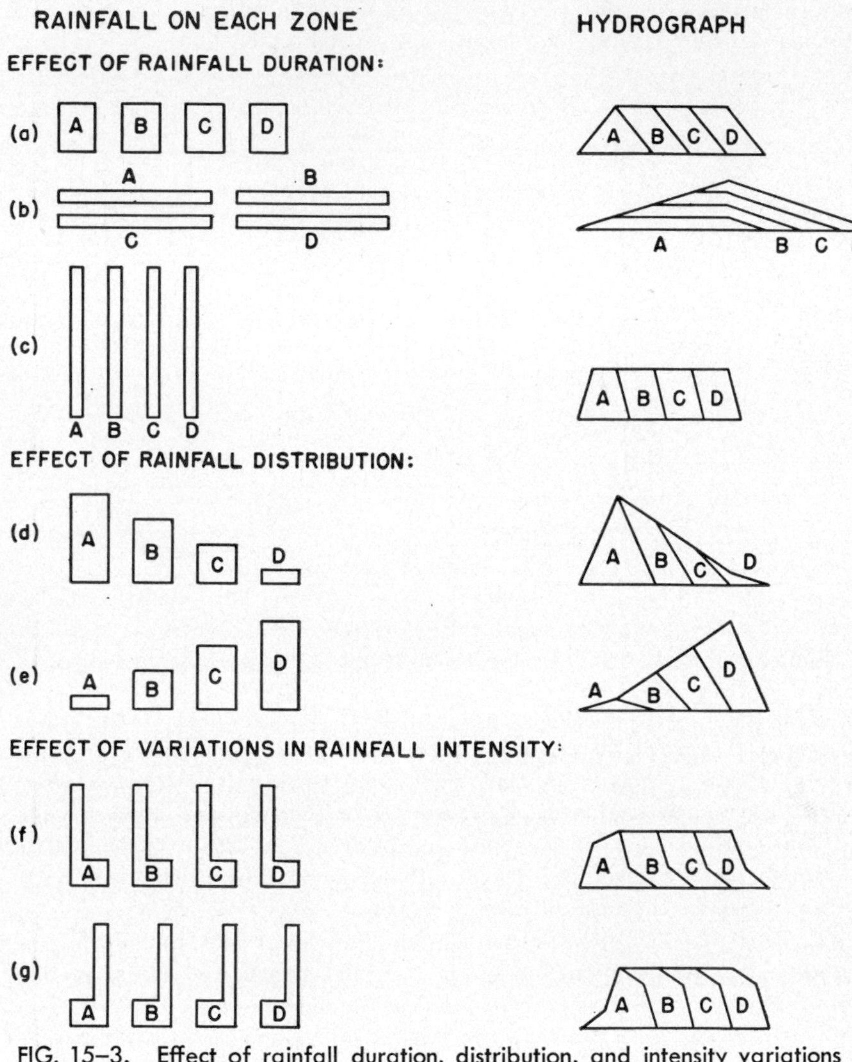

FIG. 15–3. Effect of rainfall duration, distribution, and intensity variations on hydrographs from a hypothetical basin.

Again, the time bases conform to the sum $t_c + t_R$, but because of the nonuniform distribution the hydrographs are no longer symmetrical. Heavy rainfall in the downstream portion of the basin results in a rapid rise and early peak, while heavy rainfall in the upstream areas reverses the hydrograph to yield a slow rise and late peak. In both cases the maximum ordinate equals the maximum rainfall rate anywhere within the basin.

Cases (*f*) and (*g*) indicate the results if the rainfall rate is not uniform. The hydrographs conform to the general pattern observed in the earlier cases, except that the rate of rise no longer remains uniform. In case (*f*), with heavy rain early in the storm, the concentration curve is concave

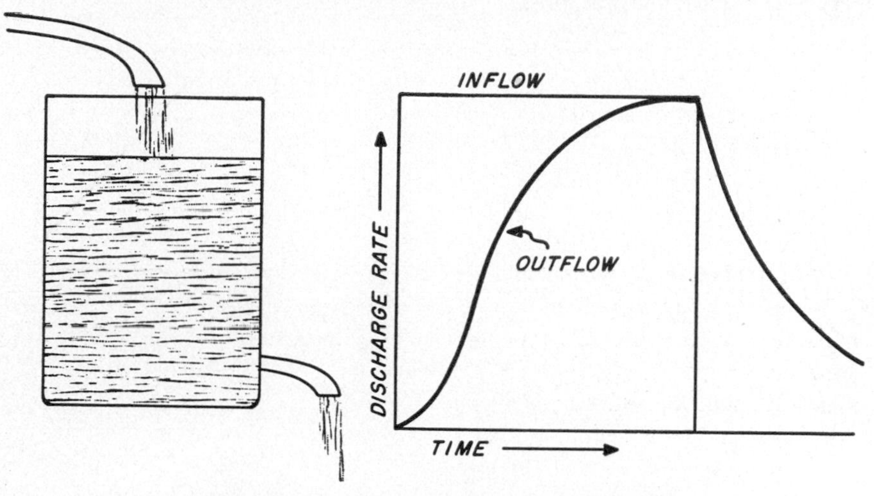

FIG. 15-4. The effect of valley storage.

downward, while case (*g*), in which the heavy rain is assumed to occur in the concluding period of the storm, produces a concentration curve which is concave upward.

The discussion thus far has avoided consideration of the effect of channel storage, which necessarily plays an important role in establishing the shape of the basin hydrograph. The effect of valley storage is demonstrated by Fig. 15-4. The rate of inflow into the barrel is assumed to be constant and equal to the discharge capacity of the orifice when the barrel is filled to the water line shown. If we start with the barrel empty, only a portion of the inflow can be discharged and the balance is stored in the barrel. As the barrel fills, the discharge rate increases and the rate of filling decreases. The time required to fill the barrel from h_1 to h_2 is

$$t = \frac{2A}{k}(\sqrt{h_1} - \sqrt{h_2}) + \frac{2IA}{k^2}[\log_e(I - k\sqrt{h_1}) - \log_e(I - k\sqrt{h_2})] \quad (15\text{-}1)$$

where A is the water-surface area in the barrel and I is the inflow rate. The coefficient $k = C_d a_c \sqrt{2\mathbf{g}}$, where C_d is the orifice coefficient and a_c the orifice area. It will be seen from this equation that the discharge rate approaches the inflow rate asymptotically, and hence an infinite time would be required to reach an equilibrium condition in which inflow equals outflow. For practical purposes, however, it may be assumed that the equilibrium condition is reached in a fairly short time. When the inflow ceases, the discharge begins to decrease at once but does not become zero until the water stored in the barrel is drained out.

Channel storage acts in a similar way on the flow in natural basins, and the hydrographs assumed in Fig. 15-3 on the basis of translatory motion must be further modified. The effect of storage is to produce an actual concentration curve below those indicated and to reduce the peak. The water removed during the period of rising flows by storage is returned to the falling limb, causing attenuation of the hydrograph. The time base of the rising limb is very definitely fixed by the duration of inflow, while the time base of the falling limb has no such limitation. Hence, the ordinary hydrograph is skewed in such a manner that the concentration curve is much shorter than the recession.

The concentration curve. Obviously, the concentration curve is a function of the time-area histogram of the basin and of the duration and uniformity of the rain. It is not possible to derive a universally applicable equation for the rising limb of a natural hydrograph, although such an equation could be derived for special cases.

In most natural basins the area between isochrones is greatest in the middle or upper portions of the basin. This tends to cause the rising limb to be concave upward, rising slowly in the early stages of the flood event and more rapidly toward the end of the rise. This tendency is further strengthened by the fact that the portion of the rainfall which is taken up by infiltration, interception, and surface detention is greater in the early stages of a storm. Hence, uniform rates of rainfall generally mean steadily increasing rates of runoff.

The peak. The peak is the highest instantaneous value of the hydrograph, but the *peak*, or *crest*, *segment* extends from the point of inflection on the rising limb to a similar inflection point on the falling side. Meyer[1] has suggested that hydrographs from storms with duration equal to or exceeding the time of concentration should show a sharp break at the end of rain. Such a break is observed in hydrographs from small plots where rainfall is artificially applied at uniform rates for periods often as long as ten or fifteen times the concentration period of the plots (Fig. 11-9). It is extremely rare for conditions over any natural basin to be particularly favorable to the establishment of equilibrium conditions. Irregular basin shape, uneven distribution and intensity of rainfall, and varying infiltration rates all preclude such an occurrence.

The time of concentration is less significant in basin hydrograph studies than *basin lag*, the time difference between the center of mass of rainfall

[1] Meyer, O. H., Analysis of Runoff Characteristics, *Trans. ASCE*, Vol. 105, pp. 83-89, 1940.

and the center of mass of resulting runoff. Basin lag is clearly determinable for any storm and basin, whereas time of concentration is not. It means very little to know that the time from the outermost fringe of the basin is t_c hr, since the water which arrives at this time may contribute to any of the three portions of the hydrograph. Because of the difficulties involved in determining the center of mass of the hydrograph, it is common practice to use an approximate definition of lag in which either the hydrograph peak or the time at which one-half the outflow has occurred is substituted for center of mass. Actual differences in time between any of these three points are small in the usual hydrograph.

The peak of the hydrograph occurs when the aggregate contribution is at a maximum. Neglecting storage, the hydrograph of the average natural basin peaks with the arrival of flow from that portion of the basin representing the highest concentration of area-inches of runoff. Under conditions of uniform rain, the peak cannot occur until the end of rain, and it ordinarily occurs after the end of rain at some time fixed by the basin characteristics. If rainfall rates are nonuniform, with highest rates early in the storm, the peak may occur before the end of rain simply because the runoff rate declines to a value insufficient to maintain the peak flow. The interval between end of rain and peak is highly dependent on the areal distribution of rain, with an early peak occurring when the rain is concentrated near the basin outlet.

It is characteristic of some basins that their hydrographs show two or more peaks from a single relatively short period of rain. A basin shaped like an hourglass may have a typical double peak as the result of the arrival of water first from the lower basin and then from the area above the constriction. The peaks may be nearly equal or markedly different in magnitude, depending on the area distribution within the basin. The double peak will always be pronounced after rains of short duration. With rainfall of long duration, the two peaks may merge. The characteristic double peak should not be confused with multiple-peak hydrographs, which can occur in every basin as the result of rainfall which is nonuniform in time.

The recession. The recession is the one portion of the hydrograph which can be reasonably well expressed by a general equation applicable to all storms within a basin. In fact, the constants in such an equation are frequently equal or nearly the same for all basins of similar size within a given region. The recession curve represents withdrawal of water from storage after all inflow to the channel has ceased. It is therefore independent of time variations in rainfall or infiltration and is essentially dependent on the physical features of the channel alone. Variations in areal rainfall distribution can have some slight effect on the recession shape. Heavy runoff in the immediate vicinity of the outlet tends to result in an unusually rapid recession, while concentration of runoff in the headwater areas results in a delayed recession. Since each component of flow follows a different path to the outflow station, their recession characteristics necessarily differ. Hence, the shape of the total recession is dependent on the proportions of the several components present.

Barnes[1] found that the recession of any component plotted approximately as a straight line on semilogarithmic paper (Fig. 15-11). The recession equation for any component can therefore be expressed as

$$q_1 = q_0 K_r \tag{15-2}$$

or

$$q_t = q_0 K_r^t \tag{15-3}$$

where K_r is a recession constant and t is the elapsed time between the occurrence of discharge q_0 and q_t.

Since the falling limb of a hydrograph represents withdrawal from storage with zero inflow, it is the differential of the storage curve. The outflow during any time unit equals the change in storage during that time. A storage curve may, therefore, be constructed by summing the increments of outflow (ΔS) from the recession. The differential equation for storage is

$$dS = q_t dt \tag{15-4}$$

Combining Eqs. (15-3) and (15-4), integrating, and substituting limits gives the following expression for the storage curve:

$$S = \frac{-q_0}{\log_e K_r} \tag{15-5}$$

The master recession curve of total flow for a basin is a useful hydrologic tool. Determination of K_r in Eq. (15-2) or (15-3) sometimes serves the purpose, but usually the factor K_r for the total recession cannot be taken as constant throughout the entire range. A master curve may be constructed by piecing together segments of recessions from several floods until a curve covering the necessary range in discharge is complete. Minor differences in the shape of recessions from different storms and lack of data within some ranges of flow often make the construction of a recession curve by this method difficult. An alternate procedure suggested by Langbein[2] involves the plotting of q_1 vs. q_2 (Fig. 15-5). If K_r were truly constant throughout all ranges of flow, this plotting would indicate a straight line. Some curvature is usually evident, and a scattering of points discloses a disagreement between recessions of different floods.

Data used in the development of a recession curve by either method should be selected from periods when no inflow to the channel is taking

[1] Barnes, B. S., Discussion of Analysis of Runoff Characteristics, *Trans. ASCE*, Vol. 105, p. 106, 1940.

[2] Langbein, W. B., Some Channel Storage and Unit Hydrograph Studies, *Trans. Am. Geophys. Union*, Vol. 21, pp. 620-627, 1940.

place. If the data have not been carefully selected, the points will scatter widely and it will be difficult to establish the true recession. Storms centering near the outflow station ordinarily display very rapid recession rates since only a small portion of the natural valley storage in the basin is involved. Such storms should be avoided in developing recession curves. Seasonal variations are noted in the recession curves for some basins as a result of variations in transpiration and evaporation.

SEPARATION OF HYDROGRAPH COMPONENTS

Because of the differing characteristics of the four components of the hydrograph, its shape is dependent, among other things, on the relative proportions of the several components present. Accurate analysis of the hydrograph would require segregation of the exact portion corresponding to each component. This is obviously a difficult problem since, except for special experimental techniques on small areas, the source of water passing a gaging station cannot be identified. Therefore, we must resort to analytical approaches if the job is to be done at all. For very small areas, where the percolation and infiltration rates are well established, the volume of the several components may be estimated for a storm. This provides some check on the separation of the elements of the hydrograph, since such a separation not only must result in a reasonable shape but also must check the estimated volumes. Over large areas local variations in rainfall, infiltration, and antecedent conditions substantially preclude any such volumetric check. It is common, therefore, in the solution of practical problems, to separate only two portions. Surface runoff, channel precipitation, and interflow are usually grouped into a single item designated as *direct*, or *storm*, runoff. Groundwater, or base, flow is treated as a separate item.

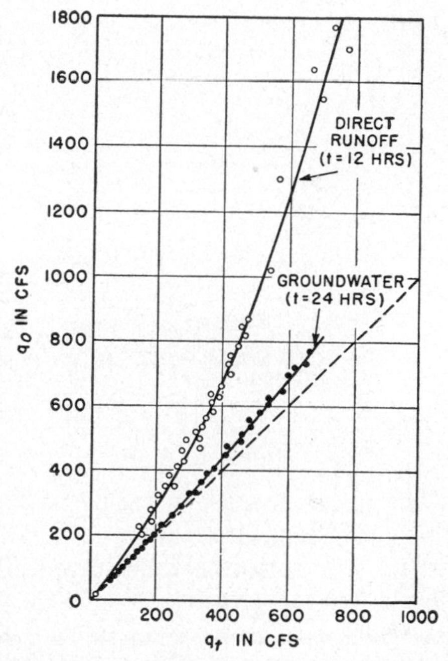

FIG. 15–5. Recession curves for the Valley River at Tomotla, North Carolina.

Several procedures for separating the hydrograph into groundwater and interflow plus surface runoff are outlined in this section. An element of subjectivity is involved in each procedure. No reliable check on the adequacy of any of the procedures is possible, but it can be presumed that the more complex procedures approach the true answer more closely than do the wholly arbitrary methods. Since the greatest use of separation techniques is to determine the amount of direct runoff associated with a particular storm and since the procedures do not differ excessively in the volumes

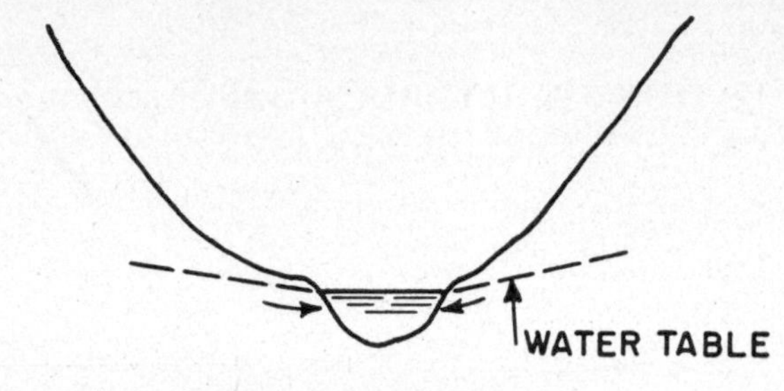

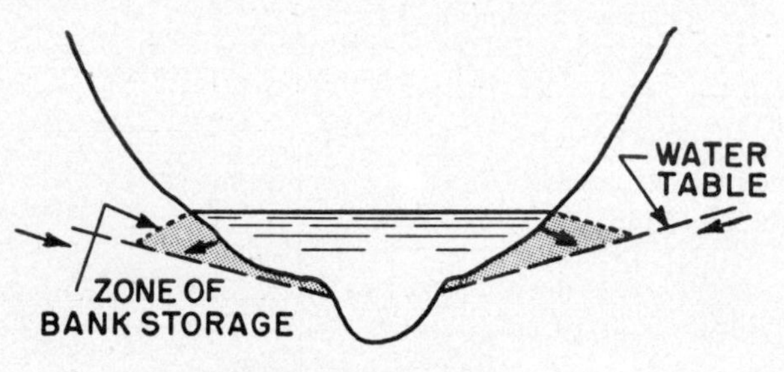

FIG. 15–6. Variation in groundwater conditions during changes in river stage.

determined, the selection of a particular method is not so important as is its consistent application throughout the study.

The groundwater hydrograph. The classification of influent and effluent streams is discussed in Chap. 14. The cross section of the channel and flood plain of a typical effluent stream during a period of low flow is shown in Fig. 15-6*a*. The entire flow is derived from groundwater sources, and the level of the water surface in the stream is normally the same as that of the groundwater at the bank. A slight slope of the water table permits discharge into the channel. When the groundwater level falls below the channel bottom, the stream becomes influent and flow from the stream to groundwater begins. If the rate of percolation to groundwater exceeds the flow in the channel, the stream becomes dry.

During flood, the stages in the stream may be expected to rise more rapidly than the level of the groundwater table. This is particularly true in regions where the soil stratification prevents rapid percolation of rainfall to groundwater. Under such conditions (Fig. 15-6*b*), the stream becomes influent, *i.e.*, water percolates from the stream into the banks. This condition persists until the peak of the streamflow has passed. In regions of sandy soil favoring high percolation rates or in areas where the groundwater table is close to the surface, a stream may remain effluent at all times. This condition is favored by flat stream slopes and slow rates of rise.

If natural streams could be classified so simply, the groundwater hydrograph could be easily determined. Actually, the conditions within a basin may be so variable that a stream can be influent in some reaches and effluent in others. In some basins a casual reconnaissance may suffice to establish that a stream is predominantly influent or effluent, but in the more geologically complex basins only careful geological exploration can indicate the relative proportions of influent and effluent channel.

Two extremes of shape are possible for the groundwater hydrograph of an effluent stream. It may be assumed that, with the beginning of surface runoff, the groundwater flow becomes zero (or negative if we consider seepage into the banks) and remains so until the crest of streamflow. As stages in the stream begin to fall, the groundwater discharge increases until the net head (elevation of water table minus elevation of water surface in the stream) begins to decrease as a result of withdrawal from groundwater storage. Thereafter, the groundwater discharge conforms to a depletion, or recession, curve. At the other extreme, it might be assumed that the groundwater hydrograph begins to rise at or shortly after the beginning of rain, reaches a peak, and declines with a hydrograph shape resembling that of the other components of flow.

The true condition probably lies somewhere between these two extremes. It follows, therefore, that the shape of the rising limb of the groundwater hydrograph is largely indeterminate, and any form of separation must be largely arbitrary. Fortunately, the volume of flow included within the period prior to the peak of groundwater hydrograph is not usually large in proportion to direct runoff, and assumptions as to the shape of the rising limb do not usually introduce serious error into subsequent computations.

Simple hydrograph separation. In many problems the exact method of separation is not important as long as the same procedure is used throughout the study. If the purpose of the analysis is to establish means of predicting the basin hydrograph for forecasting or design studies, an extremely refined separation is unnecessary, since any water omitted from one component is included in the others.

Figure 15-7 demonstrates some of the common arbitrary rules used for separation purposes. Separation by a horizontal line AA' is the simplest of all procedures, but it has the disadvantage that it yields an extremely long time base for the direct runoff hydrograph, and the time base varies from storm to storm, depending on the flow at the point of rise. As an alternate, line AB is drawn from the point of rise to an intersection with the recession N days after the crest. The time base can thus be limited to a reasonable length and will not vary beyond the variation in duration of rise. If the *initial flow,* the discharge at the beginning of rise, is high because of a previous storm, neither of these two methods gives results which are particularly realistic. The line ACB has been generally adopted as a plausible, if arbitrary, mode of separation. The line AC represents an extension of the recession existing prior to the storm to a point under the peak of the hydrograph. From this point a straight line CB connects with the hydrograph at a point N days after the crest or after the end of runoff-producing rain. Values of N vary with slope and drainage area. Approximate values of N for various drainage areas are listed in Table 15-2. While variations in slope and other factors will result in deviations from these values, the selection of N is not particularly critical in most studies. In mountainous areas, values of N shown in the table should be slightly reduced, while, for long, narrow basins or basins on flat slopes, values of N may be increased as much as 50 per cent.

TABLE 15-2. Values of N for Various Drainage Areas

Drainage Area, Square Miles	N, Days
100	2
500	3
2000	4
5000	5
10000	6

Analytical separation into two components. A groundwater depletion curve can be constructed for a basin by any of the methods discussed earlier in this chapter. It should be prepared by use of data selected from periods sufficiently long after any rain to justify the assumption that they represent groundwater flow exclusively. Beginning after a storm, when the recession is known to represent only groundwater flow, and computing successively earlier ordinates from the groundwater depletion, it will be found that the groundwater recession eventually falls below the observed recession. The point of departure (Fig. 15-8) may be taken as the end of direct runoff, and the depletion curve, extended back from this point, represents the recession of the groundwater hydrograph. The time of groundwater peak and the shape of the rising limb must be selected arbitrarily. A prepared template is useful in making this type of separation.

A modification[1] of the foregoing procedure is useful in separating the

[1] Linsley, R. K., and W. C. Ackermann, A Method of Predicting the Runoff from Rainfall, *Trans. ASCE*, Vol. 107, pp. 825-835, 1942.

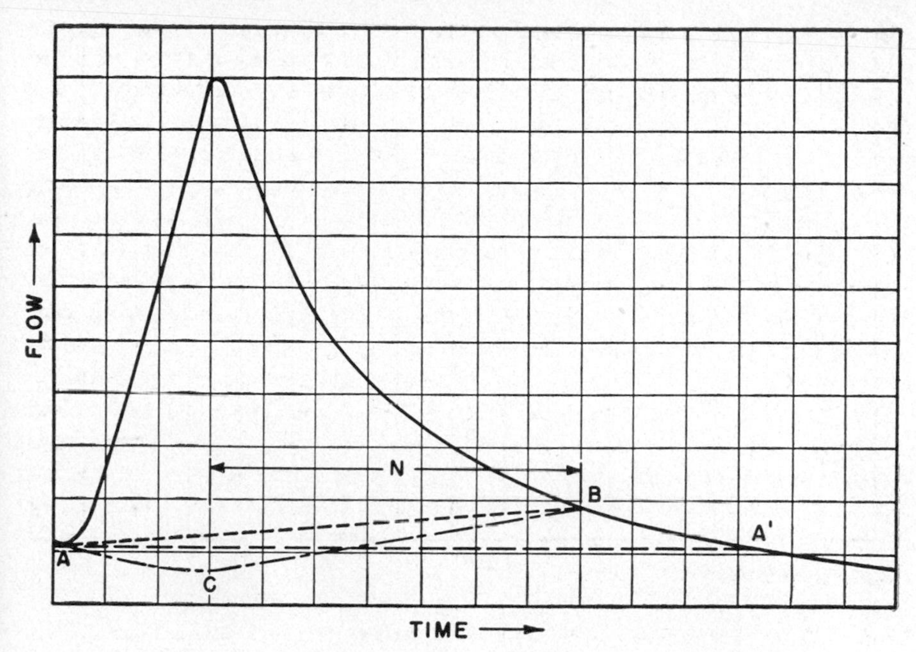

FIG. 15–7. Arbitrary methods for hydrograph separation.

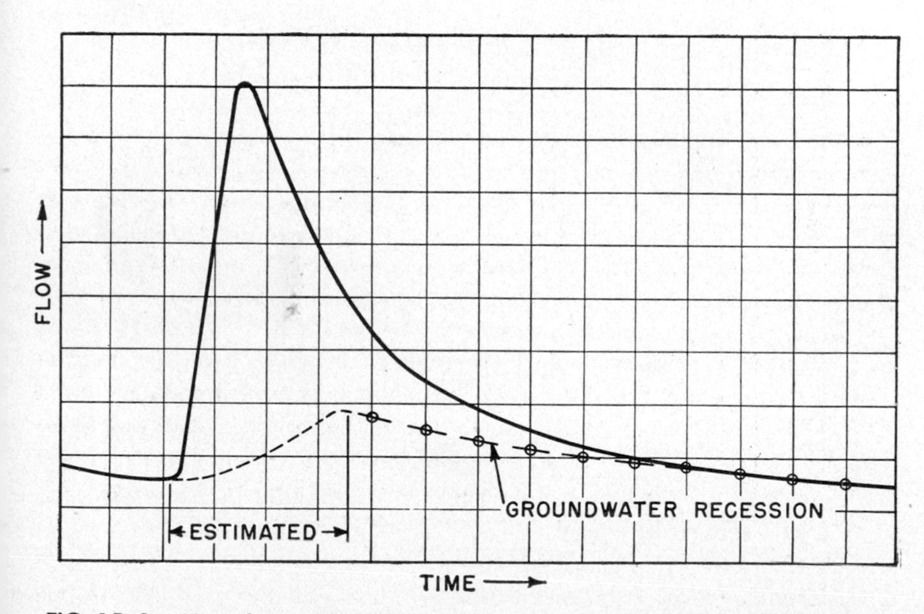

FIG. 15–8. Use of groundwater depletion for simple hydrograph separation.

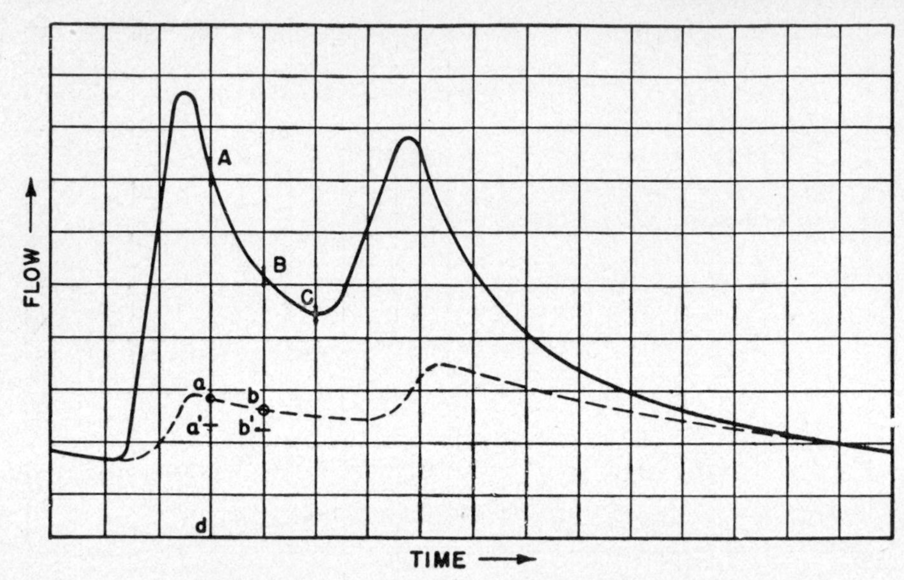

FIG. 15–9. Analysis of a complex hydrograph.

runoff from complex storms. Figure 15-9 shows two storms so close together that direct runoff does not end between the storms. The groundwater recession cannot be extended to a time earlier than the peak of the second storm. A depletion curve for direct runoff is therefore required; such a curve can be constructed by using ordinates between the groundwater recession and the total hydrograph for several storms. Both the direct-runoff and groundwater depletion curves are then replotted to show the change in discharge per unit time as a function of initial discharge (Fig. 15-10). A point on the groundwater hydrograph beneath the recession AB (Fig. 15-9) may be located as follows:

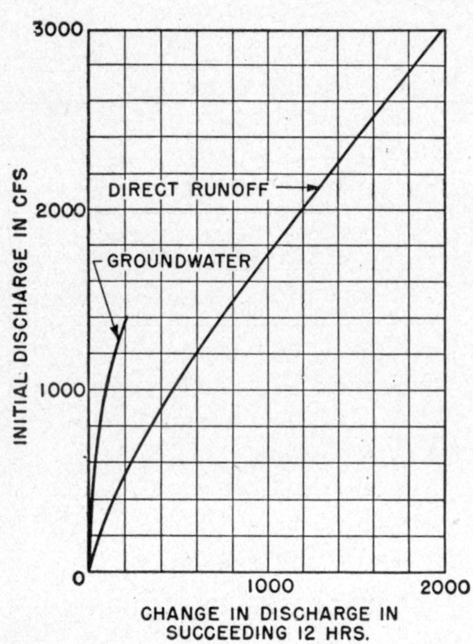

FIG. 15–10. Rate of change in flow curves for Valley River at Tomotla, North Carolina.

1. Determine the change in discharge AB (in unit time), and read a first estimate of direct runoff corresponding to this rate of change from Fig. 15-10.

2. Subtract the estimated direct runoff Aa' from the total ordinate Ad. The balance $a'd$ is a first approximation to the groundwater ordinate.
3. Determine the change in discharge corresponding to a groundwater flow $a'd$ from Fig. 15-10, and subtract this from the total change AB. The remainder is essentially the change in discharge for direct runoff and may be used to determine a new value of initial direct runoff Aa. The ordinate ad represents groundwater flow.

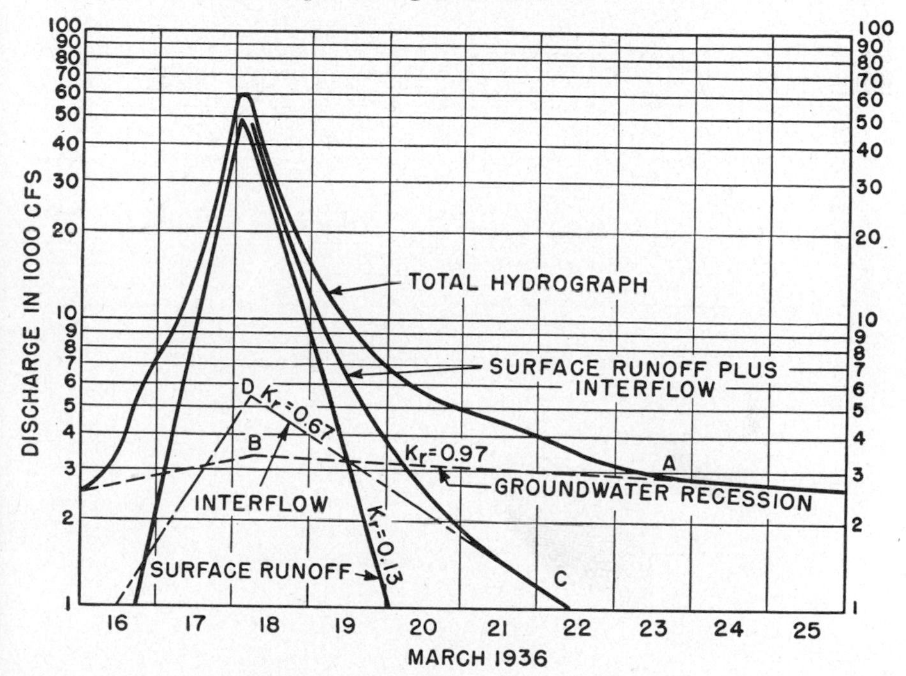

FIG. 15-11. Separation of hydrograph components using semilogarithmic plotting for Stony Creek at Johnstown, Pennsylvania.

Following the procedure outlined above, a segment of the groundwater hydrograph underneath the recession of the first storm may be determined. The balance of the groundwater hydrograph must be sketched arbitrarily. The direct-runoff recession of the first flood event can be extended under the second rise by use of the direct-runoff depletion.

Analytical separation into three components. For research studies in which it is desired to approximate the distribution of flow from each hydrograph component, an analytical procedure devised by Barnes[1] may be adopted. The procedure is displayed in Fig. 15-11, where the storm hydrograph has been plotted on semilogarithmic paper. The groundwater reces-

[1] Barnes, B. S., Structure of Discharge Recession Curves, *Trans. Am. Geophys. Union*, Vol. 20, pp. 721-725, 1939.

sion AB can be approximated by a straight line and, as such, can be extended back under the hydrograph. The residual ordinates above the groundwater hydrograph represent the combined surface runoff and interflow. This combined hydrograph is replotted and a straight line fitted to the interflow recession CD. This recession can now be extended as a straight line to separate interflow from surface runoff. The rising limb of the groundwater and interflow graphs must be estimated as in all other procedures. In all logarithmic plottings, considerable care must be exercised to avoid large errors developing in the very condensed scales at high flows.

16

RUNOFF RELATIONS

In most hydrologic studies concerned with design, river forecasting, land use, etc., it is necessary to develop relations between precipitation and runoff, possibly using other factors as parameters. Moreover, precipitation records are generally longer than those of discharge and, therefore, precipitation-runoff relations can be used to extrapolate or interpolate discharge records.

Runoff relations may be classified in two ways, (1) according to whether the precipitation is all in the form of rain or whether snow is involved and (2) according to whether the relation deals with individual storms or the total volume of runoff over an extended period of time. The nature of the precipitation is of little significance in considering long-period runoff. Therefore, runoff relations may be segregated into (1) storm-period rainfall-runoff relations; (2) short-period runoff relations involving rain and/or snow; and (3) extended-period precipitation-runoff relations. This chapter treats runoff relations according to this classification. However, before considering the numerous types of relationships, the general aspects of runoff are first discussed in order that the reader may become thoroughly familiar with the interrelations of the relevant hydrologic phenomena.

THE RUNOFF CYCLE

The *hydrologic cycle* (Chap. 1) is the term applied to the general circulation of water in its various states from the seas to the atmosphere, to the ground, and back to the seas again. The *runoff cycle* is the descriptive term applied to that portion of the hydrologic cycle between incident precipitation over land areas and subsequent discharge through stream channels or direct return to the atmosphere through evapo-transpiration.

The following discussion of the runoff cycle is similar to that presented by Hoyt.[1] However, instead of considering the cycle to be comprised of five rather arbitrary phases, depending upon the rainfall characteristics, the

[1] Hoyt, W. G., An Outline of the Runoff Cycle, *School of Engineering, Pennsylvania State College Tech. Bull.* 27, pp. 57-67, 1942.

authors have attempted to describe the sequence of events by discussing the phenomena occurring simultaneously at four specific times throughout the cycle. The conditions existing at the various times considered (Fig. 16-1) are as follows:

1. Just prior to the beginning of rainfall and after an extended dry period.
2. Shortly after the beginning of rainfall, but before interception and depression storage have been satisfied.
3. Near the end of a protracted heavy storm, but with relatively intense rain still occurring.
4. After the end of an extended storm, but before channel and retention storage have been depleted.

The figure and the discussion as well are necessarily idealized. They present what might be logically expected in a humid region.

End of dry period. Figure 16-1*A* shows an idealized cross section of a stream valley in a humid area, assuming the absence of snow, ice, and frost. All surface and channel storage resulting from the last previous rainfall has been depleted, except for that in reservoirs, lakes, and ponds. The only source of streamflow is the water *G* entering the channel from the zone of saturation. This flow is variously known as groundwater, base, or sustained, flow, or effluent seepage. It has decreased with time according to the storage-depletion curve, modified only slightly by such items as transpiration *T* from vegetation along the stream bank and evaporation *E* from the stream surface.

While the groundwater table is shown to be continuous in the figure, there may or may not be a water table, as such, under the steep slopes. Instead, there may be one or more perched water tables at various levels. In many arid regions the water supplied through precipitation is insufficient to maintain a water table tributary to stream channels, and, as a result, streamflow is intermittent, occurring only when there is runoff from surface flow or interflow. This situation is quite common in most of the western United States.

Evapo-transpiration and discharge from subterranean storage result in a gradual lowering of the water table. If the dry period has been sufficiently long to allow the water table to drop below the level of the stream channel at all points above the cross section, streamflow ceases. The cessation of streamflow from relatively large basins is common in subhumid areas and prevalent in semiarid and arid regions but occurs only in the extreme headwaters and after prolonged droughts in humid areas.

If snow, ice, or frost is present and if soil and air temperatures are below freezing, the situation is essentially unchanged. If temperatures are above freezing, however, water is being released from surface storage through melting, and conditions are more similar to those described under (*B*) and (*C*).

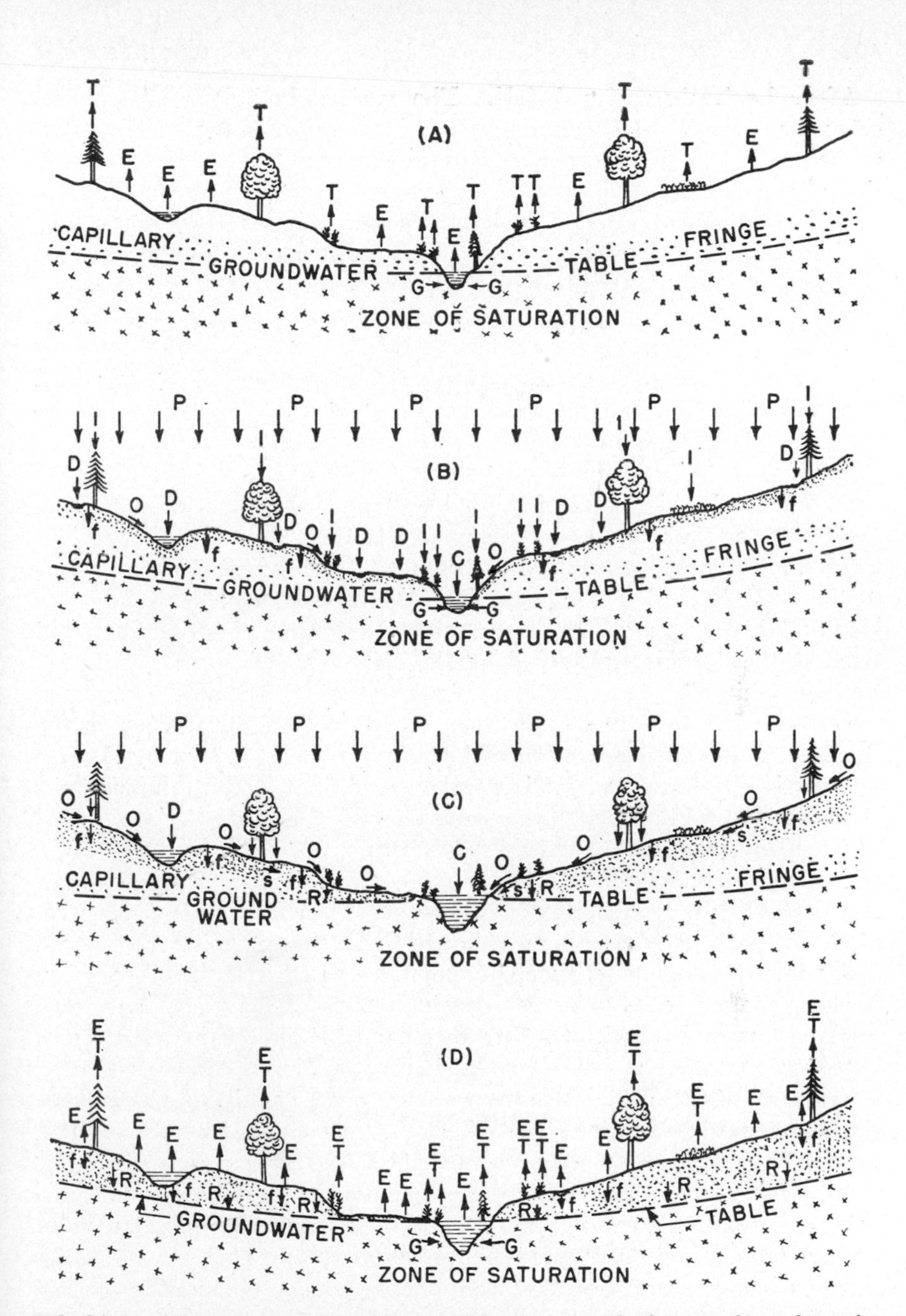

FIG. 16–1. Idealized cross sections representing specified times throughout the runoff cycle (where *T* designates transpiration, *E* evaporation, G groundwater flow, *P* precipitation, *I* interception, *D* depression storage, O overland flow, *f* infiltration, C channel precipitation, *S* subsurface or interflow, and *R* groundwater recharge).

After beginning of rainfall. The various hydrologic phenomena occurring soon after the beginning of rain P are shown in Fig. 16-1B. Part of the rain is falling directly on stream surfaces, and this channel precipitation C becomes an immediate increment of streamflow. In fact, this is essentially the only portion of the rainfall contributing to streamflow during the initial stages of the storm. Part of the precipitation is being intercepted (I) by vegetation and therefore does not contribute to runoff. This stored water is eventually returned to the atmosphere through evaporation. Most of that rain reaching the ground either is retained on the surface as depression storage D or passes through the soil surface as infiltration f. Once below the surface, this water begins to satisfy the soil-moisture deficiency which has gradually built up in the zone of aeration during the dry period.

During the initial period of rainfall, overland flow O occurs only from small portions of the basin, such as roads, buildings, and other impervious areas, and extremely steep slopes. On most of the area, infiltration, interception, and depression storage preclude overland flow unless the intensity of rainfall is very great. The rate of groundwater flow G during the initial stages of the storm is probably about the same as that just prior to the beginning of rainfall. Flow may or may not be taking place, depending upon the elevation of the water table with respect to the water surface in the channel. Rates of evaporation and transpiration are extremely slow as compared with those under fair-weather conditions, because humidity is high and because the evaporative capacity of the air tends to be satisfied by the falling rain rather than by soil moisture.

The effect of snow or frost upon runoff conditions just after the onset of rain depends on the condition of the soil or snow as the case may be. Fresh, dry snow may store some rain and delay the beginning of overland flow, while ripe snow may augment runoff. The freezing of soil with low moisture content tends to increase the infiltration capacity and thus delay overland flow and runoff. On the other hand, the infiltration capacity of frozen soil with high moisture content is very small.

Near end of rainfall. After many hours of heavy rainfall, virtually all depression and interception storage is filled, the soil-moisture deficiency is satisfied to considerable depths, and the infiltration rate is near a minimum. Figure 16-1C shows the hydrologic phenomena under these conditions. The vegetation is saturated, and rain falling on it is balanced by an equal amount falling from the vegetation to the ground, except for the small quantity being returned to the atmosphere through evaporation. Likewise, the flow into filled surface depressions is essentially balanced by overland flow and infiltration.

Overland flow O is taking place over nearly the entire basin, and streamflow is beginning to bear some relation to the rate of precipitation. Subsurface flow S is contributing to stream discharge, and subterranean storage is being replenished (R) in some portions of the basin.

If snow is present and has become saturated, it, too, will be contributing to runoff. Precipitation falling in the form of snow will have little effect on runoff until such time as melting begins.

After end of rain. In Fig. 16-1*D*, it is assumed that rainfall and overland flow have ceased and that streamflow is composed of groundwater G and channel storage. Evaporation is taking place at an active rate from soil moisture and depression and interception storage. Furthermore, transpiration has begun to take place from the vegetal cover. Water in surface depressions is continuing to enter the soil mantle through infiltration, while gravity water within the zone of aeration continues to replenish subterranean storage. The groundwater table is either rising or falling, depending upon whether the downward-percolation rate exceeds the rate at which groundwater is contributing to streamflow.

If the entire storm discussed under (B) and (C) consists of snow falling on frozen ground with subfreezing temperatures, then all four parts of the figure would be quite similar to part (A), except that under these conditions transpiration would be at a minimum. Upon the occurrence of subsequent high temperatures, melting would produce conditions similar to those discussed under (B), (C), and (D), respectively. However, groundwater and subsurface flow would be relatively greater; there would be little or no transpiration; and there would be more evaporation during runoff.

The conditions described under (D) approach those of (A) with the lapse of time, provided that there is no further precipitation. Thus, we have a complete, if oversimplified, picture of the runoff cycle. While some of the complexities of the process involved in converting precipitation to streamflow have been considered, it should be remembered that many of the minor aspects of the problem have necessarily been omitted in this idealized approach.

TIME VARIATIONS OF HYDROLOGIC PHENOMENA THROUGHOUT A STORM PERIOD

The preceding section was devoted to a discussion of the various hydrologic phenomena occurring at selected times throughout the runoff cycle by considering an idealized cross section of a basin. In such a discussion, little can be presented to explain in a qualitative manner the time variations of such factors as interception and infiltration. While each of these factors is discussed in detail in earlier chapters, it is believed that a better over-all understanding of the interrelations of the various phenomena can be gained through a qualitative analysis with respect to time. Such an analysis is shown schematically in Fig. 16-2, assuming a steady rainfall of moderate intensity. The dotted area of the figure represents that portion of the total precipitation which eventually becomes streamflow as measured at the discharge station. Because of the wide range of runoff conditions encountered in nature, the relative magnitudes of the various factors shown in the figure should not be given quantitative significance.

It will be noted that channel precipitation comprises the only increment to streamflow during the initial period of rainfall. As the streams begin to rise, their total surface area increases and consequently the volume rate

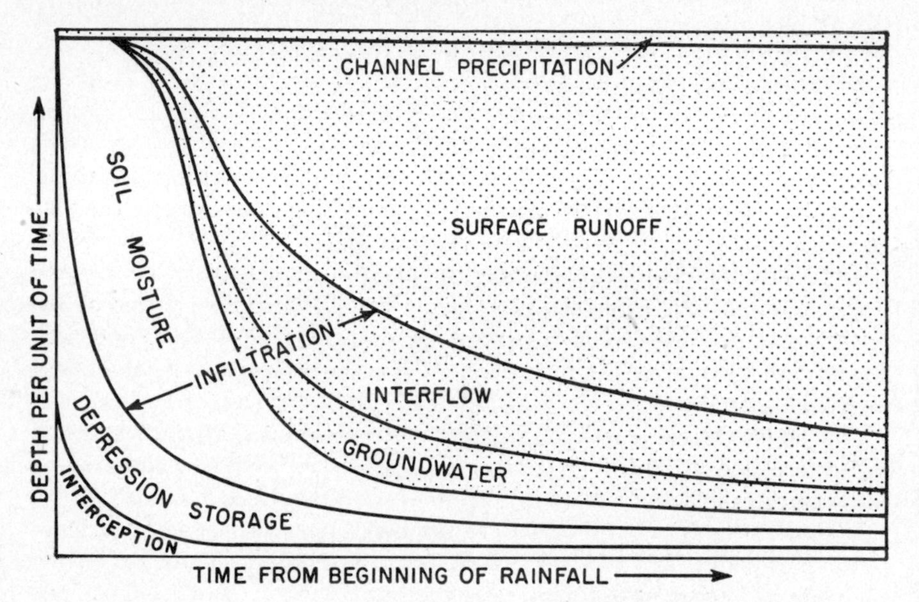

FIG. 16–2. Schematic diagram of the disposition of storm rainfall.

of channel precipitation increases. If the channels are dry at the beginning of the storm, there is no contribution to streamflow during the initial period of rainfall. While such a condition is rare in humid areas, except in the extreme headwaters, it is quite common in the subhumid and semiarid regions of the West.

The rate of interception is quite high at the beginning of rain, especially during summer in areas of dense vegetal cover. However, the available storage capacity is depleted rather quickly, so that the interception rate decreases to that required to replace water evaporated from vegetation. Most of the interception is eventually returned to the atmosphere by evaporation.

The rate at which depression storage is filled by incident precipitation decreases rapidly at first and then more gradually, reaching zero at some relatively high value of total-storm rainfall, depending upon land slope, geological structure, aspect, basin area, and other factors. While depression storage is shown as a total loss to streamflow in the simplified figure, a portion of this water does infiltrate and reach the stream as groundwater or interflow. The remainder is returned to the atmosphere through evaporation.

Except in very intense storms, the greater portion of the soil-moisture deficiency is satisfied before significant surface runoff takes place. However, some of the minute capillary pores fill very slowly, and consequently a small portion of the rain occurring late in the storm undoubtedly becomes soil moisture. Soil moisture is returned to the atmosphere during periods of no rain by evapo-transpiration.

Of that water infiltrating through the soil surface, one portion is retained in the soil against the pull of gravity (soil moisture), another percolates downward through the water table, eventually reaching the stream as groundwater, and still another portion (interflow) follows a devious path to the stream channel without reaching the water table. There is considerable difference of opinion among hydrologists regarding the quantitative breakdown between groundwater and interflow. While Fig. 16-2 shows a gradual decrease in the contribution to interflow toward the end of the period, the actual variation is dependent on many factors, such as soil type and rainfall rate.

The rate of surface runoff during a long, steady storm starts off at zero, increases slowly at first and then more rapidly, and eventually reaches a relatively constant percentage of the rainfall rate. Both the percentage and the actual rate are naturally dependent upon intensity of rainfall. The dividing line between surface runoff and interflow is no more discernible than that between groundwater and interflow. Some investigators believe that surface runoff comprises only a very small part of streamflow, even during flood periods. The question is rather academic, inasmuch as it involves the rigorousness of definitions. For example, some water flows most of the distance to the channel over the surface but does pass through the soil at one time or another. Is this water to be considered surface runoff or interflow? Since there exist all gradations, from pure surface to pure subsurface flow, it is obviously impossible to make any clean-cut analysis of the hydrograph. In view of this fact, the hydrograph is customarily separated into two components—groundwater and direct runoff—according to arbitrary procedures (Chap. 15).

The analysis here presented regarding the disposition of storm rainfall is necessarily idealized and of limited scope. Mention has not been made of some of the less important details, and conditions of frozen ground and snow do not apply to the schematic diagram. Nevertheless, an understanding of the relative time variations of hydrologic phenomena is important in considering the runoff relations presented later in the chapter.

RELATION OF STORM-PERIOD RAINFALL TO RUNOFF

The quantity of runoff from a given storm is determined by (1) the moisture deficiency of the basin at the beginning of rainfall and (2) the storm characteristics such as rainfall amount, intensity, and duration. The storm characteristics can be determined from an adequate network of recording and nonrecording precipitation gages. However, the direct determination of moisture conditions throughout the basin at the beginning of

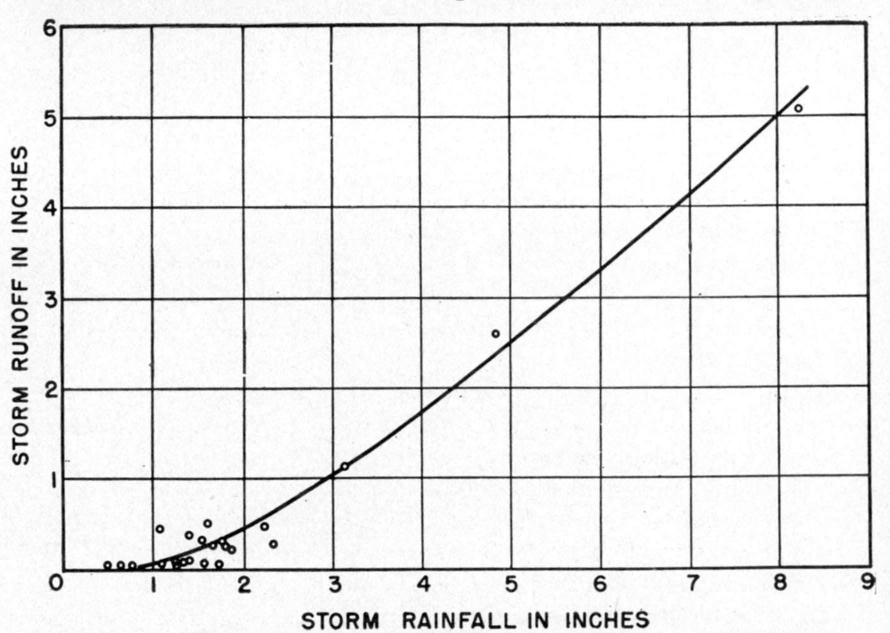

FIG. 16–3. Rainfall-runoff relation for the White River at West Hartford, Vermont.

the storm is extremely difficult. While reliable point observations of soil moisture are possible, three-dimensional measurements are required in a medium recognized for its marked physical discontinuities further emphasized by cultivation and variations in vegetal cover. Also, any complete accountability of moisture within a basin must include consideration of conditions above the soil surface, notably the storage capacity of surface depressions and vegetal cover (interception). Thus, in addition to variations in soil moisture, there is also a seasonal variation in surface storage resulting from changes in vegetal cover, farming practices, and other factors.

Because of the complex nature of a natural basin, the direct physical or analytical approach to the determination of runoff is not feasible, and resort must be had to empirical relations developed through statistical analysis of measurable factors which are directly related to runoff phenomena. The parameters to be used depend upon the required accuracy, available data, and climatic conditions and, to some extent, upon personal preference. A direct plotting of rainfall vs. runoff (Fig. 16-3) shows significant correlation for some basins and may suffice if only a rough approximation is required. However, considerable improvement will result if an index of soil conditions is added (Fig. 16-4). Soil-moisture measurements can be used to represent

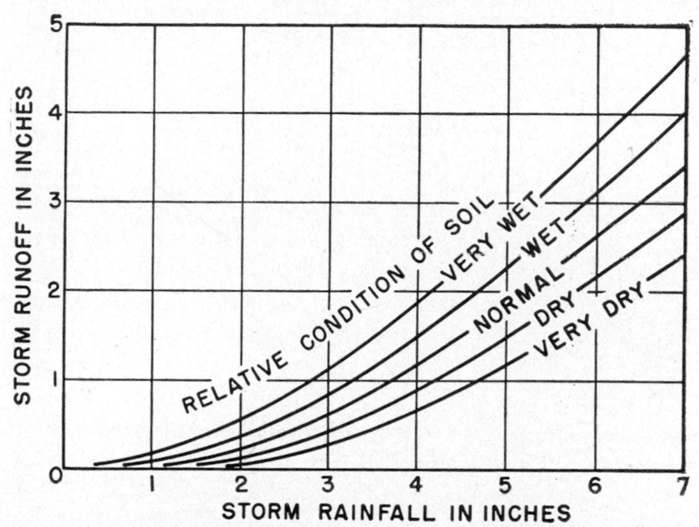

FIG. 16–4. Typical rainfall-runoff relation, using estimated soil condition as a parameter.

moisture conditions within the basin, but such observations are generally so limited with respect to areal coverage and length of record that a more indirect index must usually be employed. Stream discharge prior to the beginning of the storm is found to be a good index to moisture deficiency in humid and subhumid areas of the East, but climatic conditions of the western United States render this factor of little value—many streams being dry for a considerable portion of the year.

An examination of Fig. 16-2 shows that storm runoff (surface runoff plus interflow) effectively represents that increment of rainfall which is discharged after the moisture deficiency of the basin has been satisfied. In other words, storm runoff is the difference between precipitation and *basin recharge*. Basin recharge has often been called *loss*, because it represents loss to runoff. The term loss is actually a misnomer from an agricultural point of view, since this water is retained in the basin over a considerable period of time. Many factors used as parameters in runoff relations are more logically, if not more directly, related to the basin recharge than to runoff. Consequently, many correlations are presently being made in terms of basin recharge. Knowing the recharge and rainfall, runoff can be computed directly.

The terms surface runoff, storm runoff, and direct runoff are rather loosely used in practical hydrology, and, with respect to runoff relations, there is generally little need to draw fine distinctions. In the previous chapter, numerous arbitrary methods of hydrograph analysis, or flow separation, were described. Any one of these methods can be employed to compile runoff data for the development of relations described later in this chapter, with the exception of the direct infiltration approach. The method of flow separation used in compiling the basic data becomes an integral part of the runoff relation and must be adhered to whenever the relation is employed in subsequent studies.

Storm analysis. As in any statistical correlation, the basic data being used to develop a runoff relation must be as consistent and reliable as possible. Only that storm rainfall which produced the runoff being considered should be included. Small showers which occurred after the hydrograph had started to recede should not be included if they obviously had little or no effect upon the amount of runoff. Similarly, showers occurring sometime before the main storm should be excluded from the storm rainfall and included in the antecedent precipitation if such an index is being utilized. In general, long, complex storms should be broken up into as many short, unit storms as can successfully be accomplished through hydrograph analysis. Since hydrographs for small basins are more easily analyzed, the resulting runoff relations are more satisfactory, provided that the areas are not so small that changes in cropping in individual fields exert a significant influence on the runoff regime.

Rainfall duration need not be determined critically for most types of analysis, unless one is interested in making accurate determinations of small amounts of runoff. While experimental infiltration data indicate rates commonly in excess of 0.10 in./hr after the soil profile has become saturated, runoff relations of the types shown in Figs. 16-6 to 16-8 consistently show that the portion of basin recharge which seems to be correlated with duration takes place at rates in the order of 0.01 in./hr. The difference between these two values is largely interflow.

Indices used to represent initial basin conditions. The index to moisture conditions within the basin which is probably of the most universal application is the *antecedent-precipitation index*, P_a. It is generally defined by an equation of the type

$$P_a = b_1P_1 + b_2P_2 + b_3P_3 + \cdots + b_tP_t \qquad (16\text{-}1)$$

where b_t is a constant and P_t is the amount of precipitation which occurred t days prior to the storm under consideration. If some other index, such as base flow, is not used in the correlation, then 20 to 60 terms are generally used in the above equation, depending upon the desired accuracy and the area of application. The constant b_t is commonly assumed to be a function of t, such as $b_t = 1/t$.

If a day-by-day value of the index is required, as is the case in river forecasting, there is considerable advantage in assuming that b_t decreases with t according to a logarithmic recession rather than as a reciprocal. In other words,

$$P_{at} = P_{a0}k^t \tag{16-2}$$

where $b_t = k^t$. Letting t equal unity,

$$P_{a1} = kP_{a0} \tag{16-3}$$

Thus, the index for any day is equal to a constant k times the index of the day before. If rain occurs on any day, then the index after the rain is equal to that before the rain plus the amount of rainfall. Because of the characteristics of the logarithmic equation, errors of computation rapidly diminish with time. That is, the portion of any day's index which is accountable to conditions more than 30 days prior is extremely small.

Theoretically, the value of the recession factor k should be a function of season and should vary from one region to another. If sufficient data are available, variations of k can be determined through statistical analysis; however, it is doubtful that the time required can be justified on the basis of improved correlation. Seasonal variation can be accounted for by including "time of year" as an additional variable. With regard to regional variation, the problem is not so simple. Experience has shown that a value of 0.85 to 0.90 is applicable over most of the eastern and central portions of the United States. In any event, the antecedent-precipitation factor is only an index to moisture deficiency, and the use of an approximate value of k does not seriously affect the results. In order to use Eq. (16-3), an initial value of P_a must be computed by Eq. (16-1), making use of the fact that $b_t = k^t$. Table 16-1 gives values of k^t for various values of k and t.

In any discussion of antecedent precipitation, a question immediately arises regarding antecedent snowfall. If snow is treated in the same manner as rain, its effect will be overemphasized if it is removed from the basin through evaporation and underestimated if it is melted at a later date. In the usual sequence of events, evaporation from the snow surface is not far different from surface evaporation after a rain, and consequently snowfall can probably best be considered to have been applied to the basin on the day it melted rather than when it fell.

Since storm runoff does not, of itself, add to the residual moisture in the basin, it is evident that an antecedent index of "precipitation minus runoff," or basin recharge, should be more satisfactory than precipitation alone. This refinement requires considerable additional computational work, how-

TABLE 16-1. Values of k^t for Various Values of k and t

t \ k	0.76	0.78	0.80	0.82	0.84	0.86	0.88	0.90	0.92	0.94
1	0.760	0.780	0.800	0.820	0.840	0.860	0.880	0.900	0.920	0.940
2	0.578	0.608	0.640	0.672	0.706	0.740	0.774	0.810	0.846	0.884
3	0.439	0.475	0.512	0.551	0.593	0.636	0.681	0.729	0.779	0.831
4	0.334	0.370	0.410	0.452	0.498	0.547	0.600	0.656	0.716	0.781
5	0.254	0.289	0.328	0.371	0.418	0.470	0.528	0.590	0.659	0.734
6	0.193	0.225	0.262	0.304	0.351	0.405	0.464	0.531	0.606	0.690
7	0.146	0.176	0.210	0.249	0.295	0.348	0.409	0.478	0.558	0.648
8	0.111	0.137	0.168	0.204	0.248	0.299	0.360	0.430	0.513	0.610
9	0.085	0.107	0.134	0.168	0.208	0.257	0.316	0.387	0.472	0.573
10	0.064	0.083	0.107	0.137	0.175	0.221	0.279	0.349	0.434	0.539
11	0.049	0.065	0.086	0.113	0.147	0.190	0.245	0.314	0.400	0.506
12	0.037	0.051	0.069	0.092	0.123	0.164	0.216	0.282	0.368	0.476
13	0.028	0.040	0.055	0.076	0.104	0.141	0.190	0.254	0.338	0.447
14	0.021	0.031	0.044	0.062	0.087	0.121	0.167	0.229	0.311	0.421
15	0.016	0.024	0.035	0.051	0.073	0.104	0.147	0.206	0.286	0.395
16	0.012	0.019	0.028	0.042	0.061	0.090	0.129	0.185	0.263	0.372
17	0.009	0.015	0.023	0.034	0.052	0.077	0.114	0.167	0.242	0.349
18	0.007	0.011	0.018	0.028	0.043	0.066	0.100	0.150	0.223	0.328
19	0.005	0.009	0.014	0.023	0.036	0.057	0.088	0.135	0.205	0.309
20	0.004	0.007	0.012	0.019	0.031	0.049	0.078	0.122	0.189	0.290
21	0.003	0.005	0.009	0.015	0.026	0.042	0.068	0.109	0.174	0.273
22	0.002	0.004	0.007	0.013	0.022	0.036	0.060	0.098	0.160	0.256
23	0.002	0.003	0.006	0.010	0.018	0.031	0.053	0.089	0.147	0.241
24	0.001	0.003	0.005	0.009	0.015	0.027	0.047	0.080	0.135	0.227
25	0.001	0.002	0.004	0.007	0.013	0.023	0.041	0.072	0.124	0.213
26	0.001	0.002	0.003	0.006	0.011	0.020	0.036	0.065	0.114	0.200
27	0.001	0.001	0.002	0.005	0.009	0.017	0.032	0.058	0.105	0.188
28	......	0.001	0.002	0.004	0.008	0.015	0.028	0.052	0.097	0.177
29	......	0.001	0.002	0.003	0.006	0.013	0.025	0.047	0.089	0.166
30	......	0.001	0.001	0.003	0.005	0.011	0.022	0.042	0.082	0.156

ever, and its value depends upon the scope of the study and the accuracy of the other types of data involved in the correlation.

The time rate at which moisture is extracted from a basin through evapotranspiration is a function of such factors as air temperature and vapor-pressure difference. Therefore, a refinement of the antecedent-precipitation or -recharge indices discussed above can be accomplished through the determination or estimation of the function between k and such meteorological elements. While preliminary studies based on an assumed function between k and the vapor-pressure difference have shown promising results, it has not yet been adequately demonstrated that this approach is appreciably better than the use of a constant k value, supplemented by season as an additional parameter in the correlation.

In humid and subhumid areas where streams flow continuously, ground-water discharge at the beginning of the storm has been found to be a good index to initial moisture conditions within the basin. Since recent rains affect current moisture conditions, even though they have had no effect upon streamflow, this index should be supplemented in the correlation by some weighted measure of the rainfall for several days preceding. This is usually done by using 6 to 10 days of antecedent precipitation, weighted according to a reciprocal recession, as an additional parameter.

Evaporation, as observed at a Weather Bureau Class A station, has been used in some studies to indicate soil-moisture conditions. Linsley and Ackermann,[1] in a study of the Valley River in North Carolina, found that field-moisture deficiency at any time was approximately equal to 0.9 the total pan evaporation since the ground was last saturated, less any additions made to field moisture by intervening rains.

The use of soil-moisture observations is not to be overlooked in the event such data are available. Adequate sampling presents a difficult problem in determining the moisture deficiency of a basin. Three-dimensional measurements are required, and the selected observational sites must be representative of soil and vegetative types throughout the basin. Perhaps the most logical approach to the use of soil-moisture data is the determination of a weighted value of moisture deficiency for the basin as a whole. Here, however, one is confronted with an arbitrary decision regarding the depth of soil to be considered. Further, such an analysis assumes that moisture conditions above the soil surface are always in harmony with soil conditions, which may not be the case.

Storm precipitation. In relatively flat areas where topographic features do not cause a typical areal precipitation distribution, basin-wide precipitation data computed from station averages or Thiessen weights can be assumed to represent the average depth of precipitation over the basin.

[1] Linsley, R. K., and W. C. Ackermann, Method of Predicting the Runoff from Rainfall, *Trans. ASCE*, Vol. 107, pp. 825-846, 1942.

In this case, substitution of one rainfall station for another or additions to or deletions from the station network do not bias the basin averages. In other words, records from recently installed stations can be utilized directly without rendering the recent data incomparable with those of earlier years.

However, in mountainous areas, where topographic features create a typical areal pattern of precipitation (Chap. 6), data determined by station averages or Thiessen weights can be considered as nothing more than an *index* to average basin precipitation. In such case, storm precipitation for the entire period of record being analyzed should be based on the same station network. If this cannot be done, the data of earlier years should be adjusted to make them comparable with those being collected from the current network.

A similar problem arises in dealing with mountain basins having a snow cover in the upper elevations. Runoff from rainfall can be assumed to occur only from the snow-free area, and hence the runoff in inches over the whole basin will be less than that over the actual area of runoff. This can be accounted for by reducing the computed runoff by the percentage of noncontributing area. This does not account, however, for the varying significance of the precipitation index as the size of the contributing area varies. Linsley[1] has shown that, within certain limits, storm precipitation in mountain areas may be assumed to conform to the normal annual pattern. If, then, the storm precipitation at each station is expressed in per cent of normal annual and the average percentage is multiplied by the annual average over the contributing area, an adjusted value of the precipitation index is obtained which should be more satisfactory than a precipitation average. In studies in the San Joaquin Basin of California, this procedure greatly improved relations between runoff and rainfall. A curve of normal annual precipitation below various elevations is useful; such a curve can be obtained by planimetry on a normal isohyetal map with contours of elevation superimposed.

Three-variable relations. Since runoff is essentially the residual of precipitation after basin recharge has been removed, precipitation must necessarily be one of the independent variables in any runoff correlation. If the scope of the problem under consideration does not justify a complex correlation analysis, a simple three-way relation of the type shown in Fig. 16-4 or 16-5 may be developed. While there are numerous other factors which could be used as a parameter, such as days to last significant rain or an antecedent-precipitation index, the selected parameter should not be independent of season. The importance of this restriction becomes evident when it is realized that in some areas a 5-in. rain in August will produce less

[1] Linsley, R. K., Frequency and Seasonal Distribution of Precipitation over Large Areas, *Trans. Am. Geophys. Union*, Vol. 28, pp. 445-450, 1947.

than 10 per cent the runoff of a 5-in. storm in March, even though the number of days since last significant rain is the same in both cases.

Multi-variable coaxial relations. In most design operations and river forecasting problems, there is adequate justification for making a detailed analysis of the factors governing runoff to ensure the development of relations which will be universally applicable to the problem basin. The independent variables in the required correlation must include one or more factors which represent total moisture deficiency of the basin, as well as the

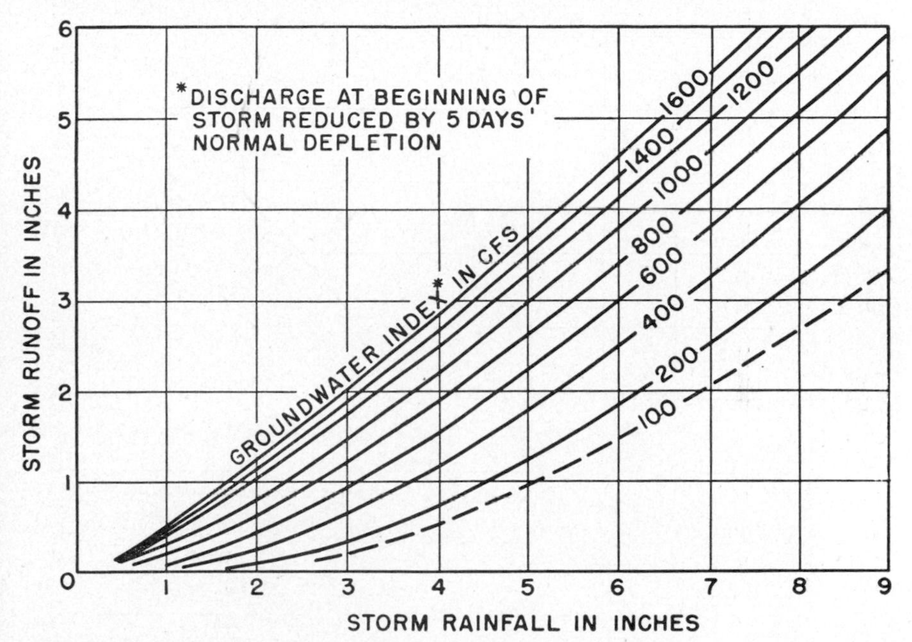

FIG. 16–5. Rainfall-runoff relation for the White River at West Hartford, Vermont, using groundwater flow as a parameter.

storm parameters (amount and duration of rainfall). Thus, there is a minimum of four variables, including runoff or basin recharge, which must be considered in the correlation. The problem is further complicated by joint functions, *i.e.*, the effect of one factor upon runoff is dependent upon the values of other variables. While analytical correlation can be used, the functional relations are extremely complex and the selection of an appropriate equation is correspondingly difficult. The coaxial method of graphical correlation (Appendix A), while perplexing to the beginner, will yield excellent results when applied by one experienced in the technique and familiar with the physical aspects of the problem involved.

The statement, "Experience is the best teacher," is amply true as applied to the coaxial correlation of runoff phenomena. As one gains familiarity with the method, he begins to realize more and more the flexibility of the procedure, and at the same time he learns how to utilize this flexibility to advantage for any particular problem. It is beyond the scope of this text to present a lengthy discussion of coaxial correlation as applied to runoff relations, but a few of the more important points are covered briefly in the following paragraphs.

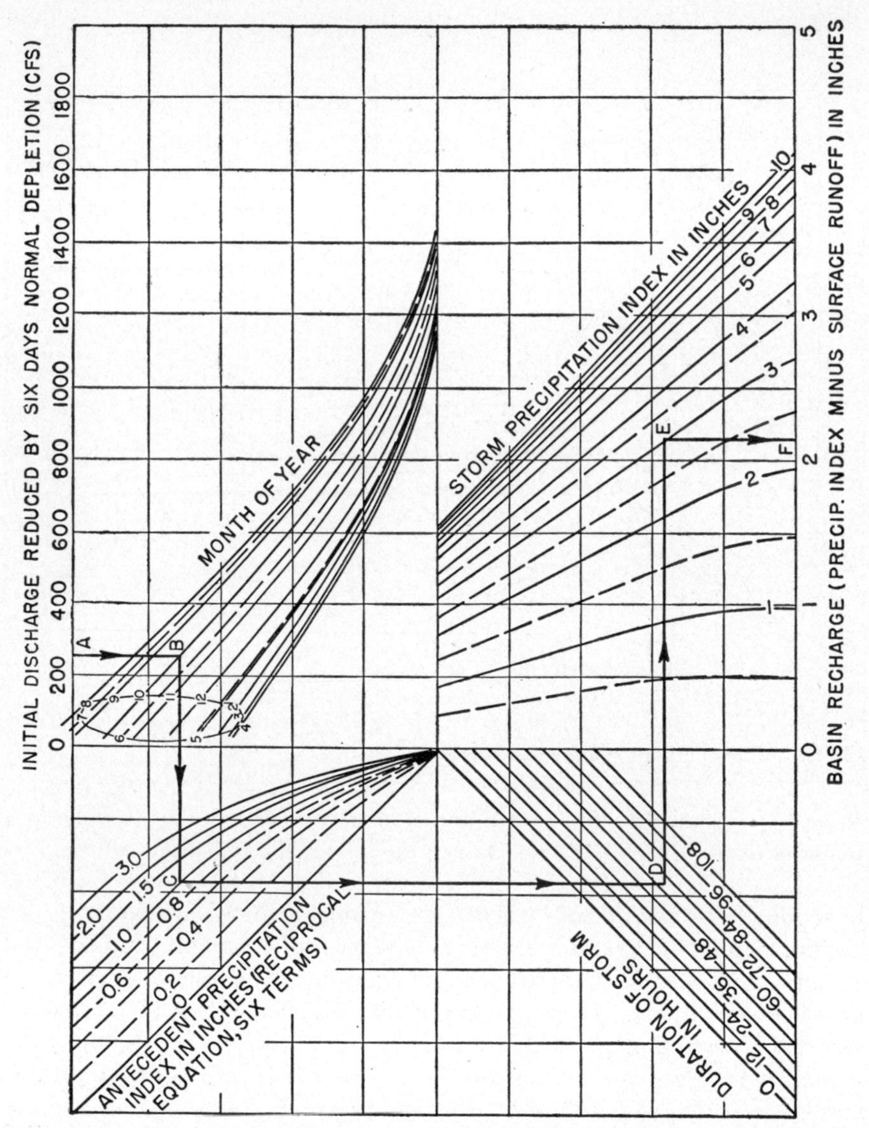

FIG. 16–6. Basin-recharge relation for the Rappahannock River near Fredericksburg, Virginia.

The independent variables can be introduced in a number of different orders, but from practical and theoretical considerations there are advantages to be gained by laying out the charts so that a unified index of initial moisture conditions is first determined, with the storm parameters being introduced last (Figs. 16-6 and 16-7). For example, many types of correlation analyses will result in a relation which is entirely adequate but which under some conditions will yield impossible values, such as negative runoff

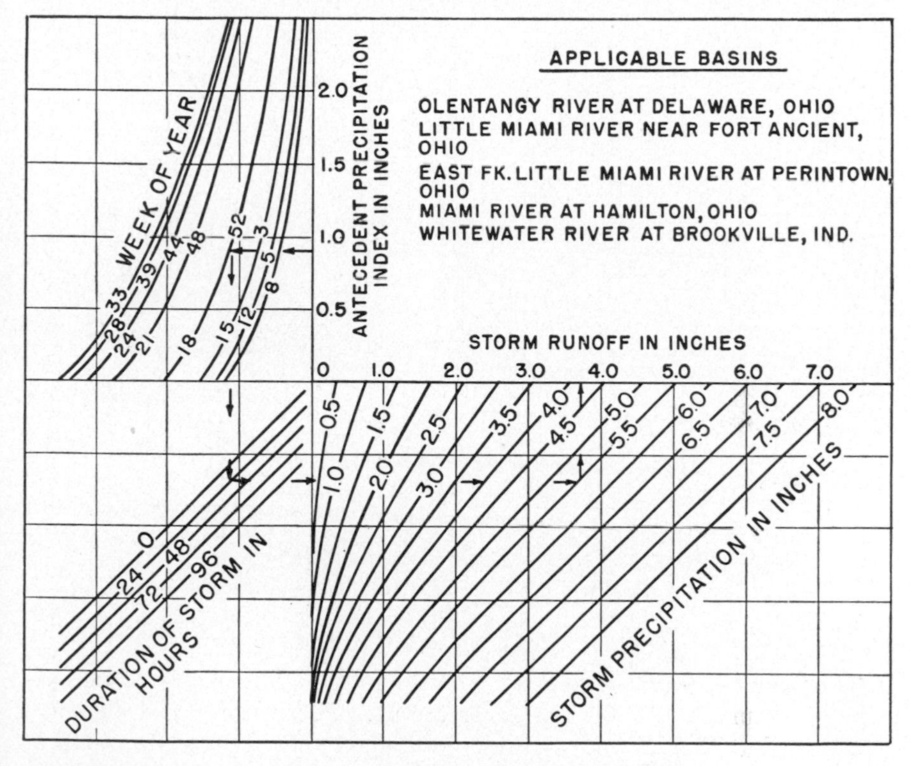

FIG. 16–7. Coaxial runoff relation developed from data for several northern tributary areas of the Ohio River Basin. *(U.S. Weather Bureau.)*

or more runoff than rainfall. Through introducing storm precipitation as the final parameter, we have a relation which in no case will yield a value of runoff that is obviously impossible. Further, while the relations are based on data derived from the storm as a whole, they may be used to compute runoff for the first part of the storm up to any given time. Consequently, incremental values of runoff can be determined by taking successive differences. That is, the runoff increment for the second 6-hr period of a storm is the difference between the runoff for the first 12- and 6-hr periods. Thus, if we are interested in computing runoff increments for application of the unit hydrograph, time can be saved by placing the moisture-deficiency indices first in the sequence of charts, since the *initial* basin conditions remain the same throughout the storm and need only be determined once.

The relation shown in Fig. 16-6 is actually designed to compute total basin recharge, while Figs. 16-7 and 16-8 have runoff as the dependent variable. Since runoff is equal to rainfall minus basin recharge, either type of

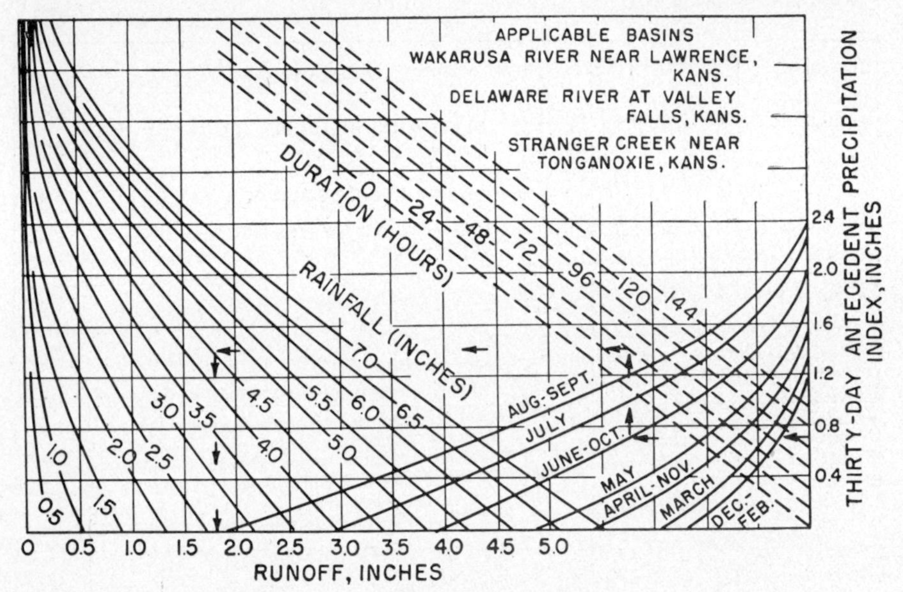

FIG. 16–8. Coaxial runoff relation with the curve families superimposed. *(U.S. Weather Bureau.)*

relation can be converted to the other by simply adjusting the storm-precipitation curves. Conditions favor the use of recharge for development purposes, but they also favor the use of runoff when the relation is to be applied. Consequently, it is customary to develop the relation in terms of basin recharge and then adjust the storm-precipitation curves to indicate runoff.

Since the most important independent variable, storm precipitation, is omitted in the first and second charts of Figs. 16-6 and 16-7, any initial plotting in these quadrants will show so little correlation that it will be difficult to construct the curve family. This difficulty can be remedied by plotting, initially, only data for storms having precipitation within rather narrow limits. However, the type of curvature and convergence can be determined by theoretical reasoning, and first-approximation curves can be constructed on the basis of limited data. Further, the relations are quite similar throughout any general area, and once such a relation is developed, all curve families but one can be used as the first-approximation curves for any other basin in the area. In fact, a single relation has been found to be applicable to as many as six or eight tributary drainages within a river basin. In any event, the first plotting will line up better if the effect of all other independent variables has been given consideration through the estimation of the respective curve families.

While relations of the types shown in Figs. 16-6 to 16-8 yield accurate results for most storms and provide a simple method of computing runoff, they nevertheless have certain deficiencies which should not be overlooked. (1) Rainfall intensity is omitted. (2) Conditions of frozen soil do not apply. (3) Snow on the ground at the beginning or end of the storm period will alter the amount of runoff. Since two of the parameters are precipitation and duration, average intensity for the entire storm period is an integral part of the relations. However, the computed runoff for a 5-in. 24-hr storm is the same whether intensity is constant or varies widely throughout the storm. This deficiency can introduce a serious error only when intensities are so great throughout the entire storm that rainfall runs off too rapidly to alleviate the moisture deficiency of the basin. Experience has shown that the relations normally yield fair results during frozen conditions, provided that the seasonal or weekly curve which indicates maximum runoff conditions is used, regardless of the date of the storm. Storms involving snowfall are discussed in the following section.

Since it is impossible to segregate the water passing the gaging station according to the portion of the basin in which it fell, statistically derived runoff relations must necessarily be determined from basin averages of the parameters. Unfortunately, because of the higher order and joint functions involved, a relation which is based on storms of uniform areal distribution will yield runoff values which are too low when applied to storms with extremely uneven distribution. This can be demonstrated by computing the runoff for 4, 6, and 8 in. of storm precipitation, assuming all other factors to remain constant. While 6 is the average of 4 and 8, the runoff depths computed from these three values of precipitation do not bear a corresponding relation. An uneven distribution of antecedent precipitation produces similar results. If, however, the runoff relations are based on data representing reasonably uniform conditions, they can properly be used to compute the runoff in the vicinity of each of the rainfall stations. The average of such computed values will, in general, more nearly approach the observed runoff. In other words, if either storm or antecedent precipitation is highly variable from one portion of the basin to another, then computed runoff depths, rather than precipitation, should be averaged.

In many hydrologic problems, such as those requiring the use of the unit hydrograph, it becomes necessary to estimate increments of runoff resulting from short periods of rainfall throughout an extended storm. This can be accomplished by computing runoff depths from accumulated precipitation up to the termini of the designated periods and subtracting successive values of runoff. As an alternative, all precipitation prior to the period of interest can be considered to be antecedent precipitation and the storm rainfall for the period used to compute the corresponding increment of runoff. For forecast purposes, where time is of the essence, the first method may be preferable. The second method, on the other hand, gives more significance to time variations of rainfall intensity and may, therefore, provide for more accurate computations. However, the relative accuracies of the two techniques are also dependent upon the adequacy of the assumed weights for antecedent precipitation, since the first method is in accord with the analysis used in developing the basin relation.

The infiltration approach. Basically, the infiltration approach is exceedingly simple, and it is considered by many to be the rational approach. In practical application to natural drainage basins of sizable proportions, however, so many complications arise that the procedure is of little value. In studies for small areas of homogeneous characteristics where a single infiltration-capacity curve can be assumed, the method can be used to advantage. During the past decade, many eminent hydrologists have attempted to use the infiltration approach for the calculation of surface runoff, and as a result many technical papers have been published on the subject.[1] The published material, which is varied in content and conclusions, has been summarized by Cook.[2]

By definition, the surface runoff produced by a given storm is equal to that portion of the rainfall which is not disposed of through (1) interception and depression storage, (2) evaporation, and (3) infiltration. Therefore, assuming that we are in a position to estimate the first two items, which may or may not be significant, we need then be concerned only with the rainfall, infiltration, and runoff. If the rainfall intensity is at all times greater than the infiltration capacity, we are then in a position to compute the surface runoff, provided that we know the duration and amount of rainfall and provided that we have an applicable curve of infiltration capacity (Chap. 12).

Since all subsurface flow is the result of infiltration, while surface runoff is composed only of water which has not infiltered, it seems plausible that the volume of either type of flow could be computed through the infiltration

[1] Horton, R. E., Determination of Infiltration Capacity for Large Drainage Basins, *Trans. Am. Geophys. Union*, Vol. 18, pp. 371-385, 1937.

Horton, R. E., Analyses of Runoff-plat Experiments with Varying Infiltration Capacity, *Trans. Am. Geophys. Union*, Vol. 20, pp. 693-711, 1939.

Horner, W. W., Role of the Land during Flood Periods, *Trans. ASCE*, Vol. 109, pp. 1269-1320, 1944.

[2] Cook, H. L., The Infiltration Approach to the Calculation of Surface Runoff, *Trans. Am. Geophys. Union*, Vol. 27, pp. 726-747, 1946.

approach. However, to the present time, the concept has been applied only to the calculation of surface runoff. Present techniques do not permit precise determination of the subsurface and surface runoff present in a hydrograph. Hence, it is impossible to develop true infiltration data through analysis of storm hydrographs from natural basins.

Since it is generally conceded that a considerable portion of the storm hydrograph may be subsurface flow, the infiltration approach, even when applicable, can be used to compute only one component of total flood flow. If a less rational method must be used to determine other major components, the value of the infiltration approach is certainly questionable. On the other hand, relations of the type shown in Figs. 16-6 to 16-8 may be used to compute the total discharge or any component, the only requirement being that the method of hydrograph analysis be common to both development and application.

The infiltration concept can be applied to the rational computation of surface runoff only when the following factors are essentially uniform throughout the area under consideration: (1) amount, intensity, and duration of rainfall; (2) infiltration characteristics; (3) surface-storage characteristics. These drastic limitations naturally preclude direct application of the infiltration approach to any area other than a small plot or experimental basin. Even if the physical characteristics, land use, and vegetal cover were uniform throughout the basin, areal variations in storm elements, and antecedent weather as well, would render the rational approach impracticable.

For a small plot with areal uniformity in every respect, experiment has shown that the infiltration-capacity curve is not stable but varies considerably with the initial condition of the soil (Fig. 12-14). Consequently, a strictly rational approach would require many test runs to determine the complex functional relation between infiltration capacity, time, and initial moisture conditions. Further, since there is no practical method for observing the moisture deficiency of a basin, an empirical parameter is required to represent initial moisture conditions. It is common practice to neglect the variations in the infiltration-capacity curve, *i.e.*, an average curve is assumed, and the time increment representing rainfall duration is shifted laterally to account for variations of initial moisture conditions.

In the simplest case, that of continuous rainfall with intensity at all times exceeding the infiltration capacity, the functional relation between capacity and time is relatively simple. Such cases, however, are seldom encountered in practice. For the general case, many questions arise, such as "How does the capacity vary with time during the initial period of the storm and in subsequent periods when the rainfall intensity is less than the infiltration capacity?" and "How does the capacity build up during rainless periods of an intermittent storm?" Such questions cannot as yet be answered on a sound basis, and, in practice, arbitrary assumptions are required.

From the foregoing discussion it should be evident that the rational infiltration approach is impracticable for the usual hydrologic problem requiring a runoff relation. In practice, therefore, many so-called "infiltration indices" have been devised by hydrologists advocating the infiltration approach. The use of such indices does not constitute a rational application of the infiltration theory, and the results derived by their use must always be considered empirical. Several of these indices are discussed briefly in the following paragraphs.

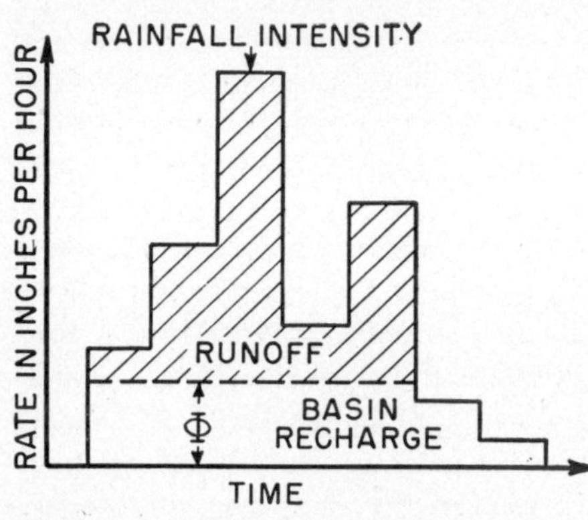

FIG. 16–9. Schematic diagram illustrating the derivation and meaning of the Φ-index.

The Φ*-index.* This index is based on the assumption that, for a specified storm with given initial conditions, the rate of basin recharge remains constant throughout the storm period. Thus, if a time-intensity graph of rainfall is constructed, the Φ-index is the average rainfall intensity above which the volume of rainfall equals the volume of observed runoff (Fig. 16-9). It will be noted from the figure that the Φ-index equals total basin recharge divided by the duration of rainfall, provided that the rainfall intensity is continuously in excess of the Φ-index. Since the maximum rate of surface retention and the infiltration capacity decrease with time throughout the storm period, the Φ concept assumes too much runoff at the beginning and too little at the end of the storm. For a single *complex* (an area of identical soil profile and surface conditions), Φ is the constant rate at which water must be extracted from the rainfall to yield the observed runoff. Since Φ represents the combined effects of interception and depression storage, as well as infiltration, some hydrologists have chosen to term it "retention rate," rather than an infiltration index. However, the term "retention" as used in this text does not include infiltration.

The **W***-index.* In the case of a single complex, the **W**-index is defined as the average rate of infiltration during the time the rainfall intensity exceeds the infiltration capacity. The equation used to derive values of **W** is

$$\mathbf{W} = \frac{F_i}{t_f} = \frac{1}{t_f}(P - Q_s - S_e) \tag{16-4}$$

where F_i is the total infiltration, t_f the time during which rainfall intensity exceeds infiltration capacity, P the precipitation, Q_s the surface runoff attributable to the storm, and S_e the effective surface storage or retention. Essentially, the **W**-index is equivalent to the Φ-index minus the rate of retention by interception and depression storage. While the segregation of infiltration and retention would appear to be a refinement of the procedure, the task of estimating the retention rate is such that combining it with infiltration is probably equally accurate. The **W**-index is commonly applied to multi-complex areas, but under these conditions it has no more physical significance than the Φ-index.

The $\mathbf{W}_{min}$*-index.* With very wet conditions, when the infiltration capacity is essentially equal to f_c and the retention rate is at a minimum, the values of **W** and Φ are almost identical. Under these conditions, the **W**-index becomes the $\mathbf{W}_{min}$-index by definition. This index is used principally in studies concerning maximum flood possibilities.

The use of infiltration indices. The foregoing discussion describes the three most commonly used infiltration indices and the methods of determining their values for specific storms for which the amount of surface runoff is known. To use such indices in practice, however, the procedure is reversed—the surface runoff is computed on the basis of an estimated value of the index. Strictly speaking, a derived value of the index is applicable only when the storm characteristics and antecedent conditions are identical to those for which it was derived. Since the variability of Φ and **W** is comparable with that of runoff, the indices are worthless unless their values can be correlated with known factors other than runoff. There is no advantage in this procedure over a direct correlation of runoff or recharge with the same factors. The introduction of such arbitrary indices into the problem of computing runoff complicates the solution without enhancing the accuracy or rationalizing the approach, and their use is not recommended.

SHORT-PERIOD RUNOFF RELATIONS INVOLVING RAIN AND/OR SNOW

The problem of predicting short-period runoff is made considerably more complex by snowfall and snowmelt when they become important or dominating factors. In the first place, data on the water equivalent of the snow cover are usually too meager, both with respect to record length and areal coverage, to permit an intensive statistical analysis. Even when the distribution of snowfall is initially uniform, subsequent drifting may result in an extremely variable snow cover. The variations in snow cover are further amplified by uneven melting, resulting from differences in elevation, slope, aspect, shading, etc. (Chap. 7). Consequently, many simultaneous observations are required to determine the water equivalent of the snow cover over a basin.

The problems of computing runoff when snow is involved may be broken down conveniently into three classes: (1) that case when the quantity of snow to be considered is small by comparison with the amount of rain; (2) that case when snow predominates throughout the basin; (3) that case when snow predominates in one portion of the basin, with rain or no precipitation in the remaining portion. Each class requires a different method of analysis. While in practice there are many borderline cases, for purposes of discussion the snow problem is considered in accordance with this classification.

Basin-wide rain and snow, predominantly rain. Storms falling into this class are usually the result of either rain falling on a thin snow cover or a rainstorm changing to snow. In either case, a rainfall-runoff relation is applicable, provided that the storm precipitation is roughly adjusted to account for the limited effect of the snow. In the first case, the estimated water equivalent of the snow cover at the beginning of rain must be added to the storm rainfall, while, in the second case, only storm rainfall need be considered.

Basin-wide snowmelt. The quantity of snowmelt occurring during a specified period depends upon many meteorological factors, such as temperature, humidity, wind, radiation, and the temperature and quantity of rainfall. Further, the snow quality and water equivalent of the pack are important factors (Chap. 7). In general, limitations imposed by the scarcity of data and the complexities of natural basins are such that, in practical application, resort must be had to purely empirical relations, except possibly in considering maximum conditions.

Air temperature is naturally one of the most important factors determining short-period snowmelt. Since snowmelt is zero for all subfreezing temperatures and is directly related to above-freezing temperatures, the index commonly used is degree days above 32°F. Thus, a day with mean temperature of 49°F represents 17 degree days. Although degree days are most commonly based on dry-bulb readings because such data are readily available, wet-bulb temperatures are probably more closely related to snowmelt. In considering small basins, the 6- or 12-hr melt is often required, and, in such cases, temperatures are expressed as *degree quarter-days* or *degree half-days*. By analogy, a 12-hr period with mean temperature of 49°F represents 17 degree half-days or 34 degree quarter-days.

Snowmelt relations are generally determined by one of two methods, (1) a direct correlation between runoff and degree days, with other parameters, and (2) a correlation between the degree-day factor and pertinent parameters. The *degree-day factor* is defined as the ratio of snowmelt (or increment of runoff) to the concurrent number of degree days. As originally conceived, the degree-day factor was expected to be relatively constant. However, there are several causes for variation in the degree-day factor.

Temperature alone is not a perfect index of the snow-melting potentialities of an air mass. Therefore, the degree-day factor may vary with different air masses over the basin, thus introducing a possible short-term fluctuation and also a seasonal fluctuation in values of melt per degree day. The implication in a constant degree-day factor is that melt and runoff are concurrent. Actually, at the beginning of a melting period much of the melt water may be stored in the snow or soil to be released at some later time. This phenomenon may cause an apparent increase in the degree-day factor as the melting period advances. In view of the fact that the degree-day factor is a variable, there is probably little advantage to be gained through its use, since the introduction of degree days and snowmelt as separate variables permits greater flexibility with respect to the functional relations.

Numerous determinations of the dry-bulb degree-day factor have been made. Clyde[1] found that the apparent degree-day factor for Gooseberry Creek, Utah, was about 0.09 in./degree day. He also exposed snow samples in a laboratory and found the degree-day factor to be 0.05 in./degree day. The difference probably represents heat supplied to the snow in the basin from radiation and from the soil which is not reflected in the air temperature. Studies by the U.S. Weather Bureau and others indicate that the dry-bulb degree-day factor varies between 0.05 and 0.15 in./degree day. Since the wet-bulb temperature is generally lower than the dry bulb, the wet-bulb degree-day factor would be somewhat higher. Wet-bulb temperatures have not been used extensively because they are observed at relatively few stations.

Studies have shown that the apparent degree-day factor computed from streamflow tends to increase with time after a freezing spell. This effect is probably largely due to the retention of early melt water in the snow and soil. One item in the determination of degree-day factors which results in considerable variation is the contributing area. Some investigators have expressed melt in inches over the entire basin, even if a portion of the area does not contribute. Others have attempted to reduce melt to inches on the actual contributing area. This latter procedure naturally results in higher values of the degree-day factor. In studies of basins in western Pennsylvania, Horton[2] found the degree-day factors to be slightly lower on heavily forested basins, with values ranging from 0.09 on basins with thin cover to 0.06 where cover was heavy.

The question of the best base for degree-day computations has been the subject of some debate. The freezing point, 32°F, has been most commonly used. However, an inversion frequently occurs over the snow surface, and crusts have been observed to form on snow while the temperature in a shel-

[1] Clyde, G. D., Snow-melting Characteristics, *Utah Agr. Expt. Sta. Bull.* 231, 1931.

[2] Horton, R. E., Infiltration and Runoff during the Snow Melting Season, with Forest Cover, *Trans. Am. Geophys. Union*, Vol. 26, pp. 59-68, 1945.

ter several feet above the snow was as high as 40°F. This suggests the possibility that better results might be obtained by using a base higher than 32°F, but no actual investigations along this line have been reported.

In studies[1] of the Susquehanna River Basin, a rather satisfactory relation was developed between snowmelt, degree days accumulated since the last freezing temperatures, and the initial water equivalent of the snow cover (Fig. 16-10). This type of relation tends to take into account the quality

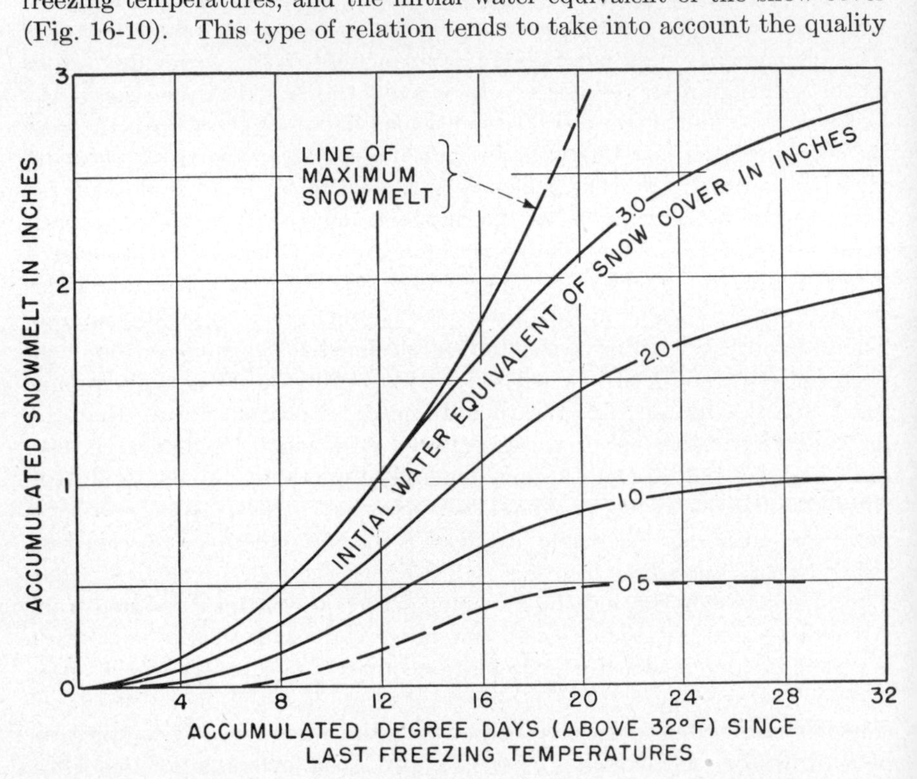

FIG. 16–10. Snowmelt forecasting curves developed by the Federal-State Flood Forecasting Service of Pennsylvania.

of the snow cover but neglects such factors as wind, humidity, and radiation, except as they may be interrelated with temperature. If a more accurate relation is required, a coaxial correlation between all significant factors should be attempted. However, in many cases, the quality and quantity of available data will prevent the development of more detailed procedures.

Because of the lag in travel through a basin, it cannot be assumed that the discharge on a given day represents that day's melt from the snow field.

[1] Snyder, F. F., "Cooperative Hydrologic Investigations," Part II, Commonwealth of Pennsylvania, Harrisburg, 1939 (mimeo.).

The outflow hydrograph should, therefore, be adjusted for this delay. This may be accomplished by a trial-and-error process of reversing the unit-graph procedure or by reversing the routing procedure with a storage curve developed from the channel recession. Since most snowmelt runoff follows subsurface paths, the routing procedure is probably more reliable than the use of unit graphs developed for rainfall but either method is susceptible to considerable error. However, computed inflows should more nearly represent the snowmelt than does observed streamflow. This adjustment does not account for water required to satisfy soil-moisture deficiency.

The occurrence of rain over a snow field further complicates the runoff problem. The volume of snowmelt caused by rainfall can be computed as outlined in Chap. 7. The portion of the incident rain which will run off depends on the ability of the snow blanket to absorb water. In any case, appreciable runoff from rainfall cannot occur in an area where the air temperature is below freezing, and this area should be deducted from the total basin drainage in computing runoff. Water retention by snow is discussed in Chap. 7. The ultimate storage capacity appears to be about 5 per cent by weight and, except in very deep packs (several feet) of snow, retention should not be assumed to exceed 0.05 in./in. of water equivalent.

Segregated areas of rain and snow. In many mountainous basins having a considerable range in elevation, winter conditions are typified by a semipermanent snow cover in the headwaters, while the lower portions of the basin have only intermittent snow cover. In other words, the *snow line* (lower limit of snow cover) is a dynamic feature, moving up and down the slopes with the passing of time. Since surface air temperature at any time is an inverse function of elevation, the rate of snowmelt decreases with elevation above the snow line. If the freezing isotherm is below the snow line, there is naturally no melting occurring at any point within the basin. Thus, above-freezing temperatures at an index station do not of themselves indicate the rate of melting over the basin—the extent of the snow cover also being an important factor.

Linsley[1] developed a method of forecasting snowmelt runoff for the tributary areas within the Central Valley of California, using weighted degree days. Through analysis of the area-elevation curve for the basin, the area within each 1000-ft zone of elevation was determined and, using an assumed lapse rate, the mean temperature within each zone for a given temperature at the index station was computed. Converting these temperatures to degree days and weighting them in proportion to the area within the zone, a weighted value of degree days for the basin was computed for various temperatures at the index station. These data were used to develop a series of curves (Fig. 16-11) which gave average degree days for the basin

[1] Linsley, R. K., A Simple Procedure for the Day-to-day Forecasting of Runoff from Snowmelt, *Trans. Am. Geophys. Union*, Vol. 24, Part III, pp. 62-67, 1943.

as a function of temperature at the index station and elevation of the snow line. Multiplying the degree days determined from these curves by the degree-day factor gives the snowmelt in inches over the basin. The degree-day factor for the area of application was rather closely related to the time of year (Fig. 16-12).

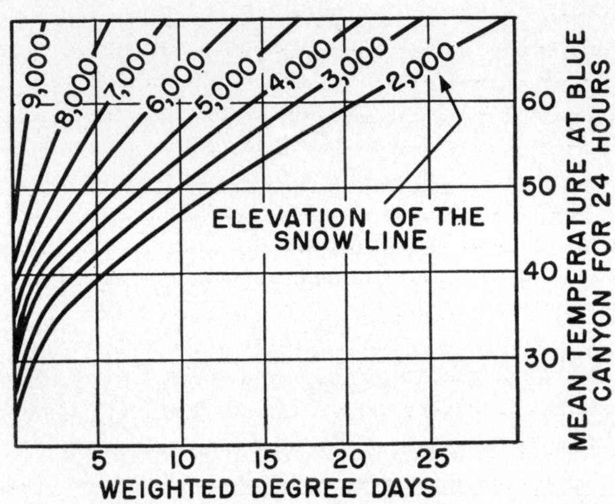

FIG. 16–11. Weighted degree-day curves for the Tuolumne River above Don Pedro Dam, California.

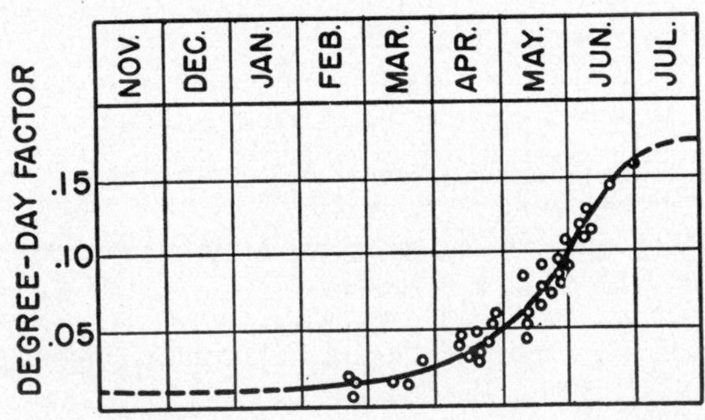

FIG. 16–12. Degree-day factor curve for the lower San Joaquin Basin, California.

The results obtained by this method can be essentially duplicated by performing a coaxial correlation between snowmelt, temperature at an index station, elevation of the snow line, and date. Such a method permits greater flexibility, since the degree-day factor may be allowed to vary with both temperature and snow-line elevation. Further, other known influences, such as wind, humidity, and radiation, can be given place in the correlation.

EXTENDED-PERIOD RUNOFF RELATIONS

The design of irrigation and power developments often requires a complete analysis of streamflow possibilities with respect to runoff, not only from individual storms but for extended periods as well. In many cases, the period covered by the precipitation records far exceeds that for discharge, and consequently an adequate annual or seasonal precipitation-runoff relation permits extrapolation of the streamflow record. The efficient operation of many irrigation, power, and flood-control developments requires that some estimate be made of the streamflow to be expected during the coming month, season, or year. Here again, runoff relations serve the purpose.

There is an important difference in the basic requirements of runoff relations as applied to design and operation. For design purposes, streamflow and related parameters can be concurrent. In operation, however, runoff must be predicted in advance of its occurrence. This means that the seasonal or annual volume of streamflow must be related to antecedent factors or parameters which can themselves be measured in advance. On a seasonal or annual basis, precipitation is the dominating factor determining streamflow. Inasmuch as the meteorologist is not yet capable of predicting precipitation far in advance, seasonal or annual runoff relations possess forecast value only in those areas where snow accumulates during the winter season, producing a seasonal rise corresponding to the upward trend of temperatures in the spring. Such conditions exist in varying degree throughout the mountainous regions of the western United States and to some extent in New England.

There are at present two schools of thought regarding the most practicable and expeditious method of forecasting water supply. One advocates the use of a relation between streamflow and the water equivalent of the snow pack at the beginning of the spring thaw as determined by snow surveys. The other contends that equally reliable forecasts can be made directly from precipitation data collected at long-established stations, the advantage being one of economy. While generally of comparable accuracy, either method may be found to yield the best results in a particular case, depending upon record lengths and relative network density.

Several other approaches to the problem of long-range water-supply forecasting have been explored with varying degrees of success. Potts[1] describes the use of photographs taken from fixed points as the basis of forecasts. The percentage of snow-covered area in a fixed portion of the photograph is used to predict subsequent streamflow. Collins[2] established

[1] Potts, H. L., Snow-surveys and Runoff-forecasting from Photographs, *Trans. Am. Geophys. Union*, Vol. 18, pp. 658-660, 1937.

[2] Collins, E. H., Relationship of Degree-days above Freezing to Runoff, *Trans. Am. Geophys. Union*, Vol. 15, pp. 624-629, 1934.

a relation between accumulated degree days and per cent of total runoff for several streams. With a known accumulation of degree days, the corresponding per cent of total runoff can be read from the curve. Knowing the runoff to date, the total for the year can be computed. Wahle[1] based his forecast on the volume and pattern of flow during the first 6 months of the water year. Although none of these methods matches those described in the following sections for accuracy, the fact that any success was attained at all shows the existence of relationships between water equivalent and area of the snow pack and between winter runoff from low-elevation rainfall and the subsequent volume of snowmelt runoff. The existence of such relations indicates that low-elevation precipitation stations or scattered snow courses should provide reliable indices of spring runoff from high-elevation snowmelt. The methods discussed below are considered to be most practicable when the problem at hand justifies an exhaustive analysis. For simpler solutions, one need only eliminate some of the refining techniques.

Precipitation-runoff relations. Many attempts have been made to develop relations between winter precipitation and spring runoff from mountainous areas where an accumulated snow cover builds up during the winter season.[2] In many cases, the results have been somewhat disappointing because of the arbitrary and simple methods of analysis employed. The precipitation and runoff periods have commonly been selected arbitrarily. Frequently, no attempt was made to determine which precipitation records were most representative of streamflow. The methods presented here are based on several years of intensive research involving basins throughout the western United States and in New England. Procedures now being used to prepare water-supply forecasts issued by the U.S. Weather Bureau are based on similar analyses.[3]

[1] Wahle, R. H., Streamflow Forecasting by Pattern-behavior, *Trans. Am. Geophys. Union*, Vol. 24, Part III, pp. 13-27, 1943.

[2] Debler, E. B., and A. F. Johnson, "Forecasting Colorado River Runoff," U.S. Bureau of Reclamation, May, 1935 (mimeo.).

Melin, R., Forecasting Spring Runoff of the Forest Rivers in North Sweden, *Trans. Intern. Comm. Snow Glaciers*, 1938, pp. 145-154.

Reedy, O. C., The Use of Precipitation-gage Measurements in Forecasting the Inflow to Lake Mead, *Trans. Am. Geophys. Union*, Vol. 19, pp. 67-69, 1938.

Alter, J. C., The Mountain Snow-survey: Its Genesis, Exodus, and Revelation, *Trans. Am. Geophys. Union*, Vol. 21, pp. 892-900, 1940.

Light, P., and M. A. Kohler, Forecasting Seasonal Runoff by Statistical Methods, *Trans. Am. Geophys. Union*, Vol. 24, Part II, pp. 719-736, 1943.

Clyde, G. D., and R. A. Work, Precipitation-runoff Relationships as a Basis for Water Supply Forecasting, *Trans. Am. Geophys. Union*, Vol. 24, Part III, pp. 43-55, 1943.

Boardman, H. P., Snow Survey versus Winter Precipitation for Forecasting Runoff of the Tuolumne River, California, *Trans. Am. Geophys. Union*, Vol. 28, pp. 752-765, 1947.

[3] Kohler, M. A., and R. K. Linsley, Recent Developments in Water Supply Forecasting from Precipitation, *Trans. Am. Geophys. Union*, Vol. 30, pp. 427-436, 1949.

Adjustment of data. In mountainous terrane the precipitation is highly variable from point to point, but the pattern from storm to storm is relatively stable (Chap. 6). Moving a rain gage a few miles may easily change the mean annual precipitation by 25 per cent. Observed precipitation can be expected to correlate well with observed runoff only when the rain gage remained at the same location throughout the period for which the records are being used.

Most of the records published by the U.S. Weather Bureau have been collected by cooperative observers without compensation. In the thinly populated sections of the West, a change of observers frequently necessitates moving the gage to a nearby ranch or village. In many such cases, the records for both sites have been published under the same name, even though the precipitation regimes are quite different. Therefore, as a preliminary step in the analysis, all precipitation records should be tested for their comparability, and indicated adjustments should be made to monthly totals of precipitation in accordance with the procedure described in Chap. 6. The accumulations should preferably be based on that period of precipitation presumed to be principally responsible for the runoff used in the correlation.

Water utilization has been a variable factor in many basins of the West. Further, changes in observational technique, discharge section, gage location, control, and other factors have all contributed to the collection of discharge records which in some cases show very definite time trends within a 30- or 40-year period. The runoff record should, therefore, be tested and any indicated adjustments made in accordance with the following procedure:

1. Plot observed seasonal values of runoff vs. average winter precipitation for several stations in and near the basin, and construct curve of best fit.
2. Compute the runoff from the derived curve for each season of record.
3. Plot double-mass curve of computed vs. observed runoff, and fit a straight line, or line segments if changes in slope are evident.
4. Adjust early records to those of recent years by ratios of the slopes of the line segments.

The runoff adjustment can be made through the direct double-mass plotting of runoff vs. the same precipitation base used to adjust precipitation data. However, this procedure assumes that the relation between precipitation and runoff is a straight line passing through the origin—a situation rarely approached in practice.

A great deal of caution should be exercised in the adjustment of basic data. Overadjustment is far less desirable than no adjustment. In many cases, the first plotting of runoff vs. precipitation will indicate such poor correlation that any adjustment from it is inadvisable. In areas where the discharge from groundwater recharge is distributed over a period of years, a long-term trend in precipitation will have a tendency to indicate an apparent time trend in the precipitation-runoff relation. Therefore, no runoff adjustment should be considered final unless it has been based on a relation between seasonal runoff and long-term precipitation or unless it has been shown that precipitation for past years is of no significance with respect to current runoff. The runoff adjustment described above is preliminary —the final adjustment is made at a later point in the analysis.

Determination of station weights. If five or more precipitation stations with sufficient length of record are strategically located within the basin being considered, an arithmetic average of their precipitation data will usually be found to be an adequate index to runoff. In the usual case, however, not more than two or three stations are found within a relatively small headwater basin, and, under these conditions, stations outside but near the basin may contribute to the correlation. A question immediately arises regarding the relative weights to be assigned to such stations. Attempts have been made in the past to assign weights on the basis of a Thiessen net, area-elevation increments, or a combination of the two. Logically, a least-squares correlation between winter precipitation at various stations and subsequent runoff from the basin should be expected to yield regression coefficients which in themselves represent the best possible weights. However, because of the high intercorrelation between precipitation at adjacent stations, the regression coefficients of a four- or five-station correlation are generally found to differ greatly, with negative coefficients being not at all uncommon. Experience has shown that weights assigned in rough proportion to the regression coefficients, but tempered toward an arithmetic average, yield consistently good results. In other words, the station with the highest positive regression coefficient is assigned the highest weight, and those with negative coefficients the lowest weights. Stations with high negative coefficients are generally dropped from the analysis. For convenience, and to minimize possible errors, the sum of the assigned weights may be set to unity.

Computation of effective basin precipitation by months. Having determined the station weights, the next step in the analysis is the computation of the effective monthly precipitation for the period of record. The *effective precipitation* is the sum of the station precipitation values multiplied by the respective station weights. For a water-year runoff correlation, effective precipitation should be computed for each month of the year. In areas where summer precipitation is insignificant, the summer months may be ignored.

While not absolutely necessary, a correlation between runoff and effective precipitation for the period used in the determination of station weights will often uncover computational errors. If the correlation coefficient of the check computation is significantly less than that obtained by the multiple correlation, all intervening computations and the cross products for the multiple correlation should be checked for errors.

Determination of monthly weights. Much fall and summer precipitation falls on bare ground in the form of rain, and consequently a sizable portion of each storm's precipitation goes toward recharging the basin. On the other hand, winter precipitation is usually in the form of snow, and each increment adds to the accumulating snow pack. Under these conditions, the portion of each increment of precipitation going toward recharging the basin is relatively insignificant. Thus, the effectiveness of precipitation in producing streamflow depends upon the time of year it occurs.

A multiple correlation between runoff and effective monthly precipitation affords a convenient and practicable means of determining monthly weights. However, a multiple correlation with eight or more independent variables based on 25 to 35 years of record is likely to yield rather erratic regression coefficients, and it is necessary to smooth the coefficients graphically. If the effectiveness of monthly precipitation is plotted against the month of occurrence, a smooth curve through the plotted data should better represent the true seasonal trend than would the individual points.

Figure 16-13 illustrates the method of determining smoothed monthly weights. Regression coefficients were computed for only 8 months. Weights for the additional months were determined by extrapolation of the smoothed curve. The discontinuity in the curve as of Oct. 1 results from the fact that the runoff period begins on that date. Thus, runoff from September rains is not included in the subsequent runoff, while that from October precipitation does affect the runoff being used in the analysis. The magnitude of the break is not determined by the analysis and is shown for academic reasons only. Theoretically, the plotted points represent mean monthly data, and the curve should be constructed in the same manner as a hydrograph based on mean daily discharge. The values taken from the curve are adjusted such that the sum of the weights is equal to unity.

Computation of seasonal precipitation index. Having determined the monthly weights, the next step in the analysis is the computation of the seasonal precipitation index for each year of record. This index is the sum of the monthly effective precipitation values multiplied by the respective monthly weights.

Determination of effect of antecedent conditions. In areas where the quantities of groundwater carried over from season to season are relatively small, antecedent conditions can usually be adequately represented by the precipitation index for the preceding year. In this case, a three-variable analytical correlation between precipitation for 2 successive years and the runoff for the second year will be found satisfactory. Converting the re gression coefficients to weights, a total precipitation index is computed for each year of record by adding to each season's index a fraction of the index for the previous year.

In regions where a considerable portion of any year's groundwater recharge is stored within the basin for 2 or more years, best results are attained by a three-variable graphical correlation between 2 successive years of runoff and the precipitation index of the latter year (Fig. 16-15).

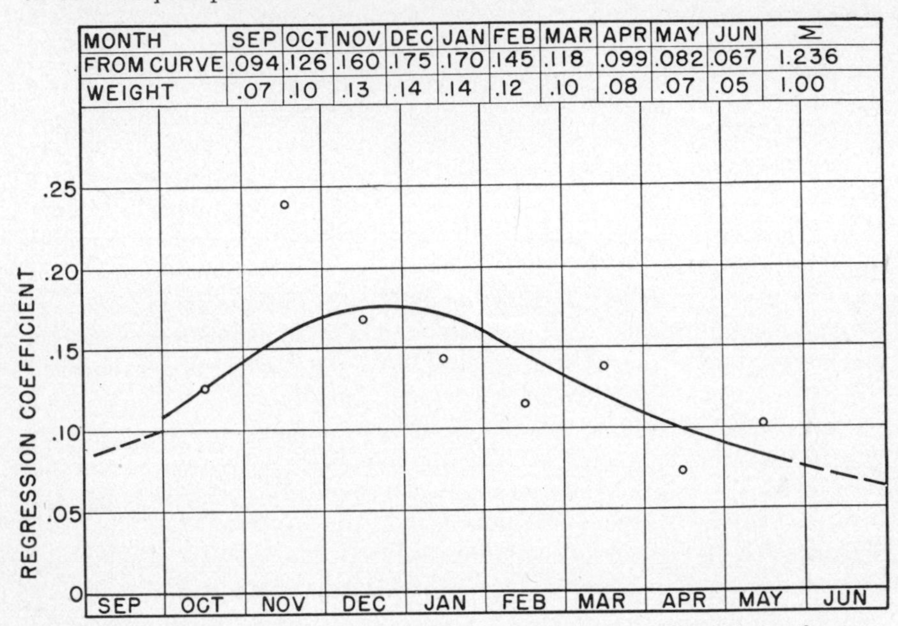

MONTH	SEP	OCT	NOV	DEC	JAN	FEB	MAR	APR	MAY	JUN	Σ
FROM CURVE	.094	.126	.160	.175	.170	.145	.118	.099	.082	.067	1.236
WEIGHT	.07	.10	.13	.14	.14	.12	.10	.08	.07	.05	1.00

FIG. 16–13. Illustration of the method of determining monthly weights from regression coefficients for the Yellowstone River above Corwin Springs, Montana. *(U.S. Weather Bureau.)*

Final runoff adjustment. The initial runoff adjustment must necessarily be based on a very rough precipitation-runoff relation. At this point in the analysis, however, we are in a much better position to adjust streamflow data since the total precipitation index is much more closely related to runoff. Therefore, a final adjustment is made in a manner similar to that described previously, except that under step 1 the total precipitation index is used. If it was necessary to use last year's runoff instead of last year's precipitation index to account for antecedent conditions, the three-variable graphical relation should be substituted in step 1. In such case, adjustments are much more difficult to establish, because last year's runoff requires the same adjustment as this year's. On the other hand, for the same reason, time trends in streamflow and precipitation have but little effect on the accuracy of the relation.

Development of final runoff relation. The end product of the analysis is a relation between runoff (final adjustment) and the total precipitation index as shown in Fig. 16-14; or, in the case of considerable groundwater carry-over, the relation is in terms of 2 successive years of runoff and the seasonal precipitation index for the later year (Fig. 16-15). The relation may be used to interpolate or extrapolate streamflow records of the past; it may be used to compute runoff to be expected from a fictitious "design season" of weather; or it may be used to forecast runoff in future years as

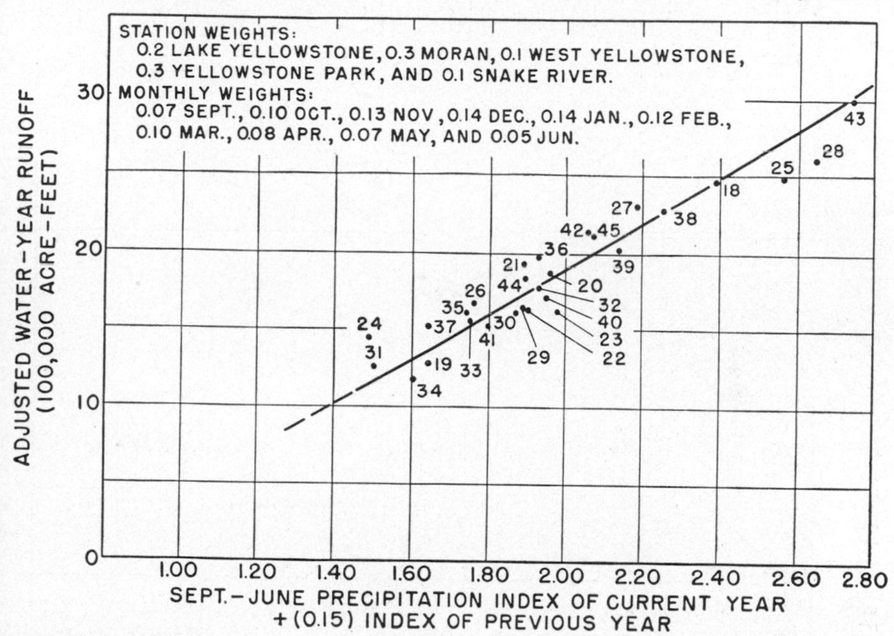

FIG. 16-14. Precipitation-runoff relation for the Yellowstone River above Corwin Springs, Montana. *(U.S. Weather Bureau.)*

discussed in Chap. 22. However, it should be remembered that the computed values are based on runoff conditions as they have existed in recent years.

Snow surveys and runoff. Unlike streamflow, river-stage, precipitation, and other hydrometeorologic observations, snow-survey measurements have been taken for a single purpose—the prediction of water supplies.[1]

[1] Church, J. E., Principles of Snow Surveying as Applied to Forecasting Streamflow, *J. Agr. Research*, Vol. 51, pp. 97-130, 1935.

Stanley, J. W., and R. E. Kennedy, Forecasting Colorado River Flow, *Trans. Am. Geophys. Union*, Vol. 28, pp. 766-779, 1947.

McDonald, C. C., Forecasting Spring Runoff from Snow Surveys for Pemigewasset River at Plymouth, New Hampshire, *Trans. Am. Geophys. Union*, Vol. 25, pp. 977-984, 1944.

To this end, the surveys of early years were made near the end of the snow-accumulation season, just prior to the beginning of the spring rise (usually about Apr. 1). In recent years, several surveys have been made each year for most of the courses, in some cases as early as Jan. 1 and as late as June 1. While forecasts can be prepared from surveys taken on any of these dates, Apr. 1 is still considered the most opportune date over most of the West.

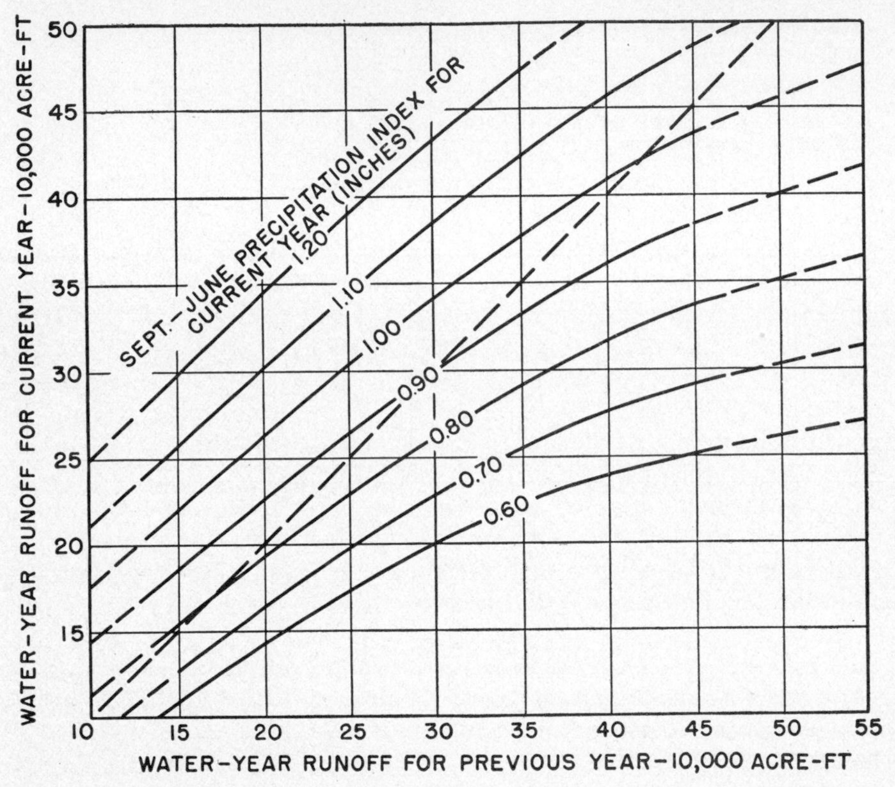

FIG. 16–15. Water-year runoff relation for the Beaverhead River at Barrats, Montana. *(U.S. Weather Bureau.)*

In view of the marked variations in snow cover within limited areas, it is not economically feasible to take enough observations of water equivalent to determine directly the volume of water in storage over a natural basin. However, by measuring at the same points year after year, the mean water equivalent over a representative course will usually constitute a reasonably adequate index to subsequent streamflow over a considerable area. A series of snow courses, so located as to give representation to elevation as well as area, will naturally result in a more accurate index.

Factors affecting the relation between snow-survey data and streamflow.

There are three factors not reflected by the water-equivalent index which can exert a pronounced influence upon subsequent runoff.[1] These are (1) groundwater storage, (2) soil-moisture deficiency, and (3) precipitation during the runoff period. In areas where base flow constitutes a sizable component of streamflow during the runoff period, the correlation can be improved by including some parameter reflecting changes in this factor. The most commonly used indices to subsequent groundwater flow are the minimum daily, weekly, or monthly flow during the snow-accumulation season or the total flow during the previous runoff season.

The moisture conditions of the soil mantle when snow begins to accumulate and the relative amount of winter melting both influence the moisture deficiency of the basin at the beginning of the runoff period. Consequently, either fall precipitation or total winter discharge (or both) are commonly used to indicate the initial conditions of the basin.

The effect of precipitation during the runoff period is dependent upon many factors such as region, extent of diversions, and time distribution. In most of California, summer rainfall is consistently very low, while in New Mexico the runoff from summer storms can approach the normal annual snowmelt runoff for small basins. If streamflow data are not adjusted for diversions, then an extensive summer storm, even though it produces no streamflow directly, will tend to reduce required diversions for irrigation and thus effectively increase observed runoff. A storm occurring in April will ordinarily produce more runoff than one in July, all other things being equal, because some of the rain falls on snow or on moist soil recently snow-covered. Moreover, the effect upon runoff of a specified monthly total of rainfall depends upon whether the entire amount fell in a single storm or was well distributed throughout the month. Taking account of all these variations in the runoff relation would require an immense amount of data and a lengthy analysis. Since quantitative forecasts of precipitation several months in advance are not presently feasible, such an elaborate analysis is seldom justified. The principal reason for including subsequent precipitation in the runoff correlation is that allowance can be made in operations for abnormal precipitation as soon as it has occurred. If subsequent precipitation is included in the relation, a forecast can be computed,

[1] Work, R. A., Adjusting Forecast Curves for Abnormal Spring and Summer Temperatures, *Trans. Am. Geophys. Union*, Vol. 25, pp. 127-140, 1944.

Marr, J. C., Effect of Soil-priming by Fall Precipitation on Spring Runoff—Upper Snake Basin, *Trans. Am. Geophys. Union*, Vol. 20, pp. 106-109, 1939.

Clyde, G. D., Soil-moisture Studies as an Aid in Forecasting Runoff from Snow Cover, *Trans. Am. Geophys. Union*, Vol. 21, pp. 871-873, 1940.

Croft, A. R., Some Factors That Influence the Accuracy of Water-supply Forecasting in the Intermountain Region, *Trans. Am. Geophys. Union*, Vol. 27, pp. 375-388, 1946.

Paget, F., A New Forecasting Curve for the Kaweah, *Trans. Am. Geophys. Union*, Vol. 27, pp. 389-395, 1946.

assuming some precipitation value which has a known probability of occurrence (Chap. 22).

Methods of weighting snow-course data. If there are numerous snow courses in and adjacent to the basin of interest, the question of how to weight the data immediately arises. The simplest method is the use of an arithmetic average. Weighting according to a Thiessen net is sometimes an improvement over the arithmetic average, especially in dealing with a

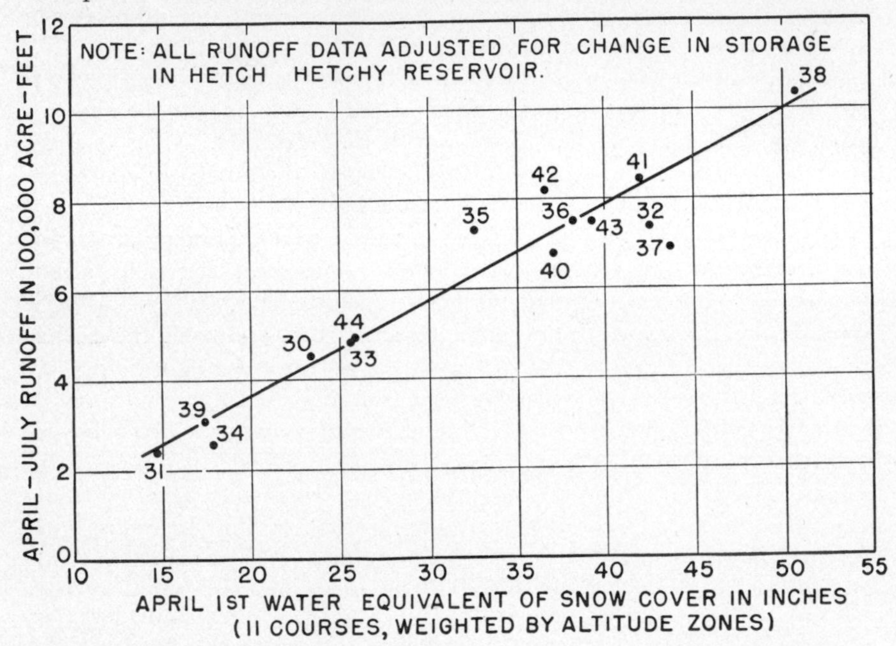

FIG. 16–16. Runoff relation for the Tuolumne River at Hetch Hetchy, California, based on snow-survey data.

particularly large basin. If the record length is sufficient, a multiple correlation between the data for each snow course and runoff can be utilized to determine weights, in the manner described for determining precipitation-station weights.

Many investigators have advocated the use of weights such that the per cent of basin area falling between two specified contours of elevation is assigned to the snow courses within that area. In practice, the area below the average elevation of the snow line on Apr. 1 is usually omitted from the percentage computations. While such a procedure seems rational since it supposedly takes into account the variation of snow cover with altitude, differences in forest cover, aspect, and slope within the basin probably produce greater simultaneous differences at one elevation than the deviations from the normal rate of change of water equivalent with elevation. The fact that winter precipitation as observed at relatively low-level stations is a good index to spring and summer runoff seems to substantiate this conclusion.

Types of relations. The period of streamflow to be related to snow-survey data depends upon the problem at hand. The period generally

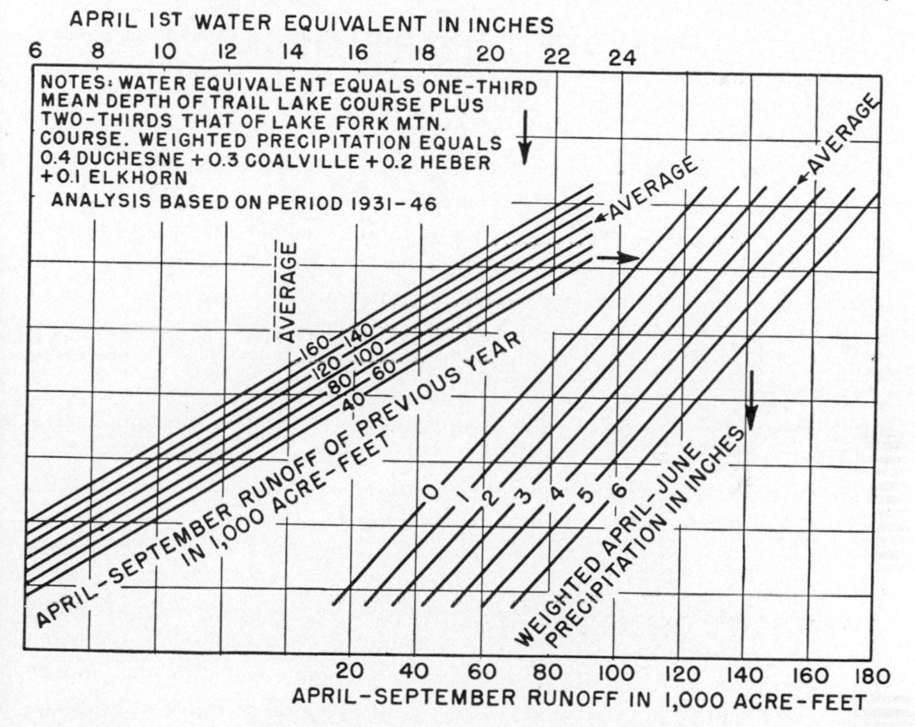

FIG. 16–17. Seasonal runoff relation for Duchesne River at Tabiona, Utah, based on snow-survey data.

extends from the date of the survey to the end of July or September or, in some cases, from July through September. A relation between April-July runoff and Apr. 1 snow cover is shown in Fig. 16-16. In this case, water-equivalent data for 12 courses were weighted by altitude zones (above 4000 ft).[1] A coaxial relation involving four variables is shown in Fig. 16-17. In this correlation, runoff of the previous season was used as an index to groundwater carry-over, and subsequent precipitation was also taken into account.

[1] Boardman, H. P., Snow Survey versus Winter Precipitation for Forecasting Runoff of the Tuolumne River, California, *Trans. Am. Geophys. Union*, Vol. 28, pp. 752-765, 1947.

17

RUNOFF DISTRIBUTION

The previous chapter discussed methods of computing the total volume of runoff associated with a particular combination of storm rainfall and antecedent weather. In certain problems, such as those involving the quantities of water available for power or irrigation storage, this volume estimate may be sufficient. More commonly, however, the estimate of runoff volume is only the first step in the determination of the outflow hydrograph from a basin. This chapter discusses techniques of determining the time distribution of flow from small and moderate drainage areas (generally under 5000 square miles).

The unit hydrograph. The discussion of hydrograph shape in Chap. 15 leads naturally to the hypothesis that identical storms with the same antecedent conditions produce identical hydrographs. This principle was expressed by Sherman[1] in introducing his theory of the *unit hydrograph*, or *unit graph*. He pointed out that all hydrographs resulting from rainfalls of a given duration have the same time base. If the rainfall distribution in the storms is similar with respect to time and area, the ordinates of each hydrograph will be proportional to its volume of runoff. The unit graph itself is the graph resulting from 1.00 in. of runoff. If the theory is sound, the hydrograph for any other similar storm of the same duration will be established by multiplying the ordinates of the unit graph by the storm runoff.

The unit hydrograph has proved to be a highly effective and simple tool for hydrologic work. It can readily be agreed that, within the limitations of a fixed duration and similar rate and areal distribution of rainfall, the hydrographs of various storms will be substantially similar in shape with ordinates approximately proportional to the runoff volumes. Obviously, this cannot be rigorously true, for the effect of channel storage varies with stage and the unit graphs of very large floods will necessarily differ somewhat from those for small rises. The unit hydrograph assumes that the time bases of all floods caused by rainfalls of equal duration are the same. A direct-runoff recession curve will show, however, that the time required for flows to

[1] Sherman, L. K., Streamflow from Rainfall by the Unit-graph Method, *Eng. News-Record*, Vol. 108, pp. 501-505, 1932.

recede to some fixed value increases with the initial flow. Since recessions approach zero asymptotically, a practical compromise is possible without excessive error.

There are limitations to the use of unit graphs which must be recognized. Reasonably similar rainfall distribution from storm to storm over very large areas is rare. Hence, unit graphs are best suited to areas under about 2000 square miles, although they have been applied to fairly large areas with varying success. Odd-shaped basins, particularly those which are long and narrow, commonly have very uneven rainfall distribution, and hence unit graphs are not well adapted to such basins. In mountainous areas subject to orographic rainfall, the areal distribution is very uneven, but the pattern tends to remain the same from storm to storm, and unit graphs may be successfully applied.

It is almost impossible to identify typical intensity patterns from storm to storm, and uniform rainfall rates over an extended period of time are uncommon. This is not so serious as it might seem at first, for nature effectively smooths a very uneven raingraph. Much of the variation in rainfall intensity is smoothed out in the course of surface detention during overland flow and further leveled by valley storage in the streams. Hence, short-period variations in rainfall intensity have little effect on the accuracy of the unit-graph method. Relatively long-period variations such as the successive bursts of rainfall accompanying a series of frontal passages must be reckoned with. This can be done by treating each such burst as an individual storm and applying the proper duration unit graph. As used in this paragraph, "short" and "long" are relative terms. On a drainage area of a few square miles, the short bursts of rain from one or more thunderstorms occurring within an hour or less may result in several streamflow peaks and may require the adoption of a time unit measured in minutes. On a basin as large as 2000 square miles, 12 or even 24 hr may be an adequate unit. Experience has shown that the time unit should approximate one-fourth the basin lag for practical application.

Derivation of the unit hydrograph from isolated storms. The unit graph can be most easily derived from the hydrograph of an isolated storm which meets the general requirements outlined in the previous section. The steps in the derivation are as follows (Fig. 17-1):

1. Separate the groundwater flow, and measure the volume of direct runoff from the storm.
2. Divide the ordinates of direct runoff by the runoff volume (expressed in inches over the drainage area). The resulting hydrograph is a unit graph for the basin.
3. Determine the effective duration of runoff-producing rain for which the unit graph is applicable by a study of the rainfall records.

General storms with runoff in excess of 1 in. are more satisfactory than smaller storms because the reduction to 1 in. tends to diminish the errors in the unit graph. When possible, unit graphs for several similar storms should be determined and averaged to obtain a mean graph for the basin. If several unit hydrographs for the same duration are superimposed so that the beginnings of rainfall excess coincide, the peaks will not necessarily coincide. If several hydrographs are averaged by averaging concurrent ordinates, the resulting average graph has a broader, and quite possibly a

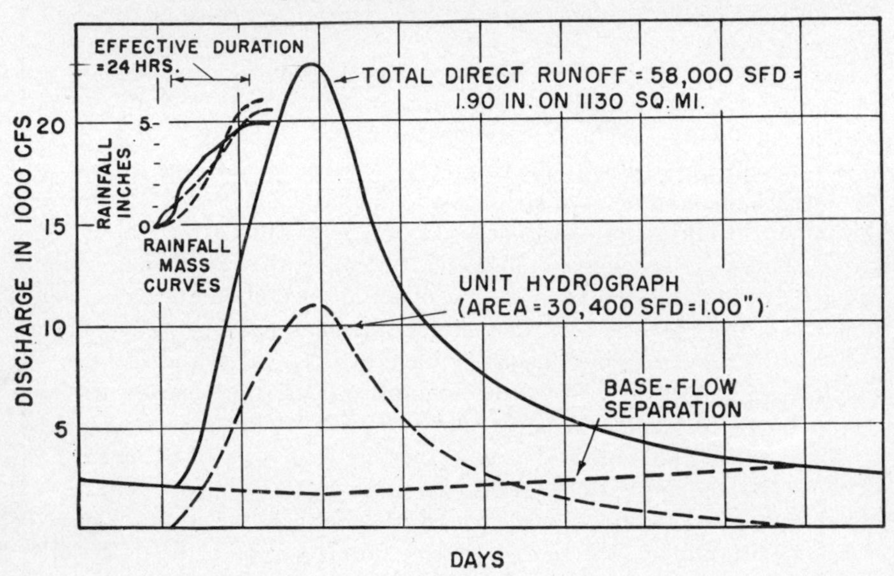

FIG. 17–1. Derivation of a unit hydrograph from an isolated storm.

lower, peak than any of the individual graphs (Fig. 17-2). The correct, average unit graph should be obtained by locating the average peak height and time and sketching a mean graph having an area equal to 1 in. of runoff and resembling the individual graphs as much as possible.

If the available storms show a wide variation in areal distribution of rainfall, it is necessary to develop several unit graphs and note on each the general nature of the rainfall distribution causing it. The effect of varying distribution or of nonuniform intensity is evident from Fig. 15-3.

In basins with two concentrations of area, the characteristic hydrograph may exhibit two peaks. Variations in rainfall distribution and intensity commonly cause a wide variation in the relative magnitudes of the two crests. Frequently, it is necessary to treat such basins in two portions or to use other methods of runoff distribution for accurate work.

Unit hydrographs from complex storms. If no better data are to be found, unit hydrographs must be developed from the records of complex storms. If the storms are sufficiently separated so that there are two peaks (Fig. 15-9), the groundwater separation can be made and the two storms may be separated by use of a direct-runoff depletion curve. The unit hydrographs may then be developed from each storm, using the procedure outlined for isolated storms.

If the only data available represent an extended period of rainfall and the hydrograph cannot be broken down into portions contributed by each

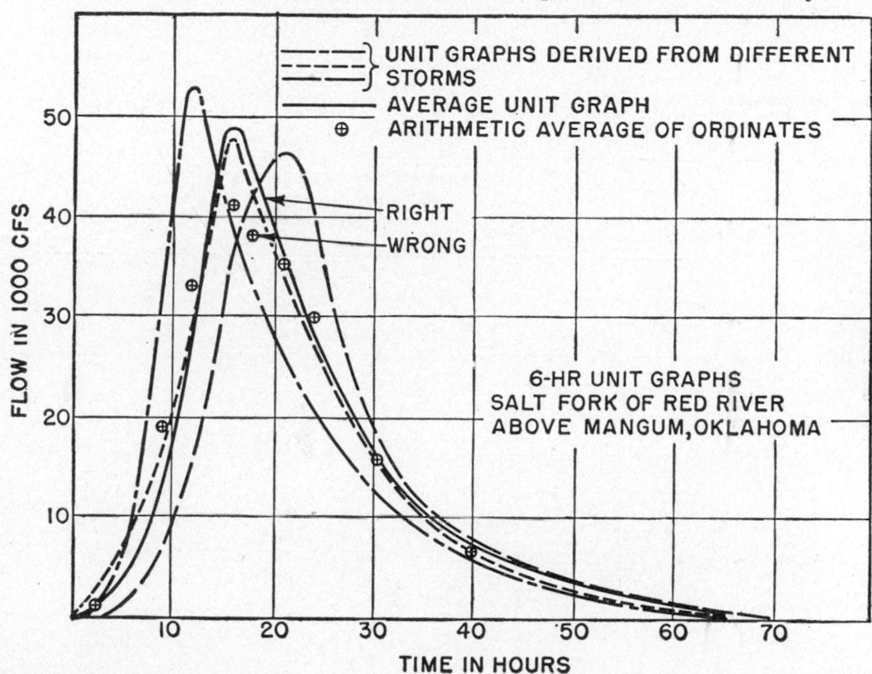

FIG. 17–2. Construction of an average unit graph. *(Data from U.S. Bureau of Reclamation.)*

burst of rain, a more specialized analysis is required. Figure 17-3 represents a hydrograph resulting from three consecutive periods of rain. Using the techniques of Chap. 16, we may compute the runoff to be expected from each period of rain. The total so computed should equal the total volume under the hydrograph (with base flow subtracted). If the observed and computed volumes do not check, the error should be prorated to the several periods in proportion to their respective runoff volumes or by some other rule. Letting U_1, U_2, U_3, etc., equal the unit-graph ordinates at times 1, 2, and 3, and Q_1, Q_2, Q_3, etc., represent the direct runoff from rain during each of the periods, then, since only Q_1 can affect the hydrograph during period 1, the discharge q_1 at the end of this period is

$$q_1 = Q_1 U_1 \tag{17-1}$$

Since q_1 and Q_1 are known, U_1 can be computed. It follows that

$$q_2 = Q_1U_2 + Q_2U_1 \tag{17-2}$$

All values except U_2 are known, and it can therefore be computed. The process may be repeated indefinitely until all necessary unit-graph ordinates have been determined.

A trial of the procedure just outlined will show that it has certain deficiencies. For example, if Q_1 is in error, the computed U_1 is likewise in error and every succeeding unit-graph ordinate is incorrect. The error may be cumulative in its effect, and in the extreme case negative ordinates can

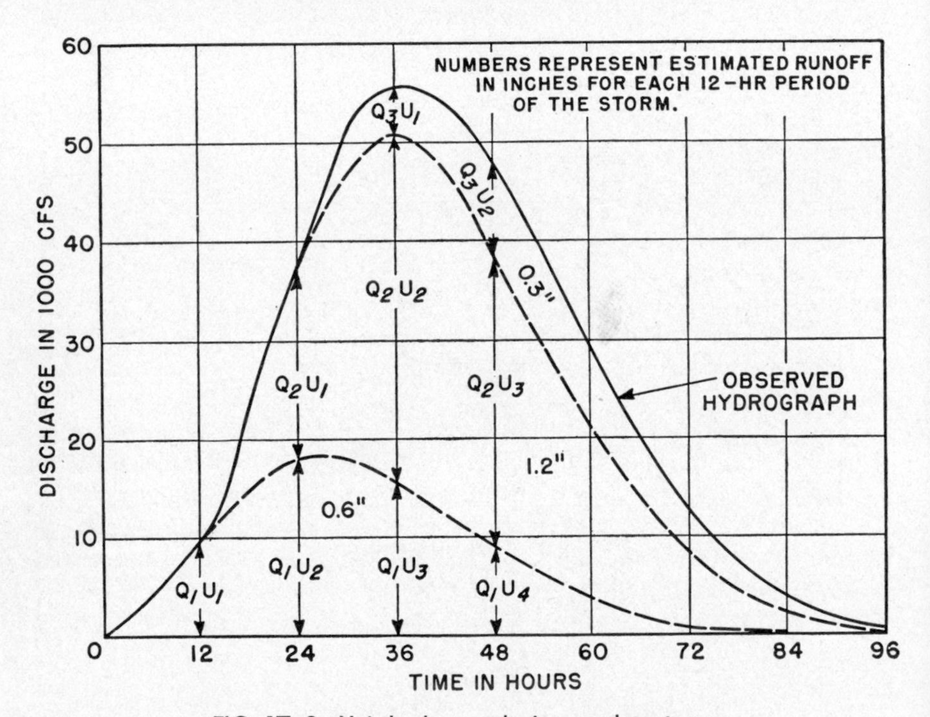

FIG. 17–3. Unit hydrographs in complex storms.

result as the computations are carried forward. If, as is quite likely, the rainfall distribution during the separate periods is not similar, a corresponding error is introduced, since the whole process is based on the assumption that the three unit graphs are identical.

A least-squares solution gives a unit graph which is the best fit for the data. The observed data are expressed in a series of equations like (17-1) and (17-2). In terms of the least-squares solution, this material may be set up in tabular form as shown in Table 17-1.

TABLE 17-1. Tabulation of Data for Development of Unit Graph by Least-squares Analysis of Complex Storms

Y	X_1	X_2	X_3	X_4	X_5	$X_6 \ldots X_n$
q_1	Q_1					
q_2	Q_2	Q_1				
q_3	Q_3	Q_2	Q_1			
.	.	.	.			
.	.	.	.			
.	.	.	.			
q_n	Q_n	Q_{n-1}	Q_{n-2}	Q_{n-3}	Q_{n-4}	$Q_{n-5} \ldots Q_1$

If the cross products are computed from this tabulation, the normal equations may be set up and solved simultaneously for the best values of U_1, U_2, etc. (b_1, b_2, etc.). Obviously, data need not be limited to one storm period but may include observations from as many periods as may be needed. At least 50 sets of data should be used for the solution of 10 normal equations.

The mathematical concept of the hydrograph has been explored by many investigators.[1] The attempts were not entirely successful because of the simplifying assumptions required for the mathematical solutions. The semiempirical approach allows the basin to integrate many of the complex functions which defy rigorous mathematical expression.

A third solution to the problem of the complex storm may be achieved by a trial-and-error process. A unit hydrograph may be assumed and the storm hydrograph reconstructed, using computed values of runoff period by period. If the reconstructed hydrograph agrees sufficiently well with the observed, then the assumed unit graph is adequate. If the agreement between the observed and reconstructed hydrographs is not sufficiently close, a study of the differences will indicate the nature of the adjustments to be made to the assumed unit graph. A second, or at most a third, trial should be sufficient to determine a satisfactory unit graph.

The distribution graph. Bernard [2] proposed a variation on the unit hydrograph, which is convenient for some purposes. He visualized the histogram of flow, which expresses discharge in a unit interval as a percentage of the total-storm volume, as representing the percentage of the drainage basin which contributes during a particular time period after the beginning of runoff. The *distribution graph* may be developed directly from the basic data, or from the unit graph by expressing flow during successive periods as a percentage of the total volume.

[1] Zoch, R. T., On the Relation between Rainfall and Streamflow, *Monthly Weather Rev.*, Vol. 62, pp. 315-322, 1934; Vol. 64, pp. 105-121, 1936.

Folse, J. A., A New Method of Estimating Streamflow, *Carnegie Inst. Wash. Pub.* 400, 1929.

[2] Bernard, M., An Approach to Determinate Streamflow, *Trans. ASCE*, Vol. 100, p. 347, 1935.

The same conditions of rainfall distribution, duration, etc., required for the unit hydrograph are also assumed in the distribution graph. The expression of the hydrograph in period averages instead of instantaneous coefficients defines its shape less clearly, particularly if the time increment is large. Hence, minor deviations between graphs from separate storms tend to be masked. The distribution graph is a simple and effective tool for problems such as forecasting of reservoir inflows, mean daily volumes of delivery, etc., where a detailed forecast of hydrograph shape is not required.

A distribution graph may be developed from such readily available data as mean daily flows. On small drainage basins, however, the distribution percentages will be materially influenced by the fortuitous occurrence of the

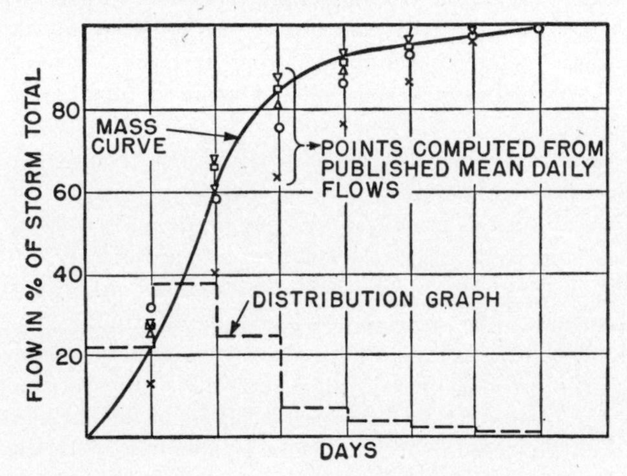

FIG. 17–4. Derivation of distribution graph by use of mass curves.

storm with respect to calendar days. Plotting of data in the form of mass curves of accumulated discharge against time (Fig. 17-4) makes it fairly simple to determine a mean curve. In all mass-curve plottings, the slope of the curves and not the absolute value is the important feature. The curves may be plotted in units of flow or in percentage of total flow.

Unit hydrographs for various durations. A unit graph developed by procedures already outlined applies, according to the basic assumptions, only to storms having a period of rainfall excess equal to that of the storm from which the unit graph was derived. The limitations of accuracy in the technique justify a limited tolerance in duration of rainfall excess. Such tolerance could easily be 10 per cent of the observed duration of rainfall excess. Thus, a 20-hr graph could apply within the range of 18 to 22 hr with very small errors, and a tolerance of 20 to 25 per cent could be accepted in many cases. Unit graphs for various durations are best obtained by analysis of data from storms covering a range of durations. If this cannot be done for lack of data, they may be developed by conversion of the available unit graphs.

The development of a unit hydrograph for a long duration from one for a shorter duration is accomplished by the simple addition of short-duration graphs. Thus, the sum of three 2-hr unit graphs with their points of beginning separated by 2 hr will yield a graph representing the hydrograph of 3 in. of runoff during a 6-hr period. If the ordinates of this derived graph are divided by 3, a 6-hr unit graph results (Table 17-2).

TABLE 17-2. Derivation of 6-hr Unit Graph from 2-hr Unit Graph

Time, hr	Ordinates of 2-hr unit graphs (1000 cfs)			Sum (1000 cfs)	6-hr unit graph (1000 cfs)
0	0	......	......	0	0
2	2.5	0	......	2.5	0.8
4	6.0	2.5	0	8.5	2.8
6	10.2	6.0	2.5	18.7	6.2
8	16.4	10.2	6.0	32.6	10.9
10	25.3	16.4	10.2	51.9	17.3
12	34.0	25.3	16.4	75.7	25.2
14	33.2	34.0	25.3	92.5	30.8
16	28.2	33.2	34.0	95.4	31.8
18	23.1	28.2	33.2	84.5	28.2
20	19.7	23.1	28.2	71.0	23.7
22	16.7	19.7	23.1	59.5	19.8
24	14.2	16.7	19.7	50.6	16.9
26	12.1	14.2	16.7	43.0	14.3
28	10.3	12.1	14.2	36.6	12.2
30	8.8	10.3	12.1	31.2	10.4
32	7.5	8.8	10.3	26.6	8.8
34	6.4	7.5	8.8	22.7	7.6
36	5.4	6.4	7.5	19.3	6.4
38	4.6	5.4	6.4	16.4	5.5
40	3.8	4.6	5.4	13.8	4.6
42	3.1	3.8	4.6	11.5	3.8
44	2.6	3.1	3.8	9.5	3.2
46	2.2	2.6	3.1	7.9	2.6
48	1.8	2.2	2.6	6.6	2.2
50	1.3	1.8	2.2	5.3	1.8
52	1.0	1.3	1.8	4.1	1.4
54	0.7	1.0	1.3	3.0	1.0
56	0.4	0.7	1.0	2.1	0.7
58	0	0.4	0.7	1.1	0.4
60	......	0	0.4	0.4	0.1
62	......	......	0	0	0

TABLE 17-3. Application of S-curve Method

Time, hr (1)	6-hr unit graph (1000 cfs) (2)	S-curve additions (1000 cfs) (3)	S curve Col. (2) + (3) (1000 cfs) (4)	S curve lagged 2 hr (5)	Col. (4) − (5) (6)	2-hr unit graph 3 × (6) (7)	S curve lagged 12 hr (8)	Col. (4) − (8) (9)	12-hr unit graph ½ × (9) (10)
0	0	......	0	......	0	0	......	0	0
2	0.8	......	0.8	0	0.8	2.4	......	0.8	0.4
4	2.8	......	2.8	0.8	2.0	6.0	......	2.8	1.4
6	6.2	0	6.2	2.8	3.4	10.2	......	6.2	3.1
8	10.9	0.8	11.7	6.2	5.5	16.5	......	11.7	5.8
10	17.3	2.8	20.1	11.7	8.4	25.2	......	20.1	10.0
12	25.2	6.2	31.4	20.1	11.3	33.9	0	31.4	15.7
14	30.8	11.7	42.5	31.4	11.1	33.3	0.8	41.7	20.8
16	31.8	20.1	51.9	42.5	9.4	28.2	2.8	49.1	24.6
18	28.2	31.4	59.6	51.9	7.7	23.1	6.2	53.4	26.7
20	23.7	42.5	66.2	59.6	6.6	19.8	11.7	54.5	27.2
22	19.8	51.9	71.7	66.2	5.5	16.5	20.1	51.6	25.8
24	16.9	59.6	76.5	71.7	4.8	14.4	31.4	45.1	22.6
26	14.3	66.2	80.5	76.5	4.0	12.0	42.5	38.0	19.0
28	12.2	71.7	83.9	80.5	3.4	10.2	51.9	32.0	16.0
30	10.4	76.5	86.9	83.9	3.0	9.0	59.6	27.3	13.6
32	8.8	80.5	89.3	86.9	2.4	7.2	66.2	23.1	11.6
34	7.6	83.9	91.5	89.3	2.2	6.6	71.7	19.8	9.9
36	6.4	86.9	93.3	91.5	1.8	5.4	76.5	16.8	8.4
38	5.5	89.3	94.8	93.3	1.5	4.5	80.5	14.3	7.2
40	4.6	91.5	96.1	94.8	1.3	3.9	83.9	12.2	6.1
42	3.8	93.3	97.1	96.1	1.0	3.0	86.9	10.2	5.1
44	3.2	94.8	98.0	97.1	0.9	2.7	89.3	8.7	4.4
46	2.6	96.1	98.9	98.0	0.9	2.4*	91.5	7.4	3.7
48	2.2	97.1	99.3	98.9	0.4	1.8*	93.3	6.0	3.0
50	1.8	98.0	99.8	99.3	0.5	1.5	94.8	5.0	2.5
52	1.4	98.9	100.3	99.8	0.5	1.2*	96.1	4.2	2.1
54	1.0	99.3	100.3	100.3	0	0.9*	97.1	3.2	1.6
56	0.7	99.8	100.5	100.3	0.2	0.6	98.0	2.5	1.2
58	0.4	100.3	100.7	100.5	0.2	0.3*	98.9	1.8	0.9
60	0.1	100.3	100.4	100.7	− 0.3	0*	99.3	1.1	0.6
62	0	100.5	100.5	100.4	0.1	0*	99.8	0.7	0.4
64	......	100.7	100.7	100.5	0.2	0*	100.3	0.4	0.2
66	......	......	100.4	100.7	− 0.3	......	100.3	0.1	0.2*
68	......	......	100.7	100.4	0.3	......	100.5	0.2	0.1

The construction of a short-period unit graph from one for a longer duration is less direct. It can be accomplished by use of any of the techniques suggested for the development of unit graphs from a complex storm. The unit graph for any fractional part of the observed duration may be determined by the S-curve method. The *S curve* is the hydrograph of flow from an infinite series of consecutive units of duration, each unit having 1 in. of runoff. The 6-hr S curve is derived by adding the ordinates of a series of 6-hr unit graphs with their points of beginning spaced 6 hr apart (Table 17-3). A continuous supply of runoff at the rate of 1 in. per 6 hr will eventually establish equilibrium conditions with a discharge volume of 1 in. every 6 hr. Hence, the maximum ordinate of the S curve will equal the flow required to discharge 1 in. of runoff in 6 hr. Once this ordinate has been attained, the S curve will continue at this constant value, and therefore the number of graphs that must be combined is not infinite but practically equals the time base of the unit graph divided by the unit duration.

The computation of the S curve is easily accomplished as shown in Table 17-3. The ordinates of the S curve during the first unit of duration (6 hr) equal the unit-graph ordinates. For the second unit of duration, the ordinates of the first 6 hr of one graph are added to those of the second 6 hr of the first graph to obtain the S-curve ordinates. For the third 6-hr period, the ordinates for the S curve in the second 6 hr are added to the unit graph for the third period. This process is continued until the S-curve ordinates become constant at a flow equal to 1 in. of runoff per unit period.

A 2-hr unit graph may then be constructed by subtracting two S curves with their initial points separated by 2 hr and multiplying the resulting differences by 3. Similarly, the difference between two S curves separated by 3 hr and multiplied by 2 would give a 3-hr unit graph. Unit graphs for any duration, either longer or shorter than that of the original unit graph, can be obtained by separating the S curves by the desired time interval and reducing the resulting hydrograph to 1 in. volume. It may be desirable to smooth the S curves and the resulting derived unit graphs by graphical plotting in order to eliminate minor irregularities occasioned by the accumulation of small errors in reading the original ordinates of the hydrograph.

The accuracy of the S-curve method is dependent on the accuracy of the estimated effective duration of the unit hydrograph from which the S curve is derived. If the assumed duration is too long, the S curve may fluctuate considerably instead of increasing steadily to a constant value. If the assumed duration is too short, there may be no indication in the shape of the S curve, but the resulting derived unit hydrographs will, of course, be in error.

The foregoing procedures should not be used if the hydrographs can be developed from actual storms. Evidence of short-duration hydrographs which have higher peaks than those determined by breakdown of long-duration graphs is available. This would be expected from theoretical considerations, since a very abrupt rain would tend to generate an abrupt translatory wave traveling in accordance with Eq. (18-19). With depths increasing behind the toe of the wave, the crest would travel faster than the toe and would overtake the earlier portions of the wave, resulting in a higher peak than from normal monoclinal waves. Some writers have suggested the possibility of streamflow rates in excess of rainfall rates because of this effect, but no cases have been cited where sufficient data were available

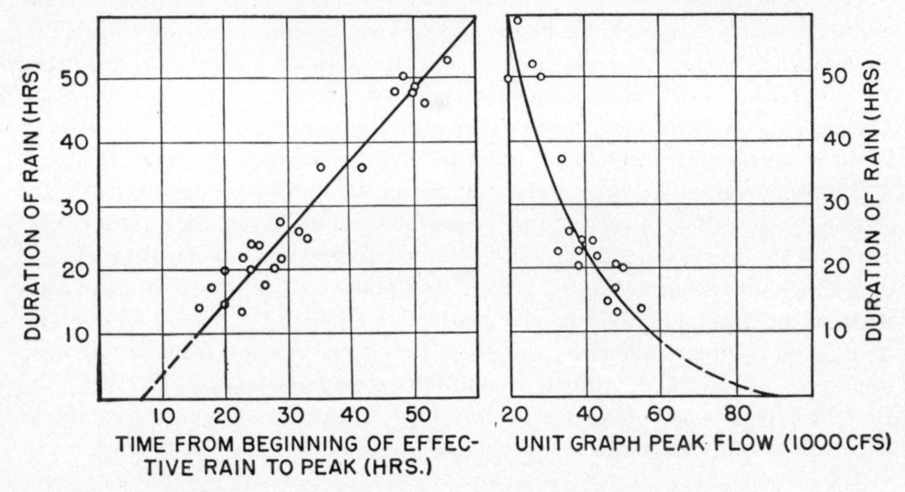

FIG. 17-5. Time to peak and unit peak-flow curves for the American River at Folsom, California.

to demonstrate clearly such an occurrence. The majority of short-duration storms producing runoff volumes large enough to warrant consideration are thunderstorms with extremely high intensities of precipitation. In contrast, long-duration storms have relatively lower rates. The high intensities of precipitation would be expected to yield a relatively greater proportion of surface runoff to interflow, and since surface runoff accumulates in the streams more rapidly than interflow, a relatively higher peak would result.

Unit peak-flow curves. If it is necessary to treat storms of widely varying durations, several unit graphs, each applicable to a different duration, must be available. It is not always possible to get a sufficient number of storms to establish the necessary unit graphs by conventional methods. In such cases, it is convenient to make use of *unit peak-flow* and *time to peak* curves (Fig. 17-5). Unit peak flow may be computed by dividing the *net peak flow, i.e.*, total peak minus base flow, by the runoff in inches. Values of unit peak flow are plotted against effective duration of the storm to determine the unit peak-flow curve, while time from beginning of effective rain to peak is plotted against duration for the time to peak curves.

Curves of this type may be developed using all available data, including that from storms which would ordinarily not be acceptable for the development of a unit hydrograph. Naturally, data from storms which most nearly conform to the basic requirements of the unit graph should be given greater weight in placing the curves than those from the less satisfactory storms, which may serve only to indicate the shape and general placement of the curves. Having established the unit peak-flow, time to peak, and depletion curves for a basin, a family of unit graphs can be constructed. With the time and height of peak established, the rising limb can be estimated, and the recession can be drawn from the depletion curve, care being taken that the resulting graph represents 1 in. of runoff.

If there is no particular need for the complete unit hydrographs, the unit peak-flow and time to peak curves may be used alone as, for example, in certain flood-forecasting problems where the principal emphasis is on forecasts of peak flow or stage. A further refinement of the procedure is obtained by plotting net peak flow against runoff with duration as a parameter (Fig. 17-6). Such curves account for variations in shape of the unit graphs resulting from floods of varying magnitude. Runoff volume may also be introduced as a parameter in the time to peak curve, but unless the data are exceptionally good, it is unlikely that any significant correlation will be evident.

Synthetic unit graphs. Many design problems require the development of hydrologic relations at points for which few, if any, data are available. It is quite natural, therefore, that considerable effort has been expended on the development of techniques to permit synthesizing of unit graphs or their transposition to points where runoff data are inadequate. The synthesis of a unit hydrograph requires the determination of the equations for the unit peak-flow and time to peak curves in terms of the physical features of the basin under study. These two curves, together with a depletion curve or a method of estimating the time base of the unit graph, provide the information for estimating the necessary unit graphs.

Snyder[1] developed a group of equations from data for the Appalachian Mountain Region which work very well in that area or in comparable terrane. Linsley[2] showed that these equations could be modified by the use of different constants for application in the Sierra Nevada. Snyder's method is based on the determination of basin lag, which he defines as the

[1] Snyder, F. F., Synthetic Unit Hydrographs, *Trans. Am. Geophys. Union*, Vol. 19, pp. 447-454, 1938.

[2] Linsley, R. K., Application of Synthetic Unit-graphs in the Western Mountain States, *Trans. Am. Geophys. Union*, Vol. 24, Part II, pp. 580-587, 1943.

time from center of mass of effective rain to peak of the unit graph. He found that the lag t_p (in hours) could be expressed by

$$t_p = C_t(L\bar{L})^{0.3} \tag{17-3}$$

The basin length L is measured along the major stream channel from the outlet station to the divide. The length to center of area $\bar{L}$ is measured along the main channel to a point opposite the center of area of the basin.

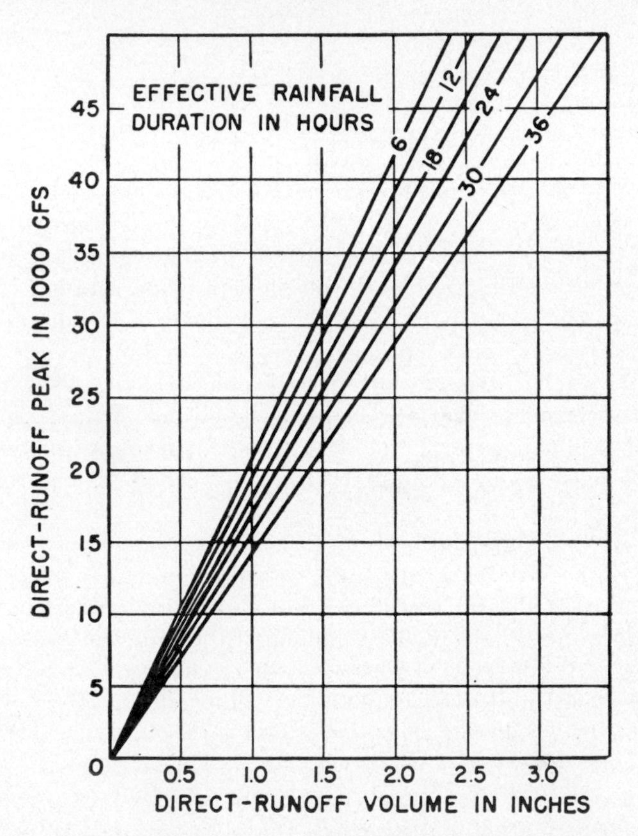

FIG. 17–6. Relation between peak of direct runoff, rainfall duration, and runoff volume for the Delaware River at Valley Falls, Kansas. *(U.S. Weather Bureau.)*

The location of the center of area may be estimated by eye or may be determined by cutting the basin outline from cardboard and marking the point of intersection of plumb lines drawn with the map suspended from different corners. In the Appalachian Mountain area the constant C_t was found to vary from 1.8 to 2.2, with some indication of lower values in basins with steeper slopes.

Snyder fixed the unit duration of rain t_r (in hours) in his study by

$$t_r = \frac{t_p}{5.5} \tag{17-4}$$

The unit-graph peak q_p for this duration may then be determined from

$$q_p = \frac{640C_pA_d}{t_p} \tag{17-5}$$

where A_d is the drainage area. The constant C_p ranged from 0.56 to 0.69 for various basins in the Appalachian Highlands.

For rainfall durations t_R (in hours) in excess of the basic duration given by Eq. (17-4), the value of lag must be modified as follows:

$$t'_p = t_p + \frac{t_R - t_r}{4} \tag{17-6}$$

The time base t (in days) of the unit graph is

$$t = 3 + 3\left(\frac{t_p}{24}\right) \tag{17-7}$$

The exact constants in Eq. (17-7) are dependent on the procedure used by Snyder for separating base flow. The time from beginning of rain to peak t_P is, from the definition of lag and a combination of Eqs. (17-4) and (17-6),

$$t_P = \frac{21t_p}{22} + 0.75t_R \tag{17-8}$$

Linsley found these equations to be applicable to basins on the western slopes of the Sierra Nevada in California, but the coefficients were generally lower. He found C_t to range from 0.7 to 1.0 and C_p to vary between 0.35 and 0.50. In view of the fact that Sierra Nevada basins are normally about one-half snow-covered during winter, floods caused by rain are produced in the lower portions of the basins. If the snow-covered area, largely noncontributing to runoff, is neglected, these coefficients agree rather well with those determined by Snyder for the Appalachian area.

Transposition of unit hydrographs. If unit graphs are available for several areas adjacent to a basin for which a unit hydrograph is required but for which necessary data are lacking, transposition of these graphs will ordinarily give better results than resort to a wholly synthetic procedure. Sherman originally proposed that the ordinates and abscissas of unit graphs for similar basins might be assumed to be proportional to the square roots of the respective drainage areas. This simple rule does not take into consideration other factors such as slope or shape of the basins.

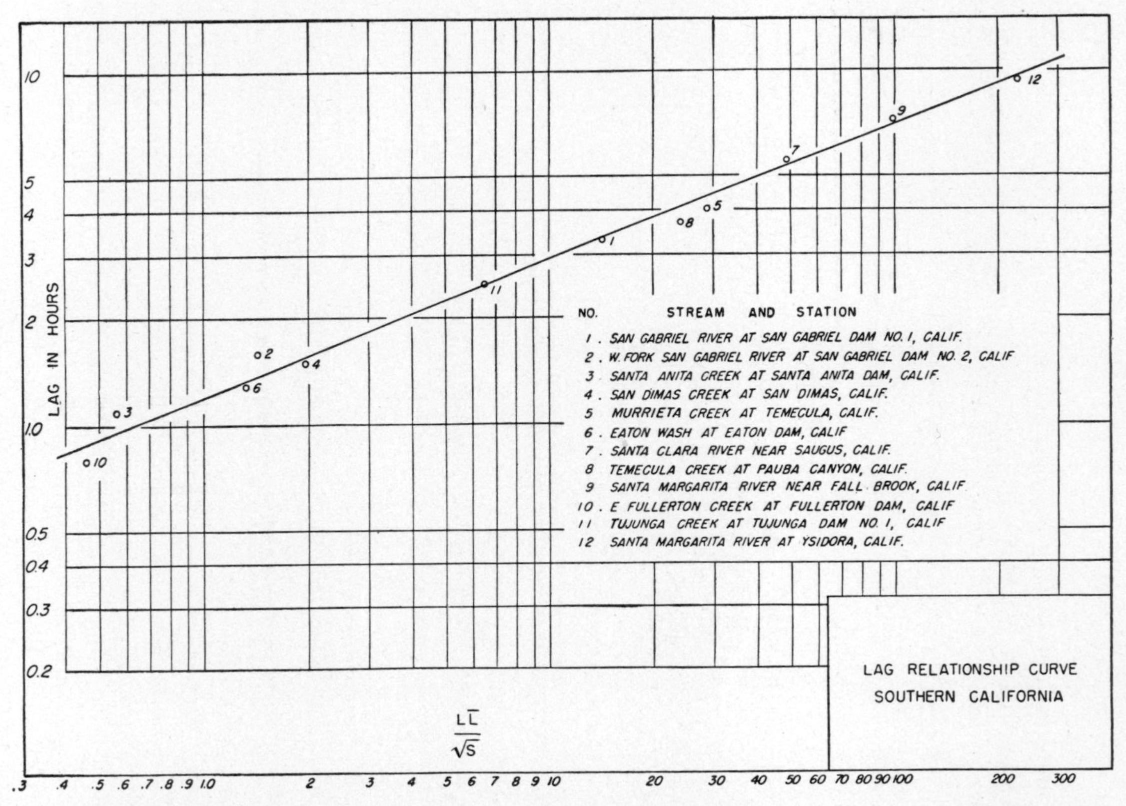

FIG. 17–7. Basin lag as a function of the physical features of basins. (U.S. Bureau of Reclamation.)

Modifying Eq. (17-3) to include the effect of basin slope s, we may write the following expression for the basin lag:

$$t_p = C_t \frac{(L\bar{L})^n}{\sqrt{s}} \tag{17-9}$$

If values of observed lag for basins having similar physiographic characteristics are plotted on logarithmic paper (Fig. 17-7) against corresponding values of $(L\bar{L})/\sqrt{s}$, they define a straight line. Figure 17-7 thus provides

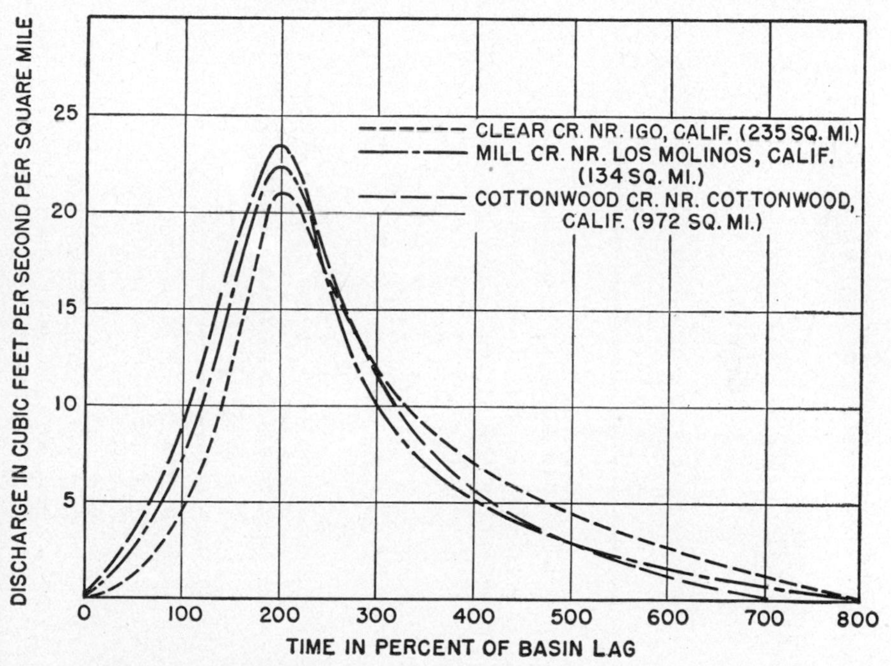

FIG. 17–8. Unit graphs for various basins, reduced to common units.

a means for estimating the lag for a basin where streamflow records are not available.

In order to compare graphs from basins of different sizes and shapes, they may be plotted in terms of percentage of lag and flow per square mile (Fig. 17-8). All graphs should represent rainfall durations having the same ratio to basin lag. The ratio should preferably be about 0.25 since the best definition of the hydrograph is obtained with unit graphs for rainfall durations considerably less than the basin lag. With a mean shape established and with the basin lag estimated from Fig. 17-7, the unit graph can be readily constructed.

Rainfall–crest-stage relations. Some problems require the development of relations for stations where stage data are available but where no discharge rating exists. River-forecasting operations may also require relations between precipitation and crest stage in the interests of conserving time in the preparation of forecasts. These requirements can be satisfied by the use of *rainfall–crest-stage relations.* Fundamentally, such relations must combine the features of the rainfall-runoff relation and the

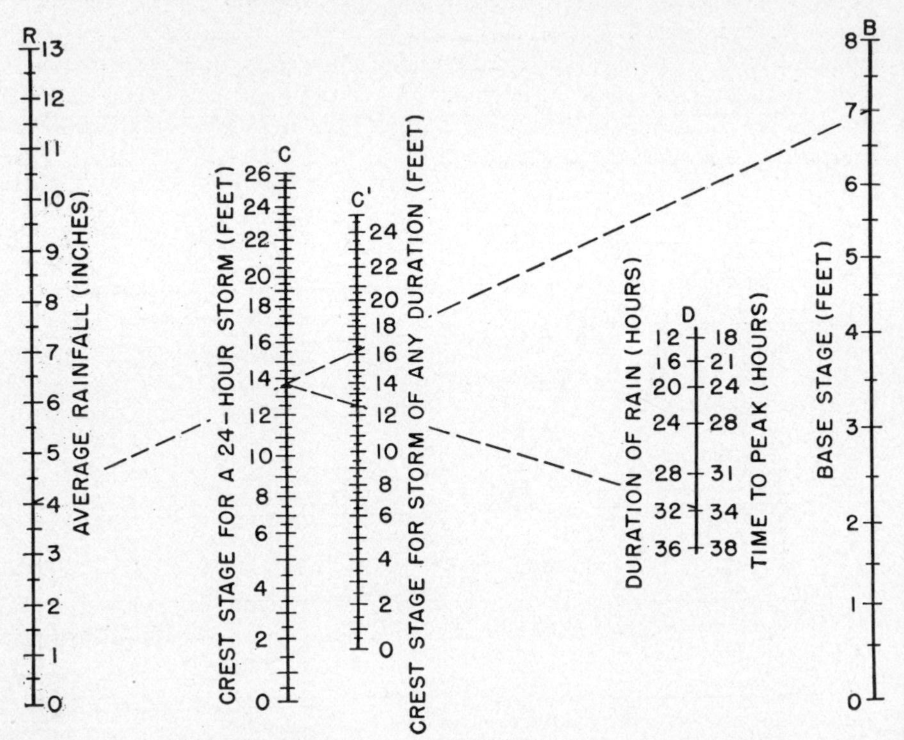

FIG. 17–9. Rainfall–crest-stage relation for the Yuba River at Colgate, California. *(U.S. Weather Bureau.)*

unit hydrograph. There are several methods by which the relations may be developed.

If discharge data for the station are available, a rainfall-runoff relation and unit hydrographs may be developed and converted into the rainfall–crest-stage relation. Duration of rain will serve a dual purpose since it influences both the amount of runoff and the peak of the unit hydrograph. In addition, base flow must be included as a parameter since the total peak is the sum of the storm-runoff peak and base flow. Unit peak-flow curves may be used in lieu of a series of unit hydrographs.

In the absence of discharge data, good results may usually be obtained by direct correlation between rainfall, stage, and suitable parameters. The choice of parameters is dictated in large measure by the desired accuracy.

Wherever base flow is a reasonable index to runoff conditions, it may be used both as an index to runoff and as a base for the flood peak. Duration may be ignored, but the results will be better if it is included. The use of antecedent precipitation, season, and an index to rainfall distribution over the basin will usually improve results but at the same time will also increase the complexity of the relation. Figure 17-9 is a rainfall–crest-stage relation for the Yuba River at Colgate, California, using duration and base stage as parameters. The nomogram was developed by direct correlation of the several parameters, using 24-hr storms to define the relation between

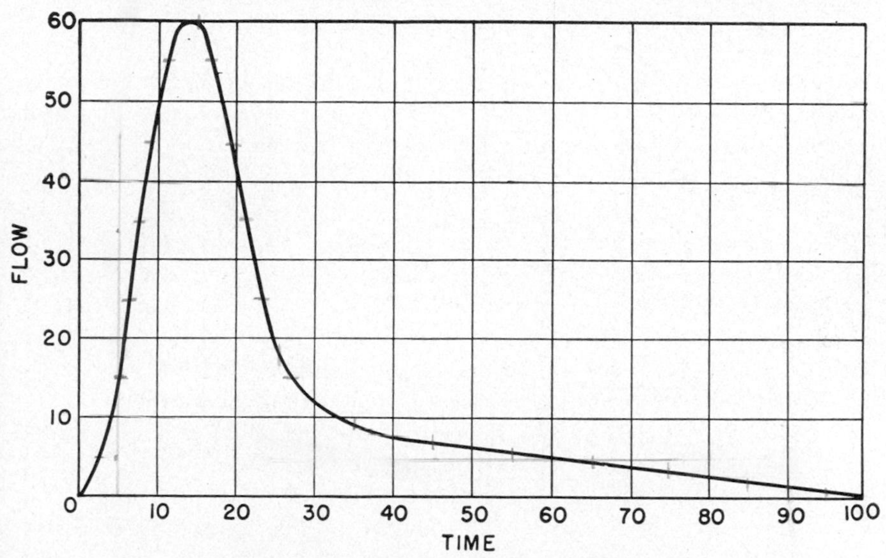

FIG. 17–10. Commons' basic hydrograph.

base flow, rainfall, and crest, and then introducing duration as a correction factor. The coaxial method is equally satisfactory for such development.

The basic hydrograph. Commons[1] developed a basic hydrograph which he found to be generally applicable as a first approximation to major floods on any basin. The graph (Fig. 17-10) was developed by averaging characteristic features of the hydrographs for many Texas floods. Its time base is divided into 100 units and the height into 60 units. The area under the curve is 1196.5 square units. Dividing the total-flood runoff in second-foot-days by 1196.5 gives the value of a square unit in second-foot-days. Dividing the peak flow by 60 gives the value of 1 unit of flow in cubic feet per second. The time unit in days may be determined by dividing the value of a square unit by that of a flow unit.

The basic hydrograph requires an estimate of the peak flow and hence is useful only for defining the hydrograph shape. For design problems

[1] Commons, G. G., Flood Hydrographs, *Civil Eng.*, Vol. 12, pp. 571-572, 1942.

in which a peak-flow estimate has been made by frequency analysis or other procedure, the basic hydrograph may prove to be a useful tool. Commons shows comparisons between the basic graph and actual floods from basins of 356 to 203,000 square miles, with time bases of 3 days and 4 months, respectively. At each extreme the reproduction of the observed graph is exceptionally good, considering the nature of the method.

Composite unit graphs. The problem of outflow from areas larger than can readily be handled by the ordinary unit graph may frequently be treated by use of a *composite unit hydrograph.* The composite unit graph is a tabular presentation of unit graphs for the important subdivisions of a larger area, with the times of beginning of rise appropriately lagged by the times of travel from the outlets of the subareas to the major gaging station (Fig. 17-11). The runoff is computed independently for each subarea and multiplied by unit-graph ordinates for that area. The sum of all flows thus computed in a vertical column gives the flow to be expected at the outlet of the basin.

The composite unit graph is obviously a simple application of the unit-hydrograph principle combined with lagging of hydrographs in lieu of routing. It does not account for variations in travel time, which may be anticipated with widely varying patterns of runoff distribution. Hence, it must be expected to yield only a first approximation to outflow from areas far greater than those ordinarily treated by the unit-graph method. Its simplicity makes it a useful tool for quick solutions such as may be required for preliminary design surveys or river forecasting.

Unit graphs of groundwater flow. The unit graph as discussed in earlier sections is applied principally to the hydrograph of direct runoff, which includes all surface runoff and most of the interflow. There appears to be no fundamental reason why the general principles of the unit graph should not apply equally well to the runoff which reaches the channels via groundwater. Linsley and Ackermann[1] demonstrated satisfactory relations between volume of groundwater runoff and the net peak rise of groundwater flow and also between duration of rain and time to groundwater peak. These two curves essentially define the unit hydrograph. The relatively flat, broad peak of the groundwater flow effectively masks any variation in peak height with duration of rain.

Little can be said about groundwater unit graphs because they are necessarily dependent on the separation technique applied to determine the groundwater hydrograph. Such unit graphs can be developed only if an entirely objective separation technique is applied. Such a technique should be one in which depletion curves are used to determine the hydrograph shape for a particular storm, rather than a procedure which is wholly

[1] Linsley, R. K., and W. C. Ackermann, A Method of Predicting the Runoff from Rainfall, *Trans. ASCE*, Vol. 107, pp. 825-835, 1942.

SUBAREA	RUNOFF	HOURS AFTER BEGINNING OF RAIN, ____ PM/AM ____ 19__											
		0	6	12	18	24	30	36	42	48	54	60	66
Pit River above Ydalpom	0.12					^{0} 0	^{4} 0.5	^{10} 12	^{16} 1.9	^{24} 29	^{34} 4.1	^{44} 5.3	^{50} 6.0
McCloud River above Baird	0.68					^{0} 0	^{1} 0.7	^{2} 1.4	^{2} 1.4	^{6} 4.1	^{14} 9.5	^{10} 6.8	^{8} 5.4
Sacramento River above Vollmers	0.95					^{0} 0	^{1} 1.0	^{2} 1.9	^{3} 2.8	^{7} 6.6	^{9} 8.6	^{6} 5.7	^{4} 3.8
Local area to Shasta Dam	0.62					^{0} 0	^{1} 0.6	^{2} 1.2	^{3} 1.9	^{4} 2.5	^{3} 1.9	^{2} 1.2	^{1} 0.6
Clear Creek near Igo	0.78					^{0} 0	^{1} 0.8	^{4} 3.1	^{5} 3.9	^{4} 3.1	^{3} 2.3	^{2} 1.6	^{2} 1.6
Cottonwood Creek nr. Cottonwood	0.45				^{0} 0	^{4} 1.8	^{9} 4.0	^{15} 6.8	^{23} 10.4	^{17} 7.6	^{12} 5.4	^{8} 3.6	^{6} 2.7
Battle Creek near Cottonwood	0.37			^{0} 0	^{2} 0.7	^{4} 1.5	^{6} 2.2	^{7} 2.6	^{5} 1.9	^{4} 1.5	^{3} 1.1	^{2} 0.7	^{1} 0.4
Local area to Red Bluff	0.21			^{0} 0	^{3} 0.6	^{6} 1.3	^{12} 2.5	^{15} 3.1	^{15} 3.1	^{12} 2.5	^{9} 1.9	^{8} 1.7	^{6} 1.3
Antelope Creek near Red Bluff	0.19			^{0} 0	^{1} 0.2	^{1} 0.2	^{4} 0.8	^{3} 0.6	^{2} 0.4	^{1} 0.2	^{1} 0.2	^{1} 0.2	^{0} 0
Mill Creek near Los Molinos	0.12			^{0} 0	^{1} 0.1	^{2} 0.2	^{3} 0.4	^{2} 0.2	^{1} 0.1	^{1} 0.1	^{1} 0.1	^{0} 0	^{0} 0
Deer Creek near Vina	0.21		^{0} 0	^{1} 0.2	^{2} 0.4	^{4} 0.8	^{4} 0.8	^{3} 0.6	^{2} 0.4	^{2} 0.4	^{1} 0.2	^{1} 0.2	^{1} 0.2
Elder Creek near Henleyville	0.28		^{0} 0	^{1} 0.3	^{3} 0.8	^{4} 1.1	^{2} 0.6	^{1} 0.3	^{1} 0.3	^{1} 0.3	^{1} 0.3	^{1} 0.3	^{0} 0
Thomas Creek near Paskenta	0.17		^{0} 0	^{1} 0.2	^{3} 0.5	^{5} 0.8	^{3} 0.5	^{2} 0.3	^{2} 0.3	^{1} 0.2	^{1} 0.2	^{1} 0.2	^{1} 0.2
Local area to Hamilton City	0.16	^{0} 0	^{4} 0.6	^{9} 1.3	^{15} 2.4	^{15} 2.4	^{12} 1.9	^{10} 1.6	^{5} 0.8	^{7} 1.1	^{6} 1.0	^{5} 0.8	^{4} 0.6
Hamilton City base flow		25	25	24	24	23	23	23	22	22	22	21	21
Hamilton City total hydrograph		25.0	25.6	26.0	29.7	33.1	40.3	47.9	51.6	55.1	59.8	49.3	43.8

All unit-graph ordinates in 1000 cfs. Applicable to storms between 20 and 28 hours in duration.

FIG. 17–11. Composite unit hydrograph for the Sacramento River above Hamilton City, California (unregulated flow).

arbitrary and hence dependent to a large extent on the features of direct-runoff hydrographs.

Unit graphs of snowmelt runoff. The unit hydrograph for a particular basin as developed from a flood event caused by rainfall runoff is not applicable to rises resulting largely from melting snow. A high percentage of the runoff from intense rainfall or a combination of heavy rain and moderate snowmelt is surface runoff. The runoff from melting snow consists largely of interflow or groundwater, depending on the rate of melt and the geological characteristics of the basin. Moreover, in basins having a wide range of elevation, only a portion of the basin (the melting zone) contributes to snowmelt at any time. Quite frequently that portion of the basin which contributes substantial volumes of snowmelt is an unimportant source area for runoff from rainfall.

There seems to be no theoretical reason why the unit-graph principle cannot be applied to runoff from melting snow. Its practical application is made difficult, if not impossible, however, by the nature of the available data. In the mountain basins of the West, the runoff from snowmelt produces a general seasonal rise and fall over a period of several months (Fig. 9-21). In nearly all cases, it is impossible to separate the runoff resulting from a given day's melt from that of the adjacent days. The difficulty of estimating daily snowmelt generally precludes the use of the least-squares approach to the analysis of a compound hydrograph.

In areas where the range in elevation is not great, the occurrence of a basin-wide snow cover is more likely, and melting periods may last only a few days. Under such conditions, the development of unit graphs by any appropriate procedure is both possible and practical. Unfortunately, such occurrences are far less frequent than the occurrence of runoff from rainfall, and the analyst may be required to work with relatively few data. The surface-runoff unit graph may be modified to produce a first approximation to the unit graph from snowmelt. Unit periods of 12 hr are generally best because of differences in melting conditions between night and day. Unit graphs for snowmelt runoff show a later and lower peak and a longer time base than a unit graph from rainfall.

18

WAVES

Waves are fluctuations in the surface level of a fluid. These variations in level may be periodic, fluctuating without period, or transient. They may be segregated into two major classes, *waves of translation* and *waves of oscillation.* Translatory waves are most commonly encountered in hydrology. The translatory wave form advances, and the water over which it passes is also moved forward in the direction of movement. It will be shown that the translatory wave is a problem in unsteady flow. Oscillatory waves, on the other hand, do not result in appreciable displacement of the water particles in the direction of motion, the particles oscillating in an orbit about a mean position. Translatory waves include flood waves in natural channels, surges, and seiches. Wind-generated ocean waves are typical oscillatory waves.

A study of translatory waves is an essential part of hydrology, since the hydrologist is frequently required to predict the hydrograph which will result at a downstream station from a known or assumed upstream hydrograph or to show the effect of various river-control works on the rate of movement and shape of a flood wave. Except for a few special cases, the general differential equation of unsteady flow is not integrable; special and approximate solutions must be used. This chapter is devoted to the consideration of such special cases for which solutions can be achieved. A subsequent chapter discusses the empirical solution, *storage routing.*

Oscillatory waves are of less interest to the hydrologist. He is, however, occasionally expected to determine the wave heights which will be generated on reservoirs or river surfaces in order that proper freeboard may be allowed in the design of a dam or levee.

The hydraulic jump is sometimes called a *standing wave.* Similar standing waves may form at other points in a flowing stream under proper flow conditions. Here the wave form remains essentially stationary, and the water flows through it. Standing waves may be important factors in hydraulic design.

Surges and seiches, though infrequent in hydrologic problems, are of occasional interest. Tides, which affect streamflow on many coastal streams, are the result of seiches and frequently induce bores, a translatory wave form.

TRANSLATORY WAVES

Uniformly progressive flow. A special case of unsteady flow possible in uniform channels is that in which the wave form moves down the channel without undergoing any change in shape. This is *uniformly progressive flow*[1] (Fig. 18-1). Though not directly applicable to an irregular

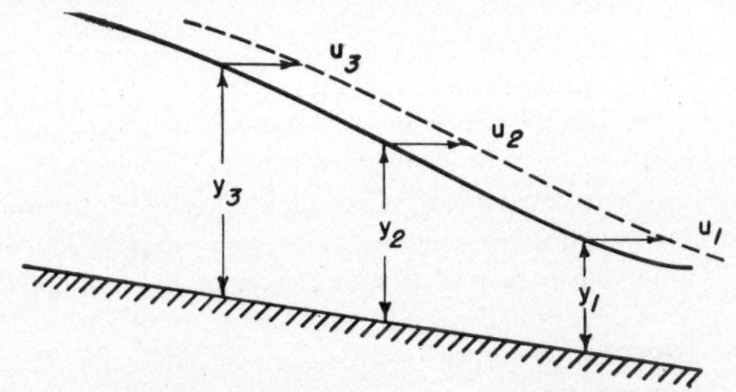

FIG. 18-1. Uniformly progressive flow.

natural channel, an investigation of uniformly progressive flow will shed some light on certain aspects of natural flood waves. From the definition of uniformly progressive flow, it follows that successive positions of the wave front must be parallel, *i.e.*,

$$u_1 = u_2 = u_3 \ldots \tag{18-1}$$

and the dotted line in Fig. 18-1 represents the position of the wave front 1 sec after the time of the initial position. The wave configuration travels downstream with celerity u, but mean water velocities in the cross section vary from section to section as the hydraulic radius and surface slope change.

Monoclinal rising wave. Figure 18-2 shows a special case of uniformly progressive flow which is called the *monoclinal rising* flood wave. Such a wave is approximately similar to the flood waves in natural streams. It can be generated by introducing into a channel, where steady uniform flow at depth D_1 and velocity v_1 is occurring, a new steady discharge q_2 which requires the stage D_2 and velocity v_2 for uniform flow. A uniform channel of constant slope is assumed. The two regions of steady flow are separated by the wave configuration *abdc* in which a condition of unsteady

[1] Thomas, H. A., "The Hydraulics of Flood Movements in Rivers," *Eng. Bull.*, Carnegie Inst. of Technology, Pittsburgh, Pa., 1937.

flow exists. This configuration tends to develop a definite and unchanging shape and to travel with a constant celerity u greater than either v_1 or v_2.

Since the wave celerity u is greater than the mean velocity of flow preceding or following the wave, a volume of water equal to $(u - v_1)a_{c1}$ must enter the front of the wave at ab, where a_{c1} is the cross-sectional area. However, because the wave configuration has a constant shape and volume, an equal quantity of water must be discharged through the section cd. The

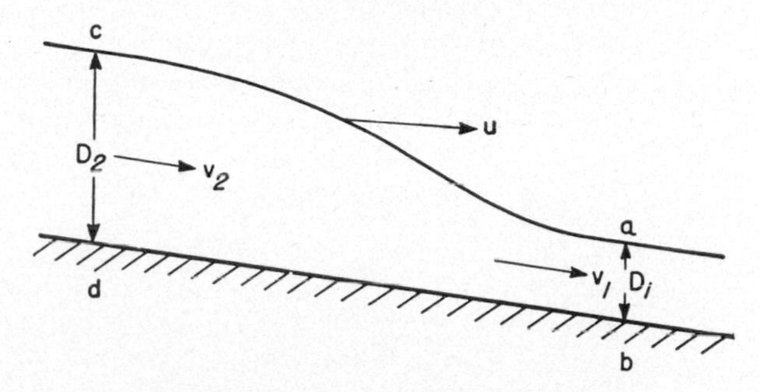

FIG. 18–2. Monoclinal rising wave.

water which flows through the wave shape is called the *overrun*, q'. It follows that

$$q' = (u - v_1)a_{c1} = (u - v_2)a_{c2} \tag{18-2}$$

Solving this equation for u,

$$u = \frac{a_{c1}v_1 - a_{c2}v_2}{a_{c1} - a_{c2}} \tag{18-3}$$

Since $q = a_c v$, Eq. (18-3) becomes

$$u = \frac{q_1 - q_2}{a_{c1} - a_{c2}} \tag{18-4}$$

Combining Eqs. (18-2) and (18-4), the overrun is found to be

$$q' = \frac{q_1 a_{c2} - q_2 a_{c1}}{a_{c1} - a_{c2}} \tag{18-5}$$

Inspection of Eq. (18-4) discloses that if there is no initial flow (q_1 and a_{c1} equal zero) then the celerity is q_2/a_{c2} or v_2. When there is initial flow, the velocity of the wave front is greater than the velocity of the water in the wave, because some water ahead of the wave is gathered up by it. The wave configuration thus moves along more rapidly than the water particles making up its volume at any instant.

It is evident from Eq. (18-4) that the velocity of a monoclinal wave is a function of the area-discharge relation for the channel. Figure 18-3 shows such a curve. Velocity usually increases with stage. Therefore, discharge, the product of area and velocity, increases at a more rapid rate than area, and the area-discharge curve is concave upward for most stations. From the figure it may be seen that

$$v_1 = \frac{q_1}{a_{c1}} = \tan\theta_1 \qquad \text{and} \qquad v_2 = \frac{q_2}{a_{c2}} = \tan\theta_2 \tag{18-6}$$

and

$$u = \frac{q_2 - q_1}{a_{c2} - a_{c1}} = \tan\theta_u \tag{18-7}$$

Since the curve is concave upward, the celerity u must always be greater than v_1 or v_2. It follows also that as q_1 approaches any given value of q_2 the celerity increases, approaching a maximum as $q_2 - q_1$ approaches zero. Therefore,

$$u_{\max} = \frac{dq}{da_c} \tag{18-8}$$

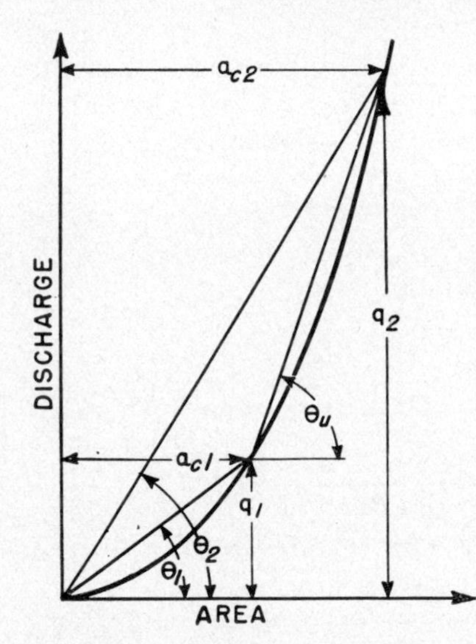

FIG. 18–3. Velocity relations in a monoclinal wave. *(After Thomas.)*

Letting B_t designate top width, $da_c = B_t\,dy$, and

$$u_{\max} = \frac{1}{B_t}\frac{dq}{dy} \tag{18-9}$$

The term dq/dy is the slope of the rating curve of the section for uniform flow.

Seddon's law. Equation (18-9) states the principle Seddon[1] developed by study of gage heights on the Mississippi and Missouri Rivers. He determined wave celerities by noting the times at which the point of rise occurred at each successive gaging station and found the celerity to be quite constant for small rises. On the Mississippi River below Cairo the wave celerity was found to be about 92 miles/day at all stages over a reach 277 miles long. For a 333-mile reach of the Missouri River below Kansas City, the celerity was found to be

$$u = 70 + 3.27\bar{g} \tag{18-10}$$

where u is in miles per day and $\bar{g}$ is the average stage in the reach. Seddon pointed out that the celerity in a reach is dependent on the mean width of the river between the stations. He even used the determination of u to compute B_t. For the reach to which Eq. (18-10) is applicable, the average rating curve (at the time of Seddon's paper) could be expressed as

$$q = 0.15(1.17\bar{g} + 19)^4 \tag{18-11}$$

[1] Seddon, J., River Hydraulics, *Trans. ASCE*, Vol. 43, pp. 217-229, 1900.

and u in feet per second as

$$u = 4.28 + 0.20\bar{g} \tag{18-12}$$

Solving Eq. (18-9) for B_t,

$$B_t = \frac{5.62(\bar{g} + 16.25)^3}{\bar{g} + 21.4} \tag{18-13}$$

The principle outlined by Seddon is applicable only to small rises. As shown by Fig. 18-3, the celerity of large waves is less than that for very small rises reaching the same crest height ($\tan \theta_u > \tan \theta_2$).

It is interesting to note that Seddon determined the celerity on the Mississippi between Carrollton and Baton Rouge to be more than 400 miles/day. This is to be expected from Eq. (18-9) since dq/dy is necessarily very large in the lower reaches of the Mississippi, approaching infinity at the outlet where stage is controlled by sea level.

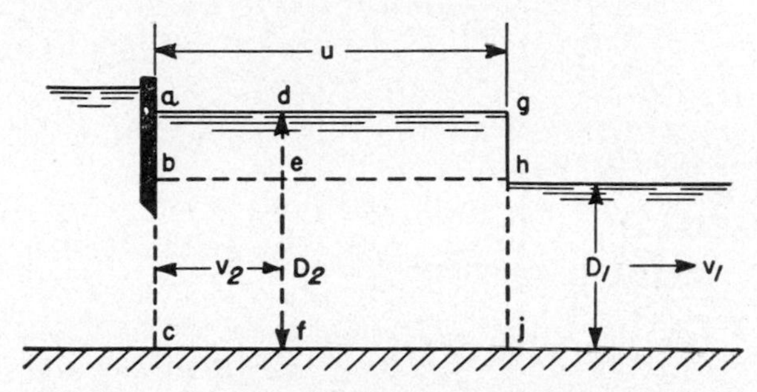

FIG. 18–4. Abrupt translatory wave. *(After King.)*

Abrupt translatory waves. An *abrupt translatory wave* is the result of an instantaneous increase in discharge. Figure 18-4 indicates conditions 1 sec after the instantaneous opening of a gate in a channel has generated an abrupt translatory wave.[1] The volume of water entering the channel in this time is $q_2 = a_{c2}v_2$(area *acfd*). The increased volume *abhg* is given by

$$q_2 - q_1 = u(a_{c2} - a_{c1}) \tag{18-14}$$

Substituting $q = a_c v$,

$$v_2 = (a_{c1}v_1 + a_{c2}u - a_{c1}u)\frac{1}{a_{c2}} \tag{18-15}$$

The volume *dfjg* has been accelerated from v_1 to v_2. The force required to produce this change in momentum is

$$F = \mathbf{m}(v_2 - v_1) = \frac{(u - v_2)(v_2 - v_1)a_{c2}w}{\mathbf{g}} \tag{18-16}$$

[1] King, H. W., "Handbook of Hydraulics," 3d ed., pp. 418-422, McGraw-Hill, New York, 1939.

where **m** is mass and w is the unit weight of water. Since F also equals the difference in hydrostatic pressure on areas a_{c1} and a_{c2},

$$F = wa_{c2}\bar{y}_2 - wa_{c1}\bar{y}_1 \qquad (18\text{-}17)$$

where $\bar{y}$ is the depth to the center of gravity of the section. Equating these values of F, eliminating w, and inserting v_2 from Eq. (18-15),

$$u = v_1 \pm \sqrt{\mathrm{g}\,\frac{a_{c2}\bar{y}_2 - a_{c1}\bar{y}_1}{a_{c1}\left[1 - \left(\frac{a_{c1}}{a_{c2}}\right)\right]}} \qquad (18\text{-}18)$$

Considering a unit width of rectangular channel we may substitute D for a_c and $D/2$ for $\bar{y}$,

$$u = v_1 \pm \sqrt{\frac{\mathrm{g}D_2}{2D_1}(D_2 + D_1)} \qquad (18\text{-}19)$$

As the height of the wave decreases (D_1 approaches D_2),

$$u = v_1 \pm \sqrt{\mathrm{g}D} \qquad (18\text{-}20)$$

Equation (18-18) is a general equation applying to any channel and any height of wave, Eq. (18-19) applies to a rectangular channel, and Eq. (18-20) is limited to waves of very small magnitude. The direction of flow is

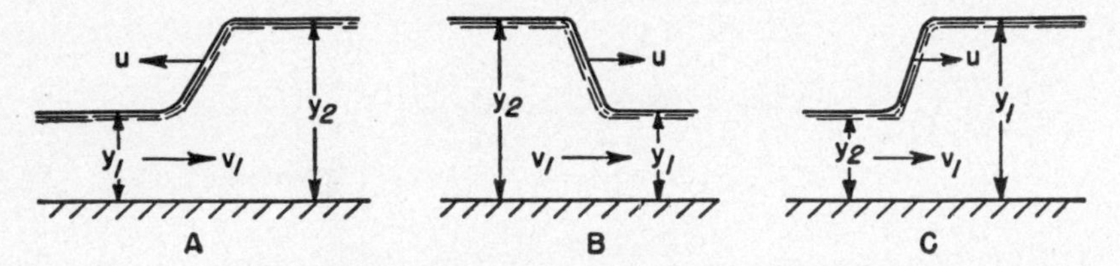

FIG. 18–5. Types of bores.

assumed to be positive downstream. If u is zero, Eq. (18-18) reduces to the general equation of the hydraulic jump. Thus, the hydraulic jump may be considered a standing wave with celerity zero.

The abrupt wave or moving hydraulic jump is known as the *hydraulic bore.* A bore can form in a rectangular channel only when

$$\frac{(u - v_1)^2}{2\mathrm{g}} > \frac{y_1}{2} \qquad (18\text{-}21)$$

In other words, the bore can form only when the initial depth in the channel is subcritical with respect to the net wave velocity $(u - v_1)$. This is analogous to the conditions under which a jump may form.

Bores occur frequently and sometimes regularly in some tidal estuaries. As the tide rises rapidly, a bore is formed and moves swiftly upstream. Such bores are to be observed on streams entering the Bay of Fundy, the

Severn River in England, and the Tsientang River in China.[1] Tidal bores are of type *A*, Fig. 18-5. The famous Johnstown flood (1889) and the Hepner, Oregon, flood (1903) were accompanied by bores of type *B*, the first being caused by the failure of a dam and the second by an intense rainstorm. The type *C* bore can result only from a decrease in flow, as by the closing of a gate in a canal or powerhouse tailrace.

Surges. Sudden changes in discharge caused by the opening or closing of a gate result in the transmission of a *surge* wave upstream from the gate. Surges are considered as positive or negative depending upon whether they are above or below the original still-water level. A positive surge (Fig. 18-6) may be caused by the sudden closing of a gate, and its celerity may be determined by an analysis similar to that applied to the abrupt translatory wave [Eq. (18-18)].

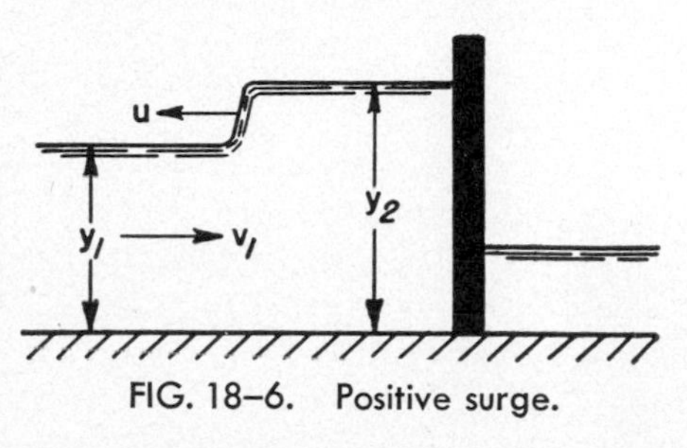

FIG. 18–6. Positive surge.

Figure 18-7 shows a negative surge such as might result from the sudden opening of a gate. The negative surge differs from the wave forms previously discussed in that it does not have constancy of form, because the upper elements of the wave travel faster than the lower elements. During

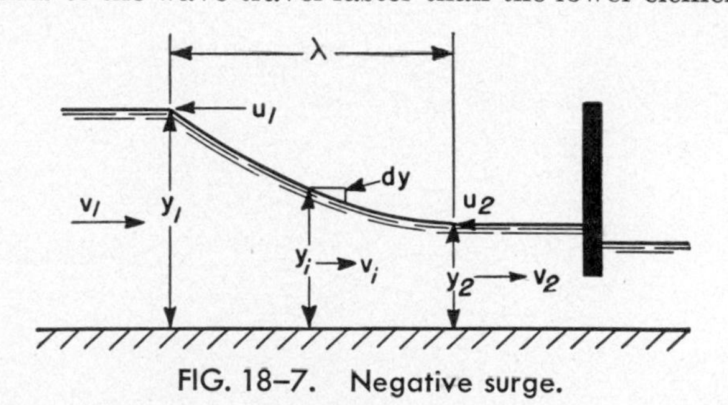

FIG. 18–7. Negative surge.

1 sec the force required to change the momentum of the vertical element intercepted by the increment of height dy is

$$F = \frac{(v - u)wa_c}{g} dv \tag{18-22}$$

The value of u is negative since we are considering a wave moving upstream. The force F is also equal to the difference in pressure across the distance $(v - u)$, *i.e.*,

$$F = \frac{wB}{2}(y - dy)^2 - \frac{wBy^2}{2} \tag{18-23}$$

[1] Mead, D. W., "Hydrology," p. 94, McGraw-Hill, New York, 1919.

where B is the width of the channel. Neglecting $(dy)^2$ this equation reduces to

$$F = -wBy\,dy = -wa_c\,dy \tag{18-24}$$

The negative sign indicates a positive force since y is decreasing and, therefore, dy is negative. Combining Eqs. (18-22) and (18-24),

$$dy = -\frac{(v-u)}{\mathbf{g}}\,dv \tag{18-25}$$

Since $v - u = \sqrt{\mathbf{g}y}$ [Eq. (18-20)],

$$\frac{dy}{\sqrt{y}} = -\frac{dv}{\sqrt{\mathbf{g}}} \tag{18-26}$$

Integrating between y_1 and y_2 and v_1 and v_2,

$$2\sqrt{y_2} - 2\sqrt{y_1} = -\frac{1}{\sqrt{\mathbf{g}}}(v_2 - v_1) \tag{18-27}$$

which can also be written

$$v_2 - v_1 = 2\sqrt{\mathbf{g}y_1} - 2\sqrt{\mathbf{g}y_2} \tag{18-28}$$

The water velocity where the depth is y_i (Fig. 18-7) is

$$v_i = v_1 + 2\sqrt{\mathbf{g}y_1} - 2\sqrt{\mathbf{g}y_i} \tag{18-29}$$

and since $v = u + \sqrt{\mathbf{g}y}$,

$$u_i = v_1 + 2\sqrt{\mathbf{g}y_1} - 3\sqrt{\mathbf{g}y_i} \tag{18-30}$$

At the crest of the wave where $y_i = y_1$,

$$u_1 = v_1 - \sqrt{\mathbf{g}y_1} \tag{18-31}$$

and at the trough of the wave,

$$u_2 = v_1 + 2\sqrt{\mathbf{g}y_1} - 3\sqrt{\mathbf{g}y_2} \tag{18-32}$$

By setting $u_2 = 0$ in Eq. (18-32), a value of $y_1 - y_2$ can be derived in terms of y_1 and v_1, namely,

$$y_1 - y_2 = \frac{5}{9}y_1 - \frac{v_1}{9\mathbf{g}}(v_1 + 4\sqrt{\mathbf{g}y_1}) \tag{18-33}$$

The rate of lengthening of the surge is

$$\frac{d\lambda}{dt} = u_2 - u_1 = 3\sqrt{\mathbf{g}}\,(\sqrt{y_1} - \sqrt{y_2}) \tag{18-34}$$

and integrating for the length of the wave,

$$\lambda = 3\sqrt{\mathbf{g}}\,(\sqrt{y_1} - \sqrt{y_2})t \tag{18-35}$$

Since $u_1t = x$, where x is measured from the point at which $\lambda = 0$, we can express λ in terms of x, the distance from the origin as

$$\lambda = \frac{3\sqrt{\mathbf{g}}\,(\sqrt{y_1} - \sqrt{y_2})x}{v_1 - \sqrt{\mathbf{g}y_1}} \tag{18-36}$$

Flood wave due to dam failure. If the dam of Fig. 18-8 is assumed to fail suddenly, a negative surge travels upstream in the reservoir with celerity u_1. Simultaneously, an advancing wave moves downstream with celerity u_0. The celerity will be zero at some point A at which v_1 also is zero, and hence, from Eq. (18-33), $z_a = 5/9 D_1$. Since $D_A = D_1 - z_a$, D_A becomes $4/9 D_1$. From Eq. (18-29),

$$v_A = 2/3\sqrt{gD_1} \tag{18-37}$$

At the toe of the wave, where $D = 0$, the celerity u_0 must equal the water velocity v_0, and, from Eq. (18-29),

$$u_0 = 2\sqrt{gD_1} \tag{18-38}$$

The derivations above are of theoretical interest but of limited practical application. The complete, instantaneous failure of any dam is most improbable, and frictional resistance would rapidly reduce any wave celerity well below that indicated by Eq. (18-38). Furthermore, Eqs. (18-29) and (18-33) were derived for a surge of very small amplitude.

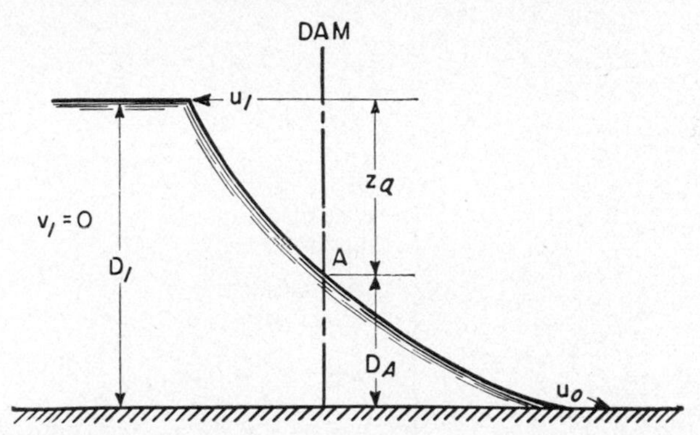

FIG. 18–8. Flood wave caused by failure of a dam.

Seiches. Oscillations of water bodies above and below their mean level are called seiches. These oscillations have a natural period depending upon the physical features of the water body. A disturbing force with the same period of oscillation as a lake or pool builds up the seiche to the point where the energy dissipated by friction equals the rate of application of energy. Seiches may be caused also by strong winds or differences in barometric pressure which cause an initial displacement of a water surface. When the force causing the displacement ceases or changes in intensity, a series of pulsations follow at the natural frequency until damped by frictional forces. Fluctuations in excess of 2 ft have been observed on the Great Lakes as a result of wind. A pressure difference of 1 in. of mercury is equivalent to 13.5 in. of water, but such a difference is rare over an area even as large as one of the Great Lakes.

A seiche may be considered to be composed of two waves traveling in opposite directions and in such phase relation that $z_a = 0$ at the nodes, and $v = 0$ at the boundaries of the basin. Figure 18-9 represents a uninodal seiche in a basin of uniform cross section. The elevation at N is

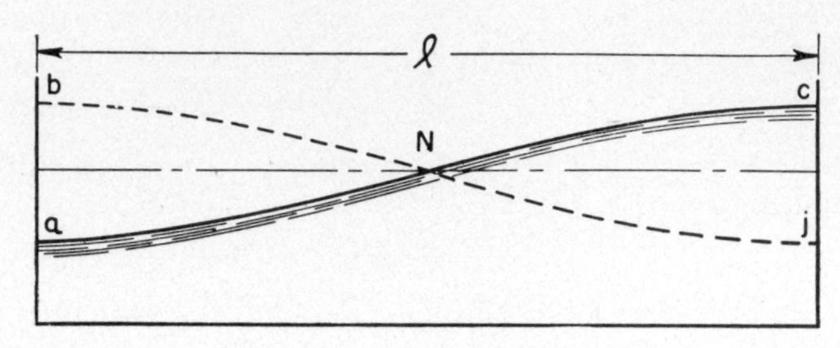

FIG. 18–9. Uninodal seiche.

constant, and the water surface at the ends fluctuates between the limits a,b and c,j. From Eq. (18-20), with $v_1 = 0$, the period of the seiche is

$$t_o = \frac{2l}{u} = \frac{2l}{\sqrt{gD}} \tag{18-39}$$

The wave length is

$$\lambda = 2l = ut_o \tag{18-40}$$

Figure 18-10 presents two cases of multinodal seiches in a closed basin of length l. If k is the number of nodes, the general expressions of Eqs. (18-39) and (18-40) are

$$t_o = \frac{2l}{k\sqrt{gD}} \tag{18-41}$$

and

$$\lambda = \frac{2l}{k} \tag{18-42}$$

In no case should more than two nodes be counted per wave length. Thus, both cases shown in Fig. 18-10 have $k = 2$.

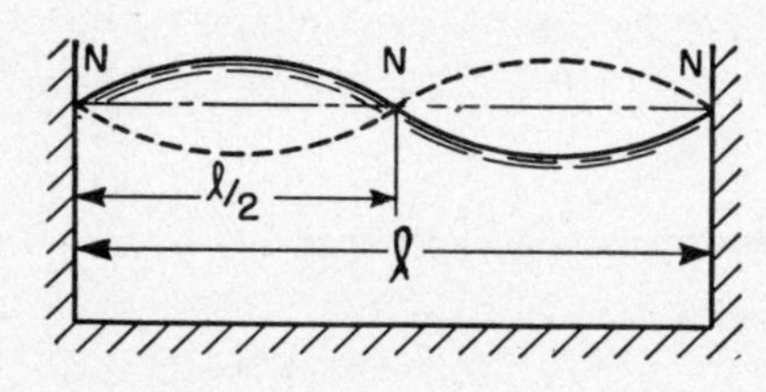

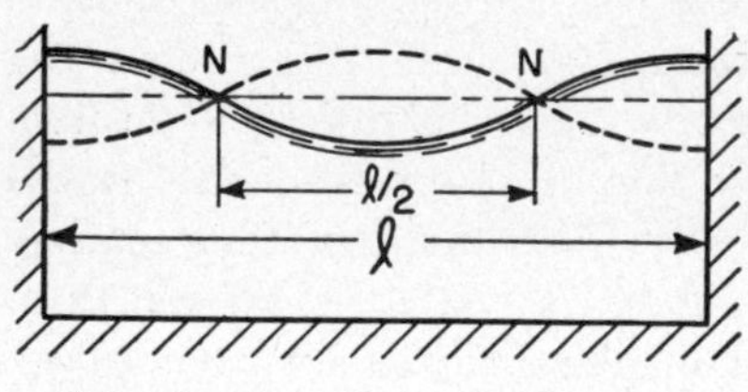

FIG. 18–10. Multinodal seiches.

If the basin is open at one end (Fig. 18-11) the water-surface elevation remains constant at this end and the seiche takes the form of that in a closed basin twice the length of the open basin. Thus, Eq. (18-41) becomes

$$t_o = \frac{4l}{k\sqrt{gD}} \tag{18-43}$$

Equations (18-39) to (18-42) have all been based on the assumption of a uniform and constant cross section in the basin. In a basin of irregular section, the period is given by integrating

$$t_o = 2\int_0^l \frac{dx}{\sqrt{gy}} \qquad (18\text{-}44)$$

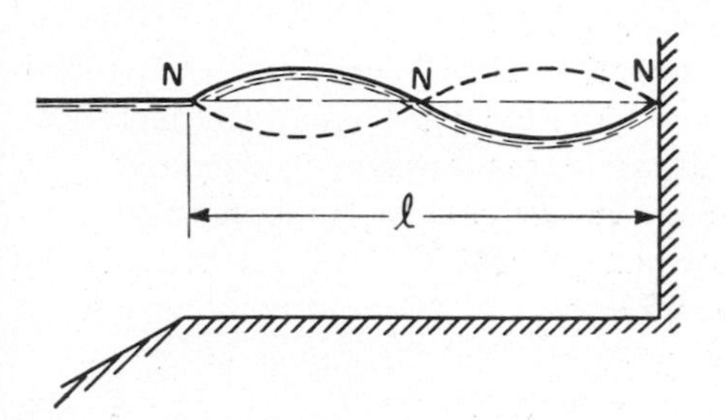

FIG. 18–11. Seiche in a basin open at one end.

Because of the usually complex relation between x and y in a natural lake or other basin, it is impossible to integrate Eq. (18-44) by analytical means. Such a basin may be treated readily by plotting $1/\sqrt{gy}$ against x and measuring the area under the resulting curve. The node will occur at the value of x dividing the area into two equal parts ($A_1 = A_2$, Fig. 18-12).

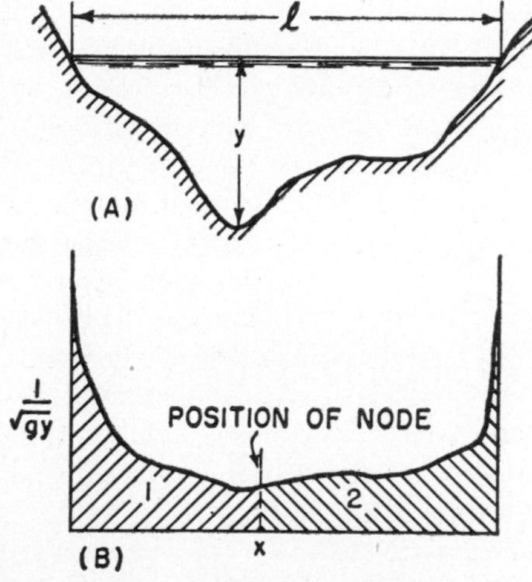

FIG. 18–12. Seiche in an irregular basin.

WAVES IN NATURAL CHANNELS

The discussions in the preceding sections of this chapter have ignored the effect of channel slope and friction on wave movement. In a short, deep channel these factors may be of little importance, but as length and slope increase and depth decreases, they exert a significant effect on wave movement. The solution of problems of unsteady flow by means of the theoretical formulas is almost impossible. In a subsequent chapter, empirical procedures used in applied hydrology to determine the movements of flood waves are discussed. The travel of natural waves is complicated, not only by friction and channel slope, but also by the fact that they are generated neither instantaneously nor at a single point but are rather the accumulation of inflow over a considerable length of stream channel.

Within their limitations the formulas presented in this chapter are applicable to the movement of flood waves, as evidenced by Seddon's experimental verification of the equation of movement for monoclinal rising waves. In reservoirs, large rivers with flat slopes, and canals and other regular channels, reasonably exact verification may be expected. At high values of u, frictional losses are tremendous. This accounts for the fact that, while observed values of u are generally less than computed values, the difference is most marked at high celerities.

Verification of theory. When the inflow into a reach can be controlled by a dam, an excellent opportunity is afforded for comparing theoretical values with observed results. Wilkinson[1] made such a comparison on three reaches in the Tennessee Valley. In two reaches, under natural river conditions, theoretical celerities agreed reasonably well with observed celerities computed from the time differences of the mid-point of rise at successive stations. Observed velocities for the beginning of rise were considerably above theoretical values computed from Eq. (18-3). If the toe of the wave is assumed to follow Eq. (18-20), the theoretical celerity at the point of beginning of rise will be well in excess of that observed. Within Wheeler Reservoir, Eq. (18-18) yielded celerities which agreed closely with the observed for some reaches, while in others the computed values were much too high. Wilkinson points out the difficulties inherent in determining the mean effective cross section through reaches of this type. Lansford in a discussion of Wilkinson's paper presents experimental data verifying Eq. (18-19) and Churchill gives data showing good verification between computed and observed wave celerities in Ft. Loudoun Reservoir.

Surges caused by levee breaks have been observed to travel at celerities in agreement with the theoretical values. Levee breaks, which generally occur at high stages, result in a sudden diversion of flow from the river, causing negative surges to travel both up- and downstream from the break. Almost instantaneous drops in stage are observed over a substantial distance along the stream in both directions from a large break. Runoff from intense local rains into already high streams sometimes produces small rises which travel as surges for considerable distances.

Zeitlinger[2] showed by experiment on waves in shallow water that because of frictional effects the actual celerity was about 0.91 of that computed by Eq. (18-20). On the other hand, Horton[3] and Moots[4] found good agreement between observed and theoretical celerities in controlled experiments. It cannot be assumed that Zeitlinger's friction factor is of universal application. The friction factor probably varies with channel features. Sherman[5] states that (1) the celerity at the toe of a wave is approximately 1.4

[1] Wilkinson, J. H., Translatory Waves in Natural Channels, *Trans. ASCE*, Vol. 72, pp. 1203-1236, 1945.

[2] Schoklitsch, A., Dam Break Waves, *Math. naturw. Klasse*, Vol. 126, pp. 1489-1514, 1917.

[3] Horton, R. E., Channel Waves Subject Chiefly to Momentum Control, *Permanent Intern. Assoc. Navigation Congr. Bull.* 27, 1939.

[4] Moots, E. E., A Study in Flood Waves, *Univ. Iowa Studies Eng. Bull.* 14, 1938.

[5] Sherman, L. K., discussion of paper by H. W. King, Translatory Waves in Open Channels, *Civil Eng.*, Vol. 3, p. 473, 1933.

times the mean celerity of the wave, which is in accord with data in Wilkinson's paper; (2) that u varies from $1.4v_2$ to $2.0v_2$; and (3) for high stages, u approaches a constant.

Whipple[1] indicates that the theoretical equations, when applied to seiches on Lake Erie, give a computed period of 14.4 hr compared with observed periods of 14 to 16 hr.

OSCILLATORY WAVES

Gaillard[2] states that the following dynamic conditions must be satisfied by a correct theory of oscillatory wave motion:

1. The effective force acting on every particle to produce acceleration is the result of the pressure of the surrounding liquid and gravity (dynamic equilibrium).
2. The mass of water may change shape during the passage of a wave, but its continuity cannot be broken.
3. The equation must take into account the character of the bottom and the atmospheric conditions at the surface (boundaries).
4. It must support the possibility of wave formation in still water with consideration of viscosity.

An example of the oscillatory wave is the wind-generated ocean wave. Observation of a floating object in fairly deep water will demonstrate that there is little forward motion of the water but rather that the particle tends to oscillate in a circular orbit.

By successive approximations based on the equation of continuity between two fluids of different density, Rayleigh[3] demonstrated that the oscillatory wave form is approximately trochoidal, with the circumference of the rolling circle equal to λ and the length of the tracing arm equal to the radius of the orbit of the surface particles r_{os}. The trochoidal form results in sharper crests and flatter troughs than indicated by simple harmonic motion. When $r_{os} = \lambda/2\pi$, the trochoidal form results in sharp cusps at the wave crests—a limiting case not observed in nature. The trochoid as discussed above is now more generally called a "curtate cycloid," *i.e.*, one in which the tracer arm is shorter than the radius of the generating circle. The trochoidal theory satisfies the first three conditions stated by Gaillard but fails to meet the fourth since it is not possible to generate trochoidal waves by application of tangential forces, such as those

[1] Whipple, G. C., "The Microscopy of Drinking Water," 4th ed., p. 162, Wiley, New York, 1927.

[2] Gaillard, D. D., Wave Action in Relation to Engineering Structures, *Corps Engrs. Prof. Paper* 31, 1904.

[3] Lamb, H., "Hydrodynamics," 6th ed., pp. 417-423, Cambridge, London, 1937.

of wind, to a liquid surface. Nevertheless, the theory is in reasonable accord with observation and experiment.

Deep-water waves. The amplitude of oscillation of a trochoidal wave becomes negligible at depths greater than one-half the wave length. Thus, waves occurring in water with a depth greater than $\lambda/2$ may be considered as deep-water waves. Figure 18-13 shows the various elements of the

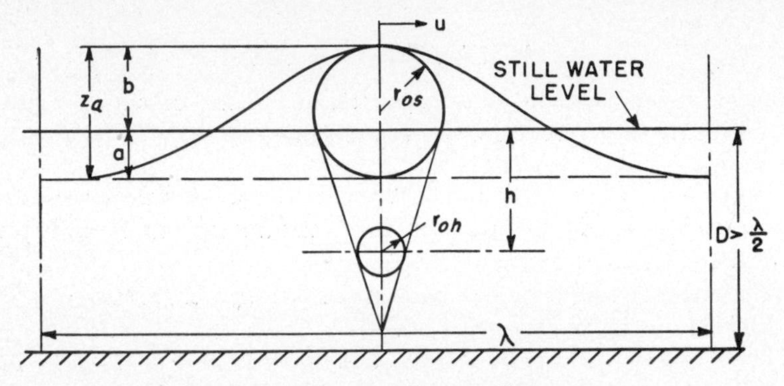

FIG. 18–13. Elements of an oscillatory wave.

trochoidal wave, and the following formulas indicate the method of computation of various factors:

$$u = \sqrt{\frac{g\lambda}{2\pi}} = 2.27\sqrt{\lambda} \qquad \text{(celerity in fps)} \tag{18-45}$$

$$r_{oh} = \frac{r_{os}}{e^{2\pi h/\lambda}} \qquad \text{(radius of orbit)} \tag{18-46}$$

$$z_a = 2r_{os} \qquad \text{(amplitude)} \tag{18-47}$$

$$a = \frac{z_a}{2} - 0.78\frac{z_a^2}{\lambda} \qquad \text{(ft)} \tag{18-48}$$

$$b = \frac{z_a}{2} + 0.78\frac{z_a^2}{\lambda} \qquad \text{(ft)} \tag{18-49}$$

$$t_o = \frac{\lambda}{u} = \frac{\sqrt{\lambda}}{2.27} \qquad \text{(period in sec)} \tag{18-50}$$

$$E = \frac{w\lambda z_a^2}{8}\left[1 - 4.94\left(\frac{z_a}{\lambda}\right)^2\right] \qquad \text{(energy per ft of crest per wave length in ft-lb)} \tag{18-51}$$

Deep-water waves are considered to be of moderate height when the ratio z_a/λ is between $\frac{1}{100}$ and $\frac{1}{25}$ and of great height when this ratio exceeds $\frac{1}{25}$. Waves of great height tend to have narrower and steeper crests and broader and flatter troughs than moderate waves. When the ratio z_a/λ exceeds $\frac{1}{7}$, the wave form becomes unstable and breaks up in numerous irregular waves of lesser height.

The trochoidal theory assumes no actual forward motion of the water particles beyond the orbital motion. Actually, a given water particle does advance a short distance in the course of each circuit through its orbit. This forward velocity[1] is

$$v = \left(\frac{\pi z_a}{\lambda}\right)^2 u \tag{18-52}$$

Shallow-water waves. If the depth of water is less than $\lambda/2$, the motion of the water particles in the vertical direction is restricted, celerity and wave length decrease, and the orbits tend to become elliptical with their major axes horizontal. The wave thus becomes more nearly a translatory wave. When $D < \lambda/25$, the wave can be considered a translatory wave. In the intermediate range, when the depth is between $\lambda/2$ and $\lambda/25$, the celerity is given by

$$u = 2.27\sqrt{\frac{c\lambda}{k}} \tag{18-53}$$

where k is the horizontal semiaxis and c is the vertical semiaxis of the orbit of the surface particles.

Wind and waves. Numerous empirical relations between wind and waves have been developed. Their verification is difficult because of the inaccuracies in estimating wave heights and because waves, once generated, tend to persist for some time, even though wind velocity changes. Stevenson[2] found that where the fetch l_f, the distance through which the wind acts on the water surface, exceeds 30 miles, the maximum wave height to be expected with high winds is

$$z_a = 1.5\sqrt{l_f} \tag{18-54}$$

For short fetches (under 30 miles) z_a appears to conform to

$$z_a = 1.5\sqrt{l_f} + 2.5 - \sqrt[4]{l_f} \tag{18-55}$$

Waves of maximum height are not generated concurrently with the onset of a given wind. Evidence indicates that the time required to develop waves of maximum height corresponding to a certain velocity increases with velocity. In general, the time required is less than 12 hr.

Molitor[3] modified Stevenson's formulas to introduce wind velocity as follows:

$$z_a = 0.17\sqrt{v_w l_f} \qquad (l_f > 20 \text{ miles}) \tag{18-56}$$

$$z_a = 0.17\sqrt{v_w l_f} + 2.5 - \sqrt[4]{l_f} \qquad (l_f < 20 \text{ miles}) \tag{18-57}$$

[1] Sverdrup, H. U., Oceanography, Sec. XIV in Berry, Bollay, and Beers (eds.), "Handbook of Meteorology," p. 1052, McGraw-Hill, New York, 1945.

[2] Stevenson, T., "Design and Construction of Harbors; A Treatise on Maritime Engineering," 2d ed., A. J. Black, Edinburgh, 1874.

[3] Molitor, D. A., Wave Pressures on Sea-walls and Breakwaters, *Trans. ASCE*, Vol. 100, pp. 984-986, 1935.

Molitor points out that empirical formulas are much less satisfactory than actual observations for a particular site because of the strong influence of local conditions.

Ride-up and set-up. In determining the proper freeboard above maximum still-water level for design of dams or levees, a safety factor must be introduced into Eqs. (18-56) and (18-57) to allow for the ride-up of waves on the sloping surface of the structure. This factor is usually taken as about 1.5.

A persistent wind will result in a shift of water from one side of a basin or reservoir to the other, increasing the water-surface elevation on the leeward side. This increase in elevation is sometimes referred to as set-up Z_w, and it must be considered in calculating freeboard on levees and dams. The formula proposed by the Lorentz Zuyder Zee Commission of Holland for this effect is

$$Z_w = 0.00125 \frac{v_w{}^2 l_f}{D} \cos \theta \tag{18-58}$$

The angle θ is measured between the fetch of the wind and a normal to the shore line where the set-up is to be computed.

TIDES

Periodic fluctuations of surface elevation in the oceans result from the gravitational attraction of the sun and moon. This gravitational potential acting on a particle of water varies directly as the mass of the attracting body and inversely as the cube of the distance from the body to the earth. The sun's mass is 26×10^6 times as great as that of the moon, but the ratio of the cube of the sun's distance from the earth to that of the moon is roughly 58×10^6. The moon, therefore, is about 2.2 times as effective as the sun in producing tidal fluctuations.

Tidal theories. A considerable amount of complex mathematical theory has been derived to explain tides. Perhaps the earliest theory ascribed the action to two primary tides, 180° longitude apart, which travel around the earth in 25 hr. There are many phenomena which cannot be explained by this theory but which do conform to the stationary-wave theory advanced by Harris.[1]

Harris's theory assumes that tides are regional phenomena depending on the geometry of the particular ocean basin in which they occur. It is assumed that the tide-producing forces of the sun and moon cause seiches whenever their period corresponds with the fundamental period or one of its harmonics in a given basin. In a seiche, the amplitude is zero at the nodes and generally a maximum at the fixed boundaries. Under this theory tides on the west coast of North America are explained by two stationary waves, one a binodal seiche with an axis from the Gulf of

[1] Harris, R. A., Manual of Tides, Appendix 8, *U.S. Coast Geod. Survey Rept.*, 1897.

Alaska to the vicinity of Ecuador with nodes near lat 20° and 33°N (San Diego), and a second from California to Australia with one of its nodes near Tahiti. The presence of a node near San Diego explains the fact that the tidal *range*, the difference in height between high and low water, increases northward along the coast. The two waves, one having a daily and the other a semidaily period, result in a *mixed tide*, a tide having two high and two low waters daily with a marked diurnal inequality in the two high and two low tides.

In the Atlantic a binodal wave is believed to exist between the eastern United States and the southern tip of Africa with a NE–SW node through the Windward Islands. This is confirmed by the fact that tides in the Windward Islands are negligible. Any body of water has natural periods of oscillation in all directions. Tidal oscillations develop in those directions along which the natural period corresponds to the period of the tide-producing forces.

Tide terminology. An extensive nomenclature has been developed to describe the complex tidal occurrences which are observed. At the time of the new and full moons, the sun, moon, and earth are in line; and the forces of the sun and moon combine to cause the highest tides, called *spring tides*. When the moon is in the first or third quarter, *i.e.*, 90° away from the sun, tides are lower and are called *neap tides*.

A *diurnal tide* has only one high and one low water daily. When a *mixed tide* occurs, there are a *higher high water* and *lower high water* and also *higher* and *lower low waters*. *Mean tide level* is midway between *mean high water*, the average of all high-water observations, and *mean low water*, the average of all low-water observations. *Mean sea level* is the elevation at which the water would stand if no tide-producing forces acted upon it.

The *mean range* is the difference in height of average high water and average low water at any point. *Spring range* and *neap range* are the mean ranges of spring and neap tides, respectively. The *diurnal range* is the difference between the elevations of mean higher high water and mean lower low water.

Harmonic analysis of tides. The U.S. Coast and Geodetic Survey publishes annual Tide Tables in which the height and time of each high and low tide for key stations and factors for computing these values for nearby stations may be found. These data are determined by a harmonic analysis of observed tidal stages as recorded on an extensive network of water-stage recorders maintained along the coast and in tidal rivers. As many as 20 or 30 separate components may be distinguished in the observed tidal cycles and may be recombined to estimate future tide heights. The lunar and solar components, though very complex as a result of the varying elliptical orbits and the time relations involved, are rather directly determinable and can be predicted from astronomical data.

Superimposed upon the tidal fluctuations caused by the sun and moon are variations in water level resulting from barometric-pressure differences, winds, freshets, and other factors. High barometric pressure off the coast and a low at the coast increase tidal heights. In estuaries, streamflow

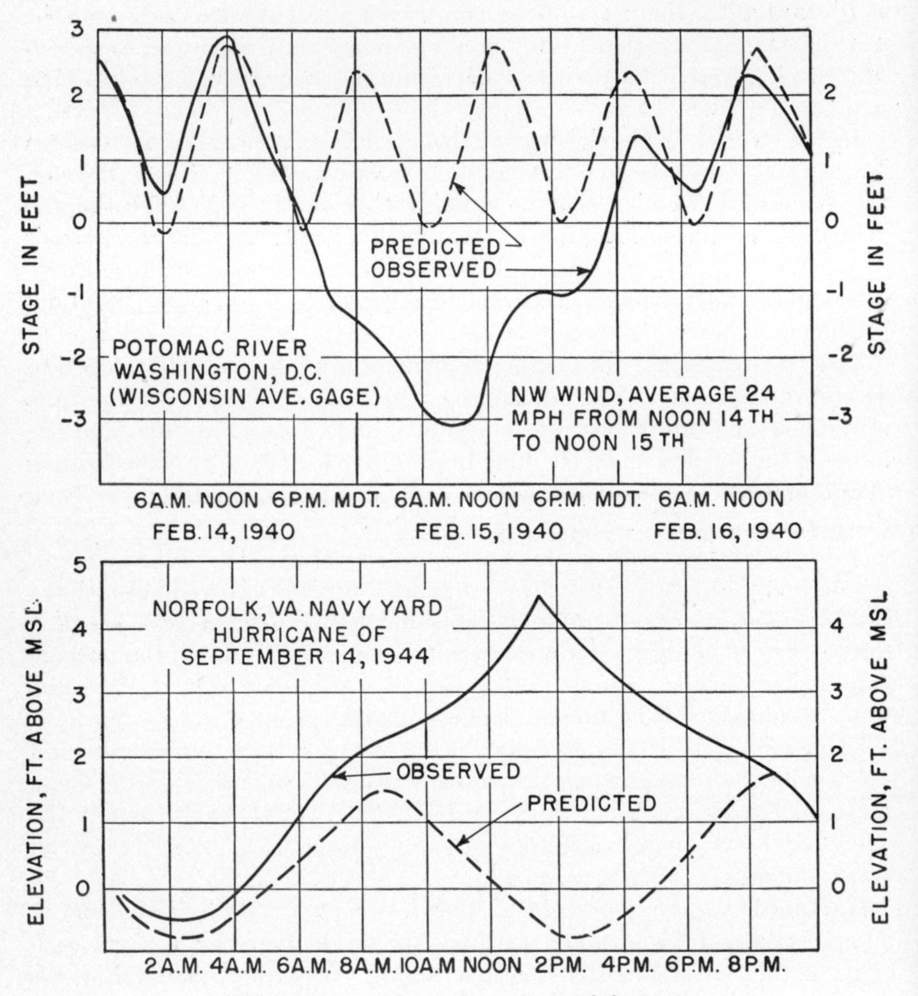

FIG. 18–14. Effect of wind on tidal stages.

from upriver or an onshore wind can raise the level above normal tidal heights, while an offshore wind can cause a much lower stage. Predicted tides are based on the normal value of these elements for the particular date involved. Thus, predicted tides in an estuary, such as the Columbia River, subject to a regular annual high water in June, will include the average effect of this high water. The normal effect of movements of semipermanent pressure centers which have a fairly regular annual cycle will also be included. Wide deviations from predicted tides may occur in estuaries and bays where freshets, winds, and pressure changes of a noncyclic nature occur.

Secondary tides. Tide-producing forces acting on the oceans do not necessarily cause true tides in rivers, bays, sounds, and other bodies of water connected to the oceans. This is supported by the fact that only a negligible amplitude can be ascribed to tides in the Great Lakes. Tides in estuaries are secondary tides generated by the occurrence of the primary tide at their mouths. Two types of secondary tides have been observed. A *progressive tide* is a moving wave progressing up and down the estuary so

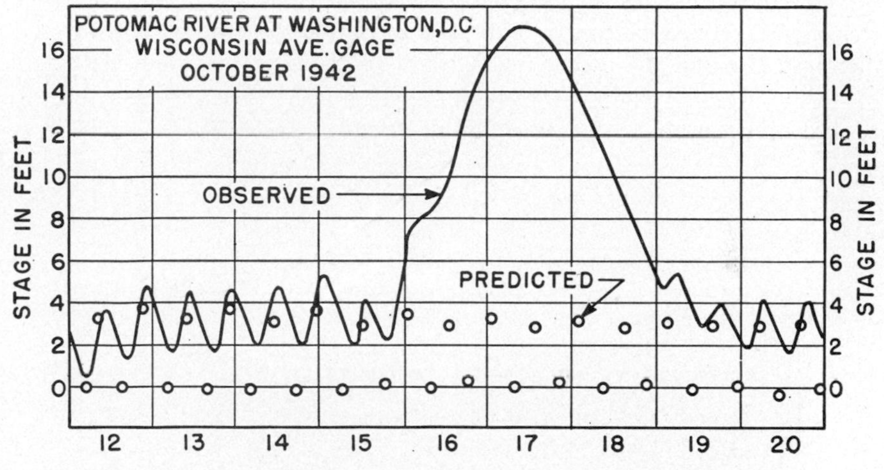

FIG. 18–15. Effect of freshets on stages of a tidal river.

that the high and low tides occur at successively later times as the wave moves along the channel.

Secondary *stationary waves* may also form, and in this case high or low tide occurs simultaneously, or nearly so, throughout the entire basin. For example, in Long Island Sound the average depth of 65 ft indicates a period of about 12 hr [Eq. (18-39)]. This coincides with the period of the primary tides and a seiche is set up in the sound with an increasing range from mouth to head, as would be expected with a node at the mouth.

Wind and tides. It has been indicated earlier that winds can produce excessively high or low tides. Typical of such occurrences is the "tidal wave," which frequently occurs in connection with hurricanes. The high winds and tremendous pressure differences associated with hurricanes move large volumes of water inshore, sometimes floating large ships inland substantial distances. Less dramatic occurrences are often observed in estuaries such as the Potomac River, where a northwest wind has been known to blow the channel at Washington nearly dry, while a southerly wind may increase stages as much as 8 ft (hurricane of August, 1933). Equation (18-58) may serve to compute this effect, although at Washington it has been observed to be cumulative, *i.e.*, height of rise increases with duration of wind. Figure 18-14 shows observed and predicted gage heights at Washington, D.C., and Norfolk, Virginia, during periods of pronounced wind effect.

Freshets and tides. Tidal effects are frequently dampened by high water in streams tributary to a tidal estuary. This effect is evidenced as the stream rises by the gradual disappearance of tidal fluctuations from stations progressively downstream. A hydrograph for the Potomac River at Washington during the October, 1942, flood (Fig. 18-15) demonstrates this effect. Its cause can probably be attributed to two factors, (1) the increased slope in the estuary as a result of rising water at its head and (2) the increased velocity of the water at high stages. These effects prevent the secondary wave from proceeding upstream.

19
STREAMFLOW ROUTING

Chapters 15 to 17 deal with the phenomena of generation of a flood wave in response to runoff resulting from rainfall or melting snow. The headwater hydrograph of a stream consists of a series of rises of varying magnitude and shape. An important problem in hydrology is that of reproducing the hydrograph at other stations downstream. In other words, we must predict the rate of movement and change in shape of each flood wave as it moves downstream.

The problem is one of unsteady flow, or wave travel. The discussion of these subjects in Chap. 18 shows that the theoretical equations are not solvable within practical limits except for a few special cases. These cases, because of simplifying assumptions ignoring friction and channel slope, are not fully applicable to practical problems in hydrology. It is necessary, therefore, to adopt an approximate solution which is within limits of practical usefulness. This solution is known as *streamflow routing*. If the critical factors governing wave movement are included in the technique and if the empirical relation is based on data representative of all possible events for the stream under study, then the techniques are generally adequate. A great number of possible routing procedures have been devised. It would be impossible to detail all these types in this chapter, but several are discussed as samples of each broad type of technique. The limitations of routing in general and of each type in particular are presented in order that the reader may judge which approach will prove most effective for a particular problem.

Natural flood waves. Two general classes of flood waves may be distinguished in natural channels, (1) those in which forces of momentum and acceleration control and (2) those in which friction is the predominant force. Waves of the first class resemble the abrupt translatory wave and usually occur in steep, dry channels as the result of cloudbursts. The length of such waves is short compared with the length of the channel system in which they move. Most natural waves are of the second type and have time bases far exceeding the time of travel through the system of streams in which they form.

During its passage through a watercourse, a flood wave may be considered to undergo *simple translation* (uniformly progressive flow) and *reservoir* or *pondage action.* Uniformly progressive flow requires a regular channel and constant wave velocity throughout the range in stage through which the wave passes. Under these conditions, the flood wave maintains a constant shape as it moves downstream, and hydrographs at successive stations differ only in time of passage of the wave. Examples of pure

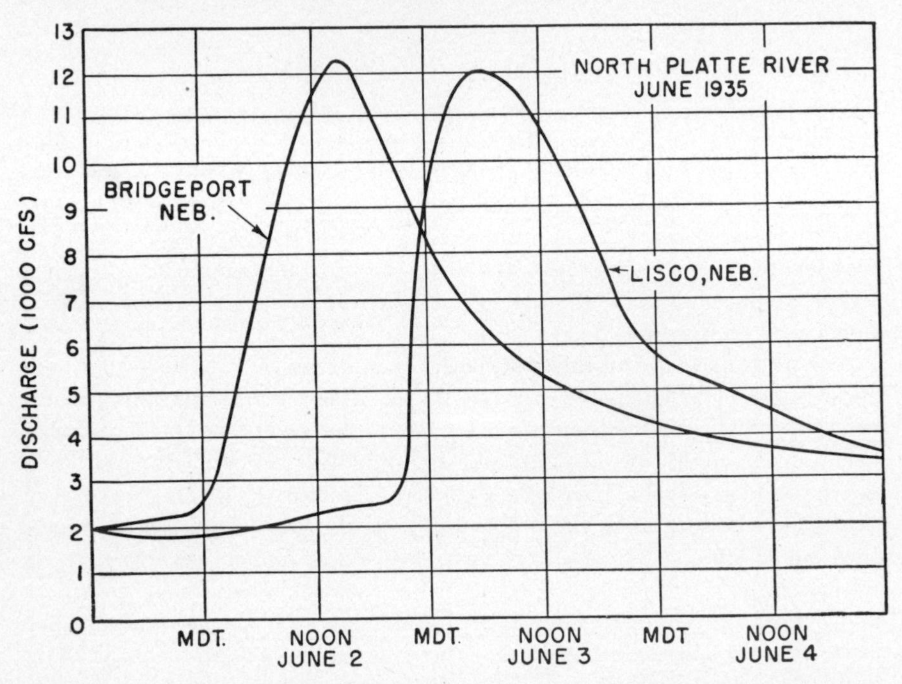

FIG. 19–1. Example of translatory wave movement, North Platte River, between Bridgeport and Lisco, Nebraska.

translatory motion in natural channels are rare, but a case without appreciable change in shape is shown in Fig. 19-1.

An ideal reservoir would have great depth and a level water surface. Water velocity in such a reservoir would be nearly zero, but the effect of inflowing water would be transmitted almost instantaneously to all parts of the pool by surge waves. If the outflow from such a reservoir were over a weir or through an orifice, such that the outflow rate were a function of head, then as water entered the reservoir the water surface would rise and the discharge from the reservoir would increase. Some water would be required to fill the reservoir as the surface rose, so that as long as the inflow increased the outflow would be less than the inflow. The pool elevation would continue to rise after the inflow began to drop, until the inflow and outflow were equal. The highest pool elevation and the outflow peak would be simultaneous and would necessarily occur at the time the outflow and inflow hydrographs cross. Few, if any, reservoirs completely fulfill these conditions, particularly in regard to the level water surface. An example that closely approaches this case is shown in Fig. 19-2.

Natural flood-wave movement is generally intermediate between the two examples cited, ranging from pure translatory movement when

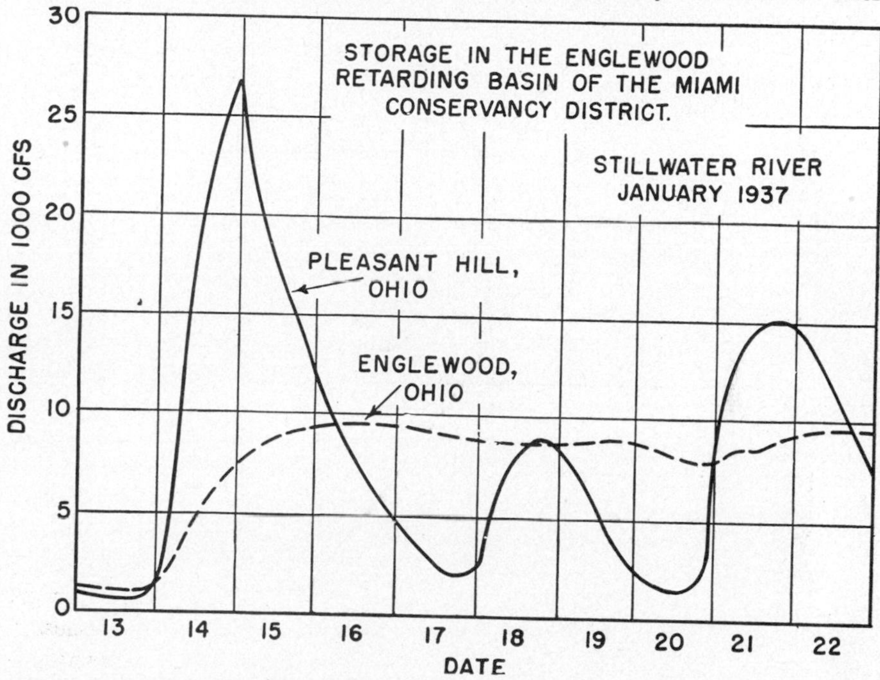

FIG. 19–2. Reduction in discharge through reservoir action, Stillwater River, Ohio.

$v/\sqrt{gD} = 1$ to pure reservoir action as $v/\sqrt{gD}$ approaches zero. Other basic differences between natural flood waves and the simplified theoretical cases may be summarized as follows:

1. The natural flood wave, unlike the abrupt translatory wave or solitary wave of translation, is never generated instantaneously, for the water supply (rainfall or snowmelt) does not become available instantaneously.
2. The natural flood wave is not generated at a point but rather is the cumulative effect of runoff entering the channels of the stream system over a considerable distance, often the entire length of the system. This introduces the complicating influence of inflow to a wave during its passage through a reach.

3. The natural flood wave is not monoclinal but instead rises to a peak, rarely sustained for a long time in relation to the time of rise, and then begins to recede. Rates of recession are usually slow, and in many cases the wave may effectively approach the monoclinal form.
4. Flood waves are frequently complex in form, being generated by rainfall, which varies in intensity with time and area. Therefore, the rate of rise, instead of being constant, may vary so that several secondary peaks are superimposed on the main wave form.

The shape of a flood wave is affected by several factors.[1] The more important of these are:

1. *Rate of rise.* A rapid rate of rise causes high velocities in the first stages of the flood, which in turn result in rapid dissipation of the first portion of the flood wave in valley storage and consequent retardation of its peak.
2. *Height of rise.* Valley storage per unit of stage increases with stage, and consequently high peaks are reduced more than low peaks.
3. *Slope of channel.* Steeper channel slopes result in higher velocities and lower stages and, consequently, less valley storage and peak reduction.
4. *Stages downstream.* If downstream stages are falling, a portion of the rising flood wave is required to maintain steady flow.
5. *Channel sections downstream.* As channel sections increase, valley storage increases, with corresponding reduction in crest flows and retardation of flood movement.
6. *Length of reach.* The longer the reach, the greater the valley storage. Storage varies as a fractional power of length of reach. Theoretically, the rise in a uniform channel would be propagated without change indefinitely, but in natural channels the curve of rate of peak reduction is concave upward.
7. *Length of crest.* The flatter the crest, the less it is reduced by valley storage.

CHANNEL STORAGE

The storage equation. The procedures of streamflow routing are based on the law of continuity expressed in the *storage equation*

$$\bar{I} - \bar{O} = \Delta S \tag{19-1}$$

In terms of differentials,

$$\frac{dS}{dt} = I - O \tag{19-2}$$

[1] Hickman, H. C., discussion of A Direct Method of Flood Routing, *Trans. ASCE*, Vol. 107, pp. 1532-1533, 1942.

This equation simply states that the rate of change of storage dS/dt is equal to the difference in the rates of inflow I and outflow O. Both forms of the storage equation are precise, *i.e.*, there is one and only one solution, and it must necessarily be exact. Unfortunately, however, most practical hydrologic problems are such that the equation cannot be used in the form given above. Certain assumptions are necessary in restating the equation, and it will be seen later that the determination of ΔS requires approximations.

Letting the subscript 1 refer to values at the beginning of any time period of length t_t and the subscript 2 refer to values at the end of the period, then the known factors in the usual routing problem are I_1, I_2, O_1, S_1, and t_t. The solution must yield a value of O_2 and, directly or indirectly, a value of S_2. Rewriting Eq. (19-1) in terms of the known and desired factors and assuming that $(I_1 + I_2)/2 = \bar{I}$ and $(O_1 + O_2)/2 = \bar{O}$,

$$\left(\frac{I_1 + I_2}{2}\right)t_t - \left(\frac{O_1 + O_2}{2}\right)t_t = S_2 - S_1 \qquad (19\text{-}3)$$

Equation (19-3) is the form of the storage equation on which most of the common solutions are based.

Determination of channel storage from surveys. It is obvious that a preliminary step to the solution of Eq. (19-3) is the determination of the volume of water in *temporary*, or *channel, storage* in the reach under consideration, and the definition of this storage in terms of some directly measurable element of the streamflow regime. The most obvious approach to the determination of channel storage is probably that of computation from surveys. If cross sections taken at reasonably short distances along the stream are available, the volume between sections may be computed by averaging end areas or by prismoidal formulas.[1] The water surface is usually assumed to be level between cross sections if the sections are close or to follow computed backwater curves or parallel the stream profile if the reaches are long.

If a suitably detailed topographic map of the channel and flood plain is available, the channel may be divided into short reaches in which the water surface may be assumed to be level and the area of water surface at successive elevations planimetered. The volume between any two elevations is equal to the average of the areas at each elevation multiplied by the difference in elevation. Total volume below any elevation may be found by summing the volumes for lower increments of elevation.

Either of the two procedures just outlined results in a series of elevation vs. storage curves for a number of short sections of the longer river reach over which the actual routing is to be performed. Backwater curves for

[1] Allen, C. F., "Railroad Curves and Earthwork," 7th ed., pp. 149-164, McGraw-Hill, New York, 1931.

various combinations of uniform and nonuniform flow must then be computed for the reach. The elevation at the mid-point of each subreach may then be determined from a given backwater curve and the corresponding storage in the subreach determined from the elevation vs. storage curve.

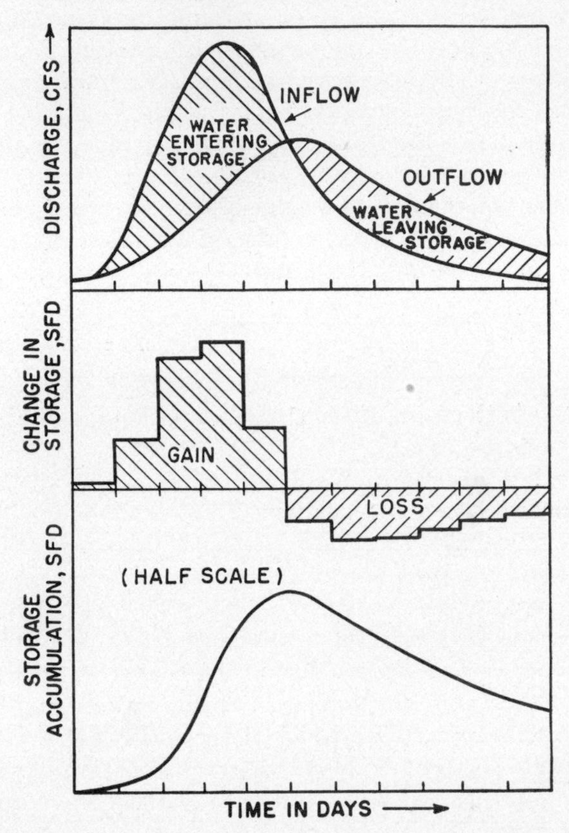

FIG. 19–3. Computation of storage from a hydrograph.

The sum of the storage in all subsections of the reach is the total reach storage under the given profile.

Determination of channel storage by hydrograph analysis. In most streams adequate survey data are lacking for the development of storage relations by the procedures outlined above. Moreover, if considerable precision is desired, a large amount of work is entailed in treating the small increments of distance and elevation into which the reach must be divided. Finally, the problem of computing the necessary backwater curves is complicated by the need for a large number of curves defining the various conditions of unsteady, nonuniform flow which may occur in the reach. An alternate solution which is usually simpler and more satisfactory lies in the derivation of storage from the hydrographs of flow through the reach.

Figure 19-3 shows the inflow and outflow hydrographs for a reach, assuming no local inflow. Under these conditions the storage equation [Eq. (19-1)] can be applied directly to compute ΔS for successive time increments, and the total storage at any time can be computed as the sum of the storage increments for all time periods from any arbitrary beginning. In actual practice, the condition of no inflow between stations is rarely observed, and adjustment for the intermediate, or *local, inflow* must be incorporated in the computations. Local inflow can be treated by selecting a period beginning and ending at the same low flow and computing the total measured flow at each gaging station for this period. The *ungaged local inflow* is equal in volume to the total outflow minus the inflow at the head of the reach minus the *gaged local inflow.* The hydrograph of ungaged local inflow can be constructed by prorating this total volume in accordance with the flow from one or more of the measured tributaries or by use of synthetic unit hydrographs. A hydrograph of total inflow is obtained by adding the local inflow hydrograph to the hydrograph of measured inflow.

With hydrographs of I and O now available, values of $\Delta S = \bar{I} - \bar{O}$ can be easily computed for short time periods and values of S determined by accumulating these increments. Since the computations are performed over a period beginning and ending at about the same low flow, the storage at the beginning and ending of the period should be about the same and the accumulation should return to zero. The length of the time increment used in computing storage as outlined above is not important so long as it is short enough to define the storage accumulation. The units of accumulation do depend, however, on the period length. Table 19-1 lists the units resulting from a given period and shows the factor by which the computed values must be multiplied to convert to second-foot-days.

TABLE 19-1. Units of Storage for Various Time Increments

Period, hr	Unit	To convert to second-foot-days multiply by
48	2 sfd	2.0
24	1 sfd	1.0
12	½ sfd *	0.5
6	¼ sfd	0.25
4	⅙ sfd	0.167
3	⅛ sfd	0.125
2	1/12 sfd	0.0833
1	1 sfh †	0.0417

* Approx. 1 acre-ft † second-foot-hours

As an example of the procedure just outlined, the channel storage for a reach of the Ohio River between Sewickley, Pennsylvania, and Wheeling, West Virginia (Fig. 19-4), during the flood of March, 1936, is computed as follows:

1. The hydrographs at Sewickley and Wheeling are shown in Fig. 19-5.

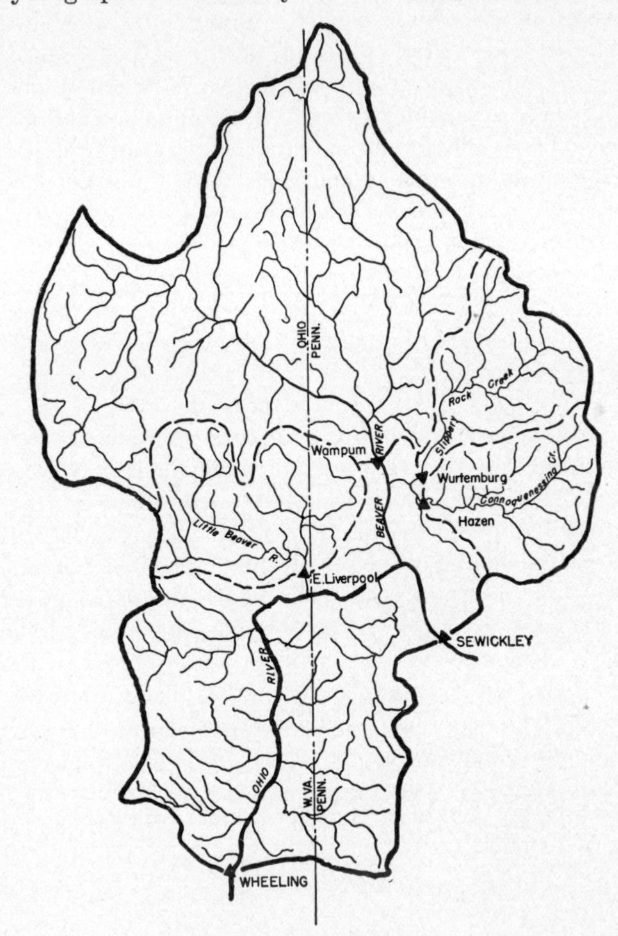

FIG. 19–4. Map of the Sewickley-Wheeling reach of the Ohio River.

The period Mar. 15 to 31 is selected as the working period since the discharges were approximately the same at the beginning and end of this period.

2. A routing period of 12 hr is chosen as being adequate to define the hydrograph shape. Therefore, the average flows at Sewickley, Wheeling, and the four tributary stations (Wampum, Hazen, Wurtemburg, and East Liverpool) are tabulated for 12-hr periods throughout the duration of the flood (Table 19-2).

3. The total measured inflow, *i.e.*, the sum for Sewickley and the four tributary stations, during the flood period, is found to be 7,443,000 acre-ft, while the outflow as measured at Wheeling is 7,830,000 acre-ft. The difference between inflow and outflow, 387,000 acre-ft, represents the total volume of ungaged inflow into the reach. The map indicates that the unmeasured tributaries are small and are apparently comparable with the

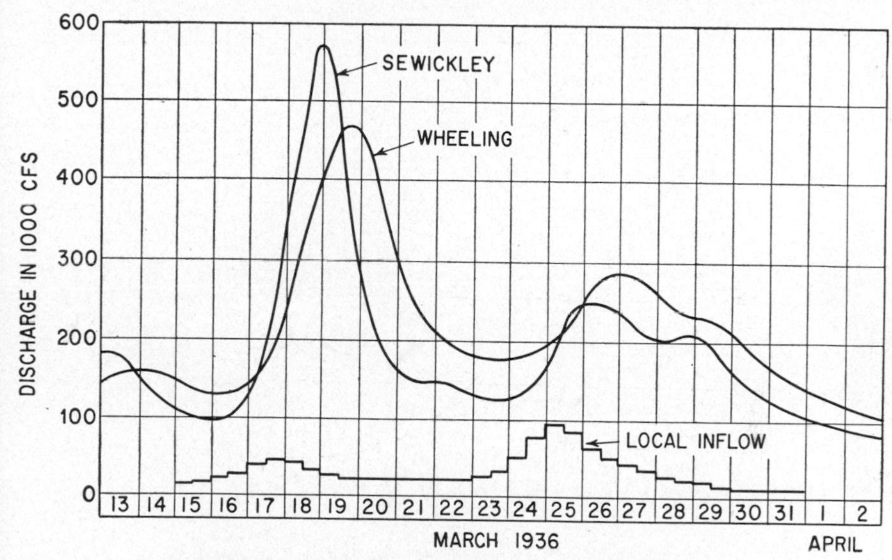

FIG. 19–5. Flood hydrographs for a typical reach.

three smaller gaged streams, Little Beaver River, and Connoquenessing and Slippery Rock Creeks. Assuming the ungaged local inflow to be distributed in time in proportion to the sum of these three measured streams, the 12-hr increments of ungaged local flow are computed by multiplying the sum of the flows on the three creeks by $387/300 = 1.29$. In actual practice, a careful consideration of rainfall distribution and other factors affecting hydrograph shape is advisable if the amount of ungaged local flow is relatively large.

4. The total local inflow is computed as the sum of the four tributaries and the ungaged local inflow and is plotted in Fig. 19-5 for comparison. The total inflow is the sum of the total local and Sewickley flows.

5. Values of ΔS are determined by subtracting the Wheeling flow from the total inflow, and values of S are computed by accumulating ΔS. For convenience, S is assumed to be zero at midnight, Mar. 16, and the accumulations are carried forward from this point to avoid large negative values of S. It will be noted that S at midnight, Mar. 14, the actual beginning of the period under study, is equal to the final value at midnight, Mar. 31.

TABLE 19-2. Computation of Channel Storage

12 hr ending		Average q in 1000 cfs for the period									ΔS (1000 acre-ft)	S (1000 acre-ft)	Instantaneous		
													Wheeling		Sewickley Stage, ft
Date	Hr	Sewickley	Wampum	Hazen	Wurtemburg	East Liverpool	Ungaged local	Total local	Total I	Wheeling			q (1000 cfs)	Stage, ft	
3/15/36	N	104	5	1	1	1	4	12	116	141	− 25	25	137	23.7	8.6
	M	102	6	1	2	2	6	17	119	133	− 14	11	127	22.3	8.3
3/16/36	N	96	7	2	2	2	8	21	117	126	− 9	2	127	22.5	8.2
	M	102	8	3	2	3	10	26	128	130	− 2	0	136	23.6	9.0
3/17/36	N	145	9	6	3	3	16	37	182	147	35	35	167	27.2	12.8
	M	245	9	9	4	2	19	43	288	189	99	134	214	32.5	22.4
3/18/36	N	388	6	9	4	2	19	40	428	254	174	308	304	41.6	31.0
	M	542	4	7	3	2	16	32	574	348	226	534	399	49.9	34.8
3/19/36	N	523	4	4	3	2	12	25	548	436	112	646	462	55.2	29.6
	M	357	4	3	3	2	10	22	379	462	− 83	563	453	54.4	20.3
3/20/36	N	240	5	3	3	2	10	23	263	423	− 160	403	386	48.8	14.4
	M	180	5	3	2	2	9	21	201	346	− 145	258	307	41.9	11.1
3/21/36	N	149	5	4	2	2	10	23	172	273	− 101	157	246	36.1	10.5
	M	145	5	3	2	2	9	21	166	225	− 59	98	211	32.2	10.6
3/22/36	N	144	4	3	2	2	9	20	164	200	− 36	62	190	29.9	10.5
	M	134	5	3	2	2	9	21	155	185	− 30	32	181	29.0	9.8

3/23/36	N	128	7	3	2	3	10	25	153	177	— 24	8	173	27.9	9.7
	M	130	10	3	2	4	12	31	161	170	— 9	— 1	169	27.5	9.8
3/24/36	N	132	18	4	4	6	18	50	182	170	12	11	174	28.1	10.0
	M	142	31	4	6	10	26	77	219	180	39	50	187	29.5	11.1
3/25/36	N	187	41	4	7	11	28	91	278	198	80	130	211	32.2	15.6
	M	236	39	4	6	8	23	80	316	230	86	216	250	36.5	17.4
3/26/36	N	245	35	3	5	5	17	65	310	265	45	261	276	39.1	17.1
	M	239	31	2	4	3	12	52	291	280	11	272	282	39.6	16.4
3/27/36	N	225	25	2	3	3	10	43	268	279	— 11	261	276	39.1	15.0
	M	205	19	2	3	3	10	37	242	269	— 27	234	259	37.4	13.8
3/28/36	N	199	13	2	2	2	8	27	226	249	— 23	211	240	35.4	13.9
	M	205	11	2	2	2	8	25	230	229	1	212	230	34.3	14.2
3/29/36	N	198	9	2	2	2	8	23	221	224	— 3	209	223	33.6	12.9
	M	172	6	2	1	1	5	15	187	220	— 33	176	211	32.2	11.8
3/30/36	N	146	6	1	1	1	4	13	159	190	— 31	145	191	30.0	10.1
	M	130	6	1	1	1	4	13	143	178	— 35	110	170	27.6	9.4
3/31/36	N	116	5	1	1	1	4	12	128	160	— 32	78	151	25.4	8.9
	M	104	5	1	1	1	4	12	116	144	— 28	50	138	23.7	8.5
Total	...	6735	408	107	93	100	387	1095	7830	7830	0				

Determination of channel storage from recession curves. In a previous chapter it was shown that storage values can be computed from the recession of streamflow after inflow to the channel has ceased. Langbein[1] has demonstrated the application of this procedure to a reach of a stream where the recession at the outflow station reflects storage in the entire stream system upstream and must therefore be corrected for storage above the inflow station. Assuming that curves showing channel storage as a function of flow in cubic feet per second per square mile have been developed for station A at the head of the reach, station B on a major tributary, and station C at the bottom of the reach, Langbein proposes the following formula for computing the storage in the channel below A and B and above C:

$$S = S_C \frac{S_C' - S_A' - S_B'}{S_C'} \tag{19-4}$$

In this formula S is the reach storage, S_C the storage above C from the storage curve, and S_A', S_B', and S_C' are storage values from each of the three curves for a common value of flow in second-feet per square mile. Although Langbein recommended that the flow selected for computing the correction factor be an average value for a particular flood, Harrold, in a discussion of the paper, states that storage values on the White River, Indiana, varied less than 2 per cent when the adjustment was made on the basis of 1 and 10 csm.

Storage computed from the recession curve by this technique is representative only of the falling side of the storage loop (see following section) and will generally prove too low during periods of rising stage. An arbitrary adjustment can be made to bring the storage determined from the recession to an approximation of the mean storage curve for both rising and falling stages. The procedure is quite simple and provides a rapid method of developing storage curves suitable for preliminary studies, approximate solutions, and other work where high accuracy is not essential.

The storage function. If values of storage (Table 19-2) are plotted against simultaneous outflow (Fig. 19-6), a loop results with storage for a given outflow greater during the rise than during the fall. A consideration of Fig. 19-7, showing a hypothetical flood wave in profile, explains the loop of Fig. 19-6. The storage in the reach may be considered to be the sum of two portions, (1) the *prism storage* beneath a line parallel to the channel bottom and (2) the *wedge storage* between this parallel and the actual water-surface profile. Discharge or stage at the outflow station is a satisfactory index of prism storage but fails to indicate the extent of wedge storage as the wave moves through the reach. Wedge storage increases the total storage volume during the rise and decreases it during falling stages.

[1] Langbein, W. B., Some Channel-storage Studies and Their Application to the Determination of Infiltration, *Trans. Am. Geophys. Union*, Vol. 19, pp. 435-447, 1938.

The second problem in developing a routing technique is that of finding a satisfactory expression of storage in terms of easily measurable factors such as flow or stage. This storage expression may be an equation, a curve, or a set of curves. It is well to emphasize that the storage equation involves

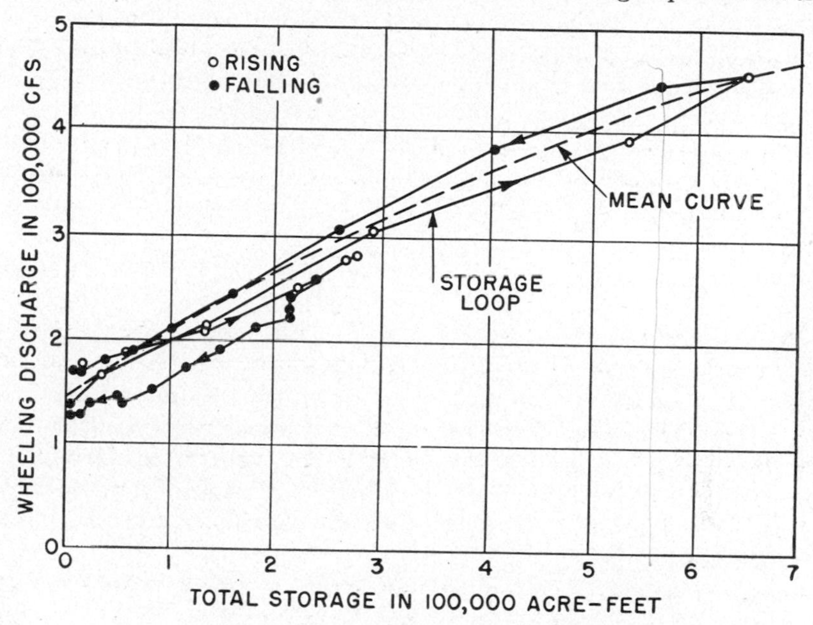

FIG. 19–6. Storage vs. outflow loop.

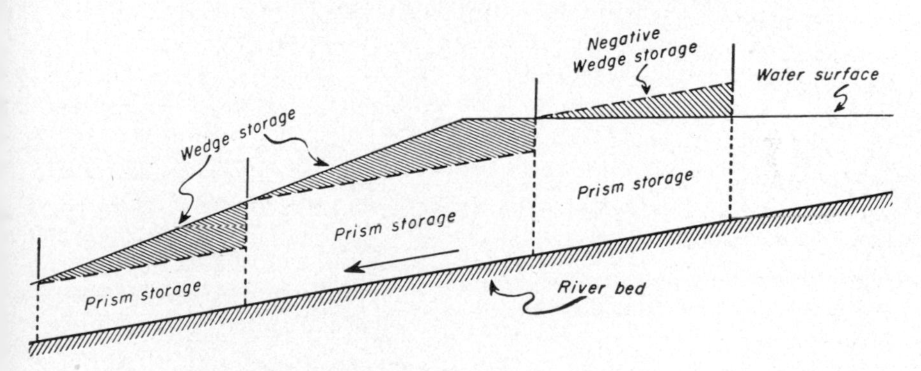

FIG. 19–7. Profile of a flood wave.

only ΔS, and that absolute values of storage are not required. Any storage function which indicates the true variation in storage with changes in the index factors is satisfactory, even though it may fail to indicate the actual total volume of water in channel storage.

The simplest of the storage functions is that relating storage to outflow, a mean curve through the loop of Fig. 19-6. If storage has been determined from surveys, a similar storage function may be obtained by plotting storage under profiles of steady flow against outflow. A storage curve of this type is subject to errors, varying in magnitude as the amount of wedge storage varies. Considering Fig. 19-7, it can be seen that this error depends on the rate of change in flow. Where changes of flow with time are small, routing methods ignoring wedge storage are reasonably successful. On streams where large changes in flow take place rapidly, such techniques are generally unsatisfactory. Obviously, in a reservoir where the water surface remains level throughout the range of outflow, storage is closely related to outflow alone.

In order to account for wedge storage, discharge or stage at the inflow station can be introduced into the storage relation. A general expression for storage in terms of flow is

$$S = \frac{b}{a}\,[xI^{m/n} + (1 - x)O^{m/n}] \tag{19-5}$$

The constants a and n are measures of the stage-discharge relations at the two ends of the reach in a formula of the form $q = ag^n$, while b and m express the mean stage-volume relation for the reach in a formula of the type $S = bg^m$. In uniform rectangular channels, storage varies with the first power of stage, while discharge varies with the 5/3 power (Manning formula). The exponent m/n is therefore about 0.6. In natural channels, m may be considerably greater than unity (wide overbank flood plains), and the ratio m/n can exceed unity. The dimensionless factor x defines the relative weights given to inflow and outflow in determining storage. If storage is entirely a function of outflow, as in a reservoir, then $x = 0$; but if the wedge storage is significant, then x will be greater than zero, with a limiting value of 0.5 when inflow and outflow have equal weight as in uniform channels.

The ratio b/a appears in most considerations of storage as a constant K. This constant expresses the ratio between storage and discharge, and a dimensional analysis will show that it has the dimension of time. It is, in fact, a measure of the *lag*, or *time of travel*, through the reach and is the slope of the storage-discharge curve. K may be determined by finding the lag, or time interval, between the occurrence of the center of mass of inflow and center of mass of outflow for the reach. It may also be approximated by determining the time of travel of critical points on the hydrograph, such as the peak.

Numerous routing techniques have been developed on the general basis of Eq. (19-5). The exponent m/n is commonly assumed to be unity, and the working equation is

$$S = K[xI + (1 - x)O] \tag{19-6}$$

To make use of this equation, storage (as determined from the hydrograph) is plotted against weighted flow in the reach, $xI + (1 - x)O$. The value of x which brings the data most closely to a single-valued curve is determined by trial (Fig. 19-8). The best value of x in Fig. 19-8 is about 0.1, indicating a decided tendency toward reservoir effect.

It has just been shown that storage can be correlated with a weighted mean flow in a reach. Meyer[1] has suggested a simple alternate approach. He assumes that the flow which is at the mid-point of a reach at any time t

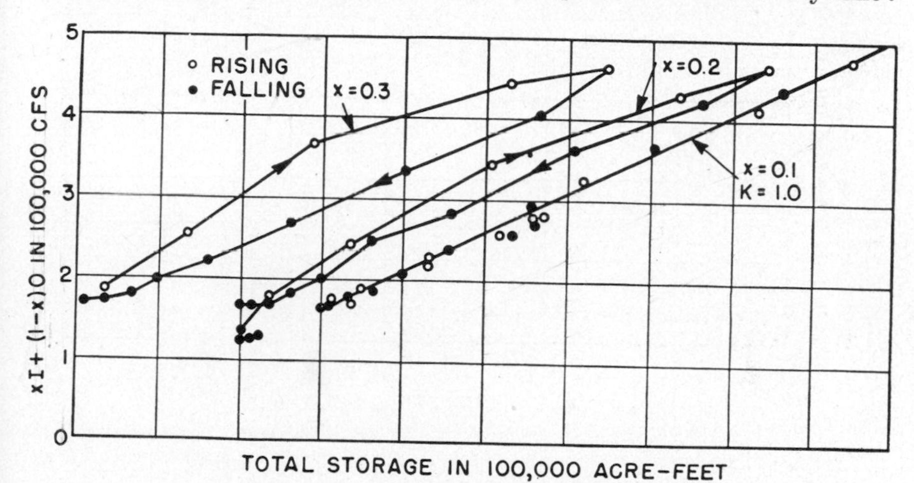

FIG. 19-8. Weighted flow vs. storage.

is a measure of the mean flow in the reach. This flow will presumably become the outflow from the reach at some later time, $t + t_u/2$, where t_u is the lag for the reach. If storage is plotted as a function of outflow at time $t_u/2$ later, we have a curve which approximates the storage vs. weighted-mean-flow curve of Fig. 19-8. In practice, the solution is not quite so simple as outlined above, since the flow at the mid-point of the reach with respect to time may not be precisely the mean flow value desired, nor will it be the outflow which arrives at the lower station at time $t_u/2$ later. A value of t_u which results in the narrowest possible storage loop can be found by trial. Storage data for the Sewickley-Wheeling reach are plotted for two values of $t_u/2$ in Fig. 19-9. It will be seen that the best value is far less than one-half the travel time. This is to be expected in a reach showing a large amount of reservoir effect. This procedure is an obvious refinement of the simple outflow vs. storage relation. It is dependent on the outflow alone and is therefore subject to errors which are avoided by introducing inflow as a parameter or auxiliary factor. Storage curves for individual floods, as

[1] Meyer, O. H., Simplified Flood Routing, *Civil Eng.*, Vol. 11, pp. 306-307, 1941.

computed by Meyer's method, will show more variation than curves including an inflow parameter.

It is well to point out that storage is truly a function of stage. However, when discharges are directly related to stage by a single-valued curve, flow will serve equally well as a storage index. If the stage-discharge relation

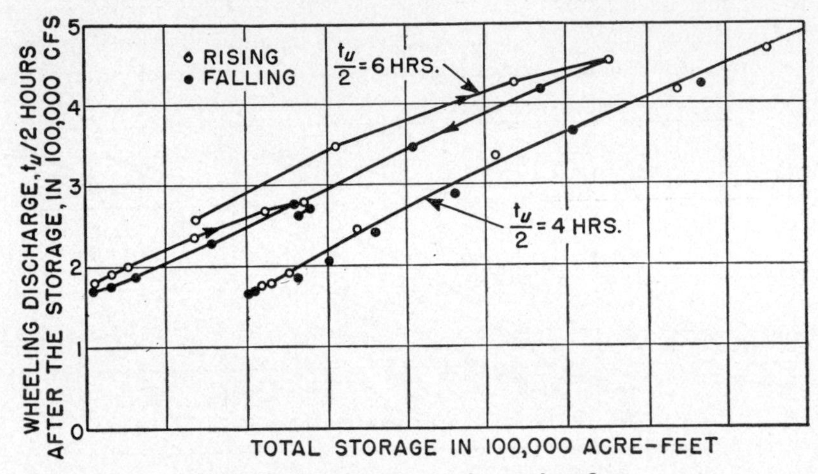

FIG. 19–9. Storage vs. lagged outflow.

is complex, involving slope, rate of rise, or backwater as a parameter, then flow is not a satisfactory index to storage. The use of flow does sometimes partly compensate for wedge storage inasmuch as discharge is higher for a given stage during the rise and lower during the fall. Under these conditions, a simple relation between outflow and storage can be superior to a relation between stage at the outflow station and storage.

A graphical procedure for constructing storage curves in terms of stage has been devised by Puls.[1] The procedure is demonstrated in Fig. 19-10*a*, using data from Table 19-2. A scale representing inflow gage height is placed at the right-hand side of a sheet which has the loop curve plotted as a function of outflow stage. This auxiliary scale is so located that, at high flows, stages representing equal flows are about opposite each other. A vertical correction axis is then located by trial and error. When properly located, all plotted storage values can be transferred to a single average curve by the procedure to be outlined. In general, the axis will lie closer to the scale representing the end of the reach having the greater storage effect. Point *A* represents the storage at a time during the rise when the upper gage height was 34.8 ft and the lower stage was 49.9 ft. A straight line is drawn from 49.9 ft on the outflow scale to 34.8 ft on the inflow-stage scale, and a

[1] "Engineering Construction-Flood Control," The Engineer School, Ft. Belvoir, Va., 1940.

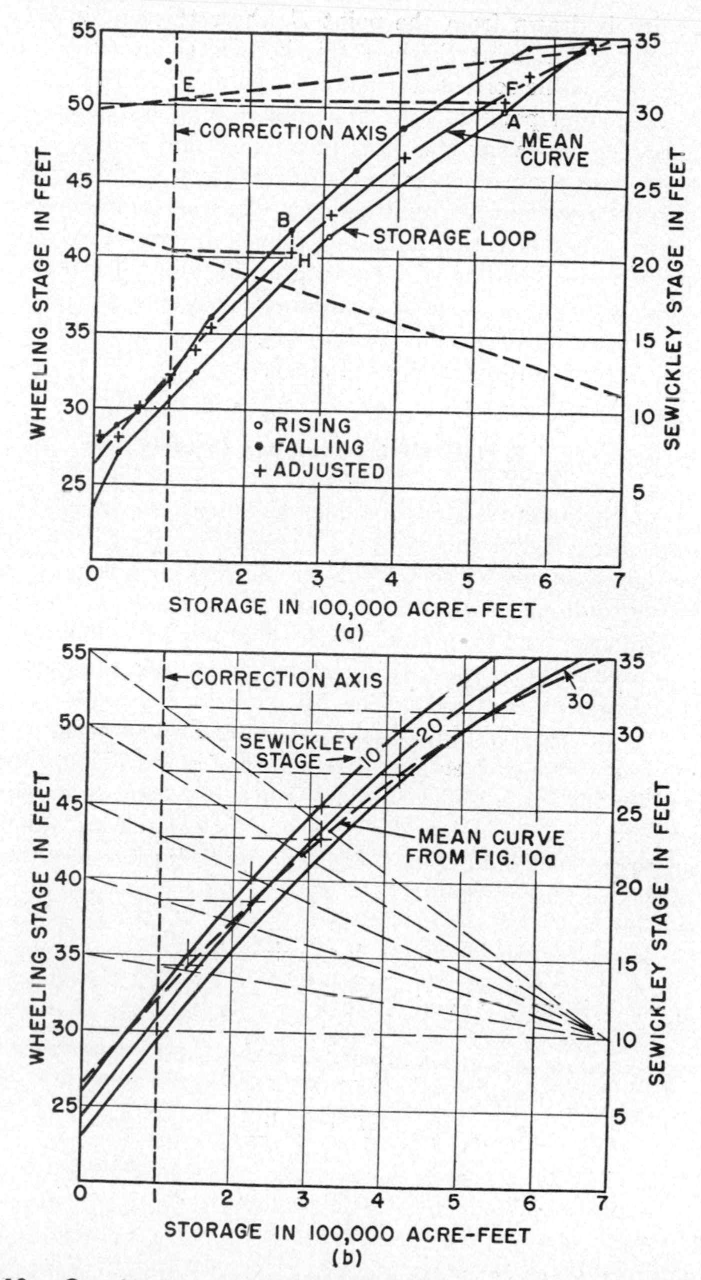

FIG. 19–10. Graphical procedures for (*a*) construction of a mean storage curve from storage loop and (*b*) construction of a family of storage curves from mean storage curve.

horizontal line is drawn from the point E where this line intersects the correction axis. The point F where this horizontal intersects a vertical drawn through A is the corrected position for point A. The point H is the corrected position for point B from the falling hydrograph determined in a like manner. By repeating the procedure for several points, an average curve is defined for the particular flood. A similar analysis should be performed for other rises and the resulting curves averaged into a mean curve for the reach. The correction axis should fall into very nearly the same position in each case. A family of curves showing storage as a function of outflow stage with inflow stage as a parameter can be constructed by reversing the process outlined (Fig. 19-10*b*). The procedure can be applied equally well in terms of flow instead of stage.

STORAGE-ROUTING METHODS

Storage-routing methods are techniques for solving the storage equation [Eq. (19-3)], using one of the storage functions described in the previous section. A great number of such techniques have been developed, and it is impracticable to discuss them all in detail. The various methods can be classified as to type; and examples of each type, as well as solutions to certain special problems encountered in streamflow routing, are discussed.

The Muskingum method. The Muskingum method developed by McCarthy[1] is an example of an analytical approach to routing. Making use of a storage curve such as Fig. 19-8, values of x and K [Eq. (19-6)] are determined for the reach under study. Values of S_1 and S_2 in Eq. (19-3) are then replaced by expressions for storage in the form of Eq. (19-6), with proper subscripts for I and O in each case. Reducing the resulting equation gives the working formula,

$$O_2 = c_0 I_2 + c_1 I_1 + c_2 O_1 \tag{19-7}$$

where the coefficients c_0, c_1, and c_2 are

$$c_0 = -\frac{Kx - 0.5t_t}{K - Kx + 0.5t_t} \tag{19-8}$$

$$c_1 = \frac{Kx + 0.5t_t}{K - Kx + 0.5t_t} \tag{19-9}$$

$$c_2 = \frac{K - Kx - 0.5t_t}{K - Kx + 0.5t_t} \tag{19-10}$$

[1] McCarthy, G. T., The Unit Hydrograph and Flood Routing, unpublished manuscript presented at a conference of the North Atlantic Division, Corps of Engineers, War Department, June 24, 1938. (See also "Engineering Construction-Flood Control," The Engineer School, Ft. Belvoir, Va., pp. 147-156, 1940.)

Adding Eqs. (19-8), (19-9), and (19-10)

$$c_0 + c_1 + c_2 = 1.00 \tag{19-11}$$

The validity of the last equation will be obvious if the case of steady uniform flow ($O_1 = O_2 = I_1 = I_2$) is considered. Equation (19-7) satisfies the condition of steady flow only if the coefficients satisfy Eq. (19-11).

The routing period t_t is selected to fit the needs of the problem. It must be sufficiently short that points t_t hr apart adequately define the hydrograph shape. This means that t_t must be equal to or shorter than the time of travel through the reach, since if it were longer than the travel time a major change in flow could traverse the reach within a routing period. For convenience, t_t is usually taken as some even fraction or multiple of a day, as 1, 2, 3, 4, 6, 12, 18, or 24 hr or 2, 3, 4, or more days. Whenever storage is computed in second-foot-days, t_t must be expressed in days.

With K, x, and t_t established, values of the coefficients in Eq. (19-7) can be computed. Since O_1, I_1, and I_2 are known at the beginning of the routing period, O_2 can be computed from Eq. (19-7). The value of O_2 for one period is the O_1 value for the subsequent routing period, and the solution can be repeated indefinitely to compute successive values of O at intervals of time t_t. Storage routing does not permit extension of the outflow hydrograph beyond the time of the last known or computed inflow value. The solution is simplest when K is a constant, *i.e.*, the storage-discharge function is a straight line. If the relation is not linear, it must be approximated by a series of straight lines and values of the coefficients changed to conform to varying values of K as routing progresses through successive ranges in stage. Table 19-3 shows the tabular work involved in the Muskingum method. Values of the routing constants are determined from Fig. 19-8, and t_t is taken as ½ day. Computed outflows are underscored.

TABLE 19-3. Solution by Muskingum Routing Method

Date and hour	I (1000 cfs)	c_0I_2 ($c_0 = 0.13$)	c_1I_1 ($c_1 = 0.30$)	c_2O_1 ($c_2 = 0.57$)	O (1000 cfs)
6/1 noon	200	....	....	....	200
6/1 midnight	300	$39 = 300c_0$	$60 = 200c_1$	$114 = 200c_2$	$\underline{213}$
6/2 noon	400	$52 = 400c_0$	$90 = 300c_1$	$121 = 213c_2$	$\underline{263}$
6/2 midnight	440	$57 = 440c_0$	$120 = 400c_1$	$150 = 263c_2$	$\underline{327}$

Semigraphical solutions. By far the greater number of routing procedures involve semigraphical solutions in which routing curves, designed to simplify the mechanics of the solution, are used in conjunction with tabular computation to complete the routing process. One such procedure, originally proposed by Goodrich[1] and subsequently used by Rutter, Graves, and Snyder,[2] uses Eq. (19-3) in the form

$$I_1 + I_2 + \frac{2S_1}{t_t} - O_1 = \frac{2S_2}{t_t} + O_2 \tag{19-12}$$

Since I and O are usually in cubic feet per second, S/t_t must be in cubic feet per second if Eq. (19-12) is to be dimensionally correct. Hence, S must be in cubic feet if t_t is in seconds or in second-foot-days if t_t is in days, etc.

Routing curves showing $(2S/t_t) + O$ as a function of O are needed (Fig. 19-11). The use of inflow as a parameter is optional, depending on the accuracy required. All terms on the left-hand side of Eq. (19-12) are

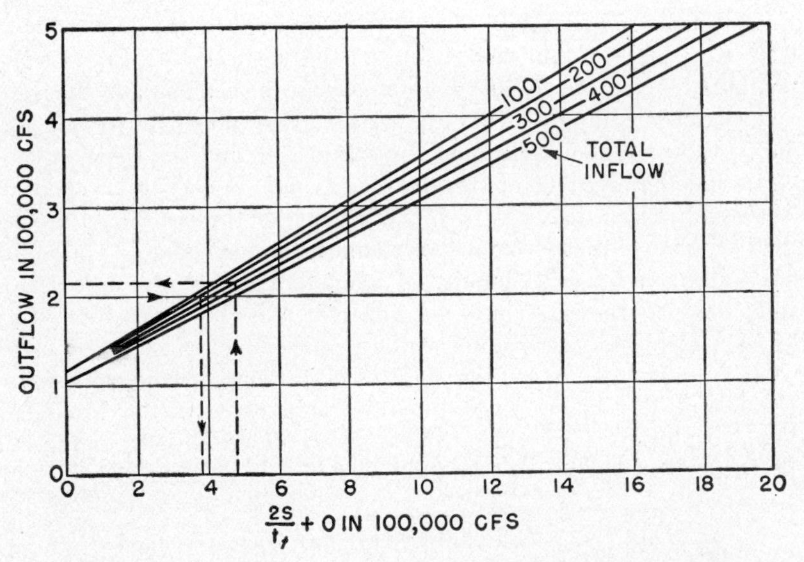

FIG. 19-11. Routing curves for Goodrich's method of routing.

known, and a value of $(2S_2/t_t) + O_2$ can be determined and $2S_2/t_t$ computed. These values of O and $2S/t_t$ become O_1 and $2S_1/t_t$ for the following routing period, and the computations can be repeated. The tabular solution is outlined in Table 19-4.

The computation of O at midnight of June 1 is accomplished as follows:

1. Enter Fig. 19-11 with the outflow at noon of June 1 (O_1) to determine $(2S/t_t) + O$.

[1] Goodrich, R. D., Rapid Calculation of Reservoir Discharge, *Civil Eng.*, Vol. 1, pp. 417-418, 1931.

[2] Rutter, E. J., Q. B. Graves, and F. F. Snyder, Flood Routing, *Trans. ASCE*, Vol. 104, pp. 275-294, 1939.

2. Compute $2S/t_t$ by subtracting O from the value determined in item 1.

3. Add inflow at noon of June 1 (I_1) and inflow 12 hr later (I_2) to the value of $2S/t_t$ determined in item 2.

4. Subtract outflow at noon of June 1 from the value determined in item 3, and enter the difference, $(2S_2/t_t) + O_2$, on the line of midnight, June 1.

5. Determine outflow at midnight of June 1 (O_2) from Fig. 19-11 by entering with the value determined in item 4.

TABLE 19-4. Solution by Goodrich's Routing Method

Date and hour	I (1000 cfs)	$\frac{2S}{t_t}$	$I_1 + I_2 + \frac{2S_1}{t_t}$	O (1000 cfs)	$\frac{2S}{t_t} + O$
6/1 noon	200	180	680	200	380
6/1 midnight	300	260	960	220	480
6/2 noon	400	480	1320	260	740
6/2 midnight	440	735	....	325	1060

Wisler and Brater[1] expressed storage as a function of $I + O$, and their storage curves thus show $I + O$ as a function of $(2S/t_t) + I + O$. The routing equation is

$$\frac{2S_1}{t_t} + I_1 + 2I_2 - O_1 = \frac{2S_2}{t_t} + I_2 + O_2 \tag{19-13}$$

Again the terms on the left-hand side are known, and the value of the sum on the right-hand side can be computed. With $(2S_2/t_t) + I_2 + O_2$ known, a value of $I_2 + O_2$ can be read from the routing curves, and since I_2 is known, O_2 can be readily computed. The process can then be repeated for subsequent routing periods.

If storage is expressed as a function of $xI + O$, a similar solution can be devised with the routing equation in the form

$$\frac{2S_1}{t_t} + I_1 + (1 + x)I_2 - O_1 = \frac{2S_2}{t_t} + xI_2 + O_2 \tag{19-14}$$

A fourth solution can be achieved by placing Eq. (19-3) in the form

$$\left(\frac{S_1}{t_t} - \frac{O_1}{2}\right) + \bar{I} = \frac{S_2}{t_t} + \frac{O_2}{2} \tag{19-15}$$

Routing curves are then plotted showing O as a function of $(S/t_t) + (O/2)$. The procedure is equally applicable if the storage curve is a single-valued function (S vs. O) or if inflow is introduced as a parameter. The solution

[1] Wisler, C. O., and E. F. Brater, A Direct Method of Flood Routing, *Trans. ASCE*, Vol. 107, pp. 1519-1529, 1942.

is similar to those previously discussed. With the terms on the left-hand side known, a value of $(S_2/t_t) + (O_2/2)$ can be determined, and O_2 can be obtained from the routing curves. Subtracting O_2 from $(S_2/t_t) + (O_2/2)$ gives a value of $(S_2/t_t) - (O_2/2)$, which permits the repetition of the solution for the subsequent period.

The same type of solution can be used with storage curves showing $(S/t_t) + (O/2)$ as a function of stage. These curves can also represent a

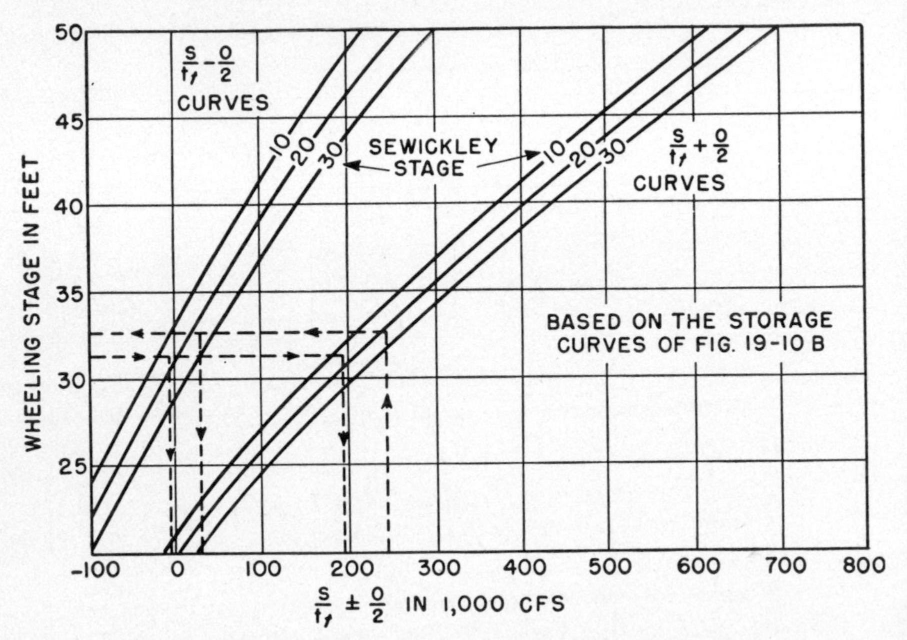

FIG. 19–12. Routing curves in terms of stage for Eq. (19-15).

single-valued function with outflow stage, but a family of curves with inflow stage as a parameter is more commonly used (Fig. 19-12). In this case O_2 cannot be determined directly from the curves. Instead, a value of $(S_2/t_t) - (O_2/2)$ must be determined by following the dotted lines (Fig. 19-12). Since $\left(\frac{S}{t_t} + \frac{O}{2}\right) - \left(\frac{S}{t_t} - \frac{O}{2}\right) = O$, O_2 can be computed. The tabular solution is demonstrated in Table 19-5.

To compute stage and discharge at the outflow station at midnight of June 1, proceed as follows:

1. With known inflow and outflow stages at noon of June 1, enter Fig. 19-12, and read values of $(S_1/t_t) \pm (O_1/2)$.

2. The sum of $\bar{I}$ for the period and $(S_1/t_t) - (O_1/2)$ is $(S_2/t_t) + (O_2/2)$, which is entered on the line for midnight of June 1.

3. Entering Fig. 19-12 with values of inflow stage and $(S/t_t) + (O/2)$ gives the outflow stage and $(S/t_t) - (O/2)$ for midnight.

4. Subtracting $(S/t_t) - (O/2)$ from $(S/t_t) + (O/2)$ gives the outflow at midnight of June 1.

TABLE 19-5. Solution of Eq. (19-15) when $S = f(g)$

Date and hour	Inflow			$\frac{S}{t_t} - \frac{O}{2}$	$\frac{S}{t_t} + \frac{O}{2}$	Outflow	
	Stage	Discharge	Average			Discharge	Stage
6/1 noon	14.0	200		−5	195	200	31.5
			250				
6/1 midnight	21.7	300		30	245	215	32.8
			350				
6/2 noon	28.0	400		108	380	272	38.2
			450				
6/2 midnight	31.6	500		218	558	340	44.5

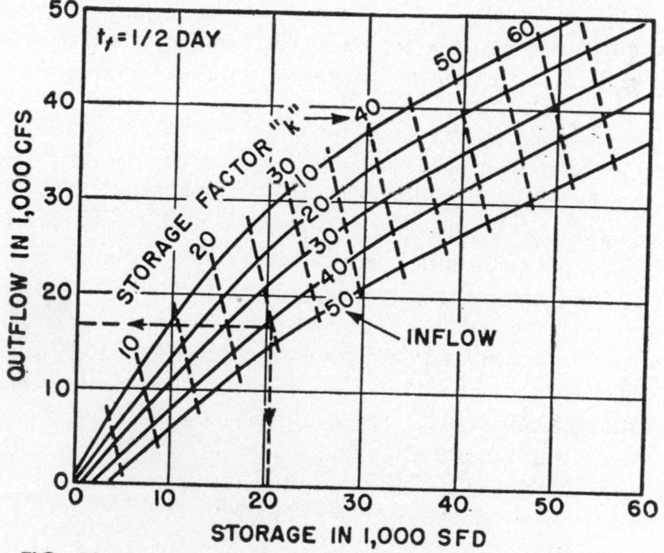

FIG. 19–13. Routing curves for Steinberg's method.

Another variation of the solutions outlined has been proposed by Steinberg.[1] For his solution the storage curves $S = f(O,I)$ are overprinted with a family of curves for a factor k, which he calls the storage factor (Fig. 19-13). He proposes the routing equation in the form

$$(I_1 + I_2 - O_1)\frac{t_t}{2} + S_1 = \frac{O_2 t_t}{2} + S_2 = k_2 \tag{19-16}$$

[1] Steinberg, I. H., A Method of Flood Routing, *Civil Eng.*, Vol. 8, pp. 476-477, 1938.

Once a value of t_t has been adopted, it is a simple matter to construct the k curves, since $k = (Ot_t/2) + S$. All factors on the left-hand side of Eq. (19-16) are known, and a value of k at the beginning of a routing period can be computed. By entering Fig. 19-13 with the parameters k and I_2, corresponding values of both O_2 and S_2 are obtained. The tabular solution is shown in Table 19-6.

TABLE 19-6. Tabular Solution by Steinberg's Method

Date and hour	I	$I_1 + I_2$	O	$I_1 + I_2 - O_1$	$(I_1 + I_2 - O_1)\frac{t_t}{2}$	S	k
(1)	(2)	(3)	(4)	(5)	(6)	(7)	(8)
7/5 noon	6		6			2	
		18		12	3		
7/5 midnight	12		6.5			4	5
		40		33.5	8.4		
7/6 noon	28		11			10	12.4
		70		59	14.8		
7/6 midnight	42		17			20.5	24.8

The development of storage curves for lag routing as proposed by Meyer has been discussed earlier in the chapter. The routing equation is used in the simple form

$$\bar{I} - \bar{O} + S_1 = S_2 \tag{19-17}$$

If the lag of the storage function equals the routing period t_t and if S_1 is known, O_2 can be read from the storage curve (Fig. 19-9). All data needed to compute a value of S_2 from Eq. (19-17) are now available. Given S_2, a value of O_3 can be determined and the process repeated indefinitely.

If the lag of the storage function is $t_t/2$, an alternate solution is possible. Then S_1 is an index to outflow at the mid-point of the routing period, which can be assumed to be the average flow during the period. This solution is one of the simplest routing techniques which have been discussed.

Graphical solutions. All the solutions discussed in the preceding section involve a simple addition of factors in the computations. Graphical techniques can therefore be readily adapted to these solutions. Two general graphical types are possible, (1) techniques which perform all computations but require that the ultimate answer be tabulated and (2) procedures by means of which the outflow hydrograph is actually reproduced without any tabulation.

Nomograms,[1] straight slide rules,[2] and circular computers[3] fall into class

[1] Linsley, R. K., Use of Nomograms in Solving Streamflow Routing Problems, *Civil Eng.*, Vol. 14, pp. 209-210, 1944.

[2] Posey, C. J., Slide Rule for Routing Floods through Storage Reservoirs or Lakes, *Eng. News-Record*, Vol. 114, pp. 580-581, 1935.

[3] Shepley, J. M., and C. B. Walton, Solving Reservoir Problems with Circular Point-by-point Computer, *Civil Eng.*, Vol. 12, pp. 154-155, 1942.

1 above. These devices can be readily set up by arbitrarily graduating scales in terms of $S + O$, $S + I + O$, k, or other storage factors, providing for the addition of I, and constructing a third scale such that, for example, $\bar{I} + \left(\frac{S}{t_t} - \frac{O}{2}\right) = \left(\frac{S}{t_t} + \frac{O}{2}\right)$. If S is a single-valued function of O, the $\frac{S}{t_t} + \frac{O}{2}$ scale can be calibrated in terms of O and the device is ready for operation. Such a device is readily adaptable to reservoir problems, and if the assumption that $S = f(O)$ is adequate for natural streams, then a like solution can be followed. If the storage function is more complex, similar computers

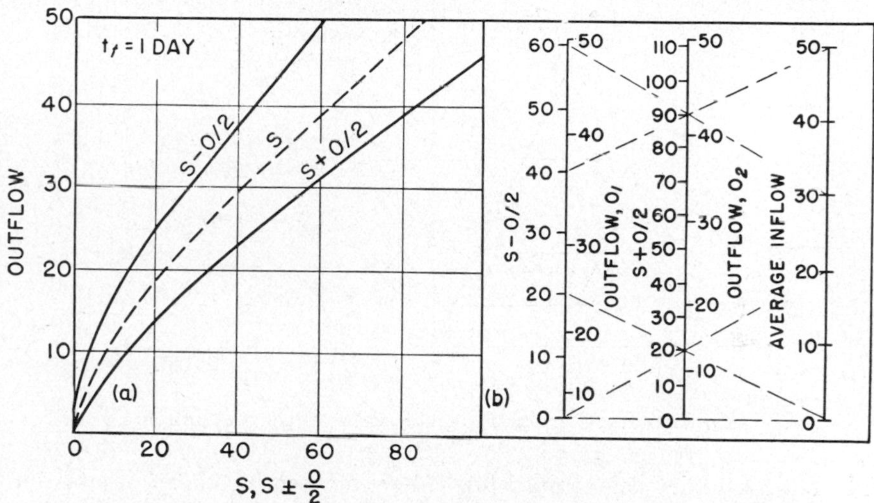

FIG. 19–14. Construction of a nomogram for streamflow routing.

can be constructed, but as a general rule they involve several operations and do not prove effective in simplifying the problem.

An illustration of the development of a routing nomogram is shown in Fig. 19-14, where the routing period t_t is equal to unity. Scales of $S - (O/2)$ and $\bar{I}$ are constructed with arbitrary graduations. From Eq. (19-15), the sum of these two terms is equal to $S + (O/2)$. Therefore, an axis must be constructed and calibrated such that its intersection with a straight line connecting any two values of $S - (O/2)$ and $\bar{I}$ is their sum. The intersection of two straight lines joining values of $S - (O/2)$ and $\bar{I}$ which have equal sums identifies one point on the $S + (O/2)$ axis. Two such points determine the location and calibration of the axis. Values of O corresponding to $S \pm (O/2)$ can be determined from Fig. 19-14*a* and the two axes recalibrated in terms of O_1 and O_2.

A solution[1] of the second type is shown in Fig. 19-15. Here, an $S + \frac{O}{2}t_t$

[1] Cheng, H. M., A Graphical Solution for Flood Routing Problems, *Civil Eng.*, Vol. 16, pp. 126-128, 1946.

curve is plotted as a function of O, and, using the same scales, a line showing the relation between $\bar{I}t_t$ and $\bar{I}$ is drawn through the origin. A horizontal line ab is drawn from O_1 until it intersects the $\left(S + \frac{O}{2}t_t\right)$ curve. The line bc is drawn parallel to the $\bar{I}t_t$ line until it intersects a horizontal fc through the average inflow $\bar{I}$. A vertical cd is then dropped to the $\left(S + \frac{O}{2}t_t\right)$ curve.

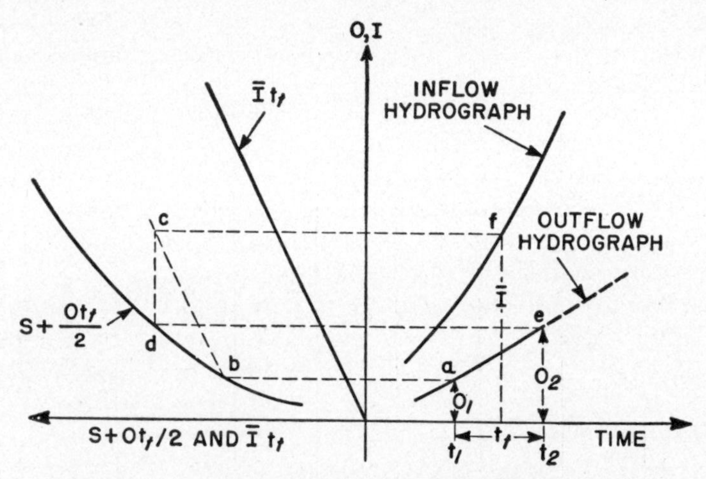

FIG. 19–15. Graphical solution of the routing equation.

The horizontal line de extended to the line representing time t_2 locates the outflow value O_2. An inspection of these operations indicates that they constitute a graphical solution of the equation

$$(\bar{I} - O_1)t_t + \left(S_1 + \frac{O_1}{2}t_t\right) = \bar{I}t_t + \left(S_1 - \frac{O_1}{2}t_t\right) = S_2 + \frac{O_2}{2}t_t \quad (19\text{-}18)$$

Equation (19-18) will be recognized as a variant form of Eq. (19-3). By inserting several $\bar{I}t_t$ lines for various values of t_t and corresponding $\left(S + \frac{O}{2}t_t\right)$ curves, the routing period can be changed at will, thus permitting closer definition of the outflow hydrograph at the crest.

NONSTORAGE ROUTING

For design problems in which a comparison of flows before and after the construction of control works or a comparison of various operation schedules is required, a true storage-routing technique must be used, since actual data for the development of relations by statistical methods will not be available. For many problems, however, it is practicable to develop a routing technique by statistical analysis of observed data.

Least-squares correlations. Inspection of Eq. (19-7) shows that it is in the exact form of a linear-regression equation. It is therefore possible to develop the coefficients of this equation by least-squares techniques. It is not necessary to limit this development to the equation shown, but it may be expanded as

$$O_4 = c_0 I_4 + c_1 I_3 + c_2 c_0 I_3 + c_2 c_1 I_2 + c_2^2 c_0 I_2 + c_2^2 c_1 I_1 + c_2^3 O_1 \quad (19\text{-}19)$$

or

$$O_4 = c_0 I_4 + (c_1 + c_2 c_0) I_3 + (c_2 c_1 + c_2^2 c_0) I_2 + c_2^2 c_1 I_1 + c_2^3 O_1 \quad (19\text{-}20)$$

Equation (19-20) is in the form of a six-variable linear-regression equation. Since all the coefficients are less than unity, the last two terms are probably negligible. By dropping the last term, we have an equation in terms of inflow alone. This has the advantage that a value of outflow can be computed at any time by use of inflow values without the necessity of routing the entire hydrograph to secure a value of O_1, which is necessary to compute O_2 by the usual methods.

Graphical correlations. The use of a linear least-squares regression has the disadvantage that it does not recognize the variation in coefficients with magnitude of rise. This may be remedied by a multiple curvilinear correlation if the nature of the variation is known or by graphical correlation using the deviations method outlined in Appendix A. None of these solutions, however, recognizes the existence of joint correlation in which the magnitude of any variable influences the effect of another variable. Yet it is recognized that the rate of change of I is a factor in the movement of a flood wave. The joint correlation can be developed by use of the coaxial technique described in Appendix A.[1]

Figure 19-16 shows a routing relation for the Sewickley-Wheeling reach of the Ohio River developed in this manner. In this chart, I_1, I_2, and I_3 are related to O_3. However, two values of inflow and two of outflow could have been correlated with approximately the same degree of accuracy.

While the storage term does not appear in such relations, its effect is reflected in the shape, slope, and spacing of the curves. In storage routing, the storage is assumed to be a function of inflow, outflow, or weighted flow in the reach. In the graphical development, the storage is assumed to be a joint function of the several independent variables used. Additional inflow values preceding I_1 can be introduced in the curves.

The chart of Fig. 19-16 is the result of numerous experiments in developing routing curves by use of the coaxial method. The order of variables shown in the figure seems to offer the simplest and most effective arrangement. It will be noted that the effect of I_2 is negative, that is, O_3 appears to vary inversely as I_2. This is in contrast to the coefficients developed by

[1] Kohler, M. A., "The Use of Crest Stage Relations in Forecasting the Rise and Fall of the Flood Hydrograph," U.S. Weather Bureau, Washington, D.C., 1944 (mimeo.).

the Muskingum method but has appeared in all such charts developed graphically. The negative effect appears to develop from the high intercorrelation between the three values of inflow. Values of I_1 and I_3 alone define the hydrograph reasonably well, and the negative effect of I_2 tends to adjust the outflow toward the mean value indicated by I_1 and I_3. In other words, if I_2 is greater than both I_1 and I_3, the negative slope of the I_2

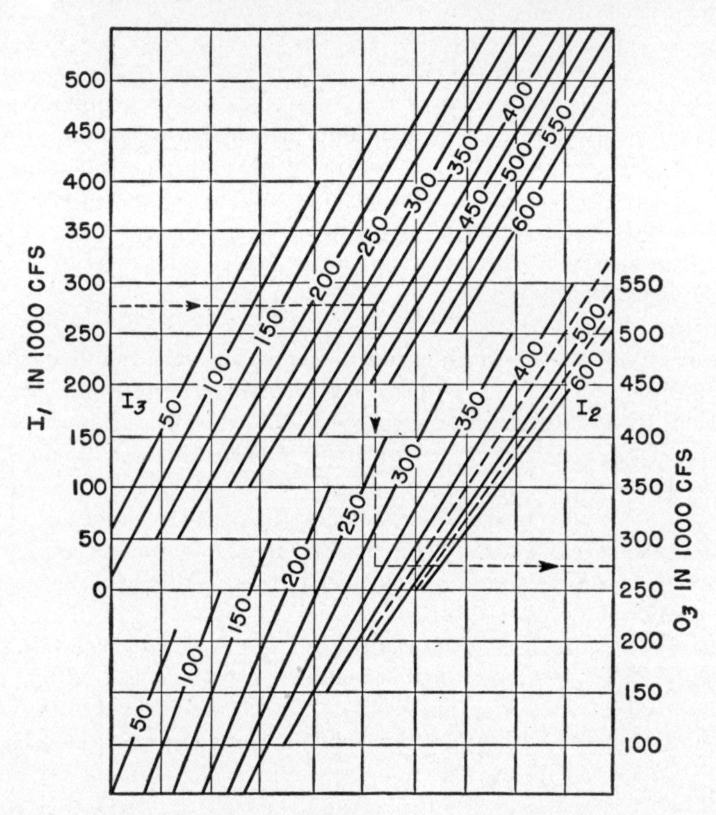

FIG. 19–16. Routing curves for the Sewickley-Wheeling reach of the Ohio River developed by coaxial correlation.

curves lowers O_3, thus cutting down the outflow peak. The higher I_2 is, *i.e.*, the sharper the inflow crest, the greater the relative reduction of the outflow crest.

The Muskingum routing equation [Eq. (19-7)] can be written

$$(O_2 - O_1) = c_0(I_2 - O_1) + c_1(I_1 - O_1) \tag{19-21}$$

The coefficient c_2 has been eliminated by use of the restriction of Eq. (19-11). Again, the equation is in the form of a simple regression equation with the terms in parentheses being treated as single variables. Maximum advantage of the new form of the equation is gained when the solution is developed graphically as a three-variable relation.

Method of successive averages. Tatum[1] developed a wholly arbitrary weighting system which is satisfactory as a preliminary technique and requires no prior development of storage curves or weights. The assumption is made that there is some point downstream from a station where the discharge at time t_2 is equal to $(I_1 + I_2)/2$. If we can ascertain the number of steps, *i.e.*, the number of successive averages occurring within the reach under study, the outflow at the downstream station can be computed by extending the averages. Tatum found that the number of steps approximated twice the time of travel divided by the length of the routing period. Having established the number of steps, the reach outflow at any instant t_n equals the inflow values at t_n, t_{n-1}, t_{n-2}, etc., multiplied by the series of factors given in Table 19-7. For example, if $2t_u/t_t = 4$, then

$$O_5 = 0.0625I_5 + 0.2500I_4 + 0.3750I_3 + 0.2500I_2 + 0.0625I_1 \quad (19\text{-}22)$$

TABLE 19-7. Coefficients for Flood Routing by Successive Averages

Number of routing steps									
1	2	3	4	5	6	7	8	9	10
0	0	0	0	0	0	0	0	0	0
.5000	.2500	.1250	.0625	.0313	.0156	.0078	.0039	.0020	.0010
.5000	.5000	.3750	.2500	.1562	.0937	.0547	.0313	.0176	.0098
	.2500	.3750	.3750	.3125	.2344	.1641	.1094	.0703	.0440
		.1250	.2500	.3125	.3126	.2734	.2187	.1641	.1172
			.0625	.1562	.2344	.2734	.2734	.2460	.2050
				.0313	.0937	.1641	.2187	.2460	.2460
					.0156	.0547	.1094	.1641	.2050
						.0078	.0313	.0703	.1172
							.0039	.0176	.0440
								.0020	.0098
									.0010

Obviously, it is not necessary to adhere to the coefficients proposed by Tatum. Equally applicable factors can be obtained by trial, using the actual inflow and outflow hydrographs. Equation (19-22) is quite similar in form to Eq. (19-20) derived from theoretical concepts. In both cases the sum of the coefficients is necessarily unity. Hence, as the number of terms increases, the values of the coefficients by either method tend to approach the same limit.

[1] Tatum, F. E., A Simplified Method of Routing Flood Flows through Natural Valley Storage, unpublished memorandum, U.S. Engineers Office, Rock Island, Ill., May 29, 1940.

ADJUSTMENT FOR LOCAL INFLOW

Local inflow is one of the most troublesome features of streamflow routing where the unmeasured local flow is a substantial portion of the total inflow to the reach. Treatment of local inflow in computing the storage curve has already been discussed. Since several storage curves should be averaged to get the mean curve for the reach, errors in treating local inflow can be assumed to compensate reasonably well. In actual application of a routing technique, errors in estimating local inflow affect the computed outflow directly.

One problem raised by local inflow is the question of whether it should be routed through storage. Usual practice in this respect is arbitrary. If the bulk of the local flow rises near the head of the reach, it is usually added to the main-stream inflow and the total is routed through storage. On the other hand, if the local flow comes largely from the lower end of the reach, the main-stream flow is customarily routed through storage and the local flow added directly to the resulting outflow hydrograph. Any arbitrary division between these two limits is obviously possible. For example, the flow of a major tributary entering near the head of the reach can be added to the main-river inflow, while the balance of the local inflow is added to the computed outflow.

Local flow from tributaries which are gaged is quite easily computed by unit hydrographs, routing, or other accepted techniques. The local inflow coming from unmeasured streams poses quite a different problem. One solution is to treat it by means of synthetic unit graphs. A more common procedure is to compute the local flow by reversing the routing process. If it is planned to add the local inflow to an outflow hydrograph computed by routing main-stream inflow, then the local inflow hydrograph can be computed by subtracting the routed main-stream hydrograph from the observed outflow.

If, on the contrary, local inflow is to be added to main-stream inflow before routing, then the routing process is reversed by computing I_1 from known values of S_1, O_1, S_2, O_2, and I_2. The measured inflow is then subtracted from the computed total inflow to obtain the unmeasured local inflow. The hydrographs obtained by either of the two procedures can be used to determine the unit hydrograph for the ungaged local area. In the procedures outlined, all routing errors are included in the unmeasured local inflow. With a highly accurate routing procedure, the resulting local-inflow hydrographs will be of reasonably normal shape. If the procedure is not precise, very irregular unit graphs will result and in extreme cases will show negative inflow values. Since the routing equation is volumetrically exact, the sum of the positive and negative values should be adjusted to 1.00 in. in developing the unit graph.

VARIABLE STAGE-DISCHARGE RELATIONS

A routing problem which is often vexing is that introduced by variable stage-discharge relations. Rating curves of this type were discussed in Chap. 9. If the storage is expressed as a function of flow, the variable rating may not prove troublesome. When stage is used as the storage index, the methods must be specially adapted to the problem. Some procedures developed by the River Forecasting Section of the Tennessee Valley Authority (TVA)[1] are used as examples.

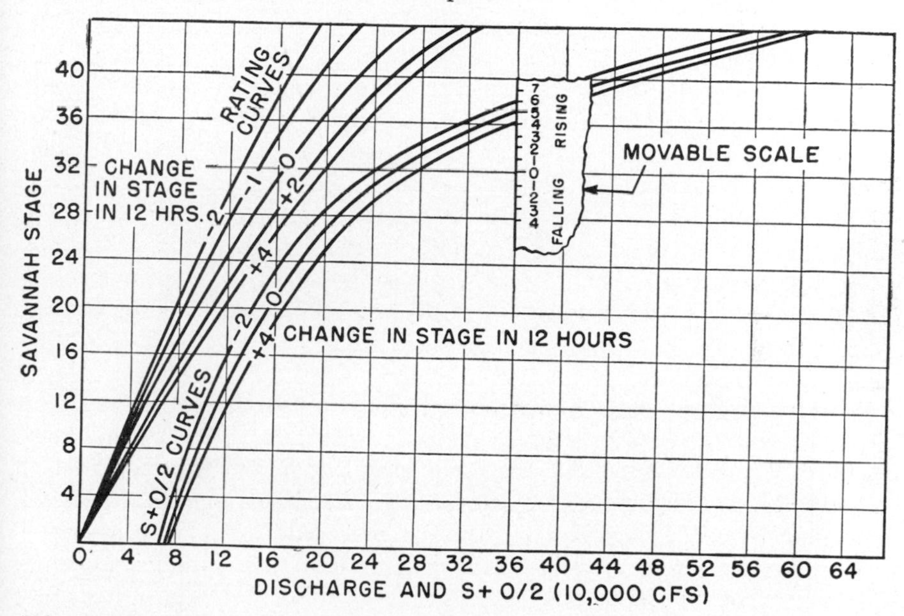

FIG. 19–17. Routing curves for the Tennessee River from Pickwick Dam to Savannah, Tennessee.

Figure 19-17 shows the routing curves developed for the reach from Pickwick Dam to Savannah. The rating curve at Savannah is a change-in-stage rating. Curves of discharge and $S + (O/2)$ were plotted against Savannah stage with the 12-hr change in stage as the parameter. Values of $\bar{I}$, O_1, $S_1 - (O_1/2)$, and the Savannah stage at the beginning of the period are known, and $S_2 + (O_2/2)$ can be computed from Eq. (19-15).

If a movable scale with graduations corresponding to the Savannah-stage scale is placed parallel to the vertical axis of the chart, with its zero point at the initial values of Savannah stage and $S_2 + (O_2/2)$, some graduation of the scale will coincide exactly with an equal value of rate of change on the

[1] The relations discussed here are no longer applicable because of the construction of Kentucky Dam near the mouth of the Tennessee River.

$S + (O/2)$ curves. This value will represent the change in stage to be expected during the routing period and, when added to the initial Savannah stage, will give the Savannah stage at the end of the period. In Fig. 19-17, the movable scale is shown with its zero point at a value of $S_2 + (O_2/2) = 360$ and an initial Savannah stage of 32 ft. The +4-ft mark coincides with the +4-ft $\left(S + \frac{O}{2}\right)$ curve, and therefore the 12-hr change in stage will be 4 ft and the final stage 36 ft.

Routing curves for the reach from Perryville to Johnsonville are given in Fig. 19-18. The rating at Johnsonville is a change-in-stage rating and,

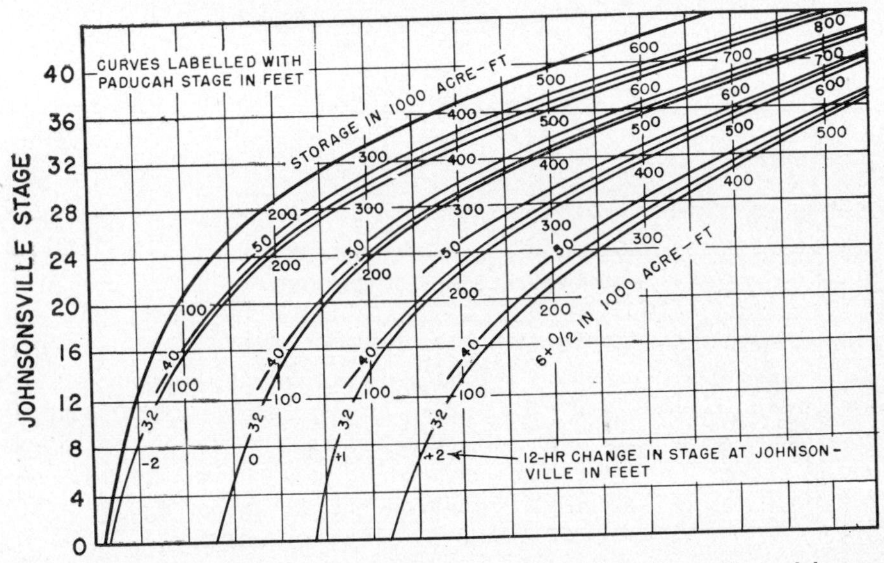

FIG. 19-18. Routing curves for the Tennessee River from Perryville to Johnsonville, Tennessee.

moreover, is complicated by backwater during high stages in the Ohio River. It is necessary, therefore, that the routing curves take both these factors into account. A curve family has been developed for each of several values of change in stage. The stage of the Ohio River at Paducah is used as a parameter in each curve family to account for backwater. From the curve for the predicted Paducah stage and the current Johnsonville stage, a value of $S + (O/2)$ for zero change in stage during the period can be determined. Similarly, a value of $S + (O/2)$ can be determined for 1 ft of rise by entering with the predicted Paducah stage and the current Johnsonville stage plus 1 ft. The procedure is repeated a third time for some other value of change in stage, and the three values of $S + (O/2)$ are plotted against the corresponding rate of change on an auxiliary sheet.

Since the final value of $S_2 + (O_2/2)$ is known, the predicted value of change in stage can be taken from this auxiliary curve and added to the current Johnsonville stage to give the predicted stage for the end of the period.

Other solutions to problems of this type are possible. Steinberg suggests the use of an index to backwater as a parameter in his routing curves. If routing curves are developed by multiple correlation (either analytical or graphical), adjustment for the effect of backwater or variable slope can be introduced by the use of suitable parameters. Occasionally, a constant-slope rating for the outflow station can be developed, using the inflow station as the slope station. With both storage and outflow expressed as a function of stages at the ends of the reach, routing curves may be constructed.

GAGE RELATIONS

The general term *gage relation*[1] and the more specific terms *stage relation, flow relation,* and *stage-flow relation* refer to empirical charts which relate the flow at a point to streamflow events at an upstream station. The average effects of ungaged local inflow and channel storage in transforming the flood wave are inherently included in most gage relations. The gage relation expresses the combined effect of so many factors that the evaluation of the influence of any one factor is often difficult. Properly developed and applied, gage relations often prove highly reliable and at the same time extremely simple. They may be considered as a primary tool in the field of flood forecasting and are frequently useful in preliminary hydrologic studies. Gage relations can be developed using either stage or discharge or a combination of the two elements. The same basic principles apply to both stage and flow relations. The choice between the two types is dependent on the particular problem to be solved.

The success of a simple gage relation depends on (1) a proportionality between flow at the upstream station and inflow between the upper and lower stations and (2) a fixed time relation between the crest at the upstream station and the crest of the inflow from the intervening area. In general, gage relations should be used only for reaches in which the two basic requirements are at least moderately well met. They apply quite satisfactorily on most streams not subject to artificial regulation. Gage relations work best on large streams where the rate of rise and fall is slow. On such streams, errors due to variation in synchronization are less than on the flashy streams (Fig. 19-19). Gage relations give best results when local inflow between stations is small in proportion to the inflow from upstream, as when a mountain stream discharges in a valley area of low rainfall or

[1] Linsley, R. K., "The Development of Flow and Stage Relations for River Forecasting," U.S. Weather Bureau, February, 1944 (mimeo.).

when a river flows through leveed channel with no appreciable local inflow. Stage relations show higher accuracy for relatively wide channel sections, where a large change in discharge results in small change in stage.

The accuracy of gage relations when applied to reaches subject to artificial regulation is dependent on the degree of regulation. Minor diversions or the existence of small reservoirs with negligible storage volume offer little hindrance to the use of such relations. If dams have fixed discharge

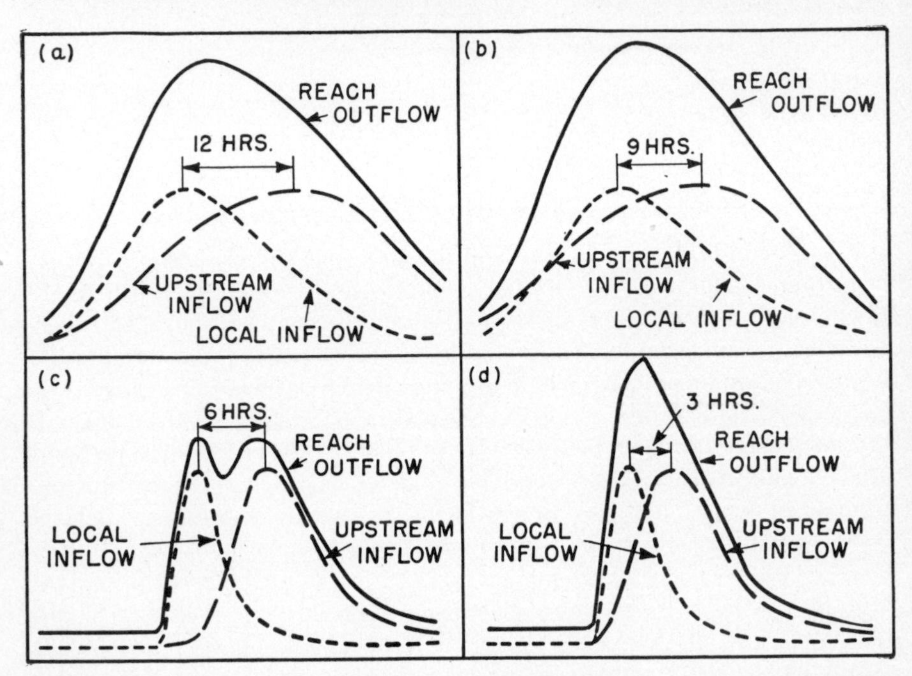

FIG. 19–19. Effect of variations in synchronization of inflows on outflow hydrograph.

capacities or operate on an established schedule during floods, gage relations can be used without serious difficulty.

In extreme floods, accurate crest stages can always be determined by observation or by floodmarks. Discharge for record-breaking floods, however, can be measured only at the time of occurrence and often must be estimated. The observed crest stage probably represents more reliable data than the estimated flow. When a river station is established, it is often possible to determine high-water marks of previous floods. These data can be used in a tentative stage relation even before actual records are collected from the newly established gage.

Simple gage relations. The simple stage relation is a plotting of *crest* at one station against the corresponding *crest* at a downstream station

(Fig. 19-20). Where the two basic requirements are well satisfied, such a relation may be fully adequate. Between Ord Ferry and Butte City the Sacramento River flows through leveed channel. Except for minor amounts of drainage water pumped over the levees, no inflow reaches the river between the two stations. This is an excellent situation for a gage relation, and an extremely accurate curve results. Diversion of water from this reach occurs at two places (in the vicinity of Ord Ferry, over the river bank to a side channel; and above Butte City at Moulton Weir, a cut in the

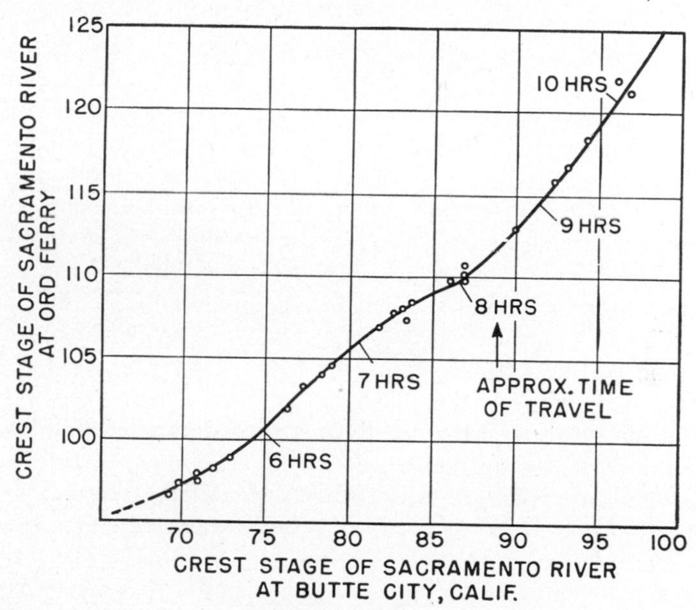

FIG. 19–20. Simple gage relation for the Sacramento River from Ord Ferry to Butte City, California. *(U.S. Weather Bureau.)*

levee with concrete spillway). These diversions always occur when the river reaches a definite height, and the amount of flow diverted is proportional to stage. Except for a slight scattering of points near an Ord Ferry stage of 108 ft, where overflow begins, these diversions have no deleterious effect on the gage relation.

Complex stage relations. As conditions depart more and more from the ideal situation, the deviations from an average stage relation become larger and larger. When the spread of data is excessive, additional variables must be introduced to explain these deviations.

If the variations from the normal curve appear to be due to variations in local inflow, the obvious parameter is a factor which expresses the amount of tributary inflow. If a single large tributary enters the reach, stages on that tributary may serve as the necessary element. If the local inflow is contributed from several small tributaries, it may be possible that stages on one will serve as an adequate index of the flow from all tributaries. This assumes a constant pattern of rainfall distribution in the local area. The largest of the tributaries should be used if possible. If the stage on a single tributary does not prove to be a satisfactory index, the stages on two or more can be used. The stage on each tributary must be used as a separate factor, since the sum of two stages is not a quantitative indication of the total discharge.

Tributary stages are the most desirable parameter for stage relations, as they provide definite information as to magnitude and volume of tributary inflow. Some cases will be found where the use of tributary stage as a third variable is impractical. In such instances, the ratio of average rainfall over the local area to that above the upper station can be used as a parameter. This presumes a definite relation between rainfall and streamflow. Chapters 16 and 17 point out quite clearly that no simple relation exists between rainfall and the shape of the resultant runoff hydrograph. The rainfall ratio serves, therefore, only as a general index. In regions of reasonably uniform rainfall, and where streams tend to be sluggish, the rainfall ratio will be most effective.

Where one of the stations is subject to backwater, a parameter may be introduced to indicate the magnitude of this effect. This condition develops most frequently when the downstream station is subject to backwater from a dam or from high stages on a connecting stream. If backwater is caused by a dam, the water-surface elevation at the dam is generally the best index to backwater. If the effect is caused by high stages in a connecting stream, stage at a station just above or below the junction is most effective. Figure 19-21 shows a gage relation between Folsom and Sacramento on the American River, with the stage of the Sacramento River at Sacramento serving as a measure of backwater. The curve of no backwater is defined by those crests on the American River which occurred with low stages on the Sacramento River. The effect of backwater is generally negligible when submergence is less than 50 per cent, and this fact may be used to extend the curve of no backwater and to determine its intersections with the parametric curves. In the example, the channel bottom at H Street Bridge is at a gage height of about 14 ft, and a stage of 24 ft at I Street Bridge represents about 10 ft of submergence. As shown on the curves, the backwater effect of an I Street stage of 24 ft becomes negligible for H Street stages in excess of 34 ft. Below this stage, backwater tends to raise the stages above those which would be experienced with no backwater.

Flow relations. Some problems arise for which the use of stage relations is impractical. In many such cases, the simplicity of gage relations can be retained by use of flow relations. As indicated in the previous section, stages should not be added but must be treated separately. If flow from several tributaries must be considered, the number of variables may be reduced by using the sum of the discharges. The tributary inflow can be added to the inflow at the head of the main-stream reach to develop a simple flow relation with the sum of the main-river and tributary inflows plotted against outflow.

Figure 19-22 presents an interesting example of a combined tributary flow and rainfall parameter. The Carbon and White Rivers join the

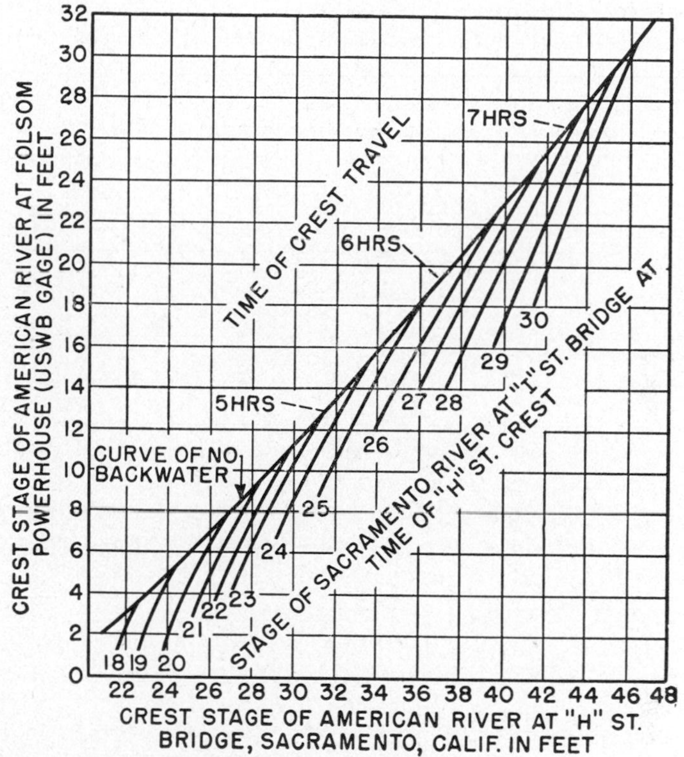

FIG. 19–21. Gage relation showing the effect of backwater. *(U.S. Weather Bureau.)*

Puyallup above the station at Puyallup, Washington. The flows at Mud Mountain and Fairfax on the White and Carbon Rivers, respectively, are added to the flow of the Puyallup River at Orting to give a combined measure of inflow from these three sources. Some measure of local inflow between these three outpost stations and Puyallup is still needed to explain fully the data from past floods. The rainfall at Puyallup during the 24 hr preceding the crest is a satisfactory index for this local inflow and is included as a variable. The heavy dash line represents the normal relation, and its intersections with the lighter solid line serve to show the normal

Puyallup rainfall for a given upstream flow. The light solid lines provide a means of estimating the Puyallup discharge for any abnormal combination of upstream and local inflow.

Flow relations are commonly used where discharge from reservoirs represents an important factor. However, any type of gage relation must be used with caution in a reach where inflow is entirely or partly controlled by reservoirs.

Flow-stage relations. The relation of Fig. 19-22 could have been made as a flow-stage relation by simply plotting the sum of the upstream

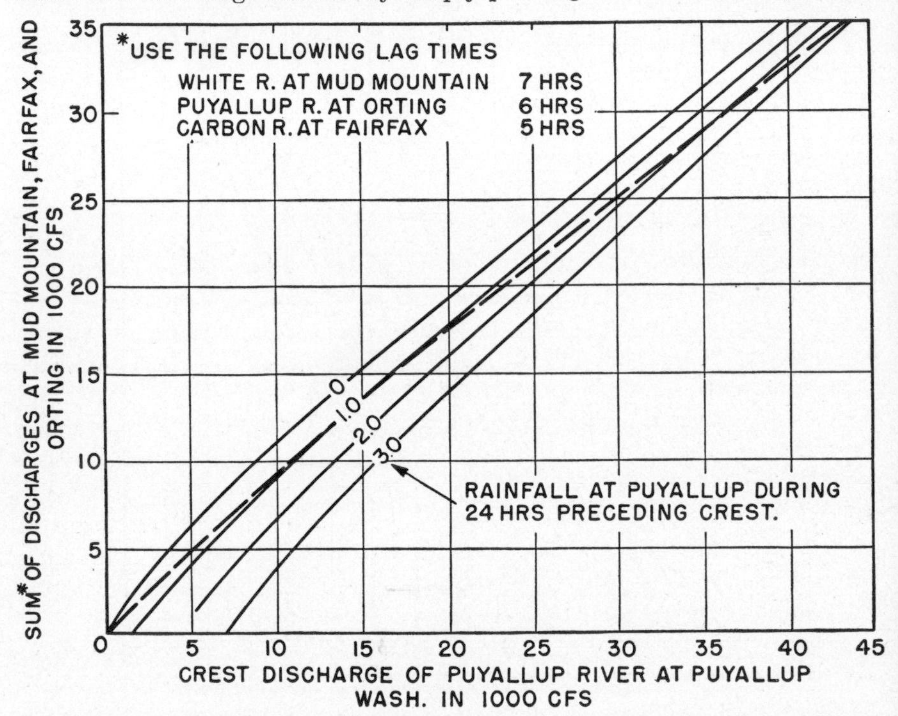

FIG. 19–22. Flow relation for the Puyallup River, Washington, using rainfall as a parameter. *(U.S. Weather Bureau.)*

flows against Puyallup stage. Flow-stage relations are perhaps most frequently used as stage-discharge relations for a station at which no discharge measurements are made. Thus, if a gage is located a few miles from a rated station, a relation can readily be plotted between stage at the gage and flow at the rated station. If no appreciable inflow can occur between the two stations, the resulting curve can be assumed to be the stage-discharge relation for the unrated station.

Selection of data. To a large extent the success or failure of a gage relation depends on the proper choice of basic data. Improperly selected data may result in a gage relation which will not at all serve the purpose intended and which may even lead to very erroneous estimates. The gage relation is essentially only a correlation of cause and effect. It is not possible, therefore, to extrapolate far beyond the range of the data with any assurance of success. In addition, extrapolation from past to future conditions or from one type of data to another must be avoided or controlled as closely as possible.

It is generally impossible to avoid extrapolation of time, *i.e.*, we must use past data as a basis for predicting future events. It is imperative to control the situation by a careful selection of data from a period of record which is believed most nearly to duplicate streamflow conditions which are expected in the immediate future. In general, only data from the period of record since the last important change in streamflow regime should be used. Such changes may be man-made or natural. The time of man-made changes, such as construction of levees, diversion works, dams, cutoffs, channel realignment, or clearing, can be determined.

A change may affect only certain ranges of data. An example might be the raising of a levee without changing the levee alignment. There would be no changes in the streamflow conditions for floods which did not overtop the old levee. Construction of a diversion weir or cutoff channel to operate at a predetermined moderate or high stage represents no change in conditions for floods below this established level. Construction of irrigation diversions to operate only during a dry season would be unimportant. Diversion of 1000 cfs would be insignificant during floods of 100,000 cfs or more but would be a material factor at much smaller flows. The construction of a small dam for diversion or recreation might not be significant at all if its storage volume is low in comparison with the total flow occurring during a flood. While the effect of a single structure may be negligible, a combination of several may be important.

Natural changes in streamflow regime may be either abrupt or gradual. Abrupt changes, such as levee failures or cutting of new channels, are easily dated. In the case of a levee break, it may be necessary to exclude data only during the period the break was open. Abrupt natural changes generally date from occurrence of a major flood. Gradual changes in channel shape or alignment by scour or silting are difficult to date with any precision. They can be treated by analyzing the data in reverse with respect to time, *i.e.*, by plotting the most recent data first and working backward until the data show a significant trend away from current conditions.

The best data for development of simple gage relations are crest stages or discharges. If stages during the rise and fall are plotted, they will define a loop similar to that of storage vs. outflow (Fig. 19-6). Moreover, local inflow during rising and falling stages is not necessarily in the same proportion as at crest. Inclusion of rising or falling stages in a gage relation will therefore result in greater deviations than when crest stages are used alone. The most reliable crest data are obtained from charts of automatic water-stage recorders. Crests reported from stations equipped with wire-weight or staff gages may also be used, but their accuracy depends on how closely the observer watched the river near time of crest. Observers' estimates of crest occurring during the night can be considerably in error.

In constructing a complex gage relation, using tributary stage as a parameter, records from automatic gages are highly desirable. *It is important in all gage relations that the stages used for upstream points be those actually influencing the crest at the downstream station.* Many attempts to construct complex gage relations have failed because this restriction was overlooked. The rule might be stated in another way. *The upstream and downstream stages must be separated by a time interval equal to the time of travel.* In developing a simple gage relation this is automatically included when actual crests are used, since these values must occur at a time interval equal to the time of crest travel. In the complex gage relation where two or more upstream stations are used to predict the downstream stage, the problem is not so simple. In tabulating data for such relations, it is necessary to select stages at upstream stations representing elements of the hydrographs which will arrive simultaneously at the downstream point. The procedure is as follows: (1) Determine the actual time of the downstream crest. (2) From this crest time, subtract the times of travel from the upstream stations. (3) Use the upstream stages at the times thus computed in developing the gage relation.

Quite often it is necessary to develop a stage relation with limited data. Under such conditions, an auxiliary relation can be constructed by plotting stages representing equal discharges on the two rating curves as a crest relation. The resulting curve may serve as an approximate guide to the shape of the crest-stage relation. The auxiliary curve assumes the translation of the flood wave without change by addition of local inflow or reduction by channel storage. It cannot be expected, therefore, to coincide with the points plotted from crest-stage data, but it may indicate the existence of possible changes in slope of the stage relation and the probable direction of the curve beyond the range of the available data. The stage relation should be drawn to best fit available data, with the auxiliary curve serving as a guide to relative slope and position of changes in slope.

If the stage relation under consideration involves three variables, *i.e.*, two upstream stations, it will frequently be observed that, because of the high intercorrelation between the upstream stations, the plotted points fall quite closely about a single line. The appearance is that of a relation in which the parameter has very little influence. What has actually happened is that in most cases when one of the upstream stations had a high crest, the other had a proportional crest. The curves for various values of the parameter, therefore, intersect the mean, or normal, curve. While it may be possible under such conditions to establish the position of a parametric curve at any one point, it is often difficult to determine the slope of such curves. Here, again, one may resort to an auxiliary family of curves constructed from the three ratings (assuming downstream flow equal to total

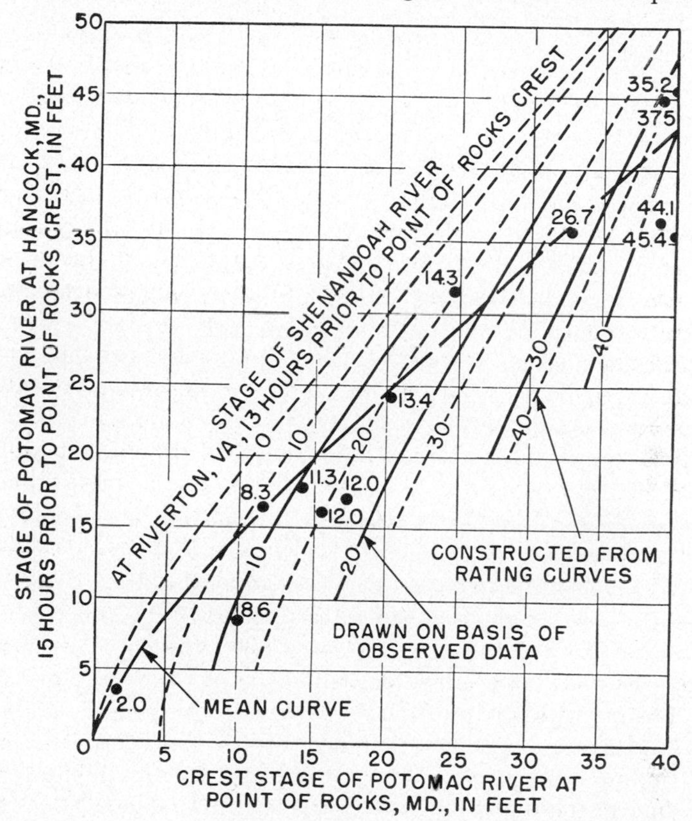

FIG. 19–23. Derivation of a complex gage relation using station rating curves.

upstream flow) as an indication of the slope and placing of the several curves for the parameter (Fig. 19-23).

If it is necessary that a stage relation involve four or more variables, it can be developed by the coaxial method outlined in Appendix A. The intercorrelation which hampers the development of a three-variable relation may become even more important in the case of lesser tributaries in a multiple-variable analysis. Not only will points tend to group in a narrow band, but the parametric curves will intersect the 45° line, which complicates the determination of the curves from the discharge ratings. These difficulties can be reduced by first constructing all but one of the curve families on the basis of stage-discharge relations. The remaining curve family, involving the two most important upstream stations, can then be determined by plotting. Such a procedure ignores the effect of channel storage on the flow of the lesser tributaries. This omission can be corrected in the second stage of the development when the curves are revised, following the procedure outlined in Appendix A.

STAGE ROUTING

It is occasionally necessary to treat a routing problem in terms of stage. Such a condition may be encountered in design when stage hydrographs are required for an unrated station. Since river forecasts are often issued in terms of stage, a successful stage-routing procedure eliminates the need for conversion of stage to discharge. Stage-routing procedures cannot be based on a quantitative solution of the storage equation.

Kohler has demonstrated that graphical correlation techniques described under Nonstorage Routing can be applied to stage routing. Values of stage representing appropriate values of I and O are used instead of flow values. Figure 19-24 shows a routing relation of this type. One of the obvious difficulties in routing stages is the problem of local inflow, since tributary stages (or flows) cannot be added to the inflow stage in the literal sense. In the figure, advantage has been taken of the fact that a crest-stage relation inherently includes the effect of local inflow. The family of curves at the lower right is a three-variable crest-stage relation between Dams 29 and 33 on the Ohio River and Chillicothe on the Scioto River. Although this relation is admittedly inadequate to define the rising and falling limbs of the hydrograph, it does serve to combine the Dam 29 and Chillicothe stages into a value (Dam 33 computed stage) which is an index to reach inflow. Stages at Dam 33 computed by this relation serve as inflow values in the routing curves on the left in the figure.

Routing of stages can also be accomplished in terms of change in stage. In Fig. 19-25, the initial stage[1] at Arkansas City and the 2-day change at Helena prior to time zero are combined to show the final stage at Arkansas City 2 days later. The effect of tributary inflow is introduced through supplementary correction curves (B and C). Curves B show the effect of the Arkansas River, using Little Rock as the index station. Since the time of travel from Little Rock to Arkansas City is about 2 days, the 2-day change in stage at Little Rock is selected as the index to the portion of the change at Arkansas City resulting from the Arkansas River. The effect of this change in stage is dependent on stages at Little Rock and Arkansas

[1] Kohler, M. A., A Forecasting Technique for Routing and Combining Flow in Terms of Stage, *Trans. Am. Geophys. Union*, Vol. 25, pp. 1030-1035, 1944.

City. In other words, a 2-ft change at Little Rock means much less water at low stages than at high, and a given amount of water from the Arkansas River will cause a much greater rise at Arkansas City during low stages than during high.

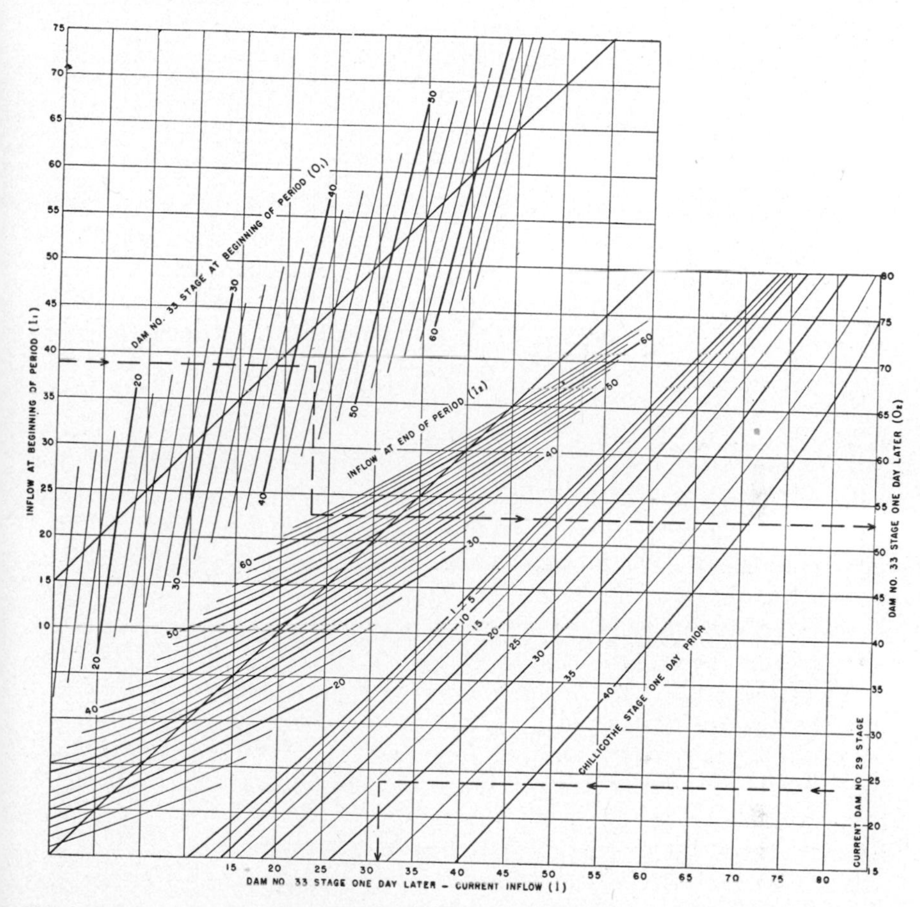

FIG. 19–24. Stage-routing curves for the Ohio River between Dam 29 and Dam 33. *(U.S. Weather Bureau.)*

In order to construct the correction curves, all changes in stage at Little Rock were first made comparable by introducing a variable representing the stage at Little Rock as shown in the upper set of curves of Fig. 19-25*B*. The horizontal axis of this chart is "change in discharge." The axis has not been labeled in the figure, because it has no significance once the curves are developed. The curves were derived directly from the rating for Little Rock. For example, points along the +2-ft curve were determined by finding the change in discharge for a 2-ft rise from various initial stages.

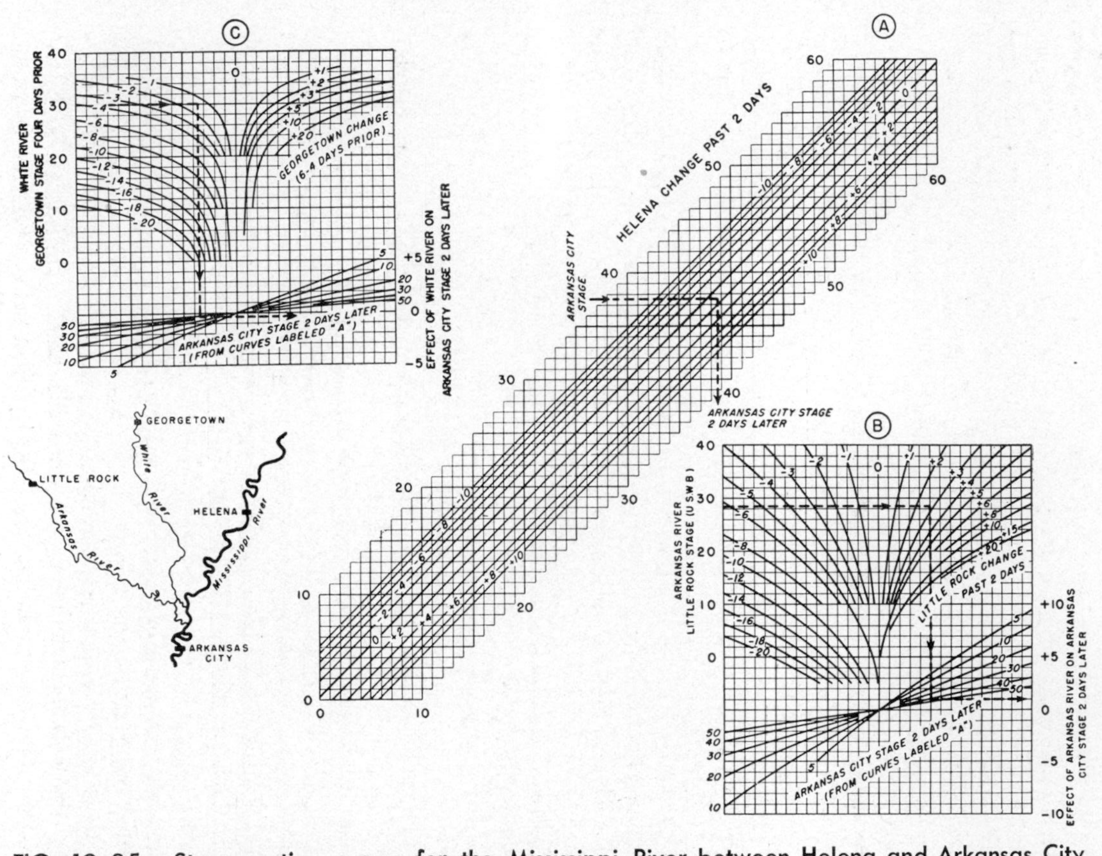

FIG. 19–25. Stage-routing curves for the Mississippi River between Helena and Arkansas City, Arkansas.

Data were then selected for periods when Little Rock stages were changing rapidly and the White River was discharging at a relatively steady rate. From these data, forecasts were made for Arkansas City from Fig. 19-25*A*, and the errors of the forecast were computed. Considering that these errors were caused by variations of inflow from the Arkansas River, they were converted to discharge and plotted against corresponding changes in discharge at Little Rock. This relation shows the "effective" change in discharge at Arkansas City for a given change at Little Rock. The lower curves in Fig. 19-25*B* were developed by converting effective change in discharge to change in stage.

Georgetown was selected as an index station for the White River, and correction curves in Fig. 19-25*C* were developed in the same manner as the curves for Little Rock. Since Georgetown is 6 days above Arkansas City, the Georgetown change 6 to 4 days prior to the current day was used as an index to the effect of the White River on the following 2-day change at Arkansas City.

In general, for this type of procedure, the period of all changes to be used as indices should be the same length and should be approximately equal to the travel time through the reach of the main stream. The period of any change to be used as an index should be in advance of the period at the downstream station by a time equal to the travel time from the index station to the lower end of the reach.

TIME OF TRAVEL

The term *time of travel* most commonly refers to the elapsed time between the occurrence of a crest at one station and the corresponding crest at a downstream station. *Lag* is ordinarily used to refer to the time difference between the occurrence of the center of mass of inflow and the center of mass of outflow. The two values are usually approximately equal since the center of mass of a hydrograph tends to bear the same time relation to the peak at both stations, but in general the lag is slightly longer than the time of travel.

The values of time of travel or lag for a particular reach are usually obtained by study of the hydrographs. If local inflow between the two stations is small, reasonably adequate values can be obtained. Inspection of Fig. 19-19 shows that, when local inflow is large, the crest at the downstream station results from the maximum combination of inflows, and not necessarily from the arrival of the upstream crest. Under such conditions, the time difference between crests is not the time of travel. Cases must be selected where only one source of inflow is contributing significantly.

Time of travel is not necessarily a constant for a particular reach. In those reaches where adequate data throughout the entire range of stage are available, time of travel will be found to be quite long at low stages, to decrease more or less rapidly to a minimum at some moderate stage, and to increase slowly again as stages pass bankfull. Quite frequently, the available data are limited to a range of stage such that the reversal in the stage–travel-time relation is not evident. In such cases, caution should be used in extrapolating the data beyond the observed range.

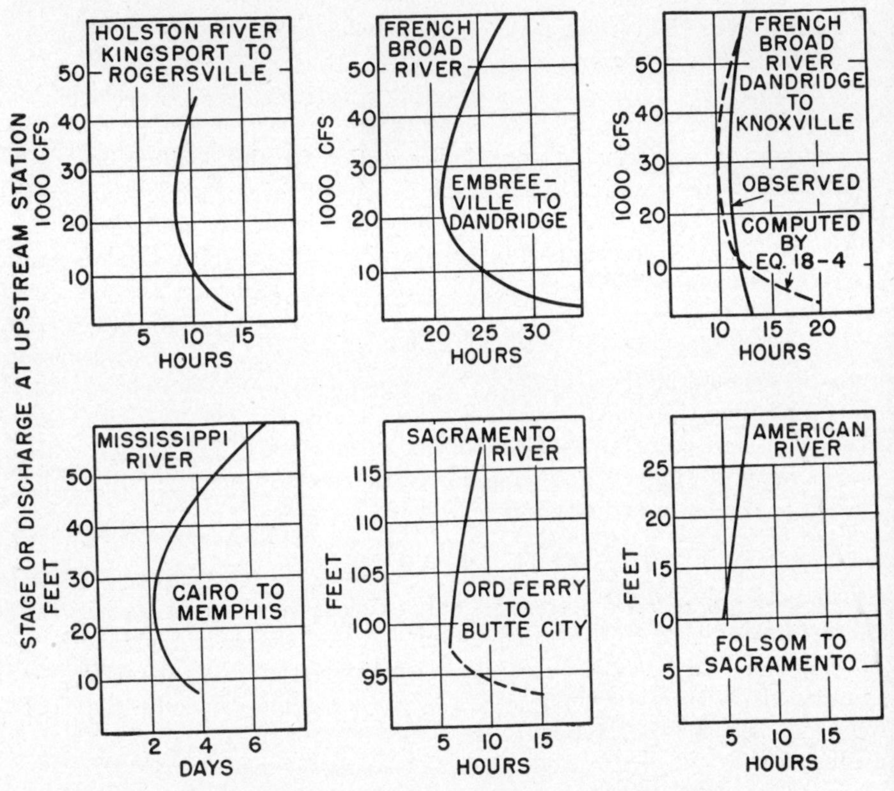

FIG. 19–26. Some typical time-of-travel curves.

Time-of-travel data are usually presented as a curve showing the relation between upstream stage or flow and travel time (Fig. 19-26). For most uses, this type of plotting is fully adequate and generally represents about the maximum accuracy which can be obtained from the available data, particularly if it has been necessary to restrict the cases used in order to eliminate the effect of some source of inflow.

The formulas for wave celerity (Chap. 18) can be used as an alternate means of determining travel time and have proved successful in many reaches in which conditions approximate the assumptions on which they are based. Consideration of these formulas indicates that celerity is a function of initial flow as well as crest height and that secondary rises moving on an already full channel will travel more rapidly than a rise from low stages to the same crest. If a particular problem requires the accuracy, a family of curves showing travel time as a function of initial and final flows can be constructed from the wave formulas and used as a guide to the determination of curves based on observed data. Average values of discharge, cross-sectional area, and depth for a reach are normally used in the formulas.

Observations have shown that wave celerity is roughly 1.4 to 2.0 times the water velocity. This offers a further means of approximation to time of travel if velocity measurements are available within the reach. Further, assuming that roughness and the hydraulic radius are comparable from stream to stream within a region, the velocity can be assumed to be proportional to the square root of slope s. Hence, if the time of travel t_{u1} in a reach is known, the time of travel t_{u2} in an adjacent reach of similar characteristics can be estimated by

$$t_{u2} = t_{u1} \sqrt{\frac{s_1}{s_2}} \frac{L_2}{L_1} \tag{19-23}$$

DETERMINATION OF BASIN OUTFLOW BY ROUTING

If we consider rainfall excess to be inflow to the stream system, the problem of hydrograph forecasting for a headwater basin becomes analogous to the problem of flood routing along a reach of a stream. In a headwater basin the flood wave is in its formative stage. Instead of a well-developed flood wave moving through a reach with moderate local inflow, we are dealing with what is, in effect, all local inflow. The various components of the hydrograph follow different paths to the stream and hence undergo different storage effects. Moreover, the contributions from various portions of the basin all pass through different amounts of storage, depending on distance to the outlet.

Despite these difficulties, routing offers a convenient and practical solution to many problems which cannot be effectively handled by direct application of the unit-graph method. In areas where unit graphs can be applied successfully, they will prove simpler and perhaps more accurate than routing. Problems for which routing procedures prove helpful include routing of runoff from (1) snowmelt in areas where protracted periods of melting occur, (2) basins of unusual shape, and (3) basins having irregular areal distribution of rainfall from storm to storm.

Determination of valley storage. Most procedures for the determination of valley storage treat it essentially as a reservoir at the outflow station. Since there is no "inflow hydrograph" in the sense used in routing flows between stations on a river, methods for determination of valley storage are limited. It is manifestly impossible to measure the storage volume in the channel system by planimetry or to correlate such volumes with inflow and outflow so as to be of practical use.

The most common procedures for determination of valley storage are based on analysis of the recession curve. The recession factor K_r can be determined by study of typical recessions and the storage-outflow curve constructed by application of Eq. (15-5). If we let K equal the reciprocal of $\log_e K_r$, Eq. (15-5) is similar in form to Eq. (19-6), which states that storage is a function of the mean flow in a reach. There is no method of determining x other than by trial routings. Clark[1] has shown that the assumption of $x = 0.3$ is practical and probably within the accuracy of the method. It is certainly reasonable to assume that, in most natural drainage basins, outflow exerts a greater influence over storage than does inflow. Exceptions would be basins with large natural storage near the headwaters in the form of lakes or swamps, where values of x may be as high as 0.5.

The storage constant K has the dimension of time and is approximately equal to the basin lag. Clark suggested that K was a function of the physical features of the basin and could be expressed by

$$K = \frac{cL}{\sqrt{s}} \tag{19-24}$$

where s is the mean slope of the basin and L the length of the main stream. Linsley, in a discussion of the same paper, proposed the modification of this formula to the form

$$K = \frac{bL\sqrt{A_d}}{\sqrt{s}} \tag{19-25}$$

The introduction of drainage area A_d provides a further expression of basin dimensions, which appears to stabilize the equation. Values of the coefficient c for east-coast streams range between 0.8 and 3.4, with the mode between 1.0 and 1.5, while values of b vary between 0.04 and 0.40, with a mode between 0.05 and 0.10. The similarity in form between Eqs. (17-9) and (19-25) suggests the use of the former for determination of K.

Routing methods. Having established a value of K, or an outflow-storage curve, several routing methods may be used. The Muskingum procedure is an obvious possibility, as is also Goodrich's technique, in which storage is treated as a function of outflow. The Meyer lag-routing procedure is also readily adaptable to the problem.

Two alternate approaches are used. In the first, a time-area concentration diagram for the basin is constructed by subdividing the basin into zones of such dimensions that the travel time from one limit of a zone to the other is relatively small with respect to the total travel time from the farthest zone to the outlet. The time-area concentration diagram then shows

[1] Clark, C. O., Storage and the Unit Hydrograph, *Trans. ASCE*, Vol. 110, pp. 1419-1488, 1945.

the area from which flows would reach the outflow station during an increment of time. By routing this diagram through storage and converting to the proper units, a unit hydrograph may be derived. This approach is simply a method of synthesizing the unit graph for a basin. The unit graph so developed is one for an instantaneous runoff event, since the time-area concentration diagram considers only the time of travel and not the continuation of runoff which would result from rain of a finite duration. The instantaneous unit graph can be converted into a unit graph for any finite duration of rain by dividing it into time increments equal to the desired duration and plotting the average ordinate for each period at the end of the period.

This first approach does not overcome any of the deficiencies of the unit hydrograph as a hydrologic tool, since it provides only a means of synthesizing a unit graph for application in the regular manner. The effect of varying rainfall duration or amount or of differing times of occurrence of rain in the various portions of the basin can be accounted for by the construction of a time-runoff concentration diagram. Here again, the basin is subdivided into zones of suitable dimensions, and a histogram showing the sum of the runoff from the several zones arriving during a given time period is constructed. This histogram, adjusted for valley storage, yields the actual hydrograph for the particular storm, including the effect of any deviations from the normal hydrograph by reason of rainfall variations with time or area.

Although this second approach is more laborious and time consuming than the first, it is necessary if application of routing methods is to yield any advantage over the unit hydrograph. It suggests also the possibility of preparing empirical routing curves by graphical or statistical correlation techniques. Once the time-runoff concentration diagram has been constructed, values of total runoff for each time period may be taken as inflow and correlated with outflow in any one of the ways previously outlined. All the advantages claimed for the statistical approach to flood routing in a river reach are again available in the problem of deriving the basin hydrograph. In view of the difficulties and approximations necessary to the determination of valley storage in a natural basin, it is quite likely that the empirical approach is relatively better in this type of problem than in main-river routing.

The problem of the long, narrow basin. If routing techniques are explored on long, narrow basins typical of many Middle Western streams, it will be found that they are not generally successful. In addition to the fact that the assumption of storage as a function of outflow is unsatisfactory in such basins, several additional complications arise. The development of a storage relation is extremely difficult because the flood events are almost entirely the result of runoff from storms striking only a section of the basin. Hydrograph shapes and recession constants vary from flood to flood, depending on the particular portion of the basin in which the flood developed. Although no completely satisfactory solution is known, a combination of the composite unit graph and routing provides the best available answer to this problem. If there are several gaging stations within the basin so that unit graphs for subareas may be derived by the usual methods, routing techniques may be prepared to route flows from these subareas to the outlet station.

Lacking actual data from subareas of the basin, an indirect solution is necessary. This solution requires division of the basin into several logical subareas (Fig. 19-27) and synthesis of a unit hydrograph for each area.

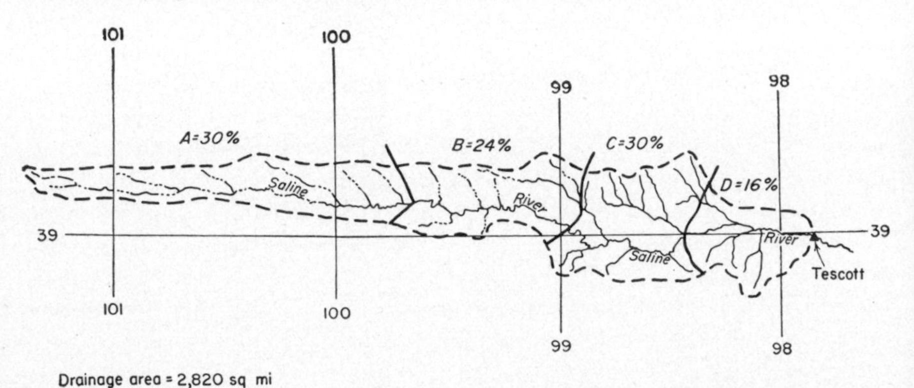

FIG. 19–27. Subdivision of the Saline River Basin above Tescott, Kansas, for outflow routing.

These unit graphs are then routed from the subareas to the outflow station. If data are not available to permit routing by any of the rational methods, a strictly empirical approach such as Tatum's method must be used. The result of the routing is a unit hydrograph of the flow from each subarea as it arrives at the outflow station (Fig. 19-28). In application, the estimated runoff from each subarea is applied to the adjusted unit graph for the particular subarea. The sum of all subarea hydrographs gives the storm runoff from the total basin.

In view of the fact that entirely synthetic unit graphs and an empirical routing technique are used, a trial-and-error adjustment is usually necessary. This is accomplished by reconstructing the hydrographs of several floods, using the estimated unit graphs. By comparing the actual and reconstituted hydrographs and considering the rainfall distribution, it is possible to determine the necessary adjustments. For example, if the reconstituted hydrographs rise too slowly, this probably means that the unit graph for the lowest subarea is too flat. If the reconstructed hydrographs are too low at peak and too high in the recession, it may be assumed that the selected time of travel to the headwater subareas is too large. If storms in which the rainfall is concentrated over a single subarea are available, the analysis of adjustments is much simplified.

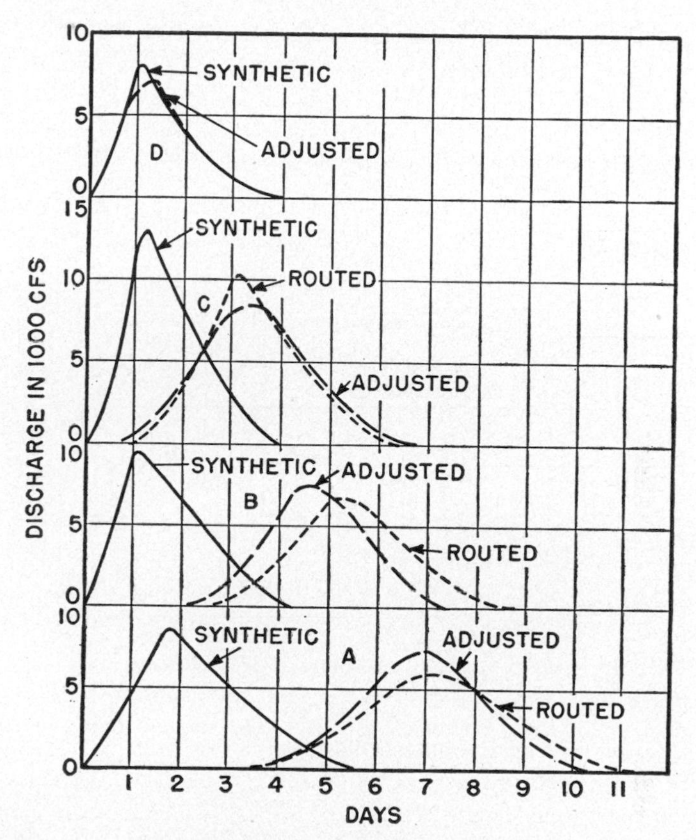

FIG. 19–28. The original synthetic, routed, and adjusted unit graphs for subareas of the Saline River above Tescott, Kansas. *(U.S. Weather Bureau.)*

ROUTING MACHINES

The routing of an extended flood by any of the techniques described earlier involves a considerable amount of computation and numerous references to curves. A machine capable of solving the storage equation would, therefore, save considerable time and effort in routing operations. If this machine could also solve the problem by use of the differential form of the storage equation [Eq. (19-2)], it would also eliminate the errors resulting from the assumption of linear hydrographs throughout a routing period [Eq. (19-3)]. This latter assumption can lead to considerable error near the point of rise and the crest of relatively sharp hydrographs.

Mechanical routing machines. Numerous mechanical devices for solving the storage equation have been constructed. Following in principle graphical solutions, such as that suggested by Cheng, a linkage can be constructed so that, when the operator follows the inflow hydrograph and storage curve with two pointers, a pencil is made to trace the resulting outflow graph on a chart.

A mechanical integrator for routing floods through reservoirs has also been designed.[1] This device consists of five drums mounted in line (Fig. 19-29). The inflow hydrograph, elevation-discharge, and elevation-storage

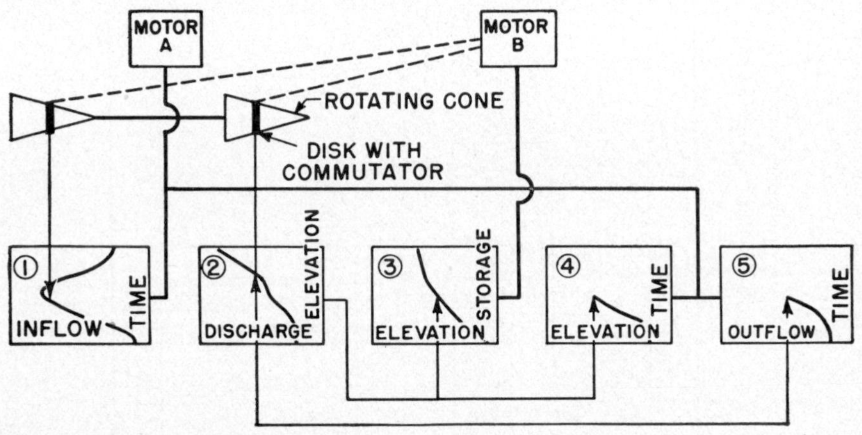

FIG. 19–29. Integrating machine for routing floods through reservoirs. *(After Corps of Engineers.)*

relations are plotted on the charts of the first three drums. Drums 1, 4, and 5 are driven continuously by motor *A*. Operators keep pointers in position on the graphs of drums 1, 2, and 3. Movement of the pointers on drums 1 and 2 position the controls of the differential motor *B*, which drives drum 3 backward or forward in accordance with the relative magnitudes of inflow and outflow. Movement of the pointer on drum 3 turns drum 2 in accordance with the instantaneous values of elevation. The pool-elevation graph and the outflow hydrograph are automatically traced on drums 4 and 5, respectively.

While mechanical routing machines can function very accurately, they require the development of a storage relation by conventional methods. Moreover, the time required to set the machine up for a particular reach is usually so long that the machines are advantageous only when a considerable volume of routing is to be performed for a single reach.

[1] "Engineering Construction; Flood Control," pp. 204-205, The Engineer School, Ft. Belvoir, Va., 1940.

Electronic routing machines. The analogy between the flow of electricity and the movement of water in a permeable medium [Eq. (14-1)] has long been used as a means of defining flow nets under dams and around drains and for other similar problems. The analogy between flow of electricity and of water can be exploited much further in the solution of flood-routing problems.

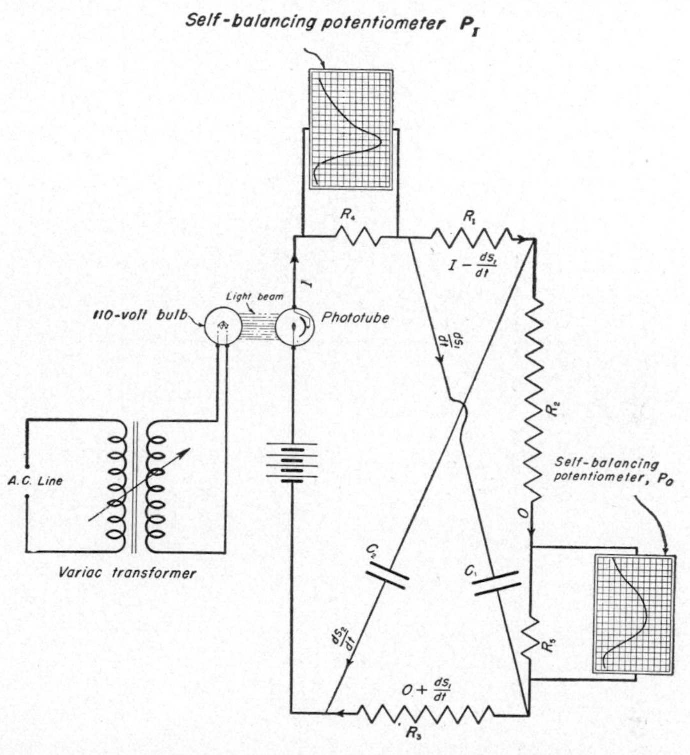

FIG. 19–30. Circuit diagram for an electronic flood-routing machine. *(U.S. Weather Bureau.)*

The charge on a condenser is a function of the potential drop across the condenser, and if the resistance of the circuit is fixed, the charge is proportional to the current. Figure 19-30 represents a circuit[1] which takes advantage of this characteristic to simulate storage in accordance with Eq. (19-6). With a given inflow current I and outflow O through the potentiometers P_I and P_O, respectively, the currents in the various portions of the circuit are shown in the diagram (the current flowing into a condenser is

[1] Linsley, R. K., L. W. Foskett, and M. A. Kohler, Electronic Device Speeds Flood Routing, *Eng. News-Record*, Vol. 141, No. 26, pp. 64-66, 1948.

equal to the time rate of change of charge S, or dS/dt. The resistances R_4 and R_5 are very small as compared with R_1, R_2, and R_3 and can be neglected. The total charge S on the condensers C_1 and C_2 at any time depends on the potential drop across them, *i.e.*,

$$S_1 = \left[\left(I - \frac{dS_1}{dt}\right) R_1 + OR_2\right] C_1 \tag{19-26}$$

and

$$S_2 = \left[\left(O + \frac{dS_1}{dt}\right) R_3 + OR_2\right] C_2 \tag{19-27}$$

Combining Eqs. (19-26) and (19-27) and simplifying, the total storage in the circuit is

$$S = IR_1C_1 + OR_2C_1 + OR_3C_2 + OR_2C_2 - C_1R_1\frac{dS_1}{dt} + C_2R_3\frac{dS_1}{dt} \tag{19-28}$$

If R_1 and R_3 are made equal and C_1 and C_2 are the same, then Eq. (19-28) can be reduced to

$$S = R_1C_1(I + O) + 2OR_2C_1 \tag{19-29}$$

In the steady state ($I = O$), this can be further simplified to

$$S = 2(R_1C_1 + R_2C_1)I \tag{19-30}$$

and since, in the steady state, $S = KI$ [Eq. (19-6)], the storage constant K for the electrical circuit is

$$K = 2(R_1C_1 + R_2C_1) \tag{19-31}$$

Substituting this value of K and the value of S given by Eq. (19-29) in Eq. (19-6),

$$R_1C_1(I + O) + 2OR_2C_1 = 2(R_1C_1 + R_2C_1)[xI + (1 - x)O] \tag{19-32}$$

Solving for x,

$$x(I - O) + O = \frac{R_1C_1(I + O) + 2OR_2C_1}{2(R_1C_1 + R_2C_1)} \tag{19-33}$$

and

$$x = \frac{R_1C_1}{2(R_1C_1 + R_2C_1)} \tag{19-34}$$

Figure 19-31 shows graphically the relation between the constants K and x and the resistances and capacitances of the circuit. Since K has the dimension of time (in seconds), it is a function of chart speed and time scales used in plotting. With fixed condensers, values of K and x may be selected at will by adjusting the three resistances. In the pilot model developed by the U.S. Weather Bureau, two recording potentiometers are inserted in the circuit across 200-ohm resistors (R_4 and R_5). The inflow current is controlled by varying the light intensity on the photocell so that the pen of potentiometer P_I follows the inflow graph plotted on its chart.

The resulting outflow graph is automatically traced on the chart of potentiometer P_O.

Because of its speed the machine can be used to advantage to determine the constants K and x, without resort to the conventional determination from hydrograph analysis. A run can be made using estimated values of the constants, and, by comparison of the resulting outflow graph with the actual data, revised values of K and x may be estimated. A test of the adopted constants on other floods in the same reach will provide a check

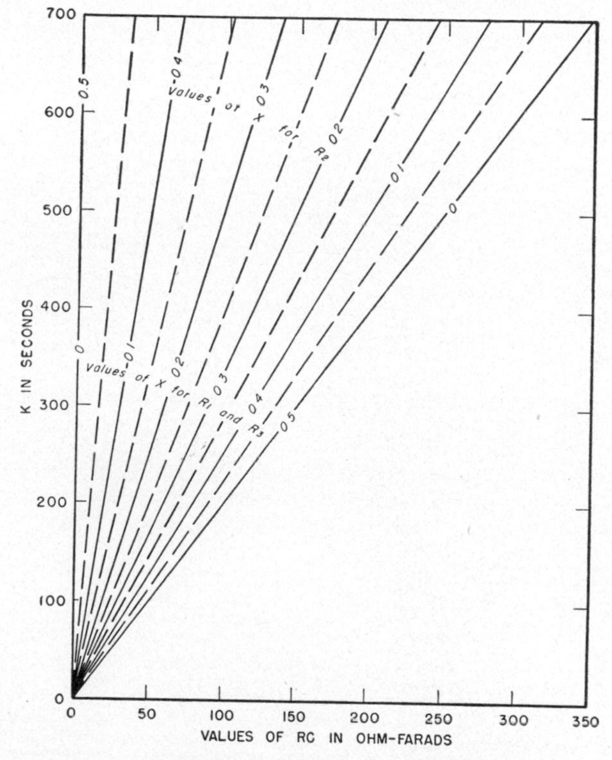

FIG. 19–31. Relation between K, x and the elements of the electrical circuit of Fig. 19–30.

on their value. Figure 19-32 shows outflow hydrographs resulting from the same inflow with various combinations of K and x.

Experience has shown that K may be taken as the average time difference between inflow and outflow crests with sufficient accuracy for preliminary trials. Differentiating Eq. (19-6) and combining with Eq. (19-2),

$$\frac{dS}{dt} = Kx\frac{dI}{dt} + (1 - x)K\frac{dO}{dt} = I - O \tag{19-35}$$

When the hydrographs cross ($I = O$),

$$x \frac{dI}{dt} = (x - 1) \frac{dO}{dt} \tag{19-36}$$

or

$$x = \frac{dO/dt}{(dO/dt) - (dI/dt)} \tag{19-37}$$

A value of x may be estimated from Eq. (19-37), or values of both K and x can be computed by applying Eq. (19-35) at two points along the hydro-

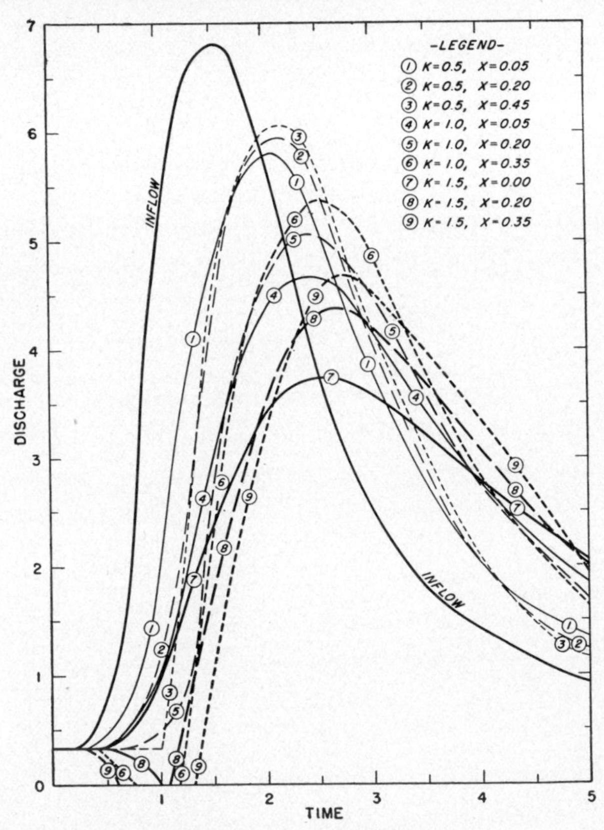

FIG. 19–32. Variation in outflow hydrographs for various combinations of K and x.

graph and solving the resulting equations simultaneously. The circuit is restricted to values of x between zero and 0.5. From Eq. (19-37) it may be concluded that the inflow must be equal to or less than the outflow at the time of the outflow peak.

Experience has demonstrated that the machine is fast and that its accuracy is within the accuracy of the basic streamflow data which are used. Two circuits can be connected so that inflow from two sources may be routed simultaneously and combined in a single outflow graph. This offers a means of independent treatment of tributary flow which is not readily obtainable with any of the other methods discussed in this chapter. Because it solves the differential form of the storage equation, the machine is particularly well adapted for routing rainfall excess from a basin to determine the outflow hydrograph. By using two or more inflow circuits runoff from different parts of the basin can be routed through different amounts of storage.

20

DESIGN CRITERIA

Engineering design requires an integrated study of many separate facets of a project. Broadly speaking, these facets may be classified as the *safety*, *efficiency*, and *appearance* of the project under study. Those projects which involve the control or disposition of surface- or groundwater on its course through the hydrologic cycle fall into the realm of hydrologic design. The ultimate appearance of a project is primarily an architectural concern and is not usually considered by the hydrologist in his studies.

Safety in design. The safety aspect of design includes consideration of the safety of the structure itself and also of life and property which might be endangered by its failure. The structure must be designed to resist any forces to which it may reasonably be subjected within its estimated economic life. Thus, a highway culvert which can be expected to be replaced within 10 to 20 years would be designed to withstand only relatively moderate flows if its failure during that period would result only in temporary inconvenience to a few motorists. On the contrary, a large dam impounding a considerable volume of water above a heavily inhabited valley must be designed to withstand extremely high flows—flows which may be greater than would be reasonably expected during the useful life of the dam. Such a design is dictated, not by the value of the structure or the inconvenience brought about by its destruction, but by the fact that the people below must be protected against the possibility that failure of the dam during a major flood would claim many lives and much valuable property. Between these two extremes, there is a wide variety of problems of different degrees of complexity.

The ideal solution to the problem of safe design would be achieved if the hydrologist could supply the hydraulic designer with an estimate of the maximum flow which would occur at the site selected for the structure during a specified period in the future. Unfortunately, the hydrologist cannot make such a positive estimate. As we shall see later in this chapter, he can provide an estimate of the maximum flow which can reasonably be expected *with a specified probability*. He can also provide, with the assistance of the meteorologist, an estimate of the maximum possible flow which can ever occur at the selected site. Beyond this point the decision as to the actual design values to be used must be a matter of judgment, established by law or by the basic policy of the designing agency.

Project efficiency. An efficient structure is one that properly performs the functions for which it is designed at minimum over-all cost. The question of efficiency is closely related to the problem of economy. The variety of problems encountered in satisfying the requirements of project efficiency probably exceeds that for any other phase of design. Consequently, the solutions are not easily standardized, and a greater amount of ingenuity, supported by a sound basic knowledge of hydrology and hydraulics, is required to accomplish an efficient design.

If a culvert is to be replaced in approximately 20 years, it may be so designed that the maximum flood which can be expected to occur in the 20-year period will not damage the structure. A culvert designed to withstand such a flood without physical damage but capable of passing without highway stoppage only the maximum flood expected to occur once every 5 years might be considerably cheaper. If the savings effected by the cheaper design outweigh the occasional inconvenience to traffic, then the hydrologist must also determine the maximum flood to be expected on the average every 5 years and this flood determination will be used by the hydraulic engineer as a basis for designing the waterway of the culvert.

At the other extreme, we may consider the large flood-control reservoir constructed on a major stream. After a tentative selection of the site and determination of the potential storage capacity, the economic justification is determined by a comparison of the capitalized benefits of the project against the estimated construction and maintenance costs. In the determination of the benefits the hydrologist must determine the number of floods of various magnitudes which can be expected during the anticipated life of the structure. He must also decide what change the reservoir could effect in the natural hydrographs of these floods, *i.e.*, how much lower the flood crests would be if the reservoir were properly operated. From these data it is possible to estimate the benefits which would accrue to the residents of the valley below the proposed reservoir. The hydrologist may be asked to compare the benefits from several possible designs in order to select that which is the most efficient, *i.e.*, which has the maximum ratio of benefit to cost. Among other things, the hydrologist must conclude whether the hydrologic features of the basin are such that it would be possible to have a sufficient foreknowledge of forthcoming floods to operate the dam successfully according to the proposed plans.

This introductory section cannot detail all the problems of hydrologic design, many of which are discussed in the next chapter. The economic aspects of design are treated in detail in various technical papers and books.

It is the purpose of this chapter to explain the methods of developing the criteria which are required in the hydrologic design of structures.

There are many possible solutions to these problems, all varying in reliability and the amount of work involved in obtaining an answer. Hence, even in the selection of a technique, the hydrologist is faced with an economic problem. Elaborate hydrometeorological studies are hardly justified for the design of a culvert on a secondary road, for the cost of such studies

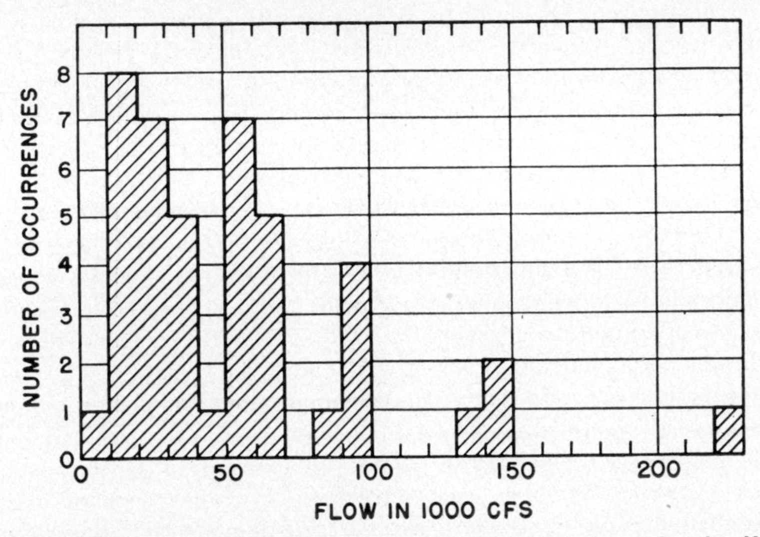

FIG. 20–1. Histogram of maximum annual mean daily flows for the Kansas River at Topeka, Kansas, 1902 to 1945.

might well exceed the cost of the culvert. On the other hand, the design of a large and expensive bridge over a major stream on the basis of doubtful rule-of-thumb techniques may constitute a far greater gamble with safety than the designer realizes.

FLOOD-FREQUENCY ANALYSIS

If the highest floods from each year of record for a particular basin are listed in order of magnitude (Table 20-7), they constitute a statistical array. Because the length of record is short, the plotted frequency histogram (Fig. 20-1) is somewhat irregular, but an infinitely long record, *i.e.*, all the floods which have or will occur on the stream, would define a smooth frequency curve. If the characteristics of this curve were known, we could predict with considerable assurance the number of floods within a specified range of magnitude which could be expected to occur during any long period of time. For example, if the distribution were normal, we could say that 68 per cent of the annual floods would fall within a range of $\pm\sigma$ about the mean flood. Unfortunately, most distributions encountered in hydrology have a pronounced skew. Because of the limited samples available, it is not easy to determine the functions which best describe the actual frequency distributions. Numerous techniques for fitting the observed data to smooth frequency curves are available, but the length of record must be multiplied several fold before we can ascertain which of the proposed techniques best fits actual events. Hence, no statistical frequency curve can be more than a guide to the judgment of the designing engineer.

Basic data. The basic data for a frequency analysis are the series of recorded observations of flow, stage, or precipitation. Since a frequency study is an application of the laws of probability, which are necessarily predicated on the use of a series of comparable data, the basic data must be reviewed for possible inconsistencies in the record. Floods caused by the failure of dams and hence not a feature of the natural regime of the stream must be excluded. Adjustments for the effect of levees, dams, cutoffs, etc., and corrections or changes resulting from station moves or revisions of measurement technique should be applied (Chaps. 6 and 16) before the data are subjected to frequency analysis. There may be good reason for considering only floods during a particular month or season, such as the growing season. In such cases, only floods during the critical season should be included in the listed data.

The data may be assembled in several different ways, depending on the purpose of the study. If extreme floods are the primary concern, it is customary to use only the *annual floods, i.e.*, the highest mean daily flow or the maximum flood peak during each year of record. Such a series ignores the second highest event in any year, which, in some cases, may exceed many of the annual maxima. This objection can be partly overcome by using *monthly floods, i.e.*, the maximum flow in each month of record. Either of these methods produces a true duration series which is subject to rigorous analysis. The second alternative, the *partial series*, or *floods above base*, makes use of all floods above a selected minimum level. The base is commonly taken to be the lowest annual flood, although it may be set higher so as to reduce the number of data. The partial series is not a true distribution series, because the flood event is not defined in terms of its occurrence but in terms of its magnitude. The shape of the resulting distribution is affected by the arbitrary selection of the base. Hence, it has not yet been demonstrated that the partial series can be analyzed by any rigorous technique. It is shown later, however, that the need for a special technique arises only in the treatment of the more extreme floods. For projects governed by events of relatively frequent occurrence, the partial series probably gives best results because it does not exclude any floods.

In selecting data for the partial series, it is important that the several events be independent, *i.e.*, only separate and distinct flood crests should be included. Every flood peak is preceded and followed by high flows, and the damage from the flood is an integral result of this series of flows. Hence, the associated flows themselves cannot be counted as individual events. In some problems it is necessary to exclude or adjust the second of two peaks occurring within a very short period of time. If flood damage at a particular point results only from sustained high flows over a period of time, then the flood event should be defined as an occurrence of flows above a specified base for a fixed duration.

A third method of summarizing the data involves the use of the full series, *i.e.*, all daily flows of record. For reasons outlined in the previous paragraph, such a series does not provide data on independent flood events and hence cannot be used for flood-frequency studies. It may be used for determining the number of days or per cent of time when flows are above or below a given value. Such information is valuable in design of water-supply, irrigation, or hydroelectric works but is useful in flood-control problems only when the flood damage is a function of the time when the river is above a critical stage. An example of the last case might be found in a railroad with tracks along a river. If damage were limited largely to the loss of revenue due to traffic stoppage by high water, then the total damage over a period of years would be a function of the number of days when flows equaled or exceeded those required to stop traffic on the road. A further discussion of the full series is given later in this chapter.

Plotting positions. Frequency analysis defines the flood which can be expected to be equaled or exceeded on the average once every N years, the *N-year flood*. This means that in a long period of record, say 10,000 years, there will be $10{,}000/N$ floods equal to or larger than the N-year flood. There is no implication that these floods will occur at more or less regular intervals of N years. Indeed, it is entirely possible, although improbable, for all such floods to occur in consecutive years. Frequency curves may be plotted in terms of the per cent of years in which a given flow will be equaled or exceeded or of the average interval in years between floods equal to or greater than the given magnitude. Three different intervals are encountered in the literature. The *exceedance interval* is defined as the average number of years between the occurrence of an event and a greater event. The *recurrence interval* is the average number of years within which a given event will be equaled or exceeded. If there are N items of data in a series from t years of record and the serial number of a particular event in order of magnitude beginning with the lowest is m, then the recurrence interval is

$$T_r = \frac{t}{N - m + 1} \qquad (20\text{-}1)$$

and the exceedance interval is

$$T_e = \frac{t}{N - m} \qquad (20\text{-}2)$$

It will be noted that T_e is infinite for the Nth observation, *i.e.*, the exceedance interval corresponding to the highest observation of the sequence is unknown. If m' is the serial number of an item in a series arranged in decreasing order of magnitude, then

$$T_r = \frac{t}{m'} \tag{20-3}$$

and

$$T_e = \frac{t}{m' - 1} \tag{20-4}$$

The percentage frequency may be computed as 100 divided by T_r or T_e.

Several plotting techniques have been introduced. The so-called "California method"[1] makes use of Eq. (20-3). This is a straightforward approach with the merit of simplicity. Hazen[2] proposed that the return period be defined as

$$T_p = \frac{2t}{2m' - 1} \tag{20-5}$$

This formula assigns a recurrence interval of $2t$ to the largest item of the record. It has been argued[3] that the maximum flood in a 10-year period is most likely to represent the median value of all possible floods in the class of flows ranging in frequency from 0 to 10 per cent of the time. Hence, it should be plotted at 5 per cent of time, as indicated by Eq. (20-5). This can be stated in another way by saying that since the actual frequency of occurrence of the maximum event in t years is not known it may be assumed to be $2t$. Equation (20-5) has been widely accepted as the proper definition of plotting position for many years. Actually, the equation does not locate the median point, as can be seen from Fig. 20-2. Moreover, no statistical device can lengthen the period of record.

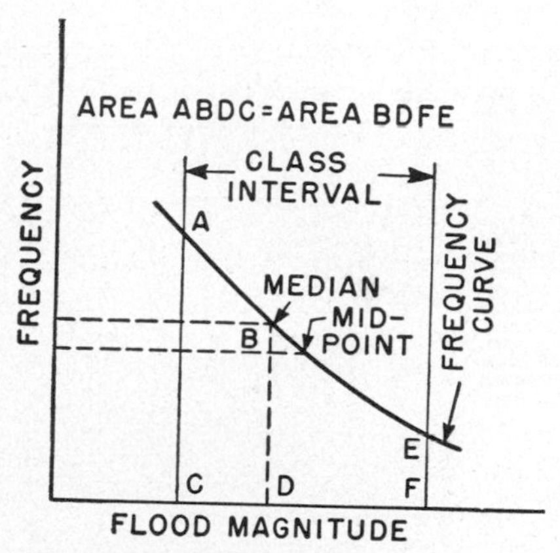

FIG. 20–2. Segment of a frequency curve demonstrating difference in frequency between mid-point and median of a class interval.

Gumbel[4] has suggested a derivation based on the characteristics of the distribution for a variable correction in lieu of Hazen's factor 2. The value

[1] Flow in California Streams, *Calif. Dept. Public Works Bull.* 5, 1923.

[2] Hazen, A., "Flood Flow," Wiley, New York, 1930.

[3] Jarvis, C. S., and others, Floods in the United States, *U.S. Geol. Survey Water Supply Paper* 771, 1936.

[4] Gumbel, E. J., On the Plotting of Flood Discharges, *Trans. Am. Geophys. Union*, Vol. 24, Part II, pp. 699-719, 1943.

of Gumbel's correction c is a function of the relative serial number m/N and the nature of the distribution. Figure 20-3 shows values of c applicable to the distribution of largest values (the annual floods) to which Gumbel believes flood flows conform. The plotting position is given by

$$T_p = \frac{t}{N - m + c} \tag{20-6}$$

or

$$T_p = \frac{t}{m' + c - 1} \tag{20-7}$$

For the largest flood $c = 1$ and $T_p = T_r$, while for the smallest flood c approaches zero and T_p approaches T_e. The theory assumes that the

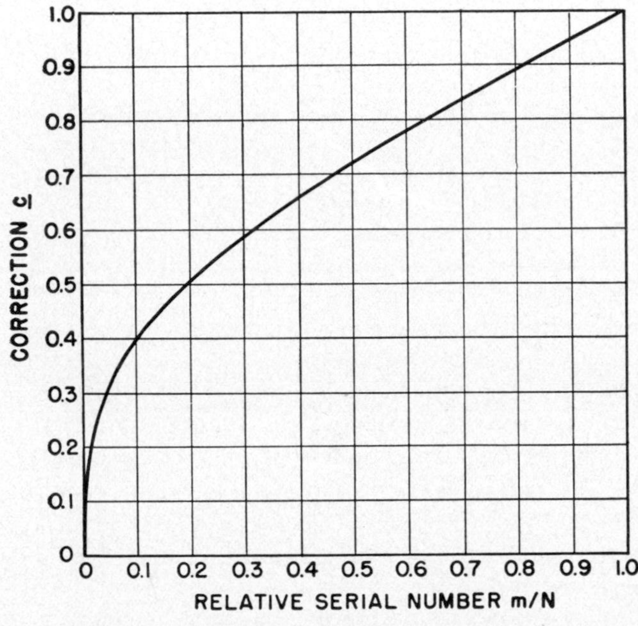

FIG. 20–3. Value of correction c for computing plotting position based on the distribution of the largest values. *(After Gumbel.)*

observed mth value of a series is the most probable, or modal, value of the mth values of all such series. Hence, its location within a class interval is skewed toward the mode of the distribution.

Table 20-1 shows values of the average return period for the five highest floods in various periods of record as a function of the probability that the indicated value will not be exceeded.[1] The table shows that there is one chance in a hundred that the true average return period for the highest

[1] Thomas, H. A., Jr., The Reliability of Hydrologic Predictions, paper given at the meeting of the *American Geophysical Union*, Cambridge, Mass., September, 1947.

TABLE 20-1. Average Return Periods for Various Levels of Probability

(After Thomas)

Rank from top, m'	No. of years of record N	Probability				
		0.01	0.25	0.50	0.75	0.99
1	2	1.11	2.00	3.41	7.46	200
	3	1.28	2.70	4.85	10.9	299
	5	1.66	4.13	7.73	17.9	498
	10	2.71	7.73	14.9	35.3	996
	15	3.78	11.3	22.1	52.6	1490
	20	4.86	14.9	29.4	70.0	1990
	30	7.03	22.1	43.8	104	2980
	60	13.5	43.8	87.0	209	5970
2	3	1.06	1.48	2.00	3.06	17.0
	4	1.16	1.84	2.59	4.12	23.8
	6	1.42	2.57	3.78	6.20	37.4
	11	2.13	4.41	6.76	11.4	71.1
	16	2.87	6.27	9.74	16.6	105
	21	3.61	8.12	12.7	21.8	138
	31	5.11	11.8	18.7	32.2	206
	61	9.62	23.0	36.6	63.4	408
3	4	1.05	1.32	1.63	2.19	7.10
	5	1.12	1.56	2.00	2.78	9.47
	7	1.31	2.06	2.75	3.95	14.1
	12	1.86	3.32	4.62	6.86	25.6
	17	2.44	4.59	6.48	9.76	37.2
	22	3.03	5.86	8.35	12.6	48.6
	32	4.21	8.41	12.1	18.4	71.6
	62	7.76	16.1	23.3	35.8	140
4	5	1.03	1.24	1.46	1.83	4.50
	6	1.09	1.42	1.73	2.24	5.78
	8	1.25	1.80	2.27	3.04	8.26
	13	1.70	2.77	3.63	5.02	14.4
	18	2.18	3.74	5.00	7.00	20.5
	23	2.67	4.72	6.36	8.98	26.6
	33	3.66	6.67	9.07	12.9	38.7
	63	6.63	12.5	17.2	24.8	75.2
5	6	1.03	1.19	1.36	1.64	3.40
	7	1.08	1.34	1.57	1.95	4.23
	9	1.21	1.64	2.00	2.55	5.85
	14	1.59	2.43	3.07	4.05	9.81
	19	2.01	3.22	4.14	5.54	13.7
	24	2.43	4.02	5.21	7.02	17.7
	34	3.28	5.60	7.35	9.99	25.5
	64	5.86	10.4	13.8	18.9	49.0

flood in 30 years is 7 years or less, an even chance that it is less than 44 years and three chances out of four that it is less than 104 years. Table 20-2 shows the distribution of actual return periods for various average return periods. The table shows that, over a long period of years, 25 per cent of the actual intervals between floods equal to or greater than the 30-year flood will be less than 8 years and an equal number will be in excess of 42 years. The return period for the maximum flood based on the assumption that the *m*th value of a series is most likely to be the median of all such values in the universe[1] is

$$T_p = 1.44N + 0.5 \tag{20-8}$$

This corresponds to the 50 per cent probability values of Table 20-1.

If the length of record t is large, the various values of T_e, T_r, and T_p obtained from Eqs. (20-1) to (20-8) converge rapidly as m' increases (Table 20-7). Thus, hydrologists dealing with return periods in the order of $t/2$ need not concern themselves greatly with the problem of the correct plotting method. The reliability of the estimated return periods increases rapidly as m' increases (Table 20-1). Equations (20-1) to (20-7) are valid whether the data series represents annual floods, monthly floods, or other period data. However, the conversion to percentage frequency is given by $100/12T_p$ for monthly data and $100/365T_p$ for daily data.

TABLE 20-2. Theoretical Distribution of the Return Period

(After Thomas)

Average return period $\bar{T}_p$	Actual return period T_p exceeded various percentages of the time						
	1%	5%	25%	50%	75%	95%	99%
2	8	5	3	1	0	0	0
5	22	14	7	3	1	0	0
10	45	28	14	7	3	0	0
30	137	89	42	21	8	2	0
100	459	300	139	69	29	5	1
1,000	4,620	3,001	1,400	693	288	51	10
10,000	46,200	30,001	14,000	6,932	2,880	513	100

It is unfortunate that Hazen's plotting method has been generally accepted as giving the most probable recurrence interval. Actually, there is no sound basis for choosing between the several methods. While Gumbel's method seems to have the best theoretical basis, it differs so little from the California method that the latter is probably the best selection because of

[1] Beard, L. R., Statistical Analysis in Hydrology, *Trans. ASCE*, Vol. 103, pp. 1110-1160, 1943.

its simplicity. It is the most conservative method from the point of view of safety but, conversely, is the least conservative in estimating project efficiency.

Extrapolation of the frequency curve. So long as the problem under consideration deals with return periods considerably less than the period of record, one may obtain a reasonably trustworthy estimate of flood frequency by interpolation. When floods approaching or transcending the maximum of record must be considered, it becomes extremely important to know the exact nature of the statistical distribution with which we are dealing.

Foster[1] suggested the use of Pearson's[2] skew functions for fitting observed flood data. Pearson adopted the general differential equation,

$$\frac{dJ}{dx} = \frac{J(x + a)}{f(x)} \tag{20-9}$$

where x is the deviation of the variable X from its mean, J the frequency corresponding to x, a a constant, and $f(x)$ a function of x. The distribution has a maximum at $-a$ (the mode) and approaches the x axis asymptotically as J approaches zero. Depending on $f(x)$, many types of curves can be derived. Two of these (types I and III) can be described by the use of the first three moments and were recommended by Foster for hydrologic use. The procedure involves the computation of a coefficient of variation (adjusted standard deviation)

$$\hat{\sigma}_x = \sqrt{\frac{\Sigma x^2}{N - 1}} \tag{20-10}$$

and a coefficient of skew

$$C_s = \frac{\Sigma x^3}{(N - 1)\,\hat{\sigma}_x^{\,3}} \tag{20-11}$$

The coefficient of skew must be adjusted for the size of the sample by

$$\hat{C}_s = C_s\left(1 + \frac{6}{N}\right) \qquad \text{(for type I curve)} \tag{20-12}$$

and

$$\hat{C}_s = C_s\left(1 + \frac{8.5}{N}\right) \qquad \text{(for type III curve)} \tag{20-13}$$

Factors corresponding to various percentage frequencies and the computed coefficients of skew can be selected from Tables 20-3 and 20-4. These factors multiplied by the coefficient of variation and added to the mean of X define the frequency curve.

Hazen[3] adopted $\hat{\sigma}_x$ and $\hat{C}_s$ as given by Eqs. (20-10), (20-11), and (20-13), but in lieu of the table of skew factors based on the Pearson curves he developed a series of factors (Table 20-5) on the assumption that the log-

[1] Foster, H. A., Theoretical Frequency Curves, *Trans. ASCE*, Vol. 87, pp. 142-173, 1924.

[2] Elderton, W. P., "Frequency Curves and Correlation," Layton, London, 1927.

[3] Hazen, A., "Flood Flows," Wiley, New York, 1930.

arithms of the variable are distributed according to the normal law. Hazen recognized that the resulting curve might not fit the actual data in all cases and suggested that, in this event, several values of C_s be tried and the one giving the best fit be selected. Reducing the coefficient of skew tends to reduce extreme values and raise those near the center of the distribution. Table 20-5 shows the per cent of items above the mean for various values of $\hat{C}_s$ and also values of $\hat{\sigma}_x$, in terms of ratio to the mean, which will yield a straight line on logarithmic probability paper.

TABLE 20-3. Skew Curve Factors for Foster Type I Curve

$\hat{C}_s$	Frequency, per cent										
	99	95	80	50	20	5	1	0.1	0.01	0.001	0.0001
0	− 2.08	− 1.64	− 0.92	0	0.92	1.64	2.08	2.39	2.53	2.59	2.62
0.2	− 1.91	− 1.56	− 0.93	− 0.05	0.89	1.72	2.25	2.66	2.83	2.94	3.00
0.4	− 1.75	− 1.47	− 0.93	− 0.09	0.87	1.79	2.42	2.95	3.18	3.35	3.44
0.6	− 1.59	− 1.38	− 0.92	− 0.13	0.85	1.85	2.58	3.24	3.59	3.80	3.92
0.8	− 1.44	− 1.30	− 0.91	− 0.17	0.83	1.90	2.75	3.55	4.00	4.27	4.43
1.0	− 1.30	− 1.21	− 0.89	− 0.21	0.80	1.95	2.92	3.85	4.42	4.75	4.95
1.2	− 1.17	− 1.12	− 0.86	− 0.25	0.77	1.99	3.09	4.15	4.83	5.25	5.50
1.4	− 1.06	− 1.03	− 0.83	− 0.29	0.73	2.03	3.25	4.45	5.25	5.75	6.05
1.6	− 0.96	− 0.95	− 0.80	− 0.32	0.69	2.07	3.40	4.75	5.67	6.25	6.65
1.8	− 0.87	− 0.87	− 0.76	− 0.35	0.64	2.10	3.54	5.05	6.08	6.75	7.2
2.0	− 0.80	− 0.79	− 0.71	− 0.37	0.58	2.13	3.67	5.35	6.50	7.25	7.8

TABLE 20-4. Skew Curve Factors for Foster Type III Curve

$\hat{C}_s$	Frequency, per cent										
	99	95	80	50	20	5	1	0.1	0.01	0.001	0.0001
0	− 2.33	− 1.64	− 0.84	0	0.84	1.64	2.33	3.09	3.73	4.27	4.76
0.2	− 2.18	− 1.58	− 0.85	− 0.03	0.83	1.69	2.48	3.38	4.16	4.84	5.48
0.4	− 2.03	− 1.51	− 0.85	− 0.06	0.82	1.74	2.62	3.67	4.60	5.42	6.24
0.6	− 1.88	− 1.45	− 0.86	− 0.09	0.80	1.79	2.77	3.96	5.04	6.01	7.02
0.8	− 1.74	− 1.38	− 0.86	− 0.13	0.78	1.83	2.90	4.25	5.48	6.61	7.82
1.0	− 1.59	− 1.31	− 0.86	− 0.16	0.76	1.87	3.03	4.54	5.92	7.22	8.63
1.2	− 1.45	− 1.25	− 0.85	− 0.19	0.74	1.90	3.15	4.82	6.37	7.85	9.45
1.4	− 1.32	− 1.18	− 0.84	− 0.22	0.71	1.93	3.28	5.11	6.82	8.50	10.28
1.6	− 1.19	− 1.11	− 0.82	− 0.25	0.68	1.96	3.40	5.39	7.28	9.17	11.12
1.8	− 1.08	− 1.03	− 0.80	− 0.28	0.64	1.98	3.50	5.66	7.75	9.84	11.96
2.0	− 0.99	− 0.95	− 0.78	− 0.31	0.61	2.00	3.60	5.91	8.21	10.51	12.81
2.2	− 0.90	− 0.89	− 0.75	− 0.33	0.58	2.01	3.70	6.20			
2.4	− 0.83	− 0.82	− 0.71	− 0.35	0.54	2.01	3.78	6.47			
2.6	− 0.77	− 0.76	− 0.68	− 0.37	0.51	2.01	3.87	6.73			
2.8	− 0.71	− 0.71	− 0.65	− 0.38	0.47	2.02	3.95	6.99			
3.0	− 0.67	− 0.66	− 0.62	− 0.40	0.42	2.02	4.02	7.25			

TABLE 20-5. Skew Curve Factors for Hazen Logarithmic Curve *

$\hat{C}_s$	Per cent of terms above mean	Frequency, per cent									$\hat{\sigma}_x$ for straight line
		99	95	80	50	20	5	1	0.1	0.01	
0	50.0	− 2.32	− 1.64	− 0.84	0	0.84	1.64	2.32	3.09	3.72	0
0.2	48.7	− 2.18	− 1.59	− 0.85	− 0.03	0.83	1.71	2.48	3.39	4.20	0.06
0.4	47.5	− 2.05	− 1.53	− 0.85	− 0.06	0.82	1.76	2.64	3.72	4.72	0.13
0.6	46.3	− 1.92	− 1.47	− 0.85	− 0.09	0.81	1.81	2.80	4.08	5.30	0.20
0.8	45.0	− 1.80	− 1.41	− 0.85	− 0.12	0.79	1.86	2.97	4.48	6.00	0.27
1.0	43.7	− 1.68	− 1.34	− 0.84	− 0.15	0.76	1.90	3.15	4.92	6.77	0.33
1.2	42.5	− 1.56	− 1.28	− 0.83	− 0.18	0.74	1.94	3.33	5.40	7.66	0.41
1.4	41.3	− 1.46	− 1.22	− 0.82	− 0.20	0.71	1.98	3.50	5.91	8.66	0.48
1.6	40.1	− 1.36	− 1.16	− 0.81	− 0.23	0.67	2.01	3.69	6.48	9.79	0.55
1.8	38.9	− 1.27	− 1.10	− 0.79	− 0.25	0.64	2.03	3.88	7.09	11.07	0.62
2.0	37.7	− 1.19	− 1.05	− 0.77	− 0.27	0.61	2.05	4.07	7.78	12.60	0.70
2.2	36.5	− 1.11	− 0.99	− 0.75	− 0.29	0.57	2.07	4.27	8.54	14.30	0.78
2.4	35.3	− 1.03	− 0.94	− 0.73	− 0.31	0.53	2.08	4.48	9.35	....	0.86
2.6	34.1	− 0.97	− 0.89	− 0.71	− 0.32	0.49	2.09	4.68	10.15	....	0.94
2.8	32.9	− 0.91	− 0.84	− 0.68	− 0.33	0.45	2.09	4.89	11.20	....	1.03
3.0	31.8	− 0.84	− 0.79	− 0.66	− 0.34	0.41	2.08	5.11	12.30	....	1.12
3.2	30.6	− 0.78	− 0.74	− 0.64	− 0.35	0.37	2.06	5.35	13.50	....	1.22
3.4	29.4	− 0.73	− 0.69	− 0.61	− 0.36	0.32	2.04	5.58	....	....	1.33
3.6	28.2	− 0.67	− 0.65	− 0.58	− 0.36	0.28	2.02	5.80	....	....	1.44
3.8	27.0	− 0.62	− 0.61	− 0.55	− 0.36	0.23	1.98	6.10	....	....	1.57
4.0	25.7	− 0.58	− 0.56	− 0.52	− 0.36	0.19	1.95	6.50	....	....	1.70
4.5	22.2	− 0.48	− 0.47	− 0.45	− 0.35	0.10	1.79	7.30	....	....	2.10
5.0	19.2	− 0.40	− 0.40	− 0.39	− 0.34	0	1.60	8.20	....	....	2.50

* Reproduced by permission from "Flood Flows" by Allen Hazen, published by John Wiley and Sons, Inc.

Hazen[1] also contributed to the techniques of frequency analysis by the introduction of probability paper. The spacing of the abscissas on such paper corresponds to the summation of the normal-probability curve. Both arithmetic and logarithmic ordinates are used. With arithmetic ordinates, data which correspond to the normal distribution will plot as a straight line, while, with logarithmic ordinates, data having logarithms conforming to the normal law will plot as straight lines. Use of his factors as described above will result in curves which approximate straight lines on logarithmic probability paper.

Slade[2] pointed out the difficulties involved in the use of higher moments in working with the limited and uncertain data usually available. Accidental variations in the data are enormously exaggerated in the computa-

[1] Hazen, A., The Storage to Be Provided in Impounding Reservoirs for Municipal Water Supply, *Trans. ASCE*, Vol. 77, p. 1549, 1914.

[2] Slade, J. J., An Asymmetric Probability Function, *Trans. ASCE*, Vol. 101, pp. 35-104, 1936.

tion of the third power of the variations. He proposed the use of a bounded function, *i.e.*, one which has an upper and a lower limit. This departs from approaches which assume that floods are unlimited variables. Actually, it is entirely reasonable to assume that there is both an upper and a lower limit to the magnitudes of most hydrologic variables. Although these limits cannot be estimated easily, the method requires only that the estimates be sufficiently extreme. A considerable difference in the assumed limits has little effect on the final answer, since the distribution approaches the X axis asymptotically. The deviation from the mean, x, corresponding to any selected frequency is given by

$$x = \frac{an - bj}{n + j} \tag{20-14}$$

where a and b are the assumed upper and lower limits of the variable, respectively, and n and j can be computed from the following equations:

$$j = \frac{a^2}{b^2}\sqrt{\frac{\sigma^2 + b^2}{\sigma^2 + a^2}} \tag{20-15}$$

$$k = \sqrt{\frac{a - b}{a + b + 2}} \tag{20-16}$$

$$\frac{1}{c} = \sqrt{\log_e \frac{a^2(\sigma^2 + b^2)}{b^2(\sigma^2 + a^2)}} \tag{20-17}$$

$$n = \mathbf{e}^{\xi/kc} \tag{20-18}$$

The parameter ξ may be obtained from Table 20-6 for any value of J.

TABLE 20-6. Values of the Factor ξ as a Function of Frequency

J, per cent	95	90	80	70	60	50	40	30	20	10	1	0.1	0.01	0.001
ξ	−1.64	−1.28	−0.84	−0.52	−0.25	0	0.25	0.52	0.84	1.28	2.33	3.09	3.72	4.26

The most recent contributions to the theory of hydrologic frequency problems have been by Gumbel, who follows the earlier assumptions that the distributions of hydrologic variables are unlimited. He makes use of the distribution of the largest values,[1] discussed by Fisher and Tippett.[2] If the sample consists of the highest values from many series, *e.g.*, the highest of 365 daily flows each year, the probability of occurrence of a value equal to or less than X is given by

$$\mathbf{P} = \mathbf{e}^{-e^{-y}} \tag{20-19}$$

[1] Gumbel, E. J., The Return Period of Flood Flows, *Ann. Math. Stat.*, Vol. 12, pp. 163-190, 1941.

[2] Fisher, R. A., and L. H. C., Tippett, Limiting Forms of the Frequency Distribution of the Largest or Smallest Member of a Sample, *Proc. Cambridge Phil. Soc.*, Vol. 24, pp. 180-190, 1928.

where $\mathbf{e}$ is the base of Napierian logarithms and y is a dimensionless variable,

$$y = a(X - X_f) \tag{20-20}$$

The mode X_f is difficult to determine from actual data, and Gumbel suggests that it be computed from

$$X_f = \overline{X} - 0.450\sigma_x \tag{20-21}$$

The factor a is given by

$$a = \frac{1}{0.7797\sigma_x} \tag{20-22}$$

The constants in both Eq. (20-21) and Eq. (20-22) are derived theoretically.

A special plotting paper can be constructed for the simple use of this method.[1] The ordinates representing flood flows and the abscissa scale for y between the approximate limits -2 and $+7$ are linear. This provides the necessary scales for plotting the function defined by Eq. (20-20), which is a straight line. In order to interpret the results in terms of frequency, or return period, an auxiliary abscissa scale in terms of probability may be constructed by use of Eq. (20-19), and the scale for the return periods may be computed from

$$T_p = \frac{1}{(1 - \mathbf{P})} \tag{20-23}$$

If the theoretical solution is applicable, the actual data should plot close to the straight line.

Example of frequency analysis. As an example of the various methods of analysis, data for the Kansas River at Topeka are analyzed in Table 20-7. The highest annual mean daily flows are listed in Col. 2, the deviations from the mean in Col. 3, and the squares and cubes of the deviations in Cols. 4 and 5, respectively. Plotting positions as computed from four different formulas are listed in Cols. 7 to 10 for comparative purposes. Values of $\hat{\sigma}_x$, C_s, and $\hat{C}_s$ are shown for the Foster and Hazen methods, and the computations of the theoretical curves defined by these values are given in Table 20-8. The three curves are plotted on logarithmic probability paper in Fig. 20-4, together with the actual data plotted according to recurrence interval (Col. 7, Table 20-7). Table 20-7 also shows the computation of σ_x, X_f, a, and y for the Gumbel method, and the curve is plotted on special probability paper in Fig. 20-5.

Although the several curves conform well to the actual data, they diverge markedly when extrapolated. Because of the logarithmic scale of flow in Fig. 20-4, the divergence is greater than appears at first glance.

[1] Powell, R. W., A Simple Method of Estimating Flood Frequency, *Civil Eng.*, Vol. 13, pp. 105-107, 1942.

Gumbel, E. J., Floods Estimated by Probability Method, *Eng. News-Record*, Vol. 134, pp. 833-837, 1945.

TABLE 20-7. Frequency Analysis for the Kansas River at Topeka, Kansas

Year	Computation of moments				Plotting positions				
	Annual flood (1000 cfs)	Deviation from mean	x^2	x^3	Serial number m'	Recurrence interval Eq. (20-3)	Exceedance interval Eq. (20-4)	Hazen Eq. (20-5)	Gumbel Eq. (20-7)
(1)	(2)	(3)	(4)	(5)	(6)	(7)	(8)	(9)	(10)
1903	220.0	165.7	27,456	4,549,540	1	43.0	......	86.0	43.0
1908	141.0	86.7	7,517	651,714	2	21.5	43.0	28.7	21.7
1935	141.0	86.7	7,517	651,714	3	14.3	21.5	17.2	14.5
1904	130.0	75.7	5,730	433,798	4	10.8	14.3	12.3	10.9
1943	98.8	44.5	1,980	88,121	5	8.6	10.8	9.6	8.7
1915	98.2	43.9	1,927	84,605	6	7.2	8.6	7.8	7.2
1941	96.3	42.0	1,764	74,088	7	6.1	7.2	6.6	6.2
1945	90.8	36.5	1,332	48,627	8	5.4	6.1	5.7	5.4
1944	89.0	34.7	1,204	41,781	9	4.8	5.4	5.1	4.8
1923	69.8	15.5	240	3,724	10	4.3	4.8	4.5	4.4
1902	69.2	14.9	222	3,308	11	3.9	4.3	4.1	4.0
1930	69.0	14.7	216	3,177	12	3.6	3.9	3.7	3.6
1929	66.9	12.6	159	2,000	13	3.3	3.6	3.4	3.3
1942	61.5	7.2	52	373	14	3.1	3.3	3.2	3.1
1927	59.3	5.0	25	125	15	2.9	3.1	3.0	2.9
1911	57.4	3.1	10	30	16	2.7	2.9	2.8	2.7
1917	55.3	1.0	1	1	17	2.5	2.7	2.6	2.5
1919	54.1	− 0.2	0	0	18	2.4	2.5	2.5	2.4
1910	53.4	− 0.9	1	− 1	19	2.3	2.4	2.3	2.3
1912	52.8	− 1.5	2	− 3	20	2.1	2.3	2.2	2.1

Computation Methods

Hazen-Foster

$$\hat{\sigma}_x = \sqrt{\frac{\Sigma x^2}{N-1}} = \sqrt{\frac{80{,}451}{42}} = 43.8$$

$$C_s = \frac{\Sigma x^3}{(N-1)\hat{\sigma}_x^3} = \frac{5{,}816{,}693}{42 \times 84{,}000} = 1.65$$

$$\left.\begin{aligned}\hat{C}_s &= C_s\left(1 + \frac{6}{N}\right)\\ &= 1.65(1 + 6/43)\\ &= 1.88\end{aligned}\right\}\text{(I)}$$

$$\left.\begin{aligned}\hat{C}_s &= C_s\left(1 + \frac{8.5}{N}\right)\\ &= 1.65\left(1 + \frac{8.5}{43}\right)\\ &= 1.97\end{aligned}\right\}\text{(III)}$$

1905	50.9	− 3.4	12	− 39	21	2.0	2.1	2.1	2.0
1916	42.0	− 12.3	151	− 1,861	22	2.0	2.0	2.0	2.0
1926	35.9	− 18.4	339	− 6,230	23	1.9	2.0	1.9	1.9
1928	34.6	− 19.7	388	− 7,645	24	1.8	1.9	1.8	1.8
1921	33.0	− 21.3	454	− 9,664	25	1.7	1.8	1.8	1.7
1922	31.9	− 22.4	502	− 11,239	26	1.7	1.7	1.7	1.7
1938	30.6	− 23.7	562	− 13,312	27	1.6	1.7	1.6	1.6
1913	28.4	− 25.9	671	− 17,374	28	1.5	1.6	1.6	1.6
1914	26.4	− 27.9	778	− 21,718	29	1.5	1.5	1.5	1.5
1939	24.7	− 29.6	876	− 25,934	30	1.4	1.5	1.5	1.5
1925	24.0	− 30.3	918	− 27,818	31	1.4	1.4	1.4	1.4
1906	22.3	− 32.0	1,024	− 32,768	32	1.3	1.4	1.4	1.4
1907	21.9	− 32.4	1,050	− 34,012	33	1.3	1.3	1.3	1.3
1918	20.6	− 33.7	1,136	− 38,273	34	1.3	1.3	1.3	1.3
1931	19.2	− 35.1	1,232	− 43,244	35	1.2	1.2	1.2	1.2
1920	18.1	− 36.2	1,310	− 47,438	36	1.2	1.2	1.2	1.2
1933	16.4	− 37.9	1,436	− 54,440	37	1.2	1.2	1.2	1.2
1924	15.7	− 38.6	1,490	− 57,512	38	1.1	1.2	1.1	1.1
1936	15.1	− 39.2	1,537	− 60,236	39	1.1	1.1	1.1	1.1
1932	14.5	− 39.8	1,584	− 63,045	40	1.1	1.1	1.1	1.1
1937	14.4	− 39.9	1,592	− 63,521	41	1.0	1.1	1.1	1.1
1934	10.6	− 43.7	1,910	− 83,453	42	1.0	1.0	1.0	1.0
1940	8.0	− 46.3	2,144	− 99,253	43	1.0	1.0	1.0	1.0
Sum.......	2333.0	− 1.9	80,451	5,816,693					
Mean......	54.3								

Gumbel

$$\sigma_x = \sqrt{\frac{\Sigma x^2}{N}} = \sqrt{\frac{80{,}451}{43}} = 43.5$$

$$X_f = \bar{X} - 0.450\sigma_x = 54.3 - 0.450 \times 43.5 = 34.9$$

$$a = \frac{1}{0.7797\sigma} = 0.0298$$

$$y = a(X - X_f)$$

X	$X - X_f$	y
10	− 24.9	− 0.74
200	+ 165.1	+ 4.91

Since the Gumbel curve plots as a straight line, it is easier to extrapolate but not necessarily more accurate.

If it is desired to compare the frequency curves for two or more basins, they may be developed in terms of ratio to the mean. In this case each

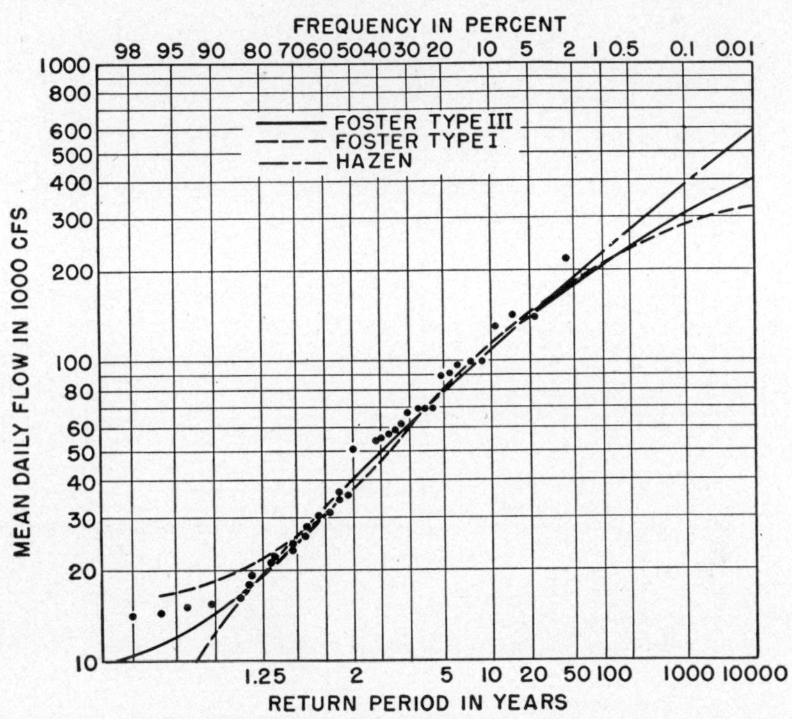

FIG. 20–4. Comparison of frequency curves for the Kansas River at Topeka, Kansas.

TABLE 20-8. Application of Skew Curve Factors

J, per cent	Foster type I			Foster type III			Hazen		
	Factor k	$k\hat{\sigma}_x$	$k\hat{\sigma}_x + \overline{X}$	Factor k'	$k'\hat{\sigma}_x$	$k'\hat{\sigma}_x + \overline{X}$	Factor k''	$k''\hat{\sigma}_x$	$k''\hat{\sigma}_x + \overline{X}$
0.01	6.24	273	327	8.14	356	410	12.37	541	595
0.1	5.16	226	280	5.87	257	311	7.67	336	390
1	3.59	157	211	3.58	157	211	4.04	177	231
5	2.11	92	146	1.99	87	141	2.05	90	144
20	0.62	27	81	0.62	27	81	0.61	27	81
50	− 0.36	− 16	38	− 0.30	− 13	41	− 0.27	− 12	42
80	− 0.74	− 32	22	− 0.78	− 34	20	− 0.77	− 34	20
95	− 0.84	− 37	17	− 0.96	− 42	12	− 1.05	− 46	8
99	− 0.85	− 37	17	− 1.00	− 44	10	− 1.20	− 53	1

item of data is first divided by the mean, and the values of $\hat{\sigma}_x$ and $\hat{C}_s$ are computed using the deviation of these ratios from their mean value, unity. The resulting frequency curves provide a measure of the relative variation from the mean for different recurrence intervals in the several basins.

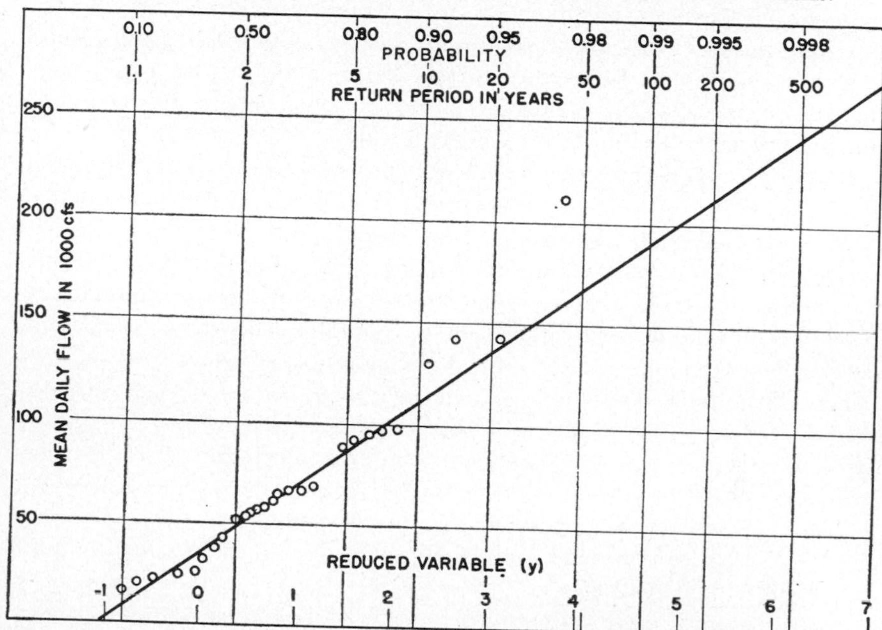

FIG. 20–5. Frequency curve for the Kansas River at Topeka plotted by Gumbel's method.

Frequency curves in terms of stage may be developed by the same procedures outlined above. Because of the exponential relation between stage and discharge, the coefficients of skew will generally be less. The effect of scouring or silting throughout the period of record may make it extremely difficult to adjust stage data to a common base so that they are suitable for statistical analysis.

RAINFALL FREQUENCY

For the design of sewer systems, drainage works, terraces, and river-control works on streams without discharge records, estimates of flood frequency may be made by analysis of rainfall data. The rainfall criteria so determined are used to compute runoff hydrographs which form the basis of design. The frequency analysis of rainfall data may be accomplished by much the same techniques suggested for flood flows. Rainfall data, though less skewed than flood data, seem to conform to the techniques described in the previous section.

A river gage reflects the results of any storm which occurs within the basin. In contrast, a rain gage samples only the rainfall over the area encompassed by its collector ring. If the maximum isohyet of a storm is assumed to encompass 10 square miles, the probability that it will be measured by a gage (based on the average United States network density) is about 1 in 30. As a rule of thumb, it has been noted that the maximum amounts observed at first-order weather stations are in the order of one-half those recorded at cooperative stations, and about one-third the amounts reported by surveys of unofficial catches. As a result of this low probability of measuring extreme storm amounts combined with the relatively short records available for study, the station-year method was devised.

The station-year method. The station-year technique was first applied to the analysis of rainfall by the Miami Conservancy District.[1] The method assumes that records from several stations in a limited area can be combined and treated as a single record whose length is equal to the sum of the individual records. The basic assumption is that the frequency curves of the individual stations would be identical if a sufficient period of record existed. This means that the entire area from which the stations are selected must be meteorologically homogeneous. Hence, the station-year approach cannot be used in mountainous areas.

There are certain restrictions which must be applied to the station-year method. First, a reasonable length of record must be available from each of the individual stations. If 1 year of record is available at each of 10 stations, the maximum observed amount would be assigned a recurrence interval of 10 years. On the basis of a single year, no reliable estimate of long-period frequencies is possible, since any particular year is likely to be abnormal. Ten years of independent record should be considered as a minimum for analysis.

Meteorological homogeneity within areas of any significant size is seldom found. Hence, the stations used in a station-year analysis should be distributed uniformly about the area to avoid the bias which might result from a concentration of gages in a particular rainfall zone.

The reliability of station-year analyses is determined by the amount of dependence or independence between the stations in the network. If the stations are so spaced that one and only one station measures each storm, then the data are wholly independent. If in a net of 15 stations an average of 3 stations samples each storm, then there are actually only $^{15}\!/\!_{3}$, or 5, independent stations. The station-year method has been the subject of much discussion[2] in attempts to evaluate its reliability. If the several stations used are entirely independent, it can be assumed that the results

[1] "Storm Rainfall in the Eastern United States," rev. ed., *Tech. Rept.* 5, Miami Conservancy District, Dayton, Ohio, 1936.

[2] Hafstad, K. C., Reliability of Station-year Rainfall Frequency Determinations, *Trans. ASCE*, Vol. 107, pp. 633-683, 1942.

are as reliable as a determination from a single station with equivalent record length. If dependence between stations exists, then the probable errors in the estimated return periods are roughly $\sqrt{N}$ greater than from a single station record, where N is the number of stations sampling each storm. Fortunately, the higher, short-period amounts are usually the result of intense, small-area thunderstorms, and the dependence between stations is fairly low.

Areal frequency. Many problems require consideration of average precipitation over areas so large that a single station cannot be considered representative. It is obviously incorrect to average the point values of a given frequency for several stations in the basin since this would assume the simultaneous occurrence of several events, each having a low probability. The resulting average would have a return period far greater than that applicable to the individual station values. The error thus introduced decreases with the frequency. Thus, while the procedure is greatly in error for 100-year storms, it is reasonably accurate for 1-year events.

The correct technique for determination of the frequency of average precipitation over an area requires computation of average values for a sufficient number of storms to establish a series which could be subjected to frequency analysis. Rainfall[1] expressed in per cent of annual or seasonal normal may be used as a common denominator in frequency studies in mountainous regions. Here orographic factors act to cause a fairly consistent pattern of distribution from storm to storm. If direction of inflow is not greatly variable, this pattern corresponds closely to the average annual distribution, *i.e.*, station values in per cent of their annual normal are nearly equal over limited areas. Under these conditions it may be reasonable to average the frequency curves for two or three index stations to determine zonal averages. Thom[2] also found a close agreement between mean annual precipitation and precipitation frequency in studies in the Pajaro River Basin of California.

Joint-frequency studies. Akin to the problem of areal rainfall frequency are several associated problems in joint frequency. If two events are mutually independent, *i.e.*, the occurrence of one is in no way related to the occurrence of the other, and their probabilities of occurrence are $\mathbf{P}_1$ and $\mathbf{P}_2$, then the probability that they will occur together is $\mathbf{P}_1\mathbf{P}_2$. Some of the problems in joint frequency which may be encountered include:

1. The occurrence of rain with snow on the ground.
2. The occurrence of heavy rain with favorable runoff conditions.
3. The occurrence of heavy runoff on a tributary coincident with a major flood on the main stream.

[1] Linsley, R. K., Frequency and Seasonal Distribution of Precipitation in Large Areas, *Trans. Am. Geophys. Union*, Vol. 28, pp. 445-450, 1947.

[2] Thom, H. C. S., On the Statistical Analysis of Rainfall Data, *Trans. Am. Geophys. Union*, Vol. 21, pp. 490-499, 1940.

It is difficult to suggest an adequate solution for problems of this type. The assumption of maximum runoff conditions coincident with a major rainstorm will result in a computed flood having a recurrence interval far greater than that for the precipitation. In areas where snow cover is normally present for extended periods, the assumption of heavy rain on snow is not so extreme, although the combination of 50-year snow cover and 50-year rain will certainly result in a flood exceeding the correct 50-year flood. In areas of intermittent and occasional snow cover the assumption of concurrence may result in a flood with a frequency approaching the product of the independent frequencies. The concurrence of simultaneous flooding on two streams depends on the particular geography of the basin and the areal extent of storms. While it is most unlikely that the Missouri and Ohio Rivers would be in extreme flood simultaneously, it is entirely possible for record floods to occur simultaneously on several streams within a small drainage area. In addition to these considerations, peak travel time is an important factor in synchronization of flood peaks.

The correct answer to joint-frequency problems would be an analysis of data segregated with respect to the second variable, *e.g.*, the frequency analysis of peak flows on one stream which occurred with concurrent flows on another stream within a specified range. Such a study would give the probability of occurrence of any desired combination of flows. Similar analyses would be possible between rainfall and snow on the ground or rainfall and antecedent precipitation. Actually, it will be found that, without an extremely long record, the number of events in any class interval will be so small that reliable analysis is not possible. In most cases, such studies will serve only as a further guide to the judgment of the engineer in selecting his design criteria.

Published rainfall-frequency data. The Miami Conservancy District made an exhaustive study[1] of frequency of excessive precipitation in that portion of the United States east of the 103d meridian. It used the station-year method and considered each 2° quadrangle of latitude and longitude as an area of homogeneity. The results of the investigation are summarized in Figs. 20-6 to 20-13, which show the amount of precipitation which may be expected once in 15, 50, or 100 years during periods of 1, 2, or 6 days.

Using data from Weather Bureau first-order stations, Yarnell[2] conducted an investigation of rains of great intensity and short duration. Figures 20-14 to 20-18 are selected charts from Yarnell's bulletin.

[1] "Storm Rainfall in the Eastern United States," rev. ed., pp. 43-93, *Tech. Rept.* 5, Miami Conservancy District, Dayton, Ohio, 1936.

[2] Yarnell, D. L., Rainfall Intensity-frequency Data, *U.S. Dept. Agr. Misc. Pub.* 204, 1935.

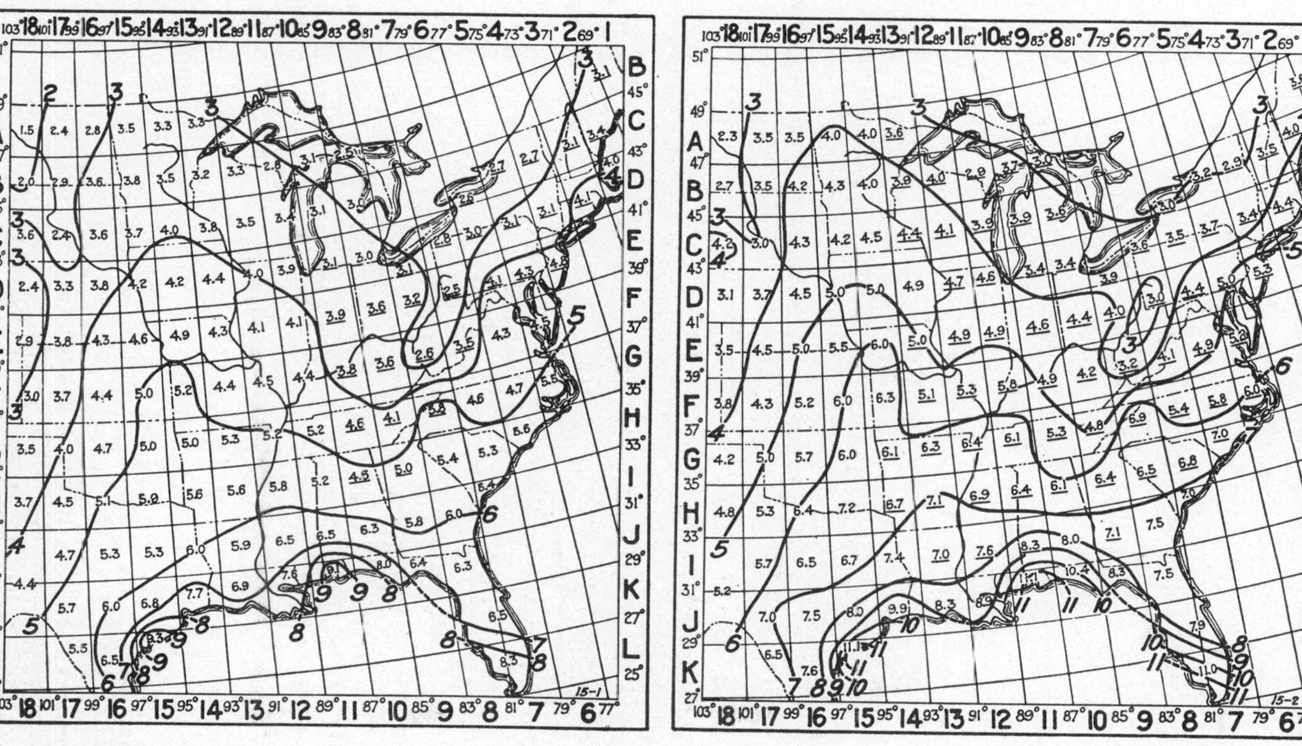

FIG. 20–6. Maximum 1-day rainfall to be expected on the average once in 15 years. (*Miami Conservancy District.*)

FIG. 20–7. Maximum 2-day rainfall to be expected on the average once in 15 years. (*Miami Conservancy District.*)

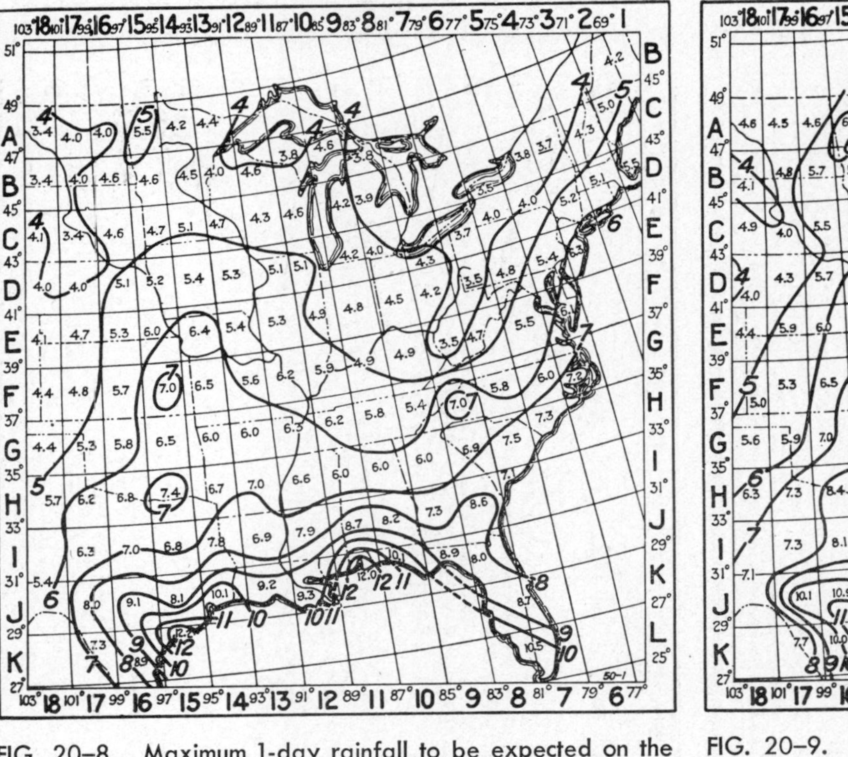

FIG. 20–8. Maximum 1-day rainfall to be expected on the average once in 50 years. (*Miami Conservancy District.*)

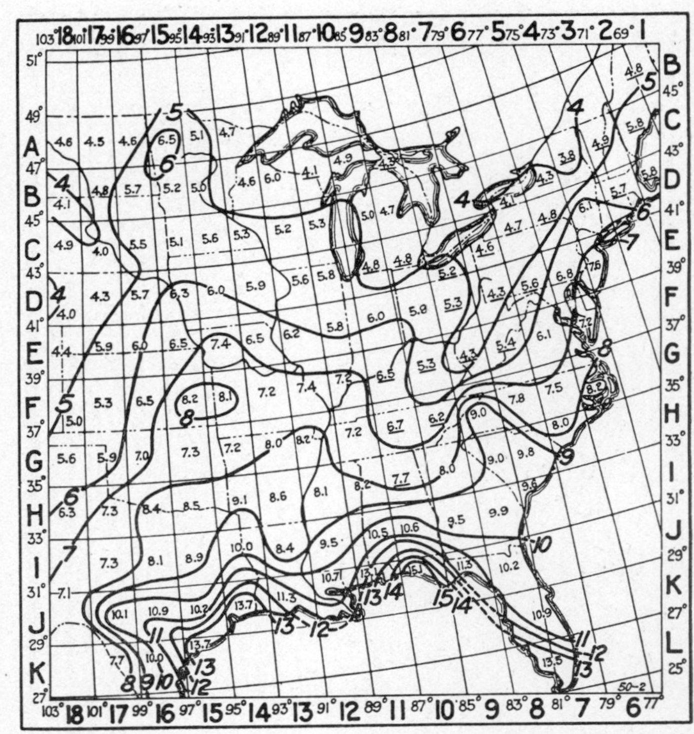

FIG. 20–9. Maximum 2-day rainfall to be expected on the average once in 50 years. (*Miami Conservancy District.*)

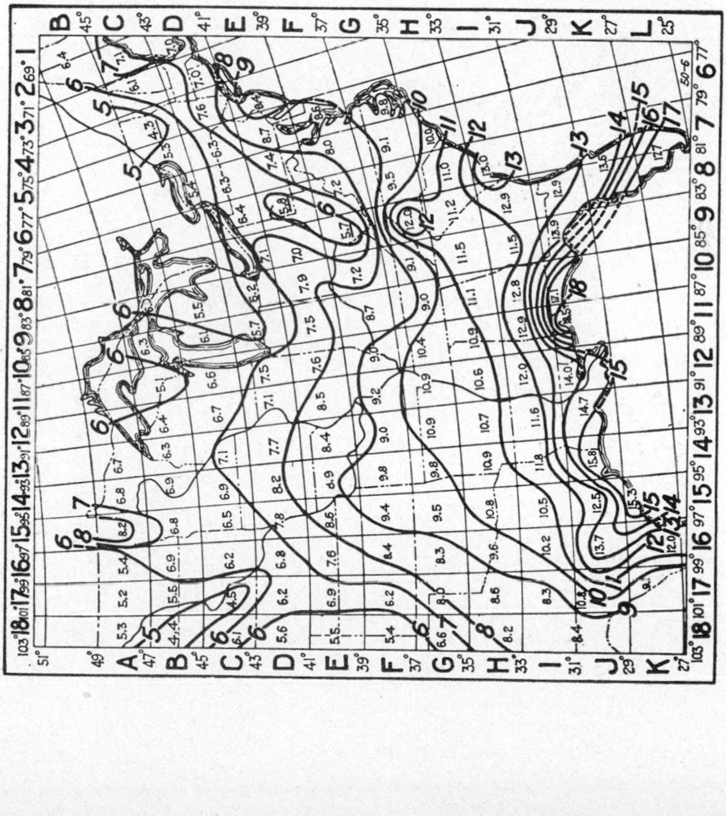

FIG. 20–10. Maximum 6-day rainfall to be expected on the average once in 50 years. (*Miami Conservancy District.*)

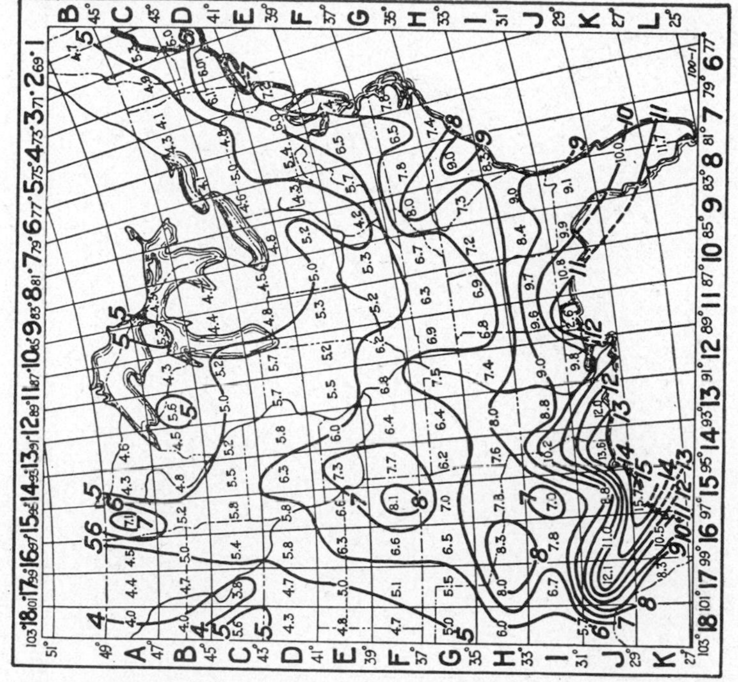

FIG. 20–11. Maximum 1-day rainfall to be expected on the average once in 100 years. (*Miami Conservancy District.*)

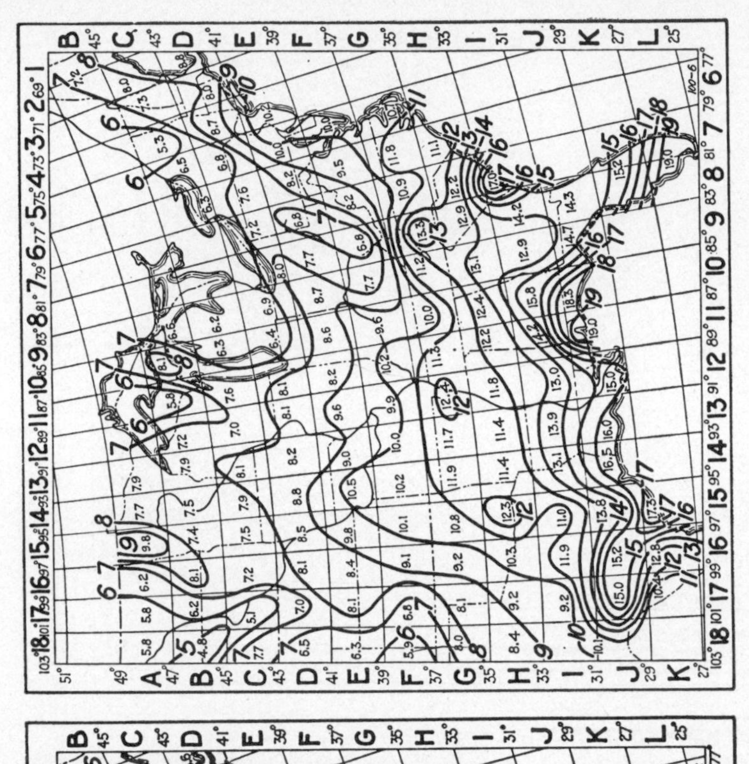

FIG. 20–12. Maximum 2-day rainfall to be expected on the average once in 100 years. (*Miami Conservancy District.*)

FIG. 20–13. Maximum 6-day rainfall to be expected on the average once in 100 years. (*Miami Conservancy District.*)

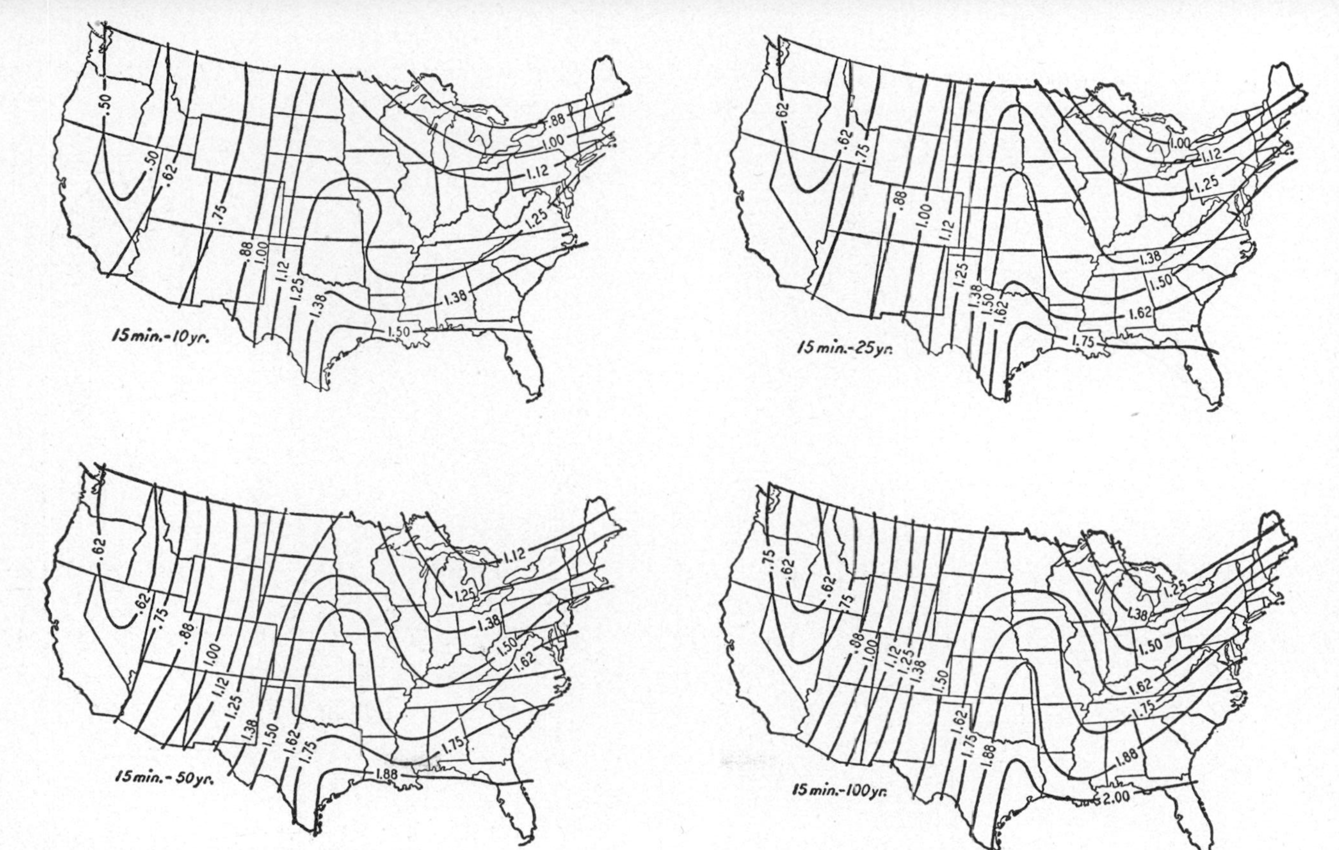

FIG. 20–14. Fifteen-minute rainfall to be expected on the average once in 10, 25, 50, and 100 years. (After Yarnell.)

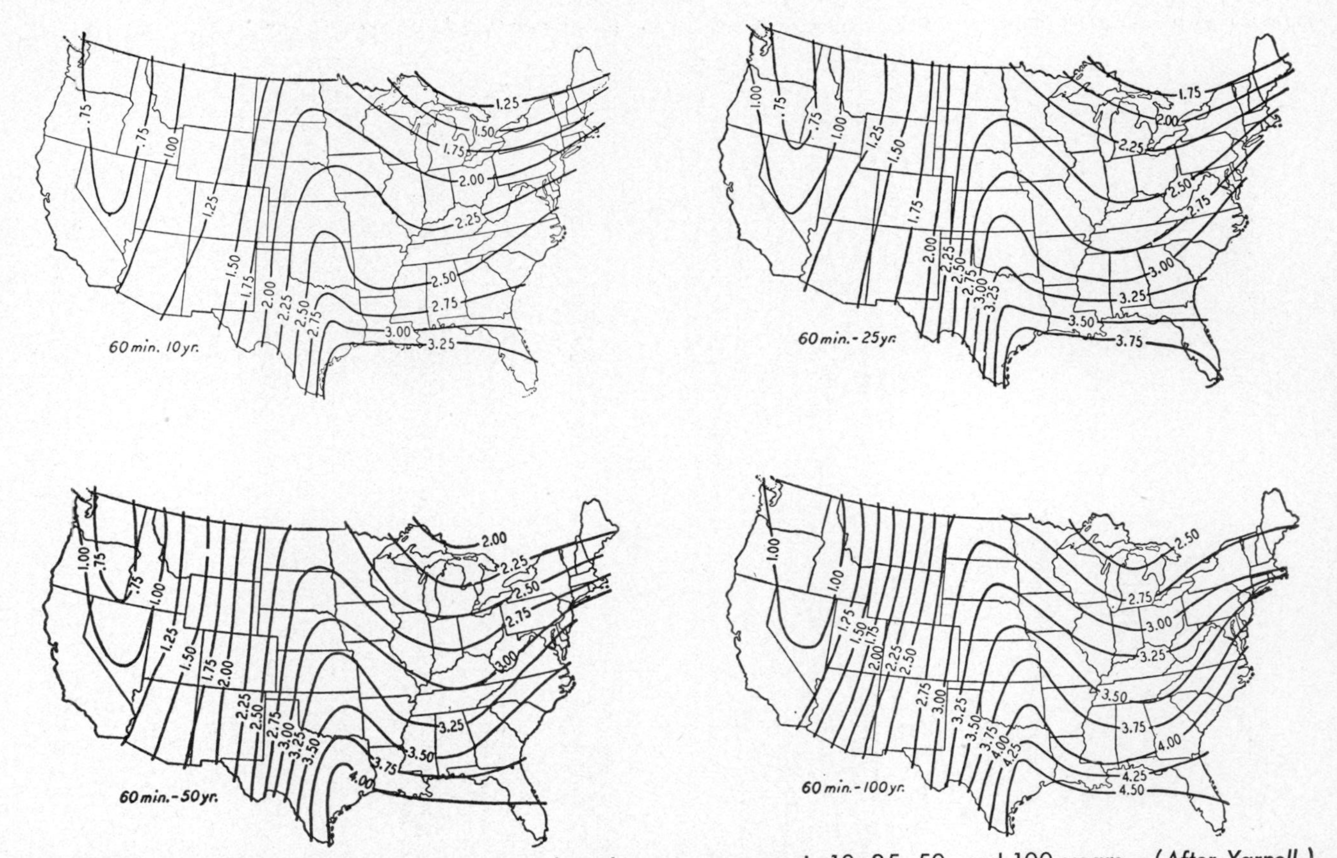

FIG. 20–15. One-hour rainfalls to be expected on the average once in 10, 25, 50, and 100 years. (After Yarnell.)

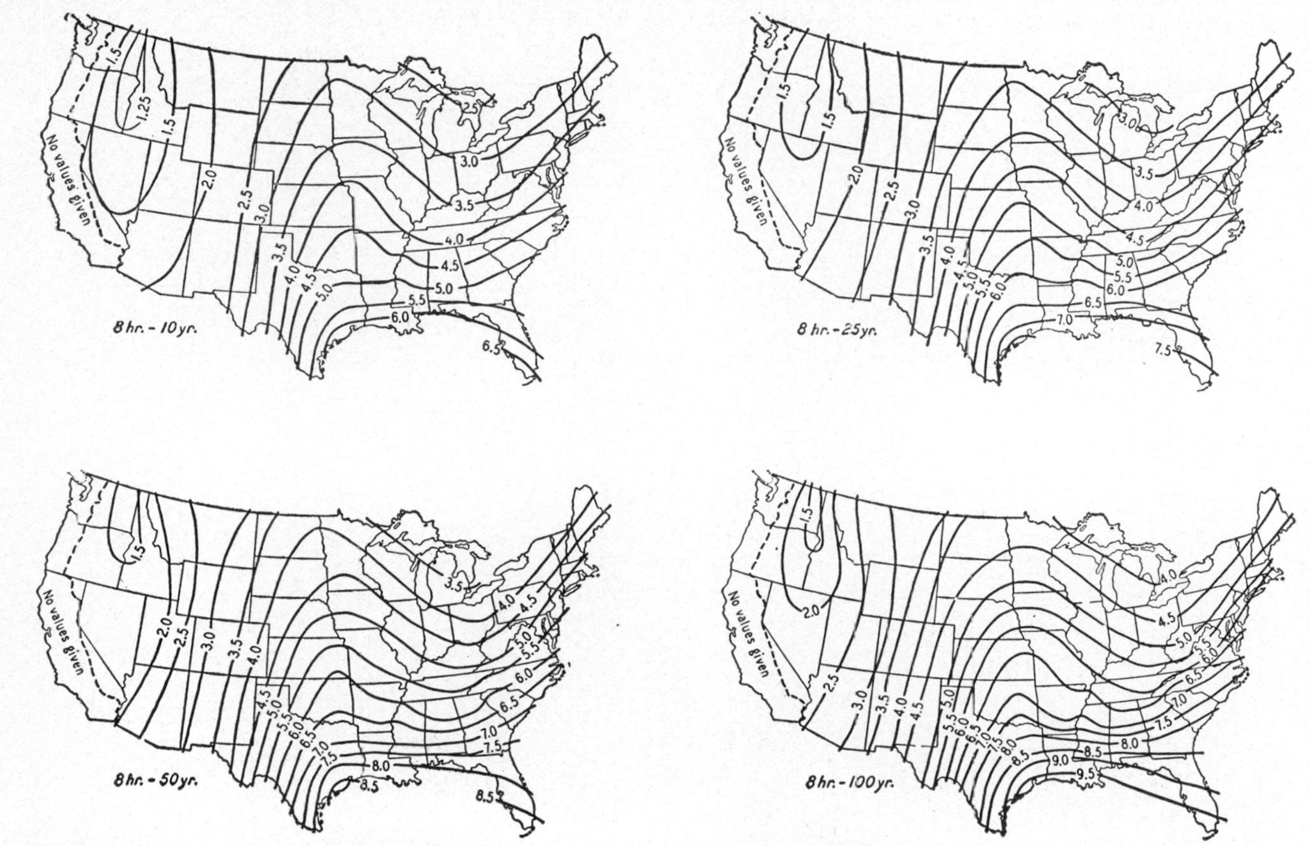

FIG. 20–16. Eight-hour rainfalls to be expected on the average once in 10, 25, 50, and 100 years. (*After Yarnell.*)

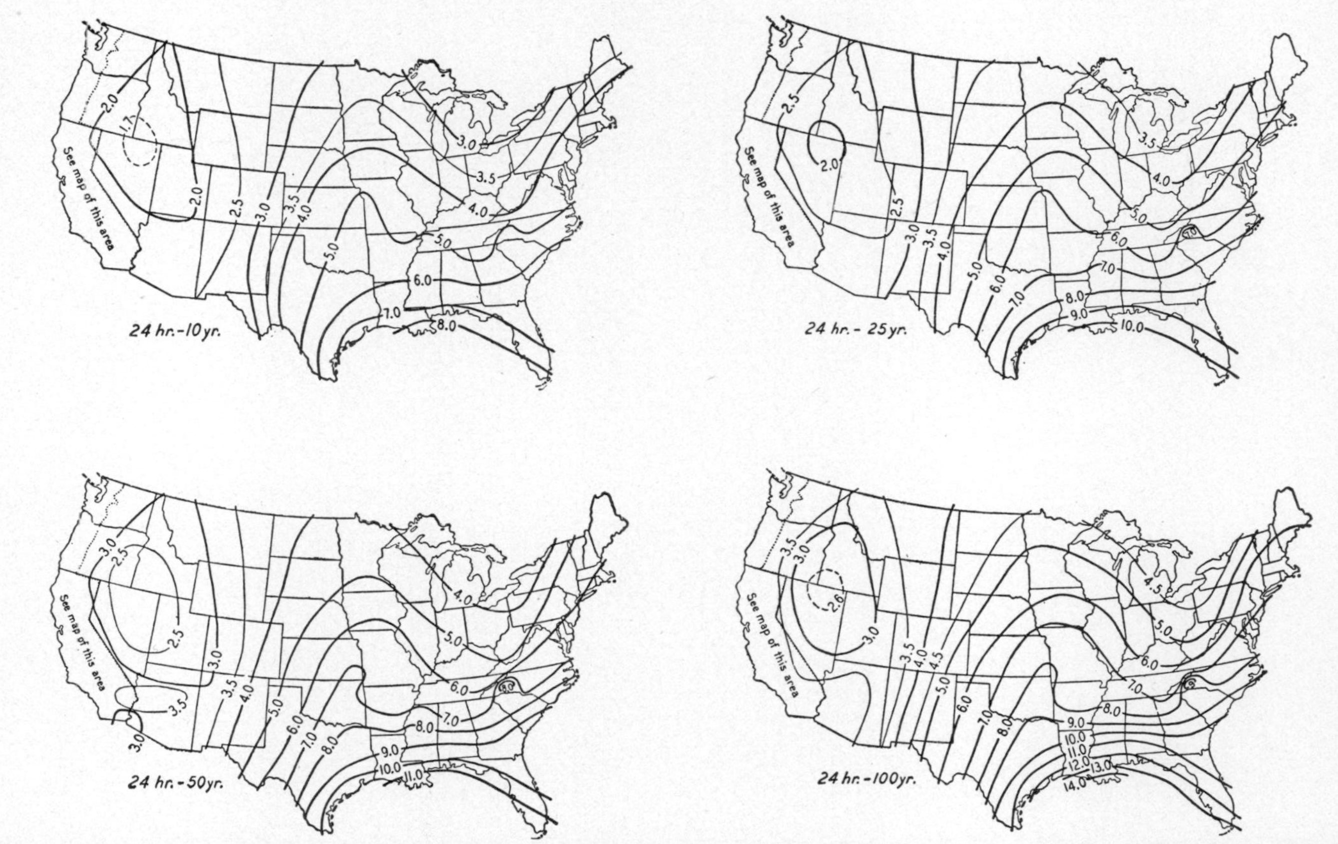

FIG. 20–17. Twenty-four-hour rainfalls to be expected on the average once in 10, 25, 50, and 100 years. (After Yarnell.)

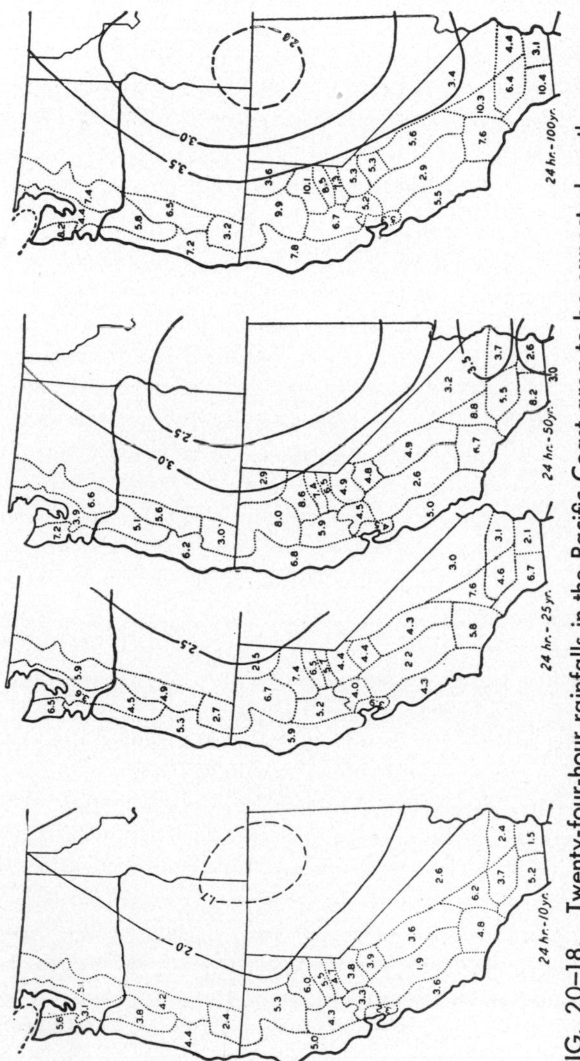

FIG. 20–18. Twenty-four-hour rainfalls in the Pacific Coast area to be expected on the average once in 10, 25, 50, and 100 years. (After Yarnell.)

The results of these studies are generally comparable, but it is to be noted that both were made some time ago and many additional data have since become available. This is particularly true in the case of short-period intensities considered in the Yarnell studies. The charts should be used for preliminary investigations only, and an actual analysis of all available data in the area of interest should be employed for final design studies.

EMPIRICAL FORMULAS

The lack of records for many small streams and the effort involved in frequency analysis of available records have led to the development of a large number of formulas for the estimation of flood flow and precipitation intensity for design purposes. The number of formulas is so large that it is quite impossible to discuss them all in detail. The various formulas are usually based on limited data for a particular region, and each involves one or more constants which must be evaluated largely by judgment. They are, therefore, difficult to apply with assurance. The general form of the various formulas is reasonably consistent, however, and best results for any particular area are obtained by determining the necessary constants from data for the area under study. A review of many of the formulas and an extensive bibliography on frequency studies and flood flows can be found in *Water Supply Paper* 771.

Extreme-flood formulas. There are a number of formulas which purport to give a value of extreme flood flow without specified frequency. If all record flood discharges within a hydrologically homogeneous region are plotted on logarithmic paper (Fig. 20-19) as a function of drainage area, the data usually define a straight-line envelope. The use of the enveloping curve is an accepted basis for determining design floods. The resulting estimates correspond to the maximum of record within the region included in the plotted data. The appropriate frequency for values determined from the enveloping curve and the related formulas cannot be defined. Representing maxima for the period of record, they would normally be assigned a recurrence interval of about 50 years. However, some of the floods plotted undoubtedly represent far greater recurrence intervals, and hence the assignable frequency depends on the position selected for the enveloping curve. A further problem associated with the enveloping curve and related formulas is the fact that basin characteristics other than area are ignored. Many of the higher points may represent basins which, because of favorable slope, land use, or precipitation regime, are capable of producing floods relatively greater than on other less favorably situated basins.

The extreme flood formulas are of the general form

$$q_c = cA_d^n \qquad (20\text{-}24)$$

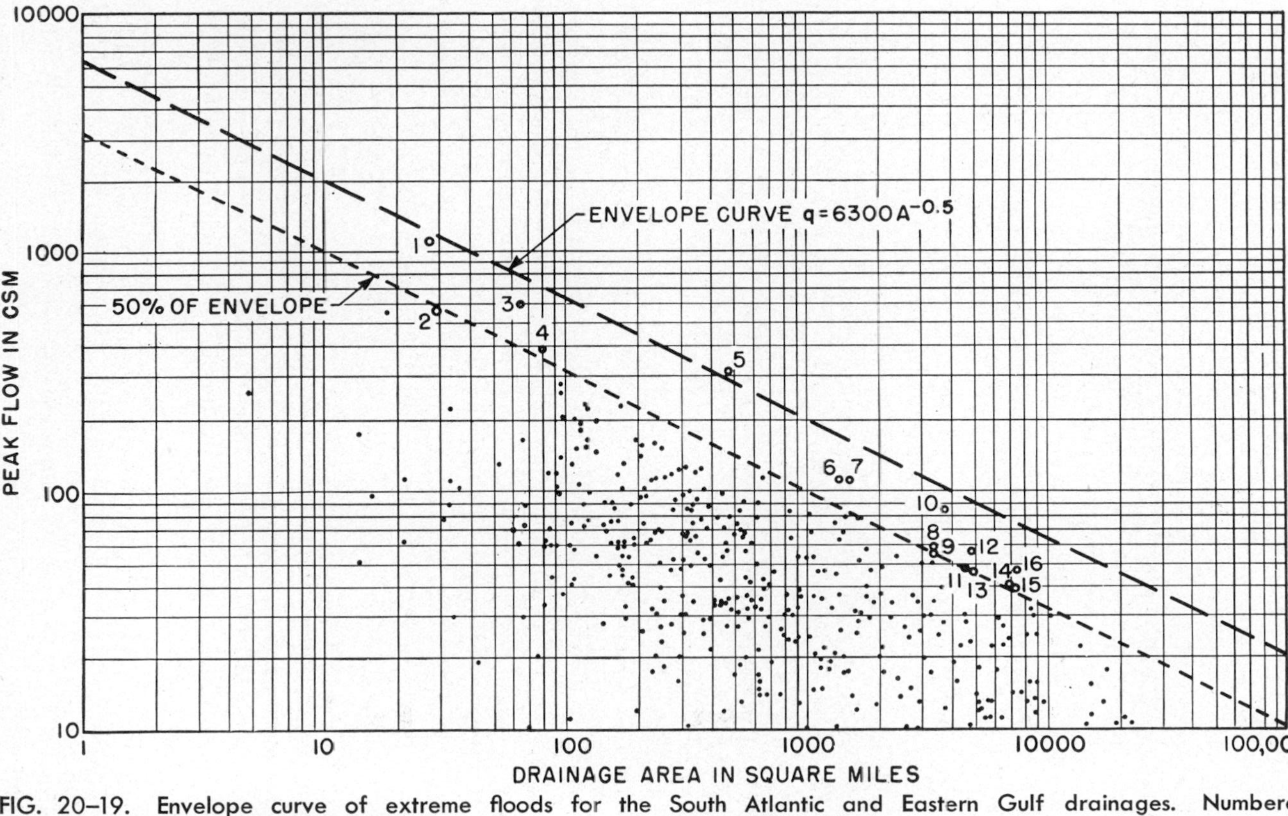

FIG. 20–19. Envelope curve of extreme floods for the South Atlantic and Eastern Gulf drainages. Numbered points are listed in Table 9–11.

where a_c is the necessary waterway area in square feet, A_d the drainage area above the site in acres, and c and n factors depending on the characteristics of the area. Formulas like Eq. (20-24) are employed in the design of culverts. The best known of these formulas is Talbot's, in which n is 0.75, and values of c are as shown in Table 20-9. Myers used n equal to 0.5 and found c to vary from 1 in flat terrane to 4 in rocky, mountainous country. In deriving the constants, each investigator assumed an average velocity of flow through the culvert. Obviously, the use of these formulas does not permit the designer to take into account the hydraulic features of the culvert. Talbot's coefficients are based on a velocity of 10 fps, and roughly fit a 10-year flood in the Middle West.

TABLE 20-9. Values of c in Eq. (20-24)

(After Talbot)

Steep, rocky ground, abrupt slopes	1
Rough, hilly country, moderate slopes	⅔
Uneven terrane, valleys very wide	½
Rolling farmland, long narrow valleys	⅓
Level terrane not affected by snow	⅕

Jarvis[1] recommended the use of a modified form of Eq. (20-24),

$$q = 100b\sqrt{A_d} \tag{20-25}$$

where q is peak flow in cubic feet per second, A_d is the drainage in square miles, and b is a constant sometimes called the *Myers rating*. Values of the Myers rating b for major floods in the United States are listed in Table 9-11.

Frequency formulas. Numerous formulas have been devised to express the flood-flow characteristics of basins[2] in terms of frequency. Fuller[3] presented the first such formula, which was in the form

$$q = \bar{q}(1 + c \log_{10} T_p) \tag{20-26}$$

where $\bar{q}$ is the average annual flood in cubic feet per second, q the flood with a return period of T_p years, and c a coefficient which Fuller found to be 0.8 for eastern streams. Lane[4] found c to be 0.69 for New England streams, and values as high as 4.5 have been found for very small streams in southern California.[5]

[1] Jarvis, C. S., Flood Flow Characteristics, *Trans. ASCE*, Vol. 89, pp. 985-1032, 1926.

[2] Richards, B. D., "Flood Estimation and Control," Chapman & Hall, London, 1944.

[3] Fuller, W. E., Flood Flows, *Trans. ASCE*, Vol. 77, pp. 564-617, 1914.

[4] Lane, E. W., discussion of paper, Flood Flow Characteristics, *Trans. ASCE*, Vol. 89, pp. 1051, 1926.

[5] "California Culvert Practice," p. 3, California Department of Public Works, Sacramento, 1944.

Horton[1] suggested the formula

$$q = q_{max}(1 - e^{-kT_e^n}) \tag{20-27}$$

where q_{max} is the maximum possible flood, q is the discharge with an exceedance interval T_e, and k and n factors varying with locality. A value of q_{max} may be assumed and k and n determined from observed frequency data. This equation, like Fuller's, is essentially a means of extrapolating the available data.

As a general equation, Horton[2] suggested the form

$$q = \frac{kT_r^n}{A_d} \tag{20-28}$$

where q is in second-feet per square mile, A_d is the drainage area in square miles, T_r the recurrence interval in years, k about 4000, and n is 0.25 for eastern Pennsylvania.

Formulas involving rainfall. By far the largest group of formulas are those which include a rainfall parameter and frequently also some measure of the physical characteristics of the basin. Perhaps the leading formula in this class is the so-called "rational formula"

$$q = ciA_d \tag{20-29}$$

where i is the rainfall intensity in inches per hour for a duration equal to the concentration time of the basin, A_d the area in acres, and c a runoff coefficient. The formula takes advantage of the fact that 1 acre-in./hr is very nearly equal to 1 cfs and assumes that for rainfall exceeding the time of concentration the rate of runoff equals the rate of rainfall reduced by an appropriate runoff factor. The peak flow for any return period is determined by using a value of i having the corresponding frequency. Bernard[3] has outlined an elaborate development of the rational method in which the coefficient c is varied with return period T_p and factors reflecting basin shape, stream pattern, and channel characteristics are introduced. Figure 20-20 is a map of c_{max} assumed by Bernard to have a return period of 100 years. Values of c for any value of T_p can be determined by

$$c = c_{max}\left(\frac{T_p}{100}\right)^x \tag{20-30}$$

where x is given in Fig. 20-25. The reference[3] contains several charts and nomograms for determining the numerous constants in the modified solution.

[1] Horton, R. E., discussion of paper, Flood Flow Characteristics, *Trans. ASCE*, Vol. 89, pp. 1081-1086, 1926.

[2] Horton, R. E., discussion of paper, Flood Flows, *Trans. ASCE*, Vol. 77, pp. 663-670, 1914.

[3] Bernard, M., "Modified Rational Method of Estimating Flood Flows," Appendix A, Low Dams, National Resources Committee, Washington, D.C., 1938.

Pettis[1] proposed the formula

$$q = cP\bar{B}^{1.25} \tag{20-31}$$

where q approximates the 100-year flood peak, P is the 100-year 1-day rainfall in inches, $\bar{B}$ the average width of the basin (A_d/L), and c a coefficient varying from about 310 in humid areas to 40 in desert regions.

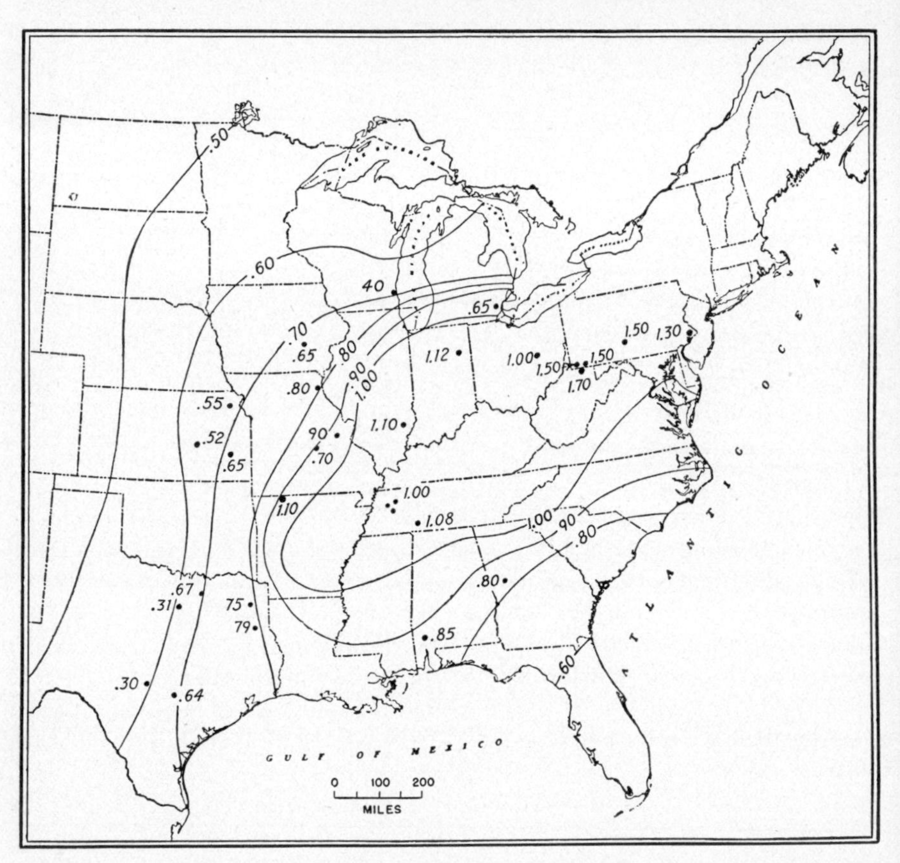

FIG. 20–20. Values of the runoff coefficient c_{max} in Eq. (20-30). (*After Bernard.*)

The many formulas relating rainfall to runoff involve coefficients having a wide range of values and complex factors designed to make them fit available data. It is probable that the rational formula [Eq. (20-29)] is as reliable as any of the more complex formulas, but most problems will justify treatment by application of the principles of hydrology outlined elsewhere in the text rather than the use of questionable empiricisms.

[1] Pettis, C. R., "A New Theory of River Flow," private publication, 1927.

Rainfall-frequency formulas. There have been many studies of rainfall pointed to the development of empirical formulas expressing precipitation for various durations as a function of frequency. The resulting formulas are generally in the form

$$i = \frac{kT_p^x}{t^n} \qquad (20\text{-}32)$$

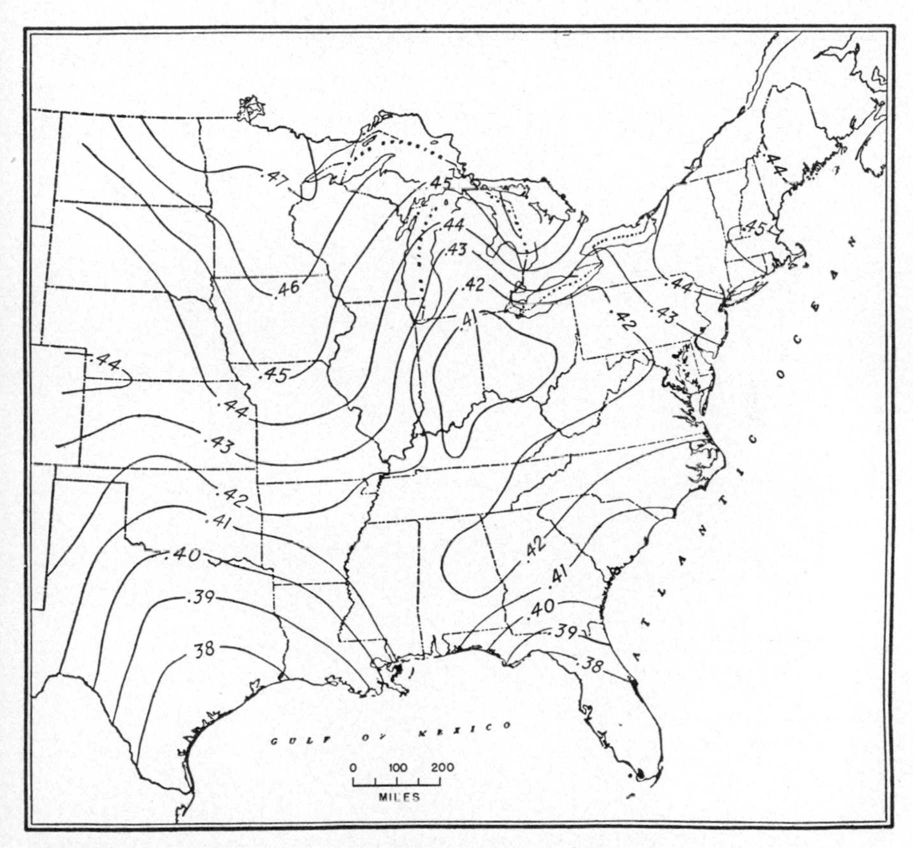

FIG. 20-21. Values of the exponent n in Eq. (20-32) for durations between 5 and 60 min. *(After Bernard.)*

where i is the rainfall intensity in inches per hour, T_p the return period, t the duration in minutes, and k, x, and n are regional constants. Figures 20-21 through 20-25 show values of the several constants as derived by Bernard[1] on the basis of Yarnell's data. It should be noted that k and n vary, depending on whether t is more or less than 60 min.

[1] Bernard, M., Formulas for Rainfall Intensities of Long Duration, *Trans. ASCE*, Vol. 96, pp. 592-624, 1932.

The relative consistency in rainfall-frequency formulas is to be expected since, unlike flood peaks, rates of rainfall are more nearly general regional characteristics. No attempt need be made to include elusive indices of basin shape, slope, etc. A general formula type has been shown to be applicable over the eastern United States; and, hence, its development is supported by a far greater amount of data than is a flood formula applicable

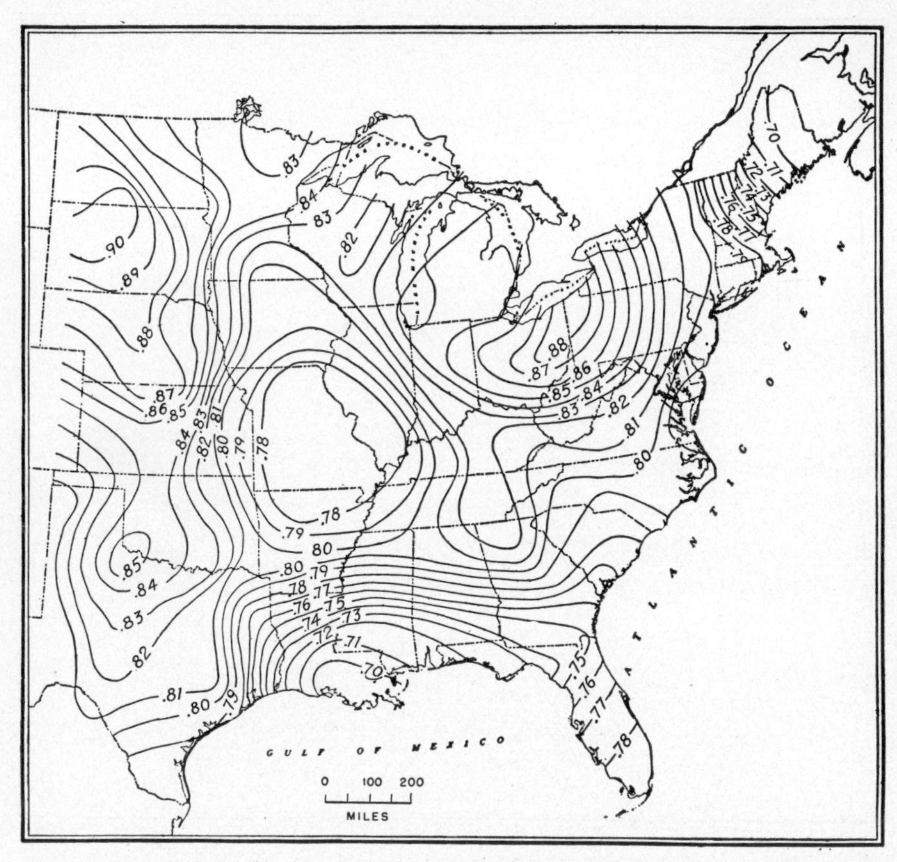

FIG. 20–22. Values of the exponent n in Eq. (20-32) for durations between 60 and 1440 min. *(After Bernard.)*

in a particular region. Hence, we may assume that the rainfall-intensity frequency formulas are generally more reliable than corresponding formulas for flood flows. Nevertheless, it is good practice to establish the necessary constants by consideration of available records in the immediate area of study. Computed rainfall values may be used in the development of flood hydrographs by accepted hydrologic techniques.

OBSERVED MAXIMA

Many simple design problems are solved by the use of the observed maximum flow or precipitation at the station as the criterion. As discussed in the section on Frequency Analysis (page 544), this provides a design value which may be presumed to have a return period approximately equal to the period of record. Actually, the true return period may be quite different

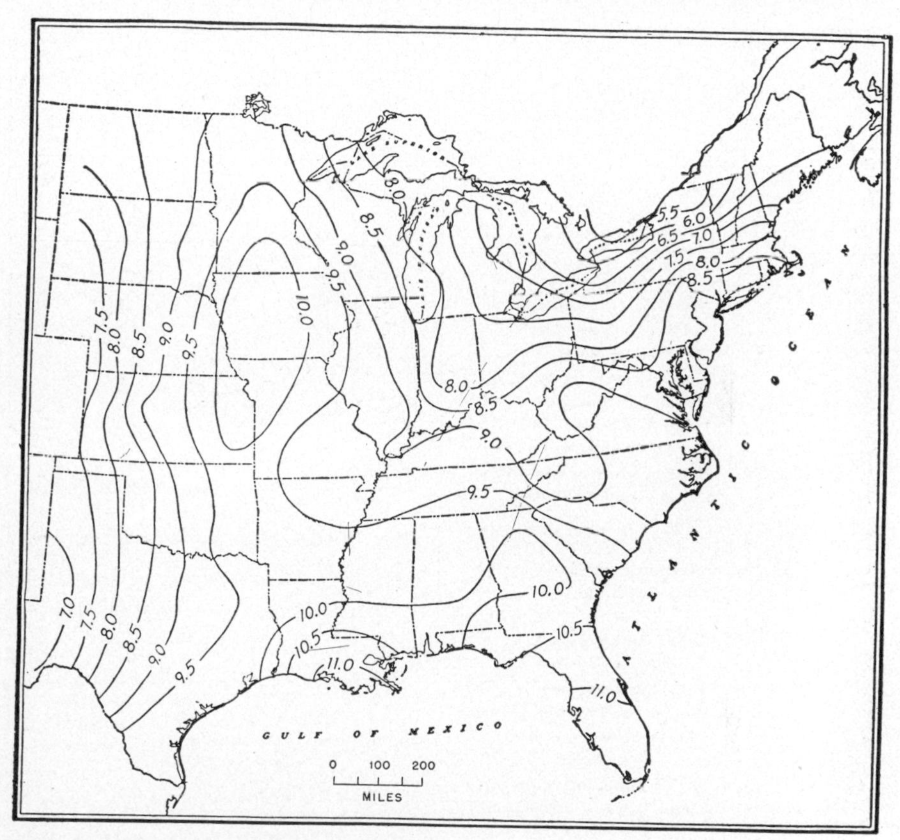

FIG. 20–23. Values of the coefficient k in Eq. (20-32) for durations between 5 and 60 min. *(After Bernard.)*

from the period of record. If frequency analysis is applied to the data, the other events in the record have a place in defining the frequency curve and may indicate that a modification of the record maximum, either up or down, is required to give a more satisfactory estimate of the t-year event, where t is the period of record. In any case, the record value should be compared with data from near-by stations as a check. The selected value should be adjusted for changes which affect the observed flow or precipitation.

Tables of record maximum flows are given in Chap. 9 and of maximum observed precipitation in Chap. 6. The maximum flood flows listed in Table 9-11 are limited to those which exceed 50 per cent of the enveloping-curve value for the drainage area of the basin. Separate enveloping curves (Table 20-10) were developed for each of the 14 regions used by the U.S. Geological Survey for publication of streamflow data. These areas are not necessarily homogeneous, and an enveloping curve does not apply equally well to all portions of a region.

TABLE 20-10. Equations for Enveloping Curves of Peak Streamflow

(Values of q in second-feet per square mile)

U.S. Geol. Survey Part No.	Area	Equation	
1	North Atlantic Slope	$q = 4800A_d^{-0.5}$	
2	South Atlantic and Eastern Gulf of Mexico drainage	$q = 6300A_d^{-0.5}$	
3	Ohio River Basin	$q = 5800A_d^{-0.5}$	
4	St. Lawrence River Basin	$q = 9800A_d^{-0.65}$	
5	Hudson Bay and Upper Mississippi drainage	$q = 4400A_d^{-0.57}$	
6	Missouri River Basin	$q = 3300A_d^{-0.5}$	
7	Lower Mississippi River Basin	$q = 6400A_d^{-0.5}$	
8	Western Gulf of Mexico drainage	$q = 5000A_d^{-0.23}$	(below 4000 sq miles)
		$q = 240{,}000A_d^{-0.87}$	(above 4000 sq miles)
9	Colorado River Basin	$q = 2500A_d^{-0.5}$	
10	The Great Basin	$q = 650A_d^{-0.5}$	(below 400 sq miles)
		$q = 15{,}000A_d^{-1.0}$	(over 400 sq miles)
11	Pacific Slope basins in California	$q = 5100A_d^{-0.5}$	
12	Pacific Slope basins in Washington and Upper Columbia River Basin	$q = 4600A_d^{-0.5}$	
13	Snake River Basin	$q = 110A_d^{-0.17}$	
14	Pacific Slope basins in Oregon and Lower Columbia River Basin	$q = 5800A_d^{-0.5}$	

DETERMINATION OF AVAILABLE FLOW

The determination of flood frequency is not the entire problem in design, particularly for projects involving use of water for power, irrigation, or water supply. An important factor in such projects is the determination of rate or volume of flow which will be available for use. A related problem is that of determining the volume of storage required to assure a specified rate of flow. Problems of this type more frequently relate to low flows than to high.

Droughts. A sustained period of time without significant rainfall is called a *drought*. Because of the variety of needs for water, it is not practicable to define a drought specifically. A period of only a few weeks without precipitation may be a serious matter for agricultural operations, particularly if the weather is hot and the humidity low. On the other hand, an

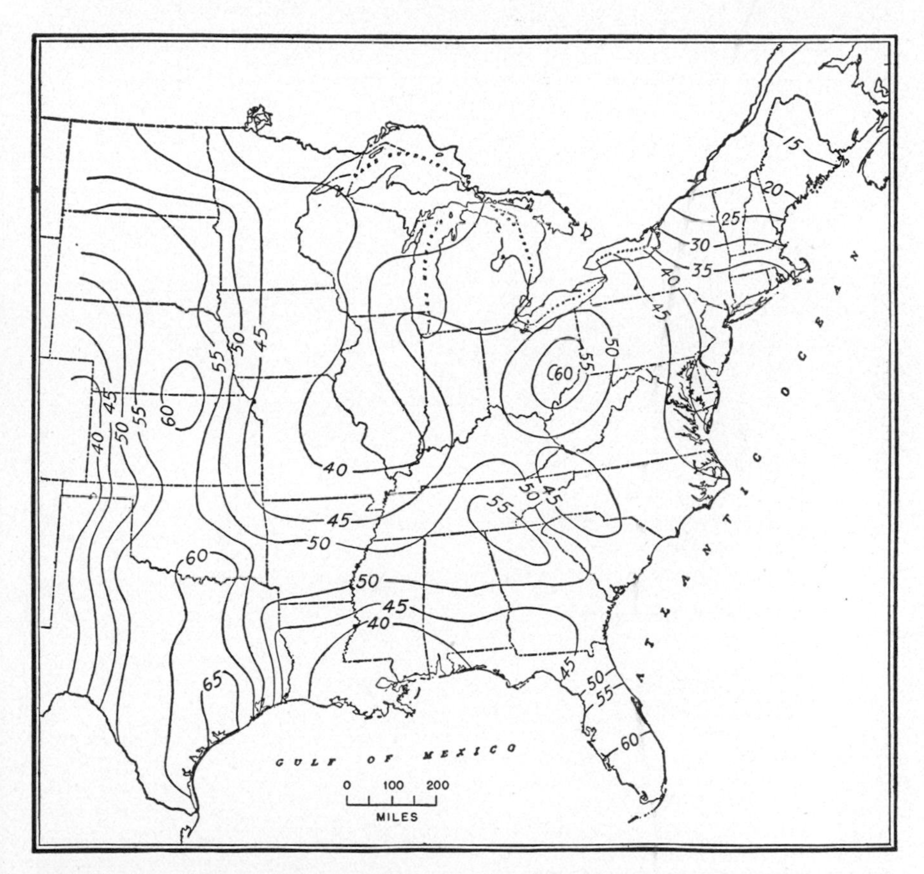

FIG. 20–24. Values of the coefficient k in Eq. (20-32) for durations between 60 and 1440 min. *(After Bernard.)*

irrigation project with adequate storage may operate several months without rain, an annual occurrence during the summer in the Central Valley of California. Because of our inability to define a drought in terms which are generally applicable to all problems, no general studies of droughts or drought frequency are available. Moreover, a drought requires an extended period of time to develop. Extreme rainfalls or floods can occur several times in one year, whereas two or three years of subnormal runoff may be required to develop a serious drought problem for projects having large volumes of storage. Hence, we do not have available a record of severe droughts which is as extensive as our records of floods. It is shown later in this chapter that it is feasible to estimate the maximum possible storm which can occur in a given basin on the basis of meteorological theory. Because of the long period involved in droughts and the great number of weather sequences which might lead to protracted dry periods,

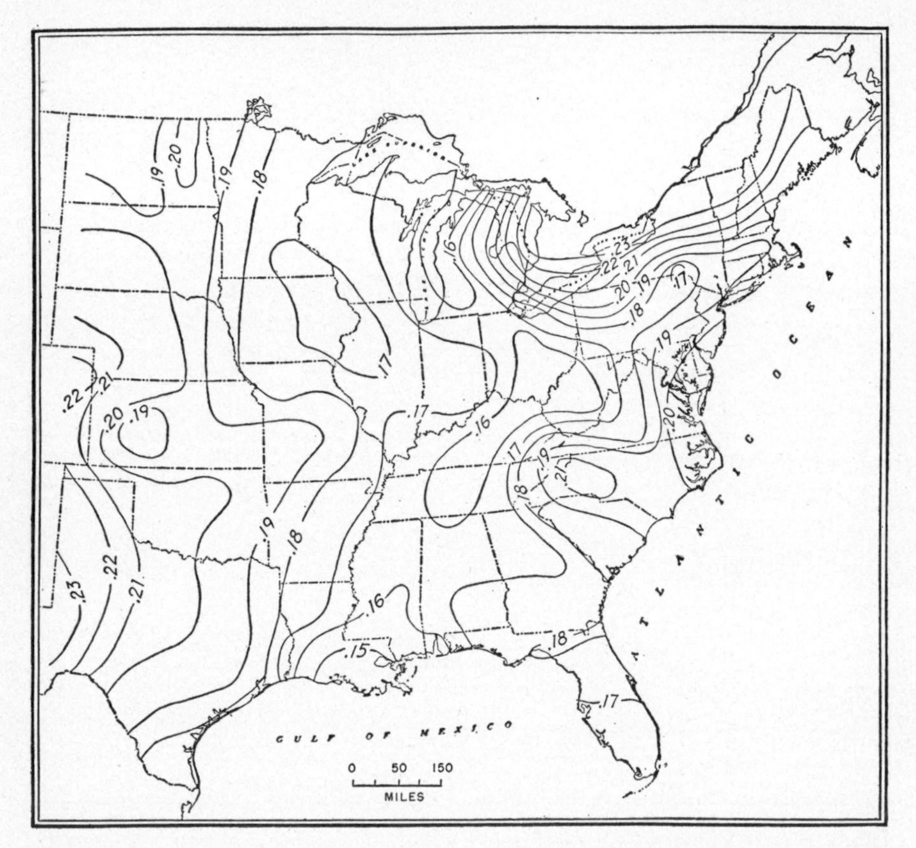

FIG. 20–25. Values of the exponent x in Eq. (20-32) for durations up to 1440 min. (*After Bernard.*)

it is not possible to estimate the worst possible drought conditions which might develop in a given area. The only alternative, then, is to deal with the most severe dry period of record, possibly modified by an arbitrary factor of safety. It should be noted that available streamflow records may be extrapolated backward by use of long-period runoff relations (Chap. 16).

Duration curves. The mean monthly flows in cubic feet per second for the Sacandaga River near Hope, New York, for the period 1936 to 1945 are shown in Fig. 20-26*a* as a frequency distribution with a class interval of 200 cfs. This diagram is prepared by counting the number of months with flows within each of the 200-cfs intervals. If values in the successive class intervals are accumulated and plotted (Fig. 20-26*b*), a cumulated histogram, or *duration curve*, results. The duration curve is thus the integral of the frequency histogram. It is ordinarily considered to be the smooth curve

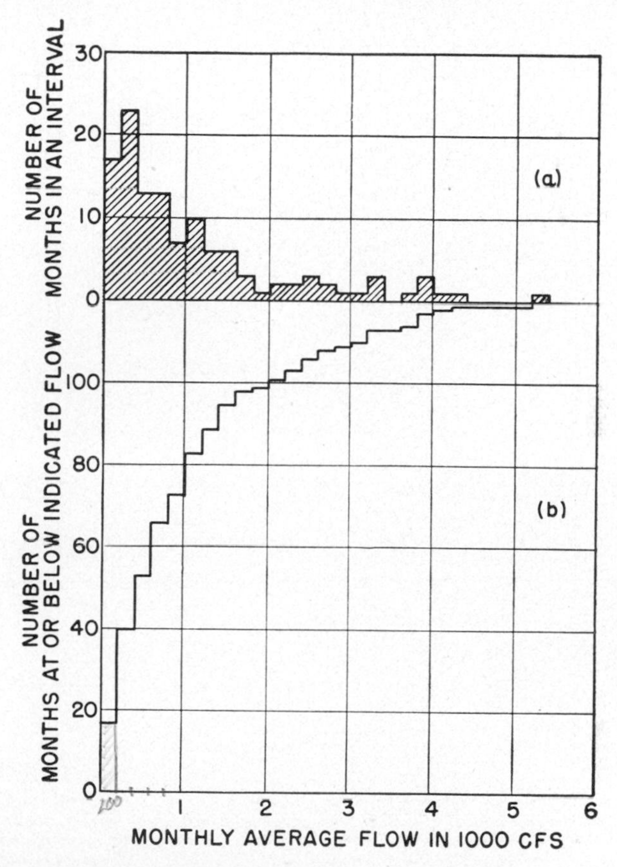

FIG. 20–26. Frequency histogram and integrated histogram of monthly flows for the Sacandaga River near Hope, New York, 1936 to 1945.

passing through the mid-points of the blocks on the cumulated histogram. This assumes that the data are evenly distributed in the class interval. If the class interval is large or the distribution within it skewed, the point representing the group is plotted at the flow and time values corresponding to the mid-value in the class. The curve of Fig. 20-26*b* shows the number of months in which flow was equal to or less than that indicated by the abscissa.

It is somewhat more convenient to show the material in the reverse order, *i.e.*, the number of events equaling or exceeding a given flow. The conversion of the time scale to percentage for comparative purposes is also common practice. Figure 20-27 shows the data for the Sacandaga River plotted on the basis of per cent of time equaled or exceeded. Three curves are shown, one based on a count of daily flows in 500-cfs intervals, the other two on the

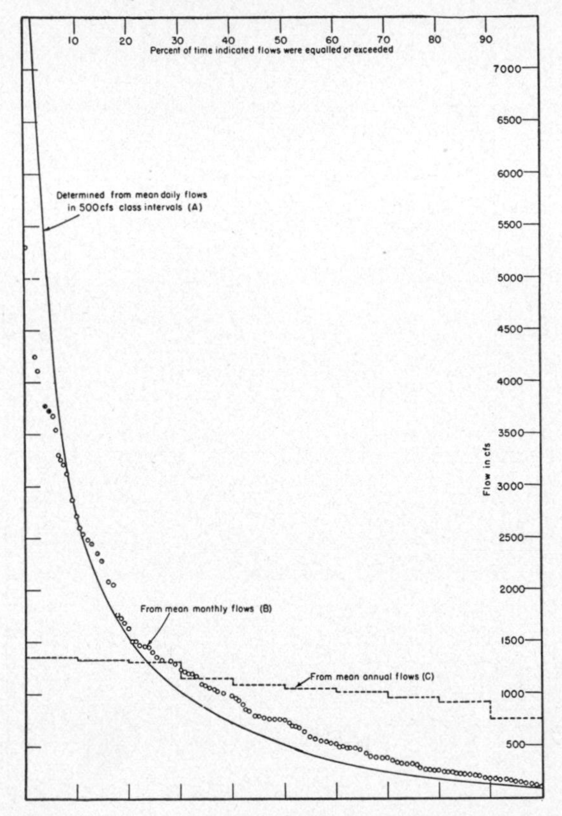

FIG. 20–27. Flow-duration curves for the Sacandaga River near Hope, New York, 1936 to 1945.

basis of individual monthly and yearly flows. Averaging of flows by months and years reduced the range of the data considerably. This point must be borne in mind in constructing a duration curve, or misleading results may be obtained. For most problems, the use of daily data is recommended, although it does require more work than the use of monthly or annual data.

For comparative purposes, duration curves are frequently plotted in terms of ratios to the average flow rather than in actual flow units. For two stations on the same stream or for adjacent streams in similar terrane, the resulting curves are often nearly identical. Hence, the duration curve developed for a station may be used as an approximation to the duration curve for an ungaged point. However, the smoothing effect of valley storage reduces the range of fluctuation in a large basin considerably more than in a small basin. Topography, vegetal cover, land use, and precipitation characteristics also influence the general shape of the duration curve. Hence, the duration curve of a basin should not be expected to apply closely in another basin of greatly different area and physical features.

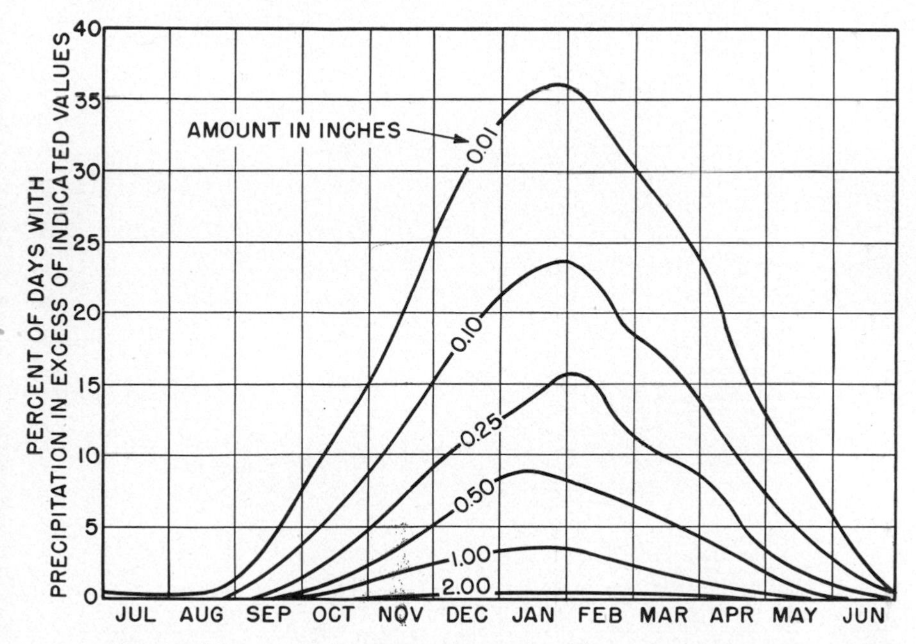

Fig. 20–28. Rainfall-duration curves for Sacramento, California.

The duration curve plotted in per cent of time may be considered to represent the hydrograph of the average year with its flows arranged in order of magnitude. Thus, from curve *A*, Fig. 20-27, the flow in the average year will be below 500 cfs 50 per cent of the time, *i.e.*, 182 days. In other words, *without storage*, a power plant of 500 cfs capacity could operate at full capacity only half the year on the average. The duration curve is most frequently used for the purpose of determining water-supply potentials for power, irrigation, or municipal use. The amount of flow available for any per cent of time, assuming no storage, can be read directly from it.

The duration curve has been widely used as the basis for power studies. In 1920 the U.S. Geological Survey adopted the flow available 50 per cent of the time, q_{50}, and the flow available 90 per cent of the time, q_{90}, as the standards of flow for water-power statistics. The q_{90} is a measure of the prime power, and the q_{50} is an index of power potential with storage. Together, the values indicated the variability of flow. Potential power is computed on the basis of gross head and 100 per cent efficiency.

It has been suggested that the duration curve may be assumed to represent an average month or other period of time. While it does, in a sense, represent the average of all months, it cannot represent any particular

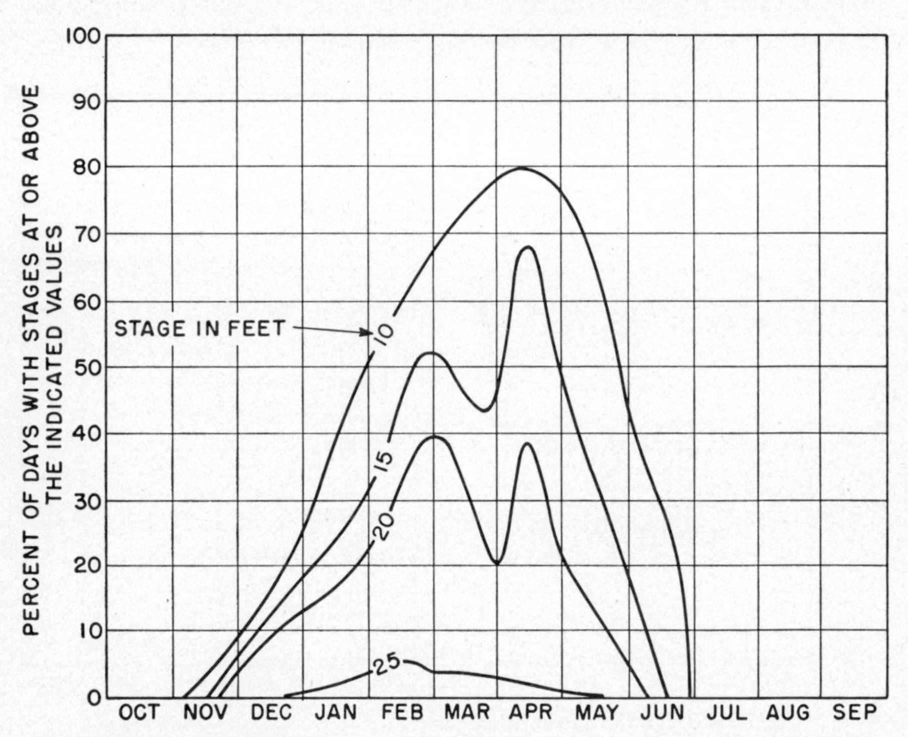

FIG. 20–29. Stage-duration curves for the Sacramento River at I Street gage, Sacramento, California.

month, unless the flows in all months of the year are essentially the same. If a pronounced seasonal cycle of streamflow is characteristic of a basin, then the duration curve representing all the data should be considered only as representative of the year. If it is desired to know the average distribution of flow in a particular month, say April, then a duration curve should be developed from all April data. Figures 20-28 and 20-29 are duration curves for rainfall and river stage at Sacramento, California, plotted to show the duration characteristics for any calendar date. These curves were developed by analyzing data for successive 10-day periods throughout the year in order to show the annual cycle. Both figures clearly show the annual variations. Figure 20-29 shows a peak of high stages in February and March, coinciding with the peak of rainfall frequency, and a secondary peak of moderate stages in April, caused by the melting of mountain snows.

The duration-area curve. A useful adjunct to the duration curve is the *duration-area curve*, described by Foster.[1] This curve shows the area beneath the duration curve and any value of flow. It is therefore the integral of the duration curve taken along the streamflow axis. When the duration curve is plotted in per cent of time, the resulting duration-area curve shows the average flow available below a given discharge.

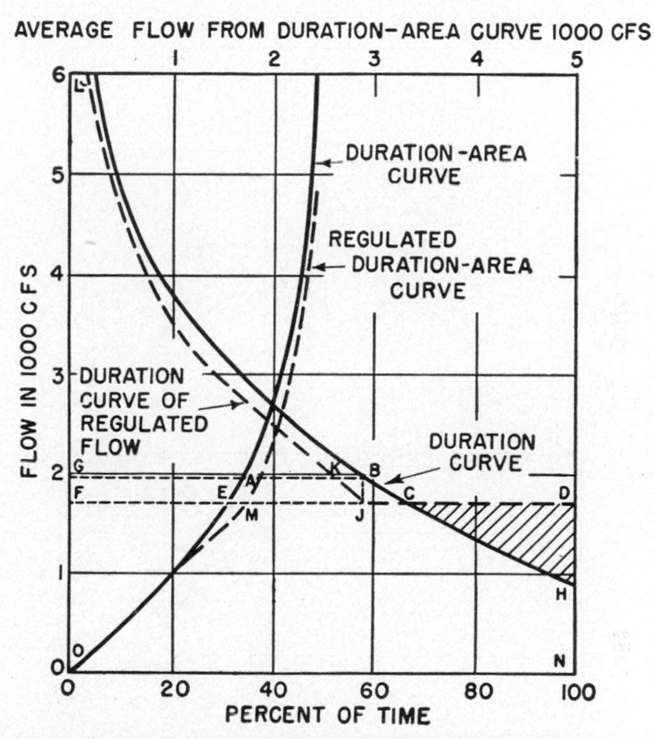

FIG. 20–30. Approximate determination of the duration curve for regulated flow.

The duration curve is not well adapted to the study of problems involving storage, because it does not present the flows in their natural order. There is no indication of the average or maximum period when flows are below any given value. With a duration-area curve it is possible to make an approximate analysis of regulated flow for preliminary studies. The method is demonstrated by use of hypothetical data in Fig. 20-30. A minimum regulated flow of 1700 cfs is assumed. The duration-area curve in-

[1] Foster, H. A., Duration Curves, *Trans. ASCE*, Vol. 99, pp. 1213-1267, 1934.

dicates this flow at A; hence the area $GBHNO$ must have an average ordinate of 1700 cfs and is equal to the area $OFDN$. The area CDH represents a volume of storage equal to $GBCF$. The duration curve of regulated flow is therefore $DJKL$, in which the segment JKL is the original duration curve displaced downward by the distance BJ. The adjusted duration-area curve follows the 45° line to a flow of 1700 cfs (point M) and then for the balance of its length is the distance AM below the original curve.

Solution of pondage problems. In the sense of river control, *storage* is water held in a reservoir for extended periods of time, while *pondage* represents only a small detention for short periods to reregulate natural

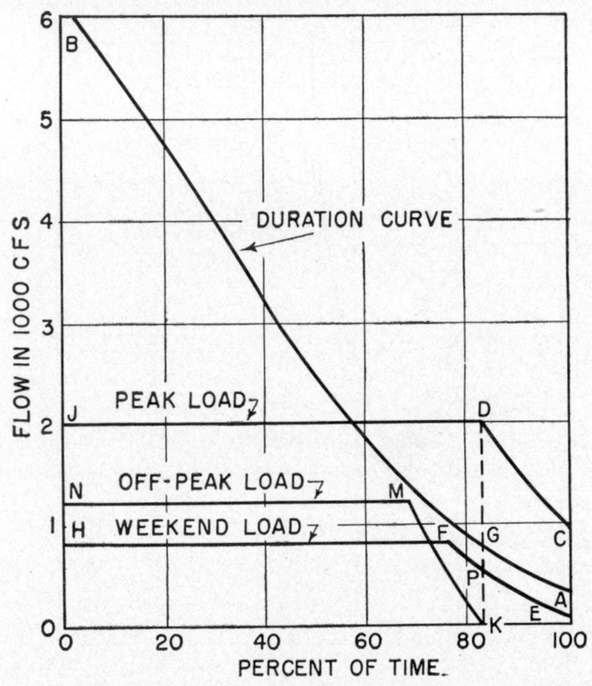

FIG. 20–31. Analysis of power production for a plant with pondage by means of a flow-duration curve.

flows, generally for hydroelectric power. The duration curve is useful in treating pondage problems because flow sequence is of little importance. Assume a plant with a turbine capacity of 2500 cfs and a forebay with a capacity of 500 sfd. The peak load occurs 10 hr/day, 5 days a week, and averages 2000 cfs. The off-peak load on these days averages 1200 cfs, and the week-end load averages 800 cfs. The natural duration curve is shown as AGB in Fig. 20-31. No week-end or off-peak power will be generated unless flows are sufficient to fill the forebay for use in development of peak power.

The forebay capacity of 500 sfd can be filled in 2 days if the flows exceed 250 cfs, and since the minimum flow is 300 cfs, it can be assumed that the forebay will be filled every week end. The flow during the 14 off-peak hours each day can be distributed over the 10 peak hours, while the 500 sfd in the forebay must be distributed over 50 peak hours during the week. The water available for peak load will then be

$$q' = q + \frac{14q}{10} + \frac{500 \times 24}{50} = 2.4q + 240 \tag{20-33}$$

The curve CD of Fig. 20-31 is plotted from Eq. (20-33) until it reaches 2000 cfs. The peak production is therefore given by the curve CDJ. Since 250 cfs per day is required to fill the forebay over week ends, the flow available for week-end power is

$$q'' = q - 250 \tag{20-34}$$

This defines the line EF to the time corresponding to a natural flow of 1050 cfs, when full week-end power is available. Because of limited forebay capacity, all off-peak flow is required for storage until point K. The flow available for off-peak use [$q''' = (24q - 17{,}600)/14$] then increases until the total daily requirement for all purposes (36,800 cfs-hours or 1530 sfd) is reached. The off-peak duration curve is the line KMN. The total annual production may be determined by computing the area under the three curves and converting to appropriate power units. It will be noted in the problem that a larger forebay would permit increased production of peak power equivalent to the area EPK, which represents water used over week ends because of lack of pondage.

Mass curves. Some problems involving storage can be solved conveniently by use of the *mass curve*. In Fig. 20-32 the accumulated monthly flows of the Sacandaga River at Hope, New York, for the water years 1939 to 1942, have been plotted as a mass curve, *i.e.*, accumulated flow up to any time plotted at that date. Straight lines on the diagram represent constant rates of flow as shown on the slope scale in the lower right of the figure. The slope of the straight line AB connecting the end points of the mass curve represents the average flow over the period, 890 cfs. The straight line CD parallel to AB and tangent to the mass curve at its lowest point G is called a *use line*. The storage volume required to permit continuous release of water at the rate of 890 cfs is given by the greatest ordinate between the use line and the mass curve, in this case EF, or 210,000 sfd. A reservoir with this capacity would be full at F (assuming it contained a volume equal to CL at time C) and would be empty at time G.

If it is desired to determine the necessary storage for some other uniform rate of flow, straight lines such as FJ and HI are drawn tangent to the high points of the mass curve, with a slope equal to the desired flow (600 cfs in this case). The required storage is given by the maximum ordinate between such lines and the mass curve, or in this case JK, which is equal to 100,000 sfd. Many other problems may be solved by application of these principles. For example, the maximum uniform flow possible with a given storage can be determined by locating the line with the smallest slope which will be tangent to the mass curve and have a maximum departure from it

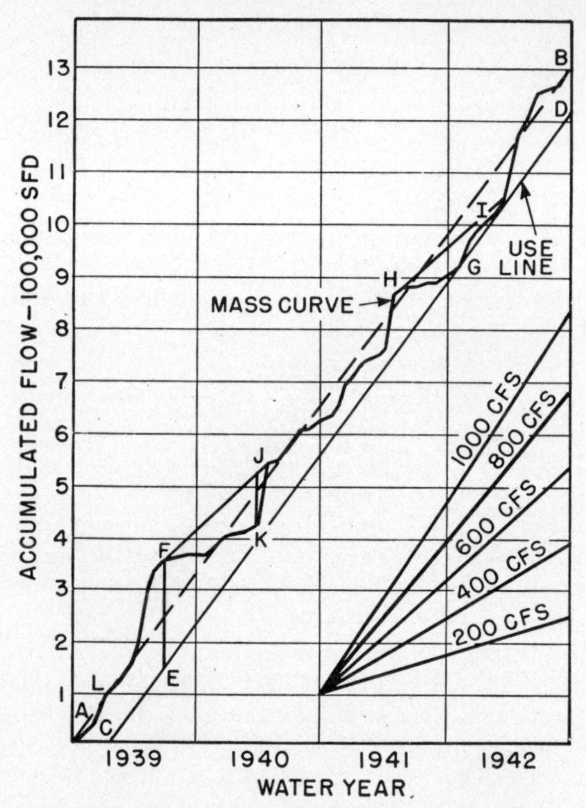

FIG. 20–32. Mass curve for the Sacandaga River at Hope, New York, showing analysis of storage requirements to maintain various flows.

equal to the assumed storage volume. Thus, in Fig. 20-33 the lines AB, CD, and EF are drawn so that their maximum departure from the mass curve in each case is 100,000 cfs. The line AB has the minimum slope. Thus, the maximum uniform flow possible with 100,000 sfd of available storage is that indicated by AB, or 630 cfs.

In practice the observed flows should be adjusted for evaporation and seepage losses before an analysis is performed. Many reservoirs have failed to deliver the expected flow because of these losses. The analysis should be applied to each segment of the record in which periods of excessively low flow occurred in order to determine the storage required in the worst case. If the withdrawal from the reservoir is not to take place at a uniform rate, a use line conforming to the expected withdrawals must be constructed. Such a problem will be encountered in irrigation work, where the withdrawal will fluctuate on a seasonal basis. The use line in such cases is a mass curve of the expected withdrawals accumulated month by month over a

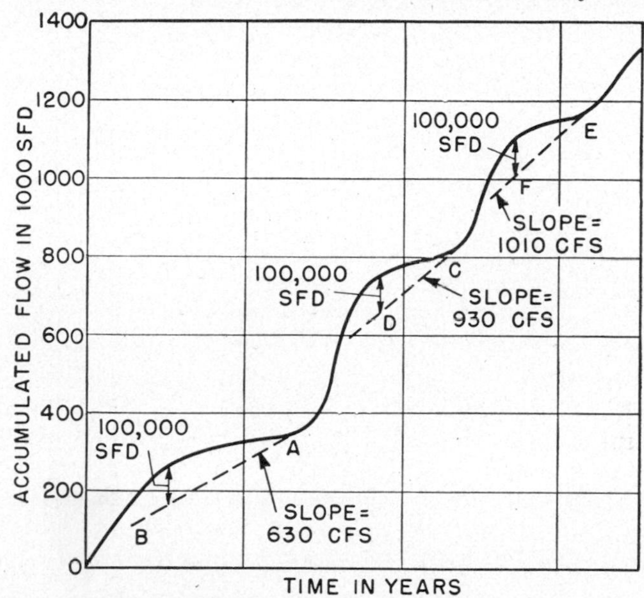

FIG. 20–33. Use of a mass curve to determine flow available with a given storage capacity.

period of several years. It should be plotted on transparent paper to the same scale as the mass curve. It may then be superimposed on the mass curve with the time scale matching, *i.e.*, December against December, and with the use line tangent to the mass curve. The maximum ordinate between the two curves represents the storage required to ensure withdrawal corresponding to the assumed use line.

HYDROMETEOROLOGICAL STUDIES

There can be little doubt that there exists some physical upper limit to the magnitudes of storms and floods. As Horton[1] has said, "A small stream cannot produce a major Mississippi River flood, for much the same reason that an ordinary barnyard fowl cannot lay an egg a yard in diameter; it would transcend nature's capabilities under the circumstances." Hazen,

[1] Horton, R. E., Hydrologic Conditions as Affecting the Results of the Application of Methods of Frequency Analysis to Flood Records, *U.S. Geol. Survey Water Supply Paper* 771, p. 438, 1936.

Foster, Gumbel, and others have outlined frequency analyses based on the assumption that no such limit exists, while Slade and Horton assume a limit in the determination of their data. Since all frequency curves show a rapid decrease in frequency for small changes in flood magnitude near the extremes of record, these differing assumptions are of little practical concern in frequency analysis.

When major projects are under consideration, some knowledge of this physical upper limit will be of value to the designer. There is no practical way of assigning a frequency to the maximum possible event, but its return period is certainly so great that it has no significance in problems of project efficiency. Moreover, the magnitude of this limiting event is likely to be so great that it is generally not feasible to effect any significant control over the resulting flood. Nevertheless, dams constructed upstream from centers of population should be properly designed to withstand such a flood so that their failure will not further augment the damage the flood would otherwise cause. Sound planning also dictates the construction of essential facilities—power plants, water works, military establishments, etc.—in locations safe from the threat of the maximum possible flood whenever feasible.

The concept of the maximum possible storm has been discussed by several writers.[1] The first practical application of meteorology to such studies dates from cooperative efforts by the Corps of Engineers and the U.S. Weather Bureau in 1937. The first study concerned the possibility of extreme concurrent floods in the Missouri and Ohio Basins—an event which was determined to be meteorologically impossible. Shortly after the completion of this study the Hydrometeorological Section was established in the U.S. Weather Bureau to perform such studies for the Corps of Engineers on a continuing basis. Most of the fundamental techniques now in use have been developed by this section in its several reports.[2]

[1] Bernard, M., The Primary Role of Meteorology in Flood Flow Estimating, *Trans. ASCE*, Vol. 109, pp. 311-382, 1944.

Showalter, A. K., and S. B. Solot, Computation of Maximum Possible Precipitation, *Trans. Am. Geophys. Union*, Vol. 23, pp. 258-274, 1942.

Bailey, S. M., and G. R. Schneider, The Maximum Probable Flood and Its Relation to Spillway Capacity, *Civil. Eng.*, Vol. 9, pp. 32-35, 1939.

[2] Maximum Possible Precipitation, Ompompanoosuc Basin above Union Village, Vermont, *U.S. Weather Bur. Hydrometeorolog. Rept.* 1, 1943.

Maximum Possible Precipitation, Ohio River Basin above Pittsburgh, Pa., *U.S. Weather Bur. Hydrometeorolog. Rept.* 2, 1942.

Maximum Possible Precipitation, Sacramento River Basin, *U.S. Weather Bur. Hydrometeorolog. Rept.* 3, 1943.

Maximum Possible Precipitation, Panama Canal Zone, *U.S. Weather Bur. Hydrometeorolog. Rept.* 4, 1943.

Maximum Possible Precipitation, San Joaquin River Basin, *U.S. Weather Bur. Hydrometeorolog. Rept.* 24, 1947.

Present-day meteorological knowledge is not adequate to explain fully the meteorological factors involved in major storms. Hence, a hydrometeorological analysis involves considerable judgment. This fact, coupled with the vast number of data which must be processed, makes such studies a job for a large staff of highly trained meteorologists. The discussion which follows is aimed, not at teaching the reader how to perform hydrometeorological studies, but rather at giving him some understanding of the basic principles involved so that he will better understand the significance of those studies which come to his attention.

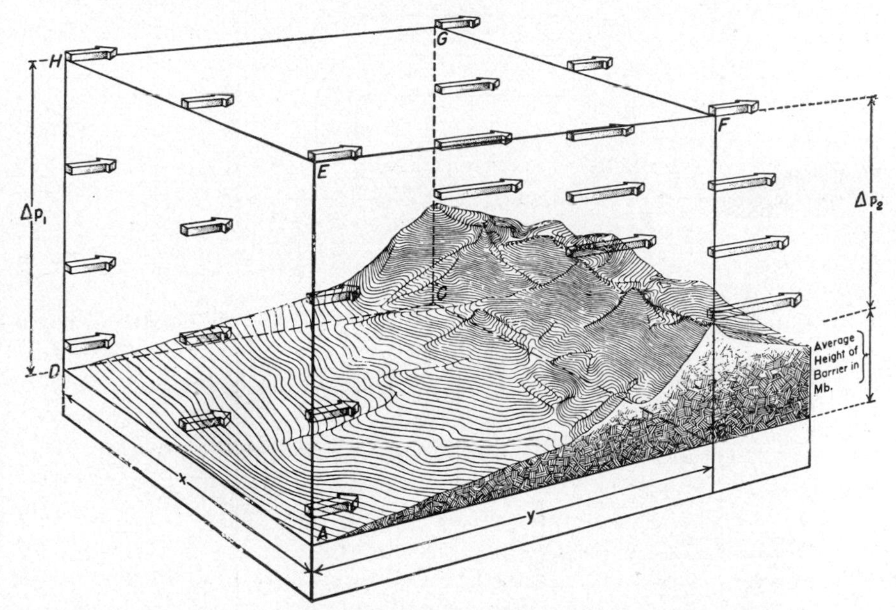

FIG. 20-34. A theoretical flow model in mountainous terrane. *(U.S. Weather Bureau.)*

The equation of continuity. The basic equation of hydrometeorology is the equation of continuity,

$$I - P = O \tag{20-35}$$

where I and O are the moisture inflow and outflow, respectively, and P is precipitation. The equation states that the volume of precipitation over a basin is equal to the difference between the volume of moisture entering the basin and that leaving it. This equation can also be expressed in terms of atmospheric models, one of which is reproduced in Fig. 20-34. As is evident from the figure, the models used must be varied to suit the particular topography and meteorological characteristics of the basin. For a very small area a simple convective cell (Fig. 20-35) may be used.

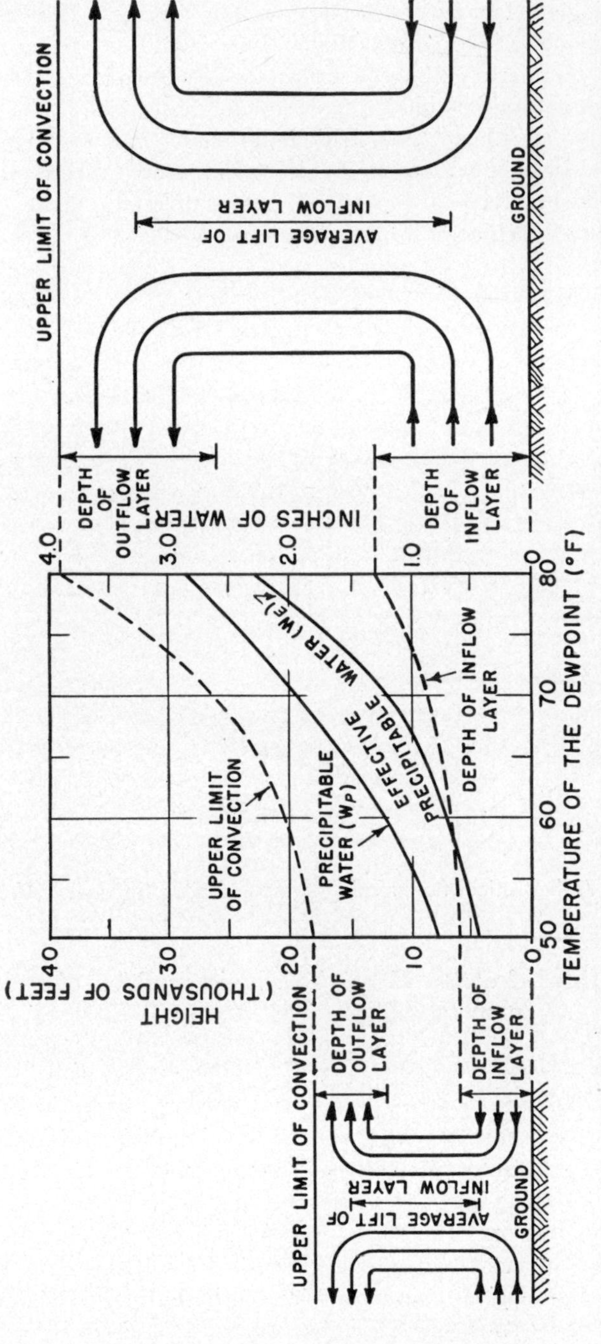

FIG. 20–35. Model of a simple convective cell showing the variation in height with dewpoint. (*U.S. Weather Bureau.*)

Moisture inflow to a basin is dependent on the humidity and rate of movement of the inflowing air. Since we are dealing with an atmosphere of considerable depth, it would be desirable to have measurements of the variation of wind and humidity with height above the ground surface. Unfortunately, observations of this type were begun only a few years ago, and even today data on upper-air winds associated with storm situations are very meager. In addition, the moisture charge must usually be estimated from surface observations.

Storm transposition. Another concept basic to hydrometeorology is that of *storm transposition, i.e.*, the application of a storm from one area to some other area within the same region of meteorological homogeneity. Storm transposition requires the determination of whether the particular storm could have occurred in the area to which it is to be transposed. For example, hurricane rains occurring along the Gulf Coast cannot be transposed more than a few miles inland since hurricanes dissipatc rapidly after crossing a shore line. On the other hand, convective thunderstorms can occur almost anywhere, and it is reasonable to transpose thunderstorm values large distances. Other types of storms are intermediate between these extremes, depending on the meteorological and topographic features of their area of occurrence. Storms in mountainous regions cannot be transposed, for the magnitude and areal distribution of precipitation are conditioned by the topography, and no method is now known by which the necessary adjustments for topography can be accomplished.

Related also to the transposition of storms are questions of change in shape and orientation of the isohyetal pattern. A storm with elliptical isohyets having their major axes perpendicular to the major axis of an elliptical basin will produce a much lower average rain over the basin than the same storm with its isohyets coinciding with the basin shape. Hence, the question of reorientation or change in shape of the isohyetal pattern may play a significant role in determining the magnitude of the storm event as expressed in average basin rainfall. Again, the problem depends largely on the meteorological characteristics of the region and the storm. For small basins in flat terrane where the governing storms are largely thunderstorms, almost any change in orientation or shape is permissible. On the other hand, the characteristic elongated patterns of rainfall occurring along a stationary front should not be changed in shape or greatly changed in orientation. In mountainous regions the rainfall pattern is largely fixed by topography; hence, the patterns are best defined by the major storms of the immediate area.

The decision that a storm may be transposed from one point to another does not completely solve the problem of transposition. It must still be decided whether the storm will be changed in magnitude by the transposition. Assuming that the dynamic features of the storm will be unchanged in transposition, then the principal factor remaining to affect the magnitude is the moisture charge. The moisture charge of the storm at its original site may be estimated from representative surface dewpoints in the warm sector by use of a precipitable-water chart (Fig. 4–2). The moisture charge must be adjusted for any difference in the height of the orographic barrier or basin elevation in the study area as compared with the original site.

Maximization. The simplest determination of the maximum possible storm involves the adjustment of observed storms upward to the precipitable-water content appropriate to the maximum observed dewpoints in the area of interest. Because the primary source of moisture in the atmosphere is the ocean, where surface temperatures in excess of 80°F are rare, surface dewpoints above 80°F cannot be considered indicative of moisture in depth. Statistical analysis[1] of observed dewpoints indicates regional limits, generally decreasing with distance from the moisture source.

It has already been stated that no adequate wind data are available for most storms; hence, it is impracticable to maximize the wind in the storm. By adjusting several storms to the maximum precipitable water on the basis of the dewpoints and selecting the largest as the maximum possible, reasonable values are obtained. This obviously involves the assumption that, among the several storms available for analysis, at least one approached the maximum dynamic efficiency possible for a storm of its type. If a sufficient number of storms are available, this assumption appears to be reasonable. It should be noted that the maximum storm of record in the region may not prove to be the storm with maximum efficiency. In many cases a lesser storm when adjusted for moisture charge will exceed the adjusted value of the recorded maximum.

The hydrometeorologist must often answer a number of other questions in connection with his study. He may be asked to determine the maximum possible or most critical snow cover prior to the storm or to define the variation in magnitude of the maximum possible storm throughout the year so that the combination of maximum winter rain and snowmelt may be compared with the maximum summer rain to determine which will cause the greatest flood. He may also be asked to indicate how soon prior to the maximum possible storm another major storm could have occurred. This latter question affects the problem of soil conditions antecedent to the maximum possible storm as well as available reservoir capacity to store its runoff. These questions and others can be answered with varying degrees of objectivity depending on the quantity and quality of data available and the meteorological complexities of the area.

Generalized charts. Complete hydrometeorological analyses involve an immense amount of work which may not be justified for preliminary

[1] Maximum Persisting Dewpoints in Western United States, *U.S. Weather Bur. Tech. Paper* 5, 1948

studies. To overcome this obstacle the Hydrometeorological Section developed a series of generalized charts[1] for small areas and short durations (Figs. 20-36 to 20-43). These charts were developed by transposing and adjusting all major storms of record to all points within their respective limits of transposition. Enveloping isopleths of maximum possible precipitation were then drawn on the maps. The mountain area of the West was not included because of the limitations of the technique, and areas of considerable relief in the East have been shaded as areas of doubtful reliability.

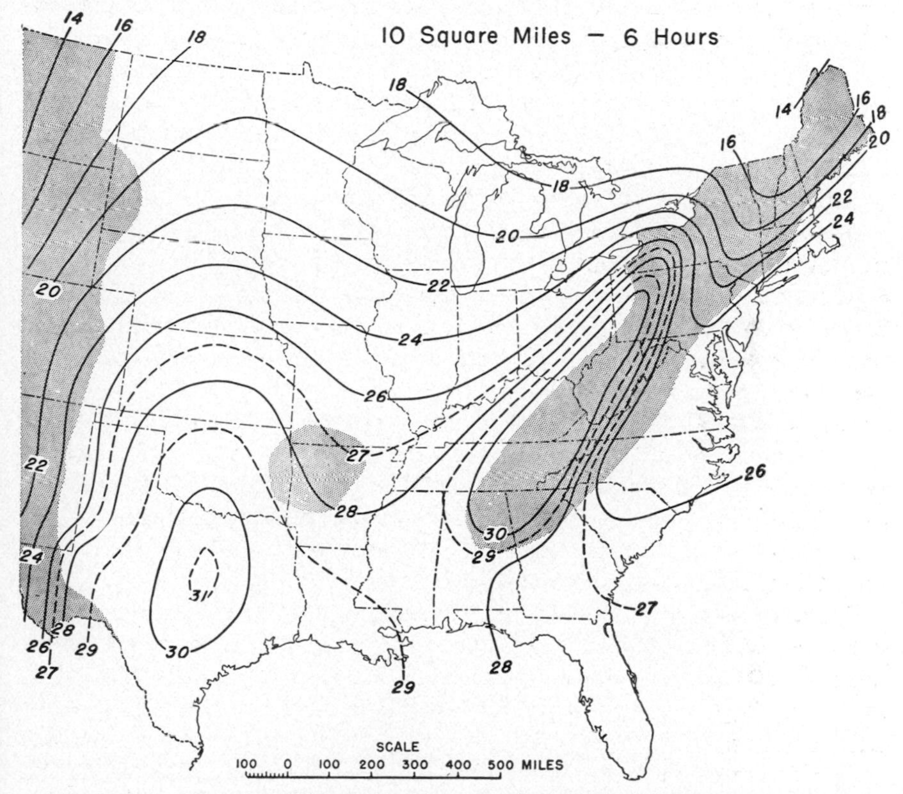

FIG. 20–36. Generalized chart of maximum possible precipitation for areas of 10 square miles and duration of 6 hr. *(U.S. Weather Bureau–Corps of Engineers.)*

In using these charts it must be constantly borne in mind that they are intended for preliminary studies only. A detailed analysis of a particular area might disclose considerable deviation from the generalized contours because of local topography or other factors. The charts are applicable only to the areas and durations shown and should not be extrapolated beyond these limits.

[1] Generalized Charts of Maximum Possible Precipitation, *U.S. Weather Bur. Hydrometeorolog. Rept.* 23, 1947.

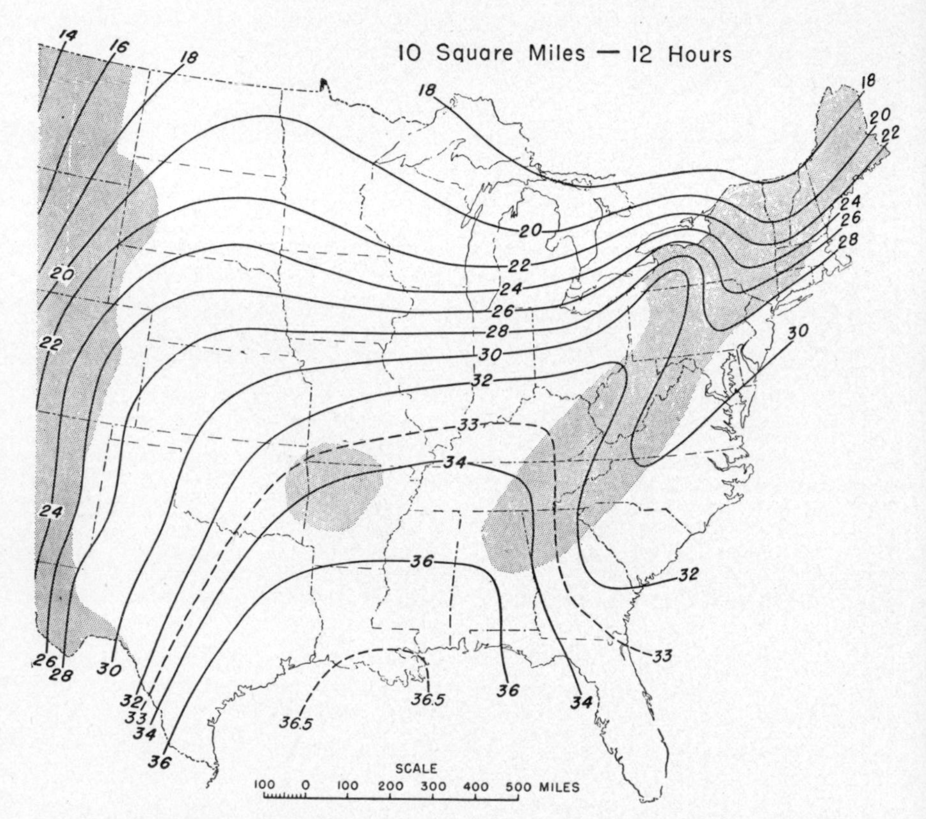

FIG. 20–37. Generalized chart of maximum possible precipitation for areas of 10 square miles and duration of 12 hr. *(U.S. Weather Bureau–Corps of Engineers.)*

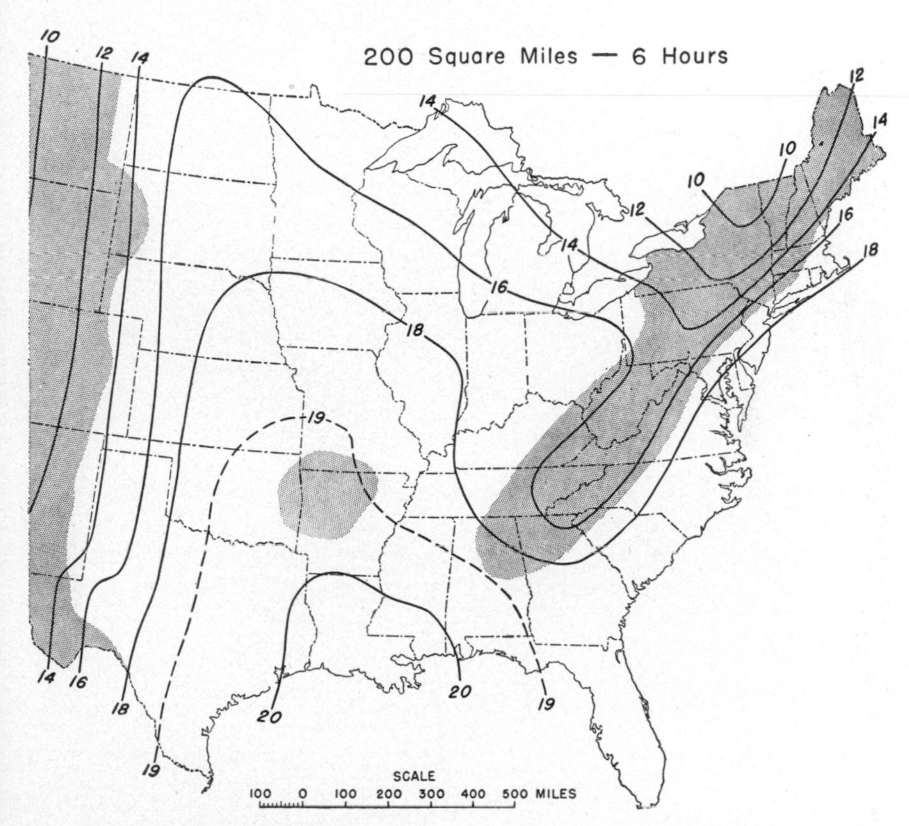

FIG. 20–38. Generalized chart of maximum possible precipitation for areas of 200 square miles and duration of 6 hr. *(U.S. Weather Bureau–Corps of Engineers.)*

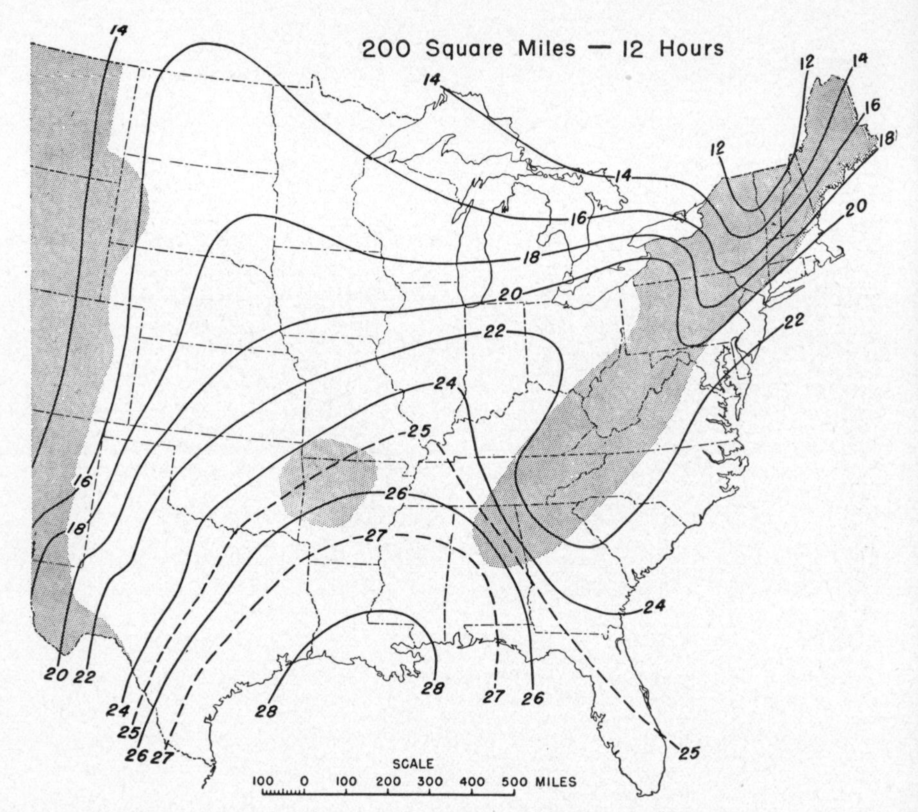

FIG. 20–39. Generalized chart of maximum possible precipitation for areas of 200 square miles and duration of 12 hr. *(U.S. Weather Bureau–Corps of Engineers.)*

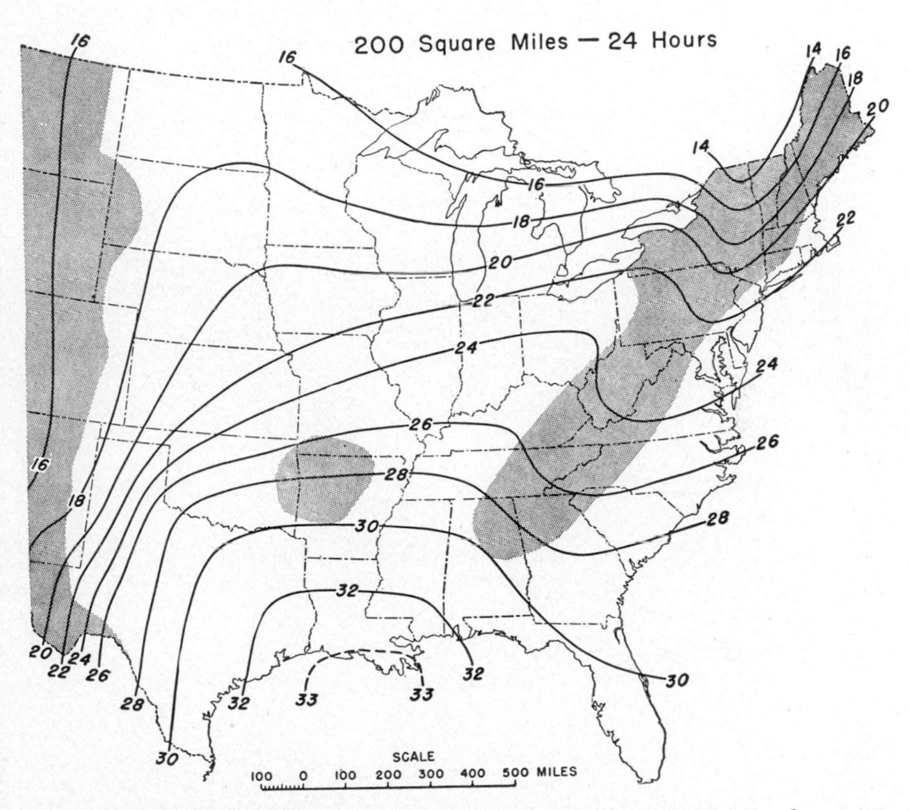

FIG. 20–40. Generalized chart of maximum possible precipitation for areas of 200 square miles and duration of 24 hr. *(U.S. Weather Bureau–Corps of Engineers.)*

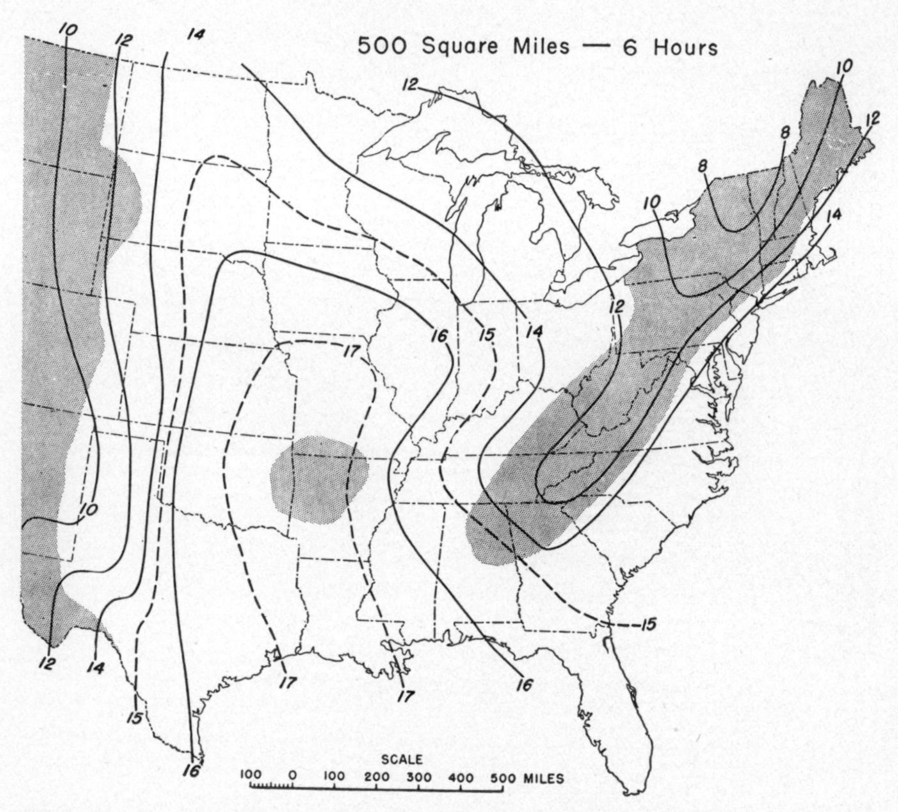

FIG. 20–41. Generalized chart of maximum possible precipitation for areas of 500 square miles and duration of 6 hr. *(U.S. Weather Bureau–Corps of Engineers.)*

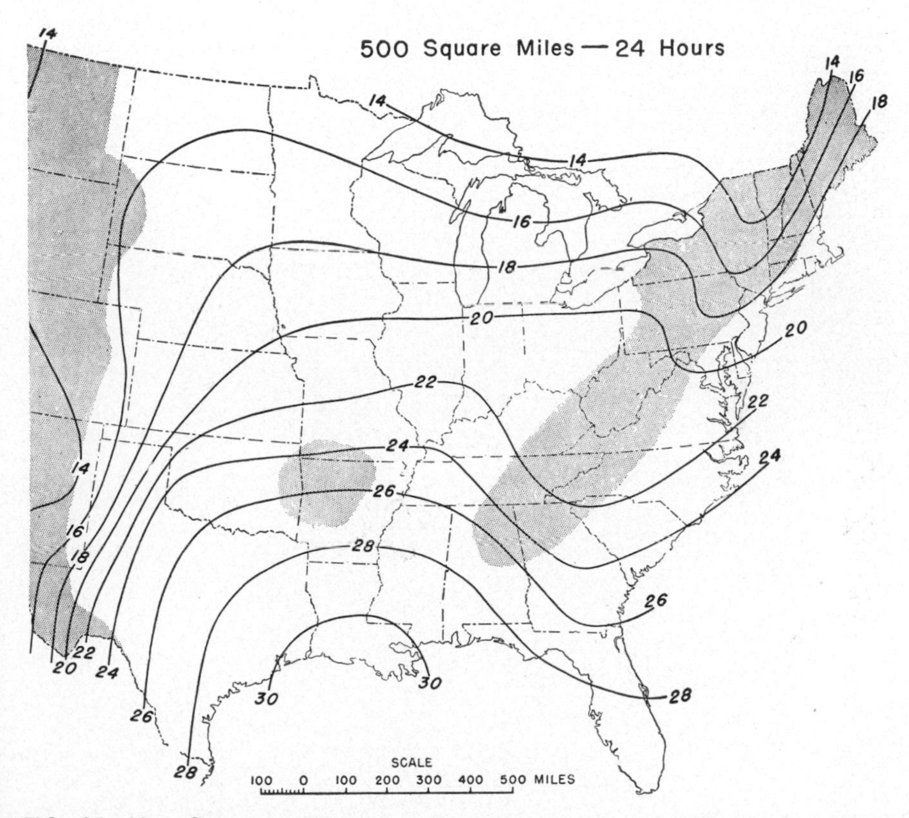

FIG. 20–42. Generalized chart of maximum possible precipitation for areas of 500 square miles and duration of 24 hr. *(U.S. Weather Bureau–Corps of Engineers.)*

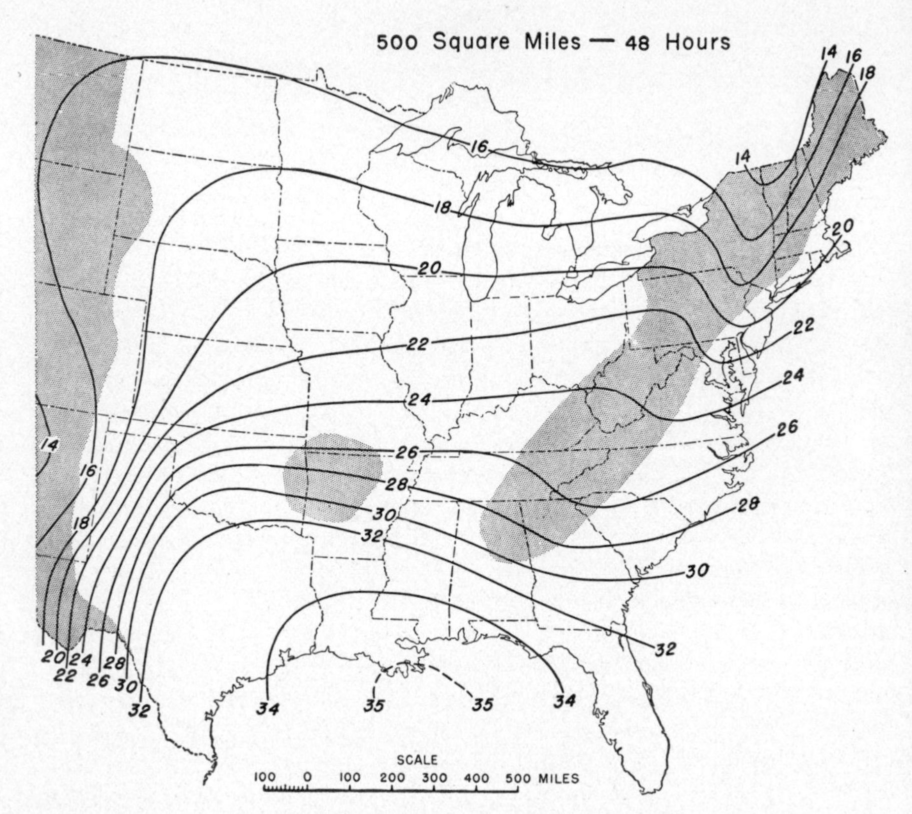

FIG. 20–43. Generalized chart of maximum possible precipitation for areas of 500 square miles and duration of 48 hr. (*U.S. Weather Bureau–Corps of Engineers.*)

21

DESIGN AND OPERATION OF WATER-CONTROL WORKS

The problems of hydrologic design depend so greatly on the physical characteristics of the basin and the project requirements that it cannot be said that a wholly standard design procedure exists. Attempts to rigorously standardize procedures into a fixed pattern would work against the attainment of maximum efficiency in design; hence, each project must be custom-built to the site. This chapter summarizes the procedures which are generally accepted and suggests those considerations which must be reviewed in all cases before the project design can be considered complete and accurate. In so doing, it relates the technical aspects of hydrology discussed in preceding chapters to the practical application in design.

The basic purpose of design is to evolve a structure which will properly serve a special purpose. In many cases river-control structures are not automatic in action, *i.e.*, they must be operated in accordance with current conditions. Unless the structure can be operated to perform its intended functions, it is worthless. Hence, operation problems are an important consideration in design, and both are discussed in this chapter.

Nature has achieved a delicate balance in the development of river systems. Encroachment on flood plains with buildings or levees, construction of reservoirs, or changes in land use disturb this balance, and nature seeks to adjust accordingly. In some cases, the natural adjustments after completion of a project have destroyed the project effectiveness. Most such failures would have been eliminated by thorough design studies. Cursory determination of a design flood by semiempirical methods is far from adequate even for modest projects. The effects that the project will have on the entire regime of the river system must be considered to ensure that they will not deprive the project of its intended economic values. This can be done best by careful study of the actual processes taking place in the basin. The use of empirical formulas or the transposition of results from adjacent basins may fail because of unrecognized deficiencies of the method. If long records are not already available on the particular stream, every effort should be made to collect as many data as possible before the final design is adopted. Better still, the need for data should be anticipated as far in advance as possible and the necessary gages installed in advance of the design work.

It should be emphasized that the cost of hydrologic design is normally a very small part of the total project cost. Consequently, short cuts in procedure to reduce this cost further are not justified. The difference between an approximate solution and a thorough study of the hydrology of the project basin is usually small when considered in terms of total project costs. It is rare indeed that either the demands of time or the need to reduce costs is sufficient to justify an inadequate design procedure. If this be the case, it is better to discontinue plans for the project until adequate funds and time are available. The instances of project failure because of inadequate design, although by no means a high percentage of the total projects constructed, are numerous enough to offset the savings achieved by short-cut design practices.

DESIGN OF DAMS AND RESERVOIRS

General requirements. The design studies for all dams and reservoirs regardless of their intended purpose have certain aspects in common. Foremost among these is that of safety, which was discussed in some detail in the introductory portion of the preceding chapter. Safety in design requires that the spillway be adequate to discharge a flood frequently known as the *spillway-design flood*. On small structures where failure would not have serious results downstream, the criterion will usually be the probable maximum flood to be expected during the economic life of the structure. Larger dams are often designed to withstand the maximum flood which can develop within the basin.

The magnitude of the spillway-design flood is best determined by estimating the rainfall to be expected under the assumed design criteria and synthesizing the reservoir-inflow hydrograph by use of a rainfall-runoff relation and a unit hydrograph. In large basins, hydrographs for subareas may be routed to the dam site. The resulting inflow hydrograph may then be reduced in accord with the storage space which may be expected in the reservoir. The amount of storage available will be determined by the anticipated operating schedule for the reservoir and by the conditions which may be assumed to precede the spillway-design flood. The two great floods of May, 1943, in the Lower Arkansas Basin and the three successive crests in the Lower Missouri and Upper Mississippi Basin in July, 1947, are indicative of conditions which would have brought any but the largest reservoir to capacity before the final flood peak and, hence, suggest the conservative estimate of a full pool prior to the crest of the spillway-design flood. In more arid portions of the country, such conservatism may not be justified.

Sediment deposits threaten the useful life of almost all reservoirs in this country (Chap. 13). Hence, any design study should include estimates of the probable sediment inflows to the reservoir. Where feasible, provisions for flushing accumulated sediment and for use of density currents to discharge silt-laden water, as well as watershed management practices in the tributary basin, may be adopted to prolong the life of the reservoir. The construction of upstream reservoirs to trap the silt is not necessarily successful. Although the inflowing silt may be deposited in the upstream reservoir, the discharge from this reservoir will pick up a new load from the reach between reservoirs. The extent of the new load will depend on the sediment delivery by intervening tributaries, the character of the stream channel, and the rate and volume of upstream discharge.

Many dams have been designed and constructed without realizing that serious leakage would develop through the reservoir banks. The effect of such leakage may be only the loss of water intended for beneficial use below the reservoir, or it may cause springs, a high water table, or swamps in the area of outflow, which may be many miles from the reservoir itself. Hence, a thorough geologic investigation of the reservoir site is necessary, particularly when the site is in a region of basalt or limestone deposits.

Flood-control reservoir. In addition to the general design requirements just outlined, there are special considerations depending on the particular purpose for which the project is intended. In the case of a proposed flood-control reservoir, it is necessary to determine the degree of flood protection offered. This requires that an operating plan for the reservoir be assumed and that actual floods of various magnitudes be routed through the reservoir following the proposed operation schedule. From the results of routing, it is possible to predict the amount of flood reduction at critical points downstream. To evaluate the monetary benefit resulting from the proposed project, it is customary to develop a curve showing the relation between stage and resulting flood damage at points of hazard. From the estimated flood-crest reduction, the known frequency of flooding, and the stage-damage curve, it is possible to make an estimate of the damage reduction which could be effected if the reservoir were to be constructed and operated over a period of years according to the assumed plan. Similar studies must be made for several different operating plans and for alternate reservoir capacities and locations until the most feasible project is determined.

In economic studies it is important to consider the potential benefits very carefully. The stage-damage curve is usually based on recorded damages during some previous flood. It frequently happens that the citizens learn from such a flood that they will suffer damage if they continue to occupy the flood plain. As a result they may take steps to remove their property from the danger zone or to provide local protection which will prevent a recurrence of such damage. Consequently, it is very often true that stage-damage data based on previous floods are too high. Even after a project has been shown to be economically justified, it should be compared with alternate methods of flood-damage reduction to determine which method has the best cost-benefit ratio.

Too often design studies are conducted without serious consideration of the operation problems. Reservoir operation is discussed in more detail in the next section, but it should be emphasized that an essential feature of design must be the assurance that adequate forecasts can be available upon which to base operating decisions. It is a fairly simple matter to decide what should have been done in a past flood with all the data at hand. It is far more difficult to make decisions in advance of a flood. Most operating plans assume that, after the flood crest is past, the accumulated storage will be discharged to provide space for a future flood. If, as in the case of the Upper Yazoo River reservoirs, 2 or 3 weeks are required for water to reach the lower portion of the river, the operator can have no assurance that a second flood will not occur during this period. If a second flood were to develop, the resulting discharges downstream might well be higher than the natural flows.

One of the most successful flood-control reservoirs is that which is self-regulating, *i.e.*, in lieu of movable gates the flow is controlled by a fixed orifice or series of orifices at different elevations. In such reservoirs, typified by the Miami River system in Ohio, the outflow is a direct function of the volume of water in storage during the flood, and the flood crest at the dam is always reduced. The reservoir automatically empties after the flood and is always ready to receive the runoff from succeeding storms. Careful design of the reservoir capacities to regulate extreme flows properly ensures the success of the operation in all floods. A feature of the design which must be carefully studied is the problem of synchronization of downstream crests. The reservoirs must be so constructed that the crest delay does not result in simultaneous arrival of flow from several tributaries at a vulnerable downstream point. Thus, the design of retarding basins requires extensive trial routing of floods through the reaches below the reservoirs to find the system which offers optimum control.

Irrigation and water supply. Problems of irrigation and water supply are concerned far more with long-period flow volumes than with flood peaks. Except for the spillway-design flood, peak flows need not be considered in the design of reservoirs solely for water storage. However, since it is usually practical to effect some flood control with any storage reservoir, potential flood-control benefits are usually determined for such projects.

The basic problem in design of water-supply and irrigation works is the determination of available flow volumes. This is usually accomplished through the use of flow-duration curves and mass curves (Chap. 20). Among other things, the study must demonstrate that the proposed reservoir will not reduce rather than increase usable water. A water-supply reservoir is intended to store water in periods of surplus and to discharge this water as required during low-flow seasons. This increases the usable water supply by reducing waste during periods of excess flow. However, additional evaporation from the water surface created by the reservoir and leakage through the reservoir banks tends to counteract these benefits. Several reservoirs in the Western states now stand empty because the induced losses more than offset the storage benefits. Therefore, the observed flows should be reduced by estimated increased evaporation and seepage losses before they are subjected to mass- or duration-curve analysis. Streamflow data should also be tested for time trend (Chap. 16) and adjusted as necessary. The evidence pointing to trend adjustments, sometimes exceeding 25 per cent in early years, cannot be ignored in project design.

Although the operation of storage works does not demand the critical analysis necessary for flood-control operations, the efficiency of storage works can be considerably increased by accurate forecasts of future inflow. Such forecasts allow advance planning of water use and are particularly important if existing water rights on the stream must be satisfied before the reservoir can be filled. Without forecasts, much flow may be wasted before it is determined that the requirements of these prior rights can be met. Hence, a study of the requirement for forecasting and the reliability of such forecasts should be an integral part of the design.

In planning domestic or industrial water-supply projects, it is necessary to be certain that the water is of satisfactory quality. While irrigation requirements do not demand the quality of water necessary for domestic consumption, a high salt content can make water unfit for irrigation use. Therefore, samples of water from the source should be checked for quality before the project design is far under way. These samples should be taken at various times of the year and under different conditions of flow so that the variations in quality may be determined.

Any water-supply project must include facilities for distributing the water to the consumer. Domestic water distribution is usually accomplished by pipe lines, which pose no problem in hydrologic design. Irrigation water is, however, commonly distributed through a system of open canals. Leakage through the bed and banks of an unlined canal can be very large. Often the cost of lining the canals with concrete or stabilizing the canal banks with soil cements, bentonite, or other filler will be repaid many times. Similar losses may be encountered if the flow from the reservoir is discharged into the stream channel. If the channel is dry before the release, heavy losses may result and several days or even weeks may be required before the full release is realized at downstream points.

If natural flows in a stream are adequate to meet the need of the users, a large reservoir is unnecessary. Usually, a small dam is constructed to establish a minimum water level at the head of the diversion canal or to increase the head in the canal. The flow quantities available for use can be determined by duration-curve analysis. If the requirements are seasonal, as is the usual case, the duration analysis should be restricted to the critical period. Diversion dams are usually small, and their failure would have little consequence on flood conditions downstream. However, the failure of such a dam might make it impossible to irrigate substantial areas if the structure could not be replaced promptly. Hence, a diversion dam should be designed to withstand a reasonably extreme flood, a flood with a recurrence interval greater than the estimated useful life of the structure.

Power development. With the exception of the problem of water quality, the design of power reservoirs is quite similar to that of irrigation reservoirs. In contrast to irrigation usage, however, power requirements do not usually show such marked seasonal variation. Hence, a more uniform delivery of water is necessary for successful hydroelectric-power operation, and the use of run-of-river plants for power development is less frequent. The fortunate occurrence of the major portion of the runoff as snowmelt during the early part of the irrigation season in much of the West makes extensive irrigation possible without storage. This same condition, however, necessitates a considerable storage reserve to provide the uniform flows required for power development.

In considering a power project in regions of wide seasonal variation in flow, it is well to consider a mixed system with steam- or diesel-operated generating equipment providing a source of auxiliary power during periods of water shortage. With reliable forecasts of long-period streamflow, it is possible to schedule use of water for maximum efficiency and to plan purchases of fuel for the auxiliary plants. System design is an important aspect of power planning. An integrated system of moderate installations on several streams is a far better guarantee of adequate power at all times than a single large plant.

An interesting example of system planning is afforded by the Lake Candlewood development of the Connecticut Light and Power Company. This reservoir is formed by a dam on Rocky River, a small tributary of the Housatonic River, in western Connecticut, and the generating station is located on the bank of the Housatonic River. Rocky River can supply only a small portion of the capacity of the reservoir. The company has several other plants, including some run-of-river plants where water was formerly wasted during off-peak periods. This water is used to develop power with which to pump water from the Housatonic River through the penstocks into the reservoir during off-peak periods. The water so stored is available for use during peak periods or periods of low flow. While the mechanical efficiency of the Lake Candlewood plant is naturally low, it is economically sound.

The amount of hydroelectric energy developed at a reservoir depends on both the volume of water available and the head through which the water falls to the turbine. Most turbines attain maximum efficiency within a narrow range of head, with efficiency decreasing in both directions from this point. Thus, a wide variation in pool elevation affects power production adversely, both through loss of head and through loss of efficiency. Therefore, it is necessary to select a turbine which has a range of maximum efficiency which will permit optimum production within the range of reservoir fluctuations.

In mountainous terrane it is often feasible to develop high-head plants by conducting water through a pressure conduit from a small reservoir at a high elevation to a power plant at a much lower elevation. Since only relatively small volumes of water are required because of the high head, the reservoir need not be large. The fluctuations of the water surface are small compared with the total head, and the turbine can function within its range of maximum efficiency at all times. A number of such plants often offers a far more economical source of power together with the advantages of system operation than the enormous projects favored by Federal agencies.

Multiple-purpose reservoirs. The recent trend in this country has been toward the construction of multiple-purpose projects. No one can deny the economic advantages of multiple-use structures, but these advantages are sometimes exaggerated. The requirements for optimum operation of a project for each of several purposes are in conflict to some degree, if not diametrically opposed. Flood control requires an empty reservoir in advance of floods if maximum benefits are to be attained. Power development requires that water levels be kept as high as possible at all times for maximum production. Irrigation operation dictates a seasonal release of water during the growing season, while power requirements are more nearly uniform throughout the year, with maximum demand, if any, during the winter season. Recreational uses require a full pool during the recreation season.

It is obvious, therefore, that the essential feature of practical multiple-use design is compromise—a compromise which must result in something less than maximum possible benefits from any one of the uses but which realizes the maximum benefits from the project as a whole. Vitally important, also, to practical multiple-use projects is an accurate forecast service. Thus, if a reliable estimate of expected water supply for the summer months is available, it is possible to schedule power releases during the winter season and yet be assured of sufficient irrigation water to meet summer needs. Similarly, with satisfactory flood forecasts, it may prove possible to draw down a combined power and flood-control reservoir in advance of floods and supply necessary storage for flood control without seriously reducing power production. The problems of operation of multipurpose projects are discussed in more detail in the following section. It is sufficient here to emphasize that knowledge of the possible accuracy of forecasts becomes essential to design, for if the planned operations cannot be carried out as intended, the multiple-purpose use fails. Such failure frequently places power development, which is a source of direct revenue, in a preferred position in contrast to flood control, which returns only indirect benefits to the operating agency.

The techniques of design of multi-purpose projects are the same as those outlined in the preceding sections for single-purpose reservoirs. Because the aim of multiple-purpose design is to attain the most beneficial combination of uses, many trials of various combinations of equipment and operating plans are required to determine which is most effective.

Reservoir systems. The benefits of system planning for power production have already been discussed. System planning of reservoirs becomes a natural consideration in multiple-use planning. Navigation, for example, requires a chain of reservoirs along a river. Enlarging the dams and installing power facilities makes it possible to generate power at these sites. However, such low-head reservoirs usually have relatively small flood-control capacity. This suggests the construction of headwater reservoirs for flood-control storage. Here, too, is a potential source of power, and the stored water is available to increase power production at the mainstream reservoirs during periods of low flow. Thus, it becomes progressively easier to justify each successive unit in the system as it contributes to the benefits of units already constructed. Fuel-burning power plants may also be added to the system to stabilize power production further.

System design has many obvious advantages in economy and efficiency, but these advantages bring with them a far more complex problem in design and operation. Once a system of reservoirs is started, there is a constant urge to add additional units because of the ease of justification. If some control is not exercised, all major stream channels in the area may be occupied by reservoirs throughout their length. Much highly productive farm land may be permanently flooded and agricultural activities forced into less valuable hillside land, with a corresponding disruption of local economy.

Far more serious, however, is the tendency for an increase in flood-peak flows. The difference between wave velocity in a natural channel and a deep reservoir is discussed in Chap. 18. Reservoirs greatly reduce the time of travel of flood peaks moving through them, and a system of reservoirs may cut several days from the normal travel time from headwaters to outlet. A general decrease in travel time acts to increase synchronization of peaks from tributaries, with resulting higher flood peaks in the lower basin. If ample storage is available in the reservoirs, skillful operation may more than overcome this effect and result in a net reduction in outflow from the system. If the storage is filled from a previous flood, there is no opportunity to control the wave movement and far greater discharge may occur downstream. Even if the peak flows are not increased, the reduced time to peak decreases the opportunity to take protective measures downstream.

Stock tanks. A practical development in water conservation which is expanding rapidly in the Middle West is the *stock-tank*, or *farm-pond*, program. These small reservoirs provide water storage for livestock and limited irrigation. At the same time, they act to retard and withhold surface runoff and must necessarily have a beneficial, although perhaps quite small, effect in reducing floods.

The efficiency of stock tanks as water-conservation structures is low. In many cases evaporation and seepage probably extract more water from the tank than is used for beneficial purposes. Evaporation can be minimized by maintaining the lowest practicable ratio of surface area to total volume. The flow volumes to be expected must be estimated from annual rainfall adjusted for evapo-transpiration and ground water accretion on the basis of soil types and land use in the contributing area. Actual precipitation or streamflow data at the site are almost never available, and the spillway-design flood is determined by use of published rainfall-frequency data and the rational formula.

RESERVOIR OPERATION

Rate of change of flow. Rapid fluctuation of discharge at low flows is undesirable if the reach below the reservoir is used for navigation. A sudden decrease in discharge may cause damage to watercraft tied up along the shore or result in the grounding of boats in transit. Sudden changes may also result in undesirable effects on scour or sedimentation immediately below the reservoir. A large increase in discharge accomplished suddenly may cause immense damage to waterside installations below the reservoir, especially if it occurs without warning. As a rule, therefore, it is necessary to place a definite restriction on the permissible rate of change in flow from a reservoir. This restriction is ordinarily not serious, since the majority of dams are not equipped with gates which can be opened simultaneously. Usually a traveling hoist must move into position over each gate successively, and considerable time is required to open all gates. In multiple-purpose design, however, a portion of the available flood-control storage is usually assumed to be that which can be emptied in advance of a flood.

This volume is sometimes limited by restrictions on maximum rates of change of flow.

Storage in long reservoirs. In short, deep headwater reservoirs, the storage may be computed on the assumption of a level pool; but on long main-stream pools such an assumption may be greatly in error. A considerable volume of water may be held in storage under the backwater profile if the inflow to the head of the reservoir is large. The storage curve for such a reservoir must therefore express the contents in terms of pool elevation at the dam and rate of inflow to the head of the reservoir. During periods of changing inflow or if an important tributary discharges into the reservoir, stages at three or more points along its length may be necessary to define the water-surface profile adequately. Before the dam is completed, the necessary storage curves can only be approximated from backwater computations. As soon as the pool is filled, several water-stage recorders should be installed along its length to obtain reliable information on the surface profile under various conditions of pool elevation and inflow.

If the inflow at the head of the pool is controlled by another dam, any change in flow at this dam has an immediate effect on the storage volume in the lower reservoir and must be carefully considered in planning an operation. A sudden decrease in discharge at the upstream dam will, for example, release a considerable volume from backwater storage in the lower pool. This water will shift to the lower end of the pool and cause a rapid rise in level at the dam. Unless the gates are adjusted to compensate for this increase in head, an increase in discharge will result.

Single-purpose operation. A reservoir planned for power or irrigation will ordinarily be maintained as nearly full as possible, with no releases in excess of current needs except when the reservoir is full. The principal operating problem for storage reservoirs is the determination of the safe rate of use during periods of low flow. On the basis of current storage reserves and expected future inflow, the operator must determine what average rate of withdrawal can be maintained until streamflow again increases above needs. Long-range forecasts of streamflow are discussed in the following chapter.

A flood-control reservoir will be maintained at minimum possible pool elevation at all times except during floods, when the release will be established at the maximum safe value and excess flows will be retained in storage. In the ideal case the operator will have before him a complete forecast of flows for such period in advance as is required to accomplish the necessary operation (Fig. 21-1). Until time A, when the volume of flow in excess of current discharge equals the available storage, all inflow will be discharged. Beginning at time A, the discharge will be regulated to a constant rate, and all inflow in excess of this rate will be stored. When the inflow again decreases to this rate, the reservoir will be full and the flood crest at the dam will have been reduced by the amount BC. The amount of reduction at downstream points will usually be less, depending on the effect of channel storage. If the constant-discharge rate is not in excess of safe flows downstream, the flow will be continued at this rate until the pool is emptied and the discharge again returns to the inflow rate. It is significant to note that this operation cannot be accomplished if the dam is not equipped with gates or valves adequate to discharge the necessary flows at low heads. High discharge capacity at normal minimum pool elevation is an important feature of a flood-control reservoir.

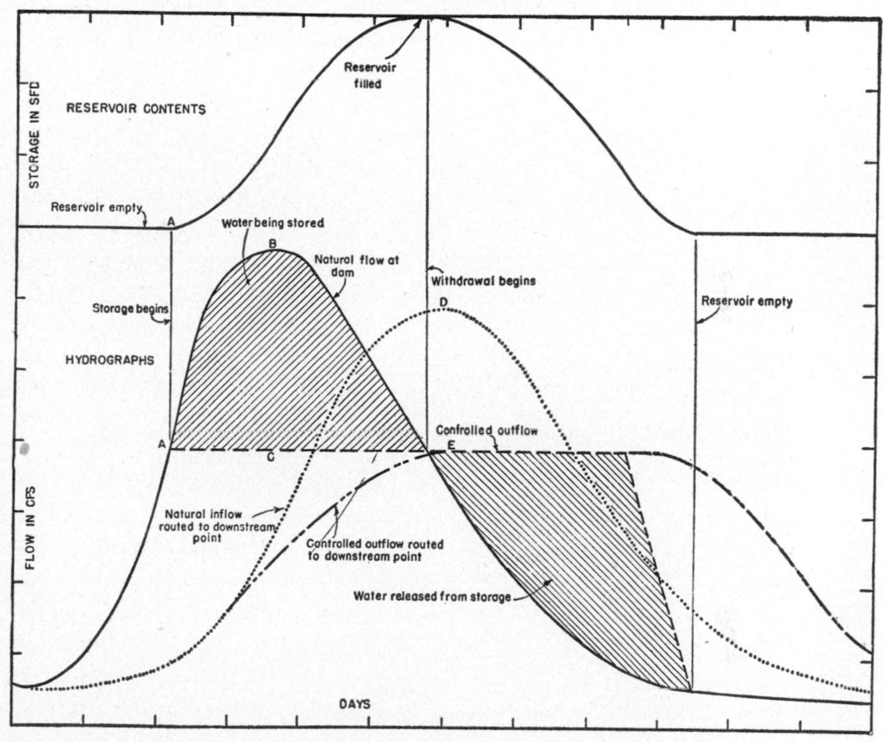

FIG. 21–1. The ideal flood-control operation.

The ideal flood-control operation necessarily requires an accurate forecast of inflows over a period of time sufficient to fill and empty the reservoir. A forecast of inflows to the stream below the dam is also necessary in order to avoid a total flow downstream in excess of the maximum safe flow. If forecasts do not extend sufficiently far in advance, there is always the risk that a subsequent storm will cause flows which cannot be properly regulated. This is a calculated risk which must be considered in design. To reduce this risk to a minimum, no more storage than is necessary to provide adequate protection downstream should be utilized during any flood, in order to reserve storage for control of a subsequent flood. The drawdown after a flood should be as rapid as possible consistent with the hazard of a subsequent flood occurring on a channel already filled by high releases from the dam. The operation plan should not be a rigorous rule devised to meet all conditions but must be a flexible plan based on the best forecasts available for maximum effectiveness. An operator who fails to take full advantage of all that the sciences of hydrology and meteorology can offer is neglectful of his responsibilities.

At some time most flood-control structures will be subjected to a flood which cannot be controlled within the established safe limits downstream. Under such conditions the operation must be planned with the utmost care. The objective is not necessarily to cut the peak off the reservoir inflow but to effect a maximum possible reduction at one or more points downstream. Figure 21-2 is a hypothetical case of the operation of a dam designed to protect the city of Riverside some distance downstream. It is assumed that the peak of the local inflow below the dam will pass Riverside before the crest from above the reservoir would arrive under natural conditions. The reservoir can be most effective by storing all possible inflow during the early stages of the flood (plan *A*). The crest reduction at the dam is less than that accomplished under plan *B*, but nevertheless the effect is to hold stages at Riverside to a minimum consistent with the streamflow and the capacity of the reservoir. This example is only one of an infinite variety of combinations which might be encountered. In each case an operation schedule must be assumed on the basis of predicted natural flows and the effect of this schedule determined by routing the proposed releases downstream. The trial may suggest a modification in the plan, which may be tested to determine its effectiveness. The process is repeated until the most effective plan is determined. It is appropriate to stress again the important role that forecasting of flows and weather plays in such an operation. The operation can be scheduled with certainty only as far ahead as reliable weather forecasts will permit the prediction of streamflow. If several days elapse between the release of water at the dam and its arrival at a downstream station, intervening rainfall may seriously affect the flow. The operator is helpless to rectify the situation once the water has left the reservoir. The relative ease with which it is possible to postulate the most effective operation when all data are before the designer should not be permitted to hide the true nature of the operating problem. Even within the time range of practicable forecasts, due allowance must be made for the inherent errors in the procedure.

The discussion has thus far dealt only with a single reservoir. If two or more reservoirs are in operation within a basin, the problem is further complicated although the operation may be more flexible. If a system of reservoirs is available, they must be operated as a system. To permit the

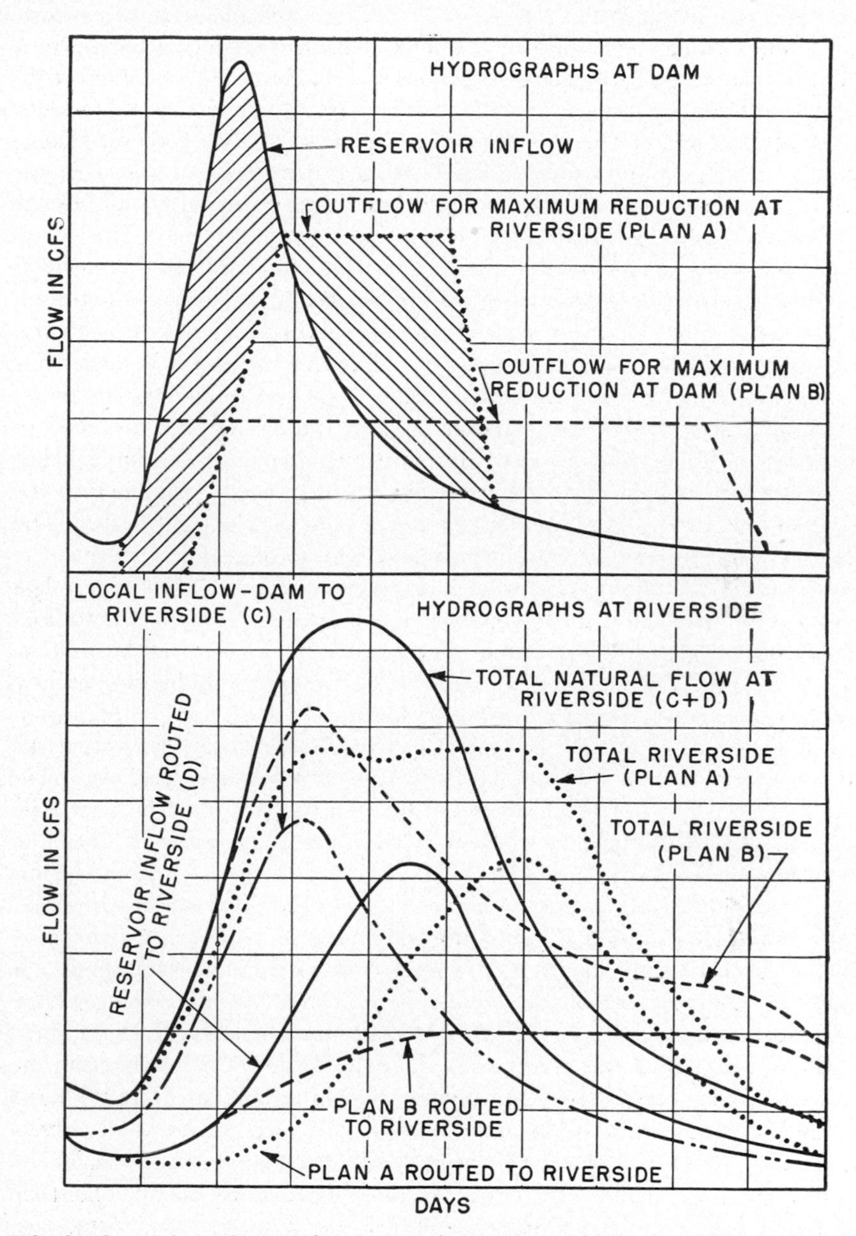

FIG. 21–2. A hypothetical flood-control operation with heavy inflow below the reservoir.

independent operation of each reservoir without consideration of proposed operations at the other dams may well result in increasing rather than decreasing the flood flows below the system. A central dispatcher's office should prepare forecasts of natural flows at each dam site and at various critical points below the reservoir and determine the best operating program by trial computations. The greater the number of reservoirs involved, the greater the flexibility of the system and the variety of possible schedules. The aim of the operation should be, not to effect maximum reduction of flow at each dam, but to minimize over-all flood damages.

Multiple-purpose operation. In essence, multiple-purpose operation does not differ greatly from single-purpose operation. The principles governing each of the separate uses are the same, regardless of the other uses for which the reservoir is intended. The principal difference lies in the need to allocate capacity for each of the several uses. If navigation is one of the several purposes, a definite minimum pool elevation is established by the minimum navigable depth over the sill of the lock. Similarly, power requirements dictate a minimum pool level below which loss in head seriously impairs efficiency of the turbines and therefore greatly reduces potential power. The minimum storage capacity necessary to achieve any successful reduction in flood flows can be determined by study of past floods. The required flood-control storage is quite frequently a seasonal feature, with maximum space reserves needed during the winter and spring months when the probability of major floods is highest.

These various limitations are usually expressed in the form of a chart known as a *rule curve*. Figure 21-3 is a rule curve for a typical high-head tributary project (Norris Reservoir), while Fig. 21-4 is for Wheeler Reservoir, a low-head main-stream project, both in the TVA system.[1] It will be seen that the rule curve is not a single curve but rather a set of upper and lower limits defining the requirements of the several purposes for which the reservoirs are to be used. Figure 21-3 is concerned primarily with power and flood control, and the rule curve shows the range in reservoir elevation necessary to ensure reasonable flood-control storage at any time. Figure 21-4 represents a reservoir designed for navigation, power, and limited flood-control operation. The minimum pool elevation is set at 550 ft to meet the needs of navigation, but during the winter months, December and January, it may be drawn down to 548 ft in advance of a flood to provide additional storage. In mid-March with the passage of the critical flood season, the pool is filled to 556 ft as flows become available, and then throughout the summer it is drawn down slowly as required for power production and mosquito control. If sufficient flow is available, the reservoir may be refilled in the fall to 555 ft to provide an extra power reserve, but

[1] Bowden, N. W., Multiple Purpose Reservoir Operation, *Civil Eng.*, Vol. 11, pp. 337–340, 1941.

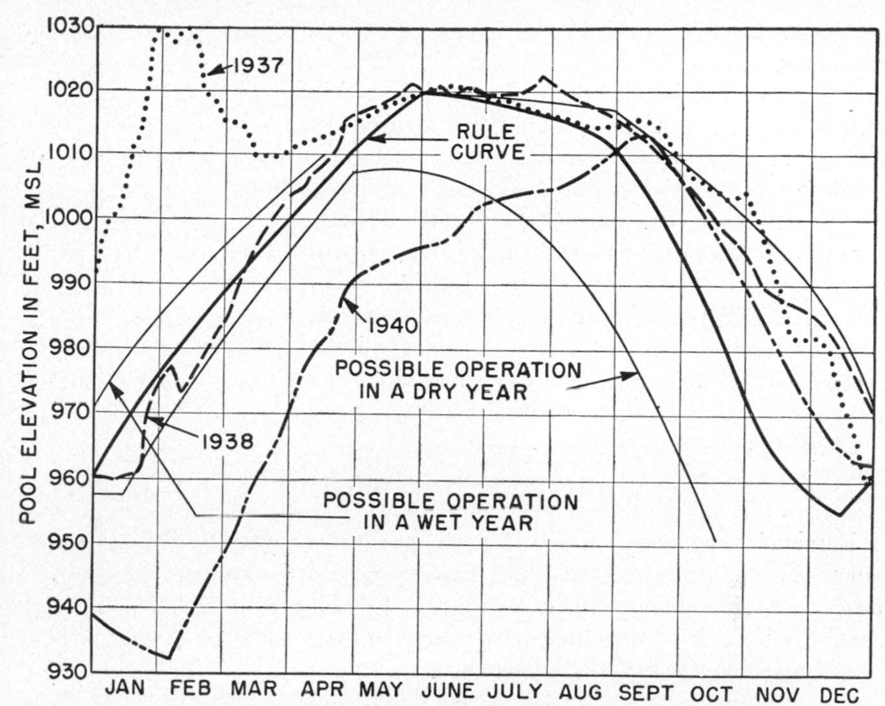

FIG. 21–3. Rule curve for a typical tributary storage reservoir. (*After Bowden.*)

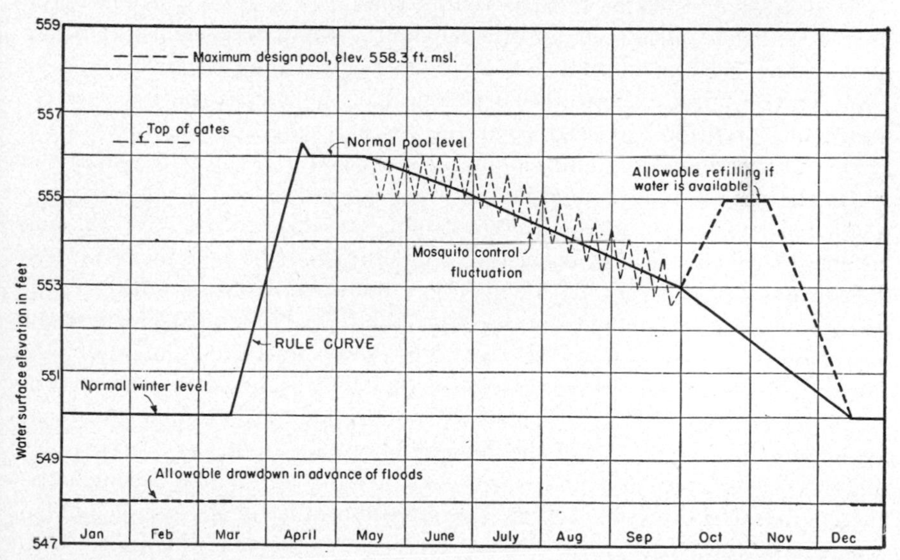

FIG. 21–4. Rule curve for a typical main-stream multiple-purpose reservoir. (*After Bowden.*)

beginning in mid-November it is drawn down again to provide winter flood-storage capacity.

The rule curve is not intended as a rigid and inflexible limit on pool elevations as of a given date. It is rather a guide based on analysis of all past records to aid the operator in his continuous gamble to attain maximum efficiency from a project designed for several basically opposed uses. During floods the storage space reserved above the rule curve is filled to regulate the flood, and the excess water is discharged as soon as possible to restore the storage capacity against future floods. In any year the actual operation curve may bear only casual resemblance to the rule curve, as unusual conditions force departure from the indicated optimum operation. Actual pool-elevation graphs are superimposed on Fig. 21-3 to show the deviations which can be expected in various years.

CHANNEL CONTROLS

Reservoirs are intended to distribute flood flows more uniformly through time, thus eliminating the high peak rates which cause excessive flood damage. Channel-control features are designed to physically prevent floodwaters from encroaching on the area to be protected.

Levees. The principal hydrologic consideration in the design of levees is the water-surface profile for the design flood. The design flood may be an actual flood of record or a synthesized flood if more extreme values are considered advisable. This flood is routed through the reach for which the levees are being considered, and the maximum stages are established at key points along the reach. Between these key points backwater computations are used to compute the water-surface profile. Since the routing must be based on conditions to exist after the levee is constructed, a tentative design must be adopted and channel-storage volumes computed from the channel cross sections as modified by the proposed levee.

All too frequently, levees are constructed as close to the river channel as possible. This restriction of the channel raises crest heights and forces higher and higher levees, with consequent increased risk of failure. Location of levees a reasonable distance from the river bank means lower crest elevations and hence lower levees. The lower initial and maintenance costs may offset the decrease in value of the lands excluded from levee protection. Several alternate plans may be studied to determine the most economical. Possible use of the flood plain outside the levees for purposes which could receive adequate protection from flood forecasts should be considered. In designing levees, consideration must be given not only to what effect the particular levee may have on the flood profile but also to its effect on existing levees elsewhere on the stream. Levees are often designed in conjunction with reservoirs so that the levee-design flood is adjusted for the anticipated effect of the reservoirs before backwater computations are made.

A feature of levee design is the problem of disposal of water accumulated behind the levees.[1] Levees are usually turned back and tied into high ground on each side of major tributaries. However, rainfall on the area enclosed within the levees, flow of small streams entering the area, and seepage through the levees must be considered. This may require a system of collecting sumps provided with pumps to discharge the accumulated flow over the levees. Occasionally, the internal drainage may be collected in a channel and conducted downstream within the levee until it can be discharged into the river under gravity. Some designs have provided detention reservoirs to withhold the internal drainage until it can be discharged through sluice gates in the levee after the river stage has receded. Often a combination of several systems is employed.

The hydrologic problems associated with disposal of internal drainage are similar to those of reservoir design. A design flood must be determined, usually on the basis of frequency studies of rainfall from which the hydrograph of internal drainage can be determined by use of runoff relations and unit hydrographs. This provides information as to the volume and rate of internal flows which must be accommodated. The frequency studies must involve consideration of the occurrence of the design flood for internal drainage coincident with high flows in the main river, *i.e.*, joint probability. After the proper design flood has been determined, the hydrologist must then route it through the pumping station, detention reservoir, or drainage channel in order to determine the relative effectiveness of the various alternate methods.

Seepage through levees has proved to be a serious problem in some areas. High river stages over long periods of time provide an opportunity for water to seep through the levee and raise the water table or leave standing pools on the land within the levee. Seepage can be very destructive to crops. Construction of the levees about an impermeable core, broadening the levee base to provide a greater thickness, or moving the levees back so that they are subjected to lesser heads are possible solutions. Hydrologically, the problem requires a determination of the probable frequency of high stages for various periods of time and the design of a levee system of such permeability that serious seepage cannot develop within the probable duration of high stages on the levees.

Weirs and by-passes. As an alternate to providing a channel between the main levees capable of discharging all floodwaters, by-pass channels are sometimes provided to carry excess flows. Water is diverted into the by-pass through a weir, spillway, or fuse-plug levee. Weirs or spillways

[1] Williams, G. R., Drainage of Leveed Areas in Mountainous Valleys, *Trans. ASCE*, Vol. 108, pp. 83-114, 1943.

are openings in the levee over which the water can discharge when stages reach predetermined levels. If it is desired to control the diversion, the weir may be provided with gates or a section of levee (fuse plug) can be breached if it becomes necessary to divert the flow.

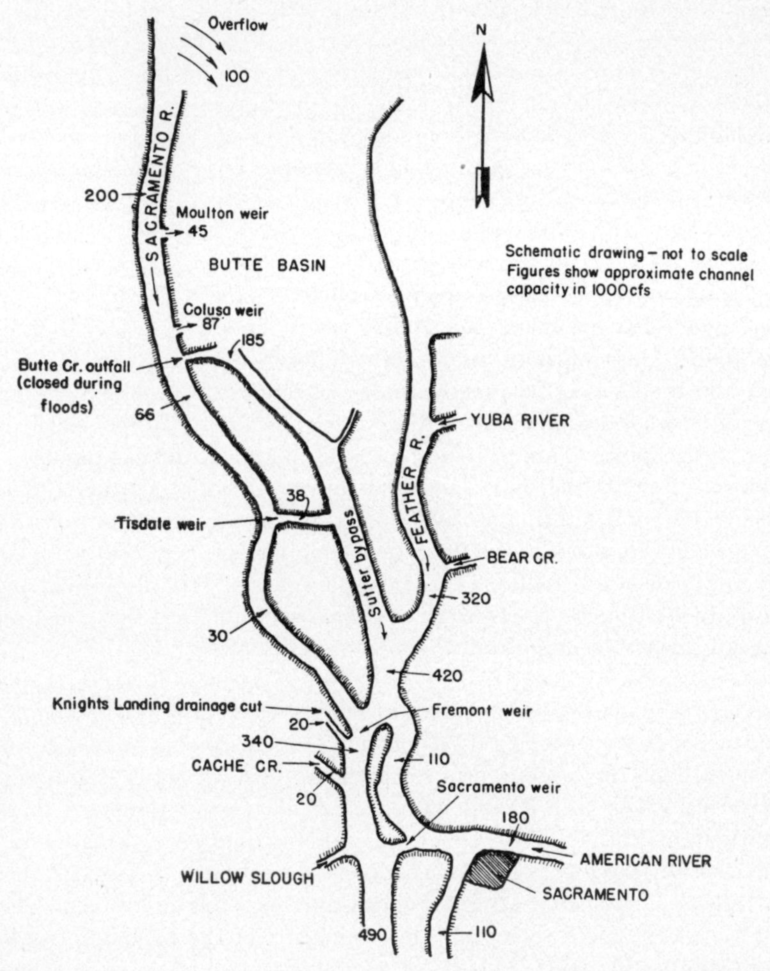

FIG. 21–5. The levee and by-pass system of the lower Sacramento Valley, California.

The determination of the effect of a weir requires a detailed study of the flow conditions in its vicinity. This can probably be best accomplished by model tests. It is important to recognize that the effect of a diversion is not merely the subtraction of a given quantity of flow from the river. A weir located downstream from the point to be protected accelerates the flow past the critical point, increases the water-surface slope, and makes possible the discharge of floodwater at lower stages than under natural conditions. A weir upstream from the critical point decreases the water-surface slope past the point to be protected, and although it may divert a portion of the flow, the stage may not fall. Figure 21-5 shows the by-pass system in the Lower Sacramento Basin of California. Sacramento Weir has a rated capacity in excess of 100,000 cfs; yet when discharging full, it reduces the Sacramento stage by less than 1 ft, although the channel capacity at Sacramento is in the order of 100,000 cfs. In addition to decreasing the water-surface slope at Sacramento, the opening of the weir accelerates flow from upstream, and a portion of the water which would normally pass over Fremont Weir is diverted down the Sacramento channel and over Sacramento Weir. Thus, the weir serves largely to provide an alternate channel for upstream flows instead of accomplishing a protective diversion. Water is diverted into the upper by-pass channels of the system over fixed weirs. These by-passes provide an auxiliary high-water channel but at the same time make it necessary to maintain extra lines of levees. It would appear that a single channel with adequate capacity would be more economical and effective.

Operation of diversion works. The decision to open a diversion way is usually based on a forecast that stages at some critical point will reach predetermined danger levels. A diversion will almost always attain its maximum effectiveness if opened early in the flood. Early opening provides faster getaway for advance elements of the flood wave and leaves a greater volume of channel storage available to reduce the crest. Such an operation is rarely followed, for several reasons. First, faster getaway of water upstream is almost certain to result in aggravation of flood conditions at points downstream. Second, the development of a major flood usually extends over some period of time, and forecasts of expected crests are not practical in the early stages. Third, velocities are usually decreased at the point of diversion, and silt deposits which may have a detrimental effect on future floods will form. Therefore, it is desirable to maintain high velocities as long as possible. Finally, but by no means least important, is the psychological factor. Despite the fact that residents of the by-pass area have sold the flowage rights over their land against such an emergency, they naturally resist the step which actually turns the water on their land. These persons can usually bring enough pressure to bear to postpone the opening of the spillway or fuse plug until the hazard to a metropolitan area is clearly evident. Therefore, the criteria for opening a diversion usually require that a specified critical stage be definitely in sight and that some lower critical stage be already reached. Determination of these criteria requires numerous trial computations based on various assumed operating plans until the one which offers maximum protection with minimum flooding of the by-pass is determined. These computations follow the established hydrologic techniques, involving principally flood routing. They are made difficult by the fact that actual data on flow through the by-pass area are rarely available, and routing curves must be determined by study of topographic maps and backwater computations.

Channel rectification. Any situation which lowers the hydraulic capacity of a channel results in higher stages for a given flow. Thus, stages can be effectively lowered by removing brush and snags and by straightening the channel through elimination of curves and meanders. The benefits from this practice are generally observed at and above the point where the channel rectification is accomplished. The removal of the restrictions makes for lower stages and faster getaway of the water upstream. This also results in a faster delivery of water to downstream points. The reduction in channel storage by shortening the channel and reducing upstream stages can serve only to increase peak rates of flow below the project reach. The acceleration of flow from upstream changes the synchronization of flows in the lower river. In small basins the effect of this change in synchronization can be predicted with some assurance. In a large river system, like the Mississippi, where synchronization is determined by the time of occurrence of storms over various portions of the basin, this effect is probably unpredictable—in some floods it may serve to increase peak flows downstream, while in others it may reduce them.

Much remains to be learned concerning cutoffs. In addition to their effect on flows through reduction of storage and changes in synchronization, they affect stages by improving the hydraulic characteristics of the channel and also by inducing changes in the channel-bottom profile through accelerated scouring upstream and deposition downstream from the cutoff. Lane[1] cites the case of the Sangamon River in Illinois and the Wyconda, Fox, and Salt Rivers in Missouri, where the effect of cutoffs has been to increase flooding in the lower reaches through the combined effects of increased discharges and silting of the channel bottom. Perhaps the outstanding example of cutoff construction in this country is found in the Lower Mississippi, where the river has been shortened by about 170 miles in a total length of 680 miles. Definite lowering of crest stages above the cutoffs has been observed, but no significant increases below the cutoffs have yet been noted although peak discharges have been increased. It is important to note, however, that no major flood has occurred since the completion of these cutoffs. Further, the establishment of equilibrium conditions in a large river is not necessarily accomplished in a few years, and the project must be observed for some years before definite conclusions can be reached. Natural lengthening of the river will in time regain the distance which has been cut off and will require that further cutoffs be

[1] Lane, E. W., The Effect of Cutting Off Bends in Rivers, *Proc. 3rd Hydraulics Conf. Univ. Iowa, Bull.* 31, pp. 230-240, 1947.

constructed to maintain the present condition. The extent of maintenance work necessary to maintain the cutoff system will not be known until many years have passed. However, the cutoffs have definitely benefited navigation by reducing the river mileage and hence the transit time.

Because of the complex problems raised by rectification, the best estimates of their effect are probably obtainable from extended hydraulic laboratory tests on movable-bed models. Approximate estimates of their effect on channel storage can be made, and the resulting increase in peak flow estimated by routing. Hydraulic computations may supply some estimate of the decrease in stage and the changes in the water-surface profile to be expected and perhaps also an approximation to the change in the conformation of the bed. However, the complex interrelations are such that it is doubtful whether or not a completely accurate prediction of the ultimate effect of rectification on a large scale can be made until the present state of our knowledge of sediment transport is greatly improved.

DRAINAGE WAYS

In the general sense, the primary purpose of drainage ways is to dispose of excess water without damage to the area being drained. Two types of drainage ways can be considered, (1) culverts and bridges intended to permit a highway or railroad to cross natural or artificial channels, and (2) drains or sewers for the purpose of disposing of excess surface waters.

Bridges and culverts. The principal hydrologic problem in the design of bridges and culverts is that of ensuring an adequate waterway for the passage of flood runoff which may be expected at the site. The primary concern is the determination of peak flow, and the designer has therefore a choice of a great variety of approaches. For small culverts he may use any of the empirical formulas, an envelope curve for the area, or, if warranted, a synthetic unit graph and rainfall intensity-frequency data. For larger culverts and small bridges on streams where discharge data are available, frequency analysis of stages or flows, envelope curves, or unit hydrographs may be employed. On the largest streams a thorough analysis involving rainfall-runoff studies, unit hydrographs, and flood routing is often justified.

In the design of a bridge on a major stream, much direct and indirect flood damage may result if the waterway is inadequate. Direct flood damage can result from the higher stages caused by backwater from the restricted section at the bridge. Indirect damage may include the interruption of business caused by closure of the damaged structure to traffic and possibly also the damage resulting from limitations of flood fighting and relief activities because of lack of access to the flooded area. To a lesser degree similar effects can result from even the smallest bridge or culvert although the majority of the smaller structures are located where backwater has no serious effects. Moreover, temporary repairs are much more readily made in the case of the smaller structures. Because of the large investment in major bridges and the potential loss from their failure or inadequate performance, it is believed that a thorough hydrologic study is justified in each case.

In some cases culverts are deliberately designed on the basis that temporary pondage of water upstream will do no harm and may make possible a more economical design because of the reduction in peak rates of flow associated with the storage. In this case volume of runoff as well as peak rates must be considered, and use of rainfall-runoff relations and unit hydrographs is to be recommended. However, many states have standard criteria for use in this type of design as well as for the simpler case where pondage is not anticipated. Some of these design standards are developed after careful study of the hydrology of the state, while others are little more than arbitrary selections of coefficients for one or more of the empirical formulas. A nomograph involving length and fall of the channel, drainage area, and 60-min rainfall expected once in 100 years has been suggested for California[1] streams. A runoff coefficient must be estimated on the basis of topography, cover, and land use.

Sewers and drains. The design of sewers and drains is normally based on rainfall of a specified return period, usually 5 to 10 years. Methods by which the assumed rainfall can be converted to a runoff hydrograph from small homogeneous areas are discussed in Chap. 11. The problem area is usually divided into small subareas on the basis of type of surface, *i.e.*, pavement, grassland, etc., and a runoff hydrograph at the point of inlet to the sewer, drain, or gutter is determined for each subarea. It is usually practicable to divide the area so that many of the subareas are identical, thus reducing the number of hydrographs which must be computed. From the point of concentration in the drain or sewer, the flows must be routed to the outlet of the system. This may be accomplished by the use of flood-routing techniques described in Chap. 19. However, the short routing period and the large number of reaches which must be considered make the use of such techniques somewhat laborious unless groups of subareas can be combined into like concentrations for which the outflow hydrographs can be assumed to be identical. Izzard,[2] Hicks,[3] and Jens[4] have suggested alternate procedures for routing flow through sewers and conduits which are reported to give essentially the same results as the more detailed methods.

[1] "California Culvert Practice," p. 6, California Department of Public Works, Sacramento, 1944.

[2] Izzard, C. F., Hydraulics of Runoff from Developed Surfaces, *Proc. Hwy. Res. Board*, Vol. 26, pp. 138-145, 1946.

[3] Hicks, W. I., A Method of Computing Urban Runoff, *Trans. ASCE*, Vol. 109, pp. 1234-1250, 1944.

[4] Jens, S. W., discussion of paper, A Method of Computing Urban Runoff, *Trans. ASCE*, Vol. 109, pp. 1255-1260, 1944.

HEADWATER CONTROL

The possibilities of headwater treatment for water and soil conservation and flood control have been debated vigorously for many years. Numerous experiments dating from the early cooperative efforts of the Forest Service and the Weather Bureau at Wagon Wheel Gap, Colorado, have been carried out. Yet today we are far from having all the facts needed as a basis for sound design of headwater-conservation practices. If anything has been learned from all the discussion and research, it is to the effect that generalized conclusions as to the value of headwater controls are not reliable. Because forest soils have generally higher infiltration rates than fallow land, it cannot be concluded per se that reforestation is a significant factor in flood control. It is necessary to study the effect of a particular measure in the light of the hydrologic and physiographic features of the basin.

Soil conservation. All experimental evidence points clearly to the fact that effective measures can be taken to reduce the amount of soil erosion resulting from intense rainfall. Erosion may be reduced in two ways, (1) by protecting the soil surface from raindrop impact through the use of a cover crop or mulch and (2) by the reduction of surface runoff by encouraging infiltration through proper selection of cover and mechanical retardation by use of contour plowing or terracing. In cultivated areas these measures can be accomplished at small cost by farmers in the course of their normal operations. There is little doubt that such costs are easily justified in terms of protection to the land as an agricultural resource. In nonagricultural areas, controlled timber cutting and grazing aid in reducing erosion. The hydrologist, in considering the problem of reservoir silting, will do well to consider the feasibility of reducing the sediment inflow by headwater-management practices. These measures provide for a considerable reduction in sediment inflow in many basins at relatively small cost. Some areas with thin soil on steep slopes will offer only slight improvements, and large areas of badlands will prove totally unsusceptible to economical treatment.

Flood control. The same techniques that control erosion are often proposed as methods for flood control. Claims as to the value of these measures have been extravagant, but the evidence is not conclusive. Test plots show considerable differences in infiltration rates with varying land uses, but quantitative application of the data from such plots, especially when artificial rainfall is used, is subject to criticism. Improved vegetal cover naturally increases interception loss, and terracing and contour plowing increase surface storage. However, no evidence has been presented to demonstrate that significant flood-crest reduction has been accomplished on a large drainage basin by headwater-control methods. Those claims which have been made for major reduction of flood flows are based largely on the occurrence of a single flood which was less severe in the areas subject to management practices than in other areas. These claims often ignore the variations in storm intensity within the basin and the inherent hydrologic differences between the areas being compared.

Looking objectively at the probable effect on flood runoff, it is evident that very great reductions in flood runoff and flood-crest heights are not to be expected.[1] Interception and depression storage are relatively small factors in major storms. Activities which increase infiltration necessarily reduce surface runoff, but this may be partly offset by an increase in interflow. The increase in infiltration tends to bring about increase in soil-moisture content which eventually offsets in part other factors tending to increase infiltration. Stock ponds and check dams retain some water from floods, but they are not operated as flood-control structures. If a heavy rain occurs while the ponds are full, they will have no beneficial effect; and the channel precipitation on the water surface of the ponds may, in some cases, more than offset the storage. Thus, it appears that the various conservation practices have, at best, only a small effect on major flood peaks—far less effect than is indicated by plot experiments concerned with surface runoff only. This effect is still further minimized by the physical limitation on application of basin-wide conservation measures. There will always be impervious areas such as roads and buildings, and the stream channels themselves, where high runoff is the rule. There will always be wastelands where conservation practices are uneconomical and there will be areas where conservation practices have no effect—steep slopes with shallow soil, shallow soil over the claypan prairies, etc. It does not appear, therefore, that the present-day engineer can consider any effective flood reduction by means of land-management practices. This does not mean that such practices should be abandoned. On the contrary, soil-conservation practices, as such, can be justified in many cases.

Water conservation. A third phase of headwater control is that of water conservation, *i.e.*, the increase in total available moisture through proper land-management techniques. It has been demonstrated that proper farming techniques can conserve the moisture which falls on the cropland by encouraging infiltration and preventing excessive evaporation. This direct conservation of water reduces the need for irrigation and makes possible greater agricultural development in regions of limited water supply.

The use of forests to conserve water has long been advocated. It was said that the forest cover reduced flash runoff of water and released it more uniformly throughout the year. Where no water-storage facilities are available, this is definitely beneficial. It is true, however, only where the in-

[1] Wilm, H. G., The Status of Watershed Management Concepts, *J. Forestry*, Vol. 44, pp. 968-971, 1946.

filtrated water can reach a groundwater table. Where the forest soil is shallow and infiltrated water is rapidly discharged as interflow, little benefit can be expected.

Recent experiments by the Forest Service[1] have demonstrated that controlled timber cutting can increase the water yield of the basin in areas where snow is a significant form of precipitation. Timber thinning reduces transpiration losses and also the quantity of snow which is intercepted by the forest cover and reevaporated. At the same time, the forest cover does protect the snow pack on the ground from evaporation. Snow within forests melts more slowly than snow in the open, with a consequent stabilization of streamflow which is advantageous where storage facilities are not available or where facilities are inadequate to store all the runoff. This effect is further enhanced by the favorable infiltration conditions in deep forest soils which permit melt water to reach the water table and be discharged as groundwater flow at a more uniform rate than it would be if all the runoff were surface runoff.

[1] Hoover, M. D., Effect of Removal of Forest Vegetation on Water Yields, *Trans. Am. Geophys. Union*, Vol. 23, pp. 969-977, 1944.

22
RIVER FORECASTING

A very practical application of hydrology is found in the field of river forecasting. Here, almost every aspect of hydrology is used to produce an end product in the form of predicted future stages or flows. The forecast problem differs from that of design in two ways: (1) It is far more frequently concerned with the more ordinary events, rather than with some possible extreme occurrence. (2) The river forecast must include not only a predicted flow or stage but also its anticipated time of occurrence.

FLOOD FORECASTING

A forecast or warning received too late to permit evacuation of residents and removal of goods from a flood-threatened area has little value. Hence, the entire operation of a flood-forecasting service must be planned around the time factor. The three phases in a flood-forecasting operation are (1) collection of weather data, (2) formulation of the forecast, and (3) dissemination of the forecast.

Collection of data. In order to formulate a forecast of streamflow, the forecaster must have reliable information as to current hydrologic conditions within the basin. He must know the amount and areal distribution of rainfall, and the water equivalent and areal distribution of snow, if present. Depending on the nature of the forecast problem and the techniques used for forecasting, he may also require information on soil conditions, duration of rainfall, and temperatures. River-stage reports are also required as a check on other data and as an up-to-the-minute verification of forecasts.

The collection of the necessary data is accomplished by means of a network of reporting stations. This reporting network must be tailored to the needs of the specific forecasting problems. In the majority of cases such networks consist of selected observers instructed to report to the forecasting office on a regular or occasional basis. Such a network may be supplemented or supplanted by automatic radio or wire-line stations.

Formulation of the forecast. The basic techniques used in river forecasting are the same as those used in other fields of hydrology. Because of time limitations, however, far more effort must be expended in the development phase to streamline the procedures so that there will be no waste motion during the forecast operation. It is usually sufficient to forecast crest height and time for small headwater areas. The rapid rate of rise and fall makes the duration above flood stage so short that there is little value in forecasting the entire hydrograph. Hence, in forecasting only for headwater areas, gage relations (Chap. 19) and relations between rainfall and crest stage (Chap. 17) will ordinarily be used to save time. For stations in the lower reaches of large rivers, where rates of rise are slow, it is important to forecast the time when various critical stages will be reached on the rise and fall, as well as time and height of crest. In such cases, the unit-hydrograph, basin-runoff routing, and flood-wave routing techniques would be used. If such forecasts are to be made for downstream points, it is usually necessary to forecast the entire flood hydrograph at headwater stations. While accuracy is the goal of any forecast, it is sometimes necessary to compromise between speed and accuracy. When a single office serves a large area, it is usually advisable to formulate a master forecast for key stations and to interpolate and localize the forecasts for intermediate points by use of simple tools such as gage relations.

While much can be done in streamlining forecasting techniques, organization is the real key to a successful forecast service. Every step from receipt of data to final preparation of the forecast should be carefully organized. A map of antecedent precipitation or other runoff index can be prepared in advance. Incoming reports can be logged on prepared forms and immediately entered on rainfall plotting maps and continuous hydrograph charts. A map of beginning and ending of rainfall can also be prepared. Work sheets for computing forecasts should be available, dated and labeled in advance. Most of this work can be done by subprofessional or junior professional employees.

No matter how complete the reporting network, there always remains some uncertainty as to the exact conditions within the basin. In addition, even the best rainfall-runoff relation will have 5 to 10 per cent of residual error. A 10 per cent error in predicted runoff volume will, according to the unit-graph theory, cause an equal error in predicted peak discharge. The error in expected peak stage depends on the slope of the rating curve at that stage. Under average conditions, forecasts for headwater areas cannot be expected to be consistently reliable to within less than 1.0 ft. On the lower reaches of large streams, the shape of the stage-discharge relation, together with the effect of channel storage, tends to reduce the effect of upstream errors, and forecasts are usually more reliable. It is misleading to the user to state a forecast in more precise terms than justified

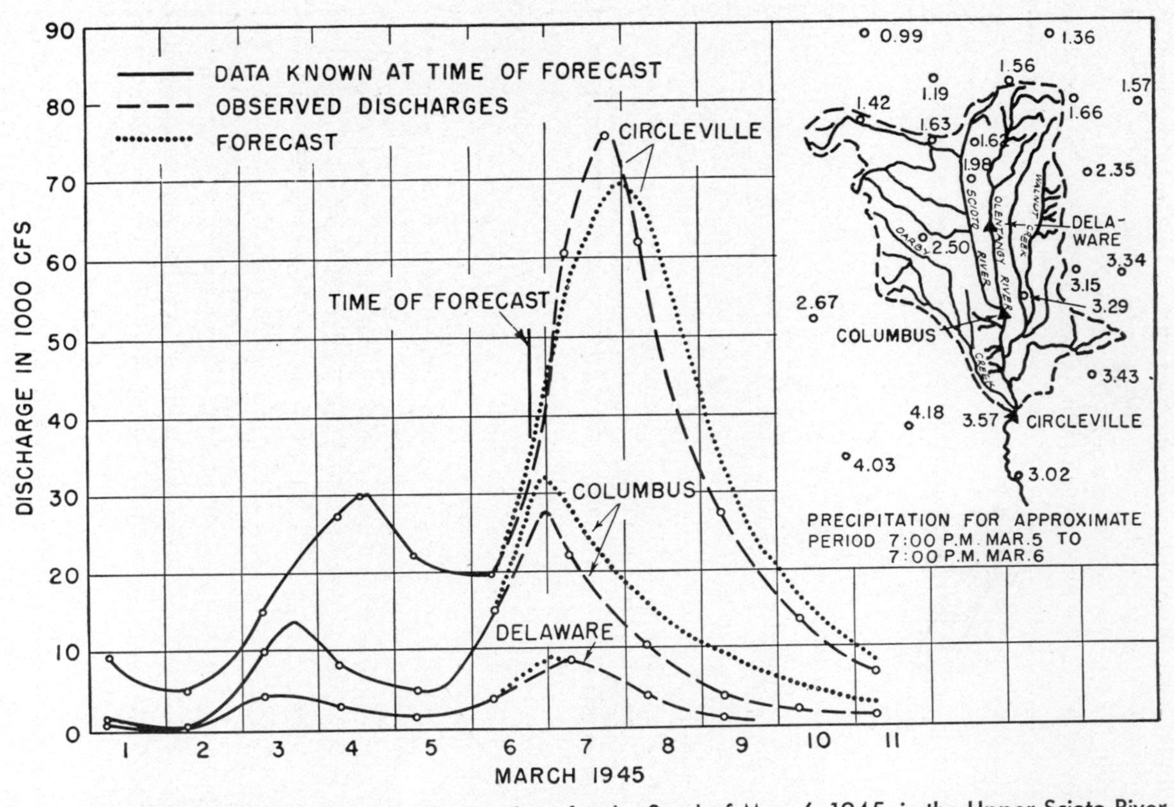

FIG. 22–1. Hydrographs and precipitation data for the flood of Mar. 6, 1945, in the Upper Scioto River Basin.

by the conditions; hence, forecasts should rarely be given to less than the nearest 0.5 ft.

Example. As an example of a typical forecast operation, a sample forecast for the Upper Scioto River Basin as of 7 P.M., Mar. 6, 1945, is developed. Total rainfall for the 24 hr beginning 7 P.M., Mar. 5, and the reported hydrographs up to the forecast time are shown in Fig. 22-1.

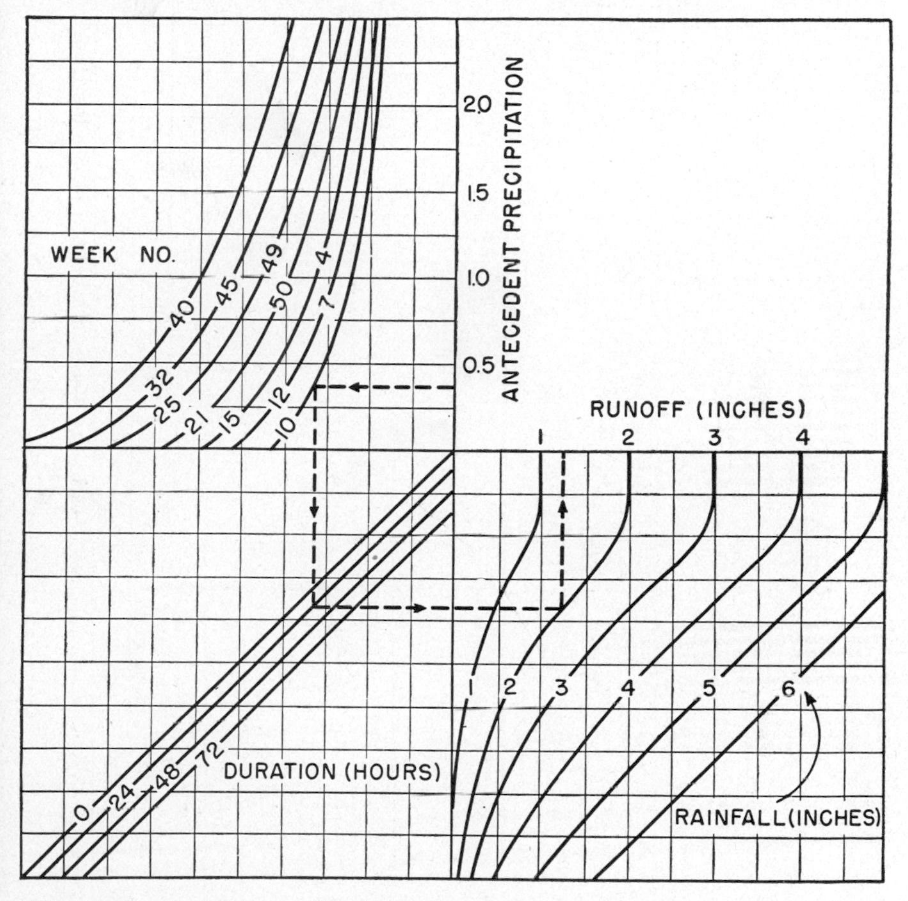

FIG. 22–2. Rainfall-runoff relation for the Scioto River Basin, Ohio. *(U.S. Weather Bureau.)*

Using the rainfall-runoff relation (Fig. 22-2), the runoff for each subarea is computed on the work sheet shown in Fig. 22-3. The rainfall is distributed into 12-hr periods on the basis of reported 6-hr amounts.

The ordinates of the unit hydrographs for each area are multiplied by the computed runoff and added to the base flow projected from the previous hydrograph to yield the final discharges for Delaware and Columbus and

STREAM & STATION	RUNOFF COMPUTATIONS		DISCHARGE IN 1000 CFS															
			March 6		March 7		March 8		March 9		March 10		March 11		March 12		March 13	
			7A	7P	7A	7P	7A	7P	7A	7P	7A	7P	7A	7P	7A	7P	7A	7P
OLENTANGY R.	ANTE. PRECIP. 0.55 INCHES WEEK NO. 10	HYDROGRAPH PREVIOUS PERIOD	3.0	6.5	4.9	3.2	2.2	1.5	1.3	1.2	1.1	1.0	0.9	09	0.8	0.8	0.7	0.7
at	TOTAL DURATION 24 HRS. TOTAL RAIN 1.70 INCHES	12 HR. UNIT GRAPH	0	2.7	7.8	6.0	3.3	2.0	0.9	0.4	0.2	0						
DELAWARE, OHIO	TOTAL RUNOFF 1.15 INCHES	DIRECT RUNOFF	0	1.2	3.5	27	1.5	0.9	0.4	0.2	0.1	0						
	PREV. RUNOFF 0.70 INCHES INCREMENT 0.45 INCHES	TOTAL FLOW	30	7.7	8.4	5.9	3.7	24	1.7	1.4	1.2	1.0	0.9	09	0.8	08	0.7	0.7
SCIOTO RIVER	ANTE. PRECIP. 0.55 INCHES WEEK NO. 10	HYDROGRAPH PREVIOUS PERIOD	138	225	14.9	11.4	8.9	7.1	5.8	4.7	3.9	3.1	2.7	27	2.6	26	2.5	2.4
at	TOTAL DURATION 24 HRS. TOTAL RAIN 2.00 INCHES	12 HR. UNIT GRAPH	0	13.1	24.5	15.8	11.5	8.2	5.8	42	29	1.8	0.7	0.2	0			
COLUMBUS, OHIO	TOTAL RUNOFF 1.35 INCHES PREV. RUNOFF 0.80 INCHES	DIRECT RUNOFF	0	7.2	13.5	8.7	6.3	4.5	3.2	2.3	1.6	1.0	0.4	01	0			
	INCREMENT 0.55 INCHES	TOTAL FLOW	13.8	29.7	28.4	20.1	15.2	11.6	9.0	70	5.5	4.1	3.1	2.8	26	2.6	25	2.4
WALNUT CREEK	ANTE. PRECIP. 0.80 INCHES WEEK NO. 10	HYDROGRAPH PREVIOUS PERIOD	6.4	13.7	15.7	17.9	14.7	6.2	2.8	1.4	0.6	0.2	0.1	0.1	0.1	0.1	0.1	0.1
LOCAL AREA	TOTAL DURATION 24 HRS. TOTAL RAIN 3.00 INCHES	12 HR. UNIT GRAPH	0	4.6	9.8	11.2	128	10.5	4.4	2.0	1.0	0.4	0.2					
	TOTAL RUNOFF 2.40 INCHES PREV. RUNOFF 1.40 INCHES	DIRECT RUNOFF	0	4.6	9.8	11.2	12.8	10.5	44	20	10	0.4	0.2					
	INCREMENT 1.00 INCHES	TOTAL FLOW	6.4	18.3	25.5	29.1	27.5	16.7	7.2	3.4	1.6	0.6	0.3	01	01	01	01	0.1
DARBY CREEK	ANTE. PRECIP. 0.70 INCHES WEEK NO. 10	HYDROGRAPH PREVIOUS PERIOD	0.6	1.3	4.5	7.7	9.1	7.0	46	32	24	18	1.0	0.4	0.2	0.1	01	01
LOCAL AREA	TOTAL DURATION 24 HRS. TOTAL RAIN 3.10 INCHES	12 HR. UNIT GRAPH	0	0.4	0.9	3.2	5.5	6.5	5.0	33	2.3	1.7	1.3	0.7	03	0.1		
	TOTAL RUNOFF 2.40 INCHES PREV. RUNOFF 1.40 INCHES	DIRECT RUNOFF	0	04	0.9	3.2	5.5	6.5	5.0	33	23	1.7	1.3	0.7	0.3	01		
	INCREMENT 1.00 INCHES	TOTAL FLOW	0.6	1.7	54	109	14.6	13.5	9.6	6.5	47	3.5	2.3	1.1	0.5	0.2	0.1	01
SCIOTO RIVER		ROUTED FLOW FROM COLUMBUS	9.0	12.7	24.5	26.5	23.5	20.0	16.2	13.2	10.5	8.0	6.2	5.5	4.0	3.5	3.0	25
at		SUM WALNUT & DARBY CREEKS	7.0	20.0	30.9	40.0	42.1	30.2	16.8	9.9	6.3	4.1	2.6	1.2	0.6	03	01	01
CIRCLEVILLE, OHIO		TOTAL FLOW	16.0	32.7	55.4	66.5	65.6	50.2	33.0	23.1	16.8	121	8.8	6.7	4.6	3.8	3.1	26

UPPER SCIOTO BASIN WORK-SHEET COMPUTED March 6 1945 FOR STORM BEGINNING 7PM March 5 COMPUTED BY RKL CKD BY MAK TIME 7PM

FIG. 22–3. Typical forecast computation form.

the local inflows for the two major subareas between Columbus and Circleville (Fig. 22-3).

In order to prepare a forecast for Circleville, the predicted Columbus hydrograph is routed to Circleville, using the relations shown in Fig. 22-4. The local-inflow hydrographs are added to the routed flows to produce the final Circleville hydrograph as shown on the computation sheet (Fig. 22-3).

The computed hydrographs and the actual flows are shown in Fig. 22-1. Approximately 0.25 in. of rain fell after the forecast time. For flood warnings the computed flows could be converted to stage through the stage-discharge relations. The errors in crest stage for this forecast would have been 0.1 ft at Delaware, 1.0 ft at Columbus, and 0.6 ft at Circleville. These errors are quite typical of forecasts for headwater areas of this type. The drainage areas above the three stations are 415, 1613, and 3217 sq miles, respectively.

WATER-SUPPLY FORECASTING

Long-range water-supply forecasting is generally limited to those areas where the lag between winter snowfall and spring runoff provides an opportunity for advance determinations. To a lesser degree, forecasts on the basis of groundwater carry-over are practicable in some areas.

Forecasts of runoff from snow. Techniques adaptable to this problem are discussed in Chap. 16. The forecasts may be based either on measurements of snow water equivalent determined from snow surveys or on precipitation data. Snow surveys provide an index to the volume of snow remaining on the basin and hence are best correlated with the runoff to be expected after the end of the accumulation season—usually during the period April to September. Precipitation data do not indicate the remaining volume of snow and must usually be correlated with full water-year runoff. Runoff measured up to the date of the forecast must then be subtracted to determine the flow to be expected during the balance of the year.

Both types of data, when properly used, yield forecasts which are of comparable accuracy. From other considerations, however, the precipitation approach seems to have the advantage. The length of available precipitation records is much greater than that of snow surveys, and hence precipitation data provide a broader sample of events and are more likely to include extreme years. Existing precipitation records make it possible to provide forecasts in almost any area, while available snow-survey records are less widely distributed. Finally, the cost of making snow surveys is quite high, since they require lengthy trips by pairs of expert skiers into remote mountain areas. The precipitation data required for water-supply forecasts are submitted to Weather Bureau section centers as a part of the routine collection of climatological data.

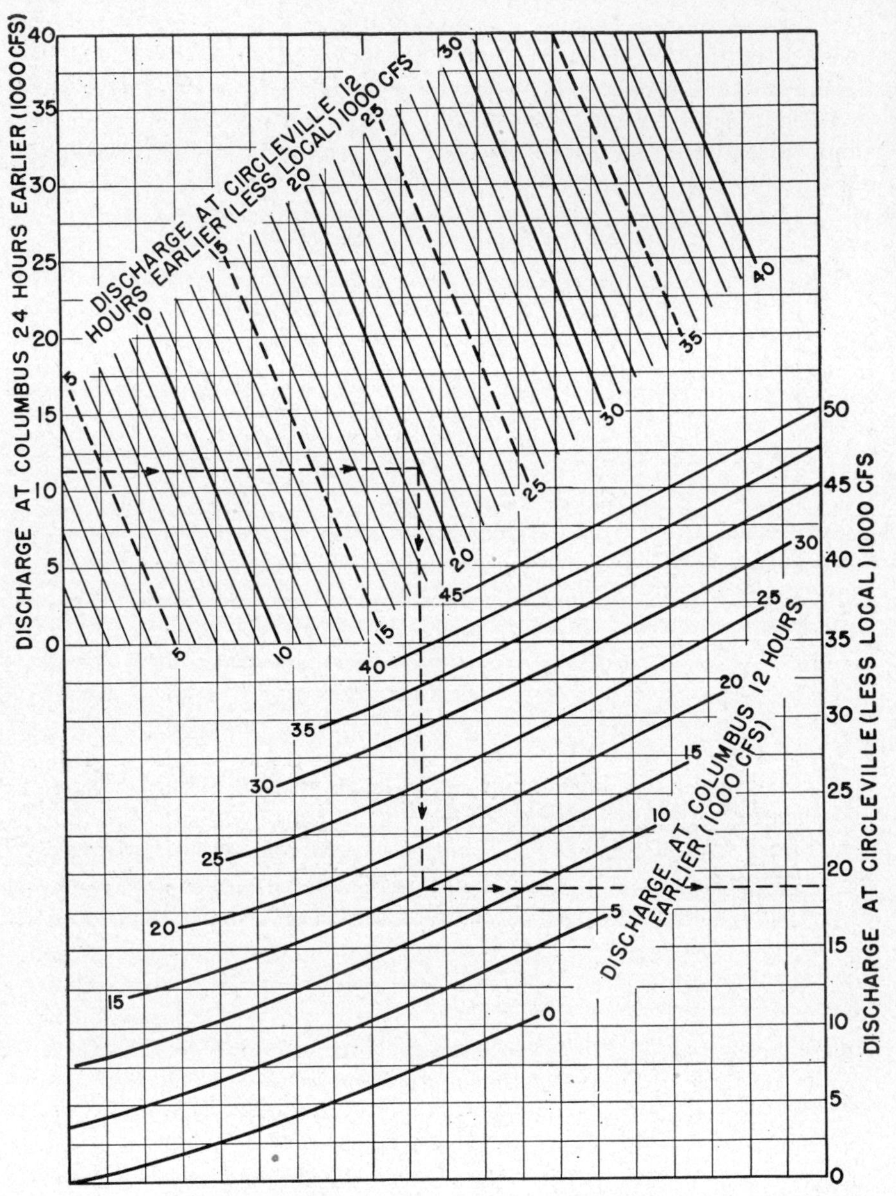

FIG. 22–4. Routing relation for the Scioto River from Columbus to Circleville, Ohio. *(U. S. Weather Bureau.)*

Final water-supply forecasts cannot be formulated until the accumulation season is ended, because the precipitation yet to come naturally influences the runoff volume. The present status of meteorology does not permit practical forecasts of future weather sufficiently far in advance to be of value in water-supply forecasting. In most of the areas where water-supply forecasting of snowmelt runoff is practicable, 85 to 90 per cent of the effective precipitation is usually observed by Apr. 1, and this date has been

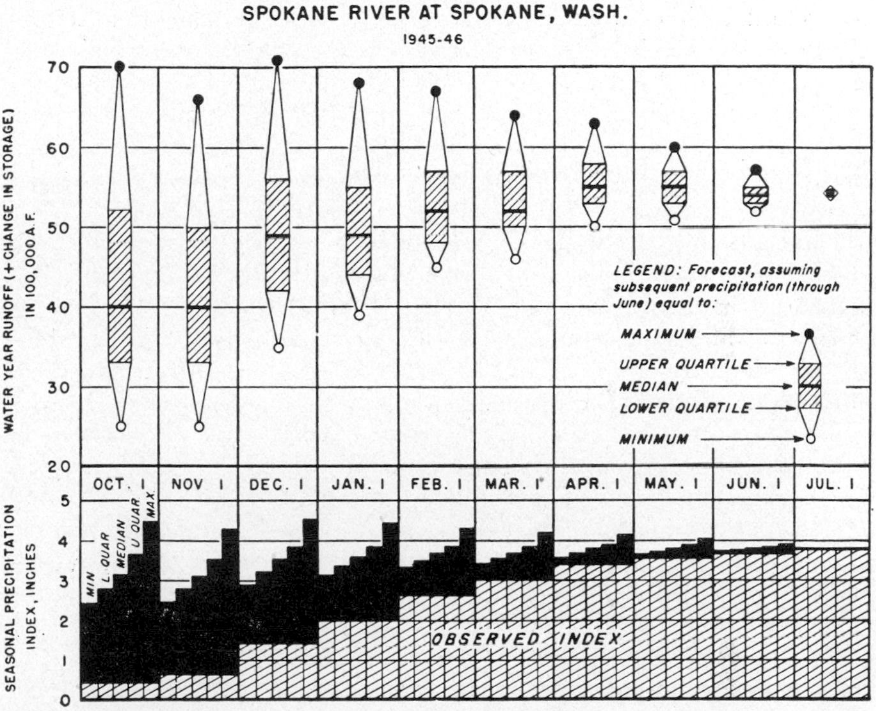

FIG. 22–5. Variation of monthly water-supply forecasts throughout a season *(U.S. Weather Bureau.)*

generally accepted as the basic date for water-supply forecasting. It is highly desirable that forecasts be available prior to Apr. 1, but such forecasts can be made only on the assumption that precipitation from the forecast date through the end of the runoff season will equal the normal (or median) value of the record. The U.S. Weather Bureau has been issuing forecasts beginning on Jan. 1, using the precipitation-runoff technique described in Chap. 16. Actual precipitation from September to December plus the effect of the previous season are known on Jan. 1. To these known data may be added the median precipitation for the balance of the season to provide a forecast of runoff. There always exists the possibility that the actual precipitation will be far from the assumed median value, and in order that the operator of a project may know what such possible departures might produce in the way of runoff, estimates may also be made on the assumption that precipitation will equal the extremes and the quartiles of record. Since some idea of the probability of occurrence of either the extremes or quartiles is known, the operator may make preliminary plans with knowledge of the approximate odds favoring the ultimate delivery of the water anticipated. Thus, a hydroelectric operator might plan to purchase fuel required in the event forecast minimum conditions prevail, while the operator of a flood-control project would naturally prepare against the possibility of maximum subsequent precipitation. Each month the range between the extremes decreases as the number of observed data increases (Fig. 22-5). A sample work sheet for computing progressive monthly water-supply forecasts from precipitation is shown in Fig. 22-6.

Forecasts on the basis of groundwater. The relation between streamflow and volume of groundwater storage during the recession is discussed in Chap. 15. Making use of this relation, it is possible to forecast *minimum* water supplies for any given period in any area. At any time, the recession hydrograph may be projected as far into the future as desired. Obviously, any accretion to streamflow by precipitation will result in more runoff than computed from the recession. Hence, such forecasts are of little value in areas where significant rainfall can be expected during the forecast period. In regions such as the Central Valley of California, where a pronounced summer dry season occurs, the technique may be used to advantage to predict summer and fall runoff volume and also to predict probable minimum discharges to be expected prior to the beginning of the rainy period.

In some areas a pronounced carry-over of groundwater storage for 2 or more years is observed. Conditions of this type are indicated by a small variation of annual flows about a relatively high normal and a poor correlation between annual precipitation and runoff. Because of the small variations in flow, forecasts are usually of less value than in areas with a greater variability in runoff. However, a series of unusually wet or dry years may have a cumulative effect which will result in a fairly large deviation from normal. The techniques for correlating effect of the previous year, discussed in Chap. 16, can be used to develop a relation for forecasting purposes. The graphical solution shown in Fig. 16-15 will be most successful. The forecasts may be made as much as a year in advance with considerable assurance, even though future precipitation is unknown. Any assumptions as to future precipitation may be introduced to provide an indication of the possible range of runoff to be expected.

U. S. DEPARTMENT OF COMMERCE — WEATHER BUREAU

DIVISON OF CLIMATOLOGICAL AND HYDROLOGIC SERVICES

COMPUTATION OF SEASONAL WATER SUPPLY FORECASTS

Sevier ~~Creek near~~ River at Hatch, Utah

1946-47 Water Year Runoff in 1,000 Acre-Feet

STATION	WGT.	SEPT Obs.	SEPT Wgtd.	OCT Obs.	OCT Wgtd.	NOV Obs.	NOV Wgtd.	DEC Obs.	DEC Wgtd.	JAN Obs.	JAN Wgtd.	FEB Obs.	FEB Wgtd.	MAR Obs.	MAR Wgtd.	APR Obs.	APR Wgtd.	MAY Obs.	MAY Wgtd.	JUNE Obs.	JUNE Wgtd.
COMPUTATION OF EFFECTIVE BASIN PRECIPITATION																					
Alton	0.3	0.09	0.03	3.59	108	2.30	0.69	1.94	0.58	0.27	0.08	0.64	0.19	.10	.03	.54	.16				
Cedar City	0.3	0.04	0.01	3.51	1.05	2.53	0.76	1.12	0.34	0.09	0.03	0.09	0.03	.26	.08	1.47	.44				
Panquitch	0.1	0.53	0.05	3.59	0.36	0.92	0.09	0.28	0.03	0.33	0.03	0.29	0.03	.12	.01	1.14	.11				
Tropic	0.3	0.50	0.15	3.41	1.02	2.42	0.73	2.04	0.61	0.31	0.09	0.55	0.16	T	0	.18	.05				
Effective Precip.(Σ)	1.0	—	0.24	—	351	—	2.27	—	1.56	—	0.23	—	0.41	—	0.12	—	0.76	—		—	

COMPUTATION OF FORECASTS (as of 1st day of following month)

		SEPT		OCT		NOV		DEC		JAN		FEB		MAR		APR		MAY		JUNE	
Monthly Weight		0.05		0.07		0.09		0.14		0.16		0.16		0.14		0.10		0.06		0.03	
Monthly Index		0.01		0.25		0.20		0.22		0.04		0.07		0.02		0.08					
Accumulated Monthly Index *		0.85 *		1.10		1.30		1.52		1.56		1.63		1.65		1.73					
Statistical Data for Balance of Year	Max.	1.67		1.57		1.42		1.22		.96		.67		.39		.15		.06		--	
	U. Qrtl.	1.38		1.28		1.14		.95		.71		.43		.20		.07		.02		--	
	Median	1.10		1.01		.87		.69		.50		.32		.16		.05		.01		--	
	L. Qrtl.	.91		.84		.73		.58		.42		.25		.12		.02		0		--	
	Min.	.59		.54		.45		.35		.22		.12		.03		.00		0		--	
	Variable	SPI	Q	SPI	Q	SPI	Q	SPI	Q	SPI	Q	SPI	Q	SPI	Q	SPI	Q	SPI	Q	SPI	Q
Total Seasonal Values 1/Q̄ = .011628	Max.	2.52	97	2.67	1.36	2.72	1.50	2.74	1.56	2.52	.97	2.30	.72								
	U. Qrtl.	2.23	67	2.38	.78	2.44	84	2.47	88	2.27	.70	2.06	.58								
	Median	1.95	52	2.11	.60	2.17	64	2.21	66	2.16	.59	1.95	.53								
	L. Qrtl.	1.76	44	1.94	.52	2.03	56	2.10	60	1.98	.54	1.88	.49								
	Min.	1.44	30	1.64	.38	1.75	43	1.87	49	1.78	.45	1.75	.43								
Flow in % Normal (1920-44)	Max.	113		158		174		181		113		84									
	U. Qrtl.	78		91		98		102		81		67									
	Median	60		70		74		77		69		62									
	L. Qrtl.	51		60		65		70		63		57									
Q̄ = 86,000 A.F.	Min.	35		44		50		57		52		50									

* Includes 0.75 x Previous Years Index (0.75 x 0.79 = 0.59) + 0.25 x Two Years Previous Index (.25 x .99 = .25) = 0.84

File HYDI. 45206

FIG. 22–6. Work sheet for computing progressive monthly water-supply forecasts from precipitation. *(U.S. Weather Bureau.)*

ROLE OF WEATHER FORECASTS IN RIVER FORECASTING

If reliable quantitative forecasts of the various weather elements affecting streamflow were possible, these forecasts could form the basis of river forecasts, exactly as do the data reported from the networks. Reasonably satisfactory temperature forecasts 24 to 48 hr in advance are now being made and can be used to extend forecasts of streamflow from snowmelt. Although the U.S. Weather Bureau has been exploring quantitative precipitation forecasts expressed in terms of averages over zones of approximately 10,000 square miles, these forecasts are not sufficiently reliable to be used as the basis of river forecasts which are to have general distribution.

Used with due regard for their limitations, quantitative precipitation forecasts will have value for special problems. The operators of large reservoirs can well afford to temper their operation program in the light of predicted rainfall, *e.g.*, by drawing down the reservoir in advance of a storm to provide extra flood-control storage. Similarly, construction crews working in a river bottom may use predicted precipitation as the basis for removing construction equipment from the channel. While the equipment may be removed unnecessarily on occasion, the cost of removal is small compared with its value. The use of weather predictions as a basis for river forecasts requires a knowledge of the specific problem and a thorough understanding of the consequences of an action on the basis of an incorrect forecast. It is only fair to the weather forecaster to point out that his forecasts vary in reliability depending on the particular weather situation. Thus, upon occasion, the forecaster may be absolutely certain that heavy rains are impending, while at other times he can only say that heavy rains are a possibility. Thus, important decisions should be based, not on published forecasts alone, but also on a discussion of the particular problem with the meteorologist.

FLOOD FORECASTING AS A PHASE OF FLOOD CONTROL

If we define flood control as "the reduction of flood damage," then flood forecasting is a very real phase of flood control. This fact has not been generally recognized in the national flood-control program. The relatively low ratio of cost to benefit in flood forecasting makes it an ideal flood-protection measure in the many areas where reservoirs or levees cannot be economically justified. The greatest possibilities lie in a planned combination of water-control structures and flood forecasting. The reservoirs of the Miami Conservancy District are an outstanding example of effective flood-control structures. Yet, because they hold water only during floods, the land behind them is not permanently removed from the natural resources of the country and may be farmed on the basis of known risks that a crop will be lost once in a certain number of years. Flood forecasts can provide a warning period during which livestock, farm machinery, trucks, and other movable equipment may be removed from the reservoir area.

Along many of our rivers it has been the practice to construct levees encroaching on the river channel. The inevitable effect is the raising of the river bottom and consequently of flood heights which necessitate higher levees. A secondary consequence is the almost inevitable failure of some, and in many cases a large percentage, of the levees, with consequent damage to property supposedly protected by them. These conditions are clearly emphasized by the floods of June and July, 1947, in the Middle West. The St. Louis crest was 7 ft higher than ever before attained for the observed discharge. At the same time only a few levees in the Lower Missouri remained intact.

In many cases it would be entirely practicable to construct the levees far back from the riverbanks. Lower levees could be constructed at correspondingly low initial cost. The wider channels would result in lower stages and provide greater channel storage, thus reducing crests downstream. The bottom land not protected by the levees could still be used for farming or pasture, depending on the expected frequency of flooding. If floods during the growing season could be expected only once in about 5 years, farming operations would probably be economical, with flood forecasts to ensure that farm equipment and movable property could be evacuated. With more frequent floods the land might be used for pasture. In this case flood forecasts would permit complete evacuation of livestock and equipment with no loss except for the cost of removal.

Bottom land in urban areas may be zoned to prevent its use for purposes which would suffer greatly from floods. The ultimate aim of such zoning should be the conversion of bottom land into parks which would not be greatly damaged by floods or to the use of industries which could take adequate precautions against damage when supplied with flood forecasts.

The chapter on Design and Operation (Chap. 21) pointed out that it is impracticable to provide protection by levees or reservoirs against the extreme floods which can be expected to occur in almost all streams at infrequent intervals. Such floods take a severe toll of levees and fill the reservoirs to the point where any attempt to regulate the flow is entirely ineffective. In this situation the only resort of those in the threatened area is to the emergency measures which can be taken on the basis of warnings. Rather than deny this possibility when flood-control structures are built and thus lull the public into false security, it should be made known so that adequate preparations for emergency measures can be made. Most flood-control structures are justified on the grounds of their benefits in reducing damage from the ordinary and frequent floods and not from the extreme.

APPENDIX A
GRAPHICAL CORRELATION

Two-variable. If a linear relation is to be used, the line of best fit must pass through the point defined by the means of the two variables. This is true not only for graphical correlations but also for the least-squares line. Having one point on the line ($\bar{Y},\bar{X}$) determined, the proper slope can be estimated by first plotting the data (Fig. A-1) and then determining average coordinates for groups of points classified according to values of the independent variable. If the total number of

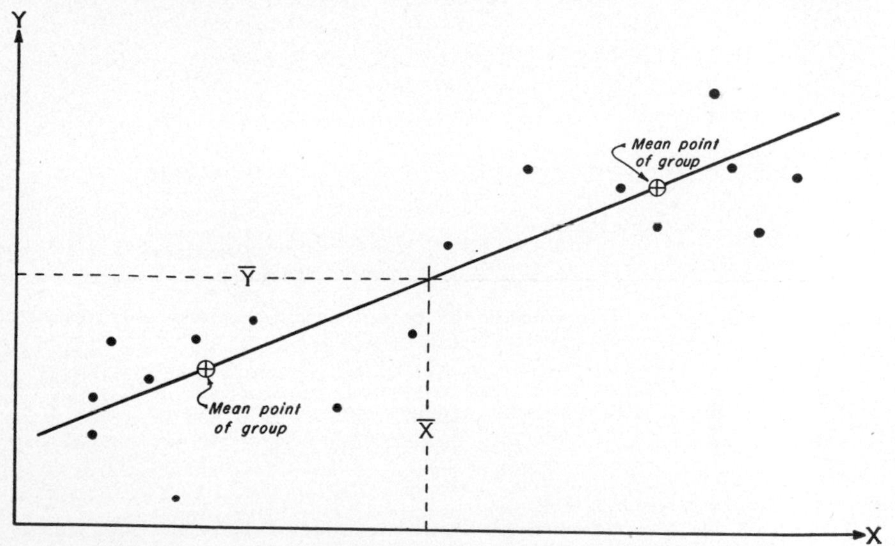

FIG. A–1. Two-variable linear correlation by graphical method.

points be divided into two groups of approximately equal size, then the line connecting their means will pass through the mean of all points and this is the best line that can be readily determined graphically.

The relation determined by *group averages* usually has a slightly steeper slope (dy/dx) than that determined by least squares. As the degree of correlation increases, the difference between the two lines diminishes and for perfect correlation they are coincident. The relation of averages tends to minimize the absolute sum of the deviations, while the least-squares relation minimizes the sum of the squares of the deviations.

The group averages can be estimated graphically by first estimating successive two-point averages (halfway between the plotted points). The four-point averages are then halfway between the two-point averages, etc. (Fig. A-2). Points should always be grouped with respect to values of the independent variable. Unless the correlation is perfect, a different line will result if points are grouped according to the dependent variable, with the difference increasing as the correlation decreases.

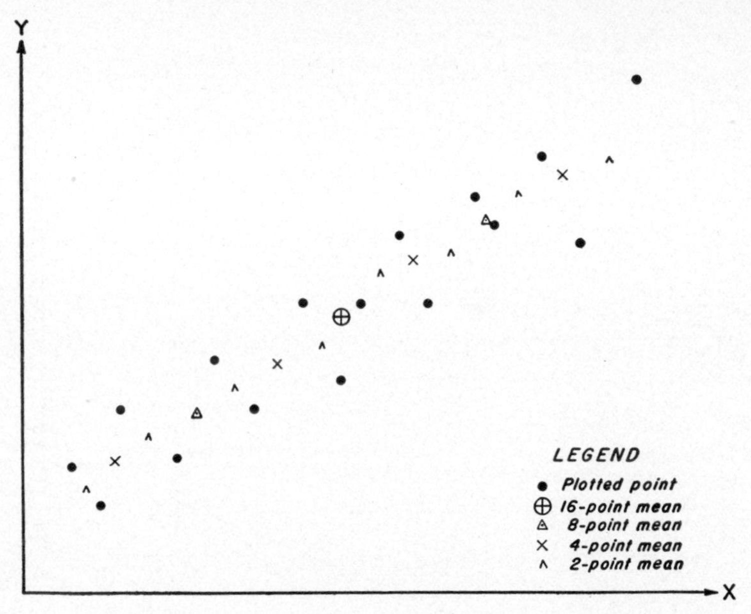

FIG. A–2. Graphical determination of group means classified with respect to X.

If, upon examination of the group averages (two-point, four-point, etc.), it is decided that the relation is curvilinear in form, then a curve can be fitted to the mean points with the aid of a celluloid curve. A curve does not necessarily pass through the mean of all the data.

Three-variable correlation by contour method. Perhaps the most logical method of presenting a three-variable relation is by means of a three-dimensional sketch. The plane surface represented by the equation $X_1 = X_2 + 2.5X_3 - 7.5$ is shown is Fig. A-3. It will be noted that the contours of X_3, that is, curves connecting equal values of X_3, are parallel straight lines and are equally spaced for equal increments of X_3. This is true of any plane surface. Given the values of any two of the variables, the third can be estimated from the chart of Fig. A-3. A close examination of the figure will disclose the fact that, once the three families of lines have been constructed on the surface *ABCD* represented by the equation, all remaining portions of the sketch become superfluous. In practice, the surface *ABCD* is projected onto one of the coordinate planes. This projection can be shown by a family of curves on cross-section paper.

A chart of the type shown in Fig. A-3 can be developed from a series of simultaneous observations by plotting X_1 against X_2, labeling the points with values of X_3, and constructing lines for which X_3 is constant. If the points scatter considerably, averages of points grouped with respect to both independent variables (X_2 and X_3) should be determined before any attempt is made to construct X_3 contours (Fig. A-4).

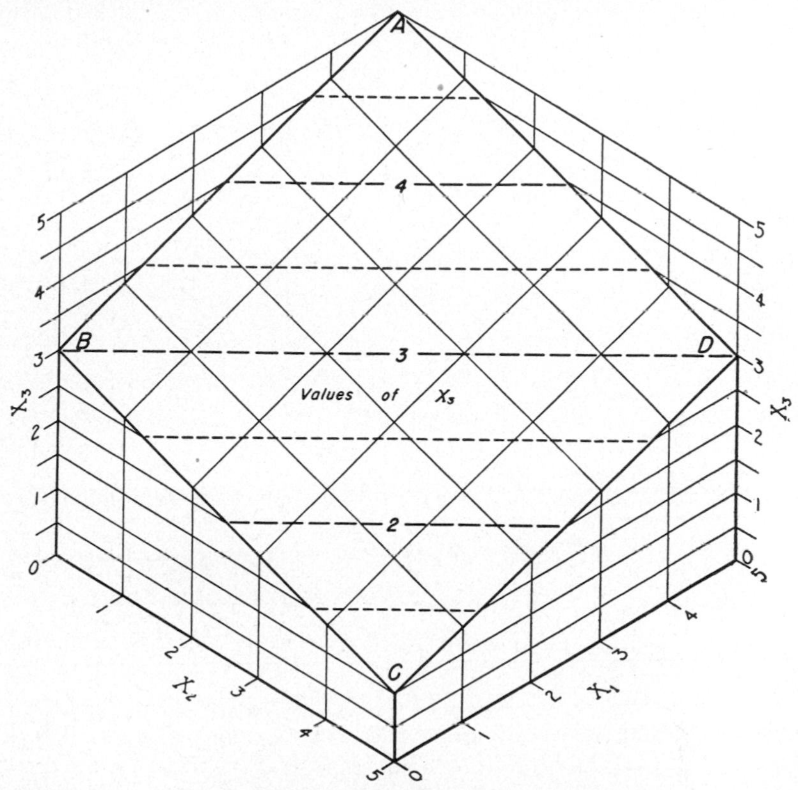

FIG. A–3. Three-dimensional figure for the solution of the equation $X_1 = X_2 + 2.5X_3 - 7.5$.

Any three-variable relation can be expressed by a chart of the type just discussed. For linear functions, the contours are equally spaced, straight, and parallel; for curvilinear functions, they may be curved, unequally spaced, or both. Contours which converge or diverge indicate the presence of a joint function.

Four or more variables (method of deviations). There are several methods for graphical correlation of four or more variables. One of the simplest is the method of deviations described by Ezekiel.[1] In this method a two-variable graphical correlation is first made between Y, the dependent variable, and X_1, the most important independent variable. Deviations from this curve $(Y - Y')$ are then

[1] Ezekiel, M., "Methods of Correlation Analysis," 2d ed., Wiley, New York, 1941.

plotted against the next most important variable X_2, and a curve is fitted to indicate the correction to be applied to the first relation, $Y = f'(X_1)$, for the effect of X_2. By plotting the residual deviations from the $\Delta Y = f'(X_2)$ curve against X_3, a second correction curve, $\Delta Y = f'(X_3)$, is determined. This process is continued until all independent variables have been introduced into the correlation.

The second approximation, $Y = f''(X_1)$, is determined by plotting the deviations from the last correction curve to be developed as deviations from the first-approximation curve, $Y = f'(X_1)$, and fitting a revised curve. The deviations from this

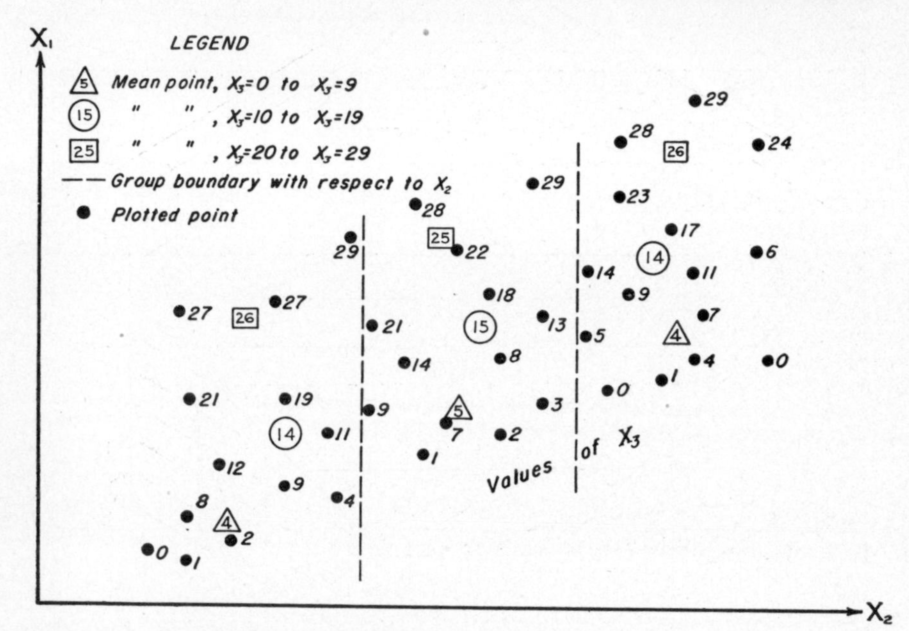

FIG. A-4. Graphical determination of means of groups of points classified with respect to two independent variables.

curve are then plotted as deviations from the first approximation to $\Delta Y = f'(X_2)$ and revisions made if necessary. This process is continued until all second-approximation curves have been determined. The third and all subsequent adjustments can be made in the same manner. However, the second approximation will seldom be materially changed by further adjustments.

For illustrative purposes, the four-variable correlation of the data series listed in the first five columns of Table A-1 is accomplished as follows:

First approximation:

1. Plot Y against X_1, labeling each point with a number identifying the observation. Determine group averages, and construct curve to fit (Fig. A-5*a*).
2. Plot deviations of Y from curve of Fig. A-5*a* against X_2, and fit a curve (Fig. A-5*b*).
3. Plot deviations from curve of Fig. A-5*b* against X_3, and fit a curve (Fig. A-5*c*).

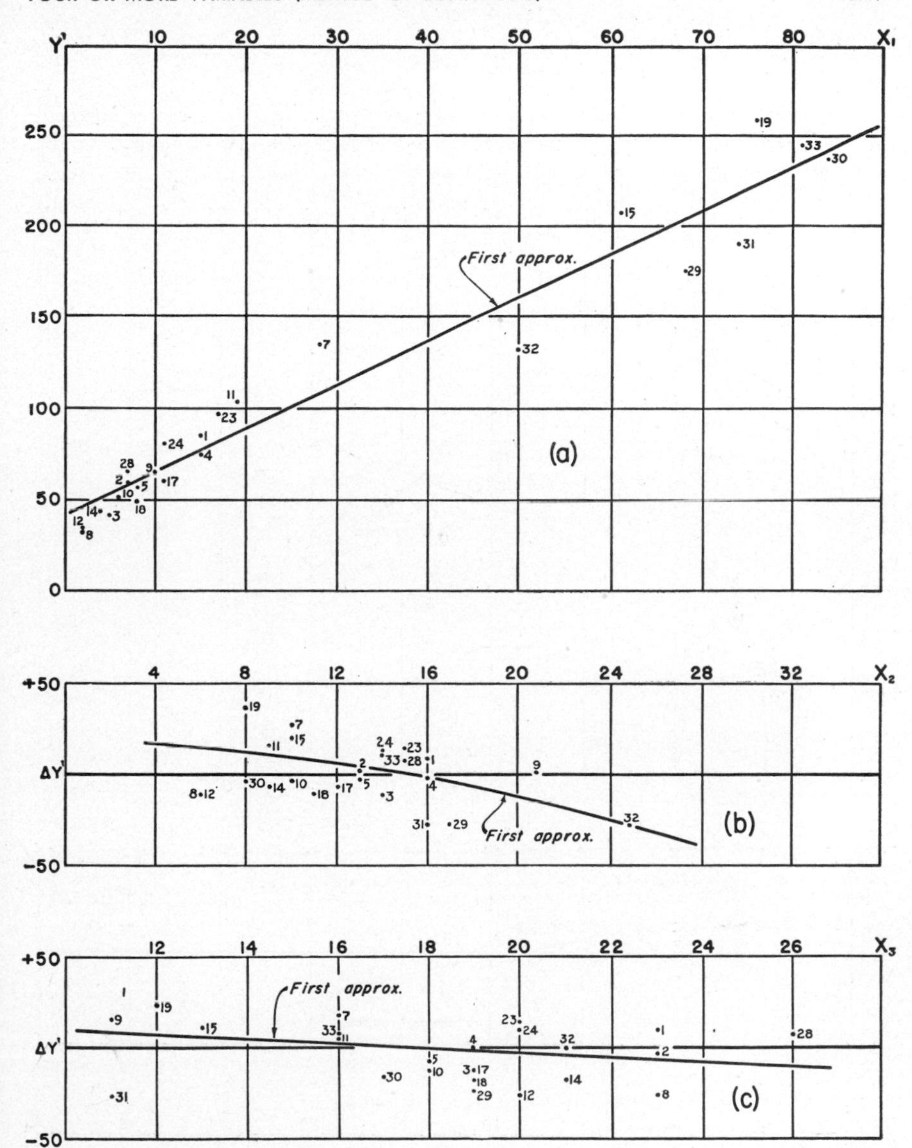

FIG. A–5. Development of first-approximation curves by deviations method (based on data from Table A–1.)

Second approximation:

1. Plot deviations of Fig. A-5*c* as deviations from curve of Fig. A-5*a*, and construct revised curve for plotted points (Fig. A-6*a*).
2. Plot deviations from curve of Fig. A-6*a* as deviations from curve of Fig. A-5*b*, and adjust previous curve (Fig. A-6*b*).

3. Plot deviations from curve of Fig. A-6*b* as deviations from curve of Fig. A-5*c*, and change first-approximation curve to fit new points.

Computed values of Y'' are determined by entering Fig. A-6 (second-approximation curves) with corresponding observations of X_1, X_2, and X_3 and adding the three values obtained from the curves, that is, $Y'' = f''(X_1) + f''(X_2) + f''(X_3)$.

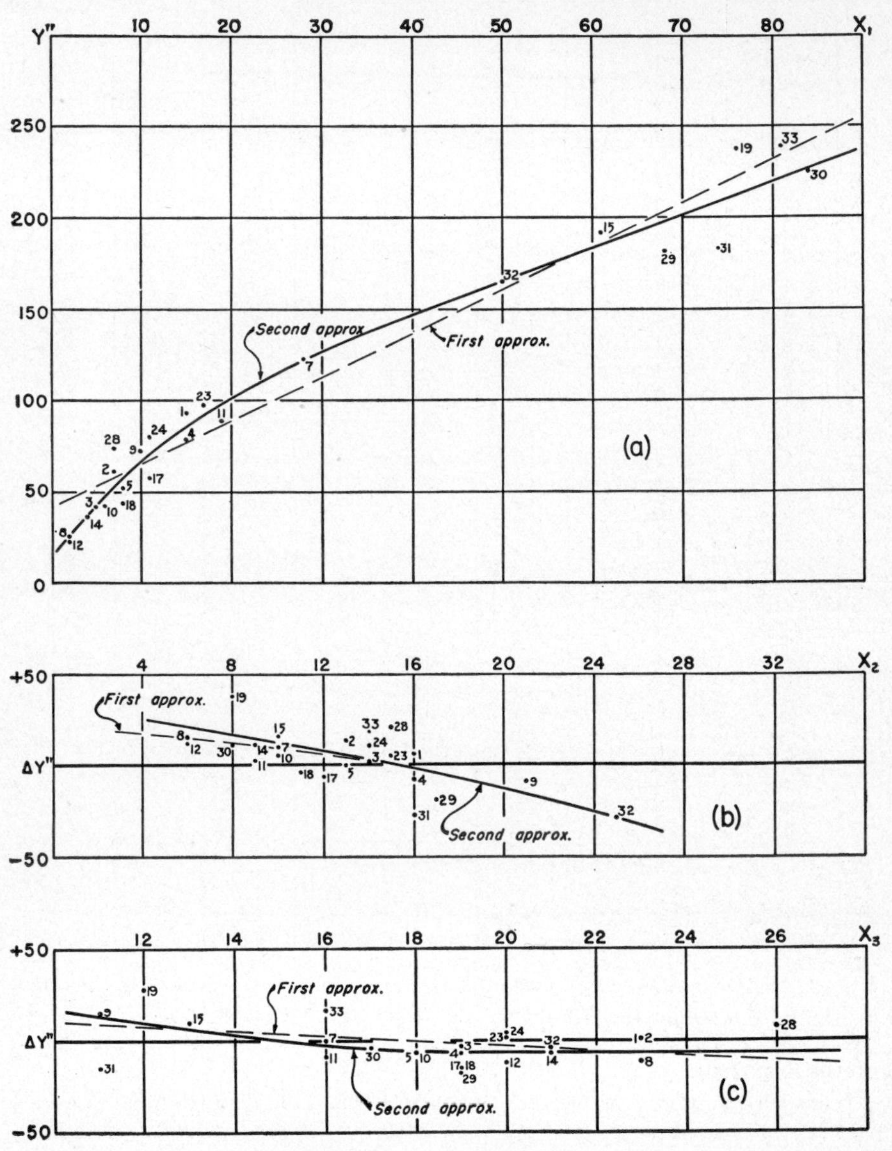

FIG. A–6. Development of second-approximation curves by deviations method (based on data from Table A–1.)

The errors of the first and second approximations, as listed in the last two columns of Table A-1, indicate that the second approximation is considerably better than the first.

TABLE A-1. Mechanical Analysis of Quebec Organic Soils *

(All data in per cent)

Observation number	Maximum moisture taken up (Y)	Loss on ignition (X_1)	Clay (X_2)	Silt (X_3)	Absolute error	
					1st approx (Fig. A-5)	2d approx (Fig. A-6)
1	86	15	16	23	17	7
2	60	7	13	23	4	7
3	42	5	14	19	11	4
4	79	15	16	19	3	0
5	58	8	13	18	6	1
7	136	28	10	16	16	2
8	34	2	6	23	19	5
9	66	10	21	11	6	2
10	52	6	10	18	12	1
11	104	19	9	16	3	6
12	35	2	6	20	23	6
14	44	4	9	21	13	0
15	208	61	10	13	5	4
17	61	11	12	19	11	8
18	50	8	11	19	17	8
19	259	76	8	12	16	18
23	97	17	15	20	17	8
24	81	11	14	20	13	10
28	66	7	15	26	18	14
29	175	68	17	19	23	11
30	237	84	8	17	17	1
31	190	74	16	11	35	28
32	132	50	25	21	4	3
33	245	81	14	16	5	18
Sum...........	......	......	......	......	314	172
Mean.........	......	......	......	......	13.1	7.2

* Oliver, W. F., Physical Properties of Some Mineral and Organic Soils of the Province of Quebec, *Can. J. Research*, Section A, Vol. 24, pp. 80-81, 1946.

The operation of transferring the deviations from one chart to the next can be greatly simplified by first transferring them to a strip of paper (Fig. A-7) and thence to the next chart.

The method of correlation just discussed is particularly applicable when the independent variables are not intercorrelated. If the type of relation is known, joint functions can be developed by introducing additional correction curves for $f(X_1X_2)$, $f(X_2X_3)$, etc.

Four or more variables (coaxial method). A somewhat more complex method of graphical correlation, but one which is better adapted to the representation of joint functions, is the *coaxial method.* In this method a three-variable correlation is first made relating the dependent variable with the two most important independent variables by the method of contours. The fourth variable is then introduced by plotting Y', as computed from this relation, $Y' = f'(X_1,X_2)$, against the observed values of Y, labeling the points with the values of X_3, and constructing

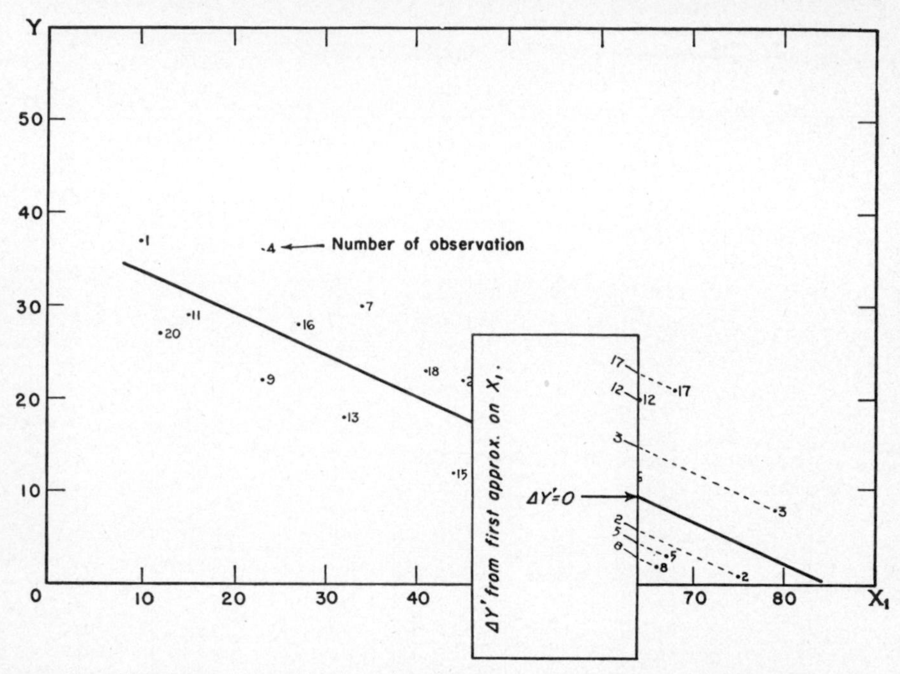

FIG. A–7. Graphical method of transferring deviations from one chart to another.

a second family of curves to fit the plotted points. A fifth variable can be introduced in a similar manner by plotting Y against $Y'' = f'(X_1,X_2,X_3)$, labeling the points with X_4, and constructing a third family of curves to fit these points. This process is repeated until all variables have been introduced. The plotting of observed values of Y against computed values can best be accomplished by laying out the axes so that the Y axis for one chart becomes the Y' axis for the following chart.

This method of correlation also requires a series of successive approximations. The $Y' = f'(X_1,X_2)$ chart is revised by plotting $f'(X_1,X_2 \ldots X_n)$ against observed values of Y and labeling the points with X_2 to see whether or not the residual errors are in any manner correlated with that variable. If an isoline for any limited class interval of X_2 deviates from the line of computed equal to observed values of Y (45° line), then a revision of that interval in the original X_2 curves is indicated. The various isolines of X_2 in such a plotting need not have a systematic arrangement, since they denote only deviations and not total values. The amount of adjustment is determined by routing the difference between an isoline of X_2 and the line of "computed equal observed" ($Y = Y''$) back through the curve families to the X_2 curves. This is accomplished by projecting the difference from the final chart onto a curve in the preceding chart. This projected difference is in turn projected into the X_2-family. The curve upon which the differences are projected should be well centered with respect to the plotted points. Further adjustments to any of the curve families are accomplished in a similar manner. The curves for the final variable can be tested and revised by replotting the data following the procedure used for the first approximation.

TABLE A-2. Data for Coaxial Graphical Correlation Illustrated in Figs. A-8 and 9

Observation number	Y	X_1	X_2	X_3	Absolute error	
					1st approx	2d approx
1	19	36	8	28	3	4
2	7	34	38	18	2	2
3	25	37	33	16	0	4
4	48	52	13	34	4	1
5	4	18	13	12	4	1
6	33	23	9	11	7	2
7	17	13	1	9	5	4
8	4	4	2	2	1	2
9	42	66	48	32	6	4
10	27	37	22	21	3	0
11	7	12	23	2	3	3
12	45	53	7	39	3	0
13	29	34	4	27	6	4
14	11	26	20	17	3	3
15	20	16	10	8	5	3
16	41	49	48	16	1	3
17	42	53	34	24	6	5
18	19	48	45	24	4	1
19	2	9	10	5	1	0
20	35	37	14	23	5	2
21	49	61	25	35	4	1
22	23	19	3	12	4	2
23	23	17	10	6	0	3
24	9	14	11	7	2	2
25	39	37	8	24	5	0
26	32	41	2	34	5	0
27	15	22	14	13	0	1
28	31	47	23	28	4	3
29	33	44	35	18	3	7
30	13	27	7	21	2	2
Sum..........	......	......	......	......	101	69
Mean.........	......	......	......	......	3.37	2.30

To illustrate this method, the correlation of the data listed in Table A-2 is performed as follows:

First approximation:

1. Plot Y against X_1, label the points with X_2, and fit a family of curves (Fig. A-8*a*) by the method of contours.
2. Plot Y against Y' as determined from Fig. A-8*a*, label the points with X_3, and fit a family of curves (Fig. A-8*b*).

Second approximation:

1. Plot Y against Y'', noting values of X_2 beside the points (Fig. A-8*c*). Examination of this chart shows that points for values of X_2 less than 20 and over 30 seem to lie along lines other than $Y = Y''$, while for intermediate values the fit is relatively good. The adjustment lines, $X_2 = 10$ and $X_2 = 35$, are constructed, and the differences *Bb*, *Cc*, *Ee*, and *Ff* are routed back through the various curve families as shown graphically in the figure. The points *A* and *D*, when routed back through the curve families, determine points in Fig. A-8*a* where the first-approximation X_2 curves are apparently correct. The points *A*, *B*, *C*, etc., define two of the second-approximation X_2 curves, and the remaining portions of the curve family are constructed by interpolation (Fig. A-9*a*).
2. Plot Y against Y' as computed from the revised X_2 curves, label the points with X_3, and fit a family of curves (Fig. A-9*b*). Figure A-9*c* shows graphically the errors of the second-approximation curves, and the errors of both approximations are listed in the last two columns of Table A-2 for comparison.

This method of multiple graphical correlation usually yields good results for many problems involving joint functions, such as rainfall-runoff and crest-stage relations, where three or more independent factors are significant. If the approximate shape and spacing of the curve families are known, the first-approximation curves for *all but one* variable can be estimated without plotting the data. The curves representing the remaining variable can then be developed by plotting in the prescribed manner. In general, it is advisable to determine the curves for the most important factor by plotting. The final position of all curve families can then be determined by the process outlined.

In some problems it is advisable to place a particular factor last in the sequence of charts in order to avoid computed values representing impossible solutions. For example, in a rainfall-runoff relation, the computed runoff should not exceed the observed precipitation.

Sometimes the best method of approach requires that all but one of the first-approximation curve families be estimated, reserving an intermediate chart for the plotting of the remaining variable. In such a case, the data are plotted by entering the chart sequence from both ends with corresponding values of all factors (including the dependent variable). The point so determined is labeled with the value of the factor for which the chart is being developed. After all the data have been plotted in this manner, the curve family is then constructed. This technique of plotting can also be utilized as an alternate method of revising the various curve

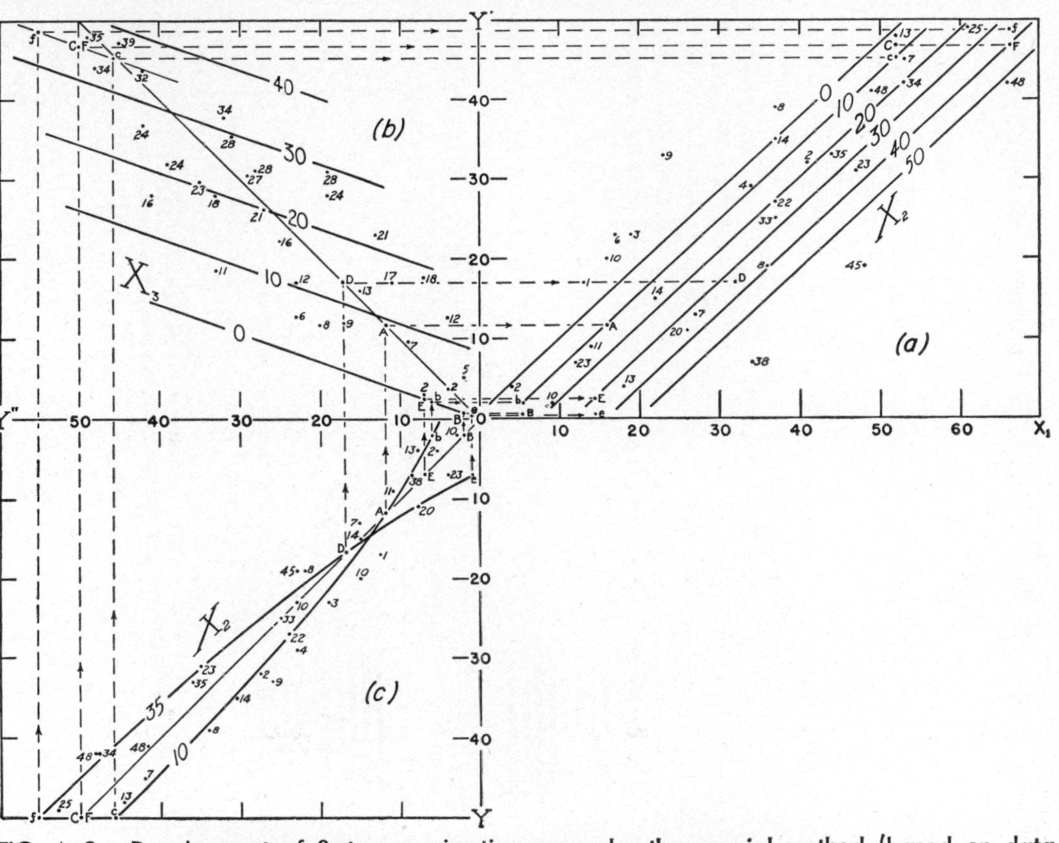

FIG. A–8. Development of first-approximation curves by the coaxial method (based on data from Table A-2).

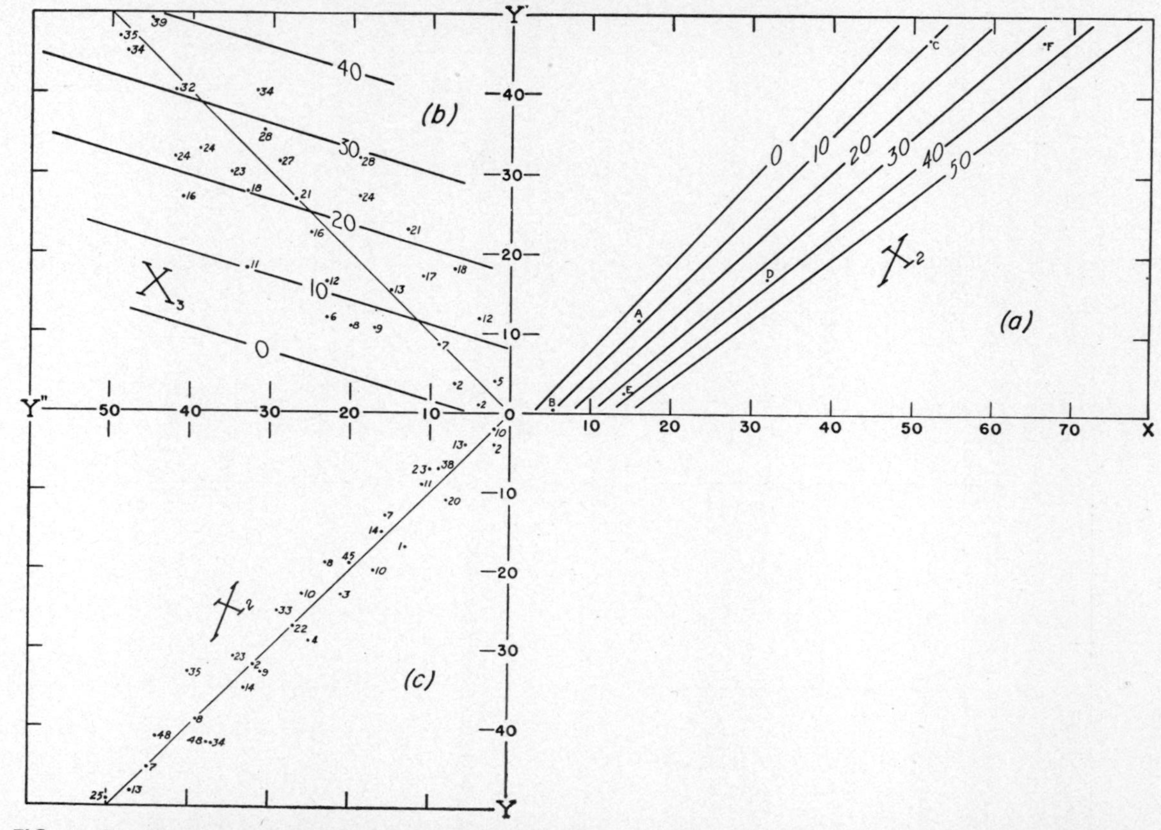

FIG. A–9. Development of second-approximation curves by the coaxial method (based on data from Table A-2).

families. Figure A-10 illustrates this method of developing the second-approximation X_2 curves, using the first-approximation X_3 curves developed in Fig. A-8. This method yields satisfactory results so long as none of the curve families entered in reverse order has slopes approaching those of the coordinate axes. In this event, deviations are either exaggerated or minimized to such an extent that the construction of the curves becomes exceedingly difficult. This deficiency can be effectively overcome, however, if the data are first stratified with respect to each variable. The charts are then entered with the average values of the variables for each class of data.

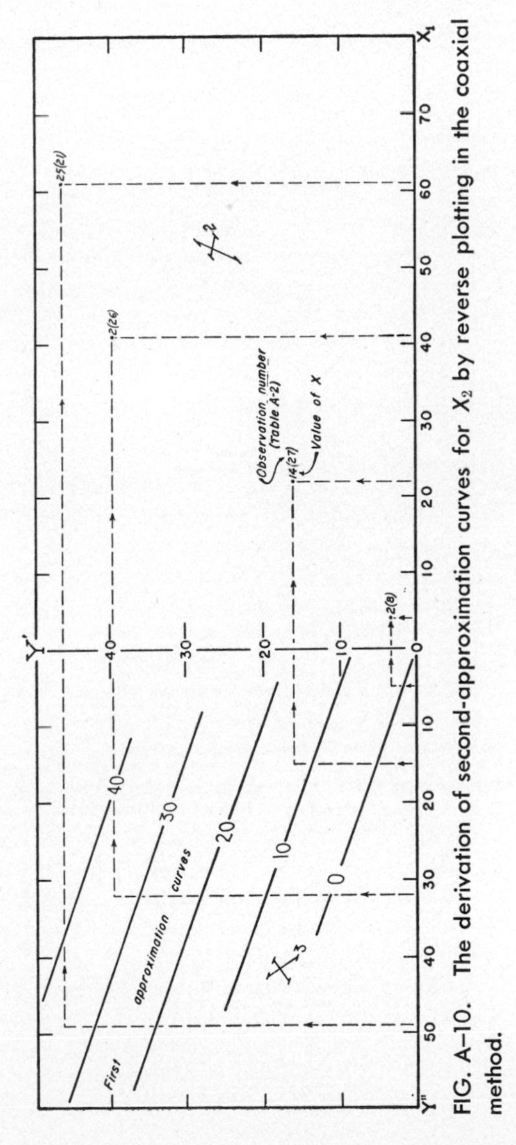

FIG. A-10. The derivation of second-approximation curves for X_2 by reverse plotting in the coaxial method.

APPENDIX B
SOURCES OF HYDROLOGIC AND METEOROLOGICAL DATA

Federal agencies are chiefly responsible for the collection and dissemination of hydrologic and meteorological data. Many state and private organizations collect hydrologic data, but the variety of such data is so great that no attempt has been made to include them in this appendix. Some data are not published but are nevertheless available upon request or through examination of the original records. Access to published data may be had at many public and university libraries which serve as depositories of Federal publications and at Federal and state offices. Much of the information given below is from *Nat. Resources Planning Board Tech. Paper* 10, "Principal Federal Sources of Hydrologic Data," by the Special Advisory Committee on Hydrologic Data of the Water Resources Committee (1943).

SOURCES

Consumptive use. Most data on consumptive use are collected by state agricultural experiment stations, the Soil Conservation Service, and the Bureau of Plant Industry. Investigations have also been made by the Bureau of Reclamation and the U.S. Geological Survey. On pages 425 to 427 of the report, "Regional Planning, Pt. VI: Upper Rio Grande," by the National Resources Committee, February, 1938, are listed 86 references to published and unpublished articles and reports. The results of accumulated studies by the Bureau of Reclamation since 1920 were summarized by Lowry and Johnson in "Consumptive Use of Water for Agriculture," *Trans. ASCE,* Vol. 107, pp. 1243-1302, 1942.

Estimates of annual water loss in the United States east of the Rocky Mountains are presented in *Water Supply Paper* 846, "Natural Water Loss in Selected Drainage Basins." Some studies by the Soil Conservation Service are reported in "Consumptive Water Use and Requirements," Part III, Section 3, The Pecos River Joint Investigation, National Resources Planning Board. Other investigations in Western states by the same agency are summarized in "Use of Water by Native Vegetation," *Calif. Dept. Pub. Works Bull.* 50.

Evaporation. The Climatological Data and Meteorological Yearbook series of the U.S. Weather Bureau are the principal sources of evaporation data. These publications contain data collected by many other Federal and state agencies. A compilation of data collected by the Bureau of Reclamation through 1923 is given in "Evaporation on United States Reclamation Projects," by Houk, *Trans. ASCE,*

Vol. 90, pp. 266-378, 1927. Evaporation records for the Lower Rio Grande Valley are published in the International Boundary Commission's *Water Bulletins.*

Floods. Reports of floods and flood damage are published in the *Monthly Weather Review,* while occasional special supplements and bulletins describe outstanding floods. Additional unpublished data are available for reference through the U.S. Weather Bureau at Washington, D.C., or its regional and river district offices in the field.

The U.S. Geological Survey publishes detailed descriptions of all outstanding floods in its series of *Water Supply Papers.* Its monthly *Water Resources Review* gives preliminary information on the magnitude of floods in the United States and Canada and shows areas of excessive streamflow.

The TVA collects complete information on past and current floods in the Tennessee Valley. Its publication, "Floods of August 1940 in Tennessee River Basin," covers recent great floods.

The Corps of Engineers prepares reports for each flood resulting in loss of life or important property damage. Flood data and analyses have been presented in a large number of *Preliminary Examination and Survey Reports* in connection with investigations of the feasibility of erecting flood-control works. Some of these reports are published as House or Senate documents, while others are available for inspection in division and district offices.

All known floods during a period of over 100 years in the Rio Grande Valley from San Marcial, New Mexico, to Devils River in Texas are recorded in the International Boundary Commission's *Water Bulletins.* This agency also prepared "Special Flood Report of the Great Rio Grande Floods of 1942."

Groundwater. The primary sources of groundwater data for the United States are the publications of the U.S. Geological Survey. Since 1935, a regular series of *Water Supply Papers* has carried annual summaries of groundwater levels as observed in a large number of wells throughout the country. Stages are reported at intervals varying from 1 day to a year. In addition, an impressive number of *Water Supply Papers* have reported special surveys of particular areas, summarizing geological conditions and groundwater resources on the basis of detailed surveys. *Water Supply Paper* 836-*D* is a summary, as of 1939, of groundwater conditions and utilization in the United States, the methods of investigation, and a bibliography of literature on groundwater. Numerous unpublished reports are also available at field offices of the U.S. Geological Survey.

The International Boundary Commission publishes records of monthly groundwater observations in the El Paso and Presidio Valleys of Texas in its *Water Bulletins.* The TVA makes groundwater observations from a network of wells around each of its reservoirs when there might be some possibility of lands being affected by the reservoirs. The Corps of Engineers collects groundwater records in Illinois, Iowa, Minnesota, Missouri, and Wisconsin. The Soil Conservation Service also collects groundwater records and makes observations in some irrigated areas.

Many states also maintain geologists who make studies of the geology and groundwater resources. Other information may be obtained from owners of producing wells and from well-drilling organizations.

Atmospheric humidity. The U.S. Weather Bureau is the principal source of humidity data. Surface and upper-air data for many of its first-order stations are presented in various publications. The Forest Service makes humidity measurements in national forests during periods of fire hazard, but most of these data are unpublished.

River and harbor ice. A tabulation of ice thickness in some of the principal rivers and harbors of the United States is published by the U.S. Weather Bureau in its *Weekly Weather and Crop Bulletin.* This agency also collects information on the dates of opening and closing of all the principal streams. The annual report of the Chief of Engineers contains information on the closing by ice of harbors on the Great Lakes. The *Water Supply Papers* of the U.S. Geological Survey show the dates when there was sufficient ice at gaging stations to affect the open-water stage-discharge relationship.

Precipitation. The U.S. Weather Bureau is the principal source of precipitation data. In addition to its own gage network, it publishes data from gages maintained by several other agencies. Daily and hourly amounts are published regularly in *Climatological Data,* and original records of both published and unpublished data may be examined at climatological section centers, river-district offices, or the Central Office in Washington. For the period 1940 to 1948, hourly data were published in the *Hydrologic Bulletins.* The *Climatic Summary* (*Bull.* W), 1930, gives monthly, annual, and average monthly and annual precipitation for the entire period of record. It also lists the average number of days with 0.01 in. or more of precipitation. Monthly, seasonal, and annual averages and extremes and a complete record of occurrences of excessive precipitation are included for first-order stations. "Average Precipitation in the United States," by McDonald, 1944, shows maps of average weekly and daily precipitation. *U.S. Weather Bur. Pub.* 1353 gives maps of seasonal precipitation in percent of normal by states from 1886 to 1938 and tables of normals and 10 wettest and 10 driest seasons and years. "Normal Weather for the United States," by Kincer (1943), gives the frequency distribution of monthly precipitation by states in addition to the average. The 1941 *Yearbook of Agriculture,* "Climate and Man," contains a large number of precipitation maps giving a variety of pertinent information. *U.S. Dept. Agr. Misc. Pub.* 471, "Crop Yields and Weather" (1942), was prepared in cooperation with the U.S. Weather Bureau and gives the departure of monthly precipitation from normal by states for all years of record.

The International Boundary Commission's *Water Bulletins* contain records of annual rainfall in the Rio Grande Basin and an index of all known rainfall records in and near the basin. The Soil Conservation Service operates several gage networks in connection with its hydrologic studies. Many of these records are published in that agency's *Technical Paper* series and in special *Progress Reports.* The Forest Service, TVA, Bureau of Reclamation, Corps of Engineers, and Bureau of Plant Industry also maintain gages. Many of these records are collected and published by the U.S. Weather Bureau.

The Corps of Engineers and the Bureau of Reclamation have undertaken the depth-area-duration analysis of storm precipitation in the United States. Several hundred storms have already been analyzed.

Quality of water. The U.S. Geological Survey publishes the results of chemical analyses of surface water and groundwater in its *Water Supply Papers.* Quality of public water supplies for all cities in the United States with a population of 20,000 or more is described in *Water Supply Paper* 658.

The TVA also analyzes water in its region. Various studies of water quality have also been made by the Bureau of Reclamation, Soil Conservation Service, Bureau of Plant Industry, Public Health Service, International Boundary Commission, and Corps of Engineers.

An inventory of data on quality of irrigation water has been prepared by the Hydrologic Subcommittee of the Federal Interagency River Basin Committee.

River and lake stages. As a part of its work in flood forecasting, the U.S. Weather Bureau collects river-stage data from about 700 stations. These data are published in *Daily River Stages.* One daily stage, usually at 7 A.M., and height and time of significant flood crests are given. A summary of factual data on gage zero, drainage area, distance from mouth, and extremes of record is presented in tabular form. Notes as to changes in gage location are also given, and reference to these notes is essential in order to ascertain the homogeneity of the data. Some data for important stations on navigable rivers are published monthly in *Climatological Data.* Current stages for some rivers are published daily in weather maps and bulletins.

The TVA maintains recording gages on its reservoirs and publishes the daily stages annually in *TVA Reservoir Elevations and Storage Volumes.* Current stages for rivers and reservoirs are published daily in cooperation with the U.S. Weather Bureau.

The Corps of Engineers maintains gages on many navigable waters of the United States. Daily stage records for main stations on the Mississippi River and its tributaries are published annually by the Mississippi River Commission.

As a phase of its streamflow-measurement program, the U.S. Geological Survey collects a large number of stage data, which are available for inspection in its field offices.

Sedimentation. Studies of reservoir sedimentation are being made by the Soil Conservation Service, Bureau of Reclamation, Corps of Engineers, and the TVA, but these data are not published regularly. These same agencies and the U.S. Geological Survey collect records of suspended load at numerous points. Summaries of these data have appeared in the *Water Supply Papers* of the U.S. Geological Survey and the *Technical Bulletins* of the U.S. Department of Agriculture.

The Soil Conservation Service has compiled a file of extracts and references on all phases of sedimentation. This file is maintained in its office at Washington, D.C.

The International Boundary Commission's *Water Bulletins* contain records showing daily samples of suspended silt in the Rio Grande and its tributaries in Mexico.

Snow. During the winter the U.S. Weather Bureau's *Weekly Weather and Crop Bulletin* contains a tabulation of snow depths at selected points and a map of the United States showing approximate snow depths. Somewhat similar data are contained in weekly *Winter Sports Bulletins* issued by some stations. Every year the results of the snow surveys of the previous winter are published, usually as a supplement to *Climatological Data,* but in the eastern United States they are issued as a supplement to *Daily and Hourly Precipitation* (*Hydrologic Bulletin*).

The Soil Conservation Service, Forest Service, and U.S. Geological Survey, often in cooperation with state agencies, also collect snow-survey data. These data are published in *Monthly Water Supply Forecast Bulletins* and for some states are summarized in the U.S. Weather Bureau's *Climatological Data.*

Soil moisture. The Bureau of Plant Industry has collected information on soil moisture in scattered areas of the Plains region and the West. The results of these observations are published in the *Technical Bulletins* of the U.S. Department of Agriculture. Many publications on soil moisture are listed by Cole in "Publications Containing Information on Soil Moisture and Soil Erosion," processed report by the Division of Dry Land Farming, U.S. Department of Agriculture. The U.S. Weather Bureau's *Weekly Weather and Crop Bulletin* describes general soil-moisture conditions by states.

Solar radiation. Measurements of solar radiant energy are published in the U.S. Weather Bureau's *Monthly Weather Review.* The December, 1937, issue of this publication (pages 415 to 441) contains information on station locations, instrumental equipment, and observational methods and a summary of data obtained through 1936.

Streamflow. The U.S. Geological Survey is the principal Federal agency engaged in the collection and publication of streamflow data. Streamflow data from about 5000 stations are now published in annual *Water Supply Papers* for each of the 14 regions outlined in Fig. B-1. An index by years to the serial numbers of these papers for the various regions and a list of data available in reports by various state organizations is given in the front of each paper in the series. In addition to mean daily flows for the water year (October through September), a description of the station, statement of mean annual flow, period of record, extremes of record, and probable accuracy of the data are given for each station. Monthly and annual totals and means and, in recent years, time and magnitude of important flood crests are shown.

Summaries of monthly and annual flows for the period of record are published in special *Water Supply Papers.* Important floods are described in special papers in which, in addition to detailed stage and discharge data, an analysis of the conditions antecedent to the flood, its meteorological aspects, and other valuable information are given.

In addition to the published data, recorder charts, rating curves and tables, and daily stage and discharge summaries are available at the district offices of the U.S. Geological Survey (Fig. B-1). Reference to data collected by other Federal, state, or local agencies can also be obtained through these offices.

The Corps of Engineers maintains gaging stations on many navigable streams, and data for the Mississippi River are published by the Mississippi River Commission. The Soil Conservation Service, International Boundary Commission, and TVA also collect streamflow data.

Air temperature. The U.S. Weather Bureau is the principal source of data on air temperature, both at the surface and in the upper air. Daily maximum and minimum temperature for several thousand stations are published monthly in *Climatological Data;* and a map of the average temperature and departure from normal is published in the *Weekly Weather and Crop Bulletin.* The *Climatic Summary* (*Bull. W*), 1930, contains mean, average maximum and minimum, and extreme temperatures for each month of record for selected stations, as well as seasonal and annual averages.

Several other summaries have also been published by the U.S. Weather Bureau. "Normal Weather for the United States," by Kincer (1943), gives the average and lowest and highest monthly temperatures by states. The 1941 U.S. Department of Agriculture *Yearbook*, "Climate and Man," presents maps of the average, maximum, and minimum annual temperatures. "Crop Yields and Weather," *U.S. Dept. Agr. Misc. Pub.* 471, 1942, prepared in cooperation with the U.S. Weather Bureau, contains departures of monthly temperature from normal by states for

FIG. B–1. Areas included in the several parts of the annual *Water Supply Papers* and the field offices of the U.S. Geological Survey.

all years of record. Summaries giving mean and average daily minimum and maximum temperatures for each week of the year are also available from the U.S. Weather Bureau. Summaries of upper-air temperature are contained in "Temperature Frequencies in the Upper Air," by Ratner (1946); "Extreme Temperature in the Upper Air," *U.S. Weather Bur. Tech. Paper* 3 (1947); and "Upper Air Average Values of Temperature, Pressure, and Relative Humidity over the United States and Alaska," *U.S. Weather Bur. Tech. Paper* 6 (1948).

Water temperatures. The U.S. Geological Survey publishes the results of groundwater-temperature observations in its *Water Supply Papers*. A summary of data on the temperature of groundwater and surface water is given in *Water Supply Paper* 520-*F*. Temperature data for over 1000 thermal springs are given in *Water Supply Paper* 796-*B*.

Federal agencies operating reservoirs often collect temperature data for operational purposes, but these records are not regularly published. The Bureau of Foreign and Domestic Commerce has compiled temperature data of water supplies for cities of 20,000 population or over (*Market Research Ser.* 17). The Fish and Wildlife Service also makes water-temperature observations in connection with fishery studies.

Wind. The U.S. Weather Bureau is the chief source of information on wind, both at the surface and aloft. Besides the wind data published on the *Daily Weather Map,* it publishes monthly in *Climatological Data* the daily movement of wind at evaporation stations and the average hourly velocity, and data regarding direction and maximum velocity for first-order stations. The *Climatic Summary* (*Bull. W*), 1930, presents for selected stations prevailing wind directions, average velocity, and direction and dates of occurrence for maximum wind velocities. Besides including information on wind storms, the *Monthly Weather Review* also contains upper-air resultant winds for selected stations and maximum upper-air wind velocity and direction for different sections of the country. Among the wind summaries available are "Normal Surface Wind Data for the United States" (1942), presenting maps showing the average hourly velocity and prevailing direction for each month; and the "Airway Meteorological Atlas for the United States" (1941), which contains a variety of summaries of wind, both at the surface and aloft.

The Soil Conservation Service, Corps of Engineers, TVA, and Forest Service also make wind observations.

BIBLIOGRAPHIES

In addition to publications already mentioned and abstracts in such publications as *Engineering News-Record, Civil Engineering, Soil Science,* and *Journal of the American Water Works Association,* the following bibliographies or reports contain abstracts and references to literature of special interest to those engaged on hydrologic problems:

"Annotated Bibliography of Economic Geology," issued semiannually by National Research Council.

"Bibliography and Index of the Publications of the U.S. Geological Survey Relating to Ground Water," *Water Supply Paper* 427 (1918).

"Bibliography of Hydrology, United States," issued annually from 1935 to 1940 by the American Geophysical Union, Section of Hydrology.

"Bibliography on Land Utilization 1918-1936," *U.S. Dept. Agr. Misc. Pub.* 284.

"Bibliography on Soil Erosion and Soil and Water Conservation," *U.S. Dept. Agr. Misc. Pub.* 312 (1938).

"Current Literature in Agricultural Engineering," issued monthly by the Bureau of Agricultural Chemistry and Engineering, U.S. Department of Agriculture.

"Deficiencies in Hydrologic Data," Water Resources Committee, National Resources Planning Board, 1936.

"Deficiencies in Hydrologic Research," Water Resources Committee, National Resources Planning Board, 1940.

"Ground Water in the United States, A Summary," *U.S. Geol. Survey Water Supply Paper* 836-*D*.

"Bibliography and Index of Publications Relative to Ground Water Prepared by the Geological Survey and Cooperating Agencies," *U.S. Geol. Survey Water Supply Paper* 992.

"Infiltration of Water into the Soil. A List of References Relative to the Physical Aspects of the Principal Factors Affecting the Rate and Movement," J. M. Davidson, Soil Conservation Service, U.S. Department of Agriculture, Bibliography 3, October, 1940.

"Inventory of Unpublished Hydrologic Data," *U.S. Geol. Survey Water Supply Paper* 837.

"A Selected Bibliography, 1938" (mimeo.), U.S. Department of Agriculture, Bureau of Agricultural Engineering.

"Bibliography on Land Drainage, 1936" (mimeo.), U.S. Department of Agriculture, Bureau of Agricultural Engineering.

"Selected Annotated Bibliography on Sedimentation as Related to Soil Conservation and Flood Control," U.S. Soil Conservation Service, SCS-MP-20, 1939. (Various other bibliographies on related subjects are available in mimeographed form in the library of the Soil Conservation Service, Washington, D.C.)

Under date of March, 1942, the National Archives published a processed report entitled, "List of Climatological Records in the National Archives." The report contains a history of the meteorologic activities of the Federal agencies from 1814 to 1891 and of the movement that resulted in the establishment of the U.S. Weather Bureau in that year. The report also presents an analysis of the various records resulting from these activities, a description of their original arrangement, and an explanation of their rearrangement by the National Archives. The list of entries is arranged alphabetically by states.

In recent years, the use of motion pictures for educational purposes has become very popular. A small number of films of hydrologic interest are listed in the "Guide to United States Government Motion Pictures," issued by the Library of Congress.

APPENDIX C

PHYSICAL CONSTANTS, CONVERSION TABLES, AND EQUIVALENTS

Conversion Table for Volume

Unit	Equivalents									
	Cm^3	$In.^3$	L	Gal	Imp gal	Ft^3	Yd^3	M^3	Acre-ft	Sfd
Cubic centimeter....	1	0.0610	0.001	2.64×10^{-4}	2.20×10^{-4}	3.53×10^{-5}	1.31×10^{-6}	10^{-6}	8.11×10^{-10}	4.09×10^{-10}
Cubic inch.........	16.4	1	0.0164	0.00433	0.00361	5.79×10^{-4}	2.14×10^{-5}	1.64×10^{-5}	1.33×10^{-8}	6.70×10^{-9}
Liter.............	1,000	61.0	1	0.264	0.220	0.0353	0.00131	0.001	8.11×10^{-7}	4.09×10^{-7}
U.S. gallon........	3,790	231	3.78	1	0.833	0.134	0.00495	0.00379	3.07×10^{-6}	1.55×10^{-6}
Imperial gallon.....	4,550	277	4.55	1.20	1	0.161	0.00594	0.00455	3.68×10^{-6}	1.86×10^{-6}
Cubic foot.........	28,300	1,728	28.3	7.48	6.23	1	0.0370	0.0283	2.30×10^{-5}	1.16×10^{-5}
Cubic yard........	7.65×10^{5}	46,656	765	202	168	27	1	0.765	6.20×10^{-4}	3.12×10^{-4}
Cubic meter........	10^{6}	61,000	1000	264	220	35.3	1.31	1	8.11×10^{-4}	4.09×10^{-4}
Acre-foot..........	1.23×10^{9}	7.53×10^{7}	1.23×10^{6}	3.26×10^{5}	2.71×10^{5}	43,560	1610	1230	1	0.504
Second-foot-day...	2.45×10^{9}	1.49×10^{8}	2.45×10^{6}	6.46×10^{5}	5.38×10^{5}	86,400	3200	2450	1.98	1

Conversion Table for Discharge

Unit	Equivalents											
	Gal/day	Imperial gal/day	Ft^3/day	M^3/day	Gpm	Imperial gpm	L/sec	gps	Imperial Gps	Acre-ft/day	Cfs	M^3/sec
U.S. gallon per day...	1	0.833	0.134	0.00379	6.94×10^{-4}	5.78×10^{-4}	4.38×10^{-5}	1.16×10^{-5}	9.64×10^{-6}	3.07×10^{-6}	1.55×10^{-6}	4.38×10^{-8}
Imperial gallon per day	1.20	1	0.161	0.00455	8.34×10^{-4}	6.94×10^{-4}	5.26×10^{-5}	1.39×10^{-5}	1.16×10^{-5}	3.68×10^{-6}	1.86×10^{-6}	5.26×10^{-8}
Cubic foot per day...	7.48	6.23	1	0.0283	5.19×10^{-3}	4.33×10^{-3}	3.28×10^{-4}	8.66×10^{-5}	7.21×10^{-5}	2.30×10^{-5}	1.16×10^{-5}	3.28×10^{-7}
Cubic meter per day..	264	220	35.3	1	0.183	0.153	0.0116	3.06×10^{-3}	2.55×10^{-3}	8.11×10^{-4}	4.09×10^{-4}	1.16×10^{-5}
U.S. gallon per minute.	1,440	1,200	193	5.45	1	0.833	0.0631	0.0167	0.0139	4.42×10^{-3}	2.23×10^{-3}	6.31×10^{-5}
Imperial gallon per minute............	1,728	1,440	231	6.54	1.20	1	0.0757	0.0200	0.0167	5.31×10^{-3}	2.67×10^{-3}	7.57×10^{-5}
Liter per second......	22,800	19,000	3,050	86.4	15.8	13.2	1	0.264	0.220	0.0700	0.0353	0.001
U.S. gallon per second	86,400	71,900	11,600	327	60	50	3.79	1	0.833	0.265	0.134	3.79×10^{-3}
Imperial gallon per second...........	1.04×10^{5}	86,400	13,900	393	72	60	4.55	1.20	1	0.318	0.160	4.55×10^{-3}
Acre-foot per day....	3.26×10^{5}	2.71×10^{5}	43,560	1,230	226	188	14.3	3.77	3.14	1	0.504	0.0143
Cubic foot per second.	6.46×10^{5}	5.38×10^{5}	86,400	2,450	449	374	28.3	7.48	6.23	1.98	1	0.0283
Cubic meter per second	2.28×10^{7}	1.90×10^{7}	3.05×10^{6}	86,400	15,800	13,200	1000	264	220	70.0	35.3	1

Discharge in Second-feet per Square Mile to Runoff Depth in Inches

Discharge, csm	Runoff, in.				
	1 day	28 days	29 days	30 days	31 days
1	0.03719	1.041	1.079	1.116	1.153
2	0.07438	2.083	2.157	2.231	2.306
3	0.11157	3.124	3.236	3.347	3.459
4	0.14876	4.165	4.314	4.463	4.612
5	0.18595	5.207	5.393	5.578	5.764
6	0.22314	6.248	6.471	6.694	6.917
7	0.26033	7.289	7.550	7.810	8.070
8	0.29752	8.331	8.628	8.926	9.223
9	0.33471	9.372	9.707	10.041	10.376

Discharge in Cubic Feet per Second to Runoff in Acre-feet

Discharge, cfs	Runoff, acre-ft				
	1 day	28 days	29 days	30 days	31 days
1	1.983	55.54	57.52	59.50	61.49
2	3.967	111.1	115.0	119.0	123.0
3	5.950	166.6	172.6	178.5	184.5
4	7.934	222.1	230.1	238.0	246.0
5	9.917	277.7	287.6	297.5	307.4
6	11.90	333.2	345.1	357.0	368.9
7	13.88	388.8	402.6	416.5	430.4
8	15.87	444.3	460.2	476.0	491.9
9	17.85	499.8	517.7	535.5	553.4

Discharge in Cubic Feet per Second to Runoff in Millions of Cubic Feet

Discharge, cfs	Runoff, millions of ft^3				
	1 day	28 days	29 days	30 days	31 days
1	0.0864	2.419	2.506	2.592	2.678
2	0.1728	4.838	5.012	5.184	5.356
3	0.2592	7.257	7.518	7.776	8.034
4	0.3456	9.676	10.02	10.37	10.71
5	0.4320	12.10	12.53	12.96	13.39
6	0.5184	14.51	15.04	15.55	16.07
7	0.6048	16.93	17.54	18.14	18.75
8	0.6912	19.35	20.05	20.74	21.42
9	0.7776	21.77	22.55	23.33	24.10

Discharge in Cubic Feet per Second to Runoff in Millions of Gallons

Discharge, cfs	Runoff, millions of gal				
	1 day	28 days	29 days	30 days	31 days
1	0.6463	18.10	18.74	19.39	20.04
2	1.293	36.20	37.48	38.78	40.08
3	1.939	54.30	56.22	58.17	60.12
4	2.585	72.40	74.96	77.56	80.16
5	3.232	90.50	93.70	96.95	100.2
6	3.878	108.6	112.4	116.3	120.2
7	4.524	126.7	131.2	135.7	140.3
8	5.170	144.8	149.9	155.1	160.3
9	5.817	162.9	168.7	174.5	180.4

Runoff in Millions of Gallons per Day to Discharge in Cubic Feet per Second

Millions of gal/day	0	1	2	3	4	5	6	7	8	9
0	.....	1.55	3.09	4.64	6.19	7.74	9.28	10.83	12.38	13.93
10	15.47	17.02	18.57	20.11	21.66	23.21	24.76	26.30	27.85	29.40
20	30.94	32.49	34.04	35.59	37.13	38.68	40.23	41.78	43.32	44.87
30	46.42	47.96	49.51	51.06	52.61	54.15	55.70	57.25	58.79	60.34
40	61.89	63.44	64.98	66.53	68.08	69.63	71.17	72.72	74.27	75.81
50	77.36	78.91	80.46	82.00	83.55	85.10	86.64	88.19	89.74	91.29
60	92.83	94.38	95.93	97.48	99.02	100.57	102.12	103.66	105.21	106.76
70	108.31	109.85	111.40	112.95	114.49	116.04	117.59	119.14	120.68	122.23
80	123.78	125.33	126.87	128.42	129.97	131.51	133.06	134.61	136.16	137.70
90	139.25	140.80	142.34	143.89	145.44	146.99	148.53	150.08	151.63	153.18

Runoff in Millions of Gallons to Runoff in Acre-feet

Millions of gal/day	0	1	2	3	4	5	6	7	8	9
0	.....	3.07	6.14	9.21	12.28	15.34	18.41	21.48	24.55	27.62
10	30.69	33.76	36.83	39.90	42.96	46.03	49.10	52.17	55.24	58.31
20	61.38	64.45	67.52	70.58	73.65	76.72	79.79	82.86	85.93	89.00
30	92.07	95.14	98.20	101.27	104.34	107.41	110.48	113.55	116.62	119.69
40	122.76	125.82	128.89	131.96	135.03	138.10	141.17	144.24	147.31	150.38
50	153.44	156.51	159.58	162.65	165.72	168.79	171.86	174.93	178.00	181.06
60	184.13	187.20	190.27	193.34	196.41	199.48	202.55	205.62	208.68	211.75
70	214.82	217.89	220.96	224.03	227.10	230.17	233.24	236.30	239.37	242.44
80	245.51	248.58	251.65	254.72	257.79	260.86	263.92	266.99	270.06	273.13
90	276.20	279.27	282.34	285.41	288.48	291.54	294.61	297.68	300.75	303.82

Discharge in Gallons per Minute to Discharge in Cubic Feet per Second

Gpm	0	1	2	3	4	5	6	7	8	9
0	.....	0.0022	0.0045	0.0067	0.0089	0.0111	0.0134	0.0156	0.0178	0.0201
10	0.0223	0.0245	0.0267	0.0290	0.0312	0.0334	0.0356	0.0379	0.0401	0.0423
20	0.0446	0.0468	0.0490	0.0512	0.0535	0.0557	0.0579	0.0602	0.0624	0.0646
30	0.0668	0.0691	0.0713	0.0735	0.0757	0.0780	0.0802	0.0824	0.0847	0.0869
40	0.0891	0.0913	0.0936	0.0958	0.0980	0.1003	0.1025	0.1047	0.1069	0.1092
50	0.1114	0.1136	0.1158	0.1181	0.1203	0.1225	0.1248	0.1270	0.1292	0.1314
60	0.1337	0.1359	0.1381	0.1404	0.1426	0.1448	0.1470	0.1493	0.1515	0.1537
70	0.1559	0.1582	0.1604	0.1626	0.1649	0.1671	0.1693	0.1715	0.1738	0.1760
80	0.1782	0.1805	0.1827	0.1849	0.1871	0.1894	0.1916	0.1938	0.1960	0.1983
90	0.2005	0.2027	0.2050	0.2072	0.2094	0.2116	0.2139	0.2161	0.2183	0.2206

Discharge in Cubic Feet per Second to Runoff in Acre-feet for a Year of 365 Days

Cfs	0	1	2	3	4	5	6	7	8	9
0	.....	724	1,448	2,172	2,896	3,620	4,344	5,068	5,792	6,516
10	7,240	7,964	8,688	9,412	10,136	10,860	11,583	12,307	13,031	13,755
20	14,479	15,203	15,927	16,651	17,375	18,099	18,823	19,547	20,271	20,995
30	21,719	22,443	23,167	23,891	24,615	25,339	26,063	26,787	27,511	28,235
40	28,959	29,683	30,407	31,131	31,855	32,579	33,302	34,026	34,750	35,474
50	36,198	36,922	37,646	38,370	39,094	39,818	40,542	41,266	41,990	42,714
60	43,438	44,162	44,886	45,610	46,334	47,058	47,782	48,506	49,230	49,954
70	50,678	51,402	52,126	52,850	53,574	54,298	55,021	55,745	56,469	57,193
80	57,917	58,641	59,365	60,089	60,813	61,537	62,261	62,985	63,709	64,433
90	65,157	65,881	66,605	67,329	68,053	68,777	69,501	70,225	70,949	71,673

Discharge in Cubic Feet per Second to Theoretical Horsepower per Foot of Fall

Cfs	0	1	2	3	4	5	6	7	8	9
0	.....	0.114	0.227	0.341	0.454	0.568	0.682	0.795	0.909	1.02
10	1.14	1.25	1.36	1.48	1.59	1.70	1.82	1.93	2.04	2.16
20	2.27	2.39	2.50	2.61	2.73	2.84	2.95	3.07	3.18	3.29
30	3.41	3.52	3.64	3.75	3.86	3.98	4.09	4.20	4.32	4.43
40	4.54	4.66	4.77	4.88	5.00	5.11	5.23	5.34	5.45	5.57
50	5.68	5.79	5.91	6.02	6.13	6.25	6.36	6.48	6.59	6.70
60	6.82	6.93	7.04	7.16	7.27	7.38	7.50	7.61	7.72	7.84
70	7.95	8.07	8.18	8.29	8.41	8.52	8.63	8.75	8.86	8.97
80	9.09	9.20	9.32	9.43	9.54	9.66	9.77	9.88	10.0	10.1
90	10.2	10.3	10.5	10.6	10.7	10.8	10.9	11.0	11.1	11.2

Variation in Density of Water with Temperature

Temp, °F	Sp gr	Wt, lb/ft^3	Temp, °F	Sp gr	Wt, lb/ft^3
32	0.99987	62.416	90	0.99510	62.118
35	0.99996	62.421	100	0.99318	61.998
39.3	1.00000	62.424	120	0.99870	61.719
40	0.99999	62.423	140	0.98338	61.386
50	0.99975	62.408	160	0.97729	61.006
60	0.99907	62.366	180	0.97056	60.586
70	0.99802	62.300	200	0.96333	60.135
80	0.99669	62.217	212	0.95865	59.843

Variation in Heat of Vaporization of Water with Temperature

Temp, °F	Heat of Vaporization, Btu/lb
32	1073
50	1059
70	1049
90	1039
110	1027
212	970

Variation in Viscosity of Water with Temperature

(From Smithsonian Tables)

Temp, °F	Absolute viscosity, lb-sec/ft^2	Kinematic viscosity, ft^2/sec
32	0.374×10^{-4}	1.93×10^{-5}
40	0.323	1.67
50	0.273	1.41
60	0.235	1.21
70	0.209	1.06
80	0.180	0.929
90	0.160	0.828
100	0.143	0.741
120	0.117	0.610
140	0.0979	0.513
160	0.0835	0.440
200	0.0637	0.341

Variation of Hydrostatic Pressure (in Pounds per Square Foot) with Head

Head, ft	0	1	2	3	4	5	6	7	8	9
0	0	62	125	187	250	312	374	437	499	562
10	624	686	749	811	874	936	998	1061	1123	1186
20	1248	1310	1373	1435	1498	1560	1622	1685	1747	1810
30	1872	1934	1997	2059	2122	2184	2246	2309	2371	2434
40	2496	2558	2621	2683	2746	2808	2870	2933	2995	3058
50	3120	3182	3245	3307	3370	3432	3494	3557	3619	3682
60	3744	3806	3869	3931	3994	4056	4118	4181	4243	4306
70	4368	4430	4493	4555	4618	4680	4742	4805	4867	4930
80	4992	5054	5117	5179	5242	5304	5366	5429	5491	5554
90	5616	5678	5741	5803	5866	5928	5990	6053	6115	6178
100	6240									

Variation of Hydrostatic Pressure (in Pounds per Square Inch) with Head

Head, ft	0	1	2	3	4	5	6	7	8	9
0	0	0.43	0.87	1.30	1.73	2.17	2.60	3.03	3.47	3.90
10	4.33	4.77	5.20	5.63	6.07	6.50	6.93	7.37	7.80	8.23
20	8.67	9.10	9.53	9.97	10.40	10.83	11.27	11.70	12.13	12.57
30	13.00	13.43	13.87	14.30	14.73	15.17	15.60	16.03	16.47	16.90
40	17.33	17.77	18.20	18.63	19.07	19.50	19.93	20.37	20.80	21.23
50	21.67	22.10	22.53	22.97	23.40	23.83	24.27	24.70	25.13	25.57
60	26.00	26.43	26.87	27.30	27.73	28.17	28.60	29.03	29.47	29.90
70	30.33	30.77	31.20	31.63	32.07	32.50	32.93	33.37	33.80	34.23
80	34.67	35.10	35.53	35.97	36.40	36.83	37.27	37.70	38.13	38.57
90	39.00	39.43	39.87	40.30	40.73	41.17	41.60	42.03	42.47	42.90
100	43.33									

Variation of Head in Feet with Hydrostatic Pressure in Pounds per Square Inch

Pressure, lb/in.^{2}	0	1	2	3	4	5	6	7	8	9
0	0	2.31	4.62	6.92	9.23	11.54	13.85	16.15	18.46	20.77
10	23.08	25.38	27.69	30.00	32.31	34.62	36.92	39.23	41.54	43.85
20	46.15	48.46	50.77	53.08	55.38	57.69	60.00	62.31	64.62	66.92
30	69.23	71.54	73.85	76.15	78.46	80.77	83.08	85.38	87.69	90.00
40	92.31	94.62	96.92	99.23	101.54	103.85	106.15	108.46	110.77	113.08
50	115.38	117.69	120.00	122.31	124.62	126.92	129.23	131.54	133.85	136.15
60	138.46	140.77	143.08	145.38	147.69	150.00	152.31	154.62	156.92	159.23
70	161.54	163.85	166.15	168.46	170.77	173.08	175.38	177.69	180.00	182.31
80	184.62	186.92	189.23	191.54	193.85	196.15	198.46	200.77	203.08	205.38
90	207.69	210.00	212.31	214.62	216.92	219.23	221.54	223.85	226.15	228.46
100	230.77									

Variation of Head in Feet with Hydrostatic Pressure in Pounds per Square Foot

Pressure, lb/ft²	0	1	2	3	4	5	6	7	8	9
0	0	0.016	0.032	0.048	0.064	0.080	0.096	0.112	0.128	0.144
10	0.160	0.176	0.192	0.209	0.225	0.241	0.257	0.273	0.289	0.305
20	0.321	0.337	0.353	0.369	0.385	0.401	0.417	0.433	0.449	0.465
30	0.481	0.497	0.513	0.529	0.545	0.561	0.578	0.594	0.610	0.626
40	0.642	0.658	0.674	0.690	0.706	0.722	0.738	0.754	0.770	0.786
50	0.802	0.818	0.834	0.850	0.866	0.882	0.898	0.914	0.930	0.946
60	0.962	0.979	0.995	1.011	1.027	1.043	1.059	1.075	1.091	1.107
70	1.123	1.139	1.155	1.171	1.187	1.203	1.219	1.235	1.251	1.267
80	1.283	1.299	1.315	1.331	1.348	1.364	1.380	1.396	1.412	1.428
90	1.444	1.460	1.476	1.492	1.508	1.524	1.540	1.556	1.572	1.588
100	1.604									

Values of *n* for the Kutter and Manning Formulas

(After Horton*)

Description of Channel	Range of *n*
Glazed brick	0.011–0.015
Brick in mortar	0.012–0.017
Neat cement	0.010–0.013
Concrete pipe	0.012–0.016
Plank flumes	0.010–0.016
Concrete-lined channels	0.012–0.018
Cement rubble	0.017–0.030
Dry rubble	0.025–0.035
Dressed stonework	0.013–0.017
Smooth metal flumes	0.011–0.015
Corrugated metal flumes	0.022–0.030
Earth canal, straight and uniform	0.017–0.025
Rock canal, trimmed smooth and uniform	0.025–0.035
Rock canal, rough	0.035–0.045
Sluggish, winding channels	0.022–0.030
Canals, stony bed, weeds along bank	0.025–0.040
Earth bottom, rubble sides	0.028–0.035
Natural channels:	
(1) Clean, straight, full stage, no pools	0.025–0.033
(2) As above with weeds and stones	0.030–0.040
(3) Winding, pools, shallows, but clean	0.033–0.045
(4) As above at low stages	0.040–0.055
(5) As (3) with weeds and stones	0.035–0.050
(6) As (4) with large stones	0.045–0.060
(7) Sluggish, weedy, or with deep pools	0.050–0.080
(8) Very weedy and sluggish	0.075–0.150

* Horton, R. E., Some Better Kutter's Formula Coefficients, *Eng. News*, Vol. 75, pp. 373-374, 1916.

Variation of Relative Humidity (Per Cent) with Temperature and Wet-bulb Depression

(Pressure = 30 in.)

Air temp, °F	Wet-bulb depression													
	1	2	3	4	6	8	10	12	14	16	18	20	25	30
0	67	33	1											
5	73	46	20											
10	78	56	34	13										
15	82	64	46	29										
20	85	70	55	40	12									
25	87	74	62	49	25	1								
30	89	78	67	56	36	16								
35	91	81	72	63	45	27	10							
40	92	83	75	68	52	37	22	7						
45	93	86	78	71	57	44	31	18	6					
50	93	87	80	74	61	49	38	27	16	5				
55	94	88	82	76	65	54	43	33	23	14	5			
60	94	89	83	78	68	58	48	39	30	21	13	5		
65	95	90	85	80	70	61	52	44	35	27	20	12		
70	95	90	86	81	72	64	55	48	40	33	25	19	3	
75	96	91	86	82	74	66	58	51	44	37	30	24	9	
80	96	91	87	83	75	68	61	54	47	41	35	29	15	3
85	96	92	88	84	76	70	63	56	50	44	38	32	20	8
90	96	92	89	85	78	71	65	58	52	47	41	36	24	13
95	96	93	89	86	79	72	66	60	54	49	44	38	27	17
100	96	93	89	86	80	73	68	62	56	51	46	41	30	21

Variation of Dewpoint with Temperature and Wet-bulb Depression and of Saturation Vapor Pressure with Temperature

(Pressure = 30 in.)

Air temp, °F	Saturation vapor pressure		Wet-bulb depression													
	Mb	In.	1	2	3	4	6	8	10	12	14	16	18	20	25	30
0	1.29	0.038	−7	−20												
5	1.66	0.049	−1	−9	−24											
10	2.13	0.063	5	−2	−10	−27										
15	2.74	0.081	11	6	0	−9										
20	3.49	0.103	16	12	8	2	−21									
25	4.40	0.130	22	19	15	10	−3	−15								
30	5.55	0.164	27	25	21	18	8	−7								
35	6.87	0.203	33	30	28	25	17	7	−11							
40	8.36	0.247	38	35	33	30	25	18	7	−14						
45	10.09	0.298	43	41	38	36	31	25	18	7	−14					
50	12.19	0.360	48	46	44	42	37	32	26	18	8	−13				
55	14.63	0.432	53	51	50	48	43	38	33	27	20	9	−12			
60	17.51	0.517	58	57	55	53	49	45	40	35	29	21	11	−8		
65	20.86	0.616	63	62	60	59	55	51	47	42	37	31	24	14		
70	24.79	0.732	69	67	65	64	61	57	53	49	44	39	33	26	−11	
75	29.32	0.866	74	72	71	69	66	63	59	55	51	47	42	36	15	
80	34.61	1.022	79	77	76	74	72	68	65	62	58	54	50	44	28	−7
85	40.67	1.201	84	82	81	80	77	74	71	68	64	61	57	52	39	19
90	47.68	1.408	89	87	86	85	82	79	76	73	70	67	63	59	48	32
95	55.71	1.645	94	93	91	90	87	85	82	79	76	73	70	66	56	43
100	64.88	1.916	99	98	96	95	93	90	87	85	82	79	76	72	63	52

Variation of Pressure, Temperature, and Boiling Point with Elevation

(U.S. Standard Atmosphere*)

Elev., ft msl	Pressure			Air temp, °F	Boiling point, °F
	In. of mercury	Mb	Ft of water		
− 1,000	31.02	1050.5	35.12	62.6	213.8
0	29.92	1013.2	33.87	59.0	212.0
1,000	28.86	977.3	32.67	55.4	210.2
2,000	27.82	942.1	31.50	51.8	208.4
3,000	26.81	907.9	30.35	48.4	206.5
4,000	25.84	875.0	29.25	44.8	204.7
5,000	24.89	842.9	28.18	41.2	202.9
6,000	23.98	812.1	27.15	37.6	201.1
7,000	23.09	781.9	26.14	34.0	199.2
8,000	22.22	752.5	25.16	30.6	197.4
9,000	21.38	724.0	24.20	27.0	195.6
10,000	20.58	696.9	23.30	23.4	193.7
11,000	19.79	670.2	22.40	19.8	191.9
12,000	19.03	644.4	21.54	16.2	190.1
13,000	18.29	619.4	20.71	12.6	188.2
14,000	17.57	595.0	19.89	9.1	186.4

* The data of this table are based on average conditions and must be adjusted to actual meteorological conditions for a specific problem.

Map Scale Conversions

Ratio	In./mile	Miles/in.
1 : 1,000,000	0.0634	15.7828
1 : 500,000	0.1267	7.8914
1 : 250,000	0.2534	3.9457
1 : 126,720	0.5000	2.0000
1 : 125,000	0.5069	1.9728
1 : 90,000	0.7040	1.4205
1 : 63,360	1.0000	1.0000
1 : 62,500	1.0138	0.9864
1 : 45,000	1.4080	0.7102
1 : 31,680	2.0000	0.5000
1 : 30,000	2.1120	0.4735
1 : 24,000	2.6400	0.3788

MISCELLANEOUS EQUIVALENTS

Discharge:

1 miner's inch = 0.025 cubic foot per second in Arizona, California, Montana, and Oregon
= 0.02 cubic foot per second in Idaho, Kansas, Nebraska, New Mexico, North and South Dakota, and Utah
= 0.026 cubic foot per second in Colorado
= 0.028 cubic foot per second in British Columbia

1 cubic foot per second = 0.000214 cubic mile per year
= 0.9917 acre-inch per hour

1 inch on 1 square mile = 2,323,200 cubic feet = 53.3 acre-feet = 26.9 second-foot-days

1 second-foot-day = 0.0372 inch on one square mile

Weight:

1 pound of water = 0.5507 inch over 8-in. circle
= 0.3524 inch over 10-in. circle
= 0.24476 inch over 12-in. circle

MISCELLANEOUS PHYSICAL CONSTANTS

$\mathbf{g}$ = 32.16 ft/sec/sec (average value)
= 981 cm/sec/sec

$\mathbf{e}$ = 2.71828 18285

π = 3.14159 26536

$\log_{10} \mathbf{e}$ = 0.43429 44819

$\log_e 10$ = 2.30258 50930

NAME INDEX

SUBJECT INDEX